PRESSURE

1 pascal = 1 newton/m^2 = 1 kg/(m·s^2) =

1 lbf/in^2 = 6894.76 pascal = 0.068 a

1 atm = 14.696 lbf/in^2 = 1.01325 × 10^5 pascal

1 bar = 10^5 pascal = 0.987 atm = 14.504 lbf/in

1 in Hg = 3376.8 pascal = 0.491 lbf/in^2

1 in H_2O = 248.8 pascal = 0.0361 lbf/in^2

ENERGY

1 joule = 1 newton·m = 1 kg·m^2/s^2 = 9.479 × 10^{-4} Btu = 0.2389 cal

1 kJ = 1000 joule = 0.9479 Btu = 238.9 cal

1 Btu = 1055.0 joule = 1.055 kJ = 778.16 ft·lbf = 252 cal

ENERGY DENSITY

1 kJ/kg = 1000 m^2/s^2 = 0.4299 Btu/lbm

1 Btu/lbm = 2.326 kJ/kg = 2326 m^2/s^2

ENERGY FLUX

1 watt/m^2 = 0.317 Btu/(hr·ft^2)

1 Btu/(hr·ft^2) = 3.154 watt/m^2

POWER

1 watt = 1 joule/s = 1 kg·m^2/s^3 = 3.412 Btu/hr = 1.3405 × 10^{-3} hp

1 kW = 1000 watt = 3412 Btu/hr = 737.3 ft·lbf/s = 1.3405 hp

1 Btu/hr = 0.293 watt = 0.2161 ft·lbf/s = 3.9293 × 10^{-4} hp

1 hp = 550 ft·lbf/s = 33,000 ft·lbf/min = 2545 Btu/hr = 746 watt

SPECIFIC HEAT

1 Btu/(lbm·°F) = 1 Btu/(lbm·R)

1 kJ/(kg·K) = 0.23884 Btu/(lbm·R) = 185.8 ft·lbf/(lbm·R)

1 Btu/(lbm·R) = 778.16 ft·lbf/(lbm·R) = 4.186 kJ/(kg·K)

TEMPERATURE

T(°F) = (9/5)T(°C) + 32 = T(R) − 459.67

T(°C) = (5/9)[T(°F) − 32] = T(K) − 273.15

T(R) = (9/5)T(K) = (1.8)T(K) = T(°F) + 459.67

T(K) = (5/9)T(R) = T(R)/1.8 = T(°C) + 273.15

ELECTRICAL UNITS

1 watt = 1 J/s = 1 V·A = 621 lumens at 5500 Å

1 kilowatt hour = 3413 Btu = 1.341 horsepower hour

1 volt = 1 joule/coulomb = 1 watt/amp = 1 ohm·amp

1 amp = 1 coulomb/second = 6.24183 × 10^{18} electrons/second

Thermodynamics

Thermodynamics

Robert T. Balmer
Professor of Mechanical Engineering
University of Wisconsin–Milwaukee

WEST PUBLISHING COMPANY
ST. PAUL   NEW YORK   LOS ANGELES   SAN FRANCISCO

Copyediting: Virginia Dunn
Cover and Text Design: David Farr, Imagesmythe Inc.
Composition: Syntax International, Pte. Ltd.
Art: Rolin Graphics
Index: Virginia Hobbs

---

50 W. Kellogg Boulevard
P.O. Box 64526
St. Paul, MN 55164-1003

Printed in the United States of America

97 96 95 94 93 92 91 90   8 7 6 5 4 3 2 1 0

Library of Congress Cataloging-in-Publication Data

Balmer, Robert T.
Thermodynamics/Robert T. Balmer.
p. cm.
Includes bibliographies and index.
ISBN 0-314-47008-5
1. Thermodynamics. I. Title.
TJ265.B195 1990
621.402′1--dc19

88-39697
CIP

This book is dedicated to you, the next generation of engineers, who through your skill and knowledge will leave your imprint on and forever change our world.

Contents

Chapter 9 Chemical Thermodynamics 573

Chapter 10 Compressible Fluid Flow 639

Chapter 11 Thermodynamics of Biological Systems 683

Preface

Thermodynamics is a very powerful engineering tool, yet it is often a conceptually difficult subject for engineering students. The nineteenth century German physicist Arnold Sommerfeld (1868–1951) seemed to voice the feelings of many when he made the following comments about thermodynamics[1]:

> Thermodynamics is a funny subject. The first time you go through the subject, you don't understand it at all. The second time you go through it, you think you understand it, except for one or two points. The third time you go through it, you know you don't understand it, but by that time you are so used to the subject, it doesn't bother you anymore.

This book was designed for a standard two-semester thermodynamics course for sophomore or junior engineering students. Since this subject inherently contains a large amount of detailed information, I have attempted to create a text that would allow the student to grasp many of the details from the reading alone, thus freeing the instructor to spend more class time working example problems and discussing complex concepts. Consequently, this book has been written in an easily readable conversational style in which common conceptual problems have been anticipated and explanations are occasionally more detailed than usual.

The first five chapters cover the basic first and second laws of thermodynamics and their application to closed and open systems. Chapters 6 through 12 cover specific topics dealing with applied engineering thermodynamics. In terms of a typical two-course sequence, I recommend covering Chapters 1 through 5 plus either Chapter 6 or Chapter 11 during the first semester. Chapter 6 continues to

1. S. W. Angrist and L. G. Helper, *Order and Chaos: Laws of Energy and Entropy*. New York: Basic Books, 1967, p. 215.

develop general thermodynamic property relations, whereas Chapter 11 focuses on applying the concepts of thermodynamics to biological systems. I have found that students generally relate well to the biological material, and in my opinion it is the better choice with which to end the semester (especially if the curriculum contains only one thermodynamics course). The second semester, or applied thermodynamics course, should then cover Chapter 6 (or 7, if 6 was covered during the first semester) through Chapter 10. Chapter 11 can then be covered if not included in the first semester, and Chapter 12 can also be covered if time permits, or if an earlier chapter was omitted.

Since the second half of the book has been designed for an applied thermodynamics course, it is primarily a survey of relevant technology. One or more books can be found on each of the topics covered in Chapters 8 through 12 in any technical library, and many individual elective courses are available on these topics. To enable students to grasp the social and cultural impact of this technology, it was decided to develop the material on heat engine cycles, refrigeration cycles, and chemical thermodynamics (Chapters 8 and 9) along a historical or chronological time line. This will provide the reader with a rare historical perspective that is unusual in engineering textbooks.

Probably the unique feature of this text is the treatment of entropy. It is presented through a balanced concept, and considerable effort has been put into developing useful auxiliary equations for entropy production so that one may effectively consider more than just "reversible" processes. Chapter 11 on biological thermodynamics is also unique to an engineering textbook. It is a natural extension of engineering thermodynamics, and is certainly a relevant topic for engineers today. A number of end of chapter computer problems have been introduced throughout the text to aid in the process of integrating the effective use of the microcomputer into the engineering curriculum. Finally, a number of end of chapter open-ended design problems have been introduced in the second half of the text to promote the development of design experience in undergraduate engineering students.

Engineering thermodynamics had its origin in the thermal technology of the eighteenth and early nineteenth centuries. It was greatly influenced by the steam and internal combustion engines, which produced the portable power that made the industrial revolution possible. Consequently, it is laced with a wide variety of technical terms, some having Greek or Latin origin, whose meaning may or may not be obvious to the reader. Appendix B provides a brief introduction to the etymology of these terms with the belief that by understanding the meaning of the words themselves they will no longer burden the learning of the subject matter of thermodynamics.

This textbook evolved after many years of teaching courses in engineering thermodynamics that were required of all undergraduate engineering students. During this time numerous people have influenced its outcome, particularly the many students who have so patiently taught me how to teach. I am also indebted to my colleagues at the University of Wisconsin–Milwaukee who allowed me to complete this work, and in particular to R. H. Merritt, S. H. Chan, K. F. Neusen, K. C. Tsao, S. Salamon, and the late I. C. Romer, Jr.

The technology of writing changed dramatically during the development of this text. The first draft of the manuscript was completely handwritten. The second draft was capably typed by Florence Widder on an electric typewriter, and the third and all subsequent drafts were word processed by Katherine Banna and myself on a microcomputer. I am very grateful for their effort. I would also like to thank Gene Menzel for his professional photographic work used in this text.

Finally, I would like to acknowledge the love and support over these many years of my family: my wife Mary Anne, my children Christine, Rob, and Theodore, and my parents, Elsie and Ted Balmer.

I have been told by my students that when reading this book they hear me lecturing in their mind. I am pleased, for I have left my voice in time.

Chapter One Dimensions and Units

We begin the study of thermodynamics with a short but exciting digression into the seemingly unimportant world of units of measure. Your understanding of the structure and fabric of such a common commodity as units of measure is really very important because the present generation of engineering students is caught up in the rather awkward transition from the old English foot–pound–second system to the new SI meter–kilogram–second system. A cultural change of this magnitude usually requires a transition phase lasting one or more generations, and consequently you must be prepared to work in a variety of coexisting units systems during your professional career. It is, therefore, vital that engineering students understand the origins of and relations between the several units systems currently in use within their profession. All of these systems are built on a very logical mathematical framework, and in fact anyone can develop a unique system of units merely by following the rules.

Most engineering subjects tend to focus on the final numerical answer as the end product of an analysis. The whole field of engineering often seems to have this rather narrow value system, that the *numerical* answer to some problem is its most important attribute. However, a calculated quantity always has two parts: the numerical value and the associated units. Therefore, the calculational result of any analysis must be correct in two separate categories: It must have the *correct numerical value* and it must have the *correct units.*

The classical branches of engineering evolved independently from each other. They developed different jargon and often used different units systems, and over the years no significant attempt has ever been made to unify them. One fundamental area in which some unification has occurred is the worldwide adoption of *Le Systeme International d'Unités*, universally called the *SI units system.* The formal study of units and dimensions is known as *metrology*. Unfortunately, many engineers consider it to be an inherently trivial subject. They seem to feel that the essence of all units systems is somehow contained in one large units conversion table. This rather condescending view of the science of measurement is not new. For many centuries people felt that units of measure were more of a nuisance than a blessing, as evidenced by the fact that the first mathematically defined system of units did not appear in any culture until the late nineteenth century. Earlier measurements were carried out with elementary and often inconsistently defined units that were at times only vaguely related to each other.

Metrology

On May 3, 1883, William Thomson (1824–1907), better known as Lord Kelvin, one of the founders of the subject of thermodynamics, delivered a speech to the British Institution of Civil Engineers in which he said

> In physical science a first essential step in the direction of learning any subject is to find principles of numerical reckoning and methods for practicably measuring some quality connected with it. I often say that when you can measure what you are speaking about, and express it in numbers, you know something about it; but when you cannot measure it, when you cannot express it in numbers, your knowledge is of a meager and unsatisfactory kind: it may be the beginning of knowledge, but you have scarcely, in your thoughts, advanced to the stage of science, whatever the matter may be.

Metrology is the source of reproducible quantification in science and engineering. It is concerned with the dimensions, units, and numbers necessary to make meaningful measurements and calculations. It does not deal with the technology of measurement, so it is not concerned with how measurements are actually made.

We call each measurable characteristic of a quantity a *dimension* of that quantity. If the quantity exists in the material world, then it automatically has three spatial dimensions (length, width, and height), all of which are called *length* (L) dimensions. If the quantity changes in time then it also has a temporal dimension called *time* (t). Some dimensions are not unique because they are made up of other dimensions. For example, an area (A) is a measurable characteristic of an object and it is therefore one of its dimensions. However, the area dimension is the same as the length dimension squared ($A = L^2$). On the other hand, we could say with equal validity that the length dimension is the same as the square root of the area dimension, and it is not obvious which of these dimensions is the more fundamental.

Even though there seems to be a lack of distinguishing characteristics that allow one dimension to be recognized as more fundamental than some other dimension, we easily recognize an apparent utilitarian hierarchy within a set of similar dimensions. We therefore arbitrarily choose to call some dimensions *fundamental,* and to call all other dimensions related to the arbitrarily chosen fundamental dimensions *secondary* or *derived.* It is important to understand that not all systems of dimensional analysis have the same set of fundamental dimensions.

Therefore, units are merely ways of quantifying dimensions. They provide us with a numerical scale whereby we can actually carry out a measurement of a quantity in some dimension. They are established quite arbitrarily, and are codified by civil law or cultural custom. How the dimension of length ends up being measured in units of feet or meters has nothing to do with any physical law. It is solely dependent upon the creativity and ingenuity of people. Therefore, whereas the basic concepts of dimensions are grounded in the fundamental logic of descriptive analysis, the basic ideas behind the units systems are often grounded in the complex roots of past civilizations and cultures.

It is evident that the meaning of a measurement depends directly on the manner in which the measurement is recorded, i.e., on the type of numerical system used. Consequently, the evolution of the systems of dimensions and units used in engineering cannot be fully understood until one gains an appreciation for certain aspects of the cultural evolution of mathematics. Both the units system and the corresponding measurement number base must be understood before the true meaning of a measurement becomes fully understood.

The Mathematics of Antiquity

Intuition tells us that civilization should have evolved using the decimal system. People have ten fingers and toes, so the base 10 (decimal) number system would seem to be the most logical system to be adopted by prehistoric people. Amazingly, this was not the case. Archaeological evidence has shown that the pre-Egyptian Sumerians used a base 60 (sexagesimal) number system, and that ancient Egyptians and early American Indians used a base 5 number system. A base 12 (duodecimal) number system was developed and used extensively during the Roman Empire. Today, mixed remains of these ancient number systems still exist deeply rooted in our culture and our measurement systems.

The development and acceptance of a particular *base* for a number system was motivated by the necessity of having a practical system of weights and measures. The base of a number system was influenced not so much by the counting of integer items as by the problem of denumerating parts of the whole, i.e., fractions. Many early civilizations developed completely functional number systems that were not initially decimal, but at some later date were converted into a decimal system for counting integers. However, for convenience in measurement these cultures usually maintained a system of fractions that was not decimal. For example, today the foot is divided into 12 parts (inches), which is called a *duodecimal* (base 12) fraction system, but the counting of feet proceeds decimally (base 10). Thus, for the past 3000–5000 years or more, people have labored under a dual base number system, one base for the integers and another base for the fractions. It seems almost unbelievable that a complete decimal system in metrology was not proposed by any nation before the late nineteenth century.

One of the fundamental elements of successful mercantile trade was that the basic units of commerce have easily understood subdivisions. Normally, the larger the base number of a particular number system, the more even divisors it has. For example, 10 has only three divisors, 1, 2, and 5. Thus, it does not make a particularly good base as far as fractions are concerned because you can divide 10 by only 3 different integers. However, 12 has five divisors (1, 2, 3, 4, and 6) and thus makes a considerably better fractional base. On the other hand, 60 has the advantage over 100 as a base number because the former has 11 divisors (1, 2, 3, 4, 5, 6, 10, 12, 15, 20, and 30) whereas the latter has only eight (1, 2, 4, 5, 10, 20, 25, and 50). Thus, the sexagesimal (base 60) system of fractions was established early in the history of commerce due to the fact that the number 60 can be subdivided by integers in more ways than, say, the number 100.

The measurements of length and time were undoubtedly the first to be of concern to prehistoric people. Perhaps the measurement of time came first, because understanding the concept of time and its passage is fundamental to survival. People had to know the relation of night to day and to understand the relevance of the seasons of the year. The most striking aspect of our current measure of time is that it is a mixture of three different numerical bases: decimal (base 10) for counting days of the year, duodecimal (base 12) for dividing day and night into equal parts (hours), and sexagesimal (base 60) for dividing hours and minutes into equal parts.

Prehistoric people first observed the sun, stars, and seasons of the year and determined that there were 360 days in the solar cycle (year). By 2000 B.C. the Sumerians had divided the total day (dark plus light) into 12 equal parts of 30 gesh each (1 gesh = 4 of our minutes). Thus, their day was divided into 12 × 30 = 360 gesh, just as the year was divided into 360 days. Claudius Ptolemaeus, a second-century A.D. Alexandrian astronomer and mathematician, was the first to divide the circle into 360 parts (degrees). He decided, for convenience, to use sexagesimal fractions and so subdivided each of the 360 parts of his circle into 60 small parts, and each of these 60 small parts was further subdivided into 60 smaller parts. In Latin, the first 60 subdivisions were called *partes minutae primae* (first small parts) and the second 60 subdivisions were called *partes minutae secundae* (second small parts). Our words *minute* and *second* come from these expressions by retaining the word *minutae* from the first phrase and *secundae* from the second. Ptolemaeus' divisions were later adopted for time measurement by dividing the total day into two 12-hour periods with 60 minutes per hour and 60 seconds per minute.

The measurement of length, being probably the next most important measure for survival, was also initially formulated in terms of the basic observations of early people. Nearly all early scales of length were based on the dimensions of parts of the adult human body. Naturally, people wanted to carry their measures with them, measures that would be universally accepted by others. Some of the early length units were the finger (digit), the hand, the forearm (cubit), the outstretched arms (fathom), the foot, and the pace. Measurements of area and volume soon followed using such units as the mouthful and handful.

Weight was probably the third fundamental measure to be established, with the development of such units as the grain (the weight of a single grain of wheat), the stone, and the talent (the maximum weight that could be comfortably carried continuously by an adult male). These units were usually related to each other in a binary (base 2) numerical system. The following sections illustrate some of the basic units of measure dating from ancient Egyptian through the Roman periods.

Length Initially, the smallest length units were the width of the finger (which is about $\frac{3}{4}$ inch wide) and the width of the thumb (which is about 1 inch wide). In modern Italian, the word *pollice* means both thumb and inch. The word *inch* comes from the old English version of the Latin word *unica*, which means *the twelfth part of*, which in turn comes from the Greek word $o\iota\chi o\sigma$ (a twelfth). Other length units were based on these in a binary (base 2) way as follows:

2 fingers = 1 half hand
2 half hands = 1 hand
2 hands = 1 span
2 spans = 1 cubit (the length of the forearm)
2 cubits = 1 arm (3 feet or 1 yard)
2 arms = 1 fathom (6 feet)

and so forth. For longer distances we have the following nonbinary length units

1 foot = 12 thumbs (inches)
1 yard = 1 pace (3 feet)
1 pole (rod) = 12 cubits (18 feet or 6 yards)
1 chain = 4 poles (24 yards)
1 bolt = 40 yards
1 cord = 10 poles (60 yards)
1 skein = 20 poles (120 yards)
1 furlong[1] = 1/8 mile (220 yards)
1 mile = 1000 double paces (1760 yards)
1 league = 6.5 miles

and so forth.

Area An area was normally given as so many lengths on a side, for example, two hands wide by three hands high. Occasionally more complex definitions were used, such as that of an *acre* of land being the amount of land that one man could plow with a team of oxen in one day.

Volume The smallest convenient volume unit available on the adult human body is the mouthful (which is equivalent to about 1 tablespoon). Other binary units are

2 mouthfuls = 1 handful
2 handfuls = 1 jack
2 jacks = 1 gill
2 gills = 1 cup
2 cups = 1 pint
2 pints = 1 quart
2 quarts = 1 pottle
2 pottles = 1 gallon
2 gallons = 1 peck
2 pecks = 1 bucket
2 buckets = 1 bushel
2 bushels = 1 strike
2 strikes = 1 coombe

and so forth.

Weight The unit of weight measured by the English pound is very old. The Latin word for weight is *pondus*, and the ancient Roman unit of weight is the *libra*.

1. The term furlong is a contraction of the phrase *furrow long* (as in plowing).

This was a convenient weight unit and it became integrated into the English system of weights and measures during the Roman occupation of Britain (43 B.C.–A.D. 410). Since the English already had a word for weight, they chose to adopt a variation of the Latin *word* for weight as the English name for the *unit* of weight. Thus, the Latin unit name *libra* was replaced in English by the name *pound* (from the Latin *pondus*). Amazingly, the abbreviation universally used for the name of this weight unit has remained lb, which is really the abbreviation of the Latin weight unit, libra.

The barleycorn (a grain of barley) is the standard upon which several medieval measures are based. The inch, for example, was defined to be the length of three medium sized barleycorns placed end to end. Thus, the foot is 12 inches or 36 barleycorns, the cubit is 18 inches or 54 barleycorns, and so forth. Although early weight units were based upon the weight of a grain of wheat, after the fourteenth century English weight units were based on the weight of a barleycorn.

During the twelfth and thirteenth centuries a series of international commercial fairs were held in the Champagne region of northeastern France. These fairs were located on the trade routes between northern Europe and the Mediterranean, and their principal products were spices, dyes, and other precious objects. The fairs were held in various French cities, one of which was Troyes. The *troy* and *avoirdupois* pound weights were established in England sometime in the fourteenth century, probably as a result of the Champagne fairs. They are both based on the weight of a certain amount of barleycorn. The avoirdupois (from the French meaning *to have weight*) pound contained 7000 barleycorns, and was divided into 16 ounces of 437.5 barleycorns each. It was used primarily for weighing ordinary commodities such as wood, bricks, and feathers. The troy pound was named after the French city Troyes and was only used to weigh precious metals (gold, silver, etc.), gems, and drugs. The English troy pound contained only 5760 barleycorns and was subdivided into 12 ounces as was the original Roman pound (the English word *ounce* is also derived from the Latin word *unica*, meaning *the twelfth part of*). Consequently, the avoirdupois pound was considerably larger (by a factor of 7000/5760 = 1.215) than the troy pound and the coexistence of both pound units has produced considerable confusion over the years. For example, a pound of feathers actually did weigh more than a pound of gold because the weight of the feathers was measured with the avoirdupois pound, whereas the weight of the gold was measured with the troy pound.

Today, all engineering calculations done in an English units system are done with the 16-ounce, 7000-grain *avoirdupois* pound.

Other early weight units are listed below. The term *grain* here means grain of barley, or barleycorn, and the term *pound* means avoirdupois pound.

1 carat = 3 grains
1 scruple = 20 grains
1 pennyweight = 24 grains
1 drachma = 60 grains
1 shekel = 131 grains
1 stone = 14 pounds
1 talent = 66 pounds
1 hundredweight (short) = 100 pounds
1 ton (short) = 2000 pounds

and so forth.

Figure 1.1 The real jack and gill are liquid measures. (Photo by Gene Menzel.)

Many of the Mother Goose nursery rhymes were not originally written for children, but were in reality British political satires. For example, in seventeenth-century England the treasury of King Charles I (1600–1649) ran low, so he imposed a tax on the popular unit of volume used for measuring honey and hard liquor, the jack. The response of the people was to avoid the tax by consuming drink measured in units other than the jack. Eventually the jack unit became so unpopular with the people that it was no longer used for anything,[2] and coincidentally, the next larger unit size (the gill) also fell into disuse. The political meaning of the following popular Mother Goose rhyme should now become clear:

Jack and *Gill* went up a hill
  to fetch a *pail of water.*
Jack fell down and broke his *crown*
  and *Gill came tumbling after.*

The Jack and Gill in this rhyme are not a little boy and girl; they are the old units of volume measure, the jack and the gill. "Jack fell down" refers to the fall of the jack from popular usage as a result of the tax imposed by the "crown," Charles I. The phrase "and Gill came tumbling after" refers to the subsequent decline in the use to the gill unit of volume measure. Figure 1.1 illustrates the "real" jack and gill of this rhyme.

---

2. One of the few existing references to the jack unit of volume measure today is in the term *jackpot*, which normally means two handfuls of coins.

Early numerical systems had no special symbol for the "nothing" number, the null or zero. Before the ninth century A.D. a zero was denoted by a blank, a bar, or a dot in a number sequence (e.g., the number 1304 was written as 13 4 or 13-4 or 13·4). The first known use of the "0" symbol for zero was in an A.D. 870 Indian inscription. Eventually the "0" became the universally accepted symbol to represent *nothing*, and by A.D. 1484 the word *null* (from *nulla figura*, Latin for *nothing figure*) was also commonly taken to mean zero. The symbol "0" itself probably comes from the first letter of the Greek word for nothing, *ουδεγ*.

The elements of mathematical symbolic logic were developed during the fifteenth- and sixteenth-century Renaissance period. The + and − signs for addition and subtraction appeared in 1489. The equality symbol (=) appeared in 1557. The multiplication symbol (×) appeared in 1631, and the division symbol (÷) in 1659. Decimal fractions were introduced in 1585, and various notational schemes for them were used. An Englishman, John Napier (1550–1617), the originator of natural logarithms, created the decimal point notation we use today.

Until the late eighteenth century units were invented at random. Particular measures became popular purely by chance, and there were major variations in the metrologies of coexisting cultures. There were few standards, and those that did exist were usually enforced only locally. Conversion factors between measures of different cultures were usually nonexistent. This did not cause much of a problem at the time because people normally "saw" what they were buying; thus, exact numerical conversion factors were unnecessary. A detailed understanding of commercial units was of value only to those involved in record keeping.

It was not until 1822 that science began to take a serious look at units and dimensions. In his remarkable book on heat transfer published in that year, Joseph Fourier (1768–1830) showed for the first time that certain measures can be expressed in terms of other, more "fundamental," measures.[3] Fourier appears to have been the first to realize that all measures can be divided into two groups: fundamental quantities and secondary or derived quantities. This was the beginning of modern dimensional analysis.

Although the decimal system today appears to be the most natural for numerical measurements, it took over 5000 years of civilization to bring it to its present form. On the other hand, it seems almost incredible that today we are using units such as the foot and the second whose basis has remained essentially unchanged for the past 2000 or more years!

Temperature Units

Thermometry is the technology of temperature measurement. Although people have always been able to experience the physiological sensations of hot and cold, the quantification and accurate measurement of these concepts did not occur until

3. Section IX of *Theorie Analytique de la Chaleur* by Jean Baptiste Joseph Fourier, 1822 (an English translation was published by Dover in 1955).

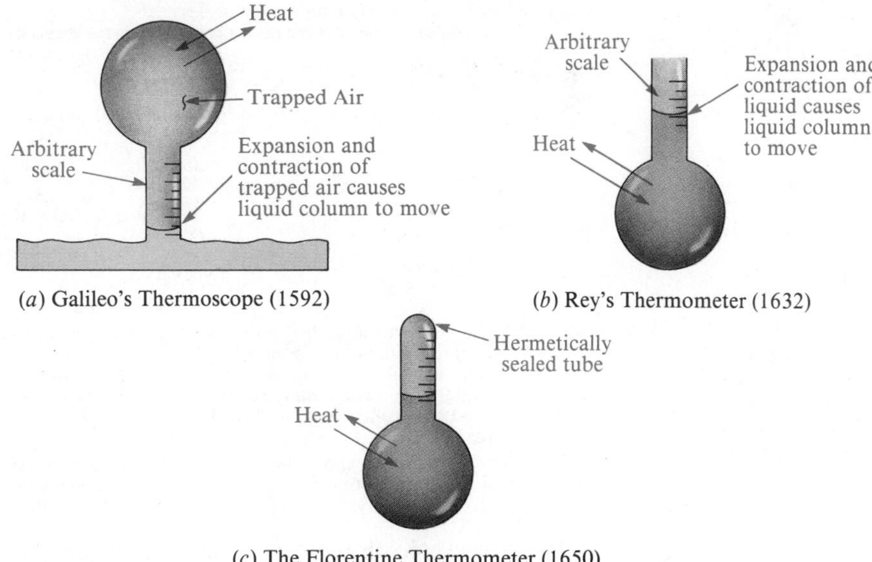

(*a*) Galileo's Thermoscope (1592)

(*b*) Rey's Thermometer (1632)

(*c*) The Florentine Thermometer (1650)

Figure 1.2 A schematic of early thermometer designs.

the seventeenth century. Ancient physicians judged the wellness of their patients by sensing fevers and chills with a touch of the hand (as we often do today). The Roman physician Galen (ca. 129–199) ascribed the fundamental differences in the health or *temperament* of a person to the proportions in which the four *humors* (phlegm, black bile, yellow bile, and blood) were mixed within the body.[4] Thus, the term for wellness (temperament) and that for body heat (temperature) were both derived from the same Latin root *temperamentum*, meaning *a correct mixture of things*.

Galileo Galilei (1564–1642) is credited with constructing the first practical thermometer (then called a *thermoscope*) in about 1592.[5] It had an arbitrary scale, and since it moved a column of colored liquid by heating or cooling the air trapped above the liquid (see Fig. 1.2*a*), it was also sensitive to changes in atmospheric pressure. In 1632 the French physician Jean Rey (1582–1645) developed a thermometer in which the indicating liquid moved due to its own expansion and contraction (see Fig. 1.2*b*), but it was still somewhat sensitive to changes in atmospheric pressure. This defect was removed in the Florentine thermometers of 1650 by completely sealing the tube containing the indicating liquid (see Fig. 1.2*c*)

4. It was thought that illness occurred when these four humors were not in balance, and that their balance could be restored by draining off one of them (i.e., by *bleeding* the patient).

5. The word *thermometer* first appears as *thermometre* in the French treatise *La Recreation Mathematique* by J. Leurechon in 1624.

Table 1.1 Early temperature scales

Inventor and date	Fixed points
Isaac Newton (1701)	Freezing water (0 °N) and human body heat (12 °N)
Daniel Fahrenheit (1724)	Freezing water (0 °F) and human body heat (96 °F)*
Rene Reaumur (1730)	Freezing water (0 °Re) and boiling water (80 °Re)
Anders Celsius (1742)†	Freezing water (0 °C) and boiling water (100 °C)

* The modern Fahrenheit scale uses the freezing point of water (32 °F) and the boiling point of water (212 °F) as its fixed points. This change to more stable fixed points resulted in changing the average body temperature reading from 96 °F on the old Fahrenheit scale to 98.6 °F on the new Fahrenheit scale.

† Initially Celsius chose the freezing point of water to be 100° and the boiling point of water to be 0°, but this scale was soon inverted to its present form.

Until the late seventeenth century thermometers were graduated with arbitrary scales. However, it soon became clear that some form of temperature standardization was necessary, and by the early eighteenth century 30 to 40 different temperature scales were in use. These scales were based on the use of two fixed calibration points (standard temperatures) with the distance between them divided into arbitrarily chosen equally spaced degrees, or else they had a single fixed calibration point with the scale divisions calculated from the known expansion properties of the enclosed liquid. Some of these early scales and their fixed calibration points are shown in Table 1.1. Note that both the Newton and the Fahrenheit scales are duodecimal (i.e., base 12).

The one hundred division (i.e., base 10 or decimal) Celsius temperature scale became very popular during the eighteenth and nineteenth centuries and was commonly known as the *centigrade* (from the latin *centi* for *100* and *gradua* for *step*) scale until 1948 when Celsius' name was formally attached to it and the term centrigrade was officially dropped.

In 1848 William Thomson (1824–1907), later to become Lord Kelvin, developed the absolute Celsius scale that now bears his name. It has a single fixed calibration point (the triple point of water, 0.01 °C or 273.16 K). Soon thereafter the absolute Fahrenheit temperature scale was developed and named after the Scottish engineer William Rankine (1820–1872). The relation between the modern temperature scales are shown below:

$$T\,(^\circ\text{F}) = \tfrac{9}{5}T\,(^\circ\text{C}) + 32 = T\,(\text{R}) - 459.67$$

$$T\,(^\circ\text{C}) = \tfrac{5}{9}[T\,(^\circ\text{F}) - 32] = T\,(\text{K}) - 273.15$$

$$T\,(\text{R}) = \tfrac{9}{5}T\,(\text{K}) = (1.8)T\,(\text{K}) = T\,(^\circ F) + 459.67$$

$$T\,(\text{K}) = \tfrac{5}{9}T\,(\text{R}) = T\,(\text{R})/1.8 = T\,(^\circ\text{C}) + 273.15$$

The Classical Mechanical and Electrical Units Systems

As Fourier realized, the establishment of a stable system of units requires the identification of certain measures which must be taken as absolutely fundamental and undefinable. For example, one cannot define force, or length, or time, or mass, or energy in terms of more fundamental dimensions. They all seem to be fundamental quantities. Since we have so many different quantities that can be taken as fundamental, we have no single unique system of units. Instead, there are many equivalent units systems, many of which are built upon different fundamental dimensions. However, all of the existing units systems today have one thing in common—they have all been developed from the same set of fundamental *equations* of physics, equations that were more or less arbitrarily chosen for this task.

All the equations of physics are mere proportionalities into which one must always introduce a *constant of proportionality* to obtain an equality. These proportionality constants, it turns out, are intimately related to the system of units used in producing the numerical calculations. Consequently, there are three basic decisions that must be made in establishing a consistent system of units:

1. The choice of the fundamental quantities on which the system of units is to be based.
2. The choice of the fundamental equations that will serve to define the secondary quantities of the system of units.
3. The choice of the magnitude *and* dimensions of the inherent constants of proportionality that appear in the fundamental equations of decision 2.

With this degree of flexibility it is easy to see why so many different measurement units systems have evolved throughout history.

The classical units systems and their fundamental equations that are commonly used today are

1. Mechanical
Wherein the fundamental equation is Newton's second law

$$F = k_1 ma \tag{1.1}$$

2. Electrical
Wherein the fundamental equations are

a) Newton's second law

$$F = k_1 ma$$

b) Coulomb's law

$$F = k_2\left(\frac{q_1 q_2}{R^2}\right) \tag{1.2}$$

c) Ampere's law

$$\frac{dF}{dL} = k_3\left(\frac{I_1 I_2}{R^2}\right) \tag{1.3}$$

d) Faraday's law

$$\nabla \times \mathbf{E} + k_4\left(\frac{\partial \mathbf{B}}{\partial t}\right) = 0 \tag{1.4}$$

The wide variety of choices that are available for the fundamental quantities that can be used in each of these classical systems has produced a large number of different units systems. Over a period of time, three systems based upon three different sets of fundamental quantities have become popular. They are the MLt system, which considers mass (M), length (L), and time (t) as independent fundamental quantities; the FLt system, which considers force (F), length (L), and time (t) as independent fundamental quantities; and the $FLMt$ system which considers all four as independent fundamental quantities. Table 1.2 shows the various popular mechanical units systems that have evolved along these lines. Also listed are the names arbitrarily given to the various derived units, and the value and units of the constant of proportionality, k_1, which appears in Newton's second law, Eq. 1.1.

In Table 1.2, the four units in boldface type have the following definitions

$$1 \text{ newton} = 1 \text{ kg}\cdot\text{m/s}^2 \tag{1.5}$$

$$1 \text{ dyne} = 1 \text{ g}\cdot\text{cm/s}^2 \tag{1.6}$$

$$1 \text{ poundal} = 1 \text{ lbm}\cdot\text{ft/s}^2 \tag{1.7}$$

$$1 \text{ slug} = 1 \text{ lbf}\cdot\text{s}^2\text{/ft} \tag{1.8}$$

These definitions are derived from Newton's second law using the fact that k_1 has been arbitrarily chosen to be unity and dimensionless in each of these units systems.

Table 1.2 Five different units systems

System name	System type	F	M	L	t	$g_c = \frac{1}{k_1}$
MKS (SI)	MLt	**newton** (N)	kilogram (kg)	meter (m)	second (s)	1 (dimensionless)
CGS	MLt	**dyne** (d)	gram (g)	centimeter (cm)	second (s)	1 (dimensionless)
Absolute English	MLt	**poundal** (pd)	pound mass (lbm)	foot (ft)	second (s)	1 (dimensionless)
Technical English	FLt	pound force (lbf)	**slug** (sg)	foot (ft)	second (s)	1 (dimensionless)
Engineering English	$FMLt$	pound force (lbf)	pound mass (lbm)	foot (ft)	second (s)	$32.2 \frac{\text{lbm}\cdot\text{ft}}{\text{lbf}\cdot\text{s}^2}$

Because of the form of k_1 in the Engineering English system, engineering texts have evolved a rather strange and unfortunate convention regarding its use. It is common to let $g_c = 1/k_1$, where g_c in the Engineering English units system is simply (see Table 1.2)

$$g_c = \frac{1}{k_1} = 32.2\,\frac{\text{lbm}\cdot\text{ft}}{\text{lbf}\cdot\text{s}^2} \tag{1.9}$$

and in all the other units systems described in Table 1.2 it is

$$g_c = \frac{1}{k_1} = 1 \text{ (dimensionless)} \tag{1.10}$$

This symbolism was originally chosen apparently because the *value* (but not the *dimensions*) of g_c happens to be the same as that of standard gravity in the Engineering English units system. However, this symbolism is awkward because it tends to make you think that g_c is the same as local gravity, *which it definitely is not*. Like k_1, g_c is nothing more than an arbitrarily chosen constant with dimensions of $ML/(Ft^2)$. Because the use of g_c is so widespread today and because it is important that you are able to recognize the meaning of g_c when you see it elsewhere, it will be used in all the relevant equations in this text. For example, we will now write Newton's second law as

$$F = \frac{ma}{g_c} \tag{1.11}$$

Until the mid twentieth century, most English-speaking countries used the Engineering English units system. But because of world trade pressures and the worldwide acceptance of the SI system, most engineering thermodynamics texts today (including this one) present example and homework problems in both the old Engineering English and the new SI units systems.

Example 1.1

In Table 1.2 the Technical English units system uses force (F), length (L), and time (t) as the fundamental dimensions. The mass unit *slug* was then defined such that k_1 and g_c came out to be unity and dimensionless. Define a new units system in which the force, mass, and time dimensions are taken to be fundamental with units of lbf, lbm, and s, and the length unit is defined such that k_1 is unity and dimensionless. Call this new length unit the *chunk* and find its conversion factor into the Engineering English and SI units systems.

Solution From Eq. 1.1 we see that the length unit must be defined via Newton's second law, $F = k_1 ma$. Since we want to have k_1 to be unity and dimensionless, we set

$$k_1 = \frac{F}{ma} = 1 \text{ (dimensionless)}$$

In our new system, we will arbitrarily require 1 lbf to be the force calculated from Newton's second law when 1 lbm is accelerated at a rate of 1 chunk/s^2. Then, from the k_1 equation above, we get

$$\frac{1 \text{ lbf}}{1 \text{ lbm } (1 \text{ chunk/s}^2)} = 1 \text{ (dimensionless)}$$

so that

$$1 \text{ chunk} = 1 \frac{\text{lbf} \cdot \text{s}^2}{\text{lbm}}$$

In the Engineering English units system, 1 lbf accelerates 1 lbm at a rate of

$$a = \frac{F}{mk_1} = \frac{F}{m}(g_c) = \frac{1 \text{ lbf}}{1 \text{ lbm}}\left(32.2 \frac{\text{lbm} \cdot \text{ft}}{\text{lbf} \cdot \text{s}^2}\right) = 32.2 \text{ ft/s}^2$$

Since lbf, lbm, and s have the same meaning in both the new system and the traditional Engineering English units system, it follows that

$$1 \text{ chunk/s}^2 \equiv 32.2 \text{ ft/s}^2$$

and that

$$1 \text{ chunk} = 32.2 \text{ ft} = (32.2 \text{ ft})/(3.218 \text{ ft/m}) = 10.0 \text{ m}$$

An electrical units system is constructed by taking one of the mechanical systems (usually the CGS or MKS system) and then adding a fourth fundamental electrical quantity, usually current (I) or charge (Q). The necessary secondary units of voltage (E), resistance (R), capacitance (C), inductance (L), magnetic induction (B), magnetic flux (Φ), and so forth are then developed from the fundamental equations (Eqs. 1.1–1.4) chosen for the system. Table 1.3 presents a few of the classical electrical units systems that have become popular, along with the names given to the secondary units and the magnitude and units of the proportionality constants k_1 through k_4. Like the previous table, Table 1.3 does not list units conversion factors for the various units. Tables 1.2 and 1.3 only afford one the opportunity to make sure that a consistent set of units is being used in any calculation.

In the late nineteenth century the English physicist and electrical engineer Oliver Heaviside (1850–1925) realized that if Coulomb's law were divided by 4, then a leading integer factor of 4 would be removed from many of the commonly used electromagnetic formulae. This modification considerably simplified calculations made using these formulae (in a precomputer age) and was, therefore, very attractive to the physicists of the time. When Coulomb's law was transformed in this way a new units system emerged that Heaviside called *rationalized*. Rationalized CGS and MKS systems became quite popular among physicists, and the structure of the rationalized MKSA system can also be found in Table 1.3. The constants k_1 through k_4 in this table are the proportionality constants in Eqs. 1.1 through 1.4.

Table 1.3 Classical electrical units systems

Quantity	MKSA (SI)	Rationalized MKSA	Electrostatic	Electromagnetic
Base mechanical system	MKS	MKS	CGS	CGS
Current (I)	amp (A)	amp (A)	statamp ($g^{1/2}\cdot cm^{3/2}\cdot s^{-2}$)	abamp ($g^{1/2}\cdot cm^{1/2}\cdot s^{-1}$)
Charge (Q)	coulomb (A·s)	coulomb (A·s)	statcoul ($g^{1/2}\cdot cm^{3/2}\cdot s^{-1}$)	abcoul ($g^{1/2}\cdot cm^{1/2}$)
Voltage (E)	volt ($m^2\cdot kg\cdot s^{-3}\cdot A^{-1}$)	volt ($m^2\cdot kg\cdot s^{-3}\cdot A^{-1}$)	statvolt ($g^{1/2}\cdot cm^{1/2}\cdot s^{-1}$)	abvolt ($g^{1/2}\cdot cm^{3/2}\cdot s^{-2}$)
Resistance (R)	ohm ($m^2\cdot kg\cdot s^{-3}\cdot A^{-2}$)	ohm ($m^2\cdot kg\cdot s^{-3}\cdot A^{-2}$)	statohm ($s\cdot cm^{-1}$)	abohm ($cm\cdot s^{-1}$)
Capacitance (C)	farad ($m^{-2}\cdot kg^{-1}\cdot s^4\cdot A^2$)	farad ($m^{-2}\cdot kg^{-1}\cdot s^4\cdot A^2$)	statfarad (cm)	abfarad ($s^2\cdot cm^{-1}$)
Induction (L)	henry ($m^2\cdot kg\cdot s^{-2}\cdot A^{-2}$)	henry ($m^2\cdot kg\cdot s^{-2}\cdot A^{-2}$)	stathenry ($s^2\cdot cm^{-1}$)	abhenry (cm)
Magnetic induction (B)	tesla ($kg\cdot s^{-2}\cdot A^{-1}$)	tesla ($kg\cdot s^{-2}\cdot A^{-1}$)	$g^{1/2}\cdot cm^{-3/2}$	gauss ($g^{1/2}\cdot cm^{-1/2}\cdot s^{-1}$)
Magnetic flux (Φ)	weber ($m^2\cdot kg\cdot s^{-2}\cdot A^{-1}$)	weber ($m^2\cdot kg\cdot s^{-2}\cdot A^{-1}$)	$g^{1/2}\cdot cm^{1/2}$	$g^{1/2}\cdot cm^{3/2}\cdot s^{-1}$
k_1	1.0	1.0	1.0	1.0
k_2	$1/\epsilon_0$	$1/(4\pi\epsilon_0)$	1.0	c^2
k_3	μ_0	$\mu_0/(4\pi)$	c^{-2}	1.0
k_4	1.0	1.0	1.0	1.0

The constants k_1 through k_4 are the proportionality constants in Eqs. 1.1 through 1.4. Also,

$$c = \text{the velocity of light} = 2.998 \times 10^{10}\ \text{cm/s} = 2.998 \times 10^{8}\ \text{m/s}$$

$$\epsilon_0 = \text{the electric permittivity of vacuum} = 8.8542 \times 10^{-12}\ \text{A}^2\cdot\text{s}^4/(\text{kg}\cdot\text{m}^3)$$

$$\mu_0 = \text{the magnetic permeability of vacuum} = 4\pi \times 10^{-7}\ \text{kg}\cdot\text{m}/(\text{A}\cdot\text{s})^2$$

Note: This is not a unit conversion table. For units conversion information consult Appendix A or the first reference at the end of this chapter.

Chemical Units

A chemical reaction equation is essentially a molecular mass balance equation. For example, the equation A + B → C tells us that one molecule of A reacts with one molecule of B to yield one molecule of C. Since the molecular mass of substance A contains the same number of molecules (6.023×10^{23}, or Avogadro's number) as the molecular mass of substances B and C, then the coefficients in the chemical reaction equation represent the number of molecular mass units involved in the reaction as well as the number of molecules. Consequently, chemists find it convenient to use a mass unit that is proportional to the molecular masses of the substances involved in a reaction. Since chemists use only small amounts of chemicals in laboratory experiments, the CGS units system has proven to be ideal for their work. Therefore, chemists have defined *the amount of any chemical substance that has a mass in grams numerically equal to the molecular mass of the substance* as their molecular mass unit, and have given it the name *mole.*

However, the mole unit is problematic in that most of the other physical sciences do not use the CGS units system, and the actual size of the molar mass unit depends upon the size of the mass unit in the units system being used. Strictly speaking, the molar mass unit used by chemists should always be called a *gram mole,* because the word mole by itself does not convey the type of mass unit being used in the unit system. Consequently, we call the molar mass of a substance in the SI system a *kilogram mole*; in the Absolute and Engineering English systems it is a *pound mole*; and in the Technical English system it is a *slug mole.* In this text we abbreviate gram mole as *gmole*, kilogram mole as *kgmole*, and pound mole as *lbmole*. Clearly these are all different amounts of mass since 1 gmole $\neq$ 1 kgmole $\neq$ 1 lbmole $\neq$ 1 slug mole. For example, 1 pound mole of water would have a mass of 18 lbm, whereas 1 gram mole would have a mass of only 18 g (0.04 lbm), so that there is an enormous difference in the molar masses of a substance depending upon the units system being used.

Since the molar amount n of a substance having a mass m is given by

$$n = \frac{m}{M} \tag{1.12}$$

where M is the molecular mass[6] of the substance, it is clear that the molecular mass must have units of mass/mass-mole. Therefore, we can write the molecular mass of water as

$$M_{H_2O} = 18 \text{ g/gmole} = 18 \text{ lbm/lbmole} = 18 \text{ kg/kgmole} = \cdots$$

The numerical value of the molecular mass is constant, but it has units that must be taken into account whenever it is used in an equation.

The Development of Modern Units Systems

The technological and scientific advances of the Renaissance contributed to the growing international commerce of the western world. After the seventeenth century development of the *decimal point* notation in number writing, it became clear that the decimal system had obvious advantages in speed and accuracy in commercial transactions. It was also becoming clear that international trade was severely impeded by the jumble of confusing units then in vogue throughout the world. In 1790 the French National Assembly requested the French Academy of Sciences to develop a system of commercial units suitable for adoption by the entire world. A decimal system based on the meter of length and the gram mass was soon established in France, but it took nearly a century before its adoption was seriously considered on a worldwide basis.

The international adoption of the French decimal units system began in 1870 when 15 nations met in Paris to discuss the issue. In 1872 a second such meeting took place with 26 nations participating, and in 1875 an international treaty entitled *The Metric Convention* was produced and signed by 17 nations (including the United States). This treaty established

1. Metric standards for length (the meter) and mass (the gram).
2. An International Bureau of Weights and Measures (BIPM).[7]

6. Most texts call M the molecular *weight*, probably out of historical tradition. However, M clearly has units of *mass*, not weight, and therefore is more appropriately named molecular mass.

7. These are abbreviations of the French language form of these titles. PM is from the French *poids et mesures* for *weights and measures*.

3. A General Conference of Weights and Measures (CGPM),[7] which was to meet every six years.
4. An International Committee of Weights and Measures (CIPM),[7] which was to meet every two years to implement the recommendations of the CGPM and to direct the BIPM.

In 1881 the International Electrical Congress recommended that the common unit of time, the second, be added to a metric units system based on the centimeter length unit and the gram mass unit to produce the CGS (centimeter–gram–second) system. In 1904 a similar addition to a system based on the meter length unit and the kilogram mass unit produced the MKS (meter–kilogram–second) units system.

In 1935 the International Electrotechnical Commission recommended that the MKS system be linked with the electromagnetic system of units by the adoption of an appropriate electrical quantity as a fourth fundamental quantity. It was decided that electrical current (I) would be the fourth fundamental quantity and the *ampere* was chosen as its unit of measure, thus producing the MKSA units system.

In 1954 the CGPM adopted a coherent system of units based on the six fundamental quantities of length (L), mass (M), time (t), electrical current (I), absolute temperature (T), and luminous intensity (I_ℓ). The four units of the MKSA system plus the absolute temperature unit, degree Kelvin (°K), and the luminous intensity unit, the candela (cd), were chosen as standard units for these fundamental quantities.

In 1960 the CGPM produced a modernized metric system of units based upon the six fundamental quantities and units adopted in 1954. They officially titled this system *The International System of Units* (or *Le Systeme International d'Unités* in French) which was to be abbreviated SI in all languages.

In 1967 the degree symbol (°) was officially dropped from the absolute temperature unit, and a notational scheme was introduced wherein *all unit names were to be written without capitalization* (unless, of course, they appear at the beginning of a sentence) regardless of whether they were derived from proper names or not. Thus, the name of the SI absolute temperature unit was reduced from *degree Kelvin* to simply *kelvin* even though the unit was named after Lord Kelvin. However, when the name of a unit is to be abbreviated, it was decided that *the name abbreviation was to be capitalized if the unit was derived from a proper name*. Therefore, the kelvin absolute temperature unit is abbreviated as K (not °K and not k or °k). Similarly, the SI unit of force, the newton, named after Sir Isaac Newton (1647–1723), is abbreviated N. The following list illustrates a variety of units from the SI and other systems which were all derived from proper names:

> ampere (A), becquerel (Bq), celsius (°C), coulomb (C), farad (F), fahrenheit (°F), gauss (G), gray (Gy), henry (H), hertz (Hz), joule (J), kelvin (K), newton (N), ohm (Ω), pascal (Pa), poiseuille (P), rankine (R), siemens (S), stoke (St), tesla (T), volt (V), watt (W), weber (Wb).

Note that we still use the degree symbol (°) with the celsius and fahrenheit temperature units. This is due partly to tradition and partly to distinguish their abbreviations from those of the coulomb and farad. In this text we have also dropped the degree symbol on the rankine absolute temperature unit even though it is not part of the SI system. This is done simply to be consistent with the SI notation scheme and because the rankine abbreviation, R, does not conflict with that of any other popular unit. Note that abbreviations use two letters only when necessary to prevent them from being confused with other established unit abbreviations, or to express prefixes (e.g., kg for kilogram).[8]

All other units whose names were *not* derived from the names of historically important people are both written and abbreviated with lowercase letters, for example, meter (m), kilogram (kg), and second (s). Obvious violations of this rule occur when any unit name appears at the beginning of a sentence, or when its abbreviation is part of a capitalized title, such as in "The MKSA System of Units."

Also, a unit abbreviation is *never* pluralized whereas the unit's name may be pluralized. For example, kilograms is abbreviated as kg, and *not* kgs; newtons as N, and *not* Ns, and so forth. And finally, unit name abbreviations are *never written with a terminal period* unless they appear at the end of a sentence: The correct abbreviation of seconds is s, not s., sec., or secs., and so forth.

In 1971 the CGPM added a seventh fundamental quantity and unit, the molar mass unit (n), and the term *mole* was chosen as its unit of measure.[9] The mole is defined to be the amount of substance containing as many *elementary entities* as there are atoms in 0.012 kg of carbon-12. Elementary entities may be such things as atoms, molecules, ions, electrons, or other well defined particles or groups of such particles. The mole unit is clearly an alternative mass unit and is useful in analysis wherein well-defined interactions of the elementary entities occur, as in the case of chemical reactions.

Table 1.4 lists the seven fundamental quantities and units of the modern SI system and their definitions. Note that the kilogram is the only fundamental SI unit that has a prefix (kilo). Table 1.5 lists various common derived secondary units of the SI system, and Table 1.6 shows the approved SI prefixes along with their names and symbols.

Care should always be taken to differentiate between the units of absolute pressure and gage pressure. In the Engineering English units system we add the letter "a" or "g" to the psi (pounds per square inch) pressure units to make this distinction. Thus, atmospheric pressure is written as 14.7 psia, or 0 psig. In the SI units system we add the *word* that applies (and *not* the letter "a" or "g") immediately after the unit name or symbol. For example, atmospheric pressure in the SI system is 101,325 Pa absolute, or 0 Pa gage. *When the clarifying term "absolute" or "gage" is not present, the pressure unit is assumed to be absolute* (i.e., the statement "15.2 kPa" is to be interpreted as "15.2 kPa absolute").

---

8. Non-SI units systems do not generally follow this simple rule. For example, the English length unit, foot, could be abbreviated f rather than ft. However, the latter abbreviation is well established within society and changing it at this time would only cause confusion.

9. This was an unfortunate choice for the name of this unit because as it is normally used it corresponds to a gram mole of a substance. Thus, the standard SI mass unit (kg) and this new molar mass unit (gram mole) do not have the same prefix.

Table 1.4 Fundamental SI units

Dimension	Unit name and definition
Length	meter (m)—the length equal to 1,650,763.73 wavelengths in vacuum of the radiation corresponding to the transition between the levels $2p_{10}$ and $5d_5$ of the krypton-86 atom (adopted by the 1960 CGPM).
Mass*	kilogram (kg)—a cylinder of platinum–iridium alloy kept by the International Bureau of Weights and Measures in France (adopted by the 1889 and 1901 CGPM).
Time	second (s)—the duration of 9,192,631,770 periods of the radiation corresponding to the transition between the two hyperfine levels of the ground state of a cesium 133 atom (adopted by the 1967 CGPM).
Electric current	ampere (A)—that constant current which, if maintained in two straight parallel conductors of infinite length, of negligible circular cross section, and placed one meter apart in a vacuum, would produce between these conductors a force equal to 2×10^{-7} newton per meter of length (adopted by the 1948 CGPM).
Thermodynamic temperature	kelvin (K)—the fraction 1/273.16 of the thermodynamic temperature of the triple point of water (adopted by the 1967 CGPM).
Amount of matter†	mole (mol)—the amount of substance of a system which contains as many elementary entities as there are atoms in 0.012 kilogram of carbon-12 (adopted by the 1971 CGPM).
Amount of light	candela (cd)—the luminous intensity, in the perpendicular direction, of a surface of 1/600,000 square meter of blackbody at the temperature of freezing platinum (2042 K) under a pressure of 101,325 newtons per square meter (adopted by the 1967 CGPM).

* This is the only fundamental unit still defined by an artifact.

† In this text we use the symbols kgmole and lbmole for this quantity.

Source: Adapted from American Society for Testing and Materials, *Standard for Metric Practice*, ASTM E 38-79, January 1980. Copyright ASTM. Reprinted with permission.

Table 1.5 Some common derived SI units

Dimension	Name	Symbol	Formula	Expression in terms of SI fundamental units
Frequency	hertz	Hz	1/s	s^{-1}
Force	newton	N	$kg \cdot m/s^2$	$m \cdot kg \cdot s^{-2}$
Energy	joule	J	$N \cdot m$	$m^2 \cdot kg \cdot s^{-2}$
Power	watt	W	J/s	$m^2 \cdot kg \cdot s^{-3}$
Electric charge	coulomb	C	$A \cdot s$	$A \cdot s$
Electric potential	volt	V	W/A	$m^2 \cdot kg \cdot s^{-3} \cdot A^{-1}$
Electric resistance	ohm	Ω	V/A	$m^2 \cdot kg \cdot s^{-3} \cdot A^{-2}$
Electric capacitance	farad	F	C/V	$m^{-2} \cdot kg^{-1} \cdot s^4 \cdot A^2$
Magnetic flux	weber	Wb	$V \cdot s$	$m^2 \cdot kg \cdot s^{-2} \cdot A^{-1}$
Pressure or stress	pascal	Pa	N/m^2	$m^{-1} \cdot kg \cdot s^{-2}$
Conductance	siemens	S	A/V	$m^{-2} \cdot kg^{-1} \cdot s^3 \cdot A^2$
Magnetic flux density	tesla	T	Wb/m^2	$kg \cdot s^{-2} \cdot A^{-1}$
Inductance	henry	H	Wb/A	$m^2 \cdot kg \cdot s^{-2} \cdot A^{-2}$
Luminous flux	lumen	lm	$cd \cdot sr$	$cd \cdot sr$
Illuminance	lux	lx	lm/m^2	$m^{-2} \cdot cd \cdot sr$

Source: Adapted from the American Society for Testing and Materials, *Standard for Metric Practice*, ASTM E 380-79, January 1980. Copyright ASTM. Reprinted with permission.

Table 1.6 SI Unit prefixes

Multiples and submultiples	Prefixes	Symbols
10^{18}	exa	E
10^{15}	peta	P
10^{12}	tera	T
10^{9}	giga	G
10^{6}	mega	M
10^{3}	kilo	k
10^{2}	hecto	h
10^{1}	deka	da
10^{-1}	deci	d
10^{-2}	centi	c
10^{-3}	milli	m
10^{-6}	micro	μ
10^{-9}	nano	n
10^{-12}	pico	p
10^{-15}	femto	f
10^{-18}	atto	a

Source: Adapted with permission from The Society for Testing and Materials, *Standard for Metric Practice*, ASTM E 380-79, January 1980.

Example 1.2 Determine the kinetic energy of a bullet having a mass of 10 grams traveling at a velocity of 3000 ft/s in both SI and Engineering English units.

Solution The formula for kinetic energy (KE) of an object with mass m travelling at velocity V is

$$\mathrm{KE} = \tfrac{1}{2}k_1 mV^2 = \frac{mV^2}{2g_c}$$

In the SI units system, $m = 10$ grams $= 0.01$ kg, and

$$V = (3000\ \mathrm{ft/s})\left(\frac{1\ \mathrm{m}}{3.281\ \mathrm{ft}}\right) = 914.4\ \mathrm{m/s}$$

From Table 1.2 we find that $g_c = 1/k_1 = 1$ (dimensionless). Therefore,

$$\mathrm{KE} = \frac{(1)(0.01\ \mathrm{kg})(914.4\ \mathrm{m/s})^2}{2} = 4181\ \mathrm{kg \cdot m^2/s^2} = 4181\ \mathrm{N \cdot m} = 4181\ \mathrm{J}$$

where $1\ \mathrm{J} = 1\ \mathrm{N \cdot m} = 1\ \mathrm{kg \cdot m^2/s^2}$. In the Engineering English units system, $V = 3000$ ft/s, and

$$m = 10\ \mathrm{grams} = 0.01\ \mathrm{kg} = (0.01\ \mathrm{kg})(2.205\ \mathrm{lbm/kg}) = 0.022\ \mathrm{lbm}$$

From Table 1.2 we find that $g_c = 1/k_1 = 32.2$ lbm·ft/(lbf·s^2). Therefore,

$$KE = \frac{(0.022 \text{ lbm})(3000 \text{ ft/s})^2}{2\left(32.2 \dfrac{\text{lbm}\cdot\text{ft}}{\text{lbf}\cdot\text{s}^2}\right)} = 3075 \text{ ft}\cdot\text{lbf}$$

$$= (3075 \text{ ft}\cdot\text{lbf})/(778 \text{ ft}\cdot\text{lbf/Btu}) = 3.95 \text{ Btu}$$

Example 1.3 Determine the potential energy of an automobile weighing 2000 lbf when it is 8 feet off the floor on a hoist in a repair shop. Express the result in both SI and Engineering English units.

Solution The formula for potential energy (PE) of an object of mass m at a distance Z above the reference height is

$$PE = k_1 mgZ = m\left(\frac{g}{g_c}\right)Z$$

We must first calculate the automobile's mass from its weight using Newton's second law, F = weight = mg/g_c. In the SI units system Table 1.2 gives $g_c = 1/k_1 = 1$ (dimensionless), so that the mass becomes

$$m = \frac{Fg_c}{g} = \frac{(2000 \text{ lbf})\left(\dfrac{1 \text{ N}}{0.2248 \text{ lbf}}\right)(1 \text{ dimensionless})}{9.8 \text{ m/s}^2}$$

$$= 907.8 \frac{\text{N}\cdot\text{s}^2}{\text{m}} = 907.8 \text{ kg}$$

Now,

$$Z = (8 \text{ ft})\left(\frac{1 \text{ m}}{3.281 \text{ ft}}\right) = 2.438 \text{ m}$$

therefore,

$$PE = (1)(907.8 \text{ kg})(9.8 \text{ m/s}^2)(2.438 \text{ m}) = 21{,}690 \text{ kg}\cdot\text{m}^2/\text{s}^2$$

$$= 21{,}690 \text{ N}\cdot\text{m} = 21{,}690 \text{ J} = 21.69 \text{ kJ}$$

In the Engineering English units system we have

$$m = \frac{Fg_c}{g} = \frac{(2000 \text{ lbf})\left(32.2 \dfrac{\text{lbm}\cdot\text{ft}}{\text{lbf}\cdot\text{s}^2}\right)}{32.2 \text{ ft/s}^2} = 2000 \text{ lbm}$$

Here $Z = 8$ ft and from Table 1.2 we find that $g_c = 1/k_1 = 32.2$ lbm·ft/(lbf·s^2).

Therefore,

$$PE = (2000 \text{ lbm})\left(\frac{32.2 \text{ ft/s}^2}{32.2 \dfrac{\text{lbm}\cdot\text{ft}}{\text{lbf}\cdot\text{s}^2}}\right)(8 \text{ ft}) = 16{,}000 \text{ ft}\cdot\text{lbf}$$

$$= (16{,}000 \text{ ft}\cdot\text{lbf})(1 \text{ Btu}/778 \text{ ft}\cdot\text{lbf}) = 20.6 \text{ Btu}$$

Summary

Units are not trivial. An accurate computation depends as much on correct units management as it does on correct numerical calculation. Engineers must have a sound understanding of how units systems are constructed and how the various units systems popular today are related to each other.

In this chapter we have reviewed the origin and development of systems of units. We have seen that units of measurement evolved from a growing need to expand and quantify the elements of commerce, and are undeniably woven into the history of civilizations. This chapter also contains an accurate description of the evolution and structure of a consistent worldwide system of units, the SI system. The United States is currently in the process of converting all of its commerce and technology into this system. Since it is not known exactly how long this will take, textbooks such as this one must present material in both the traditional Engineering English units system and the new SI units system so that you, the

Table 1.7 Glossary of technical terms introduced in Chapter 1

Metrology	The study of measurement.
Dimension	A measurable characteristic.
Duodecimal	A base 12 number system.
Sexagesimal	A base 60 number system.
Newton's second law	$F = ma/g_c$.
Newton	1 newton = 1 $kg\cdot m/s^2$.
Dyne	1 dyne = 1 $g\cdot cm/s^2$.
Poundal	1 poundal = 1 $lbm\cdot ft/s^2$.
Slug	1 slug = 1 $lbf\cdot s^2/ft$.
g_c	The dimensional proportionality constant in Newton's second law. In the Engineering English units system $g_c = 32.2$ $lbm\cdot ft/(lbf\cdot s^2)$, and in the SI units system $g_c = 1.0$ and is dimensionless.
gmole	The amount of any chemical substance that has a mass in grams numerically equal to the molecular mass of the substance. This is called simply a mole in most chemistry texts.
kgmole	The amount of any chemical substance that has a mass in kilograms numerically equal to the molecular mass of the substance.
lbmole	The amount of any chemical substance that has a mass in lbm (pounds mass) numerically equal to the molecular mass of the substance.
SI	Le Systeme International d'Unités (French).
psia	lbf/in^2 absolute pressure.
psig	lbf/in^2 gage pressure.

next generation of engineers, will be able to communicate in both systems if necessary.

Some of the important technical terms introduced in this chapter are given in the glossary shown in Table 1.7. Many of these terms will be used throughout the remainder of the text without further explanation.

Selected References

American Society for Testing and Materials, *Standard for Metric Practice.* ASTM E 380-79, January 1980.

Chiswell, B., and Grigg, E. C. M. *SI Units.* Sydney, Australia: Wiley, 1971.

Ipsen, D. C. *Units, Dimensions and Dimensionless Numbers.* New York: McGraw-Hill, 1960.

Jackson, J. D. *Classical Electrodynamics.* New York: Wiley, 1962, pp. 611–621.

Kayan, C. F. *Systems of Units.* Washington, DC: American Association for the Advancement of Science Publication, 1959.

McGlashan, M. L. *Manual of Symbols and Terminology for Physiochemical Quantities and Units.* London: Butterworths, 1971.

Menninger, K. *Number Words and Number Symbols, A Cultural History of Numbers.* Cambridge, MA: MIT Press, 1970.

Zupko, R. E. *A Dictionary of English Weights and Measures from Anglo-Saxon Times to the Nineteenth Century.* Madison, WI: Univ. of Wisconsin Press, 1968.

Chapter One Problems

1. Take ye a tube a hands breadth across and ten spans extent, to port a foul-smelling liquid of such substance as to balance three stone with one coombe. If it sloppeth out of ye tube with such a stench as to gag even its maker and with such a fury as to fill five pottle in two gesh, then what say ye to the querie, "What be the average speed of ye putrid bile in ye tube in cubits per gesh?"

2. If 1 gallon has a volume of 0.1337 ft^3, then how many mouthfuls of water are required to fill the moat of a castle that is 1 pole deep, 1 fathom wide, and 1 furlong long?

3. The *gage* of shot guns is universally expressed as the number of spheres of the diameter of the bore of the gun that can be cast from one pound of lead. This standardization procedure came from the English Gun Barrel Proof Act of 1868. Taking the density of lead as 705 lbm/ft^3, develop a formula relating the diameter of the gun barrel to the gage of the gun. Compute the barrel diameters for 20-, 12-, and 10-gage shotguns. (Note that the *caliber* of a gun is not the same as its gage. The caliber of a weapon is just the diameter of the bore expressed in inches multiplied by one hundred. For example, a 38-caliber pistol has a bore diameter of 0.38 inches).

4. If lead is measured in avoirdupois ounces and silver is measured in troy ounces, which weighs more,

a) an ounce of lead or an ounce of silver, and

b) a pound of lead or a pound of silver?

5. Most people believe that the size of a shoe is the length of the shoe in inches. Curiously, this is not the case. Shoe sizes became standardized between 1850 and 1900 as factory-made shoes became popular. The size standardization consisted of defining the smallest shoe size at some fixed insole length, and then increasing the insole length by a fixed amount for each size increment. The child's size 0 shoe was specified to have a $3\frac{11}{12}$-inch-long insole and the adult size 1 shoe (there is no size 0 adult shoe) was specified to have an $8\frac{7}{12}$-inch-long insole. It was also decided that each full size increment would

represent an increase in insole length by one barleycorn ($\frac{1}{3}$ of an inch), and an increase in girth (the internal circumference of the shoe at the ball of the foot) by $\frac{1}{4}$ of an inch. Letters were chosen to denote shoe width increments, and the difference in girth between these width increments (for example, between a C and a D width shoe) is also $\frac{1}{4}$ of an inch.
a) Determine the equations that relate the adult and child's size directly to insole length, and compute the insole length of an adult size 10 shoe.
b) Compute the size of a child's shoe that has the same insole length as a size 1 adult shoe and explain why children's shoes are not available in size 14 or larger.

6. The classification of carpenters nails is based on a units system that is at least six centuries old. The *penny* system of nail sizing, usually designated by the letter that was also the symbol for the monetary penny or pence, "d" (i.e., 3d = three penny nail), originated in medieval England.[10] At that time nails were sold by the hundred, and originally one hundred three penny nails cost 3 pennies. From this practice came the classification of nail sizes according to the price per hundred. This system had the disadvantage that inflation in the monetary system caused the size of the nails to change. By the end of the fifteenth century the classification became standardized according to the table shown below,[11] and from this point on the size of the nails no longer corresponded to their actual cost. Estimate the percentage of monetary inflation since the fifteenth century if a pound of 6d nails currently cost $1.00.

Nail Size	2d	3d	4d	5d	6d	7d	8d	9d	10d	12d	16d	20d	30d	40d	50d	60d
Length (inches)	1.00	1.25	1.50	1.75	2.00	2.25	2.50	2.75	3.00	3.25	3.50	4.00	4.50	5.00	5.50	6.00
Number per pound	845	540	290	250	165	150	100	90	65	60	45	30	20	17	13	10

7. By 1724 Gabriel Daniel Fahrenheit (1686–1736) had established his well-known temperature scale. This scale was based on two fixed points: the freezing point of a water and ammonium chloride solution (called 0 °F) and the temperature of the human body (called 96 °F). Later adjustments to the scale shifted the body temperature to 98.6 °F. What advantages did the number 96 have over, say, 100 as an upper end to this scale in 1724?

8. Determine the units of thermal conductivity k_t as defined by the following equation: $\dot{Q} = -k_t A(dT/dx)$, where $\dot{Q}$ is the heat transfer rate in watts, A is the cross-sectional area in meters squared, T is the absolute temperature in kelvins, and x is the distance in meters.

9. Determine the units of viscosity μ in the following equation in **a)** the Engineering English system, and **b)** the SI system: $\tau = \mu(du/dy)$, where τ is a shear stress, u is a velocity, and y and is a distance.

10. Develop a units conversion factor that will convert the specific heat of a substance in calories/(g·K) into Btu/(lbm·R).

11. The specific internal energy of a system is 411.7 J/kg. Express this value in the following units, **a)** ft·lbf/lbm, **b)** kcal/kg, and **c)** kW·h/lbm.

12. Determine the weight at standard gravity of 10 lbm in **a)** lbf, **b)** poundals, **c)** dynes, and **d)** newtons.

13. Determine the mass of an object whose weight on the moon, where the local acceleration of gravity is 5.3 ft/s^2, is 10 poundals, in **a)** lbm, **b)** slugs, **c)** grams, and **d)** kilograms.

---

10. The "d" is from *denarius*, the name of an old Roman silver coin.

11. Nails less than 2-penny are called *tacks* or *brads*, and nails larger than 60-penny are called *spikes*.

14. Determine the acceleration of gravity at a location where 3 slugs of mass weigh 50 newtons.

15. How much does 10 lbm weigh on a planet where $g = 322.0$ ft/s^2?

16. Determine the value of g_c at a location where a body with a mass of 270 lbm weighs 195 lbf.

17. Develop a mechanical units system in which the unit of mass is the stone, the unit of length is the angstrom (0.1 nm), and the unit of time is the century.

a) Define your own force unit and choose the magnitude of k_1.

b) Discuss the problems that would be encountered in converting between your system and the SI system.

18. Develop a mechanical units system in which force (F), mass (M), length (L), and time (t) are all independent quantities, using the kgf (kilogram-force) for F, and kgm (kilogram-mass) for M, the meter for L, the second for t, and 9.8 kgm·m/(kgf·s^2) as g_c. Note the similarities between this units system (which is used by some European engineers today) and the Engineering English units system.

19. Develop an FLt mechanical units system in which $g_c = 1.0$ (dimensionless), and the unit of force is the pound-force (lbf), the unit of length is the foot, and the unit of time is the second. Define the mass in this system to be the pound-mass (lbm) and determine the conversion between the primary units (lbf, ft, and s) and the secondary mass (lbm) unit at standard gravity. Note that this is not the same $FLMt$ system used in the Engineering English units system shown in Table 1.2. Explain the differences and the similarities between these two systems.

20. Determine the mass of 18 lbm of water in **a)** lbmoles, **b)** gmoles, **c)** kgmoles, and **d)** slug moles.

21. What will 3 kgmoles of CO_2 weigh at standard gravity in **a)** newtons, and **b)** lbf?

22. Determine the molecular mass of a substance for which 5 gmoles weighs 10,000 dynes at standard gravity.

23. Create an absolute temperature scale based on Reaumur's relative temperature scale defined in Table 1.1, and name it after yourself. Determine the boiling point of water in your new scale, and the conversion factors between your scale and the Kelvin and Rankine scales.

24. Create an absolute temperature scale based on Newton's relative temperature scale defined in Table 1.1, and name it after yourself. Determine the boiling point of water in your new scale, and the conversion factors between your scale and the Kelvin and Rankine scales.

25. Both the numerical value and dimensions of the universal gas constant $\mathscr{R}$ in the ideal gas formula $p\mathcal{V} = n\mathscr{R}T$ depends upon whether the temperature T is in Kelvin or Rankine absolute temperature units. In 1964 at Washington University in St. Louis, Professor John C. Georgian recognized that if the universal gas constant were set equal to unity and made dimensionless, then the ideal gas equation of state could be used to define an absolute temperature unit in terms of the traditional mass, length, and time dimensions from the result $T = p\mathcal{V}/n$, where p is the absolute pressure, $\mathcal{V}$ is the total volume, $n = m/M$ is the number of moles, and m and M are mass and molecular mass, respectively.

a) Using this relation, determine the equivalent Georgian temperature unit in terms of the standard SI units (m, kg, s). Call this new temperature unit the *georgian*, G.

b) Find the conversion factor between G and the SI units system absolute temperature scale K.

c) Find the conversion factor between G and the Engineering English units system absolute temperature scale unit, R.

d) Determine the triple and boiling points of water in G.

26. Show that $(4\pi\epsilon_o)(c^2 \times 10^{-7}) = 1\ C^2/(kg \cdot m)$, where c is the velocity of light in m/s and C is charge in coulombs (1 C = 1 A·s). (*Hint*: See Table 1.3.)
27. Show that $\epsilon_o \mu_o c^2 = 1.0$. (*Hint*: See Table 1.3.)
28. If the pressure inside an automobile tire is 32 psig in Engineering English units, what is its pressure in SI units?
29. If your mass is 183 lbm in the Engineering English units system, what is your weight in **a)** the Engineering English units system, and **b)** the SI units system?
30. If you weigh 165 lbf in the Engineering English units system, determine your mass in the following units system: **a)** Engineering English, **b)** SI, and **c)** Technical English.
31. Determine the potential energy of 1 lbm of water at a height of 1 ft above the ground level at standard gravity in **a)** the Engineering English units system, and **b)** the SI units system.
32. Compute the kinetic energy and the potential energy of an airplane weighing 5 tons flying at a height of 30,000 feet at 500 miles per hour. Give your answer in both SI and Engineering units.
33. The binding energy per molecule for liquid water at 100 °C is about 7×10^{-20} ft·lbf/molecule. Assuming all the binding energy is converted into mass, determine the percent gain in mass when 1 lbm (10^{25} molecules) of liquid water vaporizes. *Note*: $E = mc^2/g_c$, where, in the Engineering English units system, $g_c = 32.2$ lbm·ft/(lbf·s²) and $c = 9.8 \times 10^8$ ft/s.
34. The engine horsepower required to overcome rolling and air resistance for a passenger vehicle is given by the *dimensional* formula

$$\text{horsepower required} = [(53.0)(WV) + 6.8C_D A V^3] \times 10^{-6}$$

where W is the vehicle's weight in pounds force, V is the vehicle's road speed in miles per hour, A is the vehicle's frontal area in square feet, and C_D is a dimensionless drag coefficient. Convert this formula into a dimensional formula that uses only the four base units of
a) the Engineering English system (lbf, lbm, ft, s)
b) the SI system (N, kg, m, s).
35. Using the CGS units system, determine the kinetic energy of an automobile weighing 1.60 billion dynes traveling at 3000 cm/s.
36. Using the CGS units system, determine the potential energy of a truck weighing 27.0 billion dynes at a height of 30,000 cm.
37. Using the Absolute English units system, determine the weight of an object whose kinetic energy is 306.2 ft·poundal when it is traveling at a velocity of 10 ft/s.
38. Using the Absolute English units system, determine the kinetic energy of an object traveling at 15.3 ft/s and weighing 40 poundal at standard gravity.
39. Using the Absolute English units system, determine the potential energy of an object weighing 200 lbm·ft/s² at a height of 3000 ft at standard gravity.
40. Using the Technical English units system, determine the mass of an object having a potential energy of 705 ft·lbf when it is at a height of 25 ft at standard gravity.
41. Using the Technical English units system, determine the kinetic energy of a 197 slug mass traveling at a velocity of 33.5 ft/s.

Chapter Two Definitions, Balance Equations, State and Conservation Principles

Some students have difficulty with thermodynamics because of the global nature of its applicability. Most students are used to courses that focus on a few specific topics; statics, dynamics, computers, circuits, fluid flow, materials, etc., all deal with a very limited range of topics. Thermodynamics, on the other hand, deals with many issues that are inherent in every engineering system. A thermodynamic analysis can span the gamut from analyzing a complete power plant to analyzing the smallest component in the power plant. It can often be applied in a fairly simple way to extremely complex systems (like biological systems). One of the most powerful aspects of thermodynamics is its "black box" balance approach to system analysis. It is not necessary to know what takes place *inside* a system, it is only necessary to watch the systems boundaries and to monitor what and how much crosses them. This is the essence of the *balance concept* which is discussed later in this chapter. But we begin by introducing some basic thermodynamic terms and definitions.

Thermodynamics

This section deals with a series of definitions of technical terms that are fundamental to the subject of thermodynamics. Some of these terms are already in our everyday vocabulary as a result of the broad-based use of thermodynamics concepts in nonengineering areas. Many of the words used here have Greek or Latin origins. It was popular among the nineteenth century developers of this subject to coin descriptive terms whose names were taken from Greek or Latin instead of English. This was done in other professions, and engineers and physicists followed the same tradition. Many of the key Greek- or Latin-based terms used to describe the operation of a system are foreign to the English-speaking student, but when these terms are translated into English, we find that their English meaning is identical to their thermodynamic use. For example, the English translation of the term *isothermal* is simply *constant temperature*, which is the physical meaning of what the term isothermal is meant to imply. Consequently, when Greek or Latin based terms are introduced in this text their equivalent English translations will also be given at that point. Appendix B at the end of this book gives a more comprehensive analysis of the Greek and Latin origins of scientific and engineering terms. Though this may seem like a small point to the reader at this stage, the reader's total comprehension and ease with this subject will be greatly enhanced if particular attention is paid to the English meanings of these technical terms.

The name *thermodynamics* itself is an example of a Greek technical term. Basically, it means the process of converting heat (*thermo*) into mechanical power (*dynam*-ics). Modern thermodynamics deals with more than just thermal energy. It is more appropriately defined today as

Thermodynamics The science and technology that deals with the laws that govern the transformation of energy from one form to another.

There are four basic laws of thermodynamics, called the zeroth, first, second, and third laws. Like all of the other basic laws of physics, each of these laws is a generalization of observed events in the real world, and their "discovery" was the result of individual perception of how nature functions. Curiously, the order in which the thermodynamic laws are named does not correspond to the order of their discovery. The zeroth law is attributed to Fowler and Guggenheim in 1939, the first law to Joule, Mayer, and Colding in about 1845, the Second Law to Carnot in 1824, and the third law to Nerst in 1907. The first and second laws are the most pragmatic and consequently the most important to engineers. The zeroth and third laws are more definitional in nature.

A thermodynamic analysis involves applying the laws of thermodynamics to a *thermodynamic system.*

Thermodynamic system A volume of space containing the item chosen for thermodynamic analysis.

A thermodynamic system will often be referred to as just a *system.* Its *boundary* is defined simply:

System boundary The surface of a thermodynamic system.

The system and its boundary are always chosen by the analyst (i.e., you); they are almost never specified in a problem statement. It should be clear that if different systems are used to analyze the same quantity, they should produce the same basic results in each case. A system does not have to be fixed in space. It can move, deform, and increase or decrease in size with time. Basically, there are three different types of systems:

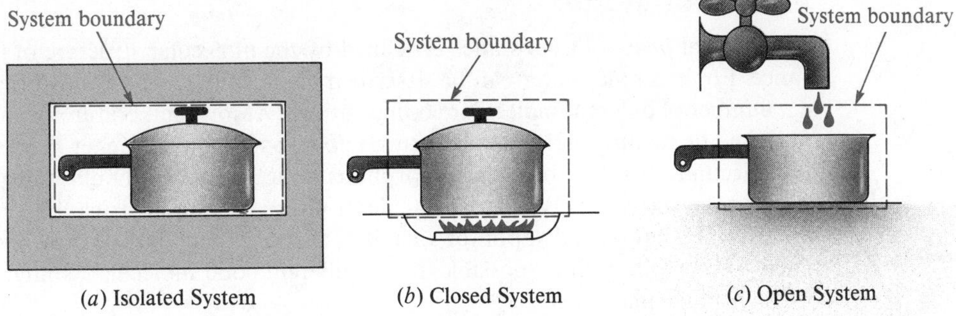

Figure 2.1 The three basic types of systems.

Isolated system Any system in which neither mass nor energy crosses the system boundary.[1]

Closed system Any system in which mass does not cross the system boundary, but energy may cross the system boundary.

Open system Any system in which both mass and energy may cross the system boundary.

Figure 2.1 illustrates each of these types of systems. In Figure 2.1*a* we have a pan of water in a mass and energy impervious insulated box, thus forming an isolated system. In Figure 2.1*b* we have a closed system wherein the contents of the pan are closed by an air-tight lid, but heat energy enters the pan from the burner. In Figure 2.1*c* we have water (mass) entering the pan by crossing the system boundary, so here the pan is an open system.

Notice that whether a system is open or closed depends on how the analyst views the system. Figure 2.1*c* could be made into a closed system if the system boundary were extended to include the faucet, all the water pipe going back to the water treatment plant, and the water supply for the plant. But such a system would be too large to analyze properly since we must be able to find all the energy that crosses its boundary, at any point along the boundary. Thus, it is much easier to view Figure 2.1*c* as an open system with a small, well-defined system boundary.

The choice of the proper system along with the proper form of the thermodynamic laws will always be decisions that you, the analyst, must make whenever beginning to solve a thermodynamics problem. Making a sketch of the system which shows the system boundary is a useful aid in making these decisions. The system sketch in thermodynamics is equivalent to the free body diagram sketch in mechanics. Its value cannot be overstated.

---

1. Einstein's mass–energy conversion relation has shown us that mass is just another form of energy. However, at the present time there are few useful mass–energy conversion technologies and so we will consider mass to be a separate entity and will assume that it is conserved in all nonnuclear reactions.

Phases of Matter

The physical *phase* of a substance is defined by the molecular structure of the substance. For example, water can be described chemically as H_2O, but it may exist in a number of different molecular configurations. At low temperatures water takes on a rigid crystalline molecular structure known as ice, but at higher temperatures its molecular structure becomes amorphous as it becomes a liquid and random as it becomes a vapor. We can easily identify three common structural phases of matter: solid, liquid, and vapor (or gas). But, whereas there may be only one liquid phase or one vapor phase possible, many different solid molecular configurations of a substance may exist.

The term *homogeneous* can be used to describe either physical or chemical uniformity. Here we use the term *pure substance* to describe substances that are chemically uniform, and reserve the term homogeneous to describe substances that are physically uniform (i.e., have a single physical phase). Thus, we define a pure substance as anything that contains the same uniform chemical composition in all its physical phases. For example, a mixture of water vapor and liquid water is a pure substance. On the other hand, air is not really a pure substance because when it is cooled sufficiently some of its components will condense into their liquid state, thus changing the composition of the remaining gases.

We further define a homogeneous substance as anything that contains a single physical phase. Air at normal atmospheric conditions is a homogeneous substance, but being a mixture of various gases it is not a pure substance. A mixture of liquid water and ice on the other hand is not a homogeneous substance, but it is a pure substance. A pure substance that is also a homogeneous substance is called a *simple substance.* Liquid water is an example of a simple substance.

Pure substances must be chemically uniform, but need not consist of a single chemical species. For example, a homogeneous mixture of uniform chemical composition can often be treated as if it were a single phase of a pure substance. Air in its gaseous state is often treated as a pure substance even though it does not satisfy the general definition of a pure substance.

System States and Thermodynamic Properties

The thermodynamic *state* of a system can be either an *equilibrium* state or a *nonequilibrium* state. A thermodynamic equilibrium state is defined by the values of its thermodynamic properties. A nonequilibrium state is much more difficult to define and generally requires the existence of a condition called *local* thermodynamic equilibrium, which exists when thermodynamic equilibrium occurs locally within a series of small volumes that make up the system. Conversely, a thermodynamic *property* is any characteristic of a system whose numerical value depends only on the (local) thermodynamic equilibrium state of the system and is independent of how that state was attained. Mass, volume, temperature, pressure, color, viscosity, magnetization, and so forth, are all possible properties.

The list of possible properties is very long. Fortunately, not all properties are independent of each other. In fact, for a homogeneous system there are relatively few independent properties. The formula relating the dependent and independent properties of a system is called a thermodynamic *equation of state*. Once the values of the independent properties are known for a particular state, this formula can then be used to calculate the values of all the dependent properties at that state. The ideal gas formula, $pv = RT$, is an example of such an equation of state for a simple system.

In classical thermodynamics there are two different types of properties, *intensive* and *extensive*.

> **Intensive property** Any thermodynamic property of a system that is independent of the system mass. Examples are pressure, temperature, density, and velocity.

> **Extensive property** Any thermodynamic property of a system that depends on the mass of the system. Examples are the system mass itself, volume, and total energy.

Most extensive properties can be converted into intensive properties by dividing the extensive property by the system mass or the number of moles in the system. Intensive properties created in this way are called *specific* properties. For example, the total volume of a system divided by the total mass of the system is the intensive property called *specific volume*, and the total volume divided by the total number of moles of the system is the intensive property called *molar specific volume*. To be able to tell the difference between extensive and intensive properties in the formulae of this book, we will adopt the following notational scheme.

> **Extensive property notation** Extensive properties are symbolized by uppercase (capital) letters.

Thus, $\forall$, E, KE, PE, etc., are the symbols for system volume,[2] energy (total), kinetic energy, potential energy, and so forth. Exceptions to this rule are temperature T (an intensive property), mass m (an extensive property), and the number of moles n (an extensive property). The use of T, m, and n for temperature, mass, and moles are the traditional symbols for these quantities and the symbols t, M, and N are the traditional symbols for time, molecular mass, and Avogadro's number, respectively.

> **Intensive property notation** Intensive mass-based properties are symbolized by lowercase letters, and intensive mole-based properties are symbolized by lowercase letters with overbars.

Thus, v, e, ke, pe, etc., are the symbols for mass-based specific volume, specific energy (total), specific kinetic energy, specific potential energy, and so forth. Similarly, $\overline{v}$, $\overline{e}$, $\overline{\text{ke}}$, and $\overline{\text{pe}}$ are the symbols for the molar specific volume, molar specific

2. In this text $\forall$ represents total volume, and V represents the magnitude of velocity.

energy (total), molar specific kinetic energy, and molar specific potential energy. Exceptions to this rule are temperature T (an intensive property), mass m (an extensive property), and the number of moles n (an extensive property), as explained above. Thus, the following relations exist:

Mass-based specific properties	Mole-based specific properties
$v = \forall/m$	$\bar{v} = \forall/n$
$e = E/m$	$\bar{e} = E/n$
$\text{ke} = \text{KE}/m = V^2/2g_c$	$\overline{\text{ke}} = \text{KE}/n = (m/n)(V^2/2g_c)$
$\text{pe} = \text{PE}/m = gZ/g_c$	$\overline{\text{pe}} = \text{PE}/n = (m/n)(gZ/g_c)$

Later we will discuss a general principle that will provide an easy way to determine the number of independent properties in any system. In the meantime we note that for a pure substance (anything with a uniform chemical composition in all its physical phases) subjected to only one work mode there are only two independent intensive properties.[3] In other words

The state of a pure substance subjected to only one work mode is determined by the values of any pair of independent intensive properties. If the pure substance is also homogeneous, then all its intensive properties are independent and any two of them will fix the state.

The pure substance can be in any physical state—solid, liquid, vapor, or any combinations of these states. Water plus ice cubes in a glass is a pure substance system if the system boundary is drawn so that it does not include the glass itself. If the system boundary is drawn outside the glass, then the system no longer contains a pure substance. This illustrates the importance of carefully considering exactly what the system is to be and where its boundaries are to be drawn.

Thermodynamic Equilibrium

An equilibrium situation implies a condition of balance between opposing factions. There are many different kinds of equilibria. A *mechanical* equilibrium exists when all the mechanical forces within a system are balanced so that there is no acceleration (the study of mechanical equilibrium is called "statics"). A *thermal* equilibrium exists within a system if there is a uniform temperature throughout the system. An *electrostatic* equilibrium exists within a system when there is a balance of charge throughout the system. A *phase* equilibrium exists within a system when there are no phase transformations (such as vaporization or melting) occurring within the system. A system is said to be in *chemical* equilibrium when there are no chemical reactions occurring within the system. Since the subject matter of

3. The work mode may be mechanical, electrical, magnetic, etc., but only one may be present in this instance. More complex systems with multiple work modes are discussed in the State Postulate section of Chapter 4.

thermodynamics contains all of these types of phenomena, we lump all of these definitions together to define

> **Thermodynamic equilibrium** A system is said to be in thermodynamic equilibrium if it does not have the capacity to spontaneously change its state after it has been isolated.

Classical equilibrium thermodynamics is based on the analysis of equilibrium states and therefore is analogous to *statics* in mechanics. Since dynamic energy systems contain nonequilibrium thermodynamic states, they are not able to be analyzed by the methods of classical thermodynamics. Hence, the term thermo*dynamics* appears to be a misnomer. Some authors have proposed that classical thermodynamics could be more accurately titled thermo*statics*, to keep it consistent with the titles used in mechanics. However, the origin of the term thermodynamics is more closely aligned with the concept of converting heat (the *thermo* part) into work (the *dynamics* part). Consequently, the *dynamics* in thermodynamics should be thought of as the dynamics of the mechanical motion associated with the various processes of converting heat into work.

Thermodynamic Processes

Engineering thermodynamics is primarily concerned with systems that undergo thermodynamic processes. A system subjected to a thermodynamic process will normally experience a change in its thermodynamic state. Consequently, we define a thermodynamic process as follows:

> **Thermodynamic process** The path of thermodynamic states that a system passes through as it goes from an initial state to a final state.

Neither the initial, final, nor any intermediate states need be in thermodynamic equilibrium during a thermodynamic process. A process can change a system from one nonequilibrium state to another nonequilibrium state via a path of nonequilibrium states. Figure 2.2 illustrates several process paths which change a system from an initial state A to a final state B.

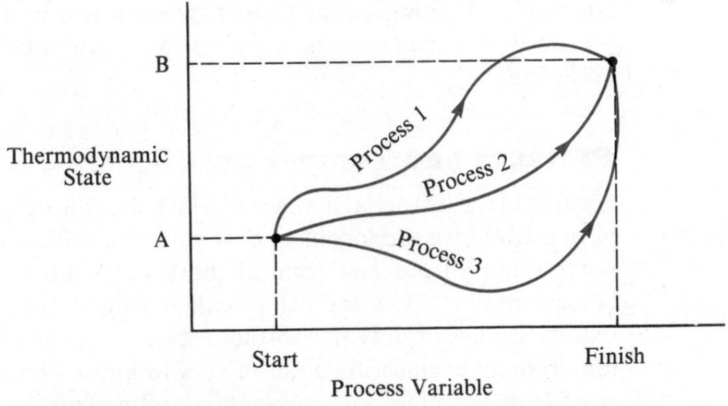

Figure 2.2 Three different process paths that change the state of the system from A to B.

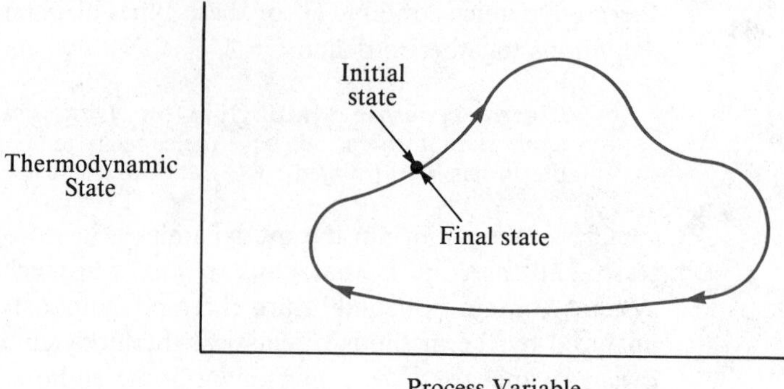

Figure 2.3 A thermodynamic cycle.

If a process path closes back on itself so that it is repeated periodically in time, then the thermodynamic process is called a *thermodynamic cycle*.

> **Thermodynamic cycle** A system process is said to go through a thermodynamic cycle when the final state of the process is identical with the initial state of the process.

Figure 2.3 illustrates the definition of a thermodynamic cycle.

There is a difference between a thermodynamic cycle and a mechanical cycle. In a mechanical cycle all of the mechanical components begin and end in the same geometrical configuration. For example, the engine of an automobile goes through a mechanical cycle once per two crankshaft rotations for a four-stroke engine, but it does not go through a thermodynamic cycle. For an automobile engine to go through a thermodynamic cycle the engine's exhaust would have to be converted back into air and fuel (the initial state) again.

Understanding the process path is *extremely* important in thermodynamic analysis because it often determines the final state of the system. In most thermodynamic textbook problem statements the process path is often only vaguely alluded to, or else it is hidden in one or more of the technical terms used. Therefore, in addition to deciding on the type of system to use in the analysis of a problem and preparing a system sketch, you must also determine the type of process that is occurring.

Pressure and Temperature Scales

Because of the historical manner in which the concepts of pressure and temperature have evolved we are forced to deal with two different scales for each. We have a *relative* and an *absolute* scale for both temperature and pressure measurement. Some formulae allow the use of either scale in calculations, but other formulae require the use of only the absolute scales in calculations. Thus, it is very important from an engineering point of view to know which scales are being used when you are given values for temperature and pressure.

There are two common absolute temperature scales, Rankine (R) and Kelvin (K). They are related as follows[4]:

$$T\ (\mathrm{R}) = \tfrac{9}{5}T\ (\mathrm{K}) \tag{2.1}$$

Each of these absolute scales has a relative scale, the common English Fahrenheit (°F) scale and the European Celsius (°C) scale.[5] These two relative scales are related to each other by

$$T\ (^\circ\mathrm{F}) = \tfrac{9}{5}T\ (^\circ\mathrm{C}) + 32 \tag{2.2}$$

and the respective absolute and relative scales are related by

$$T\ (\mathrm{R}) = T\ (^\circ\mathrm{F}) + 459.67 \tag{2.3}$$

and

$$T\ (\mathrm{K}) = T\ (^\circ\mathrm{C}) + 273.15 \tag{2.4}$$

A more detailed description of the thermodynamic meaning of pressure and temperature will be given in Chapter 6.

Pressure can be viewed as a compressive stress. Thus, absolute zero pressure corresponds to a level of zero stress. However, even though we generally do not encounter negative absolute pressures in thermodynamics, any finite tensile stress in a fluid is equivalent to its being subjected to a negative absolute pressure. There is no lack of consistency here; this is merely a standard sign convention for stress.

Because most gages manufactured to measure pressure were designed to read zero at atmospheric pressure, their readings comprise a relative pressure scale called *gage pressure*. The relation between gage and absolute pressure can be written

$$\text{absolute pressure} = \text{gage pressure} + \text{local atmospheric pressure}$$

To distinguish between gage and absolute pressure values in our writing, we append the letter "g" or "a" to the English units of the term. Thus, the English pressure units psia and psig are to be read "pounds per square inch absolute" and "pounds per square inch gage," respectively. However, the SI pressure units should carry the identifying words absolute or gage when necessary (e.g., Pa absolute or Pa gage). *When an SI pressure unit appears without such an identifier it is assumed to be an absolute pressure unit.* Unless otherwise specified in a problem statement,

---

4. Recall from Chapter 1 that since 1967 we do not use the degree prefix on the absolute temperature scales, but do retain it on the relative scales. Thus, we write 100 R for a temperature of 100 rankine, not 100 °R.

5. The Celsius scale was also commonly called the centigrade scale. However, the centigrade (from the Latin for one hundred (*centi*) divisions (*grade*)) scale was developed by the Swedish astronomer Anders Celsius in about 1742, and in 1948 the centigrade scale was officially renamed the Celsius scale.

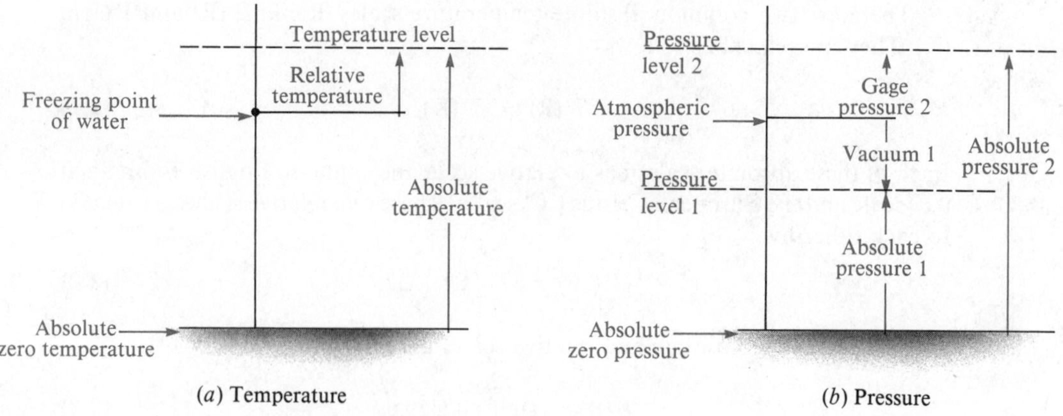

Figure 2.4 Relative and absolute temperatures and pressures.

the local atmospheric pressure should always be taken to be standard atmospheric pressure, which is 14.696 psia (or 14.7 psia) or 101,325 Pa (or 101.3 kPa).

Figure 2.4 illustrates the meanings of relative and absolute temperature and pressure.

If you are given a formula with a quantity such as p or T in it, how do you know which scale to use? The following rule of thumb will provide the answer. *If a quantity with both a relative and an absolute scale of measurement stands by itself or is raised to some power in a formula, then the values assigned to it must be in an* absolute *scale of units.* In the ideal gas equation of state,

$$pV = mRT \tag{2.5}$$

both the quantities p and T stand alone, so that the values substituted for them must always be in an absolute scale (psia and R, or Pa absolute and K). On the other hand, if a formula contains the difference in a quantity not raised to a power, such as $p_2 - p_1$ (or Δp), or $T_2 - T_1$ (or ΔT), then the values assigned to that quantity may be in either absolute or relative scale units. For example, if we have an ideal gas in a closed system of constant volume V, then when the gas is in state 1 we can write

$$p_1 V = mRT_1 \tag{2.6}$$

and when it is changed to state 2 we can write

$$p_2 V = mRT_2 \tag{2.7}$$

Now if we subtract Eq. 2.6 from 2.7 we get

$$(p_2 - p_1)V = mR(T_2 - T_1) \tag{2.8}$$

Absolute pressure and temperature scales must be used in making calculations with Eqs. 2.6 and 2.7, but either absolute or relative scales may be used in Eq.

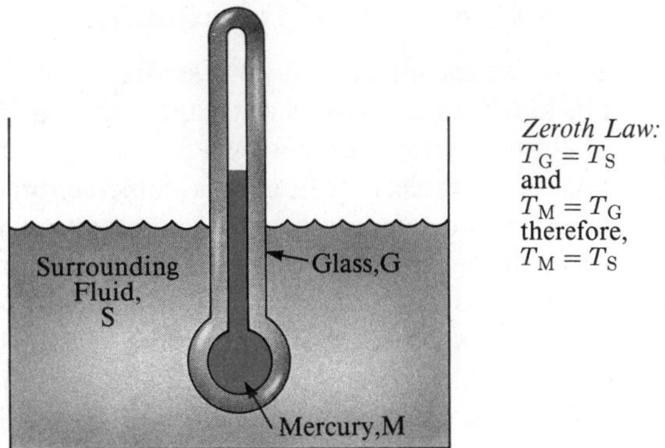

Figure 2.5 The zeroth law of thermodynamics applied to a mercury in glass thermometer.

2.8. Briefly, relative scales can be used whenever the additive term that converts a relative scale to an absolute scale cancels out within the formula, as it does when a simple difference is taken.

Using relative scale values where absolute scale values should be used clearly leads to enormous calculational errors. If in doubt, use values in the absolute scale units.

The Zeroth Law of Thermodynamics

As previously mentioned, the zeroth law was one of the last thermodynamic laws to be developed. It was introduced by R. H. Fowler and E. A. Guggenheim in 1939.[6]

> **Zeroth law of thermodynamics** Consider three thermodynamic systems, A, B, and C. If system A is in thermal equilibrium with (i.e., is the same temperature as) system C and system B is in thermal equilibrium with system C, then system A is in thermal equilibrium with system B.

This may seem trivial at first reading, but consider this: if man A loves woman C and man B loves woman C does it follow that man A loves man B? Not necessarily. One of the major values of the zeroth law is that it forms the theoretical basis for temperature measurement technology. Consider the mercury in glass thermometer shown in Figure 2.5. The zeroth law tells us that if the glass is at the same temperature as (i.e., is in thermal equilibrium with) the surrounding fluid, and if the mercury is at the same temperature as the glass, then the mercury is at the same temperature as the surrounding fluid. Thus, the thermometer can be graduated to show the mercury temperature, and this temperature will automatically (via the zeroth law) be equal to the temperature of its surroundings.

6. Fowler, R. H., and Guggenheim, E. A. *Statistical Thermodynamics*. Cambridge, MA: Cambridge Univ. Press, 1939, p. 56.

The Continuum Hypothesis

While we recognize today the existence of the atomic nature of matter, we have not found an effective way to apply the basic laws of physics to large aggregates of atomic particles except by a statistical averaging technique. This is because the number of molecules in even a cubic centimeter of gas at standard atmospheric pressure and temperature is so large (about 10^{20}) that we cannot simultaneously solve all the equations of motion for each molecule. The statistical averaging process taken over large numbers of molecules produces a *continuum model* for matter, and the *continuum hypothesis* simply states that large systems made up of many discrete molecules or atoms may be treated as though they were made up of a *continuous* (i.e., nonmolecular) material. The continuum approach to thermodynamics works well so long as the dimensions of the systems being analyzed are much larger than the dimensions of the molecules themselves, and so long as the time interval over which a process takes place is very much greater than the average time between molecular collisions. Continuum thermodynamics breaks down when these conditions are violated, such as in the rarefied gas of outer space. When continuum thermodynamics breaks down, another type of thermodynamics, called *statistical thermodynamics*, can be used to solve problems. An introduction to the structure and applications of statistical thermodynamics is presented in Chapter 12.

The vast majority of engineering problems can be solved with continuum concepts, and they will be the main focus of this text. There are two other technical terms that also express these ideas:

Microscopic system analysis The analysis of systems at the atomic level. This is the domain of statistical thermodynamics.

Macroscopic system analysis The analysis of systems at the continuum level (i.e., molecular dimensions and time scales do not enter into the analysis.) This is the domain of classical and nonequilibrium thermodynamics.

When we deal with differential quantities in continuum analysis, such as dx/dt, we do not infer that the differentials shrink down to molecular dimensions and thus invalidate the continuum concept. Also, when we speak of evaluating thermodynamic properties at a *point* in a continuum system we are extrapolating the continuum concept in a mathematical sense only. The resulting mathematical functions and relations that are developed in macroscopic system analysis are not valid in and cannot be accurately applied to microscopic systems.

The Balance Concept

The balance concept is one of the most important and, oddly enough, most underrated concepts in physical science today. It is basically nothing more than a simple accounting procedure. Consider some quantity X possessed by an arbitrary system. Then the balance of X over the system during a macroscopic time interval δt is

$$\left\{\begin{matrix}\text{The gain in } X\\ \text{by the system}\\ \text{during time } \delta t\end{matrix}\right\} = \left\{\begin{matrix}\text{The amount of } X\\ \text{transported into the}\\ \text{system during time } \delta t\end{matrix}\right\} - \left\{\begin{matrix}\text{The amount of } X\\ \text{leaving the system}\\ \text{during time } \delta t\end{matrix}\right\}$$
$$+ \left\{\begin{matrix}\text{The amount of } X\\ \text{produced by the system}\\ \text{during time } \delta t\end{matrix}\right\} - \left\{\begin{matrix}\text{The amount of } X\\ \text{destroyed by the system}\\ \text{during time } \delta t\end{matrix}\right\} \tag{2.9}$$

By using the word *net* to signify the difference between like terms, Eq. 2.9 can be simplified to

$$\left\{\begin{matrix}\text{The net gain in}\\ X \text{ by the system}\\ \text{during time } \delta t\end{matrix}\right\} = \left\{\begin{matrix}\text{The net amount of } X\\ \text{transported into the}\\ \text{system during time } \delta t\end{matrix}\right\} + \left\{\begin{matrix}\text{The net amount of } X\\ \text{produced by the system}\\ \text{during time } \delta t\end{matrix}\right\} \tag{2.10}$$

In symbol form, Eq. 2.10 can be further simplified to

$$X_G = X_T + X_P \tag{2.11}$$

where the subscripts G, T, and P refer to net gain, net transport, and net production, respectively. In equilibrium systems, Eq. 2.11 is sufficient. But in nonequilibrium systems X_G, X_T, and X_P may be functions of time. In systems in which X_G, X_T, and X_P change continuously in time, Eq. 2.11 can be differentiated with respect to time to give a *rate* balance equation of X as

$$\dot{X}_G = \dot{X}_T + \dot{X}_P \tag{2.12}$$

where $\dot{X}_G = dX_G/dt$, $\dot{X}_T = dX_T/dt$, and $\dot{X}_P = dX_P/dt$. Equations 2.11 and 2.12 provide a full and general account of the behavior of any property X of a system, and they are valid for any coordinate system.

The Conservation Concept

In classical physics a quantity is said to be *conserved* if it can be neither created nor destroyed. The basic laws of physics would not produce unique balance equations if it were not for this concept. Whereas a balance equation can be written for any conceivable quantity, conserved quantities can be discovered only by human research and observation. The outstanding characteristic of conserved quantities is that their net production is always zero, and therefore their balance equations reduce to the simpler forms

$$X_G = X_T \tag{2.13}$$

or

$$\dot{X}_G = \dot{X}_T \tag{2.14}$$

when X is conserved

This may not seem like much of a reduction at first, but it is a very significant simplification of the general balance equations. It means that we do not have to worry about property production/destruction mechanisms and how to calculate their effects. Equations 2.13 and 2.14 turn out to be very effective working equations for engineering design and analysis purposes.

Thus far scientists have empirically discovered four major entities that are conserved: mass (in nonnuclear reactions), momentum (both linear and angular), energy (total), and electrical charge. These yield the four basic laws of physics: the conservation of mass, the conservation of momentum, the conservation of energy, and the conservation of charge. The conservation of energy is also called the first law of thermodynamics.

If we let E be the total energy of a system, then its conservation is written as

$$E_P = 0 \tag{2.15}$$

or

$$\dot{E}_P = 0 \tag{2.16}$$

and its resulting balance (or *conservation law*) equation is

$$E_G = E_T \tag{2.17}$$

or

$$\dot{E}_G = \dot{E}_T \tag{2.18}$$

Equations 2.15–2.18 are elementary forms of the first law of thermodynamics. They are elementary because to be useful for calculational purposes, the terms E_T and $\dot{E}_T$ representing the systems energy transport must be expanded into a sum of terms that account for all the different energy transport mechanisms. This will be taken up in detail in Chapter 4.

Example 2.1

Whereas the total mass of a system is conserved in nonnuclear reactions, the mass of any particular chemical species is not necessarily conserved. The equation for a chemical reaction is merely the mass balance for that reaction. In a closed system undergoing a chemical reaction, the mass transport term vanishes (by virtue of the definition of a closed system) leaving only

$$m_G = m_P$$

Let us consider a simple chemical reaction that takes place over some finite time interval δt. Let the reaction be

$$n_a\text{A} + n_b\text{B} \rightarrow n_c\text{C} + n_d\text{D}$$

where A, B, C, and D are the chemical species, and n_a, n_b, n_c, and n_d are their molar amounts. For a closed system, the mass balance for each of the chemical species present can be written as $m_G = m_P = \dot{m}\,\delta t = \delta m$, or

$$m_{GA} = m_{PA} = \delta m_A$$

$$m_{GB} = m_{PB} = \delta m_B$$

$$m_{GC} = m_{PC} = \delta m_C$$

$$m_{GD} = m_{PD} = \delta m_D$$

If we add these equations together we get

$$\delta m_A + \delta m_B + \delta m_C + \delta m_D = m_{PA} + m_{PB} + m_{PC} + m_{PD}$$

Now, since total mass must be conserved, it follows that

$$\sum m_P = m_{PA} + m_{PB} + m_{PC} + m_{PD} = 0$$

and then the previous equation can be written as

$$\delta m_A + \delta m_B = -\delta m_C - \delta m_D$$

If we now convert this equation into a molar inequality by dividing each mass term by its corresponding species molecular mass, then the stoichiometric chemical reaction equation $n_a A + n_b B \rightarrow n_c C + n_d D$ results, where

$$n_a = \frac{\delta m_A}{M_A} \qquad n_c = -\frac{\delta m_C}{M_C}$$

$$n_b = \frac{\delta m_B}{M_B} \qquad n_d = -\frac{\delta m_D}{M_D}$$

and M_A, M_B, M_C, and M_D are the molecular masses of chemical species A, B, C, and D. Consequently, all stoichiometric chemical reaction equations are just molar mass balances that have utilized the conservation of total mass law.

Summary

This chapter has introduced some of the basic definitions and concepts used in the field of thermodynamics. Many of these ideas will be used in the problem solving technique that will be developed in Chapters 4 and 5.

The important technical terms introduced in this chapter are given in the glossary shown in Table 2.1. The student is urged to learn the definitions because quick and accurate evaluation of these terms will be essential later.

Table 2.1 Glossary of technical terms introduced in Chapter 2

Thermodynamics	The science and technology that deals with the laws that govern the transformation of energy from one form to another.
Thermodynamic system	A volume containing the item chosen for thermodynamic analysis.
System boundary	The surface of a thermodynamic system.
Isolated system	Any system in which neither mass nor energy crosses the system boundary.
Closed system	Any system in which mass does not cross the system boundary, but energy may cross the system boundary.
Open system	Any system in which both mass and energy may cross the system boundary.
Physical phase	A molecular configuration of matter, categorized as either solid, liquid, or vapor (or gas).
Pure substance	A substance containing a uniform chemical composition in all its physical states.
Homogeneous system	A system containing only a single physical phase of a substance.
Simple substance	A homogeneous pure substance.
Thermodynamic state	The condition of a thermodynamic system as specified by the values of its independent thermodynamic properties.
Thermodynamic property	Any characteristic of a thermodynamic system that depends on the system's thermodynamic state and is independent of how that state was achieved.
Thermodynamic equation of state	A formula relating the dependent and independent properties of a system.
Intensive property	Any property of a homogeneous system that is independent of the system mass.
Extensive property	Any property of a homogeneous system that depends on the mass of the system
Mechanical equilibrium	A situation where all the mechanical forces within a system are balanced so that there is no acceleration of the system.
Thermal equilibrium	A situation where there are no variations in temperature throughout the system.
Phase equilibrium	A situation where there are no phase transformations occurring within the system.
Chemical equilibrium	A situation where there are no chemical reactions occurring within the system.
Thermodynamic equilibrium	A situation where a system does not have the capacity to spontaneously change its state after it has been isolated.
Nonequilibrium thermodynamics	The study of systems that are not in thermodynamic equilibrium.
Thermodynamic processes	The path of thermodynamic states that a system passes through as it goes from an initial state to a final state.
Thermodynamic cycle	A situation where the final thermodynamic state of a process is identical with the initial thermodynamic state of the process.
Standard atmospheric pressure	14.696 psia, 29.92 inches of mercury, 101.325 kPa absolute.
Absolute pressure	Gage pressure plus the local atmospheric pressure.
Gage pressure	Absolute pressure minus the local atmospheric pressure.
Absolute zero temperature	273.15 °C or 459.67 °F below the freezing point of water at standard atmospheric pressure.
The zeroth law of thermodynamics	If system A is in thermal equilibrium with (i.e., is the same temperature as) system C; and system B is in thermal equilibrium with system C, then system A is in thermal equilibrium with system B.

(*Continued*)

Table 2.1—*continued*

The continuum hypothesis	Large systems made up of many discrete molecules or atoms may be treated as though they were made up of a continuous material.
Microscopic system analysis	The analysis of a system at the molecular level.
Statistical thermodynamics	The study of molecular level (i.e., microscopic) systems.
Macroscopic system analysis	The analysis of a system at the continuum level.
The balance equation	An equation that accounts for all the changes in some quantity within a system.
The conservation concept	If a quantity is neither produced nor destroyed, then it is said to be conserved.

Selected References

Bridgman, P. W. *The Nature of Thermodynamic.* Cambridge, MA: Harvard Univ. Press, 1943.

Georgescu-Roegen, N. *The Entropy Law and the Economic Process.* Cambridge, MA: Harvard Univ. Press, 1971.

Holman, J. P. *Thermodynamics*, 3d ed. New York: McGraw-Hill, 1980.

Reynolds, W. C., and Perkins H. C. *Engineering Thermodynamics*, 2d ed. New York: McGraw-Hill, 1977.

Van Wylen, G. J., and Sonntag, R. E. *Fundamentals of Classical Thermodynamics*, 3d ed. New York: Wiley, 1986.

Chapter Two Problems

1. Define the following terms: **a)** thermostatics, **b)** open system, **c)** extensive property, **d)** equilibrium, and **e)** zeroth law.

2. Define the following terms: **a)** thermodynamics, **b)** closed system, **c)** intensive property, **d)** macroscopic analysis, and **e)** isolated system.

3. Which of the following are extensive properties? **a)** Temperature, **b)** volume, **c)** density, **d)** work, and **e)** mass.

4. Are the following extensive or intensive properties? **a)** Total energy, **b)** temperature, **c)** work, and **d)** mass.

5. Identify whether the following properties are intensive or extensive: **a)** total kinetic energy, **b)** total potential energy, **c)** total energy, **d)** temperature, and **e)** molar mass.

6. Explain how color could be a thermodynamic property and indicate whether it would be an intensive or extensive property.

7. Two cubic feet of a liquid–vapor mixture of motor oil at 70 °F and 14.7 psia weighs 97.28 lbf where $g = 32.0\ \text{ft/s}^2$. List the values of three intensive and two extensive properties of the oil.

8. How many independent property values are required to fix the state of a pure substance subjected to only one work mode?

9. Determine whether the following statements are true or false.

a) The mass of a closed system is constant and its boundaries are not movable.

b) An open system is defined as a system that can exchange only heat and work with its surroundings.

c) An isolated system is completely uninfluenced by the surroundings.

d) A thermodynamic property is a quantity that depends on the state of the system and is independent of the process path by which the system arrived at the given state.

e) When a system in a given state goes through a number of different processes and its final temperature is the same as the initial temperature, the system has undergone a thermodynamic cycle.

10. Identify the proper type of system (isolated, closed or open) to be used in the analysis of each of the following, and explain the reasons for your choice: **a)** the universe, **b)** a kitchen refrigerator, **c)** an electrical generator, **d)** a hydraulic pump, **e)** a living human being.

11. An automobile internal combustion engine by itself is clearly an open system because it draws in air and exhausts combustion products. How could one construct system boundaries around an operating internal combustion engine to cause it to become a closed system?

12. A system consists of a mixture of 2 ft^3 of a liquid having a density of 50 lbm/ft^3 and 4 lbm of a second liquid having a specific volume of 0.04 ft^3/lbm. The specific volume of the mixture in the system in ft^3/lbm is **a)** 0.208, **b)** 2.08, **c)** 0.022, **d)** 2.048, or **e)** none of the above.

13. The equilibrium state of carbon at atmospheric pressure and temperature is graphite. If diamond is the equilibrium form of carbon only at very high pressures and temperatures, then why does diamond exist at atmospheric pressure and temperature?

14. Sketch the following process paths on p–v coordinates starting from state (p_1, v_1).

a) A constant pressure (isobaric) expansion from (p_1, v_1) to (p_2, v_2) where $v_2 = 2v_1$, then

b) a constant volume (isochoric) compression from (p_2, v_2) to (p_3, v_3) where $p_3 = 2p_2$, then

c) a process described by $p = p_1 + k(v - v_1)$, where k is a constant, from (p_3, v_3) back to (p_1, v_1) again.

15. Sketch the following thermodynamic cycle on p–$\mathcal{V}$ coordinates for a substance obeying the ideal gas equation of state, $p\mathcal{V} = mRT$.

a) An isothermal compression (i.e., decreasing volume) from $(p_1, \mathcal{V}_1)$ to $(p_2, \mathcal{V}_2)$, then

b) an isobaric (i.e., constant pressure) expansion (i.e., increasing volume) from $(p_2, \mathcal{V}_2)$ to $(p_3, \mathcal{V}_3)$, then

c) an isothermal expansion from $(p_3, \mathcal{V}_3)$ to $(p_4, \mathcal{V}_4)$, then

d) an isochoric (i.e., constant volume) depressurization from $(p_4, \mathcal{V}_4)$ to $(p_5, \mathcal{V}_5)$, and finally

e) an isobaric compression from $(p_5, \mathcal{V}_5)$ back to $(p_1, \mathcal{V}_1)$ again.

16. A new thermodynamic cycle for an ideal gas is described by

a) an isothermal compression from $(p_1, \mathcal{V}_1)$ to $(p_2, \mathcal{V}_2)$, then

b) an isochoric compression from $(p_2, \mathcal{V}_2)$ to $(p_3, \mathcal{V}_3)$ then

c) an isobaric expansion from $(p_3, \mathcal{V}_3)$ to $(p_4, \mathcal{V}_4)$, then

d) an isothermal expansion from $(p_4, \mathcal{V}_4)$ to $(p_5, \mathcal{V}_5)$, and finally

e) an isochoric decompression from $(p_5, \mathcal{V}_5)$ back to $(p_1, \mathcal{V}_1)$ again.

Sketch this cycle on p–$\mathcal{V}$ coordinates.

17. Convert **a)** 20 °C into R, **b)** 1 °C into °F, **c)** 56 °F into °C, **d)** 253 °C into K, and **e)** 1892 °F into R.

18. Convert the following temperatures into kelvin: **a)** 70 °F, **b)** 70 °C, **c)** 70 R, and **d)** 70 degrees Reaumur. The Reaumur temperature scale was developed in 1730 by the French scientist René Antoine Ferchault de Réaumur (1683–1757). The freezing and boiling points of water at atmospheric pressure are defined to be zero and 80 degrees Reaumur, respectively.

19. Many historians believe that Gabriel Daniel Fahrenheit (1686–1736) had established his well-known temperature scale by 1724. It was based on three easily measured fixed points: the freezing temperature of a mixture of water and ammonium chloride (0 °F), the freezing point of pure water (32 °F), and the temperature of the human body (96 °F). Later this scale was changed to read 212 °F at the boiling point of pure water, which moved the body temperature from 96 to 98.6 °F. Using the *original* Fahrenheit scale (freezing point of water = 32 °F and body temperature = 96 °F) determine

a) the temperature of the boiling point of pure water, and

b) the conversion formula between the original Fahrenheit and the modern Celsius temperature scales.

20. Convert the following pressures into the proper SI units.

a) 14.7 psia

b) 5 atmospheres absolute

c) 10^5 dynes/cm^2 absolute

d) 30 lbf/ft^2 gage

e) 12.4 poundals/ft^2 absolute

21. Convert the following pressures into psia.

a) 1000 N/m^2 gage

b) 3.0 MPa absolute

c) 11 Pa gage

d) 20.3 kN/m^2 absolute

e) 1.01 GPa absolute

22. Will the continuum hypothesis hold for the following thermodynamic states (and why)?

a) Air at 20 °C and atmospheric pressure.

b) Liquid water at 70 °F and 14.7 psia.

c) Steam at 1 psia and 100 °F.

d) Steam at 1 MPa absolute and 100 °C.

e) Air at 1 μN/m^2 absolute and 10 K.

23. An engineer is trying to fill on initially empty 10-gallon bucket with a dipper. One dipper of water is added each second, and the dipper holds 1 lbf of water. Unfortunately, the bucket has a hole in it through which water leaks at a rate of 0.5 lbm/s. How long does it take the engineer to fill the bucket? (Water weighs 8.3 lbf/gallon.)

24. In the late eighteenth century it was commonly believed that heat was some kind of colorless, odorless, weightless fluid. Today we know that heat is not a fluid (it is primarily an energy transport due to a temperature difference), but we still have many old phrases and terms in our everyday and technical language that imply that heat is a fluid (e.g., heat "pours" out of a hot stove, or heat always "flows" down a temperature gradient, and so on). Discuss whether or not heat can be generated or absorbed, and using the balance concept discuss whether or not it is a conserved quantity.

25. Is the amount of gold reserves held by a nation a conserved quantity? Explain what happens if more currency is put into circulation while the currency base (e.g., gold reserves) is held constant.

26. Use the balance concept to explain the changes in the wealth of a nation. In particular, describe methods by which a nation can add or lose wealth by transport across its boundaries, and show how it can produce or destroy wealth within its boundaries.

27. Are the natural resources of a nation conserved in a thermodynamic sense? If not, explain what would have to be done to cause them to be conserved. Give a specific example where this is currently being done.

28. Write a balance equation for the total potential energy of a system. Is this potential energy conserved? How can potential energy be produced or destroyed?

29. 2.0 kg of hydrogen (H_2) reacts with 16.0 kg of oxygen (O_2) to yield water (H_2O). Determine the chemical equation for this reaction on a kgmole basis, and find the amount of water formed in kg.

30. 12.0 lbm of carbon (C) reacts with 24.0 lbm of oxygen (O_2) to form 22.0 lbm of carbon dioxide (CO_2) plus an unknown amount of carbon monoxide (CO). Determine the amount of carbon monoxide formed in lbm, and find the chemical equation for this reaction on a lbmole basis.

Chapter Three Thermodynamic Property Values

Before the basic laws of thermodynamics can be used in engineering analysis, we must first be able to find numerical values for the thermodynamic properties of the system. Thermodynamic property values can be determined from five different sources:

1. thermodynamic equations of state,
2. thermodynamic tables,
3. thermodynamic charts,
4. direct experimental measurements, and
5. the formulae of statistical thermodynamics

This chapter deals with the first three sources. Item 4, the techniques of direct property measurement, are not discussed in this text, but the given information in many of the thermodynamic problem statements can be assumed to have come from such measurements. The fifth source is discussed in Chapter 12.

Property values are often given in thermodynamic problem statements in the *process path* designation. For example, if a system changes its state by an isothermal process at 250 °C, then we know that $T_1 = 250\ °C = T_2$. Thus, the process path statement gives us the value of a thermodynamic property (temperature in this case) in each of the two different states. Process path statements that imply that some property is held constant during a change of state are quite common in thermodynamics.

General Relations

In the previous chapter we discussed the fact that the values of any two thermodynamic properties are sufficient to fix the state of a homogeneous (single phase) pure substance subjected to only one work mode. Consequently, each thermodynamic property of such a pure substance can be written as a function of any two independent thermodynamic properties. Thus, if x, y, and z are all intensive independent properties, we can write

$$f(x, y, z) = 0 \tag{3.1}$$

or

$$x = x(y, z) \tag{3.2}$$

$$y = y(x, z) \tag{3.3}$$

$$x = z(x, y) \tag{3.4}$$

Using the chain rule for differentiating the composite functions in Eqs. 3.2 to 3.4 yields

$$dx = \left(\frac{\partial x}{\partial y}\right)_z dy + \left(\frac{\partial x}{\partial z}\right)_y dz \tag{3.5}$$

$$dy = \left(\frac{\partial y}{\partial x}\right)_z dx + \left(\frac{\partial y}{\partial z}\right)_x dz \tag{3.6}$$

$$dz = \left(\frac{\partial z}{\partial x}\right)_y dx + \left(\frac{\partial z}{\partial y}\right)_x dy \tag{3.7}$$

where the notation $(\partial x/\partial y)_z$ means the partial derivative of the function x with respect to the variable y while holding the variable z constant. Normally, the partial differential notation $(\partial x/\partial y)$ automatically implies that all the other variables of x are held constant while differentiation with respect to y is carried out. However, in thermodynamics we will always have a wide choice of variables with which to construct the function x, but when we change variables we do not always change the functional notation. Thus, we can write

$$x = x(y, z) = x(y, w) = x(y, q) \tag{3.8}$$

where each of these three functions has a different form even though they all yield x. Since these functions are *not* the same, we cannot expect their partial derivatives to be equal:

$$\left(\frac{\partial x}{\partial y}\right)_z \neq \left(\frac{\partial x}{\partial y}\right)_w \neq \left(\frac{\partial x}{\partial y}\right)_q \tag{3.9}$$

Consequently, in thermodynamics, we *always* indicate which variables are held constant in partial differentiation. This also informs the reader as to which independent variables are being used in a functional relation.

Substituting Eq. 3.6 into Eq. 3.5 and rearranging gives

$$\left[1-\left(\frac{\partial x}{\partial y}\right)_z\left(\frac{\partial y}{\partial x}\right)_z\right]dx=\left[\left(\frac{\partial x}{\partial y}\right)_z\left(\frac{\partial y}{\partial z}\right)_x+\left(\frac{\partial x}{\partial z}\right)_y\right]dz \tag{3.10}$$

Equation 3.1 tells us that two of the three variables are independent. If we choose the independent variables to be x and z, then Eq. 3.10, which relates x and z, is valid only if the coefficients of dx and dz are both equal to zero. Then we have

$$1-\left(\frac{\partial x}{\partial y}\right)_z\left(\frac{\partial y}{\partial x}\right)_z=0 \tag{3.11}$$

or

$$\left(\frac{\partial x}{\partial y}\right)_z\left(\frac{\partial y}{\partial x}\right)_z=1 \tag{3.12}$$

or

$$\left(\frac{\partial x}{\partial y}\right)_z=\left[\left(\frac{\partial y}{\partial x}\right)_z\right]^{-1} \tag{3.13}$$

and

$$\left(\frac{\partial x}{\partial y}\right)_z\left(\frac{\partial y}{\partial z}\right)_x+\left(\frac{\partial x}{\partial z}\right)_y=0 \tag{3.14}$$

or

$$\left(\frac{\partial x}{\partial y}\right)_z\left(\frac{\partial y}{\partial z}\right)_x=-\left(\frac{\partial x}{\partial z}\right)_y \tag{3.15}$$

Then, using the results of Eq. 3.13, we can write

$$\left(\frac{\partial x}{\partial y}\right)_z\left(\frac{\partial y}{\partial z}\right)_x\left(\frac{\partial z}{\partial x}\right)_y=-1 \tag{3.16}$$

Some New Thermodynamic Properties

In Chapter 2 we introduced the specific volume v, an intensive property, as

$$v=\mathcal{V}/m \tag{3.17}$$

where $\mathcal{V}$ is the total volume[1] and m is the total mass of the system. We are now free to establish v as a function of any two other independent properties. For a

1. In this text, volume is represented by the symbol $\mathcal{V}$. The symbol V is reserved for the magnitude of velocity.

single-phase (i.e., homogeneous) pure substance subjected to only one work mode, the pressure and temperature *are* independent properties, and for such a system we can then write

$$v = v(p, T) \tag{3.18}$$

Differentiating Eq. 3.18 gives

$$dv = \left(\frac{\partial v}{\partial p}\right)_T dp + \left(\frac{\partial v}{\partial T}\right)_p dT \tag{3.19}$$

The coefficients of dp and dT in Eq. 3.19 reflect the dependence of volume on pressure and temperature, respectively. Because these terms have such important physical meaning, we introduce the following notation

$$\frac{1}{v}\left(\frac{\partial v}{\partial T}\right)_p = \beta = \text{isobaric coefficient of volume expansion} \tag{3.20}$$

and

$$-\frac{1}{v}\left(\frac{\partial v}{\partial p}\right)_T = \kappa = \text{isothermal coefficient of compressibility} \tag{3.21}$$

where the thermodynamic term *isobaric* is from the Greek words *iso* meaning constant and *baric* meaning weight or pressure; the term is to be taken to mean *constant pressure* in this text. Thus, we can write Eq. 3.19 as

$$dv = -v\kappa\, dp + v\beta\, dT \tag{3.22}$$

or

$$\frac{dv}{v} = \beta\, dT - \kappa\, dp \tag{3.23}$$

If κ and β are constant (or averaged) over small ranges of temperature and pressure, then Eq. 3.23 can be integrated to give

$$\ln\frac{v_2}{v_1} = \beta(T_2 - T_1) - \kappa(p_2 - p_1) \tag{3.24}$$

or

$$v_2 = v_1\{\exp[\beta(T_2 - T_1) - \kappa(p_2 - p_1)]\} \tag{3.25}$$

Thus, v is seen to have an exponential dependence on p and T when β and κ are constant. Table 3.1 gives values of β and κ for copper as a function of temperature, and Table 3.2 gives values of β and κ of various liquids at 20 °C (68 °F).

Table 3.1 **β and κ for copper as a function of temperature**

	$\beta \times 10^6$		$\kappa \times 10^{11}$	
T(K)	R^{-1}	K^{-1}	ft^2/lbf	m^2/N
100	17.5	31.5	34.51	0.721
150	22.8	41.0	35.08	0.733
200	25.3	45.6	35.80	0.748
250	26.7	48.0	36.47	0.762
300	27.3	49.2	37.14	0.776
500	30.1	54.2	40.06	0.837
800	33.7	60.7	44.13	0.922
1200	38.7	69.7	49.30	1.030

Source: Material drawn from Mark W. Zemansky, *Heat and Thermodynamics*, 4th ed. (New York: McGraw-Hill, 1957), p. 263 (Table 13.5). Reprinted by permission of the publisher.

Table 3.2 **Values of β and κ for various liquids at 20 °C (68 °F)**

	$\beta \times 10^6$		$\kappa \times 10^{11}$	
Substance	R^{-1}	K^{-1}	ft^2/lbf	m^2/N
Benzene	0.689	1.24	4550	95
Diethyl ether	0.922	1.66	8950	187
Ethyl alcohol	0.622	1.12	5310	111
Glycerin	0.281	0.505	1010	21
Heptane (n)	0.683	1.23	6890	144
Mercury	0.101	0.182	192	4.02
Water	0.115	0.207	2200	45.9

Source: Adapted by permission of the publisher from Mark W. Zemansky, Michael M. Abbott, and Hendrick C. Van Ness, *Basic Engineering Thermodynamics*, 2d ed. (New York: McGraw-Hill, 1975), p. 32 (Table 2-1).

Example 3.1

A 1-cm^3 copper block at 250 K is heated in the atmosphere to 800 K. Find the volume of the block at 800 K.

Solution Since the copper block changes state under atmospheric (constant) pressure, it undergoes an isobaric process. When p = constant, Eq. 3.25 reduces to

$$v_2 = v_1\{\exp[\beta(T_2 - T_1)]\}$$

and multiplying both sides of this equation by the mass m of the block gives the total volume $\mathcal{V}$ as

$$\mathcal{V}_2 = mv_2 = \mathcal{V}_1\{\exp[\beta(T_2 - T_1)]\}$$

It can be seen from Table 3.1 that β is not constant in the temperature range of 250 to 800 K. To come up with a reasonable value for an average β we must see how β varies with temperature. The figure below shows the data for β vs. T for copper taken from Table 3.1. This figure shows that β varies linearly with T in the range of 250 to 800 K. Then the average value of β in this temperature range is easily found to be

$$\beta_{avg} = 54.4 \times 10^{-6}\ \text{K}^{-1}$$

Now we can calculate the final volume as

$$\begin{aligned} V_2 = mv_2 &= V_1\{\exp[\beta(T_2 - T_1)]\} \\ &= (1\ \text{cm}^3)\{\exp[(54.4 \times 10^{-6}\ \text{K}^{-1})(800 - 250\ \text{K})]\} \end{aligned}$$

or

$$V_2 = 1.03\ \text{cm}^3$$

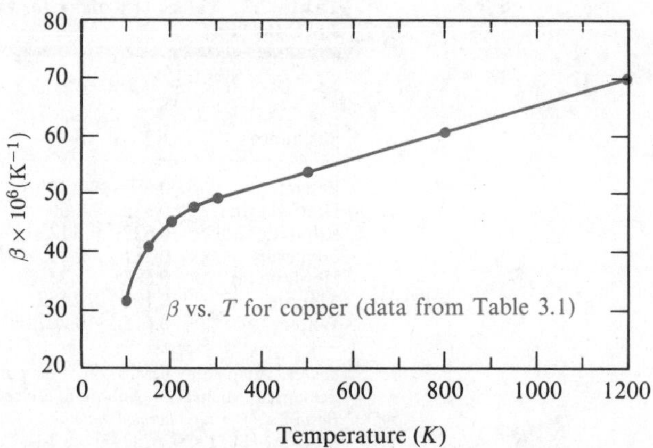

β vs. T for copper (data from Table 3.1)

Note that we could also fit a straight line to the β vs. T data between 250 and 800 K and come up with a formula of the form

$$\beta = C_1 T + C_2$$

Inserting this formula into Eq. 3.23 and then integrating it (with $dp = 0$) will yield a different (but equally valid) relation between v_1, v_2, T_1, and T_2. This is left as an exercise (Problem 13) at the end of this chapter.

For historical reasons, the total energy of a system which does not have magnetic, electric, surface, etc., effects is divided into three parts. Classical physicists recognized two easily observable forms of energy: 1) the total kinetic energy KE = $mV^2/2g_c$, and 2) the total potential energy PE = mgZ/g_c. The remaining unobservable part of the total energy is simply called the *total internal energy U*. Thus, the total energy E of a system is written as

$$E = U + mV^2/2g_c + mgZ/g_c \tag{3.26}$$

or

$$E = U + \mathrm{KE} + \mathrm{PE} \tag{3.27}$$

We will use the simpler Eq. 3.27 when writing general expressions and use the more complete Eq. 3.26 when calculations are required. Total internal energy is an all inclusive concept that includes chemical, nuclear, molecular, etc., energies within the system. Since all mass has internal energy, the only systems that have zero internal energy are devoid of matter.

We define a system's *specific internal energy* u as

$$u = U/m \tag{3.28}$$

where m is the system mass. Then we can write Eqs. 3.26 and 3.27 as

$$e = E/m = u + V^2/2g_c + gZ/g_c \tag{3.29a}$$

and

$$e = u + ke + pe \tag{3.29b}$$

where

$$\mathrm{ke} = |\mathbf{V}|^2/2g_c = V^2/2g_c \tag{3.30a}$$

and

$$\mathrm{pe} = gZ/g_c \tag{3.30b}$$

The specific internal energy u is an intensive property like pressure, temperature, specific volume, etc.; thus, it too can be written as a function of any other two independent properties. For a simple (i.e., homogeneous and pure) substance the temperature and specific volume are independent thermodynamic properties, so we can write

$$u = u(T, v) \tag{3.31}$$

and then

$$du = \left(\frac{\partial u}{\partial T}\right)_v dT + \left(\frac{\partial u}{\partial v}\right)_T dv \tag{3.32}$$

The first term in Eq. 3.32 describes the temperature dependence of u, and the coefficient of dT is written as c_v, where

$$\left(\frac{\partial u}{\partial T}\right)_v = c_v = \text{constant volume specific heat} \tag{3.33}$$

Then Eq. 3.32 becomes

$$du = c_v\, dT + \left(\frac{\partial u}{\partial v}\right)_T dv \tag{3.34}$$

For an incompressible substance, the volume is constant and $dv = 0$. Then Eq. 3.34 becomes

$$du = c_v\, dT \tag{3.35}$$

and upon integration this becomes

$$u_2 - u_1 = \int_{T_1}^{T_2} c_v\, dT \tag{3.36}$$

The constant volume specific heat is a material property that is often constant over small or moderate temperature ranges, T_1 to T_2. In this case Eq. 3.36 reduces to

$$u_2 - u_1 = c_v(T_2 - T_1) \tag{3.37}$$

Equation 3.37 is very useful for calculating changes in specific internal energy of an incompressible simple substance or a substance whose specific internal energy does not depend on specific volume.

Many of the equations of thermodynamics will have groupings of similar terms. It is convenient to simplify the writing of these equations by assigning a single symbol and name to such a grouping. This is what was done in Eq. 3.26 in defining the total system energy as the sum of three other energy terms. Also, it should be quite clear that any function of a system's thermodynamic properties is also a thermodynamic property itself. Thus, the specific energy e in Eq. 3.29 is an intensive thermodynamic property as are u, ke, and pe.

When we introduce the open system energy balance later in this text we will find that the properties u and pv are consistently grouped together. For simplicity, then, we combine these two properties into a new thermodynamic property called *enthalpy*,[2] whose total and specific forms are defined as

$$H = U + p\mathcal{V} = \text{Total enthalpy} \tag{3.38}$$

and

$$h = H/m = u + pv = \text{specific enthalpy} \tag{3.39}$$

Like specific internal energy, we can take specific enthalpy to be a function of any two independent properties for a simple substance subjected to only one work mode. For such a simple substance the temperature and pressure are independent, so we can write

$$h = h(T, p) \tag{3.40}$$

2. The quantity $u + pv$ has had many different names over the years. In the early years of thermodynamics it was known at various times as the heat function, the heat content, and the total heat. The term enthalpy comes from the Greek ενθαλποσ, meaning *in warmth*, and was introduced in 1922 by Professor Alfred W. Porter. He credited the coining of the name to the Dutch physicist Kamerlingh Onnes (1853–1926). This name was officially adopted by the American Society of Mechanical Engineers (ASME) in 1936.

and

$$dh = \left(\frac{\partial h}{\partial T}\right)_p dT + \left(\frac{\partial h}{\partial p}\right)_T dp \tag{3.41}$$

The temperature dependence of h is important in classical physics, and the coefficient of dT is written as c_p, where

$$\left(\frac{\partial h}{\partial T}\right)_p = c_p = \text{constant pressure specific heat} \tag{3.42}$$

Then Eq. 3.41 becomes

$$dh = c_p\, dT + \left(\frac{\partial h}{\partial p}\right)_T dp \tag{3.43}$$

If a process is isobaric (constant pressure) or if a substance has a specific enthalpy independent of pressure, then Eq. 3.43 reduces to

$$dh = c_p\, dT \tag{3.44}$$

and

$$h_2 - h_1 = \int_{T_1}^{T_2} c_p\, dT \tag{3.45}$$

And if c_p is constant (or averaged) over the temperature range T_1 to T_2 then

$$h_2 - h_1 = c_p(T_2 - T_1) \tag{3.46}$$

Equation 3.46 is the companion equation of Eq. 3.37. Together they can be used to determine changes in u and h in the simple systems for which these equations have been derived.

Other thermodynamic properties such as *entropy* and *availability* will be introduced later in this text when they are needed. It must be remembered, however, that not all thermodynamic properties are directly measurable. A pressure gage and a thermometer will give us numerical values for p and T, but there are no instruments that give us values of u and h directly. It takes much more sophisticated measurements to allow us to calculate accurate values for u and h. More complex mathematical relations between thermodynamic properties will be developed in Chapter 6 after the reader is thoroughly familiar with the concept of entropy discussed in Chapter 5.

Phase Diagrams

A pure substance is composed of a single chemical compound which may itself be composed of a variety of chemical elements. Water (H_2O), ammonia (NH_3), and carbon dioxide (CO_2) are all pure substances, but air is not because it is a mixture of N_2, O_2, H_2O, CO_2, and so forth. All substances can exist in one or more of the gaseous (or vapor), liquid, or solid physical states, and some solids can have a variety of molecular structures. In 1875 the American physicist Josiah Willard Gibbs (1839–1903) introduced the term *phase* to describe the different forms in which a pure substance can exist. We now speak of the gaseous, liquid, and solid phases of a pure substance and we recognize that a pure substance may have a number of different solid phases.[3] Multiple solid phases are called *allotropic*, a term that comes from the Greek words *allos*, meaning *related to*, and *trope* meaning *forms of the same substance*. For example, graphite and diamond are allotropic forms of carbon.

A substance made up of only one physical phase is called *homogeneous*, if it is composed of two or more phases it is called *heterogeneous*. Coexistent phases are separated by an interface called the *phase boundary* of finite thickness across which the property values change uniformly. A system in which two phases coexist in equilibrium is called *saturated*.[4]

The number of degrees of freedom within a heterogeneous mixture of pure substances is given by Gibbs' phase rule as

$$f = C - P + 2 \tag{3.47}$$

where f is the number of degrees of freedom, C is the number of components (pure substances) in the mixture and P is the number of phases. Also, f can be interpreted to be the number of intensive properties of the individual phases that are required to fix the state of the individual phases. For example, a homogeneous ($P = 1$) pure substance ($C = 1$) requires $f = 1 - 1 + 2 = 2$ intensive properties to fix its state. Similarly, a homogeneous ($P = 1$) mixture of two pure substances ($C = 2$) requires $f = 2 - 1 + 2 = 3$ intensive properties to fix its state, and so forth. The case of a two-phase ($P = 2$) pure substance ($C = 1$), however, is slightly misleading because here $f = 1 - 2 + 2 = 1$. But this simply means that each individual phase requires one intensive property to fix its state, thus two independent properties are required to fix the state of the complete two phase system. To find the state of a mixture of two phases we need to know how much of each phase is present, i.e., the composition of the mixture. The phase composition in a liquid–vapor mixture is given by a new thermodynamic property called the *quality* of the mixture, which will be defined shortly.

A phase diagram is made by plotting thermodynamic properties as coordinates. Figure 3.1 illustrates typical *p-T* and *p-v* phase diagrams for a substance

3. Actually, matter can exist in a bewildering variety of phases, beyond the common solid, liquid, and vapor forms. Ferromagnetic, antiferromagnetic, ferroelectric, superconducting, superfluid, nematic, smectic, and so on, are all valid phases.

4. The term *saturated* comes from the eighteenth century when heat was thought to be a fluid. At that time it was thought that a substance could be saturated with heat just like water can become saturated with salt or sugar. Today we recognize that heat is not a fluid and therefore the use of the word saturation in reference to a thermodynamic phase change is really a misnomer. However, this term is now completely entrenched in modern thermodynamic literature.

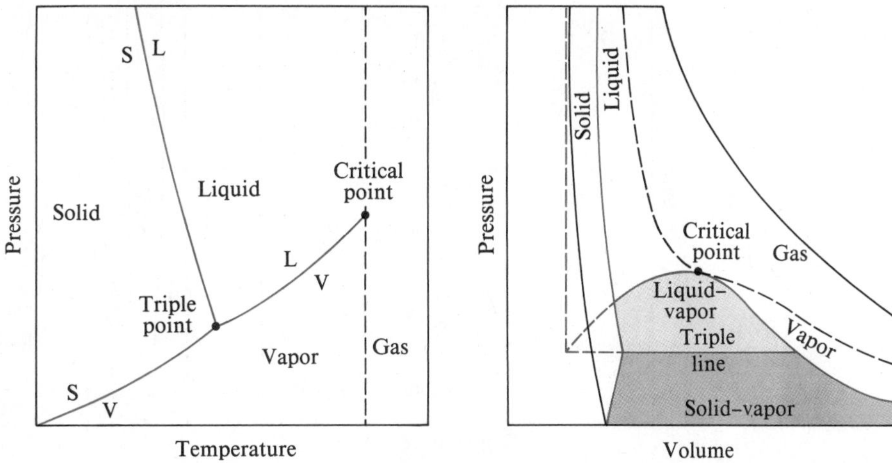

Figure 3.1 Pressure–temperature and pressure–volume diagrams for a substance that expands on freezing (like water).

that expands upon freezing (like water and antimony). When the p-T and p-v diagrams are combined to form a three dimensional p-v-T surface, thermodynamic surfaces then arise as shown in Figure 3.2. Figures 3.3 and 3.4 show the similar plots for a substance that contracts upon freezing (such as carbon dioxide and most other substances).

The expansion or contraction behavior of a substance on solidification can be deduced either from the increase or decrease in specific volume as the substance

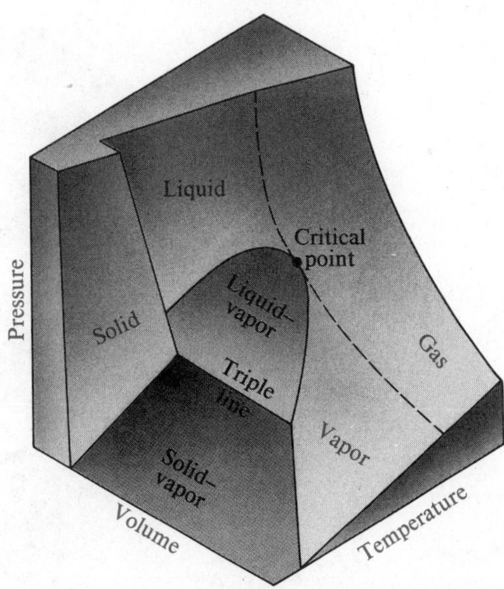

Figure 3.2 The p-v-T surface for a substance that expands on freezing (like water).

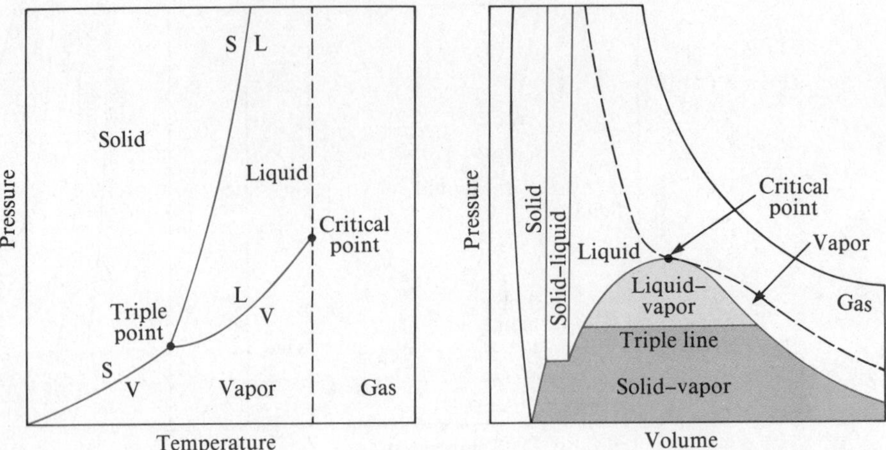

Figure 3.3 Pressure–temperature and pressure–volume diagrams for a substance that contracts upon freezing (like carbon dioxide).

goes from a liquid to a solid, or from the slope of the fusion line on the *p-T* diagram. If the *p-T* fusion line has a negative slope then the substance contracts upon melting; if it has a positive slope then it expands upon melting.

The pure substance *p-T* phase diagram shown in Figures 3.1 and 3.3 is composed of three unique curves. The *fusion line* represents the region of two-phase solid–liquid equilibrium, the *vaporization line* represents the region of two-phase liquid–vapor equilibrium; and the *sublimation line* represents the region of two-

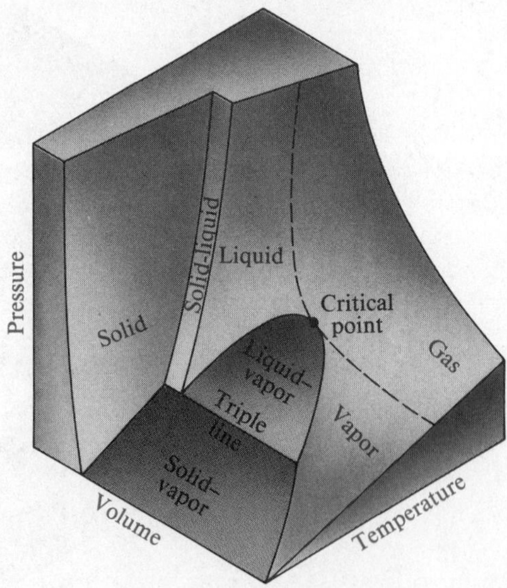

Figure 3.4 The *p-v-T* surface for a substance that contracts upon freezing (like carbon dioxide).

Table 3.3 Triple point data for various materials

Substance	*T* (R)	*T* (K)	*p* (psia)	*p* (kPa)
Ammonia (NH_3)	351.7	195.4	0.89	6.16
Carbon dioxide (CO_2)	389.9	216.6	75.98	523.8
Helium 4 (‖ point)	3.9	2.17	0.74	5.11
Hydrogen (H_2)	24.9	13.84	1.03	7.13
Neon (Ne)	44.2	24.57	6.35	43.77
Nitrogen (N_2)	113.7	63.18	1.84	12.67
Oxygen (O_2)	97.8	54.36	0.02	0.15
Sulfur dioxide (SO_2)	355.9	187.7	0.02	0.17
Water (H_2O)	491.7	273.16	0.09	0.62

Source: Adapted by permission of the publisher from Mark W. Zemansky, Michael M. Abbott, and Hendrick C. Van Ness, *Basic Engineering Thermodynamics*, 2d ed. (New York: McGraw-Hill, 1975), p. 107 (Table 5-1).

phase solid-vapor equilibrium. These three lines intersect at one point, called the *triple point*, which is the only point where all three phases can be in equilibrium simultaneously. The triple point on the p-T diagram appears as a line on the p-v diagram, with the triple point simply being an end view of this line. Table 3.3 gives the property values at the solid–liquid–vapor triple point of various substances. At the triple point of a pure substance, $C = 1$, $p = 3$, and Eq. 3.47 gives the number of degrees of freedom as $f = 1 - 3 + 2 = 0$; i.e., there is no flexibility in the thermodynamic state, and none of the properties can be varied and still keep the system at the triple point. The properties can be varied along the various two-phase boundary lines, but not at the three-phase triple point. If a substance has more than one solid phase, then it will also have more than one triple point. Figure 3.5 shows a more complete p-T phase diagram for water including seven of its known solid phases. Each intersection of three phase transition lines forms a new triple point.

The liquid to vapor phase transformation is called *vaporization*, and the vapor to liquid phase transformation is called *condensation*. Similarly, the solid to liquid phase transformation is known as *melting* and the liquid to solid phase transformation is called *freezing* or *solidification*. Finally, the solid to vapor phase transformation is known as *sublimation* and the vapor to solid phase transformation is simply *condensation* (or *frost* in the case of water).

The vaporization curve for all known substances has a peak at a curious point known as the *critical state*. This is the state at which the densities of the liquid and the vapor phases become equal and, consequently, where the physical interface between the liquid and the vapor disappears. At or above the critical state there is no longer any physical difference between a liquid and a vapor. Substances existing under these conditions are called *gases*.[5] In this text we will use the term gas to describe the state of any substance whose temperature is greater than its

5. The term gas was coined by the Belgian chemist Jan Bapist Van Helmont (1577–1644), and is derived from the Greek word *κεφσ*, meaning *gaping void*.

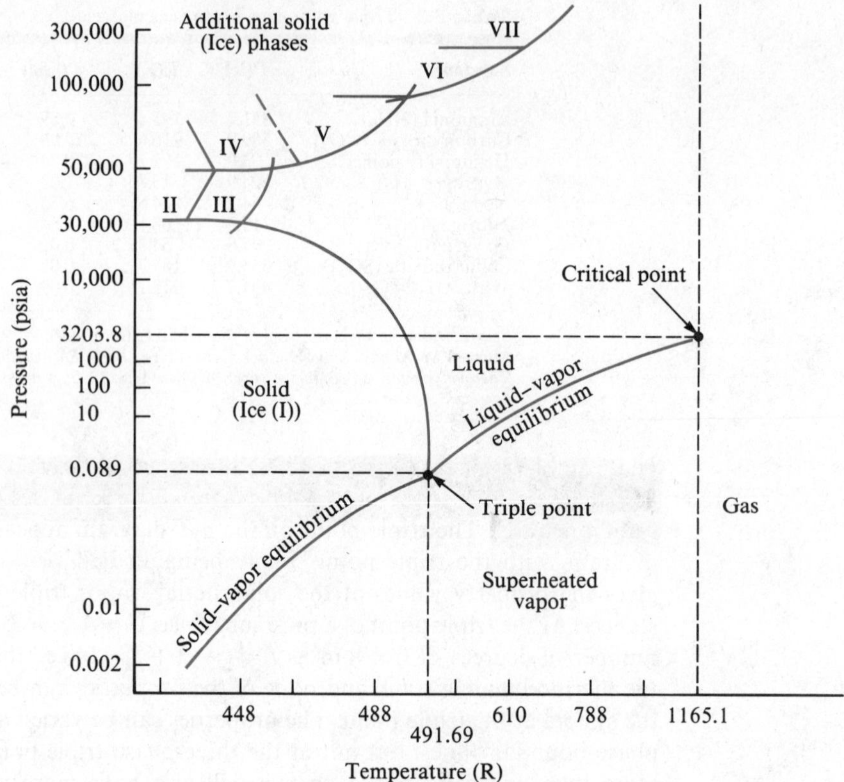

Figure 3.5 Phase diagram for water (not drawn to scale).

critical state temperature. A substance in the vapor phase that does not meet the definition of a gas is called a *superheated vapor* (sometimes just vapor). These definitions are illustrated in Figures 3.5 and 3.6. Table 3.4 gives the critical state

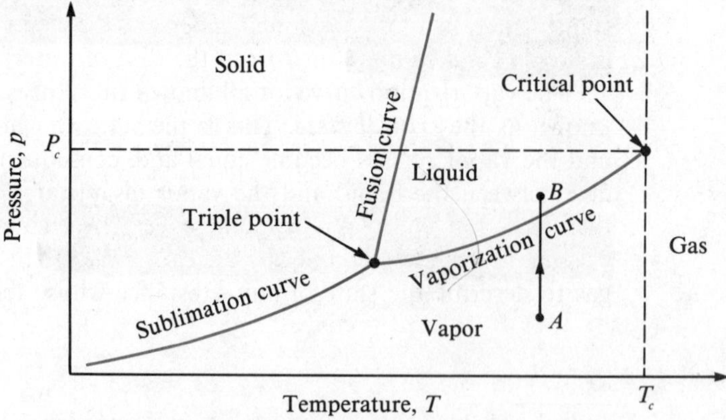

Figure 3.6 The definitions of a gas and a vapor.

Table 3.4 Critical state properties for various substances (see also Appendix C.12)

Substance	T_c (R)	T_c (K)	p_c (psia)	p_c (MPa)	v_c (ft^3/lbm)	v_c (m^3/kg)
Ammonia (NH_3)	729.9	405.5	1636	11.28	0.068	0.0043
Carbon dioxide (CO_2)	547.5	304.2	1071	7.39	0.034	0.0021
Carbon monoxide (CO)	239.4	133.0	507.0	3.50	0.053	0.0033
Helium (He)	9.5	5.3	33.2	0.23	0.231	0.0144
Hydrogen (H_2)	59.9	33.3	188.1	1.30	0.516	0.0322
Nitrogen (N_2)	227.1	126.2	491.68	3.39	0.051	0.0032
Oxygen (O_2)	278.6	154.8	736.9	5.08	0.039	0.0024
Sulfur dioxide (SO_2)	775.2	430.7	1143	7.88	0.030	0.0019
Water (H_2O)	1165.1	647.3	3203.8	22.09	0.051	0.0032

Sources: Reprinted with permission from K. A. Kobe and R. E. Lynn, Jr., *Chemical Reviews* 52 (1953): 117–236, Copyright 1953 American Chemical Society. Also from Gordon J. Van Wylen and Richard E. Sonntag, *Fundamentals of Classical Thermodynamics*, 3d ed. (New York: Wiley, 1986), pp. 684, 685 (Tables A.6E, A.6SI), Copyright © 1986 John Wiley & Sons. Reprinted by permission of John Wiley & Sons.

temperature, pressure, and specific volume for various common pure substances. A larger critical state data table is given in Appendix C. 12 at the end of this text.

Notice in Table 3.4 that at 14.7 psia and 70 °F (530 R) ammonia is a *vapor* ($T_c > 530$ R). Also, it should be clear from Figure 3.6 that to liquefy any gas whose pressure is initially less than its critical pressure simply by increasing its pressure alone, the gas must first be made into a vapor by lowering its temperature below its critical temperature. Vapor–liquid condensation is shown by process A–B in Figure 3.6. Thus, for example, no matter how high the applied pressure, hydrogen cannot be liquefied unless its temperature is below 59.9 R (see Table 3.4).

Several thermodynamic properties have discontinuities at the critical state; β, κ, and c_p become infinite there. Near the critical state a transparent substance will become almost opaque due to light scattering caused by large fluctuations in local density. This phenomenon is called *critical opalescence*, and is illustrated in Figure 3.7. Notice the appearance of the liquid–vapor interface in Figure 3.7b when the temperature becomes less than the critical temperature.

Quality

As mentioned earlier, in an equilibrium two-phase mixture temperature and pressure cannot be varied independently; therefore, either one or the other can be taken as an independent thermodynamic property, but not both. Figure 3.8*a* shows the actual *p-v* diagram for water on log–log coordinates. Notice that in the two-phase regions (liquid plus vapor and solid plus vapor) the isotherms (lines of constant temperature) are parallel to the isobars (lines of constant pressure) showing that pressure and temperature are not independent in this region. To determine other thermodynamic properties of a mixture of phases we need to know the amount of each phase present. We do this with a *lever rule* applied to one of the phase diagram coordinates. Consider the simplified liquid–vapor *p-v* diagram shown in Figure 3.8*b*. Substances whose state lie *on* the saturation curve are called *saturated*. Substances whose states lie *under* the saturation curve are called *wet*. Substances whose states are on the saturation curve but to the *left* of the

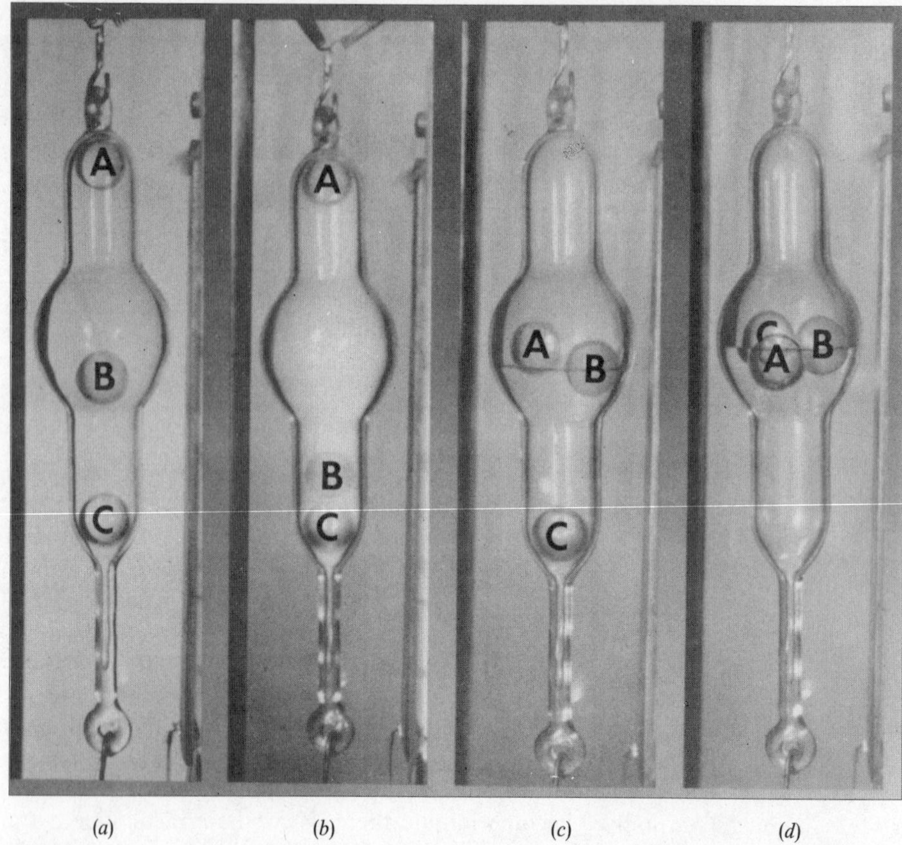

(a) (b) (c) (d)

Figure 3.7 The behavior of a fluid as the temperature is lowered past the critical temperature. The glass bulb contains carbon dioxide near the critical density ρ_c, and three balls with densities $\rho_A \lesssim \rho_c$, $\rho_B = \rho_c$, and $\rho_C \gtrsim \rho_c$ that indicate the variation in density with position and temperature inside the bulb. In (*a*) the temperature is well above the critical temperature leaving all the carbon dioxide in the gaseous state with a uniform density, so the three balls are well separated and ball B with density ρ_c floats in the center. In (*b*) the temperature is only slightly above the critical temperature and the carbon dioxide has become foggy with a *critical opalescence* that obscures the positions of the balls. Now the density distribution is very sensitive to temperature variations and ball B is no longer in the center of the bulb. In (*c*) the temperature is slightly below the critical temperature and a meniscus has developed separating the gaseous and liquid states. Since the density of the new gaseous state is significantly less than before, the ball originally at the top has fallen to the meniscus. In (*d*) the temperature is far below the critical temperature and the density of the liquid has increased to the point where all three balls now float on the surface of the liquid. *Source*: Reprinted with permission from Jan V. Sengers and Anneke Levelt Sengers, "The Critical Region," *Chemical and Engineering News* 48 (June 10, 1968): 104. Copyright 1968 American Chemical Society.

critical state are called *saturated liquids*, and those on the saturation curve to the *right* of the critical state are called *saturated vapors*. Substances whose states are to the left of the saturation curve are called *compressed* or *subcooled* liquids, and those to the right are called *superheated vapors*.

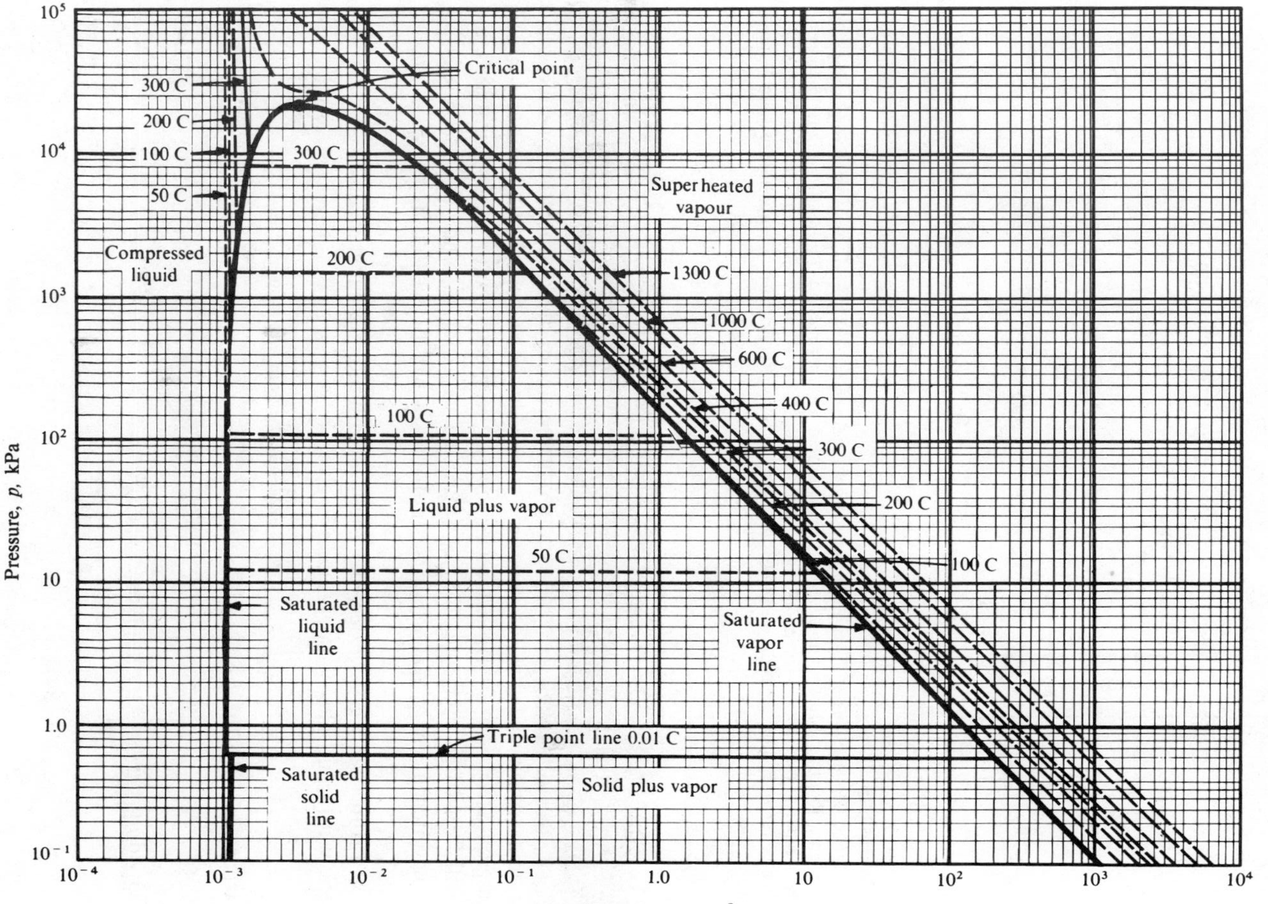

Figure 3.8a p-v diagram notation. The actual p-v diagram for water plotted on log–log coordinates. *Sources*: Barnard D. Wood, *Applications of Thermodynamics*, second edition, © 1982, Addison-Wesley Publishing Co., Inc., Reading, Massachusetts. Fig. 1.5. Reprinted with permission. Plotted from data in Joseph H. Keenan, Frederick G. Keyes, Philip G. Hill, and Joan G. Moore, *Steam Tables* (New York: Wiley, 1969), B. 16. Copyright © 1969 John Wiley & Sons. Reprinted by permission of John Wiley & Sons, Inc.

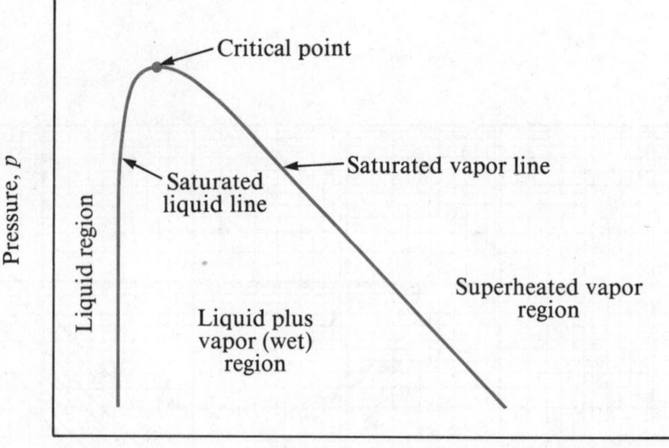

Figure 3.8b Schematic p-v diagram for the liquid, mixture, and vapor regions. *Sources*: Barnard D. Wood, *Applications of Thermodynamics*, second edition, © 1982, Addison-Wesley Publishing Co., Inc., Reading, Massachusetts. Fig. 1.5. Reprinted with permission. Plotted from data in Joseph H. Keenan, Frederick G. Keyes, Philip G. Hill, and Joan G. Moore, *Steam Tables* (New York: Wiley, 1969), B. 16 Copyright © 1969 John Wiley & Sons. Reprinted by permission of John Wiley & Sons, Inc.

To help identify the properties of a system we will adopt the convention of using an "f" subscript on the symbols of all thermodynamic properties of saturated liquids and a "g" subscript on the symbols of all thermodynamic properties of saturated vapors.[6] Thermodynamic properties in the compressed (or subcooled) liquid region, the wet (or mixture) region, and the superheated vapor (or gas) region carry *no* subscripts. Consequently, the specific volume of saturated liquid will be written as v_f and that of saturated vapor as v_g, and the associated specific internal energies, enthalpies, and masses will be written as u_f, u_g, h_f, h_g, m_f, and m_g.

From Figure 3.9 we see that the *total* volume of a substance whose state is in the wet (liquid plus vapor) region is given by

$$\forall = mv = m_f v_f + m_g v_g \tag{3.48}$$

where m is the total mass given by

$$m = m_f + m_g \tag{3.49}$$

Dividing Eq. 3.48 by m gives

$$v = m_f v_f/m + m_g v_g/m \tag{3.50}$$

6. The use of "f" and "g" as subscripts here is out of tradition. They come from the first letters of the German words *flussig* (for liquid) and *gas*. More appropriate English subscripts might be "ℓ" for liquid and "v" for vapor, but they are not used.

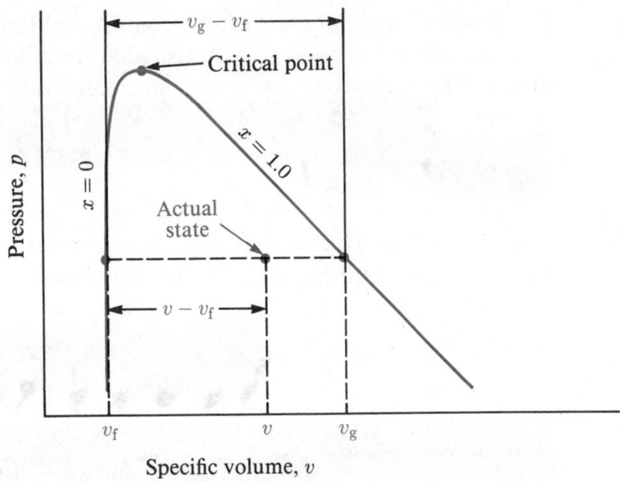

Figure 3.9 The lever rule for calculating quality.

Equation 3.50 is just a simple mass-based lever rule equation relating a mixture thermodynamic property (v) to the thermodynamic properties of the components of the mixture (v_f and v_g). We now define the *quality* x of a liquid plus vapor mixture as the relative amount of vapor present, or

$$x = m_g/(m_g + m_f) = m_g/m \tag{3.51}$$

Thus, Eq. 3.50 can be written as

$$v = (1 - x)v_f + xv_g \tag{3.52}$$

or

$$v = v_f + x(v_g - v_f) = v_f + xv_{fg} \tag{3.53}$$

where we have defined the magnitude of the liquid to vapor property change as

$$v_{fg} = v_g - v_f \tag{3.54}$$

Thus, from Figure 3.9 we see that another definition of quality is

$$x = \frac{v - v_f}{v_{fg}} \tag{3.55}$$

It should be clear from the definition of quality that its *value* has the following bounds

Saturated liquid: $x = 0.0$
Saturated vapor: $x = 1.0$
Wet region: $0 < x < 1$

In all other single-phase regions (compressed liquid, superheated vapor, gaseous) *x is not defined* because they are single-phase homogeneous regions in which the mass ratio represented by x does not constitute an independent thermodynamic property. Note that since the numerical value of quality is restricted to lie in the range from zero to one, *no correct calculation can ever give a value of x less than 0 or greater than 1.0.*

Although Eq. 3.55 was developed using specific volume, an identical argument can be used to expand it to all other intensive properties (except pressure and temperature) resulting in equations of the form

$$x = \frac{v - v_f}{v_{fg}} = \frac{u - u_f}{u_{fg}} = \frac{h - h_f}{h_{fg}} \tag{3.56}$$

The term $m_f/m = 1 - x$ in Eqs. 3.50 and 3.52 represents the relative amount of liquid present in the mixture, and is often called the *moisture* of the mixture.

Example 3.2

Saturated water at 14.696 psia and 212 °F has the following properties:

$v_f = 0.01672 \text{ ft}^3/\text{lbm}$ $v_g = 26.80 \text{ ft}^3/\text{lbm}$
$u_f = 180.2 \text{ Btu/lbm}$ $u_g = 1077.5 \text{ Btu/lbm}$
$h_f = 180.07 \text{ Btu/lbm}$ $h_g = 1150.4 \text{ Btu/lbm}$

If 0.2 lbm of saturated water at 14.696 psia is put into a sealed rigid container whose total volume is 3.0 ft^3, determine the following properties of the system:

a) the specific volume v,
b) the quality x and moisture $1 - x$,
c) the specific internal energy u,
d) the specific enthalpy h, and
e) the mass of water in the liquid and vapor phases, m_f and m_g.

Solution The system is a closed rigid container:

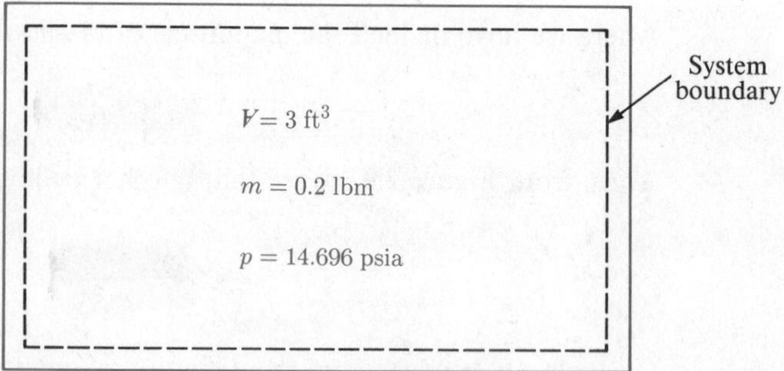

a) The specific volume can be calculated directly from its definition, Eq. 3.17 as

$$v = V/m = 3.0/0.2 = 15.0 \text{ ft}^3/\text{lbm}$$

b) The quality can be calculated from Eq. 3.55 or 3.56 and Eq. 3.54 as

$$x = \frac{v - v_f}{v_{fg}} = \frac{15.0 - 0.01672}{26.80 - 0.01672} = 0.5594$$

or $x = 55.94\%$ vapor. Thus, the amount of moisture present is $1 - x = 0.4406$, or the mixture consists of 44.06% moisture.

c) The specific internal energy can be obtained by combining Eq. 3.56 with the definition $u_{fg} = u_g - u_f$ to give

$$u = u_f + xu_{fg} = u_f + x(u_g - u_f)$$

or

$$u = 180.2 + (0.5594)(1077.5 - 180.2) = 682.2 \text{ Btu/lbm}$$

d) The specific enthalpy can be obtained by combining Eq. 3.56 with the definition $h_{fg} = h_g - h_f$ to give

$$h = h_f + xh_{fg} = h_f + x(h_g - h_f)$$

or

$$h = 180.07 + (0.5594)(1150.4 - 180.07) = 722.9 \text{ Btu/lbm}$$

e) To obtain the mass of water in the liquid and vapor phases we can use the original definition of quality given in Eq. 3.51 to get $m_g = xm = 0.5594(0.2) = 0.1119$ lbm of saturated water vapor and then $m_f = (1 - x)m = m - m_g = 0.0881$ lbm of saturated liquid water.

Example 3.3 What total mass of saturated water (liquid plus vapor) should be put into a 0.5-ft^3 sealed rigid container at 14.696 psia so that the water will pass exactly through the critical state when the container is heated? Also, determine the initial quality in the vessel.

Solution Processes carried out in sealed rigid containers are constant volume (or *isochoric*) processes. Thus, the process path on a *p-v* diagram is a vertical straight line, as shown in the *p-v* diagram below. In this problem we are given the final state (the critical state) and we are asked to determine a thermodynamic property (the mass) at the initial state. In Table 3.4 or Appendix C.1a we find for water that $p_c = 3203.8$ psia, $T_c = 1165.1$ R, and $v_c = 0.05053$ ft^3/lbm. Also, since both the volume and mass are constant here, $v_2 = v_1 = v_c$. This process can then be diagrammed as follows

Initial state	$\xrightarrow[\text{process}]{\text{Constant volume}}$	**Final state**
$p_1 = 14.696$ psia		$p_2 = p_c$
$T_1 = 212$ °F (saturated)		$T_2 = T_c$
$v_1 = v_2$ (from the process path)		$v_2 = v_c$

Therefore,

$$m = \frac{V}{v_1} = \frac{V}{v_2} = \frac{V}{v_c} = \frac{0.5 \text{ ft}^3}{0.05053 \text{ ft}^3/\text{lbm}} = 9.895 \text{ lbm}$$

We can now find the quality in the initial state by using Eq. 3.55 and the data given in Example 3.2 as

$$x_1 = \frac{v - v_{f1}}{v_{fg1}} = \frac{v_c - v_{f1}}{v_{g1} - v_{f1}} = \frac{(0.05053 - 0.01672) \text{ ft}^3/\text{lbm}}{(26.8 - 0.01672) \text{ ft}^3/\text{lbm}} = 1.26 \times 10^{-3}$$

or

$$x_1 = 0.126\% \text{ vapor}$$

Note that since the quality is not defined at the critical state (quality is one of the properties that has a discontinuity there), no value for $x_2 = x_c$ can be given.

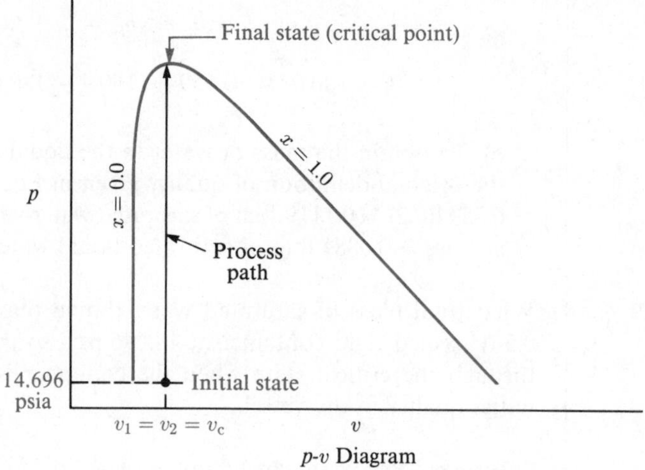

p-v Diagram

Thermodynamic Equations of State

In this section we discuss some of the basic *p-v-T* equations of state for ideal and real substances. A more comprehensive discussion of the behavior of real gases is given in Chapter 6.

The simplest equation of state is that for an incompressible material. One of the equations of state of an incompressible material is merely v = constant. This equation can be used for either a solid or a liquid, but it cannot be used for a vapor or a gas. Incompressible substances also have one other important state equation, which specifies that the specific internal energy of an incompressible material is a function of only one variable, temperature. Thus, the full set of state equations that characterize an incompressible material are

$$v = \text{constant} \tag{3.57}$$

and

$$u = u(T) \tag{3.58}$$

The constant volume specific heat of an incompressible material is given by Eq. 3.33 as

$$c_v = \left(\frac{\partial u}{\partial T}\right)_v = \frac{du}{dT} \quad \text{(since } u \text{ is independent of } v \text{ here)} \tag{3.59}$$

Since the specific enthalpy is defined as $h = u + pv$, then Eq. 3.42 gives the constant pressure specific heat of an incompressible material as

$$c_p = \left(\frac{\partial h}{\partial T}\right)_p = \frac{du}{dT} + \left(\frac{\partial(pv)}{\partial T}\right)_p = \frac{du}{dT} + pv\beta = c_v \quad \text{(when } \beta = 0\text{)}$$

since for incompressible materials v = constant and $\beta = 0$. However, note that since β is very small for most liquids and solids (see Table 3.1 and 3.2), these substances can be accurately modeled as incompressible materials. The subscripts p and v are meaningless for an incompressible material, and the simple phrase *specific heat*, represented by the symbol c without any subscripts, is sufficient. Thus, for all incompressible substances, $c_p = c_v = c$. Consequently, for these materials we can write

$$u_2 - u_1 = \int_{T_1}^{T_2} c\, dT \tag{3.60}$$

and if c is fairly constant over the temperature range from T_1 to T_2, then Eq. 3.60 becomes

$$u_2 - u_1 = c(T_2 - T_1) \tag{3.61}$$

Also, since $v_2 = v_1 = v$ here, then

$$h_2 - h_1 = c(T_2 - T_1) + v(p_2 - p_1) \tag{3.62}$$

Tables 3.5 and 3.6 list the specific heats of some materials whose liquid and solid phases accurately approximate incompressible substances.

Table 3.5 Specific heats of various liquids at atmospheric pressure

	T		*C*	
Substance	**R**	**K**	**Btu/lbm·R**	**kJ/kg·K**
Benzene	520	289	0.430	1.800
Butane (*n*)	492	273	0.550	2.303
Glycerin	510	283	0.554	2.320
Mercury	510	283	0.033	0.138
Propane	492	273	0.576	2.412
Water	492	273	1.007	4.216

Source: Material drawn from Kenneth Wark, Jr., *Thermodynamics*, 5th ed. (New York: McGraw-Hill, 1988), pp. 871, 971 (Tables A-22, A-22M). Reprinted by permission of the publisher.

Table 3.6 Specific heats of various solids at atmospheric pressure

	T		*C*	
Substance	**R**	**K**	**Btu/lbm·R**	**kJ/kg·K**
Aluminum	360	200	0.190	0.797
	540	300	0.215	0.902
	720	400	0.227	0.949
	900	500	0.238	0.997
Copper	540	300	0.092	0.386
	851	473	0.096	0.403
Graphite	527	293	0.170	0.712
Iron	527	293	0.107	0.448
Lead	540	300	0.031	0.129
	851	473	0.032	0.136
Rubber	527	293	0.439	1.84
Silver	527	293	0.056	0.233
Water (ice)	492	273	0.504	2.11
Wood	527	293	0.420	1.76

Sources: Material drawn from Kenneth Wark, Jr., *Thermodynamics*, 5th ed. (New York: McGraw-Hill, 1988), pp. 871, 971 (Tables A-22, A-22M). Reprinted by permission of the publisher. Also reprinted by permission of the publisher from William C. Reynolds and Henry C. Perkins, *Engineering Thermodynamics*, 2d ed. (New York: McGraw-Hill, 1977), pp. 648 (Table B.11).

The next simplest equation of state is that of an ideal gas. Like an incompressible substance, an ideal gas is also defined by two state equations, both of which must be obeyed if a gas is to be called ideal. The first equation of state is the common ideal gas law, which has the following four equivalent forms

$$pV\!\!\!/ = mRT \tag{3.63a}$$

$$pv = RT \tag{3.63b}$$

$$pV\!\!\!/ = n\mathcal{R}T \tag{3.63c}$$

$$p\bar{v} = \mathcal{R}T \tag{3.63d}$$

where $n = m/M$ is the number of moles, $\bar{v} = V\!\!\!/ /n$ is the molar specific volume, and $\mathcal{R}$ is the universal gas constant whose value is (see Appendix A)

$$\mathcal{R} = 1545.35 \text{ ft·lbf/(lbmole·R)} = 1.986 \text{ Btu/(lbmole·lR)}$$

$$= 8314 \text{ joule/(kgmole·K)} = 8.314 \text{ kJ/(kgmole·K)}$$

The second state equation used to define an ideal gas is that its specific internal energy is only a function of temperature, or

$$u = u(T) \tag{3.64}$$

As in the case of an incompressible substance, Eq. 3.33 gives the constant volume specific heat of an ideal gas as

$$c_v = \left(\frac{\partial u}{\partial T}\right)_v = \frac{du}{dT} \quad \text{(since } u \text{ does not depend on } v\text{)} \tag{3.65}$$

and if c_v is constant over the temperature range from T_1 to T_2, then upon integration of Eq. 3.65 we recover Eq. 3.37:

$$u_2 - u_1 = c_v(T_2 - T_1)$$

Thus, for a *constant specific heat ideal gas*, Eq. 3.37 is valid for *any* process (not just a constant volume process) because the internal energy of an ideal gas does not depend upon its volume. Thus, even for an isobaric (constant pressure) process, Eq. 3.37 is valid when a constant specific heat ideal gas is used.

Combining Eqs. 3.39 and 3.63b gives the specific enthalpy of an ideal gas as

$$h = u + pv = u + RT \tag{3.66}$$

From Eqs. 3.42 and 3.66, the constant pressure specific heat is

$$c_p = \left(\frac{\partial h}{\partial T}\right)_p = \frac{du}{dT} + R \tag{3.67}$$

or

$$c_p = c_v + R \tag{3.68}$$

If c_p is constant over the temperature range from T_1 to T_2, then upon integration of Eq. 3.67 we recover Eq. 3.46:

$$h_2 - h_1 = c_p(T_2 - T_1)$$

Thus, for a *constant specific heat ideal gas* Eq. 3.46 is valid for *any* process (not just a constant pressure process) because the enthalpy of an ideal gas does not depend upon its pressure. Thus, even for an isochoric (constant volume) process, Eq. 3.46 is valid when a constant specific heat ideal gas is used.

Note that even though the values of c_p and c_v for an ideal gas do not depend upon p and v, they may depend upon temperature. However, their temperature dependence is usually very weak, and most ideal gases can be considered to have constant specific heats over temperature ranges of a few hundred degrees. Figure 3.10 illustrates the temperature and pressure dependence of c_p and c_v for various common gases. Values of c_p, c_v, and the gas constant R are given in Table 3.7 for a variety of common gases at low pressure that behave as ideal gases. A larger table can be found in Appendix C.13 at the end of this text.

Normally, only low molecular mass real gases at high temperature or low pressure obey the ideal gas equation of state with good accuracy. For real gases with complex molecular structures or real gases approaching their saturated vapor

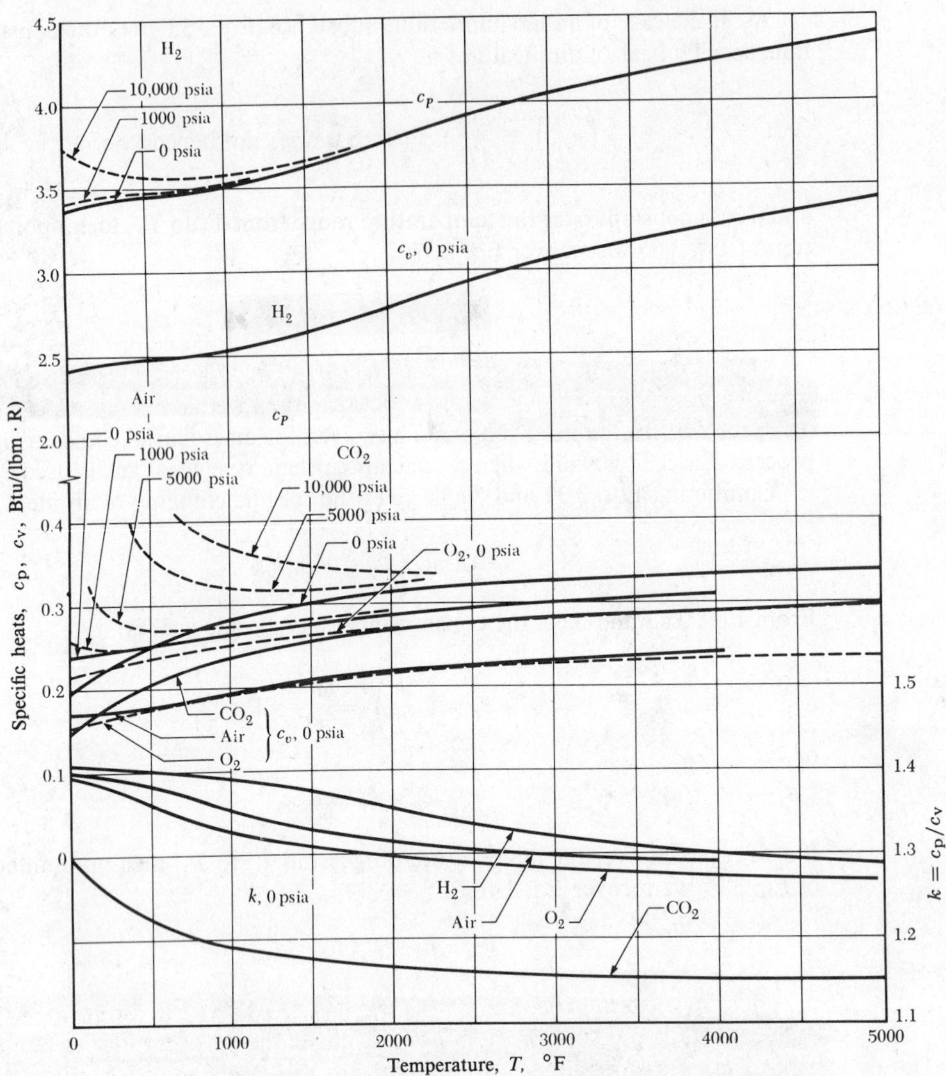

Figure 3.10 Specific heats of selected gases (data from the National Bureau of Standards). *Sources*: Reprinted by permission of the publisher from William C. Reynolds and Henry C. Perkins, *Engineering Dynamics*, 2d ed. (New York: McGraw-Hill, 1977), p. 621. Data from National Bureau of Standards.

region, more complex equations of state are required. The following equations have modifications to the ideal gas *p-v-T* equation that are intended to account for observed real gas behavior.

The Clausius equation of state accounts for the volume actually occupied by the gas molecules themselves. If we let b represent the specific volume of the molecules themselves, then the Clausius equation of state is

$$p(v - b) = RT \tag{3.69}$$

Table 3.7 Properties of various gases at low pressure (also see Appendix C.13)

		R		c_p		c_v		
Substance	M	**Btu/lbm·R**	**kJ/kg·K**	**Btu/lbm·R**	**kJ/kg·K**	**Btu/lbm·R**	**kJ/kg·K**	$k = c_p/c_v$
Air	28.97	0.0685	0.286	0.240	1.004	0.172	0.718	1.40
Argon (Ar)	39.94	0.0497	0.208	0.125	0.523	0.075	0.315	1.67
Carbon dioxide (CO_2)	44.01	0.0451	0.189	0.202	0.845	0.157	0.656	1.29
Carbon monoxide (CO)	28.01	0.0709	0.297	0.249	1.042	0.178	0.745	1.40
Helium (He)	4.003	0.4961	2.077	1.24	5.200	0.744	3.123	1.67
Hydrogen (H_2)	2.016	0.9850	4.124	3.42	14.32	2.435	10.19	1.40
Methane (CH_4)	16.04	0.1238	0.158	0.532	2.227	0.408	1.709	1.30
Nitrogen (N_2)	28.02	0.0709	0.296	0.248	1.038	0.177	0.742	1.40
Oxygen (O_2)	32.00	0.0621	0.260	0.219	0.917	0.157	0.657	1.39

Source: Reprinted by permission of the publisher from William C. Reynolds and Henry C. Perkins, *Engineering Thermodynamics*, 2d ed. (New York: McGraw-Hill, 1977), pp. 641, 642 (Tables B-6a, B-6b).

In 1873 van der Waals included a second correction factor to account for the forces of molecular attraction. These forces produce a net decrease in the observed pressure that is inversely proportional to v^2. The van der Waals equation of state has the form

$$\left(p + \frac{a}{v^2}\right)(v - b) = RT \tag{3.70}$$

The values of the molecular coefficients a and b in Eqs. 3.69 and 3.70 can be found in Appendix C.15 at the end of this text.

Other important real gas equations of state that are commonly used in engineering analysis are the Dieterici (1899) equation,

$$p(v - b) = RT \exp[-a/(RTv)] \tag{3.71}$$

and the Berthelot (1903) equation,

$$p(v - b) = RT - \frac{a}{T}\left(\frac{v - b}{v^2}\right) \tag{3.72}$$

But perhaps the most useful, best known, and most accurate equations of state for real gases are those of Beattie-Bridgeman (1928),

$$p = \left(\frac{1 - \epsilon}{v^2}\right)(v + B)RT - \frac{A}{v^2} \tag{3.73}$$

where

$$A = A_0(1 - a/v) \qquad B = B_0(1 - b/v) \quad \text{and} \quad \epsilon = \frac{c}{vT^3}$$

and Redlich-Kwong (1949),

$$p(v - b) = RT - \frac{a}{v\sqrt{T}}\left(\frac{v - b}{v + b}\right) \tag{3.74}$$

where A_0, B_0, a, b, and c are constants whose values for various gases can be found in Appendix C.15.

A more general form for a real gas equation of state is a power series expansion such as

$$pv = RT + \frac{A}{v} + \frac{B}{v^2} + \frac{C}{v^3} + \cdots \tag{3.75}$$

where $A, B, C, \ldots$ are all empirically determined functions of temperature. These equations are called *virial expansions*, and the temperature-dependent coefficients $A, B, C, \ldots$ are called the *virial coefficients.*

One way of measuring the difference between real and ideal gas behavior is through the *compressibility factor* Z, defined as

$$Z = \frac{Pv}{RT} \tag{3.76}$$

where $Z = 1$ for an ideal gas. Figure 3.11 shows that the experimental data for the compressibility factor for many different gases fall together when Z is plotted against *reduced pressure* p_R while holding the *reduced temperature* T_R constant. Figures 3.11, 3.12, and 3.13 constitute a set of compressibility charts that can be used

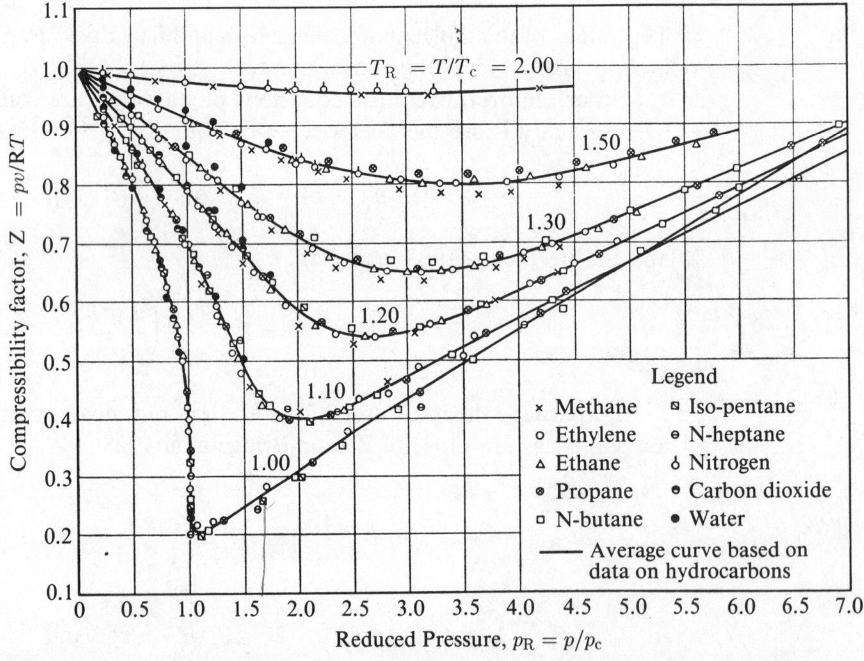

Figure 3.11 A generalized compressibility chart for various gases. *Sources*: Reprinted with permission from Gouq-Jen Su, "Modified Law of Corresponding States for Real Gases," *Industrial and Engineering Chemistry* 38, no. 8 (August 1946): 804. Copyright 1946 American Chemical Society. Also reprinted with permission of the publisher from William C. Reynolds and Henry C. Perkins, *Engineering Thermodynamics*, 2d ed. (New York: McGraw-Hill, 1977), p. 253 (Figure 8.9).

to solve real gas compressibility factor problems. The reduced variables used in these figures are defined as

$$p_R = \frac{p}{p_c} \tag{3.77}$$

and

$$T_R = \frac{T}{T_c} \tag{3.78}$$

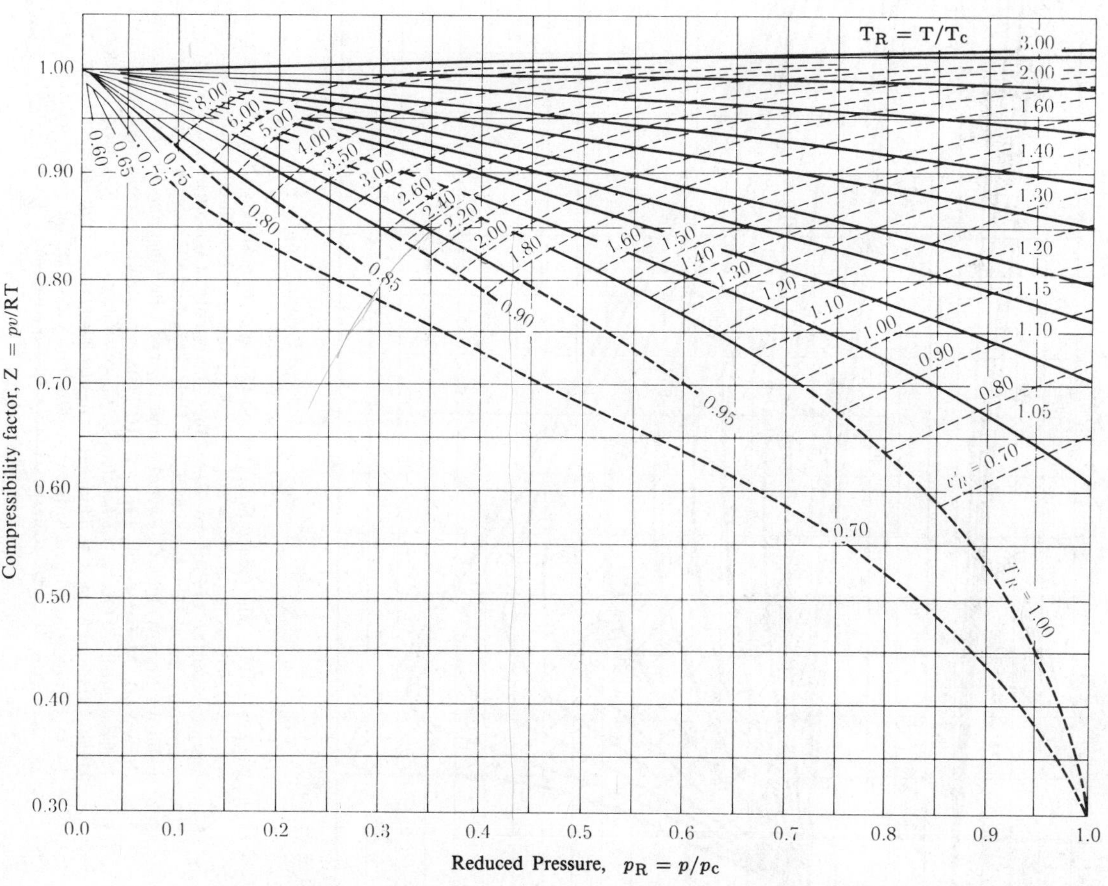

Figure 3.12a The Generalized (Nelson-Obert) compressibility chart—low-pressure range, $0 \leq p_R \leq 1.0$. Note that $v'_R = v/v'_c = vp_c/RT_c$. *Sources*: "Nelson-Obert Compressibility Charts" adapted courtesy of Professor E. F. Obert, University of Wisconsin, Madison, from E. F. Obert, *Concepts of Thermodynamics* (New York: McGraw-Hill, 1960). Data reprinted by permission of McGraw-Hill from L. C. Nelson and E. F. Obert, "Generalized Compressibility Charts," *Chemical Engineering*, vol. 61, no. 7 (1954): 203.

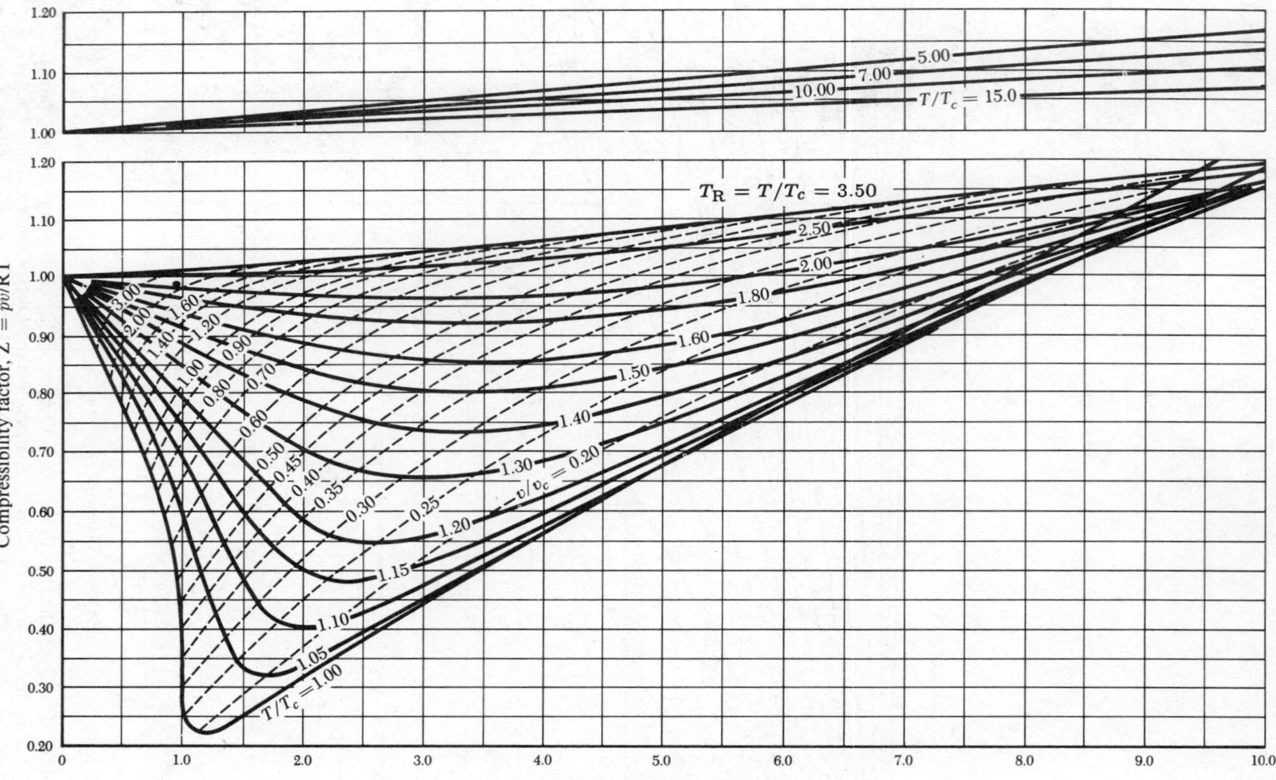

Figure 3.12b The Generalized (Nelson-Obert) compressibility Chart—low-pressure range, $0 \le p_R \le 10.0$. Note that $v'_R = v/v'_c = vp_c/RT_c$. *Sources:* "Nelson-Obert Compressibility Charts" reprinted courtesy of Professor E. F. Obert, University of Wisconsin, Madison, from Edward F. Obert, *Thermodynamics* (New York: McGraw-Hill, 1948), Fig. VII. Also reprinted by permission of the publisher from William C. Reynolds and Henry C. Perkins, *Engineering Thermodynamics*, 2d ed. (New York: McGraw-Hill, 1977), p. 616. Data reprinted by permission of McGraw-Hill from L. C. Nelson and E. F. Obert, "Generalized Compressibility Charts," *Chemical Engineering*, vol. 61, no. 7 (1954): 203; and from B. F. Dodge, *Chemical Engineering Thermodynamics* (New York: McGraw-Hill, 1944). Data also reprinted with permission from Gouq-Jen Su, *Industrial and Engineering Chemistry* 38, no. 8 (August 1946): 803-806. Copyright 1946 American Chemical Society.

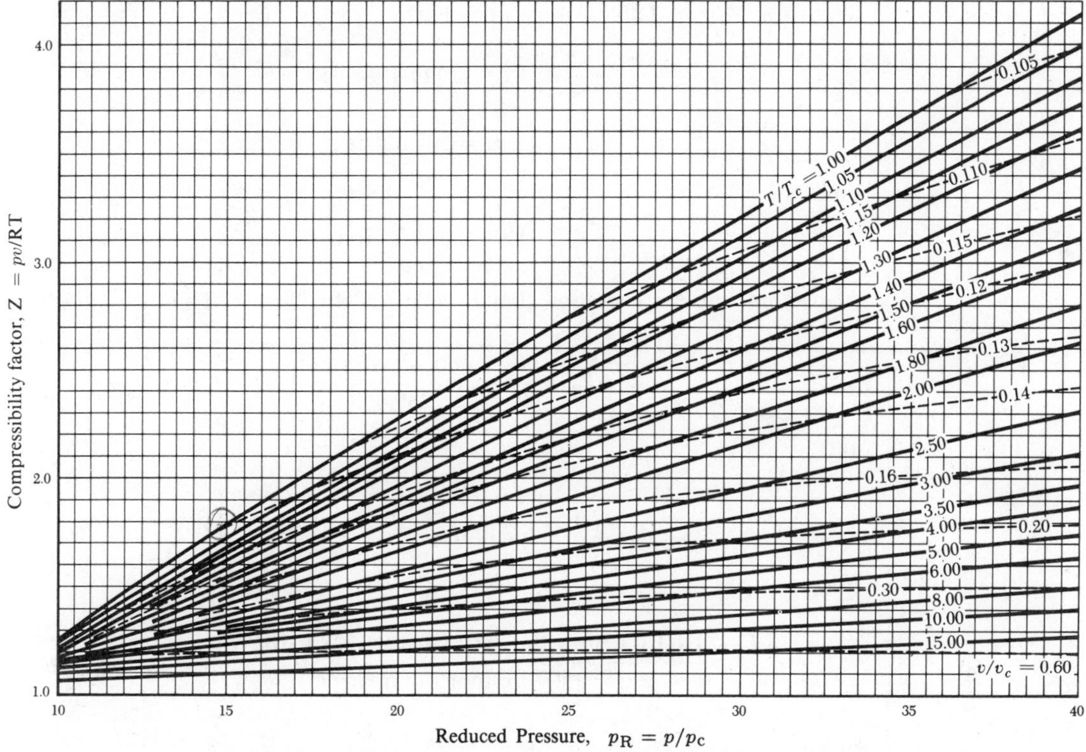

Figure 3.13 The Generalized (Nelson-Obert) compressibility chart—high-pressure range. Note that $v'_R = v/v'_c = vp_c/RT_c$. *Sources*: "Nelson-Obert Compressibility Charts" adapted courtesy of Professor E. F. Obert, University of Wisconsin, Madison, from E. F. Obert, *Concepts of Thermodynamics* (New York: McGraw-Hill, 1960). Data reprinted by permission of the publisher from B. F. Dodge, *Chemical Engineering Thermodynamics* (New York: McGraw-Hill, 1944).

where p and T are the *actual* pressure and temperature of the gas, and p_c and T_c are the *critical state* pressure and temperature of the gas (see Table 3.4 and Appendix C.12). In these figures a *pseudo* critical specific volume, $v'_c = RT_c/p_c$, has been used to calculate a *pseudo* reduced specific volume v'_R as

$$v'_R = \frac{v}{v'_c} = \frac{vp_c}{RT_c} \tag{3.79}$$

The pseudo critical specific volume has been used in these plots because the experimental data did not correlate well when the actual specific volume at the critical state was used. Note that pseudo critical specific volume v'_c is *not* the same as the actual specific volume at the critical state v_c.

Example 3.4

Using the compressibility charts, find the pressure exerted by 8.2 lbm of carbon monoxide in a 1.0 ft^3 container at -78 °F.

Solution From Table 3.4 we find that

$$T_c = 239.4 \text{ R}$$

$$p_c = 507.0 \text{ psia}$$

and

$$v_c = 0.053 \text{ ft}^3/\text{lbm}$$

Also, from Table 3.7 we find that $R = 0.0709$ Btu/lbm·R. Then we have

$$T_R = \frac{T}{T_c} = \frac{460 + (-78)}{239.4} = 1.60$$

and

$$v = \frac{1.0 \text{ ft}^3}{8.2 \text{ lbm}} = 0.122 \text{ ft}^3/\text{lbm}$$

with

$$v'_c = \frac{RT_c}{p_c} = \frac{[0.0709 \text{ Btu/(lbm}\cdot\text{R)}](239.4 \text{ R})(778 \text{ ft}\cdot\text{lbf/Btu})}{(507 \text{ lbf/in}^2)(144 \text{ in}^2/\text{ft}^2)} = 0.181 \text{ ft}^3/\text{lbm}$$

so that

$$v'_R = \frac{v}{v'_c} = \frac{0.122}{0.181} = 0.67$$ (notice that we do *not* use the actual critical specific volume v_c here)

Using $T_R = T/T_c = 1.60$ and $v'_R = v/v'_c = 0.67$ we find from Figure 3.12*b* that

$$p_R = \frac{p}{p_c} = 2.1 \quad \text{and} \quad Z = 0.85$$

Then we can calculate

$$p = p_c p_R = 34.5(2.1) = 72.5 \text{ atmospheres}$$

Thermodynamic Tables

Thermodynamic tables are generated from complex equations of state which in turn were developed from accurate experimental data. These tables are quick and easy to use but they are not available for all materials of engineering interest. Appendixes C.1 through C.11 give the thermodynamic properties of a variety of substances. There are basically only three types of tables given there: pressure and temperature entry saturation tables, superheated vapor tables, and compressed or subcooled liquid tables. The saturation table contains properties only along the saturation curve ($x = 0$ and $x = 1$) and does not contain property values of liquid–vapor mixtures. These mixture properties must be calculated from the saturation values and the quality using Eq. 3.56. The superheated vapor and compressed liquid tables provide values throughout their regions of definition. Figure 3.14 illustrates the range of applicability of these tables.

When thermodynamic data are given in problem statements you will normally not be told whether the state of the system is compressed, saturated, or superheated. To decide which table to use you must be able to deduce the state of the system from the information given. This can be done by comparing the given properties with the saturation properties at the same temperature or pressure. For example, suppose you are given water at 500 °F and 1000 psia. How can you tell if it is a compressed liquid, saturated liquid, a mixture of liquid plus vapor (i.e., wet), a saturated vapor, or a superheated vapor? The answer is obtained from the saturation data in Appendix C.1*a* or C.2*a*. These tables tell you that a 500 °F, the saturation pressure is 680.8 psia, and that at 1000 psia the saturation temperature is 544.61 °F. First of all, we could use the saturation pressure of 680.8 psia as a guide and note that the actual state (500 °F, 1000 psia) is at a pressure greater than that required to produce a saturated liquid at 500 °F, consequently the water must be in a compressed liquid state. Alternatively, we could use the saturation temperature of 544.61 °F as a guide and note that the actual state has a temperature (500 °F), which is less than that required for a saturated liquid at 1000 psia (544.61 °F), so again the water must be in a compressed (or subcooled) liquid state. Consequently we would obtain all other desired property information from Appendix C.4*a*, the compressed water table.

Similarly, in metric units, if you have water at 1.0 MPa and 200 °C, a check of the saturation data in Appendix C.1*b* reveals that at 200 °C the saturation pressure is 1.554 MPa, which is greater than the actual pressure of 1.0 MPa. Therefore,

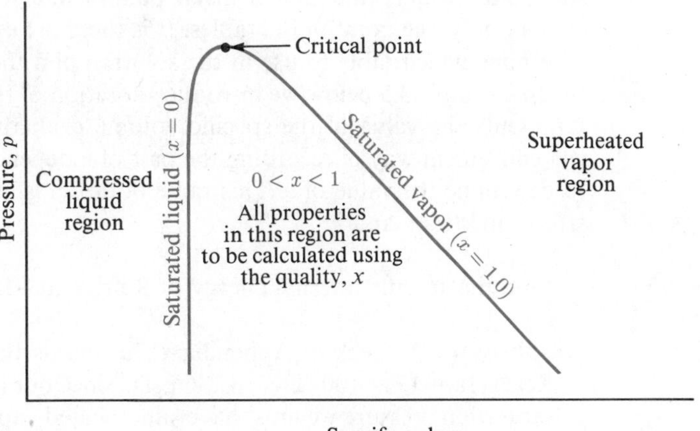

Figure 3.14 Regions of application of thermodynamic tables.

Table 3.8 The States of water fixed by various combinations of property pairs

Pair of independent properties	State and correct tables to use
$T = 500$ °F, $p = 1000$ psia	Compressed or subcooled liquid (C.4a)
$p = 1$ MPa, $T = 200$ °C	Superheated vapor (C.3b)
$T = 170$ °F, $x = 1.0$	Saturated vapor (C.1a)
$p = 14.696$ psia, $v = 5.0$ ft^3/lbm	Saturated vapor (C.2a)
$u = 500$ Btu/lbm, $p = 100$ psia	Saturated vapor (C.2a)
$h = 1500$ Btu/lbm, $T = 300$ °F	Superheated vapor (C.3a)
$p = 0.1$ MPa, $h = 200$ kJ/kg	Compressed or subcooled liquid (C.4b)
$T = 100$ °C, $v = 8.321$ m^3/kg	Superheated vapor (C.3b)
$v = 0.1$ m^3/kg, $h = 600$ kJ/kg	Saturated vapor (C.1b or C.2b)
$h = 3157.7$ kJ/kg, $u = 2875.2$ kJ/kg	Superheated vapor (C.3b)

the actual state of the water must be in the superheated vapor region. A check of Appendix C.3*b* reveals that this state can be easily found in this table.

How do you decide which table to use when you are given properties other than pressure and temperature? You use the same basic technique. For example, suppose you are given 3.0 lbm of water in a 15 ft^3 closed rigid container at 14,696 psia. The specific volume of the system, then is $v = 15/3.0 = 5.0$ ft^3/lbm. A check of Appendix C.2*a* reveals that at 14.696 psia, $v_f = 0.01672$ ft^3/lbm, and $v_g =$ 26.80 ft^3/lbm. Since the actual specific volume here falls between these two values ($v_f < v < v_g$), then the state of the water must be in the liquid plus vapor (wet) region and it therefore has a quality of $x = (5.0 - 0.01672)/(26.8 - 0.01672) =$ 0.186, or 18.6%. To get more familiar with these tables, it is recommended that the reader verify the states given in Table 3.8 for water.

While it is true that any pair of independent properties will fix the state of a simple substance subjected to only one work mode, you must be able to deduce the system's thermodynamic state (compressed liquid, saturated liquid or vapor, liquid–vapor mixture, or superheated vapor) from the data given in a problem statement in order to know which table to use to find the other properties that will be required in the analysis. It is important to remember that thermodynamic states are unique, and that a given pair of independent properties will fix the state at only one point in the tables. It is therefore essential to understand how to determine which table to use in the solution of a thermodynamics problem.

In Example 3.5 below we introduce notation of the form $v(X$ °F, Y psia) which represents the value of the specific volume evaluated at X °F and Y psia. This is a convenient way of recording the pair of independent intensive properties used to determine the value of v. This same notation is also used there with the intensive properties u and h.

Example 3.5 Find the specific internal energy of Refrigerant-12 at 100 °F and 95 psia.

Solution A check of Appendix C.7*a* reveals that the saturation pressure of Refrigerant-12 at 100 °F is 131.86 psia. Since our actual pressure is less than the saturation pressure we must have superheated vapor. A check of Appendix C.8*a* reveals that 100 °F and 95 psia is indeed in the superheated region. Appendix

C.8*a* lists h but not u, but u can be calculated from the definition of h, i.e., $u = h - pv$. Also, since 95 psia is not a direct entry into this table, we must use linear interpolation to find the needed values. Interpolating to find the specific volume gives

$$\frac{v(100\text{ °F}, 95\text{ psia}) - v(100\text{ °F}, 90\text{ psia})}{95\text{ psia} - 90\text{ psia}} = \frac{v(100\text{ °F}, 100\text{ psia}) - v(100\text{ °F}, 90\text{ psia})}{100\text{ psia} - 90\text{ psia}}$$

or

$$v(100\text{ °F}, 95\text{ psia}) = 0.48749 + \tfrac{5}{10}(0.43138 - 0.48749) = 0.45944\text{ ft}^3/\text{lbm}$$

Similarly, for the specific enthalpy h we have

$$\frac{h(100\text{ °F}, 95\text{ psia}) - h(100\text{ °F}, 90\text{ psia})}{95\text{ psia} - 90\text{ psia}} = \frac{h(100\text{ °F}, 100\text{ psia}) - h(100\text{ °F}, 90\text{ psia})}{100\text{ psia} - 90\text{ psia}}$$

or

$$h(100\text{ °F}, 95\text{ psia}) = 89.175 + \tfrac{5}{10}(88.694 - 89.175) = 88.935\text{ Btu/lbm}$$

Then, finally

$$\begin{aligned} u(100\text{ °F}, 95\text{ psia}) &= h(100\text{ °F}, 95\text{ psia}) - pv(100\text{ °F}, 95\text{ psia}) \\ &= 88.935\text{ Btu/lbm} - (95\text{ lbf/in}^2)(144\text{ in}^2/\text{ft}^2)\left(\frac{0.45944\text{ ft}^3/\text{lbm}}{778\text{ ft}\cdot\text{lbf/Btu}}\right) \\ &= 80.856\text{ Btu/lbm} \end{aligned}$$

Thermodynamic Charts

Experimental data, equations of state, and statistical thermodynamics results can all be combined into very accurate thermodynamic phase diagrams called *thermodynamic charts*. These two-dimensional property diagrams can be constructed with various useful thermodynamic properties as coordinates. For example, Figure 3.15 shows a specific volume vs. specific internal energy chart for water. This chart also includes lines of constant pressure, temperature, and quality. Thus, given a pair of independent properties such as p and T (or p and x in the wet region), the u and v values could be immediately read off from the coordinate axes. Notice that in the wet region where $0 < x < 1$ the constant temperature and constant pressure lines lie on top of each other since p and T are not independent in this region.

A series of similar charts for a variety of substances can be found in Appendix D of this text. It must be emphasized, however, that since the physical size of these charts is very small, the values taken from them will not be as accurate as those

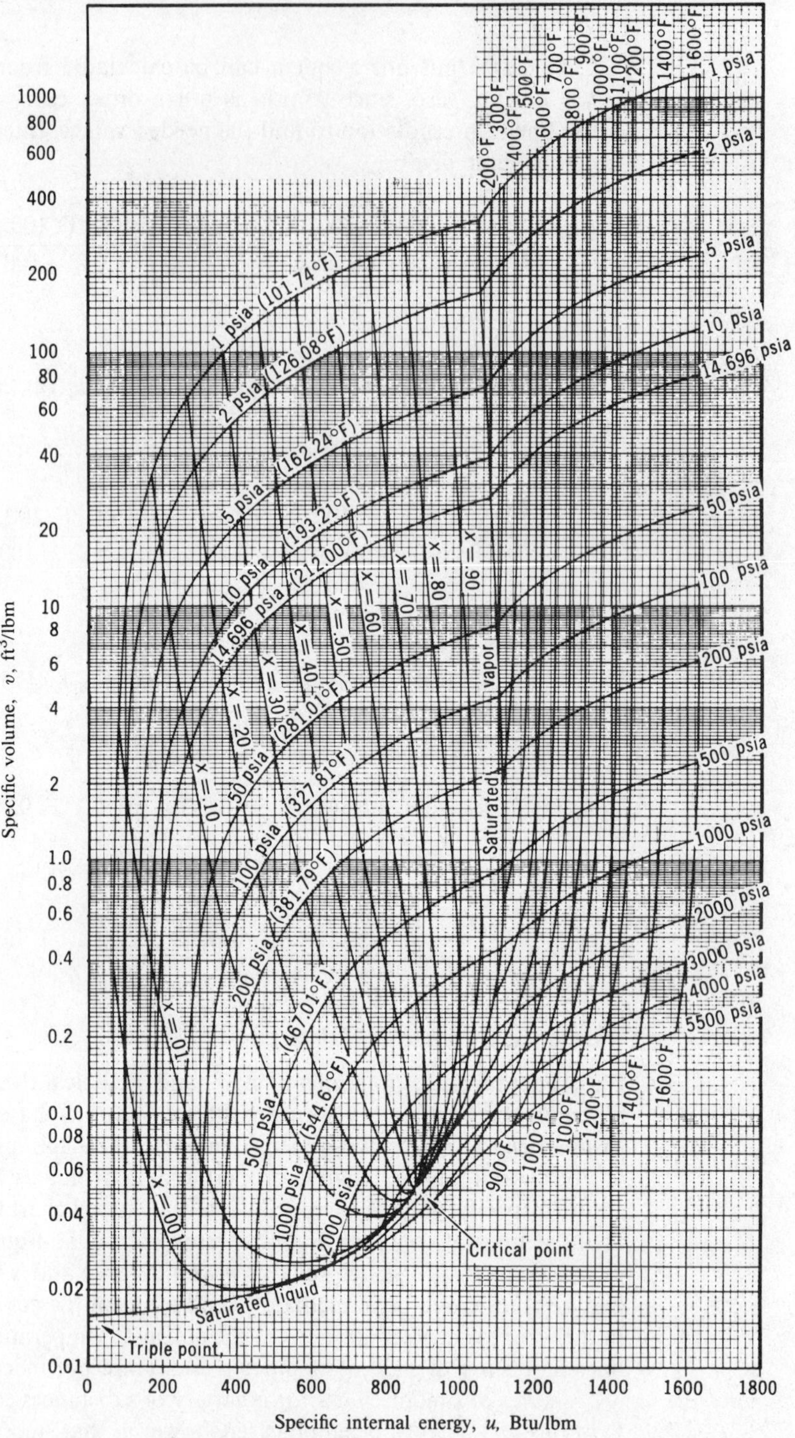

Figure 3.15 Thermodynamic properties of steam (H_2O). *Sources*: Reprinted by permission of the publisher from William C. Reynolds and Henry C. Perkins, *Engineering Thermodynamics*, 2d ed. (New York: McGraw-Hill, 1977), p. 602. Redrawn from Joseph H. Keenan and Joseph Keyes, *Thermodynamic Properties of Steam* (New York: Wiley, 1952). Copyright © 1952 John Wiley & Sons. Reprinted by permission of John Wiley & Sons, Inc.

taken from a table for the same substance, even if interpolation must be used within the table. Therefore, small charts like these are to be used only when appropriate tables are not available, or when a state is to be fixed without using either pressure or temperature. For example, given values for u and v for water it would be much easier to find the other thermodynamic properties at that state by using Figure 3.15 rather than by doing a double interpolation within the water tables (however, the accuracy would still not be as good as using the tables).

Summary

In this chapter three of the five main techniques used in obtaining values for thermodynamic properties were discussed. Equations of state, thermodynamic tables, and thermodynamic charts are all valuable tools that will be needed in the thermodynamic analyses that occur in the following chapters.

This chapter also introduced many new technical thermodynamic terms, most of which are listed in the glossary in Table 3.9 below. The reader is urged to learn

Table 3.9 Glossary of technical terms introduced in Chapter 3

Isobaric process	Constant pressure process.
Isochoric process	Constant volume process.
Internal energy	Total energy minus kinetic and potential energy.
Enthalpy	Internal energy plus the product of pressure and volume.
Constant volume specific heat (c_v)	The variation in specific internal energy with respect to temperature while holding volume constant.
Constant pressure specific heat (c_p)	The variation in specific enthalpy with respect to temperature while holding pressure constant.
Allotropic	Different solid forms of the same substance.
Triple point	The point where the solid, liquid, and vapor phases coexist in thermal equilibrium.
Vaporization	The transformation of a liquid into a vapor.
Condensation	The transformation of a vapor into a liquid or a solid.
Melting	The transformation of a solid into a liquid (synonymous with fusion).
Solidification	The transformation of a liquid into a solid (synonymous with freezing).
Sublimation	The transformation of a solid into a vapor.
Saturation	A condition that exists when two or more phases coexist in equilibrium.
Critical state	The peak of the vaporization curve.
Gas	The state of any substance whose temperature is greater than that at the critical state.
Quality	The ratio of the mass of vapor present to the total mass present.
Moisture	The ratio of the mass of liquid present to the total mass present (1.0 minus the quality).
Wet vapor	A substance whose state is under the saturation dome.
Phase	The physical state (or molecular configuration) of matter.

the definitions of these terms. They will be freely used in the remaining chapters under the assumption that their meaning is fully understood by the reader.

Selected References

Badger, P. H. *Equilibrium Thermodynamics.* Boston: Allyn & Bacon, 1967.

Compressed Gas Assoc. Inc. *Handbook of Compressed Gases*, 2d ed. New York: Van Nostrand Reinhold, 1981.

Obert, E. F., and Young, R. L. *Elements of Thermodynamics and Heat Transfer*. New York: McGraw-Hill, 1962.

Van Wylen, G. J., and Sonntag, R. E. *Fundamentals of Classical Thermodynamics*, 3d ed. New York: Wiley, 1986.

Wark, K. *Thermodynamics*, 5th ed. New York: McGraw-Hill, 1988.

Zemansky, M. W., Abbott, M. M., and VanNess, H. C. *Basic Engineering Thermodynamics*, 2d ed. New York: McGraw-Hill, 1975.

Chapter Three Problems

1. If p, v, and T are all intensive independent properties

a) show that the following relation is always valid:

$$\left(\frac{\partial p}{\partial v}\right)_T = -\left(\frac{\partial p}{\partial T}\right)_v\left(\frac{\partial T}{\partial v}\right)_p$$

b) Verify this relation for the equation of state of an ideal gas.

2. Show that the following equations are valid:

a) $c_v = -\left(\frac{\partial v}{\partial T}\right)_u\left(\frac{\partial u}{\partial v}\right)_T$

b) $c_p = -\left(\frac{\partial p}{\partial T}\right)_h\left(\frac{\partial h}{\partial p}\right)_T$

3. Show that $\beta = -(1/v)\left(\frac{\partial v}{\partial p}\right)_T\left(\frac{\partial p}{\partial T}\right)_v$

4. Show that $\kappa = (1/v)\left(\frac{\partial v}{\partial T}\right)_p\left(\frac{\partial p}{\partial T}\right)_v$

5. Show that $\left(\frac{\partial p}{\partial T}\right)_v = \beta/\kappa$

6. A 0.20-m-diameter sphere of solid copper is isothermally compressed from 0.1 to 1000.0 MPa at 500 °C. Determine the sphere's diameter after the compression process.

7. Assuming that the isothermal coefficient of compressibility is constant, determine the percent decrease in the volume of liquid water that undergoes an isothermal increase in pressure of 100,000 psia.

8. Assuming that the isobaric coefficient of volume expansion is constant, determine the percent increase in the volume of liquid water that is heated at constant pressure from 50 to 212 °F.

9. Some historical researchers believe that Gabriel Daniel Fahrenheit (1686–1736) constructed his well-known temperature scale based upon the isobaric coefficient of volume expansion of mercury rather than with fixed reference temperatures (see Problem 7 at the end of Chapter 1). It is thought that he may have defined his degree size to be the temperature change required to isobarically change the volume of mercury by 1/10,000th of its value at the zero point of his scale. Modern measurements have established that the isobaric coefficient of volume expansion of mercury at 0 °F is $1.015 \times 10^{-4}\ R^{-1}$. Consider an ordinary glass thermometer with a bore of radius r and a reservoir bulb of volume V_0 at the bottom. Ignoring the expansion of the glass itself and assuming that the isobaric coefficient of volume expansion is a constant, determine the relationship between the change in length of the mercury column (ΔL) and the bulb volume (V_0), the initial length of the mercury column (L_0), the isobaric coefficient of volume expansion (β), and the temperature change (ΔT). Is ΔL independent of L_0? If not, then the temperature interval divisions will not be the same size along the length of the thermometer. Determine the percent difference in ΔL between $L_0 = 0$ and $L_0 = 30$ cm if $V_0 = 0.5\ \text{cm}^3$ and $r = 0.1$ mm.

10. Assuming that all physical properties are constant, determine the percent change in the volume of liquid glycerin as it is heated from 20 to 150 °C while simultaneously being pressurized from 0.1 to 10.0 MPa.

11. What gage pressure would have to be exerted on liquid diethyl ether to prevent any change in its volume as it is heated from 0 to 50 °C? Assume all the physical properties are constant for this process.

12. To what temperature would mercury need to be heated to prevent any change in its volume as it is pressurized at 70 °F from 14.7 to 1000 psia? Assume all physical properties are constant for this process.

13. Using the relations p = constant and $\beta = C_1 T + C_2$, integrate Eq. 3.23 to obtain the result

$$v_2 = v_1 \exp\{[C_1(T_2 + T_1)/2 + C_2](T_2 - T_1)\}$$

and show that this is the same as

$$v_2 = v_1 \exp[\beta_{avg}(T_2 - T_1)]$$

where $\beta_{avg} = (\beta_2 + \beta_1)/2$.

14. **a)** For an ideal gas, mathematically evaluate the partial derivative $(\partial u/\partial v)_T$.
b) What is the partial derivative $(\partial h/\partial T)_p$ called for a real gas.

15. The enthalpy of a certain gas can be obtained from the following equation:

$$h = (0.21)T + (1.2 \times 10^{-4})T^2 + (0.32)p + (3.6)p^2$$

where h is in Btu/lbm, T is in R, and p is in psia. Determine the specific heat at constant pressure (c_p) for this gas when the temperature is 500 R and the pressure is one atmosphere.

16. Using the property data given in the superheated steam tables, estimate the specific heat at constant pressure for steam at 400 psia and 1000 °F.

17. Using the property data given in the superheated steam tables, estimate the specific heat at constant pressure for steam at 30 MPa and 700 °C.

18. Sketch (neatly) the common p-T and p-v diagrams for water and label
a) the critical state,
b) the triple point and triple point line, and
c) the solid, liquid, and vapor regions.
d) Indicate the correct slope of the fusion line (i.e., either a positive or negative slope).

19. Are the following statements true or false?
a) The specific volume of mercury is a function of temperature only.
b) If ice is heated sufficiently, it always melts to form a liquid.

26,256 + 5000 +

c) If water is at a pressure lower than the critical pressure, it is always in the liquid phase.
d) If a mixture of liquid ammonia and ammonia vapor is heated sufficiently in a rigid sealed tube, the content of the tube will always become a vapor.

20. Define the following terms:
a) internal energy, **d)** moisture, and
b) saturation, **e)** compressibility factor.
c) critical state,

21. Define the following terms:
a) isobaric, **d)** quality, and
b) isochoric, **e)** triple point.
c) enthalpy,

22. **a)** Is quality (x) a thermodynamic property? Explain.
b) Mathematically define the specific heat at constant pressure.
c) For a saturated mixture of liquid and vapor, explain whether or not the pressure and temperature can be varied independently.
d) Define the compressibility factor (Z) which predicts deviations from ideal gas behavior. Does the value of Z always fall within the range $0 < Z \leq 1$?

23. A vessel with a volume of 10.0 ft^3 contains 3.0 lbm of a mixture of liquid water and water vapor in equilibrium at a pressure of 100 psia. Determine
a) the mass of liquid present
b) the mass of vapor present.

24. Determine the change in specific internal energy of 3.0 kg of graphite as it is heated at atmospheric pressure from 20 to 200 °C. Assume a constant specific heat.

25. Determine the change in enthalpy of 5.0 lbm of ice as it is heated from 22 to 32 °F under constant atmospheric pressure. Assume a constant specific heat.

26. Determine the change in specific internal energy of solid aluminum as it is heated at atmospheric pressure from 300 to 500 K. Use an average specific heat over this temperature range.

27. Determine the change in specific enthalpy of solid lead as it is heated from 14.7 psia, 80 °F to 1000 psia, 200 °F. The density of lead is 710 lbm/ft^3. Assume a constant specific heat.

28. Determine the change in specific internal energy of 7.0 lbm of methane gas as it is heated from 32 to 200 °F at atmospheric pressure. Assume ideal gas bahavior.

29. Determine the change in specific enthalpy of carbon dioxide gas as it is heated isobarically from 300 to 500 K at atmospheric pressure. Assume ideal gas behavior.

30. Argon gas is heated in a constant pressure process from 20 to 500 °C. Assuming ideal gas behavior, determine
a) the ratio of the final to initial volumes,
b) the change in specific internal energy, and
c) the change in specific enthalpy of the argon.

31. Helium gas is heated in a constant volume process from −200 to 500 °F. Assuming ideal gas behavior, determine
a) the ratio of the final to initial pressures,
b) the change in specific internal energy, and
c) the change in specific enthalpy of the helium.

32. Gaseous oxygen is heated in a constant temperature process until its volume is doubled. Assuming ideal gas behavior, determine
a) the ratio of the final to initial pressures,
b) the change in specific internal energy, and
c) the change in specific enthalpy of the oxygen.

33. Using Figure 3.10, estimate the average values for the constant pressure and constant volume specific heats for the following gases and processes:

a) carbon dioxide as it is heated isobarically at 10,000 psia from 1000 to 2000 °F.

b) carbon dioxide gas as it is compressed isothermally at 1000 °F from 0 to 10,000 psia,

c) hydrogen gas as it is heated isobarically at 0 psia from 0 to 5000 °F, and

d) air as it is compressed from 0 °F, 0 psia to 1000 °F, 5000 psia.

34. In 1879 the French physicist Emile Amagat generated experimental data in a mine shaft at Verpilleux, France, for his research on the compressibility of gases. There he used a vertical column of mercury 327 m high to measure the compressibility of nitrogen at a pressure of 430 atm. Assuming the temperature at the bottom of the mine shaft was 30 °C, use the compressibility charts to determine the value of the compressibility factor for nitrogen under these conditions.

35. Determine the compressibility factor for hydrogen (H_2) gas at a temperature of 20 °C and a pressure of 11 MPa.

36. For air at 20 °C there is a unique pressure above $p_R = 1.0$ at which the compressibility factor is the same as that of an ideal gas. Use the compressibility charts to determine this pressure.

37. For air at 20 °C use the compressibility charts to determine the low pressure range in which the compressibility factor of air differs from that of an ideal gas by no more than 2% (i.e., $1.0 \leq Z \leq 0.98$). Is it reasonable to assume ideal gas behavior for air at pressures up to 3.45 MPa (500 psia)?

38. Using the compressibility charts, determine the temperature and compressibility factor of carbon dioxide (CO_2) gas when it is at a pressure of 2500 psia and has a density of 32 lbm/ft^3.

39. Calculate the specific volume of propane at 1000 psia and 300 °F using

a) the ideal gas equation of state,

b) the Clausius equation of state (use the van der Waals value for b), and

c) the compressibility charts.

40. Determine the pressure exerted by 10.0 lbm of steam at a temperature of 1300 °F in a volume of 3.285 ft^3 using

a) the steam tables,

b) the ideal gas equation of state,

c) the van der Waals equation of state, and

d) the compressibility charts.

41. a) State van der Waals equation.

b) Indicate which term corrects for the fact that the molecules occupy a finite volume.

c) Indicate which term corrects for the fact that there are attractive forces between the molecules.

d) How are the constants a and b in van der Waals equation determined, and are they the same for all gases?

42. For superheated dichlorodifluoromethane (Refrigerant-12) at 100 psia and 100 °F determine the value of the specific volume

a) from the superheated vapor table,

b) assuming it to be an ideal gas,

c) from the van der Waals equation of state, and

d) assuming it to be a real gas and using the compressibility charts.

43. Estimate the temperature to which water at the bottom of a 500-ft deep lake would have to be heated before it would begin to boil. (*Note*: hydrostatic pressure = γz, where $\gamma = 62.4$ lbf/ft^3 is the specific weight of water, and z is the depth below the free surface.)

44. One of the reasons for wearing a pressure suit in high altitude or space work is because without it the pressure in the body might become low enough to cause the blood to "boil." Assume blood behaves essentially as pure water (which is its primary component) and that the body core temperature is 100 °F. Find the pressure at which this blood will begin to "boil."

45. Refrigerant-12 contained in a tank at a pressure of 98.87 psia has a specific volume of 0.3116 ft^3/lbm. Using the proper thermodynamic table, determine the value of the enthalpy of the Refrigerant-12 under these conditions.

46. The vapor produced when the pressure on saturated liquid water is suddenly reduced during a constant enthalpy process is called *flash steam* because it occurs so quickly that part of the liquid appears to "flash" into vapor. Determine the final temperature and the percentage of flash steam (i.e., the quality) that is produced as the pressure on saturated liquid water at 2.0 MPa is suddenly reduced to 1.0 MPa in a constant enthalpy process.

47. What total mass of water must be put into a 1.0-ft^3 sealed rigid container so that when the container is heated the contents pass through the saturated vapor curve exactly at the point $p = 2000$ psia, $T = 636$ °F?

48. A rigid container contains 1.0 lbm of water at the critical state. Determine the volume of the vapor present in the container after it has been cooled to 212 °F.

49. Two-thirds of a pound mass of water is put into a 1.0-ft^3 rigid container at 14.7 psia and 212 °F and sealed. The container is then heated.

a) At what temperature will the contents become a saturated vapor or saturated liquid?
b) Which will it be—a saturated vapor or a saturated liquid?
c) Sketch this process on a *p-v* diagram.

50. A closed rigid container contains water in an equilibrium mixture of liquid and vapor at 70 °F. The mass of the liquid initially present is 10.236 times the mass of the vapor. The container is then heated until all the liquid becomes vapor. Determine

a) the initial quality, and
b) the pressure in the container when the last bit of water becomes vapor.
c) Sketch this process on a *p-v* diagram.

51. It is desired to carry out an experiment that will allow a visual observation of a material passing through the critical state. An empty transparent rigid sealed container with a 2.000-cm^3 internal volume is to be used.

a) How many grams of solid CO_2 (dry ice) should be put into the container so that when it is sealed and heated its contents will pass directly through the critical state?
b) To what temperature (in °F) must the contents be heated to be at the critical state?
c) What will be the pressure (in psia) inside the container at the critical state?

52. Using the tables for compressed liquid water (Appendix C.4), determine the pressure increase required to raise the specific enthalpy of saturated liquid water at 100 °F by 1.00 Btu/lbm.

53. Determine the properties as required in the table below

Substance	Given	Find
a) Ammonia	$T = 0$ °C $x = 0.2$	$v = ?$
b) Water	$p = 400$ psia $h = 1000$ Btu/lbm	$x = ?$
c) Water	$T = 500$ °F $p = 400$ psia	$u = ?$
d) Refrigerant-12	$p = 98.87$ psia $h = 85.282$ Btu/lbm	$v = ?$

54. The Chara Maru is a transport vessel that has inadvertently entered an enemy neutral zone. She carries 600 passengers and has radioed that she has blown her superlumen drive system. The Star Command distress codes are taken from the tables of the thermodynamic properties of water because the enemy has a very poor knowledge of this substance. Thus, if there are any errors in the code it may be a trap and not a real distress call. Is the following transmission correct? If not, what are the errors? (Variations of less than 1% are not errors.)

p (kPa)	T(°C)	v (m^3/kg)	u (kJ/kg)	h (kJ/kg)	x (quality)
600	600	0.6696	2801.7	3700.7	
0.6113	0.01	206.1	2375.3	2501.3	1.0
100	99.6	0.001043	417.3	417.4	0.0

a) The standard reply to all such distress messages is to transmit the properties of water at 100% quality and 3000 kPa. What are those values?

$p = 3000$ kPa $\quad u = ?$
$T = ?$ $\quad h = ?$
$v = ?$

b) At this point your reply is acknowledged with $T = 200$ °C, $p = 1554.9$ kPa, $x = 0.23$. Is the acknowledgment from the Chara Maru or the enemy? Explain.

55. Using the appendixes in the back of the book, fill in the missing properties in the table below.

Material	T (°F)	p (psia)	u (Btu/lbm)	v (ft^3/lbm)	ρ (lbm/ft^3)	x
Water	?	60.0	?	?	?	1.0
Water	?	80.0	?	?	?	0.6
Ref.-12	?	23.849	62.124	1.3526	?	?

56. Using Appendixes C and D in the back of the book, fill in the missing properties in the table below.

Substance	p (psia)	T (°F)	v (ft^3/lbm)	h (Btu/lbm)	u (Btu/lbm)
H_2O	300	?	0.7811	?	?
H_2O	300	600	?	?	?
Ref.-12	?	70	0.2526	?	?
Nitrogen	50.0	?	1.0	?	?

57. Using Appendixes C and D in the back of the book, fill in the missing properties in the table below.

Substance	p (psia)	T (°F)	v (ft^3/lbm)	h (Btu/lbm)
Water	1000	?	0.2326	?
Ref.-12	84.888	?	?	84.36
Water	1000	?	?	1505.9
Nitrogen	?	−160	0.25	?

58. Using the appendixes in the back of the book, fill in the missing properties in the table below.

Material	p (psia)	T (°F)	v (ft³/lbm)	h (Btu/lbm)	u (Btu/lbm)	x (if applicable)
Water	?	35	?	?	?	0.0
Water	1.0	?	?	?	?	1.0
Water	14.7	1000	?	?	?	?
Ref.-12	?	−40	?	?	?	0.5

59. **a)** Using only the thermodynamic *tables* in Appendix C at the back of the book, fill in the missing properties in the table below.

Material	p (psia)	T (°F)	v (ft³/lbm)	h (Btu/lbm)	u (Btu/lbm)	x (if applicable)
Water	14.7	300	?	?	?	?
Ref.-12	23.849	?	?	?	?	1.0

b) Using only the thermodynamic *charts* in Appendix D at the back of the book, fill in the missing properties in the table below.

Material	T (°F)	p (psia)	h (Btu/lbm)	v (ft³/lbm)	x (if applicable)
Carbon dioxide	0	?	?	?	0.2
Nitrogen	?	100	?	1.0	?

60. Using the appendixes in the back of the book, fill in the missing properties in the table below.

Material	p (psia)	T (°F)	v (ft³/lbm)	x (if applicable)
Water	5	300	?	?
Water	100	?	8.053	?
Water	1000	544.8	0.1	?
Ref.-12	?	0	?	0.0
Mercury	1.0	?	?	1.0

61. Using the appendixes in the back of the book, fill in the missing properties in the table below.

Material	p (psia)	T (°F)	v (ft³/lbm)	h (Btu/lbm)	x (if applicable)
Water	1.2	?	?	?	0.0
Water	?	220	?	?	1.0
Water	?	32.018	?	?	0.5
Water	8000	2000	?	?	?
Ref.-12	23.849	0	0.011030	8.5207	?

62. Using the appendixes in the back of the book, fill in the missing properties in the table below.

Material	p (psia)	T (°F)	v (ft³/lbm)	h (Btu/lbm)	x (if applicable)
H_2O	600	600	?	?	?
H_2O	?	200	?	?	1.0
H_2O	200	1500	?	?	?
H_2O	14.696	?	?	?	0.0
Ammonia	?	100	?	?	0.0

63. Using the appendixes in the back of the book, fill in the missing properties in the table below.

Material	p (psia)	T (°F)	v (ft³/lbm)	x (if applicable)
Water	?	300	4.0	?
Water	300	?	?	0.5
Water	1.0	1000	?	?
Mercury	1.0	?	?	1.0
Ideal gas	100	?	5.0	?

(Use the ideal gas equation of state here with $R = 50$ ft·lbf/lbm·R.)

64. Using the appendixes in the back of the book, fill in the missing properties in the table below.

Material	p (psia)	T (°F)	v (ft³/lbm)	h (Btu/lbm)	x (if applicable)
Water	40	?	?	?	0.0
Water	?	?	51.03	1240.5	?
Water	?	50	?	?	1.0
Ref.-12	249.31	?	?	?	0.5
Ref.-12	?	150	?	?	1.0
Mercury	100	?	?	?	1.0

65. Using the appendixes in the back of the book, fill in the missing properties in the table below.

Material	T (°F)	p (psia)	h (Btu/lbm)	x (if applicable)
Ammonia	60	60	?	?
Ammonia	60	?	?	0.1
Mercury	?	60	38.44	?
Ref.-12	60	?	?	1.0
Water	?	1.0	1336.1	?
Water	?	1.0	?	0.0

66. Using the appendixes in the back of the book, fill in the missing properties in the table below.

Material	p (psia)	T (°F)	v (ft³/lbm)	x (if applicable)
H_2O	466.3	460	?	0.0
H_2O	160	363.6	?	1.0
H_2O	40	?	6.0	?
H_2O	1000	1000	?	?
Ammonia	?	105	1.0	?
Ammonia	100	100	?	?
Ref.-12	?	200	?	0.5
Ref.-12	313	?	?	0.0
Mercury	1000	?	?	1.0

Computer Problems

These problems are designed to be done on any personal computer using BASIC language programming. They are problems that could not be done easily without the use of a computer. They are meant to furnish an additional learning experience by providing new insights into the operation of complex thermodynamic systems and in demonstrating the power of the personal computer in generating and manipulating thermodynamic properties. In these problems *log* is the base 10 logarithm and *ln* is the base e (i.e., natural) logarithm.

67. In 1849 William Rankine proposed the following pressure–temperature relation for saturated water:

$$\log p_{sat} = 6.1007 - 2731.62/T_{sat} - 396{,}945/T_{sat}^2$$

where p_{sat} is in psia and T_{sat} is in R. Write an interactive computer program that will return values for p_{sat} in psia when T_{sat} is input in °F. Be sure to include proper units on all screen prompts and on all output values. Using the steam tables in Appendix C.1*a* at the back of the text, plot the percent error in your calculated saturation pressure vs. input temperature utilizing data at 32, 100, 200, 300, 400, 500, 600, and 700 °F. For extra credit, modify this program to allow the user to choose to work in either the SI or Engineering English units system, and then accept either input and produce output in the user selected units system.

68. In 1905 Knoblauch, Linde, and Klebe proposed the following equation for the specific volume of superheated steam:

$$v = 0.5962\mathrm{T}/p - (1 + 0.0014p)(150{,}300{,}000/T^3 - 0.0833)$$

where p is in psia, T is in R, and v is in ft³/lbm. Write an interactive computer program that will return v when p and T are input. Allow the user to choose either SI or Engineering English units. Compare your results with steam table values at 0.1, 0.5, 1.0, 1.5, 2.0, 2.5, and 3.0 MPa along the 200 °C isotherm. Plot these results as a percent error in v vs. p for $T = 200$ °C.

69. Write an interactive computer program that will calculate the pressure of superheated ammonia vapor from the Beattie-Bridgeman equation of state when the specific volume and temperature are input from the keyboard. Allow the user to choose to work in either SI or Engineering English units. Using the superheated ammonia tables (Appendix C.6) determine the percent error between your calculated values of pressure and the correct values along the 100 °F isotherm. Plot this percent error vs. p utilizing actual pressure data of 10, 30, 50, 70, 90, 140, and 180 psia.

70. The pressure–temperature relation for saturated ammonia can be written as

$$\log p_{sat} = C_1 - C_2/T_{sat} - C_3 \log(T_{sat}) - C_4 T_{sat} + C_5 T_{sat}^2$$

where

$$C_1 = 25.5743247 \qquad C_2 = 3295.1254 \qquad C_3 = 6.4012471$$

$$C_4 = 4.148279 \times 10^{-4} \qquad \text{and} \qquad C_5 = 1.4759945 \times 10^{-6}$$

In this equation p_{sat} is in psia and T_{sat} is in R. Write an interactive computer program that will calculate in either SI or Engineering English units (user's choice) p_{sat} in either psia or kPa when T_{sat} is entered in either °F or °C. Make sure the screen prompts are clear and indicate the proper units on the requested information and on all output values. Compare the resulting output values with the corresponding saturation values given in Appendix C.5.

71. The p-v-T relation for superheated mercury vapor is

$$pv = RT - (T/v)\exp(10.3338 - 312.095/T - 2.07951 \ln T)$$

where p is in N/m^2, v is in m^3/kg, T is in K, and $R = 41.45$ J/kg·K. Write an interactive computer program that will output p, v, and T with their appropriate units when either **a)** p and T are input, or **b)** v and T are input. Allow the user to work in either the SI or Engineering English units and to choose which type of input he/she wishes to use. For extra credit create an isometric three-dimensional plot of a p-v-T surface using this equation of state.

Chapter Four The First Law of Thermodynamics with Applications to Closed and Open Systems

In this chapter we begin the formal study of the first law of thermodynamics. The theory is presented first, and then it is applied to a variety of closed and open systems of engineering interest. Consequently, this chapter has been divided into three distinct sections.

In Section I the first law of thermodynamics and its associated energy balance are presented along with a detailed discussion of the energy transport mechanisms of work and heat. A powerful problem-solving technique is also introduced, and its use is illustrated throughout the remainder of the chapter.

In Section II the focus is on applying the theory presented in Section I to a series of steady state closed systems such as sealed rigid containers, electrical apparatus, and piston–cylinder devices. Section II ends with a brief discussion of the behavior of unsteady-state closed systems.

The first law of thermodynamics presented in Section I is expanded in Section III to cover open systems, and the conservation of mass law is introduced as a second independent basic equation. Then appropriate applications are presented dealing with a variety of common open systems of engineering interest such as nozzles, diffusers, throttling devices, heat exchangers, and work producing or absorbing machines. Section III then ends with a brief discussion of the behavior of unsteady state open systems.

Chapter Four Section I The First Law of Thermodynamics and Energy Transport Mechanisms

In Section I of this chapter we focus our attention on the detailed structure of the first law of thermodyanmics. To completely understand this law we will need to study a variety of work and heat energy transport modes, and to investigate the basic elements of energy conversion efficiency. We complete this section by presenting an effective general technique for solving thermodynamics problems. This technique is then illustrated in Sections II and III of this chapter.

The First Law of Thermodynamics

The simplest and most direct statement of the first law of thermodynamics is that *energy is conserved.* That is, energy can neither be created nor destroyed. The condition of zero energy production was expressed mathematically in Eq. 2.15:

$$E_P = 0 \tag{2.15}$$

By differentiating this with respect to time we obtain an equation for the condition of a zero energy production *rate*:

$$\frac{dE_P}{dt} = \dot{E}_P = 0 \tag{2.16}$$

Whereas Eqs. 2.15 and 2.16 are accurate and concise statements of the first law of thermodynamics, they are relatively useless by themseles because they do not contain terms that can be used to calculate other variables. However, if these equations are substituted into the energy balance and energy rate balance equations, then the following equations result.

Energy balance

$$E_G = E_T + E_P \quad E_P = 0 \text{ (as required by the 1st law)}$$

or

$$E_G = E_T \tag{4.1}$$

and

Energy rate balance

$$\dot{E}_G = \dot{E}_T + \dot{E}_P \quad \dot{E}_P = 0 \text{ (as required by the 1st law)}$$

or

$$\dot{E}_G = \dot{E}_T \tag{4.2}$$

From now on we will frequently be using the phrases *energy balance* and *energy rate balance* in identifying the proper equation to use in an analysis. So, for simplicity, we introduce the following abbreviations

EB = energy balance

and

ERB = energy rate balance

In Chapter 3 we introduced the components of the total system energy E as the internal energy U, the kinetic energy $mV^2/2g_c$, and the potential energy mgZ/g_c, or[1]

$$E = U + \frac{mV^2}{2g_c} + mgZ/g_c \tag{3.26}$$

In this equation, V is the magnitude of the velocity of the center of mass of the entire system, Z is the height of the center of mass above a ground (or zero) potential datum, and g_c is the dimensional proportionality factor (see Table 1.2 of Chapter 1). In Chapter 3 we also introduced the abbreviated form of this equation:

$$E = U + \text{KE} + \text{PE} \tag{3.27}$$

---

1. In this text we use the symbol V to represent the magnitude of the average velocity $|\mathbf{V}|$, and the symbol $\forall$ to represent volume.

and similarly for the specific energy e,

$$e = \frac{E}{m} = u + \frac{V^2}{2g_c} + \frac{gZ}{g_c} \tag{3.29a}$$

and

$$e = u + \text{ke} + \text{pe} \tag{3.29b}$$

In these equations we have continued the practice introduced in Chapter 2 of using uppercase letters to denote *extensive* properties and lowercase letters to denote *intensive* (specific) properties. The energy concepts described in these equations are illustrated in Figure 4.1.

In equilibrium thermodynamics the proper energy balance is given by Eq. 4.1, where the gain in energy E_G is to be interpreted as follows. The system is initially in some equilibrium state (call it state 1) and after the application of some "process" the system ends up in a different equilibrium state (call it state 2). If we now add a subscript to each symbol to denote the state at which the property is to be evaluated (E_1 is the total energy of the system in state 1 and so forth), then we can write the energy gain of the system as

$$E_G = \text{final total energy} - \text{initial total energy} \tag{4.3}$$

or

$$E_G = E_2 - E_1 \tag{4.4}$$

and extending this to Eq. 3.26 above we obtain

$$E_G = U_2 - U_1 + \frac{m}{2g_c}(V_2^2 - V_1^2) + \left(\frac{mg}{g_c}\right)(Z_2 - Z_1) \tag{4.5}$$

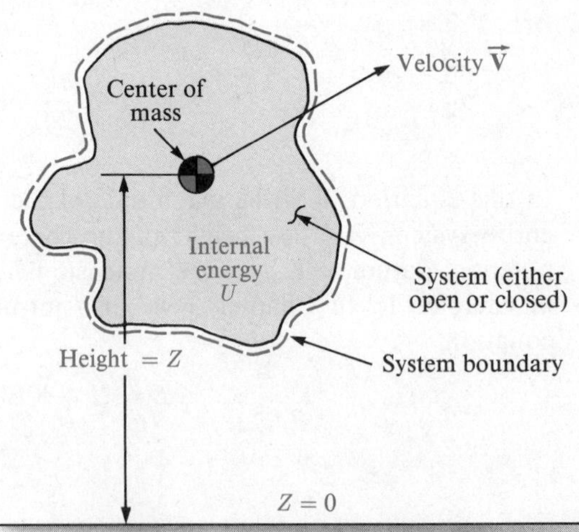

Figure 4.1 System energy components.

or

$$E_G = m\left[u_2 - u_1 + \frac{V_2^2 - V_1^2}{2g_c} + \frac{g}{g_c}(Z_2 - Z_1)\right] \tag{4.6}$$

or, alternatively,

$$E_G = U_2 - U_1 + KE_2 - KE_1 + PE_2 - PE_1 \tag{4.7}$$

and

$$E_G = m(u_2 - u_1 + ke_2 - ke_1 + pe_2 - pe_1) \tag{4.8}$$

In most of the engineering situations we will encounter, either the system will not be moving at all or it will be moving without any change in velocity or height. In these cases, $E_G = U_2 - U_1 = m(u_2 - u_1) = E_T$.

Example 4.1

Three lbm of saturated water vapor at 10 psia is sealed in a rigid container aboard a spaceship traveling at 25,000 mph at an altidue of 200 miles. What energy transport is required to decelerate the water to zero velocity and to bring it down to the surface of the earth such that its final specific internal energy is 950.0 Btu/lbm? Neglect any change in the acceleration of gravity over this distance.

Solution Let the system in this example be just the water in the container, and then the process followed by the water is a constant volume process (the water is in a "rigid sealed container"). Therefore, the problem statement can be outlined as follows:

State 1	$\xrightarrow{m = 3.0 \text{ lbm},\ v = \text{constant}}$	**State 2**
$p_1 = 10$ psia		$u_2 = 950.0$ Btu/lbm
$x_1 = 1.0$ (saturated vapor)		$v_2 = v_1 = 38.42$ ft^3/lbm
$v_1 = v_g$ (at 10 psia) $= 38.42$ ft^3/lbm		

Notice how the process path gives us the value of a property (v_2) in the final state. To determine the required energy transport we use the energy balance, Eq. 4.1, along with the definition of the energy gain term E_G from Eq. 4.5.

$$\text{EB: } E_G = E_T + \underset{0 \text{ (from the 1st law)}}{E_P}$$

and, assuming g is constant during this process,

$$E_G - E_T = U_2 - U_1 + \frac{m}{2g_c}(V_2^2 - V_1^2) + \frac{mg}{g_c}(Z_2 - Z_1)$$

Here, $V_2 = Z_2 = 0$, so

$$E_T = U_2 - U_1 - \frac{m}{2g_c}V_1^2 - \frac{mg}{g_c}Z_1$$

Appendix C.2*a* gives

$$u_1 = u_g\,(10\text{ psia}) = 1072.2\text{ Btu/lbm}$$

and the problem statement requires that $u_2 = 950.0$ Btu/lbm. Therefore

$$U_1 = mu_1 = (3.0\text{ lbm})(1072.2\text{ Btu/lbm}) = 3216.6\text{ Btu}$$

and

$$U_2 = mu_2 = (3.0\text{ lbm})(950.0\text{ Btu/lbm}) = 2850.0\text{ Bu}$$

so

$$E_T = (2850.0 - 3216.6)\text{ Btu} - \frac{3.0\text{ lbm}}{2}\left[(25{,}000\text{ mile/h})\left(\frac{5280\text{ ft/mile}}{3600\text{ s/h}}\right)\right]^2$$

$$\times\frac{\dfrac{1\text{ Btu}}{778\text{ ft}\cdot\text{lbf}}}{32.2\dfrac{\text{lbm}\cdot\text{ft}}{\text{lbf}\cdot\text{s}^2}} - \frac{3.0\text{ lbm}(32.2\text{ ft/s}^2)}{\left(32.2\dfrac{\text{lbm}\cdot\text{ft}}{\text{lbf}\cdot\text{s}^2}\right)}(200\text{ miles})(5280\text{ ft/mile})\left(\frac{1\text{ Btu}}{778\text{ ft}\cdot\text{lbf}}\right)$$

or

$$E_T = -367 - 80{,}500 - 4070 = -84{,}900\text{ Btu}$$

Thus 84,900 Btu's of energy must be transferred *out of* the water (E_T is negative here) by some mechanism. This can be done, for example, by having the water do work on the atmosphere (via aerodynamic drag) or on the retro-rockets or through heat transfer.

In nonequilibrium systems we use the energy rate balance (ERB) equation with $\dot{E}_G$ defined as

$$\dot{E}_G = \frac{d}{dt}\left(U + \frac{m}{2g_c}V^2 + \frac{mg}{g_c}Z\right)_{\text{system}} = \dot{E}_T \qquad \textbf{(4.9)}$$

Equation 4.9 can become quite complicated for open systems whose total mass is rapidly changing (such as with rockets) because it exapnds as follows (using $U = mu$)

$$\dot{E}_G = m\left[\dot{u} + \frac{V}{g_c}(\dot{V}) + \frac{g}{g_c}(\dot{Z})\right] + \left(u + \frac{V^2}{2g_c} + \frac{gZ}{g_c}\right)\dot{m} = \dot{E}_T \qquad \textbf{(4.10)}$$

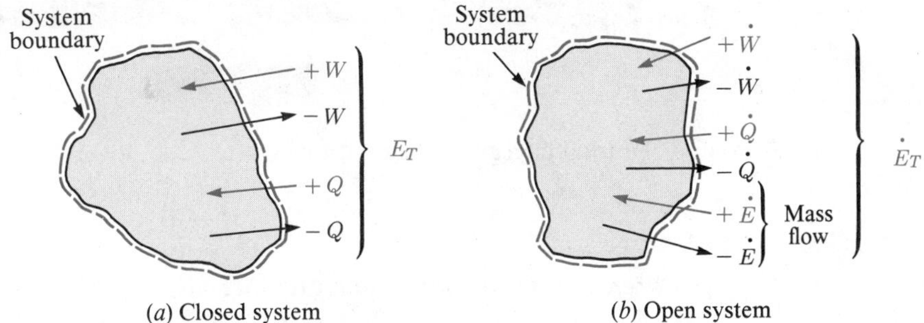

Figure 4.2 Energy transport mechanisms.

Notice that in this equation $\dot{V} = dV/dt$ is the magnitude of the instantaneous acceleration, and $\dot{Z}$ is the magnitude of the instantaneous vertical velocity.

The equilibrium thermodynamics energy balance and the nonequilibrium energy rate balance are fairly simple concepts; however, their implementation can be quite complex. Each of the gain, transport, and production terms may expand into many separate terms, all of which must be evaluated in an analysis. Next we investigate the structure of the energy transport and energy transport rate terms.

Energy Transport Mechanisms

There are three energy transport mechanisms, any or all of which may be operating in any given system: **1)** work,[2] **2)** heat, and **3)** mass flow., These three mechanisms and their sign conventions are illustrated in Figure 4.2.

By definition, a closed system has no mass crossing its system boundary, so it can experience only work and heat transport mechanisms. Also, since the gain, transport, and production terms in the balance equation are defined to be *net* values (see Eq. 2.10) we define

1. the *net* work transport of energy *into* a system $= \sum_i W_i = W$ and the *net* work transport rate of energy *into* a system $= \sum_i \dot{W}_i = \dot{W}$
2. the *net* heat transport of energy *into* a system $= \sum_i Q_i = Q$ and the *net* heat transport rate of energy *into* a system $= \sum_i \dot{Q}_i = \dot{Q}$
3. the *net* mass transport of energy *into* the system $= \sum_i E_i = E_{\substack{\text{mass}\\\text{flow}}}$ and the *net* mass transport rate of energy *into* the system $= \sum_i \dot{E}_i = \sum \dot{E}_{\substack{\text{mass}\\\text{flow}}}$

2. The types of work transports of energy that are included here are only those due to dissipative or nonconservative forces. For example, the work associated with gravitational or electrostatic forces is not considered a work mode because it is conservative (i.e., it is representable by the gradient of a scalar quantity) and is consequently nondissipative. Energy transports resulting from the actions of conservative forces have their own individual terms in the energy balance equation (such as mgZ/g_c for the gravitational potential energy).

Thus, for a *closed system*, the total energy transport becomes

$$E_T = W + Q \tag{4.11}$$

and the total energy transport rate is

$$\dot{E}_T = \dot{W} + \dot{Q} \tag{4.12}$$

For *open systems*, the same quantities are

$$E_T = W + Q + \sum E_{\substack{\text{mass}\\\text{flow}}} \tag{4.13}$$

and

$$\dot{E}_T = \dot{W} + \dot{Q} + \sum \dot{E}_{\substack{\text{mass}\\\text{flow}}} \tag{4.14}$$

In Eqs. 4.13 and 4.14 note that we write the summation signs on the net mass transport of energy terms, but for simplicity we do not write the summation signs on the work or heat transport terms. This is because you will often have open systems with more than one mass flow stream, but seldom will you have more than one type of work or heat transport present. However, you must always remember that W, $\dot{W}$, Q, and $\dot{Q}$ are also *net* terms and represent a summation of all the different types of work and heat transports of energy present. This is illustrated in the following example.

Example 4.2 Determine the energy transport rate for the system shown in the sketch below.

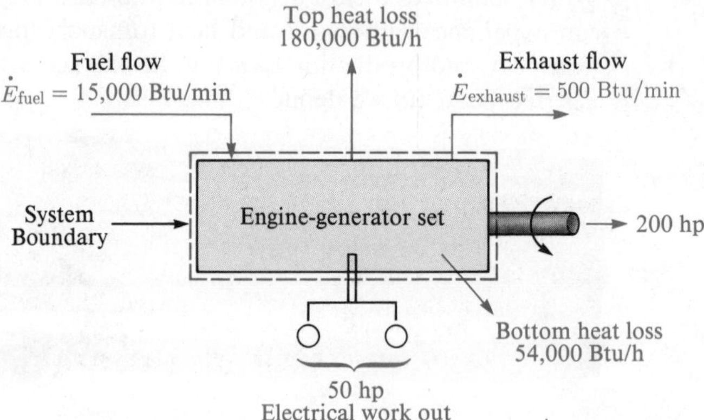

Solution From Eq. 4.14 the total energy transport rate is

$$\dot{E}_T = \dot{W} + \dot{Q} + \sum \dot{E}_{\substack{\text{mass}\\\text{flow}}}$$

where $\dot{W}$ = net work rate into the system = −200 hp − 50 hp = −250 hp (negative because they are *out* of the system), and

$$\dot{Q} = \text{net heat transfer into the system}$$
$$= -180{,}000 \text{ Btu/h} - 54{,}000 \text{ Btu/h} = -234{,}000 \text{ Btu/h}$$

while

$$\sum \dot{E}_{\substack{\text{mass}\\ \text{flow}}} = \text{net } input \text{ of mass flow energy into the system}$$
$$= 15{,}000 \text{ Btu/min} - 500 \text{ Btu/min} = 14{,}500 \text{ Btu/min}$$

So

$$\dot{E}_{\text{T}} = (-250 \text{ hp})[42.4 \text{ Btu/(hp}\cdot\text{min)}] - (234{,}000 \text{ Btu/h})\left(\frac{1 \text{ h}}{60 \text{ min}}\right)$$
$$+ 14{,}500 \text{ Btu/min} = 0.0 \text{ Btu/min},$$

The system of Example 4.2 had no *net* energy transport rate even though it had six different energy transport rates. Note that the energy rate balance (Eq. 4.2) for this system is $\dot{E}_{\text{G}} = \dot{E}_{\text{T}}$, and therefore this system also had no net gain of energy. That is, the total energy E of this system was constant in time.

Point and Path Functions

A quantity, say y, that has a value at every point within its domain of definition is called a *point function.* Its derivative is written as dy, and its integral as

$$\int_1^2 dy = y_2 - y_1$$

Thus, the value of the integral depends only on the values of y at the end points of the integration path, and is independent of the actual path taken between these end points. This is a fundamental characteristic of point functions. *All intensive and extensive thermodynamic properties are point functions.* Thus, we can write

$$\int_1^2 dE = E_2 - E_1 \qquad \int_1^2 du = u_2 - u_1 \qquad \int_1^2 dm = m_2 - m_1$$

and so forth.

A quantity, say x, whose value depends upon the mathematical *path* taken between two points within its domain of definition is called a *path function.* Since path functions do not differentiate or integrate in the same manner as do point functions, we cannot use the same differential and integral notation for both path and point functions. Let $\bar{d}x$ denote the differential of the path function x, and let its integral be written as

$$\int_1^2 \bar{d}x = {}_1x_2 \tag{4.15}$$

A path function does not have a value at a point. It only has a value for a path of points, and this value is directly determined by the effect of all the points on the path, not just its end points. For example, the area A under the curve of the point function $w = f(y)$ is a path function because

$$\bar{d}A = w\,dy = f(y)\,dy$$

and

$${}_1A_2 = \int_1^2 \bar{d}A = \int_{y_1}^{y_2} f(y)\,dy = \text{area under } f(y) \text{ between the points } y_1 \text{ and } y_2$$

Clearly, if the path $f(y)$ is changed, then the area ${}_1A_2$ is also changed. Consequently ${}_1A_2$ must be a path function.

We will see in the next sections that *both the work and heat transports of energy are path functions.* Consequently, we write the differentials of these quantities as $\bar{d}W$ and $\bar{d}Q$, and their integrals as[3]

$$\int_1^2 \bar{d}W = {}_1W_2 \qquad \textbf{(4.16)}$$

and

$$\int_1^2 \bar{d}Q = {}_1Q_2 \qquad \textbf{(4.17)}$$

Since the associated rate equations contain the time differential, we define

$$\dot{W} = \bar{d}W/dt \qquad \textbf{(4.18)}$$

and

$$\dot{Q} = \bar{d}Q/dt \qquad \textbf{(4.19)}$$

Each of the different types of work or heat transport of energy is called a *mode.* A system that has no operating work modes is said to be *aergonic.*[4] Similarly, a system that changes its state without any work transport of energy having occurred is said to have undergone an *aergonic process.* While there are only three different modes of heat transport, there are many different modes of work transport. In the following segments four mechanical work modes and five nonmechanical work modes are studied in detail.

Substituting Eqs. 4.8 and 4.11 into Eq. 4.1 gives the general closed system energy balance equation for a system undergoing a process from state 1 to state 2 as

---

3. Note that since work and heat are *not* thermodynamic properties we cannot write the work transport for a process as $W_2 - W_1$ or ΔW, and we cannot write $Q_2 - Q_1$, or ΔQ for the process heat transport.

4. The term aergonic is coined here and consequently is unique to this text. It comes from the Greek roots *a* meaning *not* and *ergon* meaning *work*, and it should be interpreted to mean "no work has occurred."

General closed system energy balance

$$
\begin{aligned}
{}_1Q_2 + {}_1W_2 &= (E_2 - E_1)_{\text{system}} \\
&= m[(u_2 - u_1) + (V_2^2 - V_1^2)/(2g_c) + (Z_2 - Z_1)g/g_c]_{\text{system}} \quad \textbf{(4.20)}
\end{aligned}
$$

and substituting Eq. 4.10 with m = constant and Eq. 4.12 into Eq. 4.2 gives the general closed system energy rate balance as

General closed system energy rate balance

$$\dot{Q} + \dot{W} = (dE/dt)_{\text{system}} = (m\dot{u} + mV\dot{V}/g_c + mg\dot{Z}/g_c)_{\text{system}} \quad \textbf{(4.21)}$$

Similarly, substituting Eqs. 4.9 and 4.14 into Eq. 4.2 gives the general open system energy rate balance as

General open system energy rate balance

$$\dot{Q} + \dot{W} + \sum_{\text{flow}} \dot{E}_{\text{mass}} = (d/dt)(mu + mV^2/2g_c + mZg/g_c)_{\text{system}} \quad \textbf{(4.22)}$$

where the mass of the system is no longer required to be constant.

Mechanical Work Modes of Energy Transport

In mechanics we recognize that work is done whenever a force moves through a distance. When this force is a mechanical force **F** we call this work mode *mechanical work* and define it as

$$(\bar{d}W)_{\text{mechanical}} = \mathbf{F} \cdot d\mathbf{x} \quad \textbf{(4.23)}$$

or

$$({}_1W_2)_{\text{mechanical}} = \int_{\mathbf{x}_1}^{\mathbf{x}_2} \mathbf{F} \cdot d\mathbf{x} \quad \textbf{(4.24)}$$

where the force **F** is assumed to be exerted *on* rather than *by* the system. Also, our sign convention requires that work done *on* the system be *positive*, while work done *by* the system be *negative*.

In thermodynamics there are four classical types of mechanical work:

1. moving system boundary work,
2. rotating shaft work,
3. elastic work, and
4. surface tension work.

These are very important work modes in engineering analysis and the following material provides a detailed discussion of their major characteristics.

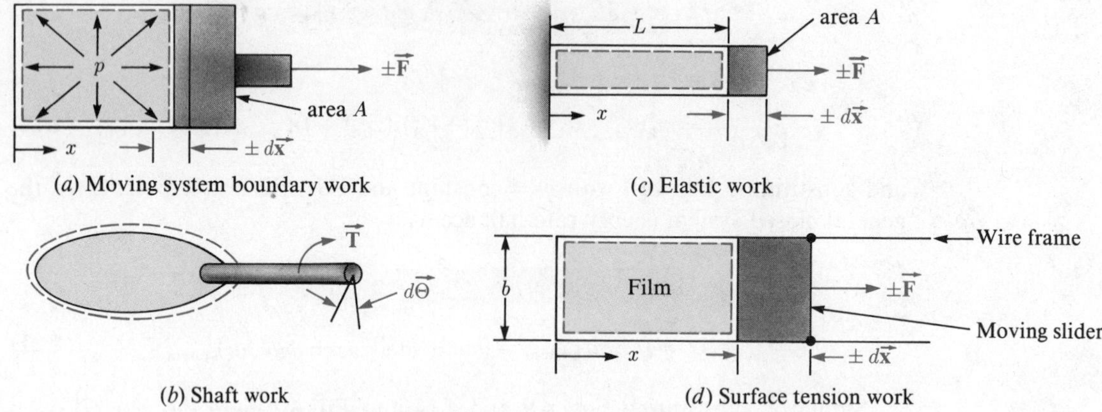

Figure 4.3 Four classical types of mechanical work.

Moving System Boundary Work Whenever a system boundary moves such that the total volume of the system changes, then moving system boundary work occurs. This is sometimes called expansion or compression work and it has wide application in mechanical power technology. In this case (see Figure 4.3*a*), $\mathbf{F} = -p\mathbf{A}$ and so $\mathbf{F} \cdot d\mathbf{x} = -p\mathbf{A} \cdot d\mathbf{x} = -p\,d\mathcal{V}$ where p is the pressure acting on the system boundary, $\mathbf{A}$ is the area vector (defined to be normal to the system boundary and pointing outward), $d\mathbf{x}$ is the differential boundary movement, and $d\mathcal{V}$ is the differential volume $\mathbf{A} \cdot d\mathbf{x}$. The minus sign appears because $p\mathbf{A}$ is the force exerted by the system but $\mathbf{F}$ is defined to be the force exerted on the system. Consequently,

$$(\bar{d}W)_{\substack{\text{moving}\\\text{boundary}}} = -p\,d\mathcal{V} \tag{4.25}$$

and

$$({}_1W_2)_{\substack{\text{moving}\\\text{boundary}}} = -\int_1^2 p\,d\mathcal{V} \tag{4.26}$$

Example 4.3

Determine the mechanical moving boundary work required to increase the pressure in a sealed rigid container of air from 14.7 psia at 70 °F to 100 psia.

Solution Let the system be the material inside the container. The process that occurs here is one of constant volume (the container is rigid). Therefore, since $\mathcal{V}$ = constant, then $d\mathcal{V} = 0$, and so

$$({}_1W_2)_{\substack{\text{moving}\\\text{boundary}}} = -\int_1^2 p\,d\mathcal{V} = 0$$

The problem statement in Example 4.3 is misleading because you cannot change the pressure in a sealed rigid container via moving boundary work alone. Indeed, a rigid container can *never* have a moving boundary that results in a volume change.

Example 4.4 A weather balloon is inflated from a constant pressure compressed gas source at 20 psia. Determine the moving system boundary work as the balloon expands from a diameter of 1.0 ft to 10 ft.

Solution Assume the balloon is a sphere, then $V = \frac{4}{3}\pi R^3 = \frac{1}{6}\pi D^3$. The process here is one of constant pressure, so $p =$ constant, and

$$
\begin{aligned}
({}_1W_2)_{\substack{\text{moving}\\\text{boundary}}} &= -\int_1^2 p\,dV = -p\int_1^2 dV = -p(V_2 - V_1)\\
&= -\left(20\,\frac{\text{lbf}}{\text{in}^2}\right)\left(\frac{144\ \text{in}^2}{\text{ft}^2}\right)\left(\frac{\pi}{6}\right)[(10^3 - 1.0^3)\ \text{ft}^3]\\
&= -1.5 \times 10^6\ \text{ft}\cdot\text{lbf}
\end{aligned}
$$

The work is negative because the balloon *does* work on the atmosphere as it expands and pushes the atmosphere out of the way.

To carry out the integration indicated in Eq. 4.26 the exact $p = p(V)$ pressure–volume function must be known. This function is usually given in the process path specification of a problem statement. For example, in Example 4.3 the process was one of constant volume (the container was rigid) so $dV = 0$; and in Example 4.4 the filling process was isobaric ($p =$ constant) and so the integral of Eq. 4.26 was very easy. In general, outside of these two cases, the integration of Eq. 4.26 is not trivial and must be determined with great care.

As an example of a nontrivial integration of Eq. 4.26, consider a process that obeys the relation

$$pV^n = \text{constant} \tag{4.27}$$

or

$$p_1V_1^n = p_2V_2^n$$

where the exponent n is a constant. Such processes are called *polytropic processes.*[5] The moving system boundary work of any substance undergoing a polytropic process is

$$({}_1W_2)_{\substack{\text{polytropic}\\\text{moving boundary}}} = -\int_1^2 p\,dV = -\int_1^2 \frac{\text{constant}}{V^n}\,dV$$

For $n = 1$ this integral becomes

$$({}_1W_2)_{\substack{\text{polytropic }(n=1)\\\text{moving boundary}}} = -p_1V_1 \ln\frac{V_2}{V_1} = -p_2V_2 \ln\frac{V_2}{V_1} \tag{4.28}$$

5. The term polytropic comes from the Greek roots *poly* meaning *many* and *trope* meaning *turns* or *paths.*

and for $n \neq 1$ it becomes

$$({}_1W_2)_{\substack{\text{polytropic } (n \neq 1) \\ \text{moving boundary}}} = \frac{p_2 \forall_2 - p_1 \forall_1}{n - 1} \tag{4.29}$$

If the material undergoing a polytropic process is an ideal gas, then it must simultaneously satisfy both of the following equations:

1. the ideal gas equation of state, $p\forall = mRT$
2. the polytropic process equation, $p\forall^n = \text{constant}$.

Combining these two equations by eliminating the pressure p gives

$$mRT\forall^{n-1} = \text{constant}$$

or, for a fixed mass system,

$$T_1 \forall_1^{n-1} = T_2 \forall_2^{n-1}$$

or

$$\frac{T_2}{T_1} = \left(\frac{\forall_1}{\forall_2}\right)^{n-1} = \left(\frac{v_1}{v_2}\right)^{n-1} \tag{4.30}$$

Similarly, eliminating $\forall$ in these two equations (for a fixed mass system) gives

$$\frac{T_2}{T_1} = \left(\frac{p_2}{p_1}\right)^{n-1/n} \tag{4.31}$$

Finally, if we have an ideal gas undergoing a polytropic process with $n \neq 1$, then its moving system boundary work is given by Eq. 4.29 as

$$({}_1W_2)_{\substack{\text{polytropic } (n \neq 1) \\ \text{ideal gas} \\ \text{moving boundary}}} = \frac{mR}{n - 1}(T_2 - T_1) \tag{4.32}$$

Rotating Shaft Work Whenever a rotating shaft carrying a torque load crosses a system boundary, then *rotating shaft work* is done. In this case (see Figure 4.3*b*),

$$(\bar{d}W)_{\substack{\text{rotating} \\ \text{shaft}}} = \mathbf{T} \cdot d\boldsymbol{\theta} \tag{4.33}$$

and

$$({}_1W_2)_{\substack{\text{rotating} \\ \text{shaft}}} = \int_1^2 \mathbf{T} \cdot d\boldsymbol{\theta} \tag{4.34}$$

where **T** is the torque vector of the shaft and $d\boldsymbol{\theta}$ is its angular displacement vector. Normally, thermodynamic problem statements do not require rotating shaft work to be calculated from Eq. 4.34. The rotating shaft work is usually openly given as part of the problem statement. For example, if you are analyzing an automobile internal combustion engine producing 150 ft·lbf of work at the crankshaft, you must be able to recognize that $({}_1W_2)_{\substack{\text{rotating}\\\text{shaft}}} = -150$ ft·lbf.

Elastic Work Whenever we compress or extend an elastic solid (like a spring) we perform elastic work. Consider a force $\pm\mathbf{F}$ applied to the end of an elastic rod (see Figure 4.3*c*). The normal stress σ in the rod is

$$\sigma = \pm\frac{|\mathbf{F}|}{A} \tag{4.35}$$

where A is the cross-sectional area of the rod. Since the force **F** and its corresponding displacement $d\mathbf{x}$ are always in the same direction, then the vector dot product $\mathbf{F} \cdot d\mathbf{x}$ always reduces to $F\,dx$, where $F = |\mathbf{F}|$ and $dx = |d\mathbf{x}|$, and the work increment can then be written as

$$\bar{d}W = \mathbf{F} \cdot d\mathbf{x} = F\,dx = \sigma A\,dx \tag{4.36}$$

Now the strain ϵ in the rod is defined as

$$d\epsilon = \frac{dx}{L} = \frac{A\,dx}{AL} = \frac{A\,dx}{\forall} = \frac{d\forall}{\forall} \tag{4.37}$$

where L is the length of the rod and AL is its volume $\forall$. Then

$$A\,dx = d\forall = \forall\,d\epsilon \tag{4.38}$$

and Eq. 4.36 becomes

$$\bar{d}W = \sigma A\,dx = \sigma\forall\,d\epsilon \tag{4.39}$$

Therefore,

$$({}_1W_2)_{\text{elastic}} = \int_1^2 \sigma\forall\,d\epsilon \tag{4.40}$$

Example 4.5

Determine an expression for the work involved in deforming a constant volume elastic solid that obeys Hooke's law of elasticity.

Solution Here we have $\forall$ = constant. Also, from strength of materials we can write Hooke's law as

$$\sigma = E\epsilon$$

where E is Young's modulus of elasticity. Then Eq. 4.40 becomes

$$({}_1W_2)_{\text{elastic}} = \int_1^2 \sigma V\, d\epsilon = \int_1^2 EV\epsilon\, d\epsilon = EV \int_1^2 \epsilon\, d\epsilon$$

$$= EV\left(\frac{\epsilon_2^2 - \epsilon_1^2}{2}\right) = \frac{V}{2E}(\sigma_2^2 - \sigma_1^2)$$

Thus, if $\epsilon_2^2 > \epsilon_1^2$ work is being put into the system, and if $\epsilon_2^2 < \epsilon_1^2$ work is being produced by the system. Note that both tensile strains ($\epsilon > 0$) and compressive strains ($\epsilon < 0$) are possible here. But the resulting work formula deals only with ϵ^2 and consequently gives the correct result regardless of the strain direction.

Surface Tension Work Surface tension work is the two-dimensional analog of the elastic work considered above. Figure 4.3*d* shows a soap film on a wire loop. One side of the loop has a movable wire slider that can either compress or extend the film. As in the case of the elastic solid, the force and deflection are always in the same direction, so we can modify Eq. 4.36 to read

$$\bar{d}W = \mathbf{F} \cdot \mathbf{dx} = F\, dx = (2\sigma_s b)\, dx \tag{4.41}$$

where σ_s is the surface tension of the film, and b is the length of the moving part of the film. The factor of 2 appears because the film normally has two surfaces (top and bottom) in contact with air. Now, $2b\, dx = dA =$ change in the film's surface area, so Eq. 4.41 becomes

$$\bar{d}W = \sigma_s\, dA \tag{4.42}$$

and

$$({}_1W_2)_{\substack{\text{surface}\\ \text{tension}}} = \int_1^2 \sigma_s\, dA \tag{4.43}$$

Example 4.6

Determine the amount of surface tension work required to inflate a soap bubble from a diameter of zero to 0.05 m. The surface tension of the soap film can be taken to be a constant 0.04 N/m.

Solution Here, $\sigma_s =$ constant $= 0.04$ N/m. So Eq. 4.43 becomes[6]

$$({}_1W_2)_{\substack{\text{surface}\\ \text{tension}}} = \sigma_s \int_1^2 dA = \sigma_s(A_2 - A_1)$$

---

6. Note that we are not calculating the surface area of the bubble here from its geometric elements, but only wish to find the change in area between states 1 and 2. Consequently, the area integral in this instance can be treated as a point function rather than as a path function.

where $A_1 = 0$. Now, since a soap bubble has *two* surfaces (the outside and inside films), then

$$A_2 = 2(4\pi R^2) = 2(4\pi)\left(\frac{0.05 \text{ m}}{2}\right)^2$$
$$= 0.0157 \text{ m}^2$$

and

$$({}_1W_2)_{\substack{\text{surface}\\ \text{tension}}} = (0.04 \text{ N/m})(0.0157 - 0 \text{ m}^2)$$
$$= 6.28 \times 10^{-4} \text{ N}\cdot\text{m} = 6.28 \times 10^{-4} \text{ J}$$
$$= (6.28 \times 10^{-4} \text{ J})(1 \text{ Btu}/1055 \text{ J}) = 5.96 \times 10^{-7} \text{ Btu}$$

Example 4.6 shows that it would take all of the surface tension energy stored in nearly 2 million 5-cm-diameter soap bubbles to raise the temperature of one pound-mass of water by one degree Fahrenheit.

Notice that in each of the four cases of classical mechanical work the work differential $\bar{d}W$ was given by the product of what we can call a *generalized force* F and a *generalized displacement* $d\chi$; that is

$$\bar{d}W = F\, d\chi \tag{4.44}$$

where F and $d\chi$ for each of the four classical mechanical work modes are identified in Table 4.1. In Eq. 4.44 the scaler or dot product is implied if F and $d\chi$ are vectors.

The application of these work modes may change the thermodynamic state of the system, and thus may produce a change in the system's thermodynamic properties. Finally, note that the generalized forces are all intensive properties, whereas the generalized displacements are all extensive properties.

We can generalize the work concept to nonmechanical systems by including any work mode given by Eq. 4.44 when the generalized for F is an intensive property *forcing function* and the generalized displacement $d\chi$ is an extensive property *response function.* We are now in a position to analyze the remaining work mode energy transport mechanisms.

Table 4.1 Generalized forces and generalized displacements

Work mode	Generalized force F	Generalized displacement dx
Moving system boundary	$-p$ (pressure)	$d\forall$ (volume)
Shaft	T (torque)	$d\theta$ (angular displacement)
Elastic	σ (stress)	$\forall\, d\epsilon$ (volume)
Surface Tension	σ_s (surface tension)	dA (surface area)

Nonmechanical Work Modes of Energy Transport

Of the wide variety of nonmechanical work modes available, the following five are of significant engineering value:

1. electrical current flow,
2. electrical polarization,
3. magnetic,
4. chemical, and
5. mechanochemical.

Materials are electrically classified as conductors, nonconductors (dielectrics or insulators), and semiconductors. A pure *conductor* is a substance that has mobile charges (electrons) free to move in an applied electric field. They constitute the flow of electrical current. Pure *nonconductors* have no free electrons whatsoever and a *semiconductor* is a material that behaves as a dielectric (nonconductor) at low temperatures but becomes conducting at higher temperatures.

As an electric field E is applied to a pure conductor the free electrons migrate to the conductor's outer surface where they create their own electric field which opposes the applied field. As more and more electrons reach the outer surface the electric field inside the object grows weaker and weaker, eventually vanishing altogether. At equilibrium, there is no electric field within a pure conductor.

A pure nonconductor has no free electrons with which to neutralize the applied electric field. The externally applied field therefore acts on the internal molecules and normally nonpolar molecules will become polar and develop *electric dipoles*. Some molecules are naturally polar in the absence of an electric field (e.g., water). The applied electric field will rotate and align the newly created or naturally polar molecules. Complete alignment is normally prevented by molecular vibrations. But when the applied field is strong enough to overcome the vibration randomizing effects and further increases in field strength have no effect on the material, the material is then said to be *saturated* by the applied field. The process of electric dipole creation, rotation, and alignment in an applied electric field is known as dielectric *polarization*.

Therefore, there are two separate work modes that arise from the application of an electric field to a material. The first is the work associated with the free electron (current) flow, and the second is the work associated with dielectric polarization. For a pure conductor the polarization work is always zero, and for a pure nonconductor the current flow work is always zero. We will always treat these as separate work modes.

Electrical Current Flow Work Electrical current flow work occurs whenever current-carrying wires (pure conductors) cross the system boundary. This is the most common type of nonmechanical work mode encountered in thermodynamic system analysis. The generalized force here is the intensive property *voltage* (the electric potential) ϕ, and the extensive property generalized displacement is the charge q.[7] Then,

$$(\bar{d}W)_{\substack{\text{electrical}\\\text{current}}} = \phi\, dq$$

and

$$({}_1W_2)_{\substack{\text{electrical}\\\text{current}}} = \int_1^2 \phi\, dq \tag{4.45}$$

Electrical current i is defined as

$$i = \frac{dq}{dt}$$

so $dq = i\,dt$, and

$$(\bar{d}W)_{\substack{\text{electrical}\\\text{current}}} = \phi i\, dt \tag{4.46}$$

Then

$$({}_1W_2)_{\substack{\text{electrical}\\\text{current}}} = \int_1^2 \phi i\, dt \tag{4.47}$$

From Ohm's law,[8] the instantaneous voltage ϕ across a pure resistance R carrying an alternating current described by $i = i_{max} \sin(2\pi ft)$ is

$$\phi = Ri = Ri_{max} \sin(2\pi ft)$$

where f is the frequency and $\phi_{max} = Ri_{max}$. Thus, Eq. 4.47 gives the electrical current work of n cycles of an alternating electrical current passing through a pure resistance from time 0 to time $t = n/f$ as

$$\begin{aligned}(W_2)_{\substack{\text{electrical}\\\text{current}}} &= \phi_{max} i_{max} \int_0^{t=n/f} \sin^2(2\pi ft)\, dt \\ &= \phi_{max} i_{max}(t/2) \\ &= \phi_e i_e t = \phi_e^2(t/R) = i_e^2 Rt \end{aligned} \tag{4.48}$$

where ϕ_e and i_e are the *effective* voltage and current defined by $\phi_e = \phi_{max}/\sqrt{2}$ and $i_e = i_{max}/\sqrt{2}$.

7. The electrical potential ϕ and the electric field strength vector **E** and related by $\mathbf{E} = -\nabla(\phi)$, where $\nabla(\ )$ is the gradient operator.

8. This law was discovered experimentally by George Simon Ohm (1787–1854) in 1826. Basically, it states that for a given conductor the current is directly proportional to the potential difference, and is usually written as $\phi = Ri$, where R is the *electrical resistance* in units of ohms, where 1 ohm = 1 volt/ampere.

Electrical work can exist in either open or closed systems (we do not consider the flow of electrons across a system boundary to be a mass flow term). When the electron supply is coming from or going into a *finite* energy reservoir such as a battery or a capacitor, then Eq. 4.45 or 4.47 is convenient to use. But, when an essentially *infinite* reservoir with a constant voltage and current is used, then it is more convenient to use the instantaneous electrical *power*, defined as

$$(\dot{W})_{\substack{\text{electrical}\\ \text{current}}} = \frac{\bar{d}W}{dt} = \phi i \tag{4.49}$$

The instantaneous electrical power ϕi of an alternating current circuit will vary in time with the excitation frequency f. However, it is common to report the electrical power of an ac device as the instantaneous power averaged over one cycle of oscillation, or

$$\begin{aligned}(\dot{W})_{\substack{\text{electrical}\\ \text{(pure resistance)}}} &= f\int_0^{1/f} \phi i\, dt = f\phi_{\max} i_{\max}\int_0^{1/f} \sin^2(2\pi f t)\, dt \\ &= \phi_{\max} i_{\max}/2 = \phi_e i_e = \phi_e^2/R = i_e^2 R \end{aligned} \tag{4.50}$$

where ϕ_e and i_e are the effective voltage and current defined earlier.

Example 4.7

Consider a 120-V, 144-Ω alternating current incandescent light bulb to be a pure resistance. Determine

a) the electrical current work when the bulb is operated for 1.5 h, and

b) its electrical power consumption.

Solution **a)** Since the voltage and current ratings of ac devices are always given in terms of their effective values, then $\phi_e = 120$ V and, from Ohm's law, $i_e = \phi_e/R = 120/144 = 0.833$ A. Then, from Eq. 4.48,

$$\begin{aligned}({}_1W_2)_{\substack{\text{electrical}\\ \text{current}}} &= \phi_e i_e t = (120\text{ V})(0.833\text{ A})(1.5\text{ h}) \\ &= 150\text{ V}\cdot\text{A}\cdot\text{h} = 150\text{ W}\cdot\text{h}\end{aligned}$$

b) From Eq. 4.50,

$$\begin{aligned}(\dot{W})_{\substack{\text{electrical}\\ \text{current}}} &= \phi_e i_e = (120\text{ V})(0.833\text{ A}) \\ &= 100\text{ V}\cdot\text{A} = 100\text{ W}\end{aligned}$$

Electrical Polarization Work The electric dipole formation, rotation, and alignment that occurs when an electric field is applied to a nonconductor or a semiconductor constitutes an electric polarization work mode. The generalized force is the intensive property **E**, the electric field strength vector, and the generalized displacement is the extensive property **P**, the polarization vector of the medium (defined to be the sum of the electric dipole rotation moments of all the molecules in the system). Then

Table 4.2 The electric susceptibility of various materials

Material	Temperature (°C/°F)	χ_e (dimensionless)
Air (14.7 psia)	20/68	5.36×10^{-4}
Plexiglass	27/81	2.40
Neoprene rubber	24/75	5.7
Glycerine	25/77	41.5
Water	25/77	77.5

Source: Reprinted by permission of the publisher from Mark W. Zemansky, Michael M. Abbott, and Henrick C. Van Ness, *Basic Engineering Thermodynamics*, 2d ed. (New York: McGraw-Hill, 1975), p. 66 (Table 3.1).

$$(\bar{d}W)_{\substack{\text{electrical}\\\text{polarization}}} = \mathbf{E} \cdot d\mathbf{P} \tag{4.51}$$

and

$$({}_1W_2)_{\substack{\text{electrical}\\\text{polarization}}} = \int_1^2 \mathbf{E} \cdot d\mathbf{P} \tag{4.52}$$

Since the effect of the electric field is to orientate the dipoles coincident with the field, then **E** and **P** are always parallel and point in the same direction. Therefore, if we let the magnitude of **E** be E and the magnitude of **P** be P, then Eqs. 4.51 and 4.52 reduce to

$$(\bar{d}W)_{\substack{\text{electrical}\\\text{polarization}}} = E\,dP \tag{4.53}$$

and

$$({}_1W_2)_{\substack{\text{electrical}\\\text{polarization}}} = \int_1^2 E\,dP \tag{4.54}$$

Many substances (particularly gases) correlate well with the following dielectric equation of state:

$$P = \epsilon_0 \chi_e \forall E \tag{4.55}$$

where $\forall$ is the volume of the dielectric substance, ϵ_0 is the electric permittivity of vacuum (8.85419×10^{-12} N/V^2) and χ_e is the *electric susceptibility* (a dimensionless number) of the material. Table 4.2 gives values of χ_e for various materials.

Example 4.8

A parallel plate capacitor is charged to a potential difference of 110 V at 25 °C. The plates are square with a side length of 0.10 m and are separated by 0.01 m. If the gap between the plates is filled with water, determine the polarization work required in the charging of the capacitor.

Solution Here we can use the dielectric equation of state, Eq. 4.55. Then Eq. 4.54 becomes

$$({}_1W_2)_{\substack{\text{electric}\\\text{polarization}}} = \int_1^2 E\,dP = \int_1^2 \forall \epsilon_0 \chi_e E\,dE$$

$$= \forall \epsilon_0 \chi_e (E_2^2 - E_1^2)/2$$

From the problem statement we have

$$\forall = AL = (0.10\ \text{m})^2\ (0.010\ \text{m}) = 10^{-4}\ \text{m}^3$$

If we assume that the electrical potential ϕ varies linearly between the plates, then we can write

$$E = |-\nabla(\phi)| = (\text{voltage difference})/(\text{plate gap})$$

So that $E_1 = 0$ (uncharged plates) and

$$E_2 = \frac{110\ \text{V}}{0.01\ \text{m}} = 1.1 \times 10^4\ \text{V/m (charged plates)}$$

From Table 4.2 we find that for water, $\chi_e = 77.5$. Then

$$\begin{aligned}({}_1W_2)_{\substack{\text{electric}\\ \text{polarization}}} &= (10^{-4}\ \text{m}^3)(8.85419 \times 10^{-12}\ \text{N/V}^2)(77.5) \\ &\quad \times [(1.1 \times 10^4)^2 - 0^2\ \text{V}^2/\text{m}^2] \\ &= 8.3 \times 10^{-6}\ \text{N}\cdot\text{m} = 8.3 \times 10^{-6}\ \text{J}\end{aligned}$$

The polarization work is a small fraction of the total energy required to charge an entire capacitor. The total work required to charge a capacitor is divided into two parts. The largest fraction goes into increasing the electric field strength **E** itself, and the remaining goes into the polarization of the material exposed to the electric field. Consequently, if the thermodynamic system you are analyzing is just the material between the plates of a capacitor, then only polarization work is done on the material and Eq. 4.54 gives the correct electrical work mode value. On the other hand, if you are analyzing the entire capacitor (plates and dielectric), then Eq. 4.47 must be used to determine the correct electrical work mode value.

Magnetic Work Materials are classified as either diamagnetic, paramagnetic, or ferromagnetic. Diamagnetic materials do not have permanently established molecular magnetic dipoles. However, when they are placed in a magnetic field their molecules develop magnetic dipoles whose magnetic field opposes the applied field (the Greek prefix *dia* means *to oppose*). Paramagnetic materials have naturally occurring molecular magnetic dipoles. When placed in a magnetic field these dipoles tend to align themselves parallel to the field (the Greek prefix *para* means *beside*). Ferromagnetic materials retain some magnetism after the removal of a magnetic field. The thermodynamic state of these materials depends not only on the present values of their thermomagnetic properties, but also on their magnetic history. In this sense ferromagnetic materials have a "memory" of their previous magnetic exposure.

As in the case of an electric field, the work associated with the initiation or destruction of a magnetic field consists of two parts. The first part is the work required to change the magnetic field itself (as though it existed within a vacuum), and the second part is the work required to change the magnetization of the material present inside the magnetic field.

For calculating the total work of magnetization the generalized force is the intensive property **H**, the magnetic field strength, and the generalized displacement is the extensive property $\mathcal{V}\mathbf{B}$, the product of the system volume and the magnetic induction. Thus,

$$(\bar{d}W)_{\text{magnetic}} = \mathbf{H} \cdot d(\mathcal{V}\mathbf{B}) \tag{4.56}$$

and since **H** and **B** are always parallel and point in the same direction in magnetic materials this reduces to

$$(\bar{d}W)_{\text{magnetic}} = H\, d(\mathcal{V}B) \tag{4.57}$$

where H is the magnitude of **H** and B is the magnitude of **B**. The magnetic induction can be decomposed into two vectors as

$$\mathbf{B} = \mu_0\mathbf{H} + \mu_0\mathbf{M} \tag{4.58}$$

where **M** is the magnetization vector per unit volume of material exposed to the magnetic field (in a vacuum, **M** is equal to the null vector **O**), and $\mu_0 = 4\pi \times 10^{-7}$ V·s/(A·m) is a universal constant called the *magnetic permeability*. Inserting this information into Eq. 4.57 gives

$$(\bar{d}W)_{\text{magnetic}} = \mu_0 H\, d(\mathcal{V}H) + \mu_0 H\, d(\mathcal{V}M) \tag{4.59}$$

Equation 4.59 is the differential of the total work associated with changing a material's magnetic field. The first term corresponds to the work required just to change the field itself (in a vacuum), and the second term corresponds to the work associated with the alignment of the molecular magnetic dipoles of the material present inside the magnetic field, and represents the work of magnetization of the material exposed to the magnetic field. Thus, we can write

$$(\bar{d}W)_{\substack{\text{material}\\ \text{magnetization}}} = \mu_0 H\, d(\mathcal{V}M) \tag{4.60}$$

A simple and useful equation of state for a magnetic field is

$$M = \chi_m H \tag{4.61}$$

where χ_m is the *magnetic susceptibility* (a dimensionless number) of the material. The magnetic susceptibility is negative for diamagnetic materials and positive for paramagnetic materials (see Table 4.3). For a constant volume magnetization process, Eq. 4.61 can be used in Eq. 4.59 to give

$$(\bar{d}W)_{\text{magnetic}} = \mu_0 \mathcal{V}(1 + \chi_m)H\, dH$$

Table 4.3 The magnetic susceptibility of various materials

Material	Temperature (°C/°F)	$\chi_m \times 10^5$ (dimensionless)
Mercury	18/26	−3.2
Quartz	25/77	−1.65
Ice	0/32	−0.805
Nitrogen (14.7 psia)	20/68	−0.0005
Oxygen (14.7 psia)	20/68	0.177
Aluminum	18/64	2.21
Platinum	18/64	29.7

Source: Reprinted by permission of the publisher from Mark W. Zemansky, Michael M. Abbott, and Henrick C. Van Ness, *Basic Engineering Thermodynamics*, 2d ed. (New York: McGraw-Hill, 1975), p. 70 (Table 3.2).

and assuming a constant volume and a constant magnetic susceptibility this can be integrated to give

$$({}_1W_2)_{\text{magnetic}} = \mu_0 \mathcal{V}(1 + \chi_m)\left(\frac{H_2^2 - H_1^2}{2}\right) \tag{4.62}$$

where the increment to the total work due to the actual magnetization of the exposed material is just

$$({}_1W_2)_{\substack{\text{material}\\ \text{magnetization}}} = \mu_0 \mathcal{V} \chi_m \left(\frac{H_2^2 - H_1^2}{2}\right) \tag{4.63}$$

Chemical Work Chemical work occurs whenever a specific chemical species is added to or removed from a system. Here the generalized force is the intensive property μ_i, the Gibbs chemical potential of chemical species i, and the generalized displacement is the extensive property m_i, the mass of the chemical species added or removed.[9] Since any number of chemical species may be manipulated in any one process, we write the associated chemical work as the sum over all k of the mobile species as

$$(\bar{d}W)_{\text{chemical}} = \sum_{i=1}^{k} \mu_i \, dm_i \tag{4.64}$$

and so

$$({}_1W_2)_{\text{chemical}} = \int_1^2 \sum_{i=1}^{k} \mu_i \, dm_i \tag{4.65}$$

When the chemical potential is constant during the mass transfer from state 1 to state 2, Eq. 4.65 can be integrated to give

$$({}_1W_2)_{\substack{\text{chemical}\\ \mu_i = \text{constant}}} = \sum_{i=1}^{k} \mu_i (m_2 - m_1)_i \tag{4.66}$$

9. In chemistry texts the chemical potential is usually defined on a molar (i.e., per unit gram mole) basis. In this text we will define it as a standard intensive (per unit mass) property.

Chemical work does not include the energy transports produced by chemical reactions, nor does it include the energy transported across the system boundary with the mass transport itself. Mass flow energy transport will be considered later in this chapter, and the energy transports of chemical reaction are studied in detail in Chapter 9. The chemical work presented here essentially deals only with those energy transports involved in the mixing or separating of chemical species.

Mechanochemical Work Mechanochemical work occurs whenever there is a direct energy conversion from chemical to mechanical energy. Animal muscles are the best example of mechanochemical devices. Small mechanochemical engines have also been built using this work mode and Figure 4.4 shows a small hydraulic pump driven by a mechanochemical contractile fiber. The "fuel" used in mechanochemical engines is not "burned" as in a standard heat engine. Often it is merely diluted and a small amount of chemical work is simultaneously extracted.

Mechanochemical work is calculated as basic mechanical work. The generalized force is the intensive property f, the force generated within the mechanochemical system, and the generalized displacement is the extensive property ℓ, the mechanical diplacement of the system. Thus,

$$(\bar{d}W)_{\text{mechanochemical}} = f\,d\ell \tag{4.67}$$

Generally, the mechanochemical force f is not constant during the contraction/expansion cycle, so the total mechanochemical work must be determined by a careful integration:

$$({}_1W_2)_{\text{mechanochemical}} = \int_1^2 f\,d\ell \tag{4.68}$$

A system may be exposed to only one of the above work modes of energy transport, or it may be exposed to several of them simultaneously. Since work is an additive quantity, to get the total (or net) work of a system that has more than one work mode present we simply add all these work terms together. Thus, we have

$$\begin{aligned}(\bar{d}W)_{\text{total}} = &-p\,dV + \mathbf{T}\cdot d\boldsymbol{\theta} + \sigma\,d\epsilon + \sigma_s\,dA + \phi i\,dt + E\,dP + \mu_0 H\,d(VM) \\ &+ \sum \mu_i\,dm_i + f\,d\ell + \cdots\end{aligned} \tag{4.69}$$

It is generally the engineer's responsibility to determine the number and type of work modes present in any problem statement or real world situation. Often the work modes of a problem are affected by how the system boundaries are drawn (recall that boundary definition is a prerogative of the problem solver). For example, if a system contains an electrical heater then electrical current work will be done on the system. However, if the boundary is drawn such as to exclude the heating element itself, then no net electrical work occurs and the energy transport becomes a heat transport from the surface of the heating element into the system.

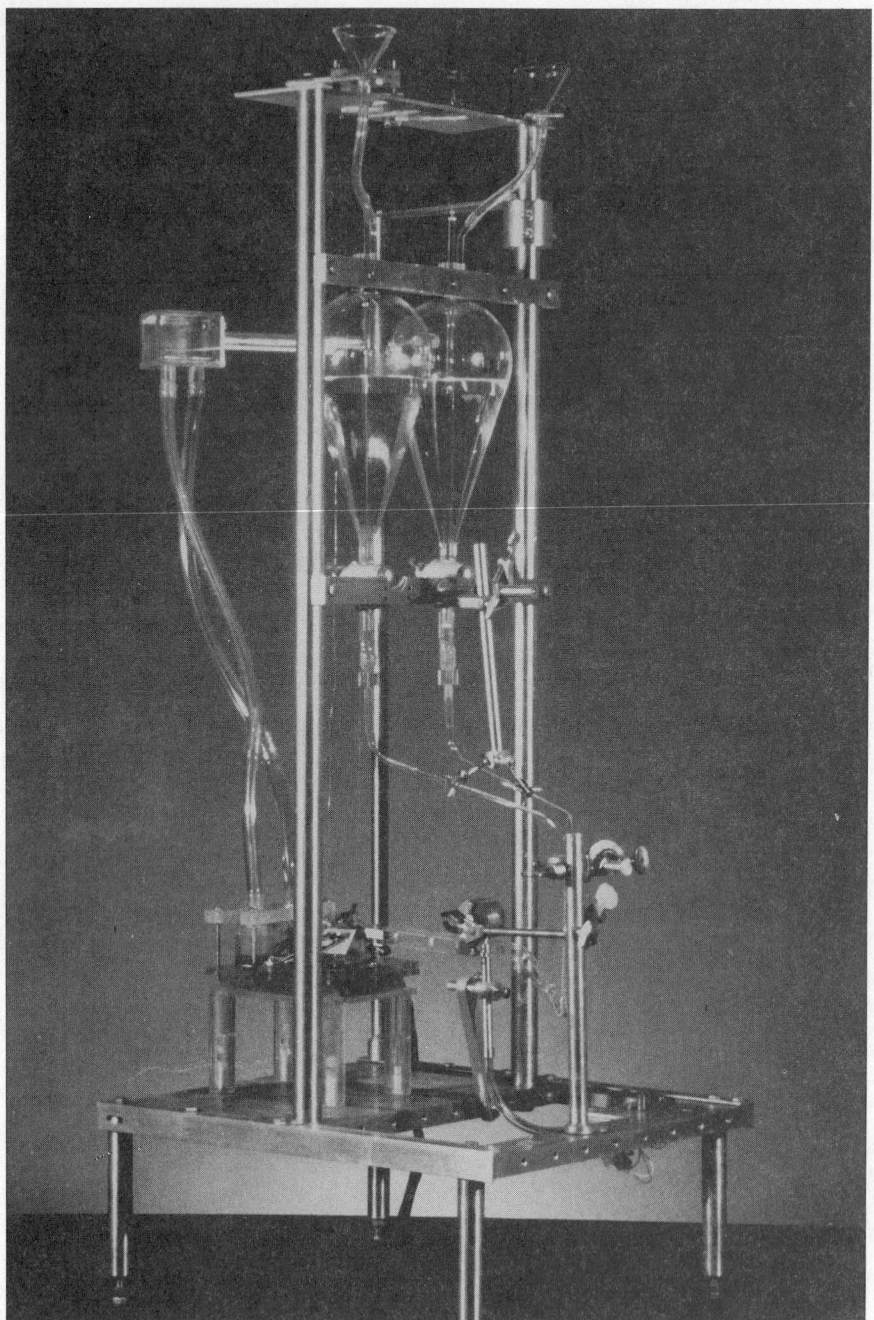

Figure 4.4 A simple mechanochemical engine and pump. Photo by Gene Menzel.

Table 4.4 Power modes of energy transport

Work mode	Power equation
Mechanical moving boundary	$(\dot{W})_{\substack{\text{moving}\\ \text{boundary}}} = -p\dfrac{d\maltese}{dt} = -p\dot{\maltese}$
Mechanical rotating shaft	$(\dot{W})_{\substack{\text{rotating}\\ \text{shaft}}} = \mathbf{T}\cdot\left(\dfrac{d\theta}{dt}\right) = \mathbf{T}\cdot\omega$
Mechanical elastic	$(\dot{W})_{\text{elastic}} = \sigma\maltese\left(\dfrac{d\epsilon}{dt}\right) = \sigma\maltese\dot{\epsilon}$
Mechanical surface tension	$(\dot{W})_{\substack{\text{surface}\\ \text{tension}}} = \sigma_s\left(\dfrac{dA}{dt}\right) = \sigma_s\dot{A}$
Electrical current	$(\dot{W})_{\substack{\text{electrical}\\ \text{current}}} = \phi i$
Electrical polarization	$(\dot{W})_{\substack{\text{nelectrical}\\ \text{polarization}}} = E\left(\dfrac{dP}{dt}\right) = E\dot{P}$
Magnetic	$(\dot{W})_{\text{magnetic}} = \mu_0\maltese(1+\chi_m)H\left(\dfrac{dH}{dt}\right) = \mu_0\maltese(1+\chi_m)H\dot{H}$
Chemical	$(\dot{W})_{\text{chemical}} = \sum \mu_i\left(\dfrac{dm_i}{dt}\right) = \sum \mu_i\dot{m}_i$
Mechanochemical	$(\dot{W})_{\text{mechanochemical}} = f\left(\dfrac{d\ell}{dt}\right) = f\dot{\ell}$

Power Modes of Energy Transport

In thermodynamics, the time rate of change of a work mode, $\bar{d}W/dt$, is called *power* and it represents the *power mode of an energy transport* $\dot{W}$. Dividing each of the previous nine differential work mode equations by the time differential dt produces an equation for the associated power mode. These results are summarized in Table 4.4, and are useful in calculating the power (i.e., work rates) in problems in which continuous rate processes occur. While continuous rate processes can occur in both closed and open systems, they are more common in open systems.

Work Efficiency

Notice that in all of the work mode formulae given above no mention was made of the *efficiency* of the work transport of energy. This is because all of the mechanical and nonmechanical work mode formulae discussed earlier were developed under the presumption of ideal circumstances in which there were no friction losses or other inefficiencies within the system. Under these conditions the work process could ideally be reversed at any time, and all the work put into a system could be removed again simply *by* reversing the direction of the generalized force. Therefore, we call all the mechanical and nonmechanical work (or power) mode formulae developed above *reversible* work (or power) formulae. Consequently, and this is very important, work or power calculations made with these formulae will not agree with the measurement of *actual* work that occurs in a real system. In real systems that absorb work, *more* actual work than that calculated from the previous formulae will be required to produce the same effect on the system, and in real work-producing systems *less* actual work will be produced than calculated from the previous formulae.

In the real world of engineering nothing is reversible. Not one of the work modes discussed earlier can actually be carried out with 100% efficiency. Some are very close to being reversible (i.e., they have very high efficiencies) but none are completely reversible. This lack of reversibility in the real world is due to the influence of the second law of thermodynamics, which will be discussed in detail in Chapter 5. Work modes with a low degree of reversibility (i.e., high irreversibility) are those carried out with systems far from thermodynamic equilibrium. Heat transfer, rapid chemical reactions (explosions), mechanical friction, and electrical resistance are all common sources of irreversibility in engineering systems.

Engineers use the concept of a work transport energy conversion efficiency to describe the difference between reversible and actual work. A general definition of the concept of an energy conversion efficiency is

$$\text{energy conversion efficiency} = \eta_E = \frac{\text{desired energy result}}{\text{required energy input}} \tag{4.70}$$

In the case of work-absorbing systems such as pumps or compressors, we can use the form of Eq. 4.70 to define a work transport energy conversion efficiency η_W:

Work-absorbing systems

$$\eta_W(\%) = \frac{W_{rev}}{W_{act}} \times 100 = \frac{\dot{W}_{rev}}{\dot{W}_{act}} \times 100 \tag{4.71}$$

In the case of work-producing systems such as engines or electrical generators the work transport energy conversion efficiency becomes

Work-producing systems

$$\eta_W(\%) = \frac{W_{act}}{W_{rev}} \times 100 = \frac{\dot{W}_{act}}{\dot{W}_{rev}} \times 100 \tag{4.72}$$

When these systems consist only of mechanical components, as, for example, in an internal combustion engine, then the work transport energy conversion efficiency is simply called the *mechanical* efficiency and η_W is usually written as η_m.

Even though work transport energy conversion efficiencies are always less than 100%, not all energy conversion efficiencies are less than 100%. The value of the efficiency depends on the nature of the desired result in Eq. 4.70. An electrical resistance can convert electrical energy (the energy input) into heat (the desired result) with an energy conversion efficiency of 100%, but when this process is reversed we find that the conversion of heat into work occurs with a much lower efficiency (a consequence of the second law of thermodynamics). On the other hand, refrigeration systems normally produce more "desired result" (cooling) than it actually costs in required energy input. Such systems normally have energy conversion efficiencies far in excess of 100%, not because they violate any law of physics, but simply because of the way their energy conversion efficiency is defined. Because it seems paradoxical to most people to speak of efficiencies in excess of 100%, we call such efficiencies *coefficients of performance* instead.

Because of the many irreversibilities that occur within a system we cannot calculate actual work absorbed or produced from a theoretical formula.All efficiency values are determined from laboratory or field measurements on the actual work of real operating systems. When energy conversion efficiencies are to be taken into account in textbook problems, the efficiency values will usually be provided within the problem statement. Experienced engineers often have a "feel" for what the efficiencies of certain devices should be, and they can use these efficiency estimations in their design calculations. Student engineers, however, are not presumed to be innately blessed with this knowledge.

The general form of Eq. 4.70 allows the creation of many different types of efficiencies. There are thermal, mechanical, volumetric, thermodynamic, and total efficiencies (to name just a few) in today's engineering literature. One should always be sure to understand the type of efficiency being used in any calculation.

The Local Equilibrium Postulate

Surprisingly, there is no adequate definition for the thermodynamic properties of a system that is not in an equilibrium state. Some extension of classical equilibrium thermodynamics is necessary for us to be able to analyze nonequilibrium (or irreversible) processes. We do this by subdividing a nonequilibrium system into many small but finite volume elements, each of which is larger than the local molecular mean free path so that the continuum hypothesis holds. We then assume that each of these small volume elements is in *local* equilibrium with its surrounding elements. Thus, a nonequilibrium system can be broken down into a very large number of very small systems, each of which is at a different equilibrium state. This technique is similar to the continuum hypothesis, wherein continuum equations are used to describe the results of the motion of discrete molecules (see Chapter 2).

The differential time quantity dt used in nonequilibrium thermodynamic analysis cannot be allowed to go to zero as in normal calculus. We require that $dt > \sigma$, where σ is the time it takes for one of the volume elements of the subdivided nonequilibrium system described above to "relax" from its current nonequilibrium state to an appropriate equilibrium state. This is analogous to not allowing the physical size of the element to be less than its local molecular mean free path as required by the continuum hypothesis. The error incurred by these postulates is really quite small because they are the result of second-order variations of the thermodynamic variables from their equilibrium values. However, just as the continuum hypothesis can be violated by systems such as rarefied gases, the local equilibrium postulate can also be violated by highly nonequilibrium systems such as explosive chemical reactions. In the case of such violations the analysis must be carried forward with techniques of statistical thermodynamics.

Because of the similarity between the local equilibrium postulate and the continuum hypothesis it is clear that the local equilibrium postulate could as well be called the continuum thermodynamics hypothesis.

The State Postulate

To carry out a reversible work mode calculation using the formulae given earlier one must know the exact behavior of both the generalized force (an intensive property) and the generalized displacement (an extensive property) for each work mode. Systems with multiple work modes have a variety of property values that must be monitored during the work process in order to utilize the proper work mode formulae. Therefore, it seems reasonable to expect that a simple relation exists between the number of work modes present in any given system and the number of independent property values required to fix the state of that system. This is the purpose of the following *state postulate*:

The number of independent intensive thermodynamic property values required to fix the state of a closed system that is

a) subject to the conditions of local equilibrium,
b) exposed to n different (nonchemical) work modes of energy transport, and
c) composed of m different pure substances

is $n + m$.

Thus, a pure substance ($m = 1$) subjected to only one work mode ($n = 1$) would require two ($n + m = 2$) independent property values to fix its state. Such systems are called *simple systems*, and

Any two independent intensive property values will fix the local equilibrium state of a simple system.

The compression or expansion of a pure gas or vapor is a simple system. The work mode is moving system boundary work, and any two independent intensive property values (p, v or p, T or v, T, etc.) will fix its state. In fact, a simple system occurs when each of the nonchemical reversible work modes discussed above is individually applied to a pure substance. On the other hand, if two of them are simultaneously applied to a pure substance, then $n + m = 3$ independent intensive property values are required to fix the state of the system.

Heat Modes of Energy Transport

We now introduce the three basic modes of heat transport of energy. Since a good heat mode analysis is somewhat more complex than a work mode analysis, and since its understanding is very important to a good engineering education, most mechanical engineering curricula include a separate heat transfer course on this subject. Consequently, this section is meant to be only an elementary introduction to this subject.

A system without any heat transfer is said to be *adiabatic*,[10] and all well-insulated systems are considered to be adiabatic. A process that occurs without any heat transport of energy is called an *adiabatic process.*

In the late eighteenth century heat was thought to be a colorless, odorless, and weightless fluid, then called *caloric.* By the middle of the nineteenth century it had been determined that heat was in fact not a fluid, but rather it represented energy in transit. Unfortunately, many of the early heat–fluid technical terms survived and are still in use today. This is why we speak of heat transfer and heat flow as though heat were something physical, but it is not. Because these conventions are so deeply ingrained in our technical culture, we will use the phrases heat transfer, heat transport, and the heat transport of energy interchangeably.

Heat transfer is broken into three modes:

1. conduction,
2. convection, and
3. radiation.

Conduction and radiation are pure heat transports of energy, but convection is really a mass flow energy transport mode. Why then is convection called a heat transfer mode? This confusion in terms occurred because the subject of heat transfer evolved faster and apart from the subject of thermodynamics. Again we yield to convention and consider convection to be a heat transfer mode rather than a mass flow energy transport mode.

After it was determined that heat was not a fluid, late nineteenth century physicists defined heat transfer simply as energy transport due to a temperature difference. In this framework, temperature was the only intensive property driving force for the heat transport of energy. However, in the twentieth century development of nonequilibrium thermodynamics it has been shown that many phenomena can be coupled together during certain processes. The result of this coupling is that one phenomenon can actually cause the occurrence of another phenomenon. For example, the flow of electrical current in certain electrical circuits can cause large heating or cooling effects. In this case the heat transfer is

10. The term adiabatic was coined by the Scottish engineer William John Macquorn Rankine (1829–1872) in 1859. It comes from the Greek word αδιαβατοσ, meaning *not to be passed through.* In thermodynamics it is universally interpreted to mean simply no heat transport of energy (or no heat transfer).

brought about by the electrical current flow rather than by a temperature difference, and the coupling effect is called *thermoelectricity.* This effect can also be reversed, and a heat transport of energy can be converted directly (at less than 100% efficiency) into electricity. Similarly, photoelectric effects arise from the coupling of electromagnetic radiation and electrical current flow, and piezoelectric effects arise from the coupling of mechanical force and electrical current flow. There are a large variety of these effects and they show great promise for the future development of new energy conversion technologies.

Today, the simplest way to define heat transport of energy is as any energy transport that is neither a work mode nor a mass flow energy transport mode. More precisely, modern nonequilibrium thermodynamics defines heat transfer as just the transport of internal energy into or out of a system. With this definition all other energy transport modes are automatically either work or mass flow modes.

The basic heat transfer mode formulae were developed empirically and, unlike the previous work mode formulae, give actual rather than reversible heat transport values. In fact, since heat transfer always occurs as a result of energy spontaneously moving *down* a potential gradient (such as from a high to a low temperature), and since the reverse cannot spontaneously occur, then no heat transfer process can be reversed in any way whatsoever. Therefore, all heat transfer processes are completely irreversible.

Heat transfer mode formulae are always (for pragmatic reasons) cast as heat transfer *rate* (i.e., $\dot{Q}$) formulae. To determine the amount of heat energy transport that occurs as a system undergoes a process from one equilibrium state to another you must integrate $\dot{Q}$ over the time interval of the process:

$$ {}_1Q_2 = \int_1^2 \dot{Q}\, dt \tag{4.73} $$

Normally, we will choose processes in which $\dot{Q}$ is constant (i.e., nontransient heat transfer processes) so that Eq. 4.73 becomes simply

$$ {}_1Q_2 = \dot{Q}(t_2 - t_1) = \dot{Q}(\Delta t) \tag{4.74} $$

where Δt is the time required for the process to occur.

Conduction Heat Transfer The basic equation of conduction heat transfer is Fourier's law,

$$ \dot{Q}_{\text{cond}} = -k_t A \left(\frac{dT}{dx}\right) \tag{4.75} $$

where k_t is the thermal conductivity of the material, A is the cross-sectional area normal to the heat transfer direction, and dT/dx is the temperature gradient in the direction of the heat transfer. The algebraic sign in Eq. 4.75 is such that a positive $\dot{Q}$ always corresponds to heat flow in the positive x direction and a negative

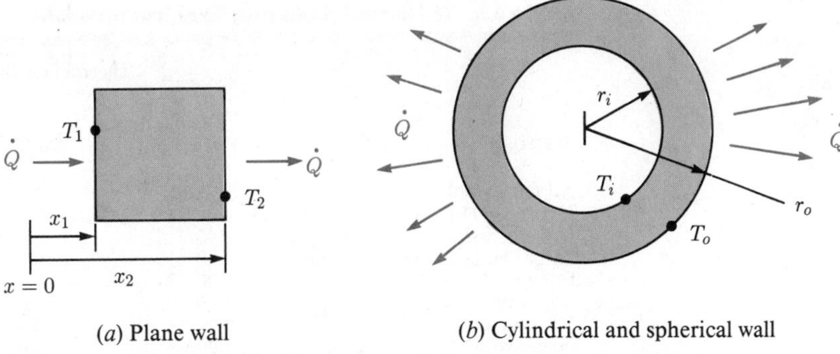

(*a*) Plane wall (*b*) Cylindrical and spherical wall

Figure 4.5 Thermal conduction notation in plane, cylindrical, and spherical geometries.

$\dot{Q}$ always corresponds to heat flow in the negative x direction. Since this is not the same type of sign convention adopted earlier in this text, the sign of values calculated from Eq. 4.75 may have to be altered to produce a positive $\dot{Q}$ when it is entering the system and a negative $\dot{Q}$ when it is leaving the system.

For steady heat transfer through a flat plane wall with a uniform surface temperature and a constant thermal conductivity, Eq. 4.75 becomes

$$(\dot{Q}_{\text{cond}})_{\text{plane}} = -k_t A\left(\frac{T_2 - T_1}{x_2 - x_1}\right) \tag{4.76}$$

where the subscripts 1 and 2 refer to the values on the two surfaces of the wall (see Figure 4.5*a*).

When the wall is cylindrical (as in the case of a pipe) with a uniform surface temperature, then the steady heat transfer area A depends on the radial distance r, and Eq. 4.75 becomes

$$(\dot{Q}_{\text{cond}})_{\text{cylinder}} = -2\pi L k_t\left[\frac{T_i - T_o}{\ln(r_i/r_o)}\right] \tag{4.77}$$

where L is the length of the cylinder and the subscripts i and o refer to the inside and outside, respectively.

Finally, if the wall is a spherical shell with a uniform surface temperature, then for steady state conditions Eq. 4.75 becomes

$$(\dot{Q}_{\text{cond}})_{\text{sphere}} = \frac{4\pi k_t(T_i - T_o)}{\dfrac{1}{r_i} - \dfrac{1}{r_o}} \tag{4.78}$$

These three geometries are illustrated in Figure 4.5. Table 4.5 gives thermal conductivity values for various materials.

Table 4.5 The thermal conductivity of various materials

Material	Temperature (°C/°F)	Thermal conductivity k_t Btu/(h·ft·R)	W/(m·k)
Air (14.7 psia)	27/81	0.015	0.026
Hydrogen (14.7 psia)	27/81	0.105	0.182
Saturated water vapor (14.7 psia)	100/212	0.014	0.024
Saturated liquid water (14.7 psia)	0/32	0.343	0.594
Engine oil	20/68	0.084	0.145
Mercury	20/68	5.02	8.69
Window glass	20/68	0.45	0.78
Glass wool	20/68	0.022	0.038
Aluminum (pure)	20/68	118.0	204.0
Copper (pure)	20/68	223.0	386.0
Carbon steel (1% carbon)	20/68	25.0	43.0

Example 4.9

Determine the heat transport rate of energy through a human skull whose average inside surface temperature is 95 °F and whose outside surface temperature is 90 °F. Assume the skull is a spherical shell 7.5 in in outside diameter and 0.25 in thick. The thermal conductivity of human bone is 0.25 Btu/h·ft·R.

Solution In Eq. 4.78, $r_o = D/2 = (7.5 \text{ in})(1 \text{ ft}/12 \text{ in})/2 = 0.313 \text{ ft}$ then, $r_i = r_o - \Delta r = 0.313 - 0.25/12 = 0.292$ ft. Now we have

$$(\dot{Q}_{\text{cond}})_{\text{sphere}} = \frac{4\pi(0.25 \text{ Btu/h·ft·R})[(95+460)-(90+460) \text{ R}]}{\left(\dfrac{1}{0.292} - \dfrac{1}{0.313}\right) \text{ft}^{-1}}$$

$$= 68.36 \text{ Btu/h}$$

Notice that since Eq. 4.78 contains a temperature *difference*, we can use either °F or R in the calculation.

Convection Heat Transfer As was mentioned earlier, convection is really a form of mass flow energy transport. However, convection is normally considered to be a heat transfer mode and, consequently, it is included in this section.

Convection energy transport normally occurs whenever an object is either hotter or colder than the surrounding fluid. The basic equation of convection heat transfer is Newton's law of cooling,

$$\dot{Q}_{\text{conv}} = hA(T_\infty - T_s) \tag{4.79}$$

where h is the convective heat transfer coefficient, A is the surface area of the object being cooled or heated, T_∞ is the bulk temperature of the surrounding fluid, and T_s is the surface temperature of the object. Table 4.6 gives typical values of h for various situations. The algebraic sign of $\dot{Q}_{\text{conv}}$ given by Eq. 4.79 has been chosen arbitrarily to be positive for $T_\infty > T_s$ (i.e., heat transfer into the object).

Table 4.6 Typical values of the convective heat transfer coefficient

	Convective heat transfer coefficient h	
Convection	**Btu/(h·ft²·R)**	**W/(m²·K)**
Air, free convection	1–5	2.5–25
Air, forced convection	2–100	10–500
Liquids, forced convection	20–3000	100–15,000
Boiling water	500–5000	2500–25,000
Condensing water vapor	1000–20,000	5000–100,000

Source: Reprinted by permission of the publisher from J. P. Holman, *Heat Transfer*, 4th ed. (New York: McGraw-Hill, 1976), p. 13 (Table 1.2).

This corresponds to our thermodynamic sign convention when the object is the system. The convective heat transfer coefficient h is always a positive, empirically determined, value.

Example 4.10 Calculate the convective heat transfer coefficient of a naked person standing in still air at 25 °C. The person's thermal energy loss rate is 150 W, average skin temperature is 34.2 °C, and surface area is 1.8 m².

Solution Assuming that all of the thermal energy loss from the person is by convection,[11] then, from Eq. 4.79,

$$\dot{Q}_{\text{conv}} = -150\text{ W} = hA(T_\infty - T_s)$$

so that

$$h = \frac{\dot{Q}_{\text{conv}}}{A(T_\infty - T_s)} = \frac{-150\text{ W}}{(1.8\text{ m}^2)(25 - 34.2\ ^\circ\text{C})} = 9.1\text{ W/m}^2\cdot\text{K}$$

Notice that h is, as it should always be, a positive number, and that the temperature difference, $T_\infty - T_s$, can be calculated in either absolute or relative temperature units. This heat transfer coefficient is related to the wind-chill factor commonly used in commercial weather forecasts.

Radiation Heat Transfer All electromagnetic radiation is classified as radiation heat transfer. Infrared, ultraviolet, and visible light, radio and television waves, X rays, and so on, are all forms of radiation heat transfer. The radiation heat transfer between two isothermal objects situated in a nonabsorbing or emitting medium is given by the Stefan-Boltzmann law,

$$\dot{Q}_{\text{rad}} = F_{1-2}\epsilon_1 A_1 \sigma(T_2^4 - T_1^4) \tag{4.80}$$

11. This may not be a good assumption. In some cases up to 70% of the thermal energy loss from a person can occur through radiation heat transfer (see Example 4.11). However, conduction heat transfer is usually negligible since only 1 or 2% of the total thermal energy loss will be by conduction through the feet to the floor.

Table 4.7 Typical emissivity values for various materials

Material	Temperature (°C/°F)	Emissivity ϵ (dimensionless)
Aluminum	100/212	0.09
Iron (oxidized)	100/212	0.74
Iron (molten)	1650/3000	0.28
Concrete	21/70	0.88
Flat black paint	21/70	0.90
Flat white paint	21/70	0.88
Aluminum paint	21/70	0.39
Water	0–100/32–212	0.96

where F_{1-2} is called the *view factor* between objects 1 and 2 (it describes how well object 1 "sees" object 2), ϵ_1 is the dimensionless emissivity (or absorptivity) of object 1, A_1 is the surface area of object 1, σ is the Stefan-Boltzmann constant (5.69×10^{-8} W/(m$^2 \cdot$K^4) or 0.1714×10^{-8} Btu/(h$\cdot$ft$^2\cdot$R^4)), and T_1 and T_2 are the average surface temperatures of the objects.

A *black* object is defined to be any object whose emissivity is unity ($\epsilon = 1.0$). Also, if object 1 is completely enclosed by object 2, then $F_{1-2} = 1.0$. For a completely enclosed black object, Eq. 4.80 reduces to

$$(\dot{Q}_{rad})_{\substack{black\\enclosed}} = A_1\sigma(T_2^4 - T_1^4) \tag{4.81}$$

The sign convention in Eqs. 4.80 and 4.81 has been arbitrarily chosen to make $\dot{Q}_{rad}$ positive when $T_2 > T_1$. Therefore, the system should be object 1 to achieve the correct thermodynamic sign convention. Also note that Eqs. 4.80 and 4.81 contain temperature raised to the fourth power. This means that absolute temperature units (K or R) must always be used in these equations.

Table 4.7 gives some typical emissivity (or absorptivity) values for various materials. The hotter surface is said to *emit* energy and the colder surface is said to *absorb* it. At thermal equilibrium, the emissivity and absorptivity coefficients are equal.

Example 4.11

Determine the radiative energy transport from a nude person standing in a room with 25 °C walls. The person's average skin temperature and surface area are 34.2 °C and 1.8 m^2. The emissivity of the skin is 0.97.

Solution Let the person be object 1 and the room be object 2. Since the person is completely enclosed by the room, we have $F_{1-2} = 1.0$. Then using Eq. 4.80 with $T_1 = 34.2 + 273.16 = 307.36$ K and $T_2 = 25 + 273.16 = 298.16$ K we get

$$\dot{Q}_{rad} = (1.0)(0.97)(1.8\ \text{m}^2)[5.669 \times 10^{-8}\ \text{W/(m}^2\cdot\text{K}^4)][(298.16)^4 - (307.36)^4\ \text{K}^4]$$
$$= -101.1\ \text{W}$$

The radiative energy loss calculated in Example 4.11 is 67% of the normal amount of thermal energy generated by the body (see Example 4.10). This (among other reasons) explains why we wear clothes, and why mammals have hair and birds have feathers.

A Technique for Solving Thermodynamic Problems

Thermodynamic problem statements sometimes have the appearance of being vaguely worded stories full of technical jargon, liberally sprinkled with random numbers. All too often a student's first instinct upon being faced with such a situation is to calculate something—anything—because the act of calculation brings about the euphoria of apparent progress toward a solution. However, this approach is quickly stilled by the inability to reach the final answer, and then long frustrating periods of shoe shuffling and window staring commence until either enlightenment, discouragement, or sleep occurs. This is definitely the wrong problem-solving technique. A good technique must have definite starting and ending points, and it must contain clear and logical steps that carry the user toward a solution.

As a perlude to discussing the details of the problem-solving technique, you should realize that the general structure of a thermodynamic word problem usually contains the following three humanistic features.

1. A thermodynamic problem statement is usually too long to be completely and accurately stored in your memory, regardless of how many times you read it. So simply reading the problem statement is usually not enough; you must restructure it into your own environment by adding a schematic, writing down relevant assumptions, and so forth.
2. To completely understand the problem statement you must first "decode" it. That is, you must dissect and rearrange the problem statement until it fits into a familiar pattern. Any problem-solving technique is, of course, based upon the premise that the problem has a solution. Curiously, it is very easy to construct problem statements that are not solvable without the introduction of extraneous material (judiciously called *assumptions*).
3. Thermodynamic problem statements tend to be very global. They can be written about virtually any type of system and can deal with virtually any form of technology. To give the problem statements a pragmatic engineering flavor they are usually written as tiny stories or *scenarios* that are designed to motivate as well as to educate the reader.

Unfortunately, many students facing thermodynamics for the first time are often overwhelmed by these factors. How are you supposed to know anything about how a nuclear power plant operates, or how the combustion chamber of a turbojet engine functions, or how a boiler feed pump works? The key here is that you really do not have to know much about any of these things to carry out a good thermodynamic analysis of them. But you do have to understand how problem statements are written and how to analyze them correctly. This is the technique of problem solving.

Actually, it would be possible to write a computer program that would solve any thermodynamic word problem. Instead, what we are going to do in this and the following chapter is to try to show you how to solve thermodynamic problems by using a computer-like flowchart approach.

The technique is really very simple. First you must learn to formulate a general starting point. Then you must learn to identify the key logical decisions that have to be made as the solution progresses. Finally, when all the analysis and algebraic manipulations are complete, you make the necessary calculations (paying close attention to units) to obtain the desired results.

The secret to solving thermodynamic problems is to *do the analysis first* and to *do the calculations last*, and not the other way around.

The basic elements of a problem statement that you must be able to identify are

1. The *unknowns*—what are you supposed to find?
2. The *system*—is it open or closed? Always draw a sketch of it.
3. If the system is closed, what are its *initial and final thermodynamic states*? If the system is open, what are its *inlet and outlet flowstream thermodynamic states*?
4. If the system is closed, what is the *process* that carries it from its initial to its final state? If the system is open, what is the *process* connecting the inlet and outlet flowstream states?

The steps that are to be followed are shown in Figure 4.6, and each step is discussed in detail below.

Step 1 *Start* Carefully read the problem statement completely through once.

Step 2 *Identify the unknown(s)* Now reread the problem statement and pick out all the things that you are supposed to determine. Write them down at the top of your work sheet.

Step 3 *Identify the system* Make a *sketch* of the device described in the problem statement on your work sheet. Then carefully define the part(s) you choose to analyze (i.e., the system) by inserting a dashed line as the system boundary. Now decide whether the system you have chosen is open or closed. Remember that it is often possible to convert from an open to a closed system (and vice versa) by a careful placement of the system boundary.

Step 4a *Closed system?* If your system is closed, identify as many of the state properties as you can. Most problems will have only two states (initial and final) but some will also have intermediate states that you will have to contend with. To keep the numerical values and units of the state properties straight, list each one under a "state" heading. For example, if you have a closed system that is initially at 14.7 psia with a specific volume of 0.5 ft^3/lbm and then by some process it ends up at 200 psia at a quality of 90%, you should write this information

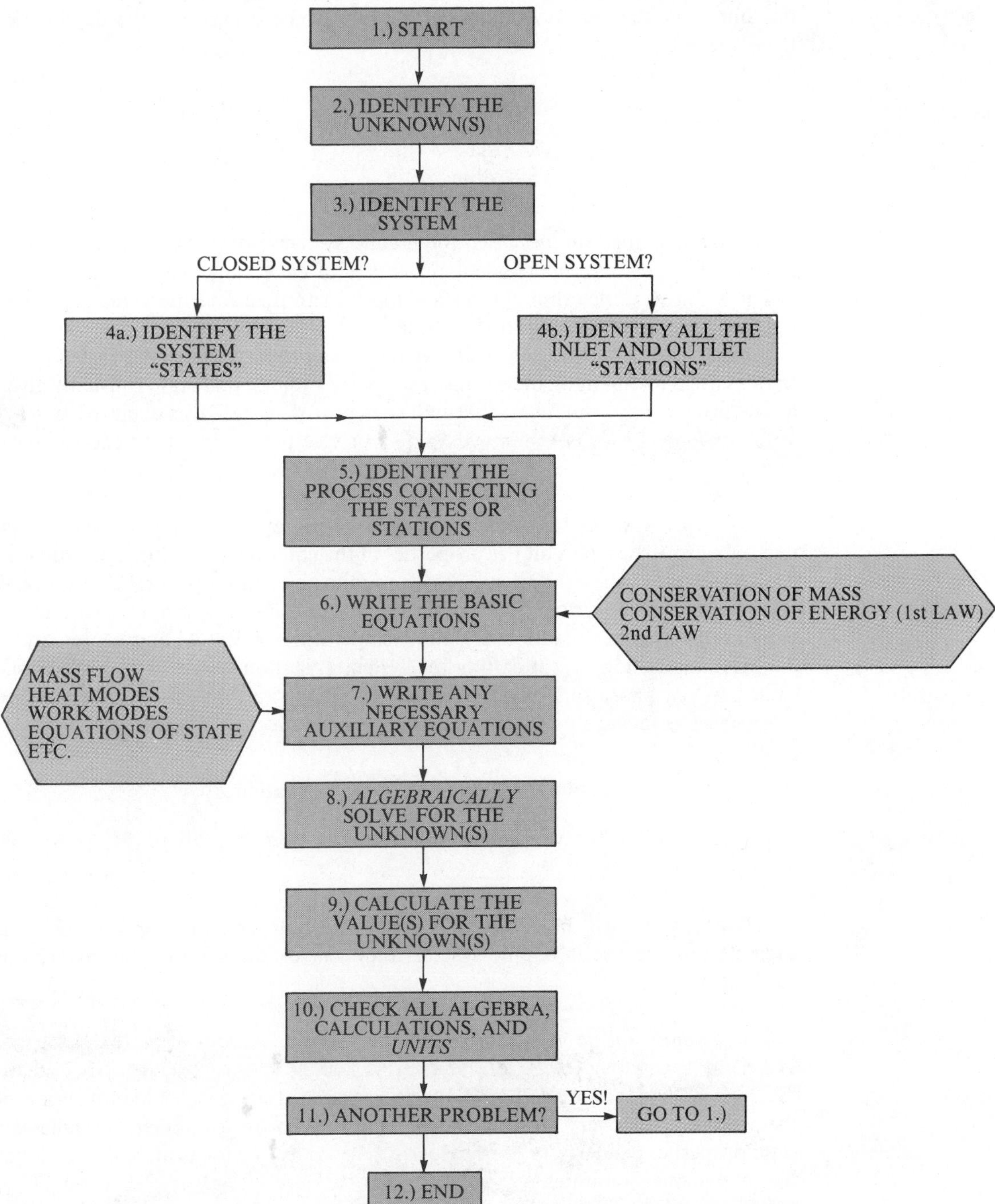

Figure 4.6 Flowchart for solving thermodynamic problems.

on your work sheet in the following form (always be sure to include the *units* on these values):

State 1	$\xrightarrow{\text{Process path}}$	**State 2**
$p_1 = 14.7$ psia		$p_2 = 200$ psia
$v_1 = 0.5$ ft^3/lbm		$x_2 = 0.9$

Notice that for "simple" thermodynamic systems we will always be looking for the values of two independent properties in each state. These two property values will fix (i.e., determine) the state and we can then find the values of any of the other properties needed at that state.

Often a problem statement will give only one property value at a system state. In this case the remaining independent property value at that state is usually given by the process path statement that indicates how that state was achieved (e.g., an isothermal process tells us that $T_2 = T_1$), or else it may be an unknown to be solved for.

Step 4b *Open system?* Here we are interested in any changes that occur in system bulk properties, plus all the properties of the entering and exiting flowstreams. Flowsteam properties are referred to as monitoring *station* properties, to clearly separate them from system bulk properties. For example, if you have a flowstream entering the system at station 1 with a temperature of 300 °C and a pressure of 1.0 MPa, and a flowstream exiting the system at station 2 with a specific volume of 26.3 m^3/kg and a quality of 99%, you should write this information on your work sheet as (always be sure to include the *units* on these values)

Station 1	$\xrightarrow{\text{Process path}}$	**Station 2**
$p_1 = 1.0$ MPa		$v_2 = 26.3$ m^3/kg
$T_1 = 300$ °C		$x_2 = 0.99$

Here, too, we will be trying to identify two independent property values at each station because in simple systems they will fix the state of the material at that station.

Step 5 *Identify the process connecting the state or stations* The process path statement is usually given in technical terms such as "a closed rigid vessel," meaning an isochoric (or constant volume) process will occur. Proper identification of the process path is very important because it often provides numerical values for state properties (e.g., $v_2 = v_1$ for a closed rigid vessel), or for heat, work, or other thermodynamic quantities (e.g., an insulated or adiabatic system would have ${}_1Q_2 = \dot{Q} = 0$, an aergonic system would have ${}_1W_2 = \dot{W} = 0$, and so forth). When two independent property values are given in the problem statement for each state and/or station of the system, then the process path is not necessary unless it provides values for heat, work, kinetic energy, or potential energy.

The easiest way to show the process path on your worksheet is as the statement "Process: process name" on a connecting arrow between the state or station data sets. In the example used in Step 4a above, if the state change occured in a closed rigid vessel and we did not know the final quality, then we would write

State 1	Process: v = constant →	State 2
$p_1 = 14.7$ psia		$p_2 = 200$ psia
$v_1 = 0.5$ ft^3/lbm		$v_2 = v_1 = 0.5$ ft^3/lbm

And if the system of step 4b above was operated at a constant pressure (i.e., an isobaric process) and we did not know the final quality, then we would write

Station 1	Process: p = constant →	Station 2
$p_1 = 1.0$ MPa		$v_2 = 26.3$ m^3/kg
$T_1 = 300$ °C		$p_2 = p_1 = 1.0$ MPa

Step 6 *Write the basic equations* At this point your worksheet should have all the details of the problem on it and you should not have to look at the problem statement again. The actual solution to the problem is begun by automatically writing down (whether you think you need them or not) all the relevant basic equations. In thermodynamics there are only three basic equations:

a) The *conservation of mass* (which is also called the mass balance)
b) The *first law of thermodynamics* (which is also called the energy balance and the conservation of energy)
c) The *second law of thermodynamics* (which is also called the entropy balance).

In closed systems the conservation of mass is automatically satisfied and need not be written down. Also, since the entropy balance will not be introduced until Chapter 5, it will not enter into the solution of any problems until then. So, for solving the closed system problems of Section II of this chapter there is really only one relevant basic equation—the first law of thermodynamics. For working the open system problems of Section III of this chapter there will be two relevant basic equations—the conservation of mass and the first law of thermodynamics.

Always write down the *general* form of the appropriate basic equations. Do not try to second guess the problem by writing specialized forms of the basic equations that were developed for specific applications. Then cross out all terms that vanish as a result of given constraints or process statements. For example, for a closed, adiabatic, stationary system we would write the energy balance as (see Eq. 4.20)

$$\underbrace{{}_1Q_2}_{0\ \text{(adiabatic)}} + {}_1W_2 = m(u_2 - u_1) + \underbrace{\mathrm{KE}_2 - \mathrm{KE}_1 + \mathrm{PE}_2 - \mathrm{PE}_1}_{0\ \text{(stationary)}}$$

Notice that we write why each crossed out term vanishes ("adiabatic" and "stationary" in this case). This makes the solution easier to follow and to check later if the correct answer was not obtained.

Step 7 *Write any necessary auxiliary equations* All the equations developed in this book that are not one of the three basic equations discussed above are called *auxiliary equations.* For example, all equations of state (ideal gas and incompressible materials), all work mode equations (mechanical, electrical, etc.), all heat mode equations (conduction, convection, radiation), all property-defining equations (specific heats, enthalpy, etc.), and all specialized equations (such as $\dot{m} = \rho AV$, $\text{KE} = \text{m}\text{V}^2/2g_c$, etc.) are auxiliary equations. If the problem statement describes a mechanical, electrical, etc., work mode, then write the equation for calculating the value of that work mode. Auxiliary equations ultimately provide numerical values for use in the basic mass, energy, and entropy balance equations.

Step 8 *Algebraically solve for the unknown(s)* By algebraically manipulating the basic and auxiliary equations you should be able to develop a separate equation for each unknown. Remember, you can solve for only as many unknowns as you have independent equations. All of the basic equations and most of the auxiliary equations are independent, so many times unknowns are determined directly from an auxiliary equation. For example, in the problem statements dealing with closed systems we will only have *one* applicable basic equation, the first law of thermodynamics (the energy balance). Therefore, if there is more than one unknown in these problem statements, then all but one of these unknowns must be determined directly from an appropriate auxiliary equation.

Incidentally, unlike in some other engineering subjects, you will not be able to find all the algebraic manipulations already done for you in example problems within the text or by the instructor in class. There are simply too many possible variations on a problem theme to do this. Therefore, you will have to carry out the mathematical manipulations suggested here to develop your own working formulae in almost every problem. This is a fact of thermodynamic problem solving.

Step 9 *Calculate the value(s) of the unknown(s)* Once all the algebra has been completed, then and only then should you begin to calculate numerical values. By this point you should be able to see your way to the end of the problem because the mechanism for finding each of the unknowns should now be clear. Determine the units on each value calculated and make sure that all values that are added together or subtracted from each other have the same units. Often one of the unknowns will be needed to find another; for example, you may need to find ${}_1W_2$ from a work mode auxiliary equation to solve for ${}_1Q_2$ from the energy balance equation.

Step 10 *Check all algebra, calculations, and units* This is self-explanatory but pay particular attention to checking the units. With the calculational accuracy of today's inexpensive electronic calculators and microcomputers, most of your errors will occur as a result of poor units handling rather than from numerical manipulations.

Step 11 *Another problem?* Is the assignment finished? If not, go back to step 1 and start again.

Step 12 *End* Recopy your work if necessary to provide an organized, neat and professional-looking result.

These twelve steps will lead you through even the most difficult thermodynamic problems. Once you become familiar with them the solutions will flow quite rapidly and naturally. It must be emphasized that these steps are not the only solution technique possible, but they have proven successful for many engineering students.

Problem Classifications

It would be helpful if we could categorize to some degree the wide variety of problems that are commonly encountered in thermodynamics. There are three effective bases upon which such a classification could be built. The first is classification by thermodynamic process, the second is classification by scenario (i.e., the story in the problem statement), and the third is classification by problem unknown (Q, W, etc.). Since the number of variations within these three bases is enormous, we will briefly discuss each before continuing.

Problem Classification by Thermodynamic Process A list of common thermodynamic processes used in most thermodynamic texts is given in Table 4.8. The entropy-based processes listed there will be explained in detail in the next chapter. Since many problems involve more than one process, or involve unknown processes, it is clearly not practical to base a classification scheme upon the process path alone.

Problem Classification by Problem Scenario Unfortunately, the list of possible engineering scenarios is much longer than the list of known processes. Consequently, a classification based on problem scenario is also doomed to failure because literally any device that obeys the continuum hypothesis (up to and including planetary systems) can be thermodynamically analyzed. However, over

Table 4.8 Common thermodynamic processes

Process name	Characteristic
Isochoric	Constant volume (e.g., a rigid vessel or container)
Isobaric	Constant pressure
Isothermal	Constant temperature
Isenthalpic	Constant enthalpy
Isentropic	Constant entropy
Polytropic	$P\mathcal{V}^n$ = constant
Adiabatic	No heat transport of energy (i.e., insulated)
Aergonic	No work transport of energy
Reversible	No entropy production

Table 4.9 Some typical thermodynamic scenarios

Scenario name	Characteristics
Piston in cylinder	a) When liquids are used this is known as *hydraulics.* b) When gases are used this is known as *pneumatics.* c) When vapors or chemical reactions occur this is known as an *engine.* d) The *p-v* relation must be known before $W = -m \int p\, dv$ can be evaluated.
Spring-loaded piston in cylinder	a) Comments a–d above apply here also. b) The work to or from the spring must be included in an energy balance.
Heaters and coolers (there are many different types)	a) Electrical heaters/coolers require an electrical work mode of energy transport. b) Simple two-fluid heat exchangers. c) Condensation or evaporation phase changes are commonly used as heaters/coolers.
Thermal mixing	a) The mixing of two or more components at different temperatures is usually done at constant pressure. b) Gases, vapors, liquids, and solids can be mixed simultaneously. c) Materials of different chemical composition can be thermally mixed.
Sealed rigid containers	a) Always have isochoric processes ($V\!\!\!/$ and m are constant). b) Always have zero mechanical moving boundary work because $V\!\!\!/ = \text{constant}$ and so $dV\!\!\!/ = 0$. c) May have mechanical work via a rotating shaft crossing the system boundary.
Nozzles	a) A nozzle converts pressure energy into kinetic energy. b) In subsonic flows they are formed with converging side walls.
Diffusers	a) A diffuser converts kinetic energy into pressure energy (usually to recover energy that would otherwise be lost). b) In subsonic flows they are formed with diverging side walls.
Throttling devices (there are many)	a) A throttling device is any device across which a large pressure drop occurs irreversibly. Thus, any flow control valve or other internal flow restriction is a throttling device. b) A throttling device is aergonic (i.e., does no work). c) An insulated throttling device with equal inlet and exit areas produces an isenthalpic process.
Turbines, heat pumps, air conditioners, and refrigerators	a) They are all engines running either forward or backward. b) Their main function is to transport energy (either work or heat) to or from a system.
Biological systems	a) They always generate thermal energy. b) They are always open systems.
Other energy conversion devices	a) Electrical: batteries, thermoelectric, etc. b) Chemical: fuel cells, combustion, etc.

the years a series of "typical" scenarios have been highlighted in engineering thermodynamics textbooks. They are listed in Table 4.9. This list is not exhaustive because obviously a very large number of such scenarios can be constructed.

Problem Classification by Problem Unknown Finally, we must consider possible classification by problem unknowns. The main unknowns are the variables carried within the first law formulae. The general closed system energy balance (EB) is given in Eq. 4.20 as

$$ {}_1Q_2 + {}_1W_2 = m\left[(u_2 - u_1) + \frac{V_2^2 - V_1^2}{2g_c} + \frac{g(Z_2 - Z_1)}{g_c}\right]_{\text{system}} \tag{4.20} $$

and the general closed system energy rate balance (ERB) is given in Eq. 4.21 as

$$ \dot{Q} + \dot{W} = (\dot{U} + \dot{\mathrm{KE}} + \dot{\mathrm{PE}})_{\text{system}} \tag{4.21} $$

Any of the variables listed in Eq. 4.20 or 4.21 can be an unknown in a problem statement. The number of variables (and possible unknowns) in an open system is equal to four times the number of flowstreams present (i.e., $\dot{m}$, h, V, and z for each flowstream) plus those listed in Eqs. 4.20 and 4.21. Thus, a problem classification scheme based upon problem unknown would be equally ineffective due to the large number of unknowns possible.

Since none of these classification schemes is significantly better than any other, they will not be pursued further. The illustrative examples presented in Sections II and III of this chapter are drawn from a variety of topics and do not represent any single classification base. They are designed to illustrate certain basic concepts rather than a specific problem classification technique.

Chapter Four Section II First Law Closed System Applications

In Section II of this chapter we present a series of detailed engineering analyses of the application of the first law of thermodynamics to closed systems. The purpose of this material is to demonstrate good thermodynamic problem-solving technique through a variety of worked examples. In the first three example problems that follow, the numbered steps in the solution are the same as the first nine steps shown in Figure 4.6. As we continue with the examples and the reader becomes more familiar with the technique we will condense the solutions by omitting the delineation of each solution step. In so doing we will also introduce some flexibility into the technique

Sealed Rigid Containers

One of the most innocuous technical incantations in basic thermodynamics is the phrase *sealed rigid container* (or *tank* or *vessel*). This phrase is composed of the following three technical terms:

1. *sealed*, meaning a *closed* system,
2. *rigid*, meaning the system has a *constant volume*; thus $\Psi =$ constant and $d\Psi = 0$, and consequently there is no moving boundary mechanical work (i.e., $-\int p\, d\Psi = 0$), and
3. *container* (sometimes tank or vessel), meaning *the system boundary lies inside the enclosure* because the material we want to analyze is inside the enclosure. Normally we are not given enough information about the enclosure itself (e.g., the material from which it is made) to be able to include it in our system and analysis.

The following example illustrates a typical problem of this type.

Example 4.12

STEP 1 Read the problem statement: A sealed rigid container whose volume is 1.0 m^3 contains 2.0 kg of liquid water plus water vapor at 20 °C. The container is heated until the temperature inside is 95 °C. Determine

a) the quality in the container when the contents are at 20 °C,
b) the quality in the container when the contents are at 95 °C, and
c) the heat transport of energy required to raise the temperature of the contents from 20 to 95 °C.

Solution

STEP 2 Here there are three unknowns: x_1, x_2, and ${}_1Q_2$.

STEP 3 Take the system to be the material *inside* the closed rigid container. Since we do not know the type or amount of material making up the container itself, the container cannot be part of the system. Also, since all of the unknowns pertain to the container's contents, detailed knowledge of the container's construction is not relevant to the solution.

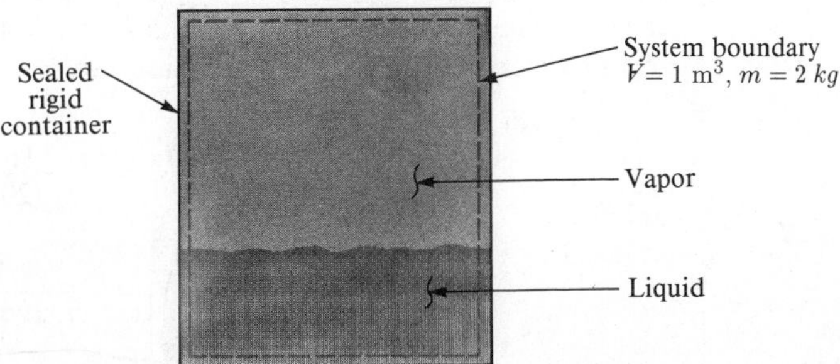

STEP 4a To fix the system's states we note that we are given the initial and final temperatures of the water, but to find other properties (such as quality) we will need the value of one more independent property in each state. Notice, however, that we are given both the total volume and the total mass, and that these do not change during the change of state. Therefore, we can calculate the system's specific volume in each state as

$$v_1 = v_2 = \forall/m = 1.0 \text{ m}^3/2.0 \text{ kg} = 0.5 \text{ m}^3/\text{kg}$$

Now we can write the states and process path as

State 1	Process: $v_1 = v_2 =$ constant →	**State 2**
$T_1 = 20$ °C		$T_2 = 95$ °C
$v_1 = 0.5$ m^3/kg		$v_2 = v_1 = 0.5$ m^3/kg

STEP 5 The process here is one of constant volume (the container was specified as rigid), and the process path has already been indicated on the state property value listing above.

STEP 6 The only basic equation we have thus far for closed systems is Eq. 4.20, the energy balance (EB) equation,

$$ {}_1Q_2 + {}_1W_2 = m[(u_2 - u_1) + \text{ke}_2 - \text{ke}_1 + \text{pe}_2 - \text{pe}_1]_{\text{system}} $$

In this case, nothing in the problem statement leads us to believe that the vessel undergoes any change in specific kinetic or potential energy during the heating process, so we will assume that $\text{ke}_2 = \text{ke}_1$ and $\text{pe}_2 = \text{pe}_1$. Also, since the container is rigid, $V =$ constant and $dV = 0$, then the mechanical moving boundary work is zero (i.e., $-\int p\,dV = 0$). Since no other work modes are suggested in the problem statement we will then assume that ${}_1W_2 = 0$. Applying these results to the general energy balance above yields the following simplified EB equation as the resulting governing equation for this problem.

$$ {}_1Q_2 = m(u_2 - u_1) $$

STEP 7 Since we now know the values of two independent properties in each state we can find the values of any other properties in those states by use of thermodynamic tables, charts, or equations of state. In particular, the qualities can be determined from the saturation tables and the auxiliary equations

$$ x_1 = \frac{v_1 - v_{f1}}{v_{fg1}} = \frac{v_1 - v_f(20\ ^\circ\text{C})}{v_{fg}(20\ ^\circ\text{C})} $$

and

$$ x_2 = \frac{v_2 - v_{f2}}{v_{fg2}} = \frac{v_2 - v_f(95\ ^\circ\text{C})}{v_{fg}(95\ ^\circ\text{C})} $$

Since we are not given enough information to use the conduction, convection, or radiation heat transfer equations, we must find ${}_1Q_2$ from the above energy balance. The values of u_1 and u_2 needed can be found by using the saturation tables and the following auxiliary equations:

$$ u_1 = u_{f1} + x_1 u_{fg1} = u_f(20\ ^\circ\text{C}) + x_1 u_{fg}(20\ ^\circ\text{C}) $$

and

$$ u_2 = u_{f2} + x_2 u_{fg2} = u_f(95\ ^\circ\text{C}) + x_2 u_{fg}(95\ ^\circ\text{C}) $$

STEP 8 At this point we have algebraic equations for all the unknowns, and we know where all the numbers in these equations are to be found.

STEP 9 We are now ready to make the calculations. From Appendix C.1*b* we find that

a) at 20 °C

$$ v_{f1} = 0.001002\ \text{m}^3/\text{kg} $$

$$ v_{g1} = 57.79\ \text{m}^3/\text{kg} $$

and

$$v_{fg1} = v_{g1} - v_{f1} = 57.789 \text{ m}^3/\text{kg}$$

Also,

$$u_{f1} = 83.9 \text{ kJ/kg}$$

$$u_{g1} = 2402.9 \text{ kJ/kg}$$

and

$$u_{fg1} = u_{g1} - u_{f1} = 2319.0 \text{ kJ/kg}$$

b) at 95 °C

$$v_{f2} = 0.00104 \text{ m}^3/\text{kg}$$

$$v_{g2} = 1.982 \text{ m}^3/\text{kg}$$

and

$$v_{fg2} = v_{g2} - v_{f2} = 1.981 \text{ m}^3/\text{kg}$$

Also,

$$u_{f2} = 397.9 \text{ kJ/kg}$$

$$u_{g2} = 2500.6 \text{ kJ/kg}$$

and

$$u_{fg2} = u_{g2} - u_{f2} = 2102.7 \text{ kJ/kg}$$

So the unknowns can now be determined as

a) $$x_1 = \frac{0.5 - 0.001}{57.789} = 8.63 \times 10^{-3} = 0.863\%$$

b) $$x_2 = \frac{0.5 - 0.00104}{1.981} = 0.2519 = 25.19\%$$

c) $$u_1 = 83.9 + (8.63 \times 10^{-3})(2319.0) = 103.9 \text{ kJ/kg}$$

and

$$u_2 = 397.9 + (0.2519)(2102.7) = 927.6 \text{ kJ/kg}$$

so that

$$\begin{aligned} {}_1Q_2 &= m(u_2 - u_1) \\ &= (2.0 \text{ kg})(927.6 - 103.9 \text{ kJ/kg}) = 1647 \text{ kJ} \end{aligned}$$

Electrical Devices

There are a vast number of closed and open systems whose primary work mode is electrical. We call these systems *electrical devices*, and recognize that one of the appropriate auxiliary equations to be used in their analysis is the electrical work or power mode equation introduced earlier. The following example illustrates a typical closed system electrical device problem.

Example 4.13

STEP 1 Read the problem statement: An incandescent light bulb is a simple electrical device. Using the energy rate balance on a light bulb determine

a) the heat transfer rate of an illuminated 100-W incandescent light bulb in a room, and

b) the rate of change of its internal energy if this bulb were put into a small sealed insulated box.

Solution

STEP 2 The unknowns are **a)** $\dot{Q}$ and **b)** $\dot{U}$.

STEP 3 The system in each case is the entire light bulb, the glass bulb plus its contents, rather than just the contents as in the first example.

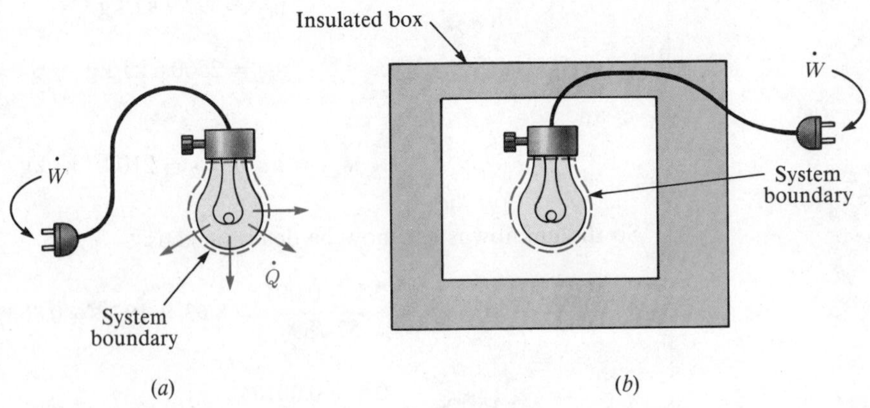

(*a*) (*b*)

STEP 4a This is a closed system for which we are not given specific thermodynamic properties in the problem statement. Presumably they are not needed in the solution.

STEP 5 The following processes occur:

- In part a: The bulb does not change its thermodynamic state so its properties must remain constant. In particular, the process path (after the bulb has warmed to its operating temperature) is $U =$ constant.
- In part b: The bulb is insulated so it undergoes an adiabatic (i.e., $\dot{Q} = 0$) process.

STEP 6 The only basic equation thus far available for a closed system rate process is Eq. 4.21, the general closed system energy rate balance (ERB) equation,

$$\dot{Q} + \dot{W} = \dot{U} + \dot{\text{KE}} + \dot{\text{PE}}$$

Since both parts a and b imply that the light bulb is to be stationary during analysis, we will assume $\dot{\text{KE}} = \dot{\text{PE}} = 0$. This reduces the governing ERB equation for this problem to

$$\dot{Q} + \dot{W} = \dot{U} = \frac{d}{dt}(mu)$$

STEP 7 The only relevant auxiliary equation needed here is the recognition that the light bulb has an electrical work *input* of 100 W, so that

$$\dot{W} = 100 \text{ W}$$

STEP 8 Algebraically solving for the unknowns we have for part a,

$$\dot{Q} = \dot{U} - \dot{W}$$

and for part b,

$$\dot{U} = \dot{Q} + \dot{W}$$

STEP 9 Since we are assuming a constant bulb temperature in part a, then U = constant and $\dot{U} = 0$. Then our calculations give

$$\textbf{a)} \quad \dot{Q} = -\dot{W} = -100 \text{ W}$$

(the minus sign tells us that the heat is *leaving* the system). Thus, all the electrical work put into a lighting system ends up as heat. Architects use the lighting within a building to supply part of the heating requirements of the building.

In the second part of this problem the bulb is inside a small insulated box, so it cannot transport any heat energy through its boundaries. Thus, $\dot{Q} = 0$ here (the bulb undergoes an adiabatic process), and the reduced ERB yields

$$\textbf{b)} \quad \dot{U} = \dot{W} = 100 \text{ W}$$

Consequently, the internal energy of the light bulb must increase at a rate of 100 J/s. This means that its temperature must continually increase. Treating the bulb as a simple incompressible substance we can write (see Eq. 3.61)

$$\dot{U} = mc\dot{T} = 100 \text{ W}$$

where m is the mass of the bulb, c is its specific heat, and $\dot{T}$ is the time rate of change of its temperature. Thus, so long as $\dot{U}$ is constant and positive the temperature of the bulb continually increases until the glass or the filament eventually melts.

Power Plants

An electrical power-generating facility is a very complex set of open and closed systems. However, if the entire facility is taken to be the system and the system boundaries are carefully chosen, then it can be modeled as a closed system. We call such systems *power plants*, and a simple thermodynamic analysis can provide important information about their operation, as the next example illustrates.

Example 4.14

STEP 1 Read the problem statement: A basic vapor cycle power plant consists of the following four parts:

a) the boiler where high-pressure vapor is produced,
b) the turbine where energy is removed from the high-pressure vapor as shaft work,
c) the condenser where the low-pressure vapor leaving the turbine is condensed into a liquid, and
d) the boiler feed pump that pumps the condensed liquid back into the high-pressure boiler for reheating.

In such a power plant the boiler receives 950,000 Btu/h from the burning fuel, and the condenser rejects 600,000 Btu/h to the environment. The boiler feed pump requires a 30-hp input, which it receives directly from the turbine. Assuming that the turbine, pump, and connecting pipes are all insulated, determine the net power of the turbine.

Solution

STEP 2 The unknown here is $(\dot{W}_T)_{net}$.

STEP 3 The system is the entire power plant. If we choose only the turbine as the system it would be an open system and we do not wish to deal with open systems until Section III of this chapter.

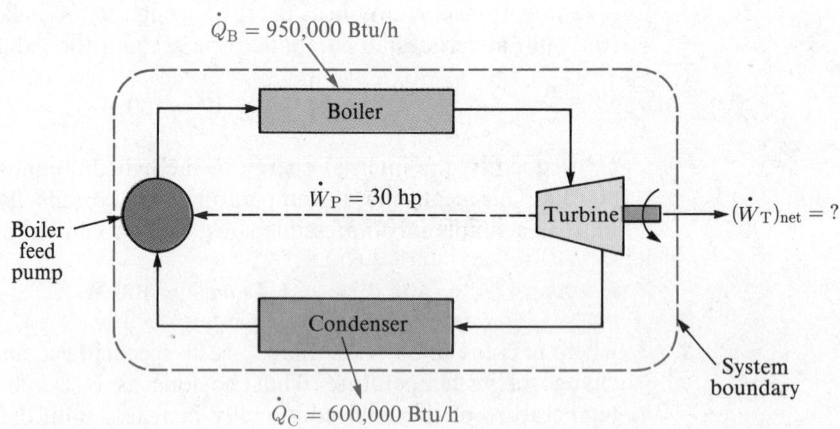

STEP 4a This is a closed system, and no specific information is given to identify the thermodynamic states of the system. Presumably it is not needed in the solution.

STEP 5 We assume a steady state process with no changes in kinetic or potential energy. Then U, KE, and PE are all constants.

STEP 6 The only basic equation applicable here is the general closed system energy rate balance (ERB), Eq. 4.21,

$$\dot{Q} + \dot{W} = \underset{0}{\dot{U}} + \underset{0}{\dot{KE}} + \underset{0}{\dot{PE}} = 0$$

which reduces to

$$\dot{W}_{\text{net}} = -\dot{Q}_{\text{net}} = (\dot{W}_{\text{T}})_{\text{net}}$$

STEP 7 No auxiliary equations are needed here.

STEP 8 Algebraically solving for the net power of the turbine gives

$$(\dot{W}_{\text{T}})_{\text{net}} = -\dot{Q}_{\text{net}} = -(\dot{Q}_{\text{B}} + \dot{Q}_{\text{C}})$$

STEP 9 The calculations then give

$$(\dot{W}_{\text{T}})_{\text{net}} = -[950{,}000 + (-600{,}000)]\ \text{Btu/h} = -350{,}000\ \text{Btu/h}$$

$$= (-350{,}000\ \text{Btu/h})\left(\frac{1\ \text{hp}}{2545\ \text{Btu/h}}\right) = -137.5\ \text{hp}$$

The negative sign tells us that the net power is coming *out* of the turbine

To simplify the solutions from this point on we will omit the description of each step in the solution technique. The steps will all be there, but now the solutions will flow in a more continuous manner.

Incompressible Liquids

Perhaps the auxiliary equations most often used in thermodynamic analysis are equations of state. The two most common equations of state are those for ideal gases and incompressible liquids. Since most students are more familiar with ideal gases than they are incompressible liquids, we have chosen the next example to illustrate the latter case. Note that this example could also be described as another illustration of the analysis of an electrical device.

Example 4.15 A food processor has a cutting/mixing blade driven by a 0.25-hp electric motor. The machine is initially filled with 1.0 quart of water at 60 °F, 14.7 psia. It is then turned on at full speed for 10 min. Assuming the entire machine is insulated and that the mixing takes place at constant pressure, determine the temperature of the water when the machine is turned off.

Solution

- Unknown: T_2
- System: Closed, the 1.0 quart of water.

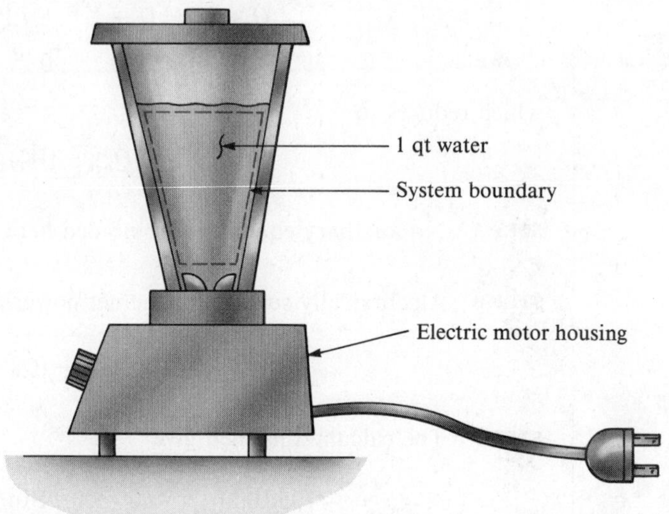

The system states and processes are

State 1	Process: Constant pressure → mechanical mixing	State 2
$p_1 = 14.7$ psia		$p_2 = p_1 = 14.7$ psia
$T_1 = 60$ °F		

Note that in this problem we do not know the values of two independent properties in the second state, nor does the process path give us any information about an additional second-state property. This example illustrates how the energy balance itself can be used to find the value of a state property.

The basic energy balance (EB) equation for this system is

$$ {}_1Q_2 + {}_1W_2 = m(u_2 - u_1) + \text{KE}_2 - \text{KE}_1 + \text{PE}_2 - \text{PE}_1 $$

Since we were given no information about the kinetic or potential energies of the system, we will assume that they do not change during the process under analysis, that is, that $\text{KE}_2 - \text{KE}_1 = \text{PE}_2 - \text{PE}_1 = 0$.

The auxiliary equations needed here are for the heat and work energy transport modes. They are ${}_1Q_2 = 0$ (insulated system), and in this case the work mode is shaft work, but it can be calculated from the definition of power as ${}_1W_2 = \dot{W}(\Delta t)$, where Δt is the time interval of the process.

Since 14.7 psia is much greater than the saturation pressure at 60 °F (0.2563 psia) state 1 is seen to be a compressed liquid. We could find u_1 by interpolating the pressure between the saturation and compressed liquid tables at 60 °F, and then use the energy balance to find u_2. Then with u_2 and p_2 we could presumably find T_2 by again interpolating in these tables. Or else we could treat the water as a simple incompressible material and use the auxiliary equation for specific heat (Eq. 3.61), $u_2 - u_1 = c(T_2 - T_1)$. The latter approach is the simplest in this case, so we will use it and take the specific heat of water to be 1.0 Btu/(lbm·R).

The mass of one quart of water at 60 °F is given by $m = \rho V = V/v$, where

$$V = (1.0 \text{ qt})\left(\frac{1 \text{ gal}}{4 \text{ qt}}\right)(0.13368 \text{ ft}^3/\text{gal}) = 0.03342 \text{ ft}^3$$

and

$$v = v_f(60\ °\text{F}) = 0.01603 \text{ ft}^3/\text{lbm} \qquad \text{(from Appendix C.1}a\text{)}$$

Therefore,

$$m = \frac{0.03342 \text{ ft}^3}{0.01603 \text{ ft}^3/\text{lbm}} = 2.085 \text{ lbm}$$

Then the energy balance gives

$$u_2 - u_1 = c(T_2 - T_1) = \frac{{}_1Q_2}{m} + \frac{{}_1W_2}{m}$$

and

$$T_2 = T_1 + \frac{{}_1Q_2}{mc} + \frac{{}_1W_2}{mc}$$

$$= 60\ °\text{F} + 0 + \frac{(0.25 \text{ hp})(10 \text{ min})(1 \text{ h}/60 \text{ min})[2545 \text{ Btu}/(\text{hp}\cdot\text{h})]}{(2.085 \text{ lbm})[1.0 \text{ Btu}/(\text{lbm}\cdot\text{R})]}$$

$$= 111\ °\text{F}$$

Piston–Cylinder Devices

One of the oldest pieces of effective technology is the piston in cylinder apparatus. It was used in early Roman pumps, and its use in the steam engine of the eighteenth century brought about the industrial revolution. It is still commonly used today in piston-type pumps and compressors, and in a wide variety of internal and external combustion engines. The following example illustrates its use in a refrigeration process.

Example 4.16 0.1 lbm of Refrigerant-12 initially at 180 °F and 100 psia in a cylinder with a movable piston undergoes the following two-part process. First, the refrigerant is expanded adiabatically to 30 psia and 120 °F, and then it is isobarically compressed to half its initial volume.

Determine:

a) the work transport of energy during the adiabatic expansion,
b) the heat transport of energy during the isobaric compression, and
c) the final temperature at the end of the isobaric compression.

Solution This is an example of a multiple-part process.

- Unknowns: **a)** ${}_1W_2$, **b)** ${}_2Q_3$, and **c)** T_3.
- System: The refrigerant in the cylinder.

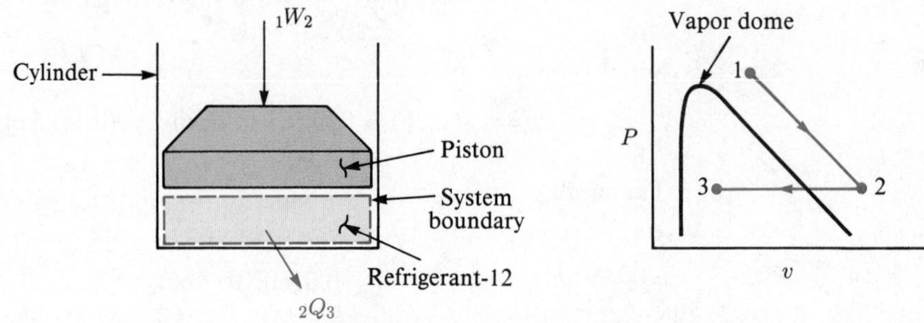

Because this is a two-part process there are three states involved, as shown below.

State 1	Process: Adiabatic expansion →	State 2	Process: Isobaric compression →	State 3
$p_1 = 100$ psia $T_1 = 180$ °F		$p_2 = 30$ psia $T_2 = 120$ °F		$p_3 = p_2 = 30$ psia $v_3 = v_1/2$

The basic EB equations for these two processes are

$${}_1Q_2 + {}_1W_2 = m(u_2 - u_1) + \mathrm{KE}_2 - \mathrm{KE}_1 + \mathrm{PE}_2 - \mathrm{PE}_1$$

and

$${}_2Q_3 + {}_2W_3 = m(u_3 - u_2) + \mathrm{KE}_3 - \mathrm{KE}_2 + \mathrm{PE}_3 - \mathrm{PE}_2$$

Since we are not given any potential or kinetic energy information we will assume that no changes occur in these variables. As auxiliary equations we have ${}_1Q_2 = 0$ (because the process from state 1 to state 2 is adiabatic), and consequently the resulting EB equation for the solution to part a is

$${}_1W_2 = m(u_2 - u_1)$$

Also, since the process from state 2 to state 3 is isobaric, then work for this process is given by ${}_2W_3 = -m\int_2^3 p\,dv = -mp_3(v_3 - v_2)$ and the EB for the process from 2 to 3 gives the formula for the solution to part b as

$$ {}_2Q_3 = m(u_3 - u_2) + mp_3(v_3 - v_2) $$

The solution to part c must be determined from the values of the independent properties p_3 and v_3, and the use of the R-12 tables. From Appendix C.8*a* we find that at $p_1 = 100$ psia and $T_1 = 180$ °F, $v_1 = 0.52291$ ft³/lbm, and $h_1 = 102.257$ Btu/lbm. Then we can calculate the value of u_1 from the definition of the specific enthalpy as

$$ \begin{aligned} u_1 &= h_1 - p_1 v_1 \\ &= 102.257\ \text{Btu/lbm} - (100\ \text{lbf/in}^2)(144\ \text{in}^2/\text{ft}^2)(0.52291\ \text{ft}^3/\text{lbm})\left(\frac{1\ \text{Btu}}{778\ \text{ft}\cdot\text{lbf}}\right) \\ &= 92.578\ \text{Btu/lbm} \end{aligned} $$

Similarly, at $p_2 = 30$ psia and $T_2 = 120$ °F we find from Appendix C.8*a* that $v_2 = 1.6600$ ft³/lbm and $h_2 = 94.843$ Btu/lbm, then

$$ \begin{aligned} u_2 &= h_2 - p_2 v_2 \\ &= 94.843\ \text{Btu/lbm} - (30\ \text{lbf/in}^2)(144\ \text{in}^2/\text{ft}^2)(1.6600\ \text{ft}^3/\text{lbm})\left(\frac{1\ \text{Btu}}{778\ \text{ft}\cdot\text{lbf}}\right) \\ &= 85.626\ \text{Btu/lbm} \end{aligned} $$

The final answers are

a) $$ \begin{aligned} {}_1W_2 &= m(u_2 - u_1) \\ &= (0.1\ \text{lbm})(85.626 - 92.578\ \text{Btu/lbm}) = -0.695\ \text{Btu} \end{aligned} $$

b) $$ {}_2Q_3 = m(u_3 - u_2) + mp_3(v_3 - v_2) $$

where we already have numerical values for m, u_2, p_3, and v_2, but we also need values for v_3 and u_3. From the problem statement for the process from 2 to 3 we find that

$$ v_3 = \frac{v_1}{2} = 0.2615\ \text{ft}^3/\text{lbm} $$

From Appendix C.7*a* we find that since state 3 is at 30 psia,

$$ v_f(30\ \text{psia}) < v_3 < v_g(30\ \text{psia}) $$

consequently state 3 is a mixture of liquid plus vapor. It therefore has a quality given by

$$x_3 = \frac{v_3 - v_{f3}}{v_{fg3}}$$

Interpolating in Appendix C.7*a* at 30 psia we get $v_{f3} = 0.01117\ \text{ft}^3/\text{lbm}$, $v_{g3} = 1.3007\ \text{ft}^3/\text{lbm}$, $h_{f3} = 10.910$ Btu/lbm, and $h_{g3} = 78.444$ Btu/lbm so that

$$\begin{aligned} u_{f3} &= h_{f3} - p_{3\text{sat}}v_{f3} \\ &= 10.910\ \text{Btu/lbm} - (30\ \text{lbf/in}^2)(144\ \text{in}^2/\text{ft}^2)(0.01117\ \text{ft}^3/\text{lbm})\left(\frac{1\ \text{Btu}}{778\ \text{ft}\cdot\text{lbf}}\right) \\ &= 10.848\ \text{Btu/lbm} \end{aligned}$$

and

$$\begin{aligned} u_{g3} &= h_{g3} - p_{3\text{sat}}v_{g3} \\ &= 78.444\ \text{Btu/lbm} - (30\ \text{lbf/in}^2)(144\ \text{in}^2/\text{ft}^2)(1.3007\ \text{ft}^3/\text{lbm})\left(\frac{1\ \text{Btu}}{778\ \text{ft}\cdot\text{lbf}}\right) \\ &= 71.222\ \text{Btu/lbm} \end{aligned}$$

We can now calculate the quality at state 3 as

$$x_3 = \frac{0.2615\ \text{ft}^3/\text{lbm} - 0.01117\ \text{ft}^3/\text{lbm}}{1.3007\ \text{ft}^3/\text{lbm} - 0.01117\ \text{ft}^3/\text{lbm}} = 0.1941 = 19.41\%$$

Finally, we get the other state 3 properties as

$$\begin{aligned} u_3 &= u_{f3} + x_3 u_{fg3} \\ &= 10.848\ \text{Btu/lbm} + 0.1941(71.222 - 10.848\ \text{Btu/lbm}) \\ &= 22.567\ \text{Btu/lbm}, \end{aligned}$$

and then

$$\begin{aligned} {}_2Q_3 &= m(u_3 - u_2) + mp_3(v_3 - v_2) \\ &= (0.1\ \text{lbm})(22.567 - 85.626\ \text{Btu/lbm}) \\ &\quad + (0.1\ \text{lbm})(30\ \text{lbf/in}^2)(144\ \text{in}^2/\text{ft}^2)(0.2615 - 1.6600\ \text{ft}^3/\text{lbm})\left(\frac{1\ \text{Btu}}{778\ \text{ft}\cdot\text{lbf}}\right) \\ &= -7.082\ \text{Btu} \end{aligned}$$

c) Since state 3 is saturated (a mixture of liquid and vapor), T_3 must be equal to the saturation temperature at 30 psia. Interpolating in the pressure—temperature data of Appendix C.7*a* gives T_3 as

$$\frac{T_3 - 10\ °F}{20\ °F - 10\ °F} = \frac{30.0\ \text{psia} - 29.335\ \text{psia}}{35.736\ \text{psia} - 29.335\ \text{psia}}$$

or

$$T_3 = 11.04\ °F$$

Closed System Unsteady State Processes

One of the most difficult thermodynamic processes to analyze is an unsteady state process. This is largely due to the fact that there are many more unknowns in these processes. In addition, they usually involve integrating the rate form of the basic equations, so some knowledge of the solution techniques for ordinary differential equations is essential before a complete thermodynamic analysis can be carried out. The following example about a nonexistent automotive "muffler bearing" illustrates this type of problem.

Example 4.17

The muffler bearing of a 1923 Detroit Electric automobile consists of a 1-ft-diameter rigid hollow steel sphere of negligible wall thickness. During its fabrication the bearing undergoes a heat-treating operation in which it is initially filled with helium at 20 psia and 200 °F, and then it is plunged into cold water at 50 °F for 5 s. The convective heat transfer coefficient of the sphere in the water is 2.0 Btu/(h·ft^2·R). Neglecting any changes in kinetic or potential energy and assuming the helium behaves as an ideal gas, determine

a) the final temperature of the helium, and
b) the change in total internal energy of the helium.

Solution

- Unknowns: After 5 s have passed, **a)** $T_2 = ?$ and **b)** $U_2 - U_1 = ?$
- System: The helium in the sphere.

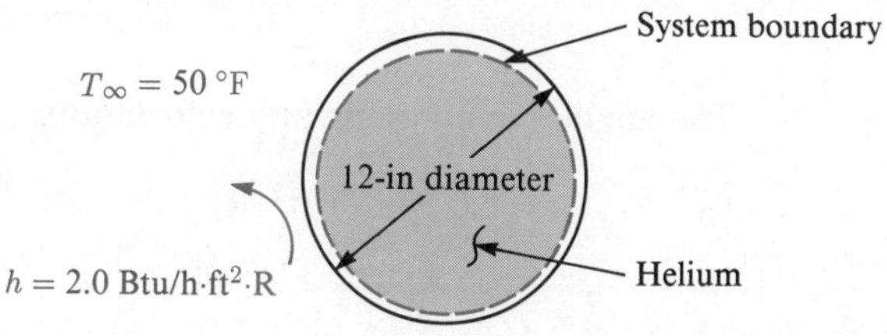

The basic equations here are the closed system energy balance (EB)

$$_1Q_2 + {}_1W_2 = U_2 - U_1 + \underbrace{KE_2 - KE_1 + PE_2 - PE_1}_{\text{Neglect}}$$

and the closed system energy rate balance (ERB)

$$\dot{Q} + \dot{W} = \dot{U} \quad \text{(neglecting } \dot{\text{KE}} \text{ and } \dot{\text{PE}}\text{)}$$

The auxiliary equations needed here are

1. the mechanical work mode

$${}_1W_2 = \dot{W} = 0 \quad \text{(a rigid hollow sphere)}$$

2. the convective heat transfer mode

$$\dot{Q} = -hA(T_s - T_\infty) \quad \text{(the negative sign is necessary here because the helium loses heat)}$$

3. Assuming the helium to be an ideal gas, then the internal energy can be represented as $\Delta u = c_v(\Delta T)$, and then $\dot{U} = m\dot{u} = mc_v\dot{T}_s$. Putting these results into the ERB equation gives (assuming T_∞ = constant)

$$\dot{Q} = -hA(T_s - T_\infty) = \dot{U} = mc_v\dot{T}_s$$

or

$$\dot{T}_s = \frac{dT_s}{dt} = \frac{d(T_s - T_\infty)}{dt} = -\frac{hA}{mc_v}(T_s - T_\infty)$$

This is a first-order ordinary differential equation with the initial condition $T_s = T_1$ when $t = 0$. Its solution is

$$T_s = (T_1 - T_\infty)\exp\left(-\frac{hAt}{mc_v}\right) + T_\infty$$

where $T_2 = T_s$ at $t = 5$ s. The remaining part of the solution is given by the EB equation as

$$U_2 - U_1 = mc_v(T_2 - T_1)$$

The auxiliary equations and calculations are

$$h = 2.0 \text{ Btu/(h·ft}^2\text{·R)}$$

$$T_\infty = 50\ ^\circ\text{F}$$

$$\forall = \frac{\pi}{6}(D)^3 = \frac{\pi}{6}(1 \text{ ft})^3 = 0.5236 \text{ ft}^3$$

$$A = \pi D^2 = \pi(1 \text{ ft})^2 = 3.1416 \text{ ft}^2 \quad \text{(the surface area of a sphere)}$$

$$c_v = 0.744 \text{ Btu/(lbm·R)} \quad \text{(from Appendix C.13}a\text{)}$$

And from the ideal gas equation of state for helium, $m = PV/RT$, Appendix C.13*a* gives $R = 386.0$ ft·lbf/(lbm·R). Then

$$m = \frac{(20 \text{ lbf/in}^2)(144 \text{ in}^2/\text{ft}^2)(0.5236 \text{ ft}^3)}{[386.0 \text{ ft}\cdot\text{lbf/(lbm}\cdot\text{R)}][(200 + 460) \text{ R}]} = 5.92 \times 10^{-3} \text{ lbm}$$

$$\frac{hA}{mc_v} = \frac{[2.0 \text{ Btu/(h}\cdot\text{ft}^2\cdot\text{R)}](3.1416 \text{ ft}^2)}{(5.92 \times 10^{-3} \text{ lbm})[0.744 \text{ Btu/(lbm}\cdot\text{R)}]} = 1427 \text{ h}^{-1}$$

And at $t = 5$ s,

$$\begin{aligned} T_2 &= (T_1 - T_\infty)\exp(-hAt/mc_v) + T_\infty \\ &= [(200 - 50)\ {}^\circ\text{F}]\exp\left[-(1427 \text{ h}^{-1})\left(\frac{5 \text{ s}}{3600 \text{ s/h}}\right)\right] + 50\ {}^\circ\text{F} \\ &= 70.7\ {}^\circ\text{F} \end{aligned}$$

Then,

$$\begin{aligned} U_2 - U_1 &= mc_v(T_2 - T_1) \\ &= (5.92 \times 10^{-3} \text{ lbm})[0.744 \text{ Btu/(lbm}\cdot\text{R)}][(70.7 - 200)\ {}^\circ\text{F}] \\ &= -0.569 \text{ Btu} \end{aligned}$$

The Explosive Energy of Pressure Vessels

The explosion of a pressure vessel such as a steam boiler is an example of a very unsteady state process. But since it is such an important topic from a safety point of view, it will be treated as a separate subject here.

Not many engineers realize just how dangerous a high-pressure gas or vapor can be. The explosive energy of a pressure vessel is defined to be its capacity to do work adiabatically on its surroundings. Consider a pressure vessel whose initial state is just before the explosion and whose final state is immediately after all the debris has come to rest and thermodynamic equilibrium has beeen reestablished. The explosion process is considered to be adiabatic with no net change in system kinetic or potential energies. The explosive energy can be determined from the closed system energy balance as

$$\text{explosive energy} = -{}_1W_2 = m(u_1 - u_2)$$

where we have introduced the minus sign because we want the work done by the system on the environment, not that done on the system. The explosive energy per initial unit volume of the pressure vessel is defined to be Γ, where

$$\Gamma = m(u_1 - u_2)/V_1 = (u_1 - u_2)/v_1 \qquad \textbf{(4.82)}$$

If the pressure vessel contains an ideal gas with constant specific heats, then Eqs. 3.37 and 3.63b can be used to give the explosive energy per unit volume as

$$(\Gamma)_{\text{ideal gas}} = c_v(T_1 - T_2)/(RT_1/p_1) = p_1(1 - T_2/T_1)/(k - 1) \quad \textbf{(4.83)}$$

where $R/c_v = k - 1$. If, on the other hand, the pressure vessel contains an incompressible liquid, then Eq. 3.61 can be used to give

$$(\Gamma)_{\substack{\text{incompressible}\\ \text{liquid}}} = c(T_1 - T_2)/v = \rho c(T_1 - T_2) \quad \textbf{(4.84)}$$

A liquid that does not change phase during decompression will undergo the process very nearly isothermally, so $T_2 = T_1$ and its explosive energy is zero. Thus, the explosive energy of high-pressure liquids is very slight in comparison with gases and vapors at the same pressure, and this is why liquids are often used to hydrostatically test pressure vessels to failure.

Example 4.18

On March 10, 1905, a catastrophic boiler explosion occurred in a shoe factory in Brockton, Massachusetts, that killed 58 and injured 117 people. This and similar explosions brought about the development of the ASME Boiler and Pressure Vessel Code in 1915. Suppose that the Brockton shoe factory had a 250-ft^3 boiler, and that right before the explosion it contained superheated steam at 600 psia and 800 °F. After the explosion the steam quickly condensed into saturated liquid water at 70 °F.

a) Determine the explosive energy per unit volume of superheated steam.

b) How many 1-lbm sticks of TNT would it take to equal the explosion of the boiler? The explosive energy per unit mass of TNT is 1400 Btu/lbm.

Solution

a) From the superheated steam table, Appendix C.3*a*, we find that at 600 psia and 800 °F

$$u_1 = 1275.4 \text{ Btu/lbm}$$

$$v_1 = 1.190 \text{ ft}^3\text{/lbm}$$

and from the saturated steam table, Appendix C.1a, we have

$$u_2 = u_f(70\ °\text{F}) = 38.1 \text{ Btu/lbm}$$

so Eq. 4.82 gives

$$\Gamma = (1275.4 - 38.1 \text{ Btu/lbm})/(1.190 \text{ ft}^3\text{/lbm}) = 1039.7 \text{ Btu/ft}^3$$

b) For a 250-ft^3 boiler, the explosive energy is then

$$(1039.7 \text{ Btu/ft}^3)(250 \text{ ft}^3) = 2.6 \times 10^5 \text{ Btu}$$

Therefore. it would take $(2.6 \times 10^5 \text{ Btu})/(1400 \text{ Btu/lbm}) = 186$ one-pound sticks of TNT to match the boiler explosion.

Chapter Four Section III — First Law Open System Applications

Section III of this chapter contains detailed solutions to a variety of classical open system thermodynamic problems. These solutions use the generalized problem-solving procedure discussed in Sections I and II (see Figure 4.6) and focus on illustrating the use of the conservation of mass law and the first law of thermodynamics. The availability of these two basic equations plus many auxiliary formulae means that there are usually more unknowns to be solved for in open system problems than in closed system problems.

Open system problems are written with their flowstream thermodynamic properties evaluated at inlet and outlet data-monitoring stations. This is done in an attempt to simulate the way in which engineering data are provided from experimental or field measurements. The bulk properties inside an open system will not normally change from one equilibrium thermodynamic state to another during the process of interest as do closed system bulk properties. In fact, the vast majority of open systems of engineering interest are not in any equilibrium state since the thermodynamic properties of the material passing through them are continually changing inside the system between the inlet and the outlet flowstreams. However, most open systems do reach a "steady state" nonequilibrium operating condition in which the total mass and energy that they contain does not change with time. Any open or closed system can be indefinitely maintained in a steady nonequilibrium state if it has the proper energy transports and/or mass flows passing through it.

In addition, many thermodynamic properties are only mathematically defined for equilibrium conditions. If the steady-state properties within a system do not exhibit large variations between two neighboring points, then we say that these points are in *local thermodynamic equilibrium*. The local equilibrium postulate introduced earlier in this chapter states that a small volume large enough for the continuum hypothesis to hold is in local equilibrium so long as its internal properties do not vary significantly within its borders. This means that the properties cannot change significantly in a distance of the order of the molecular mean free path at the point in question.[12] Most nonequilibrium processes of engineering interest obey this postulate. A few systems, such as those containing shock waves, do not. For example, if rapid explosions occur within a piston–cylinder apparatus (as in an internal combustion engine) or if the piston speed exceeds the speed of sound in the cylinder, then the gas in the cylinder is far from equilibrium and an accurate thermodynamic analysis becomes very difficult, from both a measurement and a theoretical point of view.

Mass Flow Energy Transport

Mass flow energy transport occurs whenever mass crosses the system boundary. It consists of two parts. The first part is the total energy associated with the flowstream mass itself, and the second is the energy required to push the flowstream mass across the system boundary (this part is often called the *flow work*). Let an increment of flowstream mass dm be added to or removed from a system. The total energy dE_{m} associated with dm crossing the system boundary is given by

$$dE_{\mathrm{m}} = (u + \mathrm{ke} + \mathrm{pe})\, dm$$

Figure 4.7 shows an incremental slug of mass with velocity $\mathbf{V}$ crossing a system boundary. The slug's volume is $d\mathcal{V} = A\, dL$, and its mass is $dm = \rho\, d\mathcal{V} = \rho A\, dL$, where ρ is the mass density of the slug. In the time increment dt the slug moves a distance $|\mathbf{V}|\, dt = V\, dt$ and sweeps out an incremental volume $d\mathcal{V} = AV\, dt$, which has an associated mass of $dm = \rho\, d\mathcal{V} = \rho AV\, dt$. Dividing by dt gives

$$\frac{dm}{dt} = \dot{m} = \rho AV \tag{4.85}$$

This equation is a very convenient way to calculate the flowstream mass flow rate from the easily measured variables of density (ρ), cross-sectional area (A), and average fluid velocity ($|\mathbf{V}| = V$).

The incremental energy required to push the mass slug across the system boundary is the product of the force acting on it pA and the distance moved dL. Consequently, the flow work energy increment is

$$\bar{d}W_{\substack{\text{mass}\\ \text{flow}}} = pA\, dL = p\, d\mathcal{V} = \frac{p}{\rho}\, dm = pv\, dm$$

where $v = 1/\rho$ is the specific volume of the slug.

12. In air at STP the molecular mean free path is approximately 8×10^{-8} m, or 3×10^{-6} in.

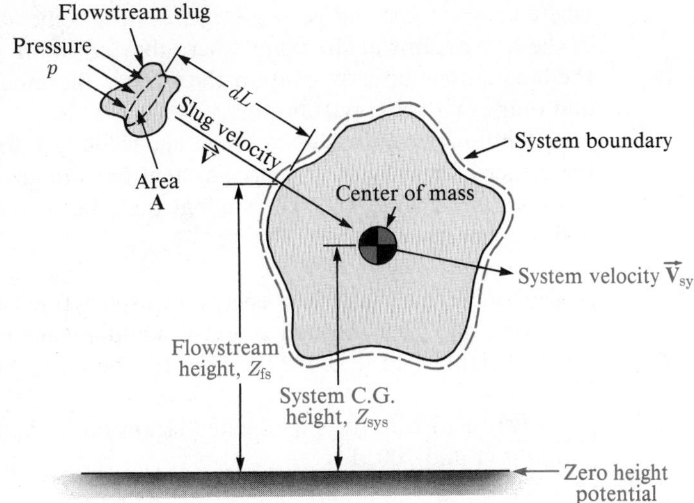

Figure 4.7 Open system flowstream and system energies.

The total mass flow energy for this incremental mass is then

$$\begin{aligned} dE_{\substack{\text{mass}\\ \text{flow}}} &= dE_m + \bar{d}W_{\substack{\text{mass}\\ \text{flow}}} \\ &= (u + \text{ke} + \text{pe})\, dm + (pv)\, dm \\ &= (u + pv + \text{ke} + \text{pe})\, dm \end{aligned} \tag{4.86}$$

Because the sum of the terms u and pv always appears in this equation, it is convenient to combine them into a single term (as explained in Chapter 3) called specific enthalpy, $h = u + pv$.

In general we will have more than one mass flowstream in any given open system. To accurately account for all the mass flow energies we will sum them in two groups. One group will account for all inlet flowstreams and the other for all exiting flowstreams. Thus, we will write

$$dE_{\substack{\text{mass}\\ \text{flow}}} = \sum_{\text{inlet}} (h + \text{ke} + \text{pe})\, dm - \sum_{\text{outlet}} (h + \text{ke} + \text{pe})\, dm \tag{4.87}$$

Upon dividing Eq. 4.87 through by dt we obtain

$$\dot{E}_{\substack{\text{mass}\\ \text{flow}}} = \sum_{\text{inlet}} \dot{m}(h + \text{ke} + \text{pe}) - \sum_{\text{oulet}} \dot{m}(h + \text{ke} + \text{pe}) \tag{4.88}$$

And upon integration of this equation we obtain

$${}_1(E_{\substack{\text{mass}\\ \text{flow}}})_2 = \sum_{\text{inlet}} \int_1^2 \dot{m}(h + \text{ke} + \text{pe})\, dt - \sum_{\text{outlet}} \int_1^2 \dot{m}(h + \text{ke} + \text{pe})\, dt \tag{4.89}$$

where $ke = V^2/2g_c$ and $pe = gZ/g_c$ are the specific kinetic and potential energies of the flowstreams at the point where they cross the system boundary. Note that these equations already contain the proper thermodynamic signs for input (+) and output (−) energy transport.

Each flowstream has its own average velocity V and height Z, and in addition the center of gravity of the entire system has unique and usually different V and Z values (see Figure 4.7). The student must be careful not to get these velocities and heights confused.

Example 4.19 Determine the mass flow energy transport rate of steam at 100 psia, 500 °F leaving a system through a 6-in-inside-diameter pipe at a velocity of 300 ft/s at a height of 15 ft above the floor (the zero height potential).

Solution From the superheated steam table, Appendix C.3*a*, we find that at 100 psia and 500 °F

$$v = 5.587 \text{ ft}^3/\text{lbm}$$

$$h = 1279.1 \text{ Btu/lbm}$$

Now, since $\rho = 1/v$, we can find $\dot{m}$ from Eq. 4.85:

$$\dot{m} = \rho A V = \frac{AV}{v} = \frac{[\pi(\frac{3}{12})^2 \text{ ft}^2](300 \text{ ft/s})}{5.587 \text{ ft}^3/\text{lbm}} = 10.54 \text{ lbm/s}$$

Then,

$$\text{ke} = \frac{V^2}{2g_c} = \frac{(300)^2 \text{ ft}^2/\text{s}^2}{2\left(32.2 \dfrac{\text{lbm}\cdot\text{ft}}{\text{lbf}\cdot\text{s}^2}\right)} = 1397.5 \frac{\text{ft}\cdot\text{lbf}}{\text{lbm}}$$

$$= \left(1397.5 \frac{\text{ft}\cdot\text{lbf}}{\text{lbm}}\right)\left(\frac{1 \text{ Btu}}{778 \text{ ft}\cdot\text{lbf}}\right) = 1.796 \frac{\text{Btu}}{\text{lbm}}$$

and

$$\text{pe} = \frac{gZ}{g_c} = \frac{(32.2 \text{ ft/s}^2)(15 \text{ ft})}{32.2 \dfrac{\text{lbm}\cdot\text{ft}}{\text{lbf}\cdot\text{s}^2}} = 15 \frac{\text{ft}\cdot\text{lbf}}{\text{lbm}}$$

$$= \left(15 \frac{\text{ft}\cdot\text{lbf}}{\text{lbm}}\right)\left(\frac{1 \text{ Btu}}{778 \text{ ft}\cdot\text{lbf}}\right) = 0.019 \text{ Btu/lbm}$$

In this problem we only have one flowstream, consequently

$$\dot{E}_{\substack{\text{mass}\\\text{flow}}} = \dot{m}(h + \text{ke} + \text{pe})$$

$$= (10.54 \text{ lbm/s})[(1279.1 + 1.796 + 0.019) \text{ Btu/lbm}]$$

$$= 1.35 \times 10^4 \text{ Btu/s}$$

Note that the ke and pe terms in Example 4.19 amount respectively to only 0.14% and 0.0015% of the total mass flow energy. This is because the specific enthalpy of steam (and most vapors) usually has a large numerical value while the specific kinetic and potential flow energies for most engineering problems usually have much smaller values when converted into the same units.[13]

The Conservation of Energy and Mass Equations for Open Systems

To obtain a general working formula for the first law of thermodynamics for open systems we will begin by constructing a general energy rate balance (ERB) equation for these systems. The general open system energy rate balance is given by Eq. 4.22 as

$$\dot{E}_G = \dot{W} + \dot{Q} + \dot{E}_{\substack{\text{mass}\\\text{flow}}}$$

where the rate of gain of total system energy $\dot{E}_G$ is given by Eq. 4.9 as

$$\dot{E}_G = \frac{d}{dt}\left(U + \frac{m}{2g_c}V^2 + mgZ/g_c\right)_{\text{system}}$$

and the mass flow energy transports are given by Eq. 4.88 as

$$\dot{E}_{\substack{\text{mass}\\\text{flow}}} = \sum_{\text{inlet}} \dot{m}(h + \text{ke} + \text{pe}) - \sum_{\text{outlet}} \dot{m}(h + \text{ke} + \text{pe})$$

where

$$(\text{ke})_{\text{inlet}} = V^2{}_{\text{inlet}}/2g_c$$

$$(\text{ke})_{\text{outlet}} = V^2{}_{\text{outlet}}/2g_c$$

and

$$(\text{pe})_{\text{inlet}} = gZ_{\text{inlet}}/g_c$$

$$(\text{pe})_{\text{outlet}} = gZ_{\text{outlet}}/g_c$$

are the specific kinetic and potential energies of each inlet and outlet flowstream. Combining the above equations gives the general ERB for open systems.

General open system energy rate balance (ERB)

$$\dot{Q} + \dot{W} + \sum_{\text{inlet}} \dot{m}(h + V^2/2g_c + gZ/g_c) - \sum_{\text{outlet}} \dot{m}(h + V^2/2g_c + gZ/g_c)$$
$$= \frac{d}{dt}(U + mV^2/2g_c + mgZ/g_c)_{\text{system}} \quad \textbf{(4.90)}$$

13. Actually, because of the form of the first law of thermodynamics, we will normally be comparing values of the change in enthalpy Δh with the changes Δke and Δpe. Here, too, we will find that Δh usually dominates.

It must be remembered that the $\dot{Q}$ and $\dot{W}$ terms in this equation are the *net* heat and work transport rate terms, that is,

$$\dot{Q} = \sum_{\text{all}} \dot{Q} \quad \text{and} \quad \dot{W} = \sum_{\text{all}} \dot{W} \tag{4.91}$$

where proper input (+) and output (−) signs are to be used in the summations. Also, the kinetic and potential energy terms on the right side of Eq. 4.90 are of the center of gravity of the entire system, whereas the kinetic and potential energy terms in the flowstream summation terms on the left side of this equation apply only to the point of entry or exit of the flowstream from the system (see Figure 4.7 for an illustration of this notation).

As a working equation, Eq. 4.90 is really too complex to remember or to write down conveniently during the solution of each thermodynamic problem we face. Since most of our problems will involve systems operating at steady state with a single-inlet and a single-outlet flowstream we will simplify Eq. 4.90 to fit this case. For a steady-state process, the entire right side of Eq. 4.90 vanishes:

Steady state

$$\dot{E}_G = \frac{d}{dt}(U + mV^2/2g_c + mgZ/g_c)_{\text{system}} = 0 \tag{4.92}$$

Note that this does not necessarily mean that $\dot{U}$, $\dot{\text{KE}}$, and $\dot{\text{PE}}$ are all zero, but only that their sum vanishes.

At this point we introduce the conservation of mass law for open system. This law can easily be cast into the form of a rate balance by using the general form of Eq. 2.14 as $\dot{m}_G = \dot{m}_T$, where the mass transport rate is simply given by

$$\dot{m}_T = \sum_{\text{inlet}} \dot{m} - \sum_{\text{outlet}} \dot{m} \tag{4.93}$$

Thus, the general mass rate balance for the rate of gain of mass $\dot{m}_G$ for an open system is simply

$$\dot{m}_G = \left(\frac{dm}{dt}\right)_{\text{system}} = \sum_{\text{inlet}} \dot{m} - \sum_{\text{outlet}} \dot{m} \tag{4.94}$$

Now, if a system is operating at steady state, then by definition,

$$\left(\frac{dE}{dt}\right)_{\text{system}} = \left(\frac{dm}{dt}\right)_{\text{system}} = \dot{E}_G = \dot{m}_G = 0 \tag{4.95}$$

so that Eq. 4.94 gives the steady state mass rate balance as

$$\sum_{\text{inlet}} \dot{m} = \sum_{\text{outlet}} \dot{m} \tag{4.96}$$

The condition of equal mass inflows and outflows described by Eq. 4.96 is often called a *steady flow* condition:

Steady flow

$$\sum_{\text{inlet}} \dot{m} = \sum_{\text{outlet}} \dot{m} \tag{4.97}$$

It should be clear from this development that any steady-state open system is also (by definition) a steady flow system. To keep this clearly in mind we will often write both statements, steady state and steady flow, explicitly, even though it is not really necessary to do so.

If the system has only one inlet and one outlet flowstream, then the summation signs can be dropped in Eqs. 4.90, 4.93, 4.94, 4.96, and 4.97. The steady flow condition for a system with a single-inlet and a single-outlet flowstream then becomes

$$\dot{m}_{\text{inlet}} = \dot{m}_{\text{outlet}} = \dot{m} \tag{4.98}$$

Note that the inlet/outlet direction subscripts on the mass flow rate term can now be dropped because they are superfluous.

Substituting Eqs. 4.92 and 4.98 into Eq. 4.90, and abbreviating the terms inlet and outlet as simply "in" and "out" gives a simplified energy rate balance. We call the resulting formula the *modified energy rate balance*, and introduce the following abbreviations for referring to this formula and its integrated alternative:

■ MERB = modified energy rate balance
■ MEB = modified energy balance

Thus, the open system MERB applies only to systems that are

1. steady state ($\dot{E}_G = 0$),
2. steady flow ($\dot{m}_G = 0$), and
3. single-inlet and single-outlet ($\dot{m}_{\text{inlet}} = \dot{m}_{\text{outlet}} = \dot{m}$)

and has the following form:

The modified open system energy rate balance (MERB)

$$\dot{Q} + \dot{W} + \dot{m}[h_{\text{in}} - h_{\text{out}} + (V_{\text{in}}^2 - V_{\text{out}}^2)/(2g_c) + (Z_{\text{in}} - Z_{\text{out}})(g/g_c)] = 0 \tag{4.99}$$

Integrating Eq. 4.99 over time gives the open system MEB:

The modified open system energy balance (MEB)

$$_1Q_2 + {}_1W_2 + \int_1^2 \dot{m}[h_{\text{in}} - h_{\text{out}} + (V_{\text{in}}^2 - V_{\text{out}}^2)/(2g_c) + (Z_{\text{in}} - Z_{\text{out}})(g/g_c)]\, dt = 0 \tag{4.100}$$

However, the vast majority of open system problems are set up on a rate basis, so the MERB will be the equation most often used in open system analysis.

When the conditions of steady state (or steady flow), or single inlet, or single outlet do not exist in any particular problem, then we must return to the more general energy rate balance of Eq. 4.90 as a starting point for the analysis. This will be illustrated with the unsteady-state examples presented later in this chapter.

The Flowstream Specific Kinetic and Potential Energies

Before we can begin analyzing thermodynamic problems we must establish a criterion as to when the specific kinetic and potential energy flowstream terms of Eqs. 4.90 and 4.99 are important and when they are not. To get some feeling for the importance of these terms we will look at how their magnitude varies over a wide range of velocities and heights. First consider the specific kinetic energy term, $V^2/2g_c$. If we work in the Engineering English units system, then V is normally in feet per second, and $g_c = 32.2\ \text{lbm}\cdot\text{ft}/(\text{lbf}\cdot\text{s}^2)$. Then,

$$\frac{V^2}{2g_c} = \frac{[V]^2\ \text{ft}^2/\text{s}^2}{2(32.2)\dfrac{\text{lbm}\cdot\text{ft}}{\text{lbf}\cdot\text{s}^2}} = \frac{[V]^2}{64.4}\frac{\text{ft}\cdot\text{lbf}}{\text{lbm}}$$

where the symbol $[V]$ stands for the numerical value of V in units of ft/s. The remaining term in the flowstream energy transport equation to which the specific kinetic and potential energy terms are to be added is the specific enthalpy h. In the Engineering English units system the specific enthalpy has units of Btu/lbm. If we convert the specific kinetic energy into these units we get

$$\frac{V^2}{2g_c} = \left(\frac{[V]^2}{64.4}\frac{\text{ft}\cdot\text{lbf}}{\text{lbm}}\right)\left(\frac{1\ \text{Btu}}{778\ \text{ft}\cdot\text{lbf}}\right) = \frac{[V]^2}{50{,}100}\frac{\text{Btu}}{\text{lbm}} \tag{4.101}$$

Table 4.10 gives values of the specific kinetic energy for various velocities using Eq. 4.101. Since the specific enthalpy values for most substances fall roughly between 100 and 1000 Btu/lbm, Table 4.10 shows that the specific kinetic energy is very small when compared to these h values for velocities less than about 250 ft/s (76 m/s), or $V^2/2g_c < \sim 1.0$ Btu/lbm (2.3 kJ/kg). Consequently, it is common to neglect the effect of a flowstream's specific kinetic energy when the flow-

Table 4.10 The effect of velocity on kinetic energy

V (ft/s)	$V^2/2g_c$ (Btu/lbm)
0	0
1	2×10^{-5}
10	2×10^{-3}
100	2×10^{-1}
1000	20

stream velocity is less than about 250 ft/s (76 m/s). This is a relatively high velocity (~170 miles/h or 270 km/h), and most engineering applications do not have such rapid flowstreams.

There are, of course, exceptions to this rule of thumb. If $h_{in} - h_{out} \approx 0$, then the enthalpy term loses its dominance. In this case a small specific kinetic energy term may be quite significant to the analysis. A nozzle or a diffuser is an example of such an exception.

Now consider the specific potential energy term, gZ/g_c. Taking $g = 32.2$ ft/s^2 and $g_c = 32.2$ lbm·ft/(lbf·s^2), then

$$\frac{gZ}{g_c} = ([Z]\ \text{ft})\left(\frac{32.2\ \text{ft/s}^2}{32.2\dfrac{\text{lbm}\cdot\text{ft}}{\text{lbf}\cdot\text{s}^2}}\right) = [Z]\,\frac{\text{ft}\cdot\text{lbf}}{\text{lbm}}$$

where the symbol $[Z]$ stands for the numerical value of Z in units of feet. Again, converting to Btu/lbm gives

$$\frac{gZ}{g_c} = \left([Z]\,\frac{\text{ft}\cdot\text{lbf}}{\text{lbm}}\right)\left(\frac{1\ \text{Btu}}{778\ \text{ft}\cdot\text{lbf}}\right) = \frac{[Z]}{778}\,\frac{\text{Btu}}{\text{lbm}} \tag{4.102}$$

Table 4.11 gives values of specific potential energy for various heights using Eq. 4.102. Note that for systems with normal engineering dimensions, say less than 1000 ft (305 m) high, the specific potential energy is very small. Consequently, it is common to neglect the effect of a flowstream's specific potential energy when the flowstream enters the system less than 1000 ft (305 m) above or below the potential energy baseline of the system, or $gZ/g_c < \sim 1.0$ Btu/lbm (2.3 kJ/kg).

There are also exceptions to this rule of thumb. Again, if $h_{in} - h_{out} \approx 0$, then flowstream height changes may be very important in the analysis. A hydroelectric power plant is an example of such an exception.

Deciding whether to neglect factors such as specific kinetic and potential energies is not always an easy task for the beginner. Self-confidence comes only with experience. There is, however, one more rule of thumb that applies to most textbook thermodynamic problems: *If values for velocity and height are not given in the problem statement and are not among the problem's unknowns, then you are supposed to neglect the kinetic and potential energy terms in your analysis.* This means that the person who wrote the problem knew that either $V_{in} \approx V_{out}$ and

Table 4.11 **The effect of height on potential energy**

Z (ft)	gZ/g_c (Btu/lbm)
0	0
1	1.29×10^{-3}
10	1.29×10^{-2}
100	1.29×10^{-1}
1000	1.29

$Z_{in} \approx Z_{out}$, or that all the velocities and heights were relatively small. The only exception to this last rule of thumb is when you know the mass flow rate $\dot{m}$, the diameter D or cross-sectional area A, and the fluid density ρ or specific volume v of a flowstream. With this information you can calculate the flowstream velocity using Eq. 4.85 as

$$V = \frac{\dot{m}}{\rho A} = \frac{\dot{m}v}{A} = \frac{4\dot{m}v}{\pi D^2} \tag{4.103}$$

If you can make this calculation for V, then you might as well use it in your energy rate balance equation unless it is so small that you are certain it will not affect the results of your analysis.

Nozzles and Diffusers

A nozzle is the generic name of any device whose primary function is to convert the pressure energy $\dot{m}pv$ of an inlet flowstream into the kinetic energy $\dot{m}V^2/2$ of an outlet flowstream. Thus, a nozzle is a very simple energy conversion device. Similarly, a diffuser is the generic name of any device whose primary function is to convert the kinetic energy of an inlet flowstream into the pressure energy of an outlet flowstream. Note that nozzles and diffusers perform opposite functions. In their simplest form, a nozzle is merely a converging duct and a diffuser is merely a diverging duct as shown schematically in Figure 4.8.[14]

Most commercial nozzles and diffusers are well insulated (abiabatic). However, they need not be and therefore may have either a heat loss or a heat gain. On the other hand, the simple mechanical nature of nozzles and diffusers prevents them from either performing or absorbing work. Therefore, they can generally be taken to be aergonic devices.

Since both nozzles and diffusers are clearly single-inlet, single-outlet devices, we can carry out an analysis of their steady state operation by using the modified energy rate balance of Eq. 4.99. Also, either both nozzles and diffusers are oriented horizontally as shown in Figure 4.8 so that $Z_{in} = Z_{out}$, or else they have such small changes in height between the inlet and outlet that the enthalpy change dominates the specific potential energy change as discussed above. This allows us to neglect the change in flowstream specific potential energy in nozzle and diffuser analysis.

However, the flowstream specific kinetic energies are not necessarily negligible because in both nozzles and diffusers at least one of the flowstreams normally has a high velocity. Consequently, we will ignore the low-speed flowstream specific kinetic energy in each case and set $V_{in} \approx 0$ for the nozzle and $V_{out} \approx 0$ for the diffuser.

14. This figure is accurate only for subsonic flow. When the flow becomes supersonic the relative shapes of nozzles and diffusers are not the same as those shown here.

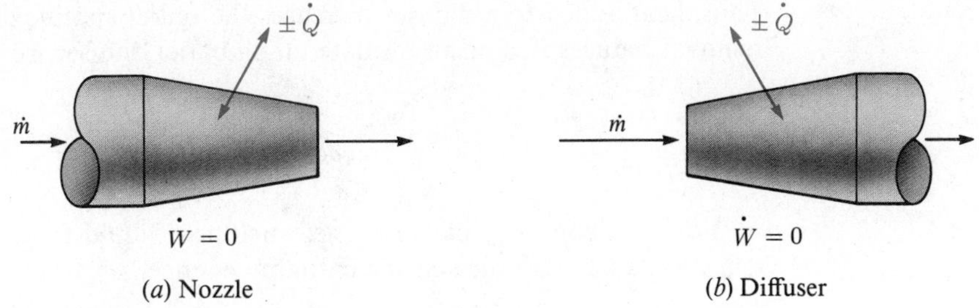

Figure 4.8 Nozzles and diffusers.

At this point we have developed the following set of assumptions for these devices

Nozzle	**Diffuser**
$\dot{W} = 0$	$\dot{W} = 0$
$Z_{in} - Z_{out} \approx 0$	$Z_{in} - Z_{out} \approx 0$
$V_{in} \approx 0$	$V_{out} \approx 0$

Applying the assumptions listed above for nozzles to the MERB of Eq. 4.99 gives the following results:

$$\dot{Q} + 0 + \dot{m}(h_{in} - h_{out} - V_{out}^2/2g_c + 0) = 0$$

or

$$V_{out}\Big|_{\text{nozzle}} = [2g_c(\dot{Q}/\dot{m} + h_{in} - h_{out})]^{1/2} \tag{4.104}$$

Notice that adding heat to the nozzle will increase the outlet velocity, whereas removing heat will decrease it. If the nozzle is insulated (adiabatic), then $\dot{Q} = 0$ and

$$V_{out}\Big|_{\substack{\text{adiabatic}\\ \text{nozzle}}} = \sqrt{2g_c(h_{in} - h_{out})} \tag{4.105}$$

Applying the assumptions for diffusers listed above to the MERB of Eq. 4.99 gives the following results:

$$\dot{Q} + \dot{m}(h_{in} - h_{out} + V_{in}^2/2g_c) = 0$$

or

$$h_{out}\Big|_{\text{diffuser}} = h_{in} + V_{in}^2/2g_c + \dot{Q}/\dot{m} \tag{4.106}$$

Thus, heat added to a diffuser increases the outlet specific enthalpy whereas heat removal reduces it. For an insulated (adiabatic) diffuser we have

$$h_{out}\Big|_{\substack{\text{adiabatic}\\ \text{diffuser}}} = h_{in} + V_{in}^2/2g_c \tag{4.107}$$

For an incompressible substance such as a liquid flowing through these systems, Eq. 3.62 gives the specific enthalpy change as

$$h_{in} - h_{out} = c(T_{in} - T_{out}) + v(p_{in} - p_{out}) \tag{4.108}$$

where c is the specific heat of the material and v is its specific volume. Then Eqs. 4.104 and 4.105 become

$$V_{out}\Big|_{\substack{\text{nozzle}\\ \text{incompressible}\\ \text{fluid}}} = \{2g_c[\dot{Q}/\dot{m} + c(T_{in} - T_{out}) + v(p_{in} - p_{out})]\}^{1/2} \tag{4.109}$$

and

$$V_{out}\Big|_{\substack{\text{adiabatic}\\ \text{nozzle}\\ \text{incompressible}\\ \text{fluid}}} = \sqrt{2g_c[c(T_{in} - T_{out}) + v(p_{in} - p_{out})]} \tag{4.110}$$

and Eqs. 4.106 and 4.107 can be similarly rearranged to give

$$p_{out}\Big|_{\substack{\text{diffuser}\\ \text{incompressible}\\ \text{fluid}}} = p_{in} + (1/v)[c(T_{in} - T_{out}) + V_{in}^2/2g_c + \dot{Q}/\dot{m}] \tag{4.111}$$

and

$$p_{out}\Big|_{\substack{\text{adiabatic}\\ \text{diffuser}\\ \text{incompressible}\\ \text{fluid}}} = p_{in} + (1/v)[c(T_{in} - T_{out}) + V_{in}^2/2g_c] \tag{4.112}$$

For an ideal gas with constant specific heats (such as air at atmospheric pressure and temperature), Eq. 3.46 gives[15]

$$h_{in} - h_{out} = c_p(T_{in} - T_{out}) \tag{4.113}$$

15. Note that this formula can be used here even though this is not a constant pressure process because the enthalpy of an ideal gas depends only on temperature and is therefore independent of pressure (see Chapter 3).

where c_p is the constant pressure specific heat. Then Eqs. 4.104 and 4.105 become

$$V_{out}\Big|_{\substack{\text{nozzle}\\\text{ideal gas}}} = \{2g_c[\dot{Q}/\dot{m} + c_p(T_{in} - T_{out})]\}^{1/2} \quad \textbf{(4.114)}$$

and

$$V_{out}\Big|_{\substack{\text{adiabatic}\\\text{nozzle}\\\text{ideal gas}}} = \sqrt{2g_c c_p(T_{in} - T_{out})} \quad \textbf{(4.115)}$$

and Eqs. 4.106 and 4.107 become

$$T_{out}\Big|_{\substack{\text{diffuser}\\\text{ideal gas}}} = T_{in} + (1/c_p)(V_{in}^2/2g_c + \dot{Q}/\dot{m}) \quad \textbf{(4.116)}$$

and

$$T_{out}\Big|_{\substack{\text{adiabatic}\\\text{diffuser}\\\text{ideal gas}}} = T_{in} + V_{in}^2/(2g_c c_p) \quad \textbf{(4.117)}$$

We are now ready to carry out a thermodynamic analysis of an open system. We begin with simple examples and work toward more difficult ones. The example problems are designed to illustrate the text material that immediately precedes the example. Therefore, the analysis section of the solution will often be abbreviated with appropriate reference made to the previous text material wherein the analysis has already been carried out. Do not be misguided by this. Homework and examination problems usually do not simply mimic textbook examples. The purpose of these examples is *not* to give you a set of ready-made formulae that you can plug numbers into to solve specific problems. Their function is to teach you analysis techniques so that you will have the ability and self-confidence to solve any thermodynamics problem whatsoever, whether you have seen one similar to it or not.

Example 4.20

The nozzle on a lawn or garden hose has a 1.0-in inlet inside diameter and an inlet pressure of 80 psig at 60 °F. The mass flow rate of water through the nozzle is 0.8 lbm/s. Assuming the water flows through the nozzle isothermally, determine

a) the outlet velocity from the nozzle, and

b) the height to which the stream of water will rise above the nozzle outlet when the nozzle is pointed straight up.

Solution The unknowns in this problem are V_{out} and Z_{out} (see the schematic below). We assume from our experience with garden hose nozzles that the system is a steady state, steady flow, single-inlet, single-outlet open system.

The material flowing through this system is water at 80 psig (94.7 psia) and 60 °F. A check of the saturation tables for water shows us that the water is in

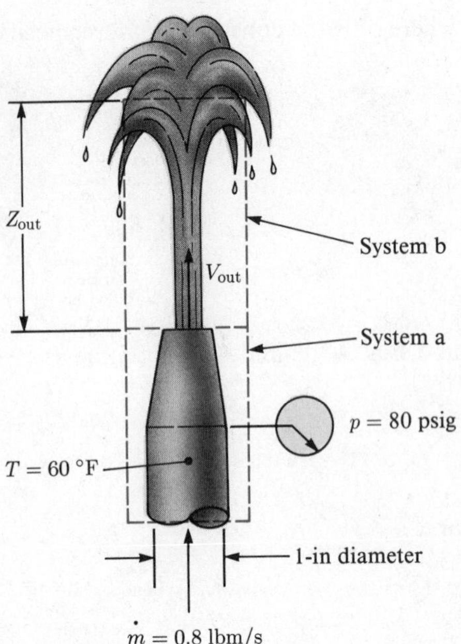

a compressed liquid state and therefore can be considered to be an incompressible fluid. Also, since the amount of excess pressure here is relatively small (94.7 psia vs. the saturation pressure of 0.2563 psia at 60 °F) we need not use the compressed water tables but rather we can get sufficient accuracy by using the saturated liquid tables at 60 °F for all the inlet properties we may need.

The first law formulation that applies to this problem is the MERB, Eq. 4.99. The auxiliary equations needed include the equation of state for an incompressible fluid (Eq. 4.108) and the mass flow rate formula (Eq. 4.85). For the case of system a shown in the schematic above we have the standard nozzle configuration, except that we can calculate V_{in} in this problem from Eq. 4.103 as

$$V_{in} = 4\dot{m}v/\pi D^2$$

where $v \approx v_f(60\ °\text{F}) = 0.01603\ \text{ft}^3/\text{lbm}$. Then,

$$V_{in} = \frac{4(0.8\ \text{lbm/s})(0.01603\ \text{ft}^3/\text{lbm})}{\pi(1\ \text{in})^2(1\ \text{ft}/12\ \text{in})^2} = 2.35\ \text{ft/s}$$

Now, this V_{in} will probably produce a negligible inlet kinetic energy, but since we have its value we will carry it along in the solution for the time being.

The solution to part a is obtained by solving the MERB for V_{out} with the enthalpy values given by Eq. 4.108. This produces an equation similar to Eq. 4.109 except with a V_{in} term included. Since we have no information about any heat transfer to or from the nozzle we will assume that there is none. This is justifiable on the following basis: Since the nozzle is very small (hand size), the water is not inside of it long enough for any significant heat transfer of energy to occur. This is a common circumstance that often occurs in obviously uninsulated small systems that have no significant heat transfer. If the residence time of the fluid in the system is very small, then, in the absence of an extraordinarily large temperature difference between the environment and the system, there is simply insufficient time for any significant heat transfer to occur, regardless of whether the system is insulated or not.

The MERB reduces to a modified form of Eq. 4.110:

$$V_{out} = \{V_{in}^2 + 2g_c[c(T_{in} - T_{out}) + v(p_{in} - p_{out})]\}^{1/2}$$

The problem statement told us to assume the water flow through the nozzle is isothermal, so we set $T_{in} = T_{out}$. Actually, the water flow will not be exactly isothermal due to an increase in internal energy of the water due to viscous effects, turbulence, and so forth. However, for a small nozzle, these effects will be negligible. For an isothermal flow we obtain

$$V_{out} = [V_{in}^2 + 2g_c v(p_{in} - p_{out})]^{1/2}$$

The data for this problem are as follows:

$$V_{in} = 2.35 \text{ ft/s}$$

$$v = v_f(60\ °\text{F}) = 0.01603 \text{ ft}^3/\text{lbm}$$

$$p_{in} = 80 \text{ psig} = 94.7 \text{ psia}$$

$$p_{out} = 0 \text{ psig} = 14.7 \text{ psia}$$

Then

$$V_{out} = \{(2.35 \text{ ft/s})^2 + 2\left(32.2\,\frac{\text{lbm}\cdot\text{ft}}{\text{lbf}\cdot\text{s}^2}\right)(0.01603 \text{ ft}^3/\text{lbm})[(80 - 0) \text{ lbf/in}^2]$$
$$\times (144 \text{ in}^2/\text{ft}^2)\}^{1/2} = 109 \text{ ft/s}$$

Notice that V_{in} was only about 2% of V_{out} and therefore could have been neglected in this case.

Part b of this example is basically a mechanics problem, but it can be easily solved by using system b shown in the example schematic, and the MERB. The following assumptions are now made for system b[16]:

$$\dot{Q} = \dot{W} = 0 \qquad Z_{out} = ?$$
$$V_{in} = 109 \text{ ft/s} \qquad p_{in} = p_{out} = 14.7 \text{ psia}$$
$$V_{out} \approx 0 \text{ ft/s} \qquad T_{in} = T_{out} = 60\ °\text{F}$$
$$Z_{in} = 0$$

16. V_{out} is $\ll V_{in}$ here because the water stream spreads into a large fan at the top of its trajectory and therefore exits system b through a large surface area. The conservation of mass law for an incompressible fluid requires that $\dot{m}$ = constant and so $V_{out} = V_{in}(A_{in}/A_{out}) \ll V_{in}$ here.

These assumptions imply a negligible aerodynamic drag on the water stream and negligible viscous dissipation within the stream itself. When these conditions are applied to the MERB we obtain

$$\underset{0}{\dot{Q}} + \underset{0}{\dot{W}} + \dot{m}(h_{\text{in}} - h_{\text{out}} + (V_{\text{in}}^2 - 0)/2g_c + (0 - Z_{\text{out}})g/g_c) = 0$$

or

$$Z_{\text{out}} = (g_c/g)(h_{\text{in}} - h_{\text{out}}) + V_{\text{in}}^2/2g$$

The change in specific enthalpy for this example is again given by Eq. 4.108, and under the assumptions listed for system b it is clear that this change is zero. Then our working MERB reduces to

$$Z_{\text{out}} = V_{\text{in}}^2/2g$$

or

$$Z_{\text{out}} = \frac{(109 \text{ ft/s})^2}{2(32.2 \text{ ft/s}^2)} = 184 \text{ ft}$$

Note that our calculations for both V_{out} and Z_{out} in this example gave numbers that will be somewhat higher that we would observe if we measured these values in an experiment. This is because we have ignored the viscous dissipation effects in the water and surrounding air. Dissipation effects are considered in more detail in the next chapter on the second law of thermodynamics.

Throttling Devices

A *throttling device* is the generic name of any device or process that simply dissipates pressure energy $\dot{m}pv$ by irreversibly converting it into thermal energy. Unlike nozzles and diffusers, throttling devices provide no form of useful energy recovery. They merely convert pressure energy into thermal energy through dissipative viscous flow (usually turbulent) processes. In fact, any device that incurs a large irreversible pressure drop can be thought of as a throttling device. Figure 4.9 schematically illustrates a variety of common throttling devices.

A throttling device may be thought of as any aergonic device whose primary purpose is to offer a resistance to flow. Throttles may or may not be insulated, but they are usually such small devices and have such high flow rates that the residence time of the fluid in them is too short for significant heat transport of energy to occur. Consequently, a throttling device is commonly taken to be adiabatic regardless of whether it is actually insulated or not.

The small physical size of most throttling devices also prevents them from having a significant change in specific potential energy between their inlet and outlet flowstreams. However, a throttle need not have the same inlet and outlet flow velocities and, therefore, it may have a significant specific kinetic energy change across it.

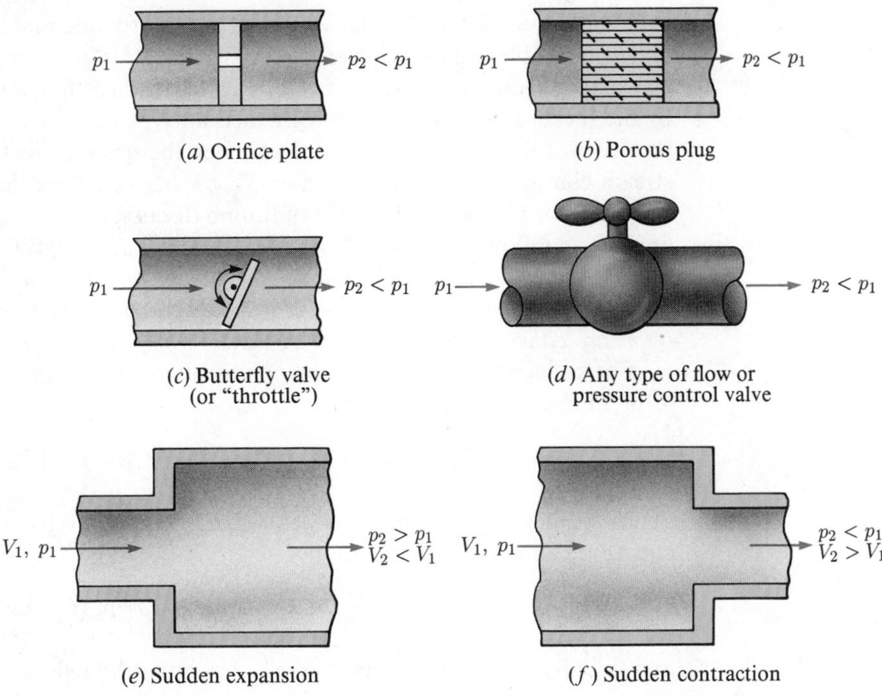

Figure 4.9 Some common throttling devices.

Consequently, we will define a throttling device with the following set of thermodyanmic conditions:

Throttling Devices

$\dot{Q} = 0$

$\dot{W} = 0$

$Z_{in} - Z_{out} \approx 0$

Applying these conditions to the MERB of Eq. 4.99 gives

$$0 + 0 + \dot{m}[h_{in} - h_{out} + (V_{in}^2 - V_{out}^2)/2g_c + 0] = 0$$

or

$$h_{out} = h_{in} + (V_{in}^2 - V_{out}^2)/2g_c \quad \textbf{(4.118)}$$

If $V_{in} = V_{out}$ as when the fluid is incompressible and the inlet and outlet areas of the throttle are equal (e.g., cases *a–d* in Figure 4.8), then Eq. 4.118 reduces to the simpler form

$$h_{out} = h_{in} \quad \textbf{(4.119)}$$

Such throttling devices are said to be *isenthalpic* (i.e., they have a constant enthalpy).

Even if the inlet and outlet velocities are clearly unequal in some problem you may still be able to justify using the simpler Eq. 4.119 as the result of your analysis. The high-velocity flowstream of an unequal area throttling device is always limited by the speed of sound in the flowing medium.[17] Consequently, if h is large, say of the order of 1000 Btu/lbm (2300 kJ/kg), then the specific kinetic energy of the flowstream can never be more than 2 or 3% of this value and may therefore be considered to be negligible. The rule of thumb discussed earlier in this chapter can be applied as follows: *If you are given a throttling device problem without adequate velocity information and where a velocity is not an unknown that you are required to find as part of the solution, then you should assume that the specific kinetic energy terms are either equal (and therefore cancel each other) or that they are negligible.*

For an incompressible fluid flowing through a throttling device we can use Eq. 4.108 in Eq. 4.118 to produce

$$c(T_{\text{in}} - T_{\text{out}}) + v(p_{\text{in}} - p_{\text{out}}) + (V_{\text{in}}^2 - V_{\text{out}}^2)/2g_c = 0 \quad \textbf{(4.120)}$$

and if we neglect the specific kinetic energy terms (or have $V_{\text{in}} = V_{\text{out}}$) then this equation can be rearranged to give

$$T_{\text{out}} = T_{\text{in}} + (v/c)(p_{\text{in}} - p_{\text{out}}) \quad \textbf{(4.121)}$$

and since p_{in} is usually greater than p_{out}, this equation tells us that there is normally a temperature rise in an incompressible fluid flowing with a negligible specific kinetic energy change through a throttling device.

For an ideal gas with constant specific heats we can substitute Eq. 4.113 into Eq. 4.118 to obtain

$$T_{\text{out}} = T_{\text{in}} + (V_{\text{in}}^2 - V_{\text{out}}^2)/(2g_c c_p) \quad \textbf{(4.122)}$$

This equation tells us that in the case of negligible change in specific kinetic energy that the throttling of an ideal gas is an isothermal process.

The actual throttling device outlet temperature for a pure substance is dependent upon its Joule-Thomson coefficient μ_J, defined as

$$\mu_J = (\partial T/\partial p)_h \quad \textbf{(4.123)}$$

Since μ_J is defined completely in terms of intensive thermodynamic properties, it too is an intensive thermodynamic property. A throttling process that has a negligible change in specific kinetic energy is a process of constant h, so the Joule-Thomson coefficient for any pure substance can be approximated from data taken during such a throttling process as

$$\mu_J \approx (\Delta T/\Delta p)_{\substack{\text{throttling}\\ \text{process}}} \quad \textbf{(4.124)}$$

17. Supersonic nozzles or diffusers usually have a flowstream velocity greater than the sonic velocity. But, with the rare exception of supersonic flow at the inlet to a throttling device, subsonic flow prevails throughout throttling devices.

Table 4.12 The maximum Joule-Thomson inversion temperature for various common gases

Substance	Maximum inversion temperature K	R
Air	659	1186
Argon	780	1404
Carbon dioxide	1500	2700
Helium	40	72
Hydrogen	202	364
Neon	231	416
Nitrogen	621	1118
Oxygen	764	1375

Source: Reprinted by permission of the publisher from Mark W. Zemansky, Michael M. Abbott, and Henrick C. Van Ness, *Basic Engineering Thermodynamics*, 2d ed. (New York: McGraw-Hill, 1975), p. 313 (Table 10.1).

If we take $\Delta p = p_{out} - p_{in}$, then Δp will normally be a negatively number for such a process. Then, clearly, a positive value for μ_J means that the temperature drops during such a throttling process ($\Delta T = T_{out} - T_{in} < 0$) and a negative value for μ_J means that the temperature increases. For an isothermal throttling process (such as occurs with an ideal gas), $\mu_J = 0$.

A gaseous pure substance that has a positive Joule-Thomson coefficient could undergo a continuous decrease in temperature and eventually become liquified by a properly designed throttling process. This was the basis of a process introduced in 1895 by Karl von Linde (1842–1934) for the large-scale production of liquid air. The temperature at which $\mu_J = 0$ for a real pure substance is called its *inversion temperature* T_{inv}, and $\mu_J > 0$ for $T < T_{inv}$ and $\mu_J < 0$ for $T > T_{inv}$. Thus, the temperature of a real gas will decrease in a throttling process if its inlet temperature is less than its inversion temperature. However, the temperature of a gas cannot be lowered via the Joule-Thomson effect if the gas inlet temperature exceeds its "maximum" inversion temperature (see Table 4.12).[18]

Figure 4.10 shows the variation in the Joule-Thomson coefficient with pressure and temperature for air and carbon dioxide.

The Throttling Calorimeter

A *throttling calorimeter* is a device that expands (i.e., throttles) a mixture of liquid plus vapor into the superheated vapor region. Under the vapor dome temperature and pressure are not independent properties; therefore, their measurement alone cannot be used to fix the thermodynamic state of a substance. If, however, the thermodynamic state can be moved into a region where pressure and temperature are independent properties, then its state can be.determined from a pressure gage and a thermometer reading. This is the purpose of a throttling calorimeter, as illustrated in the following example.

18. Since the condition $\mu_J = 0$ can occur at more than one temperature, a gas may have several inversion temperatures, the largest of which is its "maximum" inversion temperature.

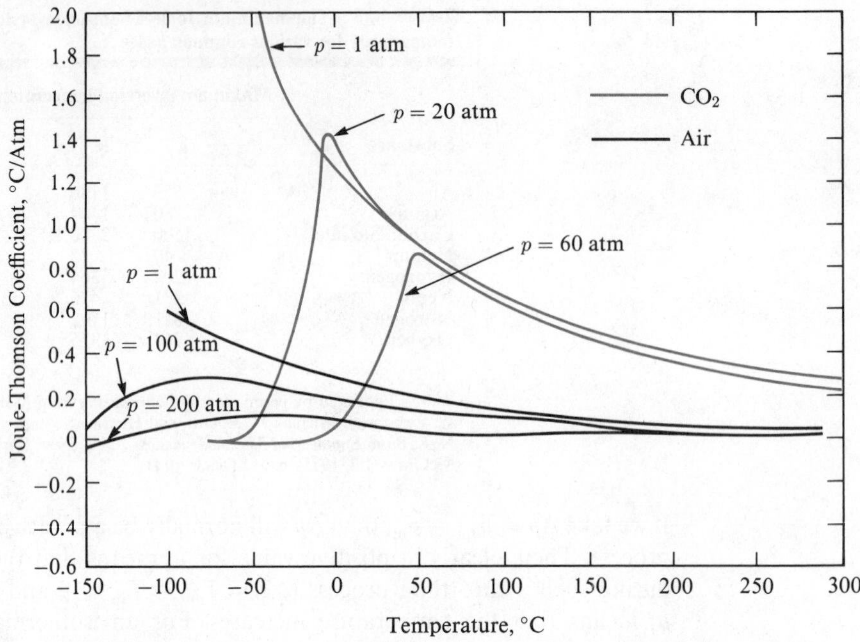

Figure 4.10 The variation in the Joule-Thomson coefficient of air and carbon dioxide with pressure and temperature.

Example 4.21 Wet (i.e., a mixture of liquid plus vapor) steam flows in a pipe at 300 psia. An insulated throttling calorimeter is attached to the pipe and a small portion of the steam is withdrawn and throttled to atmospheric pressure. The temperature of the throttled steam in the calorimeter is 300 °F. Determine the quality of the wet steam in the pipe and estimate its Joule-Thomson coefficient μ_J.

Solution A throttling calorimeter is clearly a steady state, steady flow, single-inlet, single-outlet device. The material flowing is steam, and the unknown is the quality of the inlet flowstream ($x_{in} = x_1 = ?$). The system and its properties are shown below.

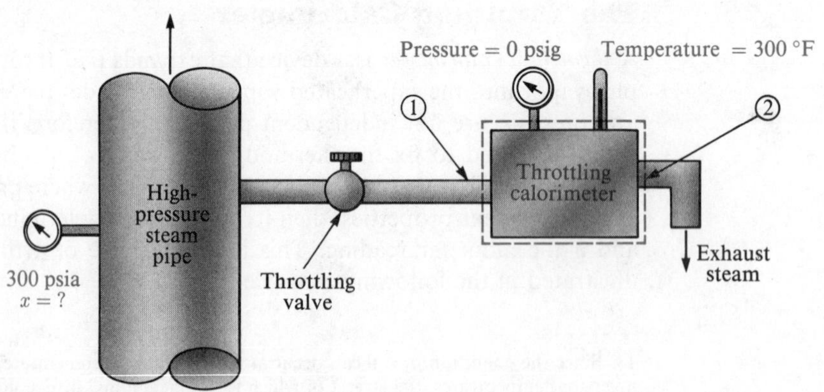

Station 1 (inlet)	$\xrightarrow[\text{process}]{\text{Throttling}}$	Station 2 (outlet)
$p_1 = p_{sat} = 300$ psia		$p_2 = 14.7$ psia
		$T_2 = 300$ °F
$x_1 = ?$		$h_2 = 1192.6$ Btu/lbm

This is an example of a problem where the process path plus three of the four state properties needed to fix the two states are given, and the unknown is a property in the undetermined state. This is a common problem format.

A quick check of the steam tables shows that the outlet state is in the superheated region, and thus all of the outlet properties are easily found from the superheated steam table. Since we are given no information on mass flow rates or velocities we will assume that the changes in flowstream specific kinetic and potential energies are negligible. The calorimeter was stated to be insulated, so it will have no heat transfer, and we will acknowledge the fact that this device can neither do work nor have work done upon it. Under these conditions the MERB reduces to Eq. 4.119, or

$$h_{in} = h_1 = h_{out} = h_2$$

From the superheated steam table (Appendix C.3*a*) we find that

$$h_2 = h(14.7 \text{ psia}, 300\ °\text{F}) = 1192.6 \text{ Btu/lbm}$$

and this value is listed above as part of the data for station 2. Therefore, from the MERB, we have

$$h_1 = h(14.7 \text{ psia}, ?) = 1192.6 \text{ Btu/lbm}$$

and the pair of independent properties $p_1 = 300$ psia and $h_1 = 1192.6$ Btu/lbm now fix the inlet state. From the saturation tables for water we find that at 300 psia

$$h_{f1} = h_f(300 \text{ psia}) = 394.1 \text{ Btu/lbm}$$

$$h_{fg1} = h_{fg}(300 \text{ psia}) = 809.8 \text{ Btu/lbm}$$

$$h_{g1} = h_g(300 \text{ psia}) = 1203.9 \text{ Btu/lbm}$$

Since $h_{f1} < h_1 < h_{g1}$, we can now use the auxiliary formula for quality x to determine its value at station 1 as

$$x_1 = (h_1 - h_{f1})/h_{fg1} = (1192.6 - 394.1)/809.8 = 0.9860$$

So that $x_1 = 98.6\%$, which is the quality of the steam in the pipe.

A rough estimate for the Joule-Thomson coefficient for this process is given by Eq. 4.124 as

$$\mu_J \approx (\Delta T/\Delta p)_{\substack{\text{throttling}\\ \text{process}}}$$

where, from the saturation tables, $T_1 = T_{sat}(300 \text{ psia}) = 417.4\ °F$. Then

$$\mu_J \approx (417.4 - 300)/(300 - 14.7) = 0.411 \text{ R}\cdot\text{in}^2/\text{lbf}$$

Note that this is not a particularly accurate value since μ_J is a point function and consequently the values of ΔT and Δp used in its calculation should really be much smaller than those used in the above calculation. This calculation does, however, provide a reasonable *average* value of μ_J for this throttling process.

Heat Exchangers

A *heat exchanger* is the generic name of any device whose primary function is to promote a heat transport of energy from one fluid to another fluid. Most heat exchangers have two separate fluid flow paths which do not mix the fluids, but instead promote the transfer of heat from one fluid to another across a thermally conducting but otherwise impermeable barrier. These heat exchangers have four flowstreams, two inlets and two outlets. Since the primary function of a heat exchanger is a heat transfer process, they are characteristically aergonic devices. Also, all of the heat transfer should take place *inside* the heat exchanger and therefore most heat exchangers are normally adiabatic devices when the entire heat exchanger is insulated and taken to be the system. It is normal for an uninsulated heat exchanger to have a net heat transfer to or from its surroundings, but when environmental heat transfer values are not supplied in a problem statement and are not an unknown or otherwise determinable, you are to assume that the entire heat exchanger is an adiabatic system. Figure 4.11 illustrates a typical heat exchanger schematic and operating characteristics.

A heat exchanger can be considered to be a pair of steady state, steady flow, single-inlet, single-outlet systems that have equal but opposite heat transfer rates. It can also be analyzed as a steady state, steady flow, double-inlet, double-outlet system that has no (assuming it is insulated) external heat transfer. In both cases

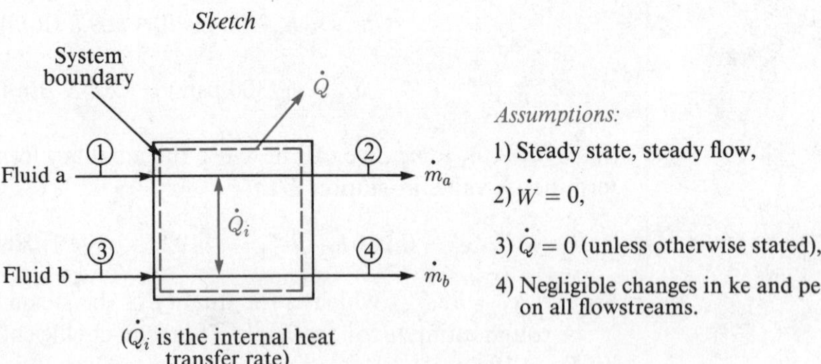

Figure 4.11 Typical heat exchanger operating characteristics.

it is common to neglect any changes in flowstream specific kinetic or potential energy across the system. The general ERB (Eq. 4.90) for the latter case reduces to

$$\dot{Q} + \dot{m}_1 h_1 + \dot{m}_3 h_3 - \dot{m}_2 h_2 - \dot{m}_4 h_4 = 0$$

The conservation of mass law requires that $\dot{m}_1 = \dot{m}_2 = \dot{m}_a$, and that $\dot{m}_3 = \dot{m}_4 = \dot{m}_b$, where the subscripts a and b refer to the two different fluids. Therefore, the ERB becomes

$$\dot{Q} + \dot{m}_a(h_1 - h_2) + \dot{m}_b(h_3 - h_4) = 0 \tag{4.125}$$

and if the heat exchanger is insulated then $\dot{Q} = 0$ and this equation further reduces to

$$\dot{m}_a(h_1 - h_2) = \dot{m}_b(h_4 - h_3) \tag{4.126}$$

If both fluids a and b are incompressible (e.g., liquids), then Eq. 4.108 can be used to give

$$\dot{m}_a[c_a(T_1 - T_2) + v_a(p_1 - p_2)] = \dot{m}_b[c_b(T_4 - T_3) + v_b(p_4 - p_3)]$$

where c_a and c_b are the specific heats of fluids a and b, respectively. For liquids, not only are v_a and v_b small numbers, but the pressure drops $p_1 - p_2$ and $p_3 - p_4$ across the heat exchanger are also small. Therefore, it is common to ignore the pressure terms in the previous equation giving the final incompressible fluid heat exchanger ERB as

$$\dot{m}_a c_a(T_1 - T_2) = \dot{m}_b c_b(T_4 - T_3) \tag{4.127}$$

If both fluids are ideal gases with constant specific heats, then the use of Eq. 4.113 gives

$$\dot{m}_a(c_p)_a(T_1 - T_2) = \dot{m}_b(c_p)_b(T_4 - T_3) \tag{4.128}$$

where $(c_p)_a$ and $(c_p)_b$ are the constant pressure specific heats of gases a and b, respectively.

If one fluid, say a, is an ideal gas (e.g., air) and the other fluid is an incompressible liquid with a negligible pressure drop across the device, then the insulated heat exchanger ERB becomes

$$\dot{m}_a(c_p)_a(T_1 - T_2) = \dot{m}_b c_b(T_4 - T_3) \tag{4.129}$$

Several other combinations of flowstream fluid types are also possible.

If we now return to the two-system heat exchanger model and treat the two fluids as separate systems, we can apply the MERB individually to each of them to obtain

$$\dot{Q}_a + \dot{m}_a(h_1 - h_2) = \dot{Q}_b + \dot{m}_b(h_3 - h_4) = 0$$

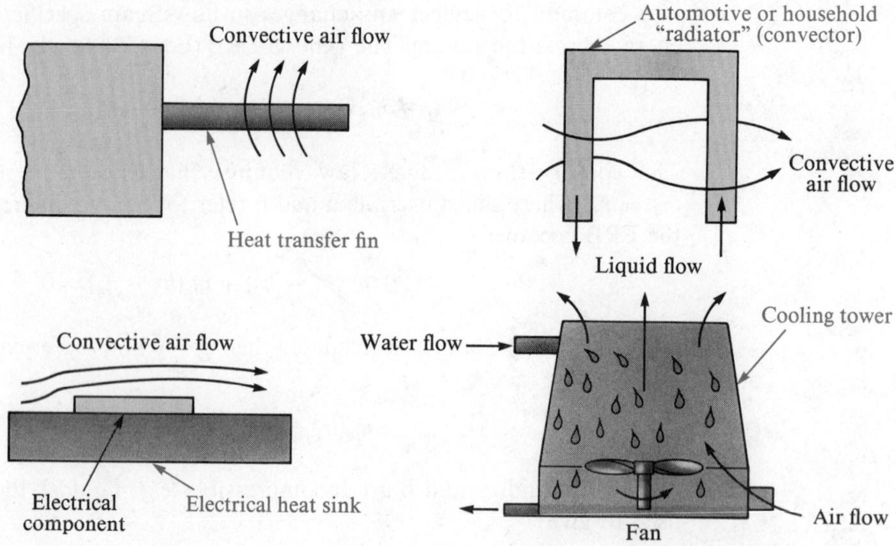

Figure 4.12 Heat exchangers where the environment is one of the heat transfer fluids.

or

$$\dot{Q}_a = \dot{m}_a(h_2 - h_1) \tag{4.130}$$

and

$$\dot{Q}_b = \dot{m}_b(h_4 - h_3) \tag{4.131}$$

Since the internal fluid to fluid heat transfer rate is $\dot{Q}_a = -\dot{Q}_b$, then adding Eqs. 4.130 and 4.131 produces Eq. 4.126. Thus, both types of system analysis give the same results.

In some cases the environment itself is one of the heat transfer fluids. Heat transfer fins, automobile radiators, electrical heat sinks, and so on, are all designed to transfer heat to or from the environment. Some of these devices are single-flowstream systems and must be analyzed using Eq. 4.129. These systems are illustrated in Figure 4.12.

Example 4.22

A *condenser* is a heat exchanger that is designed to condense a vapor into a liquid. Determine the flow rate of cooling water taken from a local river required to condense 12.0 kg/min of water vapor at 1.0 MPa and 500 °C into a saturated liquid at 1.0 MPa. The river water can be considered to be an incompressible fluid with an inlet temperature of 15 °C. The cooling water must be returned to the river and is restricted by environmental code requirements not to exceed 20 °C.

Solution The unknown is the river water mass flow rate $\dot{m}_w$. We will treat this as a steady state, steady flow, double-inlet, double-outlet open system problem. Since no information was given about heat loss or gain from the environmental surface of the condenser we will assume that it is insulated and is therefore adiabatic. Also, since no pressure loss information was given for the river cooling water flowstream we will assume that it is negligible.

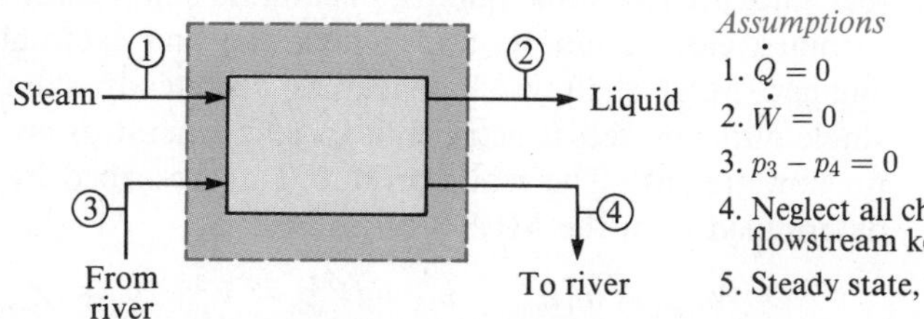

Assumptions

1. $\dot{Q} = 0$
2. $\dot{W} = 0$
3. $p_3 - p_4 = 0$
4. Neglect all changes in flowstream ke and pe terms
5. Steady state, steady flow

This particular case is not covered by any of the equations developed in the above discussion of heat exchangers. It is a combination of a pure substance (water vapor) and an incompressible fluid (river water). However, its ERB can be quickly arrived at by beginning with the general ERB for heat exchangers, Eq. 4.125, and adding the auxiliary formulae for the specific enthalpy change of an incompressible fluid given in Eq. 4.108. This gives

$$\underbrace{\dot{Q}}_{0} + \dot{m}_s(h_1 - h_2) = \dot{m}_w(h_4 - h_3)$$

$$= \dot{m}_w[c_w(T_4 - T_3) + v_w\underbrace{(p_4 - p_3)}_{0}]$$

Then solving for the river water mass flow rate $\dot{m}_w$ we get

$$\dot{m}_w = \dot{m}_s\{(h_1 - h_2)/[c_w(T_4 - T_3)]\}$$

This equation tells us what properties we need to calculate the unknown. The station data are listed below:

Station 1	Station 2	Station 3	Station 4
$p_1 = 1.0$ MPa	$x_2 = 0.0$ (sat. liq.)	$T_3 = 15$ °C	$T_4 = 20$ °C
$T_1 = 500$ °C	$p_2 = 1.0$ MPa		
$h_1 = 3478.4$ kJ/kg	$h_2 = 762.8$ kJ/kg		

Appendix C.3b gives us $h_1 = 3478.4$ kJ/kg, and Appendix C.2b gives us $h_2 = h_f(1.0\text{ MPa}) = 762.8$ kJ/kg. Both of these values have been added to the station data list above. Also, Table 3.5 in Chap. 3 gives the specific heat of liquid water as $c = 4.2$ kJ/(kg·K). The condensate flow rate was given in the problem statement to be $\dot{m}_s = 12.0$ kg/min, so that the required river water flow rate is

$$\dot{m}_w = (12.0\text{ kg/min})[(3478.4 - 762.8)\text{ kJ/kg}]/\{[4.2\text{ kJ/(kg·K)}](20 - 15\text{ K})\}$$

$$= 1552\text{ kg/min}$$

Shaft Work Machines

Shaft work machines are devices whose primary function is to promote a work input or output through a rotating or reciprocating shaft.[19] Common shaft work machines are hydraulic pumps, pneumatic compressors and fans, gas or hydraulic turbines, electric motors and generators, and external and internal combustion engines. Most shaft work machines are steady state, steady flow, single-inlet, single-outlet devices (electric motors and generators are exceptions since they have no flowstreams). The work produced or absorbed by such devices can then be determined from the MERB of Eq. 4.99 as

$$\dot{W}_{\text{shaft}} = \dot{m}[h_{\text{out}} - h_{\text{in}} + (V_{\text{out}}^2 - V_{\text{in}}^2)/2g_c + (Z_{\text{out}} - Z_{\text{in}})g/g_c] - \dot{Q} \quad \textbf{(4.132)}$$

This equation shows that the effect of heat loss ($\dot{Q} < 0$) from a work-producing device ($\dot{W} < 0$) is to *reduce* the device's power output. Therefore, most work—producing systems (engines, turbines, etc.) are insulated to improve their efficiency. Similarly, heat loss from a work-absorbing device (such as a compressor) will require that more work be supplied to produce the same state change in the flowstreams. Consequently, most of these devices are also insulated to increase their efficiency. Massive amounts of heat loss from these systems by external cooling usually indicates the need to lower their internal temperatures due to the existence of large internal irreversibilities. This is a consequence of the second law of thermodynamics and will be discussed in the next chapter.

Most shaft work machines have negligible change in specific kinetic and potential energies of their flowstreams. Obvious exceptions are hydroelectric water turbines in which the specific potential energy change of the water is the energy source for the turbine, and windmills in which the specific kinetic energy change of the air is the energy source for the windmill. The resulting ERB for an insulated shaft work machine with negligible changes in specific kinetic and potential flowstream energies, operating in a steady state, steady flow, single-inlet, single-outlet manner is obtained from Eq. 4.132 as

$$\dot{W}_{\text{shaft}} = \dot{m}(h_{\text{out}} - h_{\text{in}}) \quad \textbf{(4.133)}$$

Figure 4.13 illustrates the graphical symbols used to represent several common shaft work machines.

If an incompressible fluid is used in a shaft work machine described by Eq. 4.133, then Eq. 4.108 can be used to describe the change in specific enthalpy as

$$\dot{W}_{\text{shaft}}\Big|_{\substack{\text{incomp.}\\\text{fluid}}} = \dot{m}[c(T_{\text{out}} - T_{\text{in}}) + v(p_{\text{out}} - p_{\text{in}})] \quad \textbf{(4.134)}$$

Normally, there is very little temperature change across such devices as hydraulic pumps, motors, and turbines, so that Eq. 4.134 reduces to

$$\dot{W}_{\text{shaft}}\Big|_{\substack{\text{isothermal}\\\text{incomp.}\\\text{fluid}}} = \dot{m}v(p_{\text{out}} - p_{\text{in}}) \quad \textbf{(4.135)}$$

19. Shaft work output machines are often called *prime movers*.

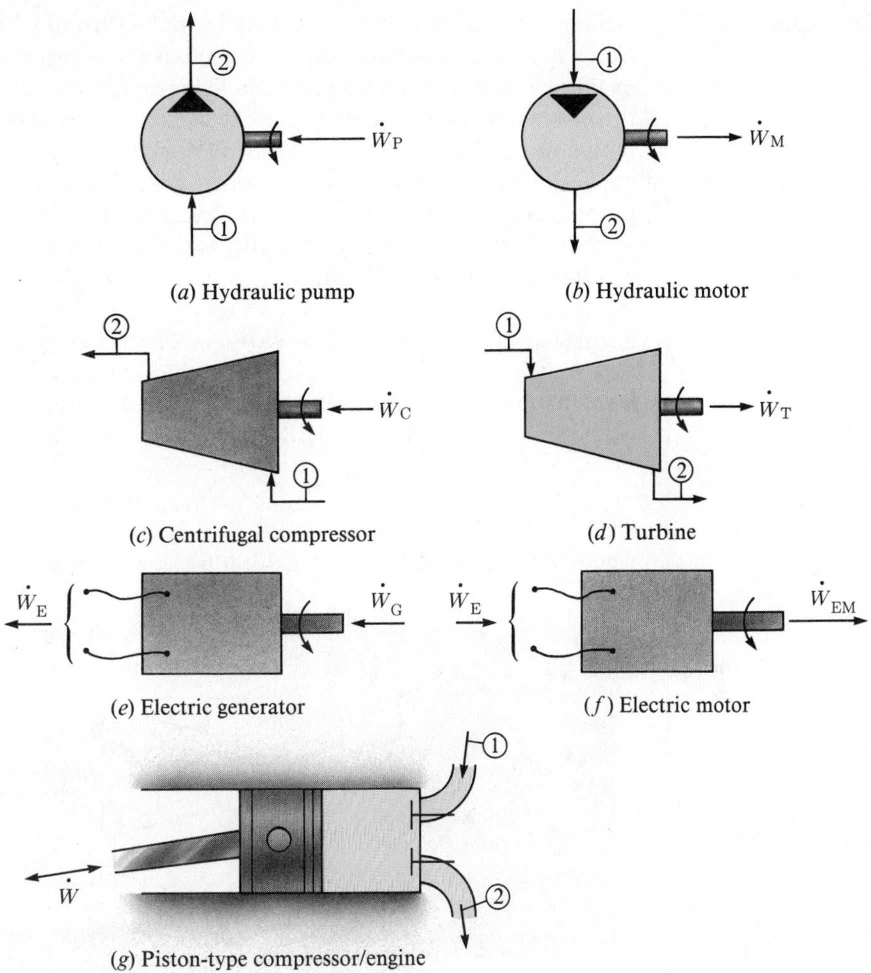

Figure 4.13 Graphical symbols for common shaft work machines.

Notice that in this equation,

$$\dot{m}v = (\rho AV)v = \frac{AV}{v}(v) = AV \tag{4.136}$$

where AV is the volume flow rate.

If an ideal gas with constant specific heats is used in a shaft work machine described by Eq. 4.133, then Eq. 4.113 can be used to describe the change in specific enthalpy, and Eq. 4.133 becomes

$$\dot{W}_{\text{shaft}}\Big|_{\substack{\text{ideal}\\\text{gas}}} = \dot{m}c_p(T_{\text{out}} - T_{\text{in}}) \tag{4.137}$$

Example 4.23 Nearly every urban home has water supplied from a local water main. This water is used in washing and cooking, but its pressure could also be used as an energy supply. Suppose you installed a small hydraulic motor or turbine on the inlet water pipe of your house. Every time water was used in the house the motor or turbine would produce shaft work that could be used to run a small appliance or to drive an electric generator and charge a battery. How much power could you realize in this way if you used an average of 20 gal of water over an eight- (8.0) hour period, with an inlet water pressure of 85 psig and an exit water pressure of 10 psig?

Solution The unknown here is $\dot{W}_{\text{shaft}}$. The water is an incompressible fluid, and we will ignore any changes in specific kinetic or potential energy of the flowstream plus any heat transfer that may occur. For steady state, steady flow, isothermal conditions our MERB becomes Eq. 4.135 above, or

$$\dot{W}_{\text{shaft}} = \dot{m}v(p_{\text{out}} - p_{\text{in}})$$

where $\dot{m}v$ = 20 gal/8.0 h = 2.5 gal/h (on the average).

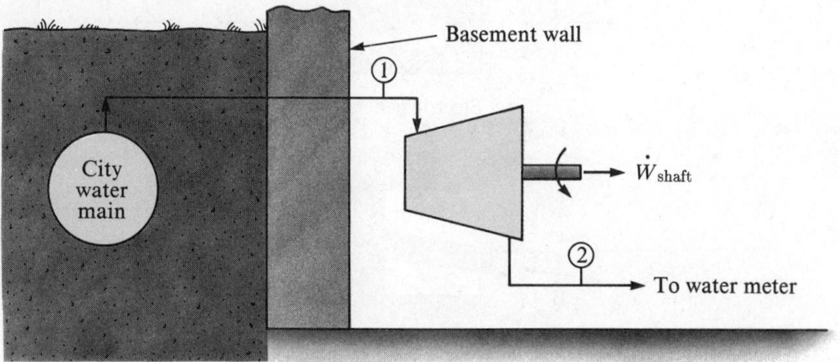

Now, (2.5 gal/h)(0.13368 ft³/gal)(1 h/3600 s) = 9.28×10^{-5} ft³/s. Then,

$$\begin{aligned}\dot{W}_{\text{shaft}} &= (9.28 \times 10^{-5}\ \text{ft}^3/\text{s})[(10 - 85)\ \text{lbf/in}^2](144\ \text{in}^2/\text{ft}^2) \\ &= -1.00\ \text{ft}\cdot\text{lbf/s} \\ &= (-1.00\ \text{ft}\cdot\text{lbf/s})[1\ \text{hp}/(550\ \text{ft}\cdot\text{lbf/s})] = -1.82 \times 10^{-3}\ \text{hp} \\ &= (-1.82 \times 10^{-3}\ \text{hp})(746\ \text{W/hp}) = -1.36\ \text{W}\end{aligned}$$

Thus, the amount of power we would get out of such a device would be extremely low and probably would not justify its initial expense.[20]

20. This conclusion might change if we were dealing with the domestic water flow into a large factory or multistory office or apartment building.

Suppose, now, we calculate an instantaneous power instead of the average power. For this calculation we will assume an instantaneous water flow of 5 gal/min. Then the hydraulic power produced would be

$$\dot{W}_{shaft}\Big|_{instantaneous} = (-1.36\text{ W})(5\text{ gal/min})(60\text{ min/h})[1/(2.5\text{ gal/h})] = -163\text{ W}$$

which is more reasonable. This is enough power to light two 75-W light bulbs, but since this water flow rate does not occur continuously the bulbs would not be lit very often.

Example 4.24 Determine the quality of the steam at the outlet of an insulated steam turbine producing 2000 kJ of energy per kilogram of steam flowing through the turbine. The steam at the inlet of the turbine is at 2.0 MPa, 800 °C and the outlet pressure is 1.0 kPa. Neglect any changes in specific kinetic or potential energy of the flowstream, and assume a steady state operation.

Solution The unknown here is the turbine's outlet quality x_2, as shown in the schematic below.

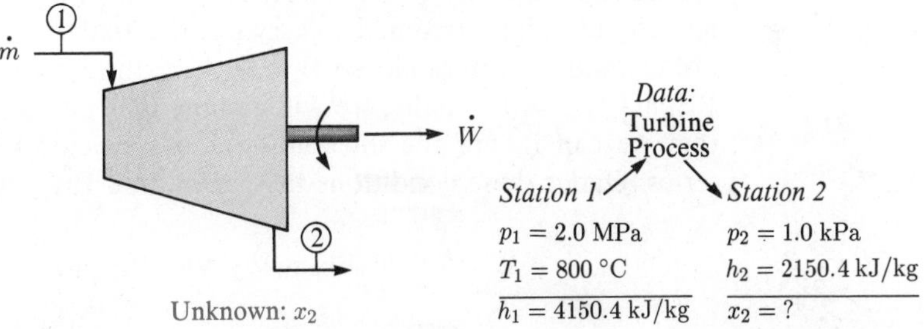

The MERB for the conditions described in the problem statement is Eq. 4.133:

$$\dot{W}_{shaft} = \dot{m}(h_2 - h_1)$$

We do not know $\dot{m}$ here, but we do know the energy produced per kilogram of steam flowing, $W/m = \dot{W}/\dot{m} = -2000$ kJ/kg, so

$$-2000\text{ kJ/kg} = h_2 - h_1$$

From Appendix C.3*b* we have $h_1 = 4150.4$ kJ/kg, and from Appendix C.2*b* we have $h_{f2} = 29.30$ kJ/kg, $h_{fg2} = 2484.9$ kJ/kg, and $h_{g2} = 2514.2$ kJ/kg (all at 1.0 kPa). Therefore,

$$h_2 = \dot{W}/\dot{m} + h_1 = -2000 + 4150.4 = 2150.4\text{ kJ/kg}$$

These values of h_1 and h_2 have been added to our station data list above. Thus, the values of $h_2 = 2150.4$ kJ/kg and $p_2 = 1.0$ kPa are a pair of two independent properties in the outlet state. Therefore, the outlet quality can be found from the auxiliary formula for quality:

$$x_2 = (h_2 - h_{f2}(1.0\text{ kPa}))/h_{fg2}(1.0\text{ kPa})$$
$$= (2150.4 - 29.30)/2484.9 = 0.854$$
$$= 85.4\%\text{ vapor at the turbine's outlet}$$

Open System Unsteady State Processes

There are a wide variety of open system unsteady state processes in industry. Most are too complex to analyze easily, but one of the simpler cases involves the filling or emptying of a rigid tank or vessel.

Consider the tank-filling process illustrated in Figure 4.14. In this system a rigid tank is connected through a valve to a high-pressure supply pipe. When the valve is opened, the rigid tank is filled from the supply pipe until the tank pressure is equal to that of the supply pipe. This is the filling process that we wish to analyze.

The filling process is neither steady state nor steady flow since the mass of the system is continually changing. Also, the system has a single-inlet flowstream but has no outlet flowstream. To carry out the analysis we note that the system does not contain a work mode, so $\dot{W} = 0$. Also, the system is not moving, so $[d(\text{KE} + \text{PE})/dt]_{\text{system}} = 0$. Finally, we will assume that the tank is filled slowly enough so that we can ignore the inlet flowstream's specific kinetic and potential energy terms. Under these conditions the generalized ERB equation becomes

$$\dot{Q} + 0 + \dot{m}_{\text{in}}(h_{\text{in}} + 0 + 0) - 0 = (dU/dt + 0 + 0)_{\text{tank}}$$

or

$$\dot{Q} + \dot{m}_{\text{in}} h_{\text{in}} = [d(mu)/dt]_{\text{tank}}$$

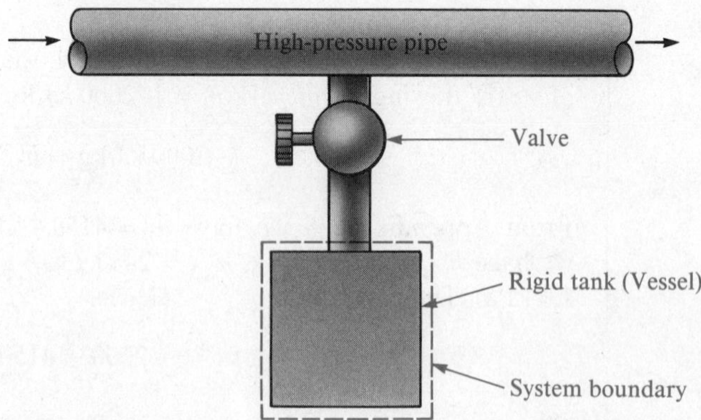

Figure 4.14 Filling a rigid vessel.

Then multiplying through by dt and integrating over the filling process gives

$$ {}_1Q_2 + \int_1^2 h_{\text{in}}\, dm_{\text{in}} = (m_2u_2 - m_1u_1)_{\text{tank}} \tag{4.138} $$

where state 1 is the initial state inside the tank and state 2 is the state inside the tank after it has been filled. When the tank is filled from a pipe of unlimited supply as shown in Figure 4.14, then h_{in} = constant, and Eq. 4.138 becomes

$$ {}_1Q_2 + h_{\text{in}}m_{\text{in}} = (m_2u_2 - m_1u_1)_{\text{tank}} \tag{4.139} $$

where the conservation of mass law for the filling process gives

$$ m_{\text{in}} = (m_2 - m_1)_{\text{tank}} \tag{4.140} $$

Equation 4.139 can then be rearranged to produce

$$ u_2 = u_1(m_1/m_2) + {}_1Q_2/m_2 + h_{\text{in}}(1 - m_1/m_2) \tag{4.141} $$

where the numerical subscripts refer exclusively to states inside the tank from this point on.

By knowing p_2 from the filling process and by calculating u_2 from Eq. 4.141 we have fixed the final thermodynamic state of the filled tank and can then find the value of any other property we desire, say its final temperature T_2. To illustrate this, let's assume the tank is insulated (${}_1Q_2 = 0$) and initially evacuated ($m_1 = 0$). Then Eq. 4.141 becomes

$$ u_2 = h_{\text{in}} \tag{4.142} $$

If we now assume that the tank is filled with an incompressible fluid, then we can utilize Eq. 4.108 and write

$$ u_2 = cT_2 = h_{\text{in}} = cT_{\text{in}} + vp_{\text{in}} $$

or

$$ T_2\Big|_{\substack{\text{filling}\\ \text{incomp.}\\ \text{fluid}}} = T_{\text{in}} + (vp_{\text{in}})/c \tag{4.143} $$

and the compression process of pressurizing the tank would cause T_2 to be greater than T_{in} by an amount $(vp_{\text{in}})/c$. On the other hand, if we assume that the tank is filled with an ideal gas, then we can utilize Eq. 4.113 to get

$$ u_2 = c_vT_2 = h_{\text{in}} = c_pT_{\text{in}} $$

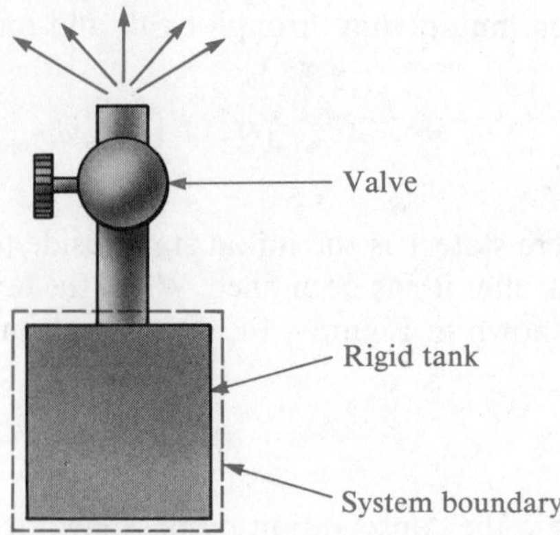

Figure 4.15 Emptying a rigid vessel.

or

$$T_2\Big|_{\substack{\text{filling}\\ \text{ideal}\\ \text{gas}}} = (c_p/c_v)T_{\text{in}} = kT_{\text{in}} \tag{4.144}$$

In the case of an ideal gas the compression process generates a considerable amount of internal energy. For air $k = 1.4$, and if $T_{\text{in}} = 70\ °\text{F} = 530\ \text{R}$ then $T_2 = 1.4(530\ \text{R}) = 742\ \text{R} = 282\ °\text{F}$. Thus, bottled gas tanks can get quite hot during their filling process and should be cooled to minimize any rupture potential.

The tank-emptying process is illustrated in Figure 4.15. Again we neglect flowstream specific kinetic and potential energies, and require that the tank remain stationary and have no work transport of energy.

When the valve is opened, the initially pressurized rigid tank empties into the environment. The generalized ERB for this process reduces to

$$\dot{Q} + 0 + 0 - \dot{m}_{\text{out}}(h_{\text{out}} + 0 + 0) = (dU/dt + 0 + 0)_{\text{tank}}$$

or

$$\dot{Q} - \dot{m}_{\text{out}}h_{\text{out}} = [d(mu)/dt]_{\text{tank}}$$

Again multiplying through by dt and integrating gives

$${}_1Q_2 - \int_1^2 h_{\text{out}}\, dm_{\text{out}} = (m_2u_2 - m_1u_1)_{\text{tank}} \tag{4.145}$$

where 1 is the filled state and 2 is the empty state (the reverse of the filling process). Unlike the filling process described above, the emptying process does not have a constant flowstream specific enthalpy ($h_{\text{out}} \neq$ constant), therefore the integral in Eq. 4.145 cannot be evaluated. However, we can devise a way of dealing with this by defining an average specific enthalpy for the discharge flowstream as

$$h_{avg} = (1/m_{out}) \int_1^2 h_{out}\, dm_{out} \tag{4.146}$$

where, from the conservation of mass law, $m_{out} = (m_1 - m_2)_{tank}$. Approximating h_{avg} as $[(h_1 + h_2)/2]_{tank}$, Eq. 4.145 becomes

$${}_1Q_2 - h_1(m_1 - m_2)/2 - h_2(m_1 - m_2)/2 = m_2u_2 - m_1u_1 \tag{4.147}$$

where the numerical subscripts refer exclusively to states inside the tank from this point on.

The effect of the emptying process can be more easily seen by simplifying the analysis somewhat. Let's stipulate that the tank is insulated (so ${}_1Q_2 = 0$) and that $m_1 \gg m_2 \approx 0$. Then Eq. 4.147 can be rearranged to give

$$h_2 = 2u_1 - h_1 \tag{4.148}$$

In the case of emptying a pressurized incompressible fluid, we can write $u = cT$ and $h = cT + vp$, and then Eq. 4.148 gives

$$T_2\Big|_{\substack{\text{emptying}\\ \text{incomp.}\\ \text{fluid}}} = T_1 - (v/c)(p_1 + p_2) \tag{4.149}$$

In the case of emptying a pressurized ideal gas, we can write $u = c_vT$ and $h = c_pT$ and then Eq. 4.148 gives

$$T_2\Big|_{\substack{\text{emptying}\\ \text{ideal}\\ \text{gas}}} = T_1[(2/k) - 1] \tag{4.150}$$

Equation 4.149 tells us that the expansion process that accompanies the emptying process of an incompressible fluid always causes the final temperature inside the tank to be less than the initial temperature inside the tank. There is also a temperature drop for the emptying of a pressurized ideal gas when $1 < k < 2$. In the case of air, $k = 1.4$, so if $T_1 = 70\ °F = 530$ R, then $T_2 = (530\text{ R})[(2/1.4) - 1] = 227.1\text{ R} = -232.9\ °F$. Since a continuous expansion process lowers the temperature of the remaining contents, this explains why pressurized paint, deodorant, etc., cans become very cold when they are continuously discharged.

Example 4.25 An insulated rigid tank on a spacecraft contains nitrogen at 2000 psig and 70 °F. It is desired to discharge the tank isothermally to supply constant temperature nitrogen to the attitude control thrustors. This can be done if a portion of the discharged nitrogen is recycled back to the tank through a heater and compressor as shown in the schematic. Assuming nitrogen to be an ideal gas and ignoring any changes in tank or flowstream kinetic and potential energies, determine

a) an expression for the ratio of recycled mass flow rate ($\dot{m}_R$) to discharge mass flow rate ($\dot{m}_D$) so that the temperature of the nitrogen in the tank (T_T) is constant in time, and

b) the values of $\dot{m}_R/\dot{m}_D$ and $\dot{Q}_H$ for $T_R = 200\ °F$, $T_T = 70\ °F$, $\dot{m}_R = 0.5$ lbm/s, and $\dot{W}_C = 3.0$ hp.

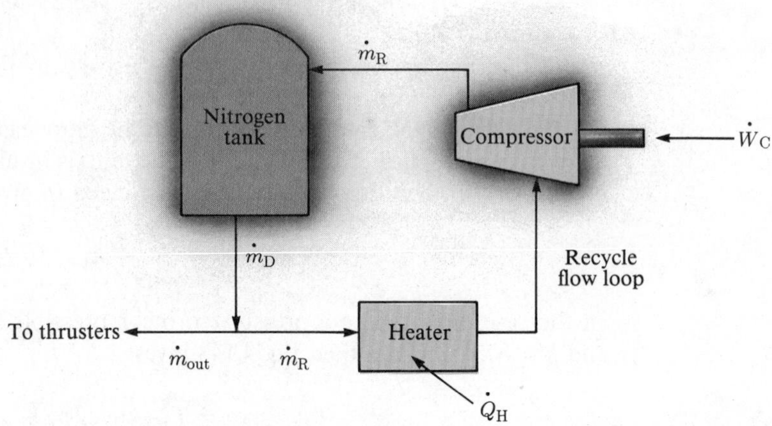

Solution The unknown here is to find a formula for $\dot{m}_R/\dot{m}_D$ and then to find its value for a specific set of conditions. Since $\dot{m}_R$ and $\dot{m}_D$ are mass flow rates into and out of the tank, let's first apply the general ERB to the tank alone and see what happens.

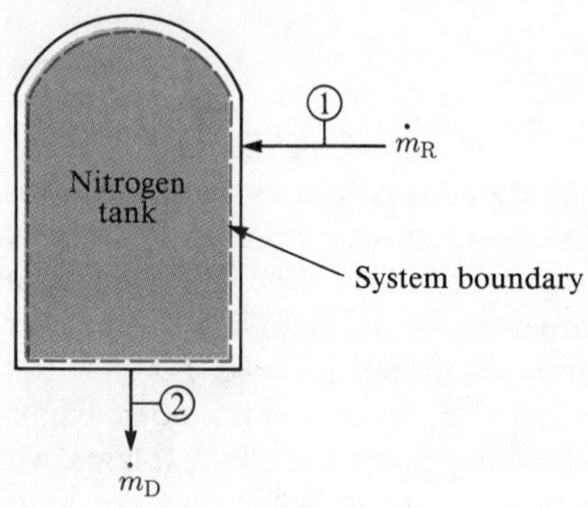

Assumptions

1. $\dot{Q} = 0$ (tank is insulated).
2. $\dot{W} = 0$ (no work done on or by the tank itself).
3. $T_T = T_2 = 70\ °F$ = constant (isothermal discharge).
4. Neglect changes in KE and PE of the flowstreams and the tank.
5. Treat N_2 as an ideal gas.

Then the general ERB becomes

$$\underbrace{\dot{Q}}_{0} + \underbrace{\dot{W}}_{0} + \dot{m}_R(h_1 + \underbrace{V_1^2/2g_c + gZ_1/g_c}_{0}) - \dot{m}_D(h_2 + \underbrace{V_2^2/2g_c + gZ_2/g_c}_{0})$$

$$= d(mu)_T/dt + \underbrace{d(KE + PE)_T/dt}_{0}$$

or

$$\dot{m}_R h_1 - \dot{m}_D h_2 = d(mu)_T/dt = \dot{m}_T u_T + m_T \dot{u}_T$$

Now, $\dot{u}_T = du_T/dt = d(c_v T_T)/dt = 0$ since T_T = constant. The conservation of mass law gives

$$\dot{m}_T = \dot{m}_R - \dot{m}_D$$

Then the ERB becomes

$$\dot{m}_R h_1 - \dot{m}_D h_2 = (\dot{m}_R - \dot{m}_D) u_T$$

or

$$\dot{m}_R/\dot{m}_D = (h_2 - u_T)/(h_1 - u_T)$$

Now,

$$h_2 = c_p T_2 = c_p T_T$$

and

$$u_T = c_v T_T$$

Then,

$$\dot{m}_R/\dot{m}_D = [(c_p - c_v)T_T]/(c_p T_1 - c_v T_T) = R/[c_p(T_1/T_T) - c_v]$$
$$= 1/[(c_p/R)(T_1/T_T) - c_v/R]$$

Since

$$c_p/R = c_p/(c_p - c_v) = k/(k-1)$$

and

$$c_v/R = c_v/(c_p - c_v) = 1/(k-1)$$

then

$$\dot{m}_R/\dot{m}_D = (k-1)/[k(T_1/T_T) - 1]$$

In part b we are given that $T_T = 70\ °F = 530\ R$ and $T_1 = 200\ °F = 660\ R$.

Appendix C.13*a* gives us the specific heat ratio for nitrogen as $k = 1.4$. Therefore, our resultant equation gives

$$\dot{m}_R/\dot{m}_D = (1.4 - 1)/[1.4(660/530) - 1] = 0.538$$

Thus, 53.8% of the discharge mass must be recycled to keep the tank temperature constant.

To find the rate of recycle heat transfer required in part b, we must analyze the heater and compressor as a separate system.

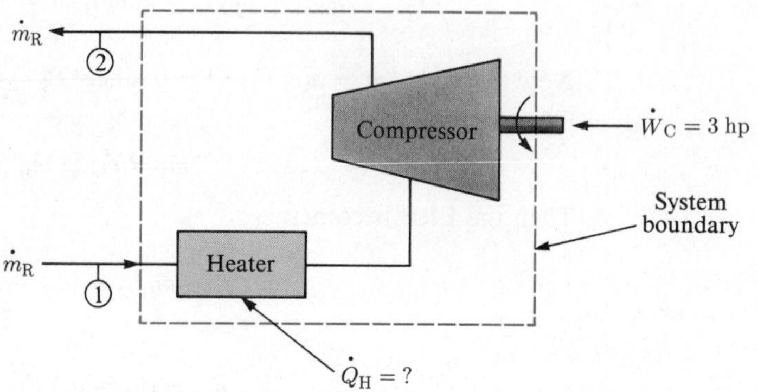

In general, $\dot{m}_R$ will not be constant in time in this system. We will assume that a feedback control system exists that will automatically scale down $\dot{W}_C$ and $\dot{Q}_H$ as $\dot{m}_R$ goes to zero and the tank empties. We will also assume that the internal, kinetic, and potential energies of the entire system are constant in time so that we will have a steady state, steady flow, single-inlet, single-outlet system. Under these conditions the MERB becomes

$$\dot{Q}_H + \dot{W}_C + \dot{m}_R(h_1 - h_2) = 0$$

where we have again neglected any changes in flowstream specific kinetic and potential energies. Using the ideal gas relationship for specific enthalpy gives

$$\dot{Q}_H = \dot{m}_R c_p(T_2 - T_1) - \dot{W}_C$$

Appendix C.13*a* gives $c_p = 0.248$ Btu/(lbm·R) for nitrogen. Then,

$$\begin{aligned}\dot{Q}_H &= (0.5 \text{ lbm/s})[0.248 \text{ Btu/(lbm}\cdot\text{R)}](660 - 530 \text{ R})\\ &\quad - (3.0 \text{ hp})[550 \text{ ft}\cdot\text{lbf/(s}\cdot\text{hp)}][1 \text{ Btu/(778 ft}\cdot\text{lbf)}]\\ &= 14 \text{ Btu/s}\end{aligned}$$

Summary

In Section I of this chapter we studied the basic energy balance and a variety of energy transport mechanisms. Since energy can be neither created nor destroyed, the resulting energy balance reduced to having the net gain in energy by a system equal the net transport of energy into the system. The three basic energy transport mechanisms (work, heat, and mass flow) were discussed in detail and it was pointed out that they are mathematically all path functions (i.e., their numerical values depend on the process path itself through an integral along the path) and that they can all be represented as the product of a generalized force (an intensive property) and a generalized displacement (an extensive property). Then we established a workable technique for solving thermodynamic word problems and went on in Section II to demonstrate the use of this technique in the analysis of closed systems utilizing the first law of thermodynamics. In Section III of this chapter we demonstrated the use of the first law of thermodynamics and the conservation of mass law in analyzing open system problems.

The example problems discussed in this chapter were not meant to cover all the possible aspects of closed and open system energy analysis. They were chosen to illustrate the problem-solving technique, thermodynamic table usage, and how to make basic assumptions about process variables. You must learn how to successfully apply a generalized problem solution technique, such as the one used in

Table 4.13 Glossary of technical terms introduced in Chapter 4

EB	The energy balance.
ERB	The energy rate balance.
$_1Q_2$ and $\dot{Q}$	Heat transfer and heat transfer rate.
$_1W_2$ and $\dot{W}$	Work and work rate (power).
Aergonic	No work.
Reversible work	No losses (i.e., no friction, heat transfer, etc.).
Work efficiency	A measure of the losses within a machine.
Coefficient of performance	The name we give energy conversion efficiency when it is more than 100%.
Conduction heat transfer	The heat transport of energy that obeys Fourier's law.
Convection heat transfer	The heat transport of energy that obeys Newton's law of cooling.
Radiation heat transfer	The heat transport of energy that obeys the Maxwell-Boltzmann law.
Adiabatic	No heat transfer.
Steady state	A thermodynamic state that is constant in time.
Steady flow	A state wherein the mass of an open system is constant in time.
Flowstream	Where mass crosses a system boundary.
Station	A data-monitoring point on a flowstream.
MEB	The modified energy balance.
MERB	The modified energy rate balance.
Pressure energy	Sometimes called the pressure *head*, $\dot{m}pv$.
Nozzle	A device for converting pressure energy into kinetic energy.
Diffuser	A device for converting kinetic energy into pressure energy.
Heat exchanger	A device for promoting heat transfer from one fluid to another.

this chapter and illustrated in the flow chart of Figure 4.6. More problem-solving skills will be gained by doing problems at the end of this chapter.

Table 4.13 lists some of the new technical thermodynamic terms introduced in this chapter. These terms will be used without further explanation in the chapters that follow. It is recommended that the student learn their definitions before proceeding to the next chapter.

Selected References

Burghardt, M. D. *Engineering Thermodynamics with Applications*, 2d ed. Cambridge, MA: Harper & Row, 1982.

Cravalho, E. G., and Smith, J. L., Jr. *Engineering Thermodynamics.* Boston: Pitman, 1981.

Faires, V. M., and Simmang, C. M. *Thermodynamics*, 6th ed. New York: MacMillan, 1978.

Faires, V. M., Simmang, C. M., and Brewer, A. V. *Problems on Thermodynamics*, 5th ed. New York: Macmillan, 1970.

Haberman, W. L., and John, J. E. *Engineering Thermodynamics.* Boston: Pitman, 1981.

Holman, J. P. *Heat Transfer*, 4th ed. New York: McGraw-Hill, 1976.

Kestin, J. *A Course in Thermodynamics*, rev. printing, Vol. 1. New York: Hemisphere, 1979.

Reynolds, W. C., and Perkins, H. C. *Engineering Thermodynamics*, 2d ed. New York: McGraw-Hill, 1977.

Van Wylen, G. J., and Sonntag, R. E. *Fundamentals of Classical Thermodynamics*, 3d ed. New York: Wiley, 1986.

Wark, K. *Thermodynamics*, 5th ed. New York: McGraw-Hill, 1988.

Chapter Four Problems

Problems for Section I

1. Determine the energy transport required to increase the temperature of 3.5 kg of air from 20 to 100 °C. Assume the air is stationary and behaves as an ideal gas with constant specific heats.

2. Determine the energy transport necessary to decrease the temperature of 15.0 kg of methane from 500 to 20 °C. Assume the methane is stationary and behaves as an ideal gas with constant specific heats.

3. Determine the gain in energy of a stationary system of 5.0 lbm of argon whose temperature is increased from 70 to 1000 °F. Assume ideal gas behavior with constant specific heats.

4. Determine the gain in energy of a stationary system of 11.0 kg of oxygen whose pressure is increased from 0.1 to 100 MPa isothermally. Assume ideal gas behavior with constant specific heats.

5. 150 Btu are transported into a system via a work mode while 75 Btu are removed via heat transfer and mass flow modes. Determine the net energy gain for this system.

6. A jet aircraft with a constant specific internal energy of 3500 Btu/lbm consumes fuel at a rate of 50 lbm/min while flying horizontally at an altitude of 30,000 ft with a constant velocity of 500 ft/s. Determine the net energy transport rate of the aircraft.

7. An automobile transmission has 175 hp of power entering from the engine, 167 hp leaving to the wheels, while losing 5000 Btu/h to the surroundings as heat. What is the net energy transport rate of the transmission?

878.22
860.35

8. To keep the transmission in the previous problem from overheating it was decided to cool it by circulating a coolant through its case. If the coolant enters the transmission with a mass flow energy rate of 10.0 Btu/s, what is its mass flow energy rate as it leaves the transmission?

9. Determine the heat transfer rate, in Btu/h, required to cool a 200-kW electric generator that is driven by a 300-hp diesel engine. *Note*: The generator will run cool if it has a zero net energy transport rate.

10. In a stationary dynamometer test, an internal combustion automobile engine had a fuel energy input rate of 1.9 million Btu/h while producing 150 hp of output power. What other energy transport mechanisms are present and what are their magnitudes. Assume that the net energy transport rate is zero.

11. Determine the heat transfer per lbm necessary to raise the temperature of a closed rigid tank of saturated water vapor from 0.14 MPa to 800 °C.

12. A rigid vessel of volume 5.0 ft^3 contains steam at 100 psia with 83.91% moisture. If 9490.4 Btu of heat are added to the steam, find the final pressure and quality (if wet) or temperature (if superheated).

13. A rigid vessel having a volume of 20.0 ft^3 is filled with steam at 100 psia and 500 °F. Heat is transferred from the steam until it exists as saturated vapor. Calculate the amount of heat transferred during this process.

14. A sealed rigid tank of 10.0-ft^3 capacity is initially filled with steam at 100 psia and 500 °F. The tank and its contents are then cooled to 260 °F. Find **a)** the final quality in the container and the amounts of liquid water and water vapor (in lbm), and **b)** the amount of heat transfer required (in Btu).

15. A sealed rigid vessel contains 5.0 kg of water (liquid plus vapor) at 100 °C and a quality of 30.375%.

a) What is the specific volume of the water?

b) What is the mass of water in the vapor phase?

c) What would be the saturation pressure and temperature of this water if it had the specific volume determined in part a above and a quality of 100%?

d) What heat transfer would be required to completely condense the saturated vapor of part c above into a saturated liquid?

16. One pound of saturated liquid water at a pressure of 40.0 psia is contained in a rigid, closed, stationary tank. 3000 ft·lbf of work is done on the system by a paddle wheel, while heat is transferred to or from the system. The final pressure of the system is 20.0 psia. Calculate the amount of heat transferred and indicate its direction.

17. Identify the following as either point or path functions:

a) $u^2 + 3u - 5$ **b)** $T(h^2 - u^2) - 3(u - pv) + 4$

c) $\sin u^3 + \sin h^3$ **d)** $\int_1^2 V\, dp$ where $V = V(p)$.

18. Identify the following as either point or path functions:

a) RT/v **b)** $\int_1^2 p\, dV$ where $p = p(V)$

c) $h + pv$ **d)** $u + V^2/2g_c + gZ/g_c$.

19. Explain whether $u_2 - u_1 = \int_1^2 c_v\, dT$ is a point or a path function for a given system.

20. Explain whether $h_2 - h_1 = \int_1^2 c_p\, dT$ is a point or a path function for a given system.

21. Explain the meaning of the notation ${}_1Q_2$ and ${}_1W_2$. Why do we not write ${}_1E_2$, ${}_1u_2$ or ${}_1h_2$?

22. Determine the moving boundary work transport of energy when 10.0 lbm of water expands at constant pressure from saturated liquid to saturated vapor while at 70 °F.

23. Determine the moving boundary work done by the atmosphere (14.7 psia) as a cube of ice 2 in on a side melts into a pool of liquid water. At 32 °F, the density of ice is 57.2 lbm/ft^3 and that of liquid water is 62.4 lbm/ft^3.

24. Determine the moving boundary work done by a cube of solid CO_2 2 in on a side as it vaporizes at atmospheric pressure (14.7 psia). The density of solid CO_2 is 97.561 lbm/ft^3 and that of CO_2 vapor is 0.174 lbm/ft^3.

25. A weather balloon is filled with helium at 50 °F so that its volume is 500 ft^3. The balloon is left anchored in the sun and its temperature rises to 110 °F. How much moving boundary work is done by the balloon on the atmosphere as its volume increases due to the increase in temperature? Assume that helium is an ideal gas and that the balloon skin is sufficiently thin so that the pressure in the balloon remains approximately atmospheric.

26. 2.0 m^3 of air (considered an ideal gas) is initially at a pressure of 101.3 kPa and a temperature of 20 °C. The air is compressed at a constant temperature in a closed system to a pressure of 0.5 MPa. **a)** How much work is done on the air to compress it? **b)** How much energy was transferred as heat during the compression process?

27. Show that the first law of thermodynamics requires that for an ideal gas with a constant specific heat ratio $c_p/c_v = k$ undergoing a polytropic process (i.e., pv^n = constant), that

a) n must be greater than k for $T_2 < T_1$ when there is heat transfer from the gas, and that

b) n must be less than k for $T_2 < T_1$ when there is a heat transfer to the gas.

28. Find the moving boundary work done on a gas in compressing it from $\mathcal{V}_1 = 10.0$ ft^3, $p_1 = 10.0$ psia to $\mathcal{V}_2 = 1.0$ ft^3 according to the relation $p\mathcal{V}^3$ = constant.

29. A brilliant young engineer claims to have invented an engine that runs on the following thermodynamic cycle:

a) an isochoric pressurization from p_1 to $p_2 = 2p_1$,

b) an isobaric expansion from $\mathcal{V}_2$ to $\mathcal{V}_3 = 2\mathcal{V}_2$.

c) an isochoric depressurization from p_3 to $p_4 = p_1$, and

d) an isobaric compression back to the initial state, p_1, $\mathcal{V}_1$.

Determine the net moving boundary work done during this cycle if $p_1 = 25.0$ kPa and $\mathcal{V}_1 = 0.03$ m^3. Sketch this cycle on a p-$\mathcal{V}$ diagram.

30. A balloon filled with air at 0.1 MN/m^2 absolute is heated in sunlight. As the balloon is heated, it expands according to the following pressure–volume relation:

$$p = 0.1 + 0.15\mathcal{V} + 0.06\mathcal{V}^2$$

where p is in MN/m^2 and $\mathcal{V}$ is in m^3. Determine the moving boundary work transport of energy as the balloon expands from 1.0 to 2.0 m^3.

31. One lbm of an ideal gas with molecular weight 6.44 lbm/lbmole is compressed reversibly in a closed system from 100 psia, 600 R to a final specific volume of 8.0 ft^3/lbm. At all points during the compression, the pressure and specific volume are related by

$$p = 50 + 4v + 0.1v^2$$

where p is in psia and v is in ft^3/lbm. Determine the moving boundary work required and the heat transfer during this compression if the gas has a constant volume specific heat of 0.20 Btu/(lbm·R).

32. Three lbm of a substance is made to undergo a reversible expansion process within a piston–cylinder device starting from an initial pressure of 100 psia and an initial volume of 2.0 ft^3. The final volume is 4.0 ft^3. Determine the moving boundary work produced by this expansion for each of the process paths listed below. Note which process produces the maximum work and which produces the minimum.

a) Pressure remains constant ($p = K$).
b) Pressure times volume remains constant ($pV = K$).
c) Pressure is proportional to volume ($p = KV$).
d) Pressure is proportional to the square of volume ($p = KV^2$).
e) Pressure is proportional to the square root of volume ($p = K\sqrt{V}$), where K is a constant in each case.

33. The magnitude of the torque T on a shaft is given in N·m by

$$T = 6.3 \cos\theta \qquad \text{where } \theta \text{ is the angular displacement.}$$

If the torque and displacement vectors are parallel, determine the work required to rotate the shaft through one complete revolution.

34. The magnitude of the torque vector normal to the axis of a shaft is given in ft·lbf by

$$\begin{aligned} T &= 21.7 \sin\theta && \text{for } 0 < \theta \leq \pi \\ &= 0 && \text{for } \pi < \theta \leq 3\pi/2 \\ &= 50.4 && \text{for } 3\pi/2 < \theta \leq 2\pi \end{aligned}$$

Determine the work done in one complete revolution of the shaft.

35. When the torque and angular displacement vectors are parallel, the torque–displacement relation for the drive shaft of a 1909 American Underslung automobile is given by

$$T\theta^n = K$$

where K and n are constants. Determine a general formula for the shaft work when **a)** $n = 1.0$, and **b)** $n \neq 1.0$.

36. How much elastic work is done in uniaxially stretching an initially unstrained elastic steel bar (Young's modulus $= 3 \times 10^7$ psi = constant) whose volume (also a constant) is 5.0 in^3 to a total strain of 0.002 in/in?

37. When a rubber band is stretched it exerts a restoring force (F) that is a function of its initial length (L) and of displacement (x). For a certain rubber band this relation is

$$F = K\left[\frac{x}{L} + \left(\frac{x}{L}\right)^2\right] \qquad \text{where } K = 0.81 \text{ lbf.}$$

Determine the elastic work (with the appropriate sign) required to stretch the rubber band from an initial length of 2.0 in to a final length of 3.0 in.

38. A 10.0-cm soap bubble is blown on the end of a large-diameter blowpipe. When the blowpipe end opposite the bubble is uncovered, the surface tension in the soap bubble causes it to collapse, thus sending its contents through the blowpipe and into the atmosphere. Estimate the velocity of the air in the blowpipe as the bubble collapses. For the soap bubble, $\sigma_s = 0.04$ N/m.

39. At 68 °F the surface tension of acetic acid is 1.59×10^{-4} lbf/in. A film of acetic acid is maintained on the wire frame as shown in the drawing. Determine the surface tension work done when the wire is moved 1.0 in in the direction indicated.

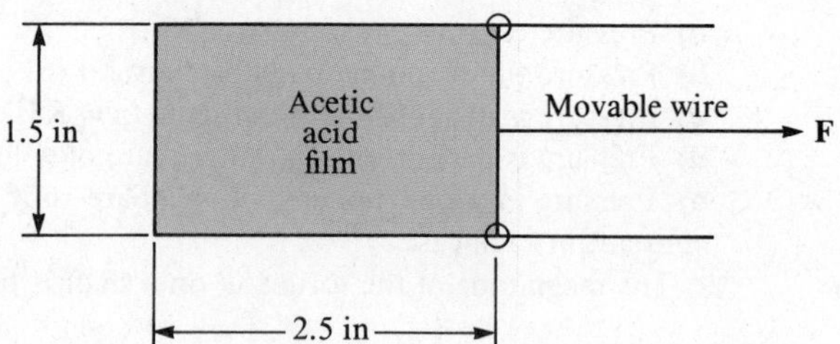

40. A 12-V automobile battery receives a constant charge from the engines generator. The voltage across the terminals is 12.5 V dc, and the current is 9 A. Determine the electrical work energy transport rate from the automobile's engine to the battery in both watts and horsepower.

41. A battery-powered wheelchair uses a standard 12-V automotive lead–acid battery with a capacity of 20 A·h. Peukert's law for the discharge of lead–acid batteries is

$$\sigma i^{1.4} = K$$

where σ is the discharge time, i is the discharge current, and K is a constant that depends upon the battery size. The capacity of the battery is given by

$$\text{capacity} = \sigma i = K i^{-0.4}$$

and the average voltage during discharge is given by

$$\phi = 11.868 - 0.0618 i$$

a) How much current is drawn from the battery if the torque on the drive shaft is 1.0 ft·lbf when it is rotating at 1.0 rev/s?

b) How long will the wheelchair operate with this current drain before the battery is discharged?

c) Evaluate the constant K for this battery with this current drain.

42. Determine the electrical current power averaged over one period, T, for a sawtooth current waveform passing through a pure resistance R described by

$$i = i_{max}(t/T) \qquad \text{for } 0 < t < T$$

43. In an ac circuit in which a phase angle Θ exists, the voltage and current are written as

$$\phi = \phi_{max}\cos(2\pi f t).$$

$$i = i_{max}\cos(2\pi f t - \Theta).$$

Show that the electrical current power averaged over one period $(1/f)$ is

$$(\dot{W})_{\text{electrical avg.}} = (1/2)\phi_{max} i_{max}\cos(\Theta) = \phi_e i_e \cos(\Theta)$$

and thus that the average power of any purely reactive ($\Theta = \pi/2$) circuit consisting entirely of ideal inductors and capacitors is zero. The term $\cos(\Theta)$ is called the *power factor*, and the product $\phi_e i_e$ is called the *apparent* power. For a purely resistive circuit $\Theta = 0$, and the average power equals the apparent power.

44. Show that the polarization work required to charge a parallel plate capacitor is given by

$$ {}_1W_2 = C\phi^2/2 $$

where $C = \epsilon_o \chi_e A/d$ is the capacitance, ϕ is the voltage difference, A is the area of the plates, and d is their separation distance.

45. An electrical capacitor constructed of two parallel conducting plates of area A, separated by a distance d, has a capacitance C given by

$$ C = \epsilon_o \chi_e A/d $$

where C is in faradays (1 F = 1 J/V^2). Determine the polarization work required to charge an initially discharged 10.0-μF parallel plate capacitor when the plates are separated by 0.005 m of plexiglass and are subjected to a potential difference of 300 V at 27 °C.

46. A typical storm cloud at an altitude of 3000 ft has a cross-sectional area of 10^8 ft^2 and a surface potential relative to the earth of 10^8 V. Determine the amount of electrical energy stored in the cloud by calculating the polarization work required to charge the earth–cloud capacitor.

47. A square aluminum bar 0.03 m on a side and 1.0 m long is wrapped with a current-carrying wire. When the current in the wire is turned on, it exposes the aluminum core to a magnetic field strength of 456,000 A/m. Determine the total magnetic work that occurs when the current is turned on and determine what percentage of this work is associated with the alignment of the aluminum's molecular magnetic dipoles.

48. A quartz rod 0.01 m in diameter and 0.1 m long is to be subjected to a magnetic intensity of 10,000 A/m. Determine the total magnetic work required for this process if the initial magnetic intensity of the rod is zero.

49. A Curie substance has a magnetic susceptibility given by

$$ \chi_m = C'/T $$

where C' is the Curie constant for the substance and T is its absolute temperature. Determine an expression for the work per unit volume for isothermal material magnetization of a constant volume Curie substance. Evaluate this for $C' = 153$ K, $T = 300$ K, $M_1 = 0$, $M_2 = 1000$ A/m.

50. The chemical potential of a professor's brains in a single species cranium is constant at -13.2 MJ/kg. Determine the chemical work required to remove 3.77 kg of this valuable substance from the cranium.

51. Two lbm of chemical species A ($\mu_A = -5700$ Btu/lbm) is removed from a system while 7.3 lbm of species B ($\mu_B = -3850$ Btu/lbm) and 11.1 lbm of species C ($\mu_C = 1050$ Btu/lbm) are added to the system. Determine the net chemical work involved. Assume constant chemical potentials.

52. If the total internal energy of an adiabatic stationary closed system is given by

$$ U = p\mathcal{V} + \sum \mu_i m_i + f\ell $$

show that the following formula must hold

$$ -\mathcal{V}\,dp + \sum m_i\,d\mu_i + \ell\,df = 0. $$

(*Hint*: Start from the differential form of the energy balance, $\bar{d}Q + \bar{d}W = dE$).

53. A simple mechanochemical engine operates on the thermodynamic cycle shown in the drawing. The mechanochemical contractile work output ($f\ d\ell$) comes from a chemical work input (μdm) due to the aqueous dilution of a single chemical species ($i = 1$).

a) Show that the net chemical transport per cycle of this engine is given by

$$(W)_{\substack{\text{chemical}\\ \text{cycle net}}} = (\mu_2 - \mu_1)(\Delta m) \qquad \text{where } \Delta m = m_3 - m_2 = m_4 - m_1$$

b) Write an expression for the work transport energy efficiency of this engine.

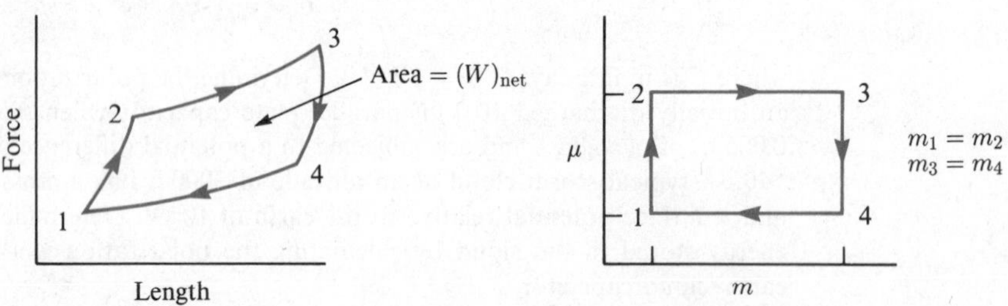

54. A refrigeration cycle is chosen to maintain a freezer compartment at 10 °F in a room which is at 90 °F. If 200 Btu/min are extracted from the freezer compartment by heat transfer, and the freezer is driven by a 1.0-hp electric motor, determine the coefficient of performance of the unit.

55. An automobile engine produces 127 hp of actual output power. If the friction, heat transfer, and other irreversibilities consume 23 hp, determine the work transport energy efficiency of this engine.

56. 60 kW enter a mechanical gear box at its input shaft but only 55 kW exit at its output shaft. Determine its work transport energy efficiency.

57. Find the heat transport rate of energy from a circular pipe 2.0 in in outside diameter, 20 ft long with a wall thickness of 0.15 in. The inside and outside surface temperatures of the pipe are 212 and 200 °F, respectively. The pipe is made of carbon steel.

58. A freezer wall is made up of $\frac{1}{16}$ in of carbon steel, 1 in of glass wool, and $\frac{1}{16}$ in of carbon steel. Determine the heat transport rate per unit area through the wall when the outside temperature is 80 °F and the inside temperature is 10 °F.

59. A thermopane window consists of two $\frac{1}{8}$-in glass panes separated by a $\frac{1}{4}$-in air gap. Compare the heat transport rate per unit area of a single $\frac{1}{8}$-in-thick window pane with this thermopane. Take the inside and outside temperatures to be 70 and 0 °F, respectively.

60. Find the surface temperature of a bare 40-W fluorescent light tube, 3.6 cm in diameter and 1.22 m long in room air at 20 °C. The convective heat transfer coefficient of the tube is 4.8 W/(m^2·K).

61. An experiment has been conducted on a small cylindrical antenna 12.7 mm in diameter and 95 mm long. It was heated internally with a 40-W electric heater. During the experiment it was put into a cross flow of air at 26.2 °C and 10.0 m/s. Its surface temperature was measured and found to be 127.8 °C. Determine the convective heat transfer coefficient for the antenna.

62. An automobile is parked outdoors on a cold evening when the surrounding air temperature is 35 °F. The convective heat transfer between the roof of the automobile and the surrounding air is 1.5 Btu/(h·ft^2·R). The night sky is cloudless and forms a radiation sink at an effective temperature of −30 °F. By performing a convective–radiation balance on the roof determine

a) the roof temperature, and

b) whether or not frost will form on the roof (and why).

63. Determine the radiation heat transfer rate per unit area between an infant at 37 °C in a crib and a nearby window at −10 °C in the winter. The view factor between the infant and the window is 0.31.

64. Determine the radiation heat transfer rate per unit area from a nuclear fire ball at 10,000 °F and a nearby building at 70 °F covered with white paint. The view factor between the building and the fire ball is 0.01.

65. Define the following terms:

a) adiabatic **b)** mechanical work

c) reversible **d)** the state postulate.

66. Define the following terms:

a) aergonic **b)** the local equilibrium postulate

c) enthalpy **d)** work efficiency.

67. A closed system undergoes a cycle made up of three processes. Fill in the missing data in the table below. All the values are in kilojoules.

Process	Q_{cond}	Q_{conv}	Q_{rad}	W_{mech}	W_{elect}	W_{magn}	W_{chem}	$E_2 - E_1$
1–2	5	13	−34	45	2	−23	11	?
2–3	12.3	56.1	121.	0.0	85.0	0.0	?	211.0
3–1	1.1	−23.3	?	−44.8	89.9	−47.3	14.2	0.0

Section I Computer Problems

The following computer-programming assignments were designed to be carried out on any personal computer using BASIC as the programming language. They are meant to be exercises in input/output screen formatting and manipulation of some of the basic formulae of this section of Chapter 4. They may be used as part of a weekly homework assignment.

68. Write an interactive computer program that will calculate the work transport for an ideal gas undergoing a polytropic moving boundary process. Have the user input all necessary data from the key board by responding to properly worded screen prompts. Make sure that units are specified when requesting user data input. Output the polytropic work and all the input data (with corresponding units).

69. Write an interactive computer program that will calculate the work transport for a Hookean elastic solid. Have the user input all necessary data from the key board by responding to properly worded screen prompts. Make sure that units are specified when requesting user data input. Output the elastic work and all the input data (with corresponding units).

70. Write an interactive computer program that will determine the work transport in a constant volume magnetization process. Have the user input all necessary data from the key board by responding to properly worded screen prompts. Make sure that units are specified when requesting user data input. Output the magnetic work, the work of magnetization of the exposed material and all the input data (with corresponding units).

71. Write an interactive computer program that will determine the chemical work transport for a system with constant chemical potentials. Have the user input all the μ_i and the initial and final m_i from the keyboard by responding to properly worded screen prompts.

Make sure that units are specified when requesting user data input. Output the chemical work (with corresponding units).

72. Write an interactive computer program that determines the total heat transfer rate from the sum of one or more of the three heat transport modes (conduction, convection and radiation). Have the user select from a menu which heat transport mode or combination of heat transport modes he/she wishes to use. Then have the user input all necessary data from the key board by responding to properly worded screen prompts. Output the heat transport rate and all input data (with corresponding units).

Problems for Section II

73. One kg of liquid water at 20 °C is poured from a height of 10 m directly onto the floor. After a short time, the specific internal energy of the water on the floor has returned to its initial value before it was poured.

a) What total heat transport of energy occurred during this process (ignore evaporation effects)?

b) In which direction was this heat transport of energy, into or out of the water?

74. Determine the direction and amount of heat transfer required to raise the temperature of the contents of a rigid sealed subterranean silicon sphere containing 10.0 lbm of saturated water vapor from 280 to 1000 °F, 100 psia. Fill in the following table (with correct units) and show all calculations.

State 1	Process = ? →	State 2
$x_1 = 1.0$		$p_2 = 100$ psia
$T_1 = 280$ °F		$T_2 = 1000$ °F
$p_1 = ?$		$x_2 = ?$
$u_1 = ?$		$u_2 = ?$

Unknown: ${}_1Q_2 = ?$

75. Determine the direction and amount of heat transfer that occurs as 3.0 kg of superheated blood (essentially steam) expands isothermally from 800 °C, 80 MPa to 0.1 MPa doing 500 kJ of work in the process. Fill in the following table (with correct units) and show all calculations.

State 1	Process = ? → ${}_1W_2 = 500$ kJ	State 2
$p_1 = 80$ MPa		$p_2 = 0.1$ MPa
$T_1 = 800$ °C		$T_2 = ?$
$v_1 = ?$		$v_2 = ?$
$u_1 = ?$		$u_2 = ?$

Unknown: ${}_1Q_2 = ?$

76. A rigid sealed 1936 DeSoto coupe contains an equilibrium water liquid–vapor mixture with a quality of 8.8333% at 3.0 psia. After 500 Btu of heat energy were added to the coupe the contents became a saturated vapor. What was the total mass of water in the coupe? Fill in the following table (with correct units) and show all calculations.

$$\textbf{State 1} \xrightarrow[{}_1Q_2 = 500\text{ Btu}]{\text{Process} = ?} \textbf{State 2}$$

State 1	State 2
$p_1 = 3$ psia	$p_2 = ?$
$x_1 = 0.088333$	$x_2 = 1.0$
$v_1 = ?$	$v_2 = ?$
$T_1 = ?$	$T_2 = ?$
$u_1 = ?$	$u_2 = ?$

Unknown: $m = ?$

77. The makers of a new breakfast cereal, have a process in which a rigid sealed vessel contains 1.0 kg of saturated water vapor at 10 MPa. Energy is removed from the vessel as heat transfer until the pressure has dropped to 0.1 MPa. Determine the heat transfer, state its direction, fill in the following table (with correct units), and show all calculations.

$$\textbf{State 1} \xrightarrow{\text{Process} = ?} \textbf{State 2}$$

State 1	State 2
$x_1 = 1.0$	$T_2 = ?$
$p_1 = 10$ MPa	$p_2 = 0.1$ MPa
$v_1 = ?$	$v_2 = ?$
$T_1 = ?$	$x_2 = ?$
$u_1 = ?$	$u_2 = ?$

Unknown: ${}_1Q_2 = ?$

78. A rigid sealed fossilized goat's bladder contains water in a liquid–vapor equilibrium at 70 °F. After 300 Btu of heat were added to the bladder its contents were converted into a saturated vapor with a specific volume of 50.2 ft^3/lbm. What was the total mass of water in the bladder?

79. A rigid vessel having a volume of 5.0 ft^3 is filled with steam at 100 psia and 500 °F. Heat is then transferred from the steam until it has a quality of 100% while the contents of the vessel are stirred with a mixing blade requiring 10 W·h of work input. Determine **a)** the final pressure in the vessel, and **b)** the total heat transfer.

80. 1.73 kg of water vapor is contained in a piston–cylinder assembly at a pressure of 1.0 MPa and temperature 600 °C. The vapor is isothermally compressed to 80.0 MPa. Determine the sum of the work and heat energy transports in this process.

81. One pound of Refrigerant-12 is put into a piston–cylinder assembly at an initial pressure and temperature of 200 psia and 200 °F. The R-12 is then slowly heated at constant pressure until the temperature reaches 300 °F. Determine the work done on or by the system and the heat transferred to or from the system.

82. The pressure in an isochoric automobile tire increases from 28 psia at 70 °F to 35 psia on a trip during hot weather. Assume the air behaves as an ideal gas. **a)** What was the air temperature inside the tire at the end of the trip. **b)** How much heat was absorbed per unit mass of air in the tire during the trip?

83. A small room 15 × 15 × 10 ft high contains air at 70 °F and 14.7 psia. It is the camera stage of a television broadcasting studio, and contains many bright lights for illumination. The room is closed, sealed, and insulated to isolate the performers from outside distractions. Assuming air is an ideal gas, find the temperature and pressure in the room 1.0 h after eight

1000-W lights are turned on. Assume there is no ventilation or air conditioning and ignore the effect of people in the room.

84. A room heating system uses steam radiators to heat the room air. A radiator that has a volume of 3.0 ft^3 is filled with saturated vapor at a pressure of 15.3 psia and then the inlet and exit valves are closed. How much energy will have been transferred to the room air as heat at a time when the pressure in the radiator reaches 3.3 psia. Assume the room air is at 14.7 psia and 70 °F during the entire process.

85. The human body under the stress of exercise can release 230 W as heat. Assume the human body to be a closed system and neglect any changes in internal and kinetic energy. Determine the power produced by the human body as a 68-kg person runs up a staircase having a vertical height of 15 m in 60 s with a constant velocity.

86. 14 kg of herpes duplex virus scum is compressed from a volume of 4.5 to 1.5 m^3 in a process where p in N/m^2 is given by $p = 60/V + 30$ when V is in m^3. During the compression process the virus gives off 20 J of heat and turns a putrid yellow in color. Determine the change in the specific internal energy of the virus for this process.

87. 3.7 kg of nitrogen gas at 0 °C and 0.1 MPa is put into a cylinder with a piston and compressed in a process defined by pV^2 = constant. When the final pressure in the cylinder reaches 10 MPa, and assuming ideal gas behavior, determine **a)** the amount of work done on the nitrogen by the piston, and **b)** the final temperature of the nitrogen.

88. Heat is transferred to 0.1 lbm of air contained in a frictionless piston–cylinder apparatus until its volume expands from an initial value of 1.0 ft^3 to a final value of 1.5 ft^3. Calculate the work transport of energy and the heat transfer when the system is the air in the cylinder. The initial temperature of the air is 70 °F. Consider air to be an ideal gas.

89. 0.1 lbm of air (an ideal gas) initially at 50 psia and 100 °F in a cylinder with a movable piston undergoes the following two-part process. First, the air is expanded adiabatically to 30 psia and 24 °F, then it is compressed isobarically (constant pressure) to half its initial volume. Determine

a) the final temperature at the end of the isobaric compression,
b) the work produced during the adiabatic expansion, and
c) the heat transfer during the isobaric compression.

90. A 1000-kg battery-powered adiabatic electric vehicle has a fully charged battery containing 20 MJ of stored energy. If it requires 12 kW of power to keep it moving at a constant velocity on a horizontal road, determine how long the vehicle will operate before its battery is fully discharged.

91. How many watt hours of electricity are needed to heat the contents of a sealed rigid insulated chamber pot containing 0.3 lbm of water from 50 °F with a quality of 1.0% to a saturated vapor. The chamber pot has an internal electrical resistance heater with a power cord that plugs into a standard 110-V ac outlet.

92. A small sealed rigid container holding 0.5 kg of water is heated in a microwave oven drawing 1600 W at 2460 MHz. The oven's timer is set for one minute. The initial thermodynamic state of the water is 20 °C at 1.0 atm. After the one-minute heating period determine **a)** the water's work transport of energy, **b)** the water's heat transport of energy, **c)** the change in specific internal energy of the water, and **d)** the final temperature and pressure assuming the liquid water to be an incompressible liquid with a specific heat of 4.5 kJ/(kg·K).

93. 30.5 kg of H_2O contained in a 1.0 m^3 rigid tank are at an initial pressure of 10 MPa. The contents of the tank are cooled at constant volume until a final pressure of 2.0 MPa is reached. Determine the final temperature, the final value of the specific internal energy, and the process heat transfer.

94. A small rigid tank 1.0 ft^3 in volume contains saturated water vapor at 300 °F. An initially evacuated rigid container 3.4549 ft^3 in volume is then attached to the first tank and the interconnecting valve is opened. The combined system is then brought to equilibrum at 300 °F by an appropriate heat transport of energy. Determine the final pressure in the system and the required heat transfer.

95. A pressure vessel that has a volume of 0.2 ft^3 is filled with saturated liquid Refrigerant-12 at 70 °F. An evacuated container 4.0 ft^3 in volume is attached to the vessel and the interconnecting valve is opened. The combined system is then brought to equilibrium at 70 °F Calculate the heat transport of energy to (or from) the system.

96. A mixture of hydrazine and cow manure happens to have the same thermodynamic properties as pure water. A secret process requires that this mixture be vaporized and then injected into light bulbs. Determine the work and heat transport of energy that occurs when 1.3 kg of this mixture is isothermally converted from a saturated liquid to a saturated vapor at 40 °F.

97. A lead bullet weighing 0.02 lbf and traveling horizontally at 3000 ft/s is suddenly stopped by a perfectly rigid object that does not deform during the impact. Find the temperature rise of the bullet assuming the impact occurs so rapidly that the impact process can be considered to be adiabatic. For lead, use $\Delta u = 0.131(\Delta T)$ in Btu/lbm where T is in °F or R.

98. As a bullet travels down the barrel of a pistol the pressure from the burning propellant behind it increases linearly with the volume V displaced by the bullet as $p = V \times 10^3$ in psia where V is in in^3. The total volume of the barrel is $\pi R^2 L$ where R is the radius of the bore and L is its total length. Determine the velocity of the bullet at the end of the barrel if it travels horizontally and adiabatically down the barrel without changing its internal energy, and without friction.

Data

Barrel length = 6 in
Barrel diameter = 0.380 in
Bullet mass = 5 g

99. A rubber band weighing 10^{-3} lbf that obeys Hooke's law of elasticity is stretched horizontally and adiabatically from an initial length of 3.0 to 4.0 in.

a) Determine the change in total internal energy of the rubber band when it is stretched if its elastic modulus is 10^3 lbf/in^2 and its cross sectional area remains approximately constant at 7.8×10^{-3} in^2.

b) If the stretched rubber band is suddenly released horizontally and adiabatically, determine its final velocity neglecting air friction and any height change during its flight.

100. A thin glass sphere 0.025 ft^3 in volume is completely filled with 1.0 lbm of saturated liquid nitrogen. The glass sphere is sealed inside a large rigid, evacuated, insulated container whose volume is 10 ft^3. What will be the final pressure and quality (if any) inside the larger container if the glass sphere breaks.

101. 1.0 ft^3 of saturated liquid water at 14.7 psia is poured into an initially evacuated rigid insulated vessel whose volume is 100 ft^3. Inside the 100-ft^3 vessel is an electric heater that draws an effective 10 A at an effective 100 V. Once this heater is turned on, how long will it take the contents of the 100-ft^3 vessel to reach 40 psia?

102. A rigid vessel having a volume of 3.0 m^3 initially contains steam at 0.4 MPa and a quality of 40.2%. If 23.79 MJ of heat is added to the steam, determine its final pressure and temperature.

103. A thermoelectric generator consists of a series of semiconductor elements heated on one side and cooled on the other. It is a type of *thermal engine*, except that the output is electrical rather than mechanical work. Electric direct current output is produced as a result of an input heat transport of energy. In a particular experiment the steady state direct current was measured to be 0.5 A and the potential across the unit was 0.8 V. The heat input to the hot side was 5.5 W. Determine the heat transfer rate from the cold side and the energy conversion efficiency of this device.

104. A rigid sealed pressure cooker has a volume of 0.7 ft^3 and contains 1.279 lbm of water (liquid plus vapor) in equilibrium at 14.7 psia. The pressure cooker is then slowly heated until all of the water inside becomes a vapor.

a) What are the internal temperature and pressure when the last bit of liquid vaporizes.
b) How much heat transfer is required (in Btu) to vaporize all the water.
c) Sketch the process path on a *p-v* diagram for water.

105. A pressure cooker whose volume is 0.3 m^3 contains 2.0 kg of water. It is placed on a heating element of an electric stove that continuously draws 220 V (effective) and 0.5 A (effective). Assuming all the heat generated in the element goes into the pressure cooker, determine the rate of heat loss from the pressure cooker to the environment when it has reached steady state conditions (i.e., $(dE/dt)_{\text{system}} = 0$).

106. A tea kettle initially contains 5.0 lbm of water (liquid plus vapor) and has a total volume of 0.5 ft^3. The atmospheric pressure (and thus the initial pressure in the tea kettle) is 14.7 psia. The kettle has a "pop-off" valve that keeps the water vapor in the kettle until its pressure reaches 5.3 psig. At this internal pressure the value opens and allows the vapor to escape into the atmosphere in such a way as to maintain the internal pressure constant. The kettle is heated on a stove until all the remaining water inside becomes saturated vapor.

a) Take the water that remains in the kettle at the final state as a system. Sketch the *p-v* diagram for this system for the process described above.
b) List two intensive properties at each of the states shown below

Initial state	**State when valve opens**	**Final state**
1)	1)	1)
2)	2)	2)

c) Determine the mass of water in the kettle when it reaches the final state.
d) Determine the work done by the escaping steam in pushing aside the atmosphere.

107. A small electrically heated steam boiler with a total volume of 10 ft^3, can be considered to be a perfectly rigid, insulated vessel with three valves: an inlet valve, an exit valve, and a safety relief valve. During a test the boiler operator closed both the inlet and exit valves while leaving the heater on. The safety relief valve will stay closed until a pressure of 160 psia is reached. If there are 4.477 lbm of water in the boiler and the pressure is 100 psia at the time the valves are closed, how much energy will have been transferred to the water as heat when the safety relief valve first opens?

108. Helium that is contained in a cylinder fitted with a piston expands according to the relation $p\forall^{1.5}$ = constant. The initial volume of the helium is 2.0 ft^3, the initial pressure is 70 psia, and the initial temperature is 400 R. After expansion the pressure is 30 psia. The specific heat of the helium is given by the relation $c_v = a + bT$ where $a = 0.4$ Btu/(lbm·R) and $b = 10^{-3}$ Btu/(lbm·R^2). Determine the heat transfer and indicate its direction.

109. A student weighs 1333 N and wishes to lose weight. The student climbs with a constant velocity to the top of a staircase with a vertical height of 250 m.

a) Assuming the student is a closed adiabatic system (which is really not a very accurate assumption here), determine the change in total internal energy of the student.
b) How much weight would the student lose if this total internal energy change were the result of the conversion of body fat, where 1.0 kg of body fat contains 32,300 kJ of energy.

c) The student decides to take more drastic action and designs a machine that will squash him from an initial volume of 0.3 m^3 to a final volume of 0.1 m^3 according to the relation $pV^{0.5}$ = constant. If the student's initial internal pressure is 0.11 MPa, determine his final internal pressure and the work done in squashing the student.

110. A Newcomen steam engine, built in 1720, pumped water from a coal mine by condensing water vapor in the piston–cylinder device shown in the sketch. If the piston had a cross-sectional area of 1.5 ft^2, determine

a) the work done by the atmosphere (at 14.7 psia) on the piston in the cylinder when the water vapor volume is decreased by 6.0 ft^3, and

b) the work done in lifting the water from the mine for the same process as part a. What accounts for the difference in the answers?

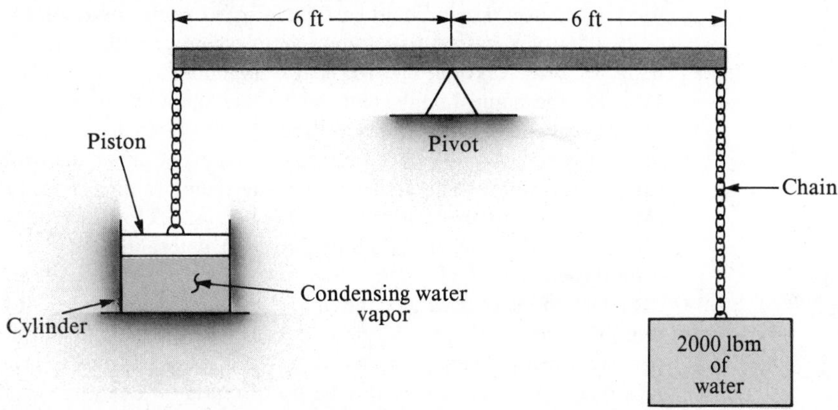

111. Determine the surface temperaturre of an automobile engine initially at 90 °C four hours after it has stopped running on a winter day when the air temperature is −30 °C and the convective heat transfer coefficient is h = 70 W/(m^2·K). Assume the engine to be approximately spherical in shape with the following physical properties: density = 7750 kg/m^3, specific heat = 0.4645 kJ/(kg·K), volume = 0.5 m^3, and thermal conductivity = 36 W/(m·K).

112. A lunar orbiting module is on its way back to earth. At 200 miles above the surface of the earth the module's velocity is 2000 miles/h. At this point an astronaut seals a rigid insulated container holding saturated water vapor at 10 psia.

You are a NASA engineering supervisor at Control Headquarters. Suddenly two wild-eyed engineers run up to you with the following emergency:

Engineer A: "That sealed container aboard the lunar module may explode when it lands! Its bursting pressure is only 80 psia, and the internal energy of the water *must* increase due to the decrease in the potential and kinetic energies on landing."

Engineer B: "Engineer A is incorrect! That container is a sealed rigid insulated vessel, so it cannot do any work or have any heat transfer. Therefore, its internal energy cannot change on landing."

Write a brief paragraph stating **a)** which engineer you support, **b)** why (make this part very clear), and **c)** what action (if any) you would take as engineering supervisor.

113. When the pressure on saturated liquid water is suddenly reduced to a lower pressure in an adiabatic aergonic process, the liquid temperature must also be reduced to reach a new equilibrium state. Consequently, part of the initial liquid is very quickly converted into a saturated vapor at the lower pressure, and the resulting heat of vaporization cools the remaining liquid to the proper temperature. Vapor formed in this manner is called *flash steam* because the liquid appears to "flash" into a vapor as the pressure is reduced. Determine the final temperature and the percent of flash steam produced as a closed system containing saturated liquid water suddenly bursts and the pressure drops from 1.0 to 0.1 MPa in an adiabatic and aergonic process.

114. In 1798 the American Benjamin Thompson (Count Rumford, 1753–1814) carried out a series of cannon-boring experiments in which he established that heat was not a material substance. (It was commonly believed at that time that heat was a colorless, odorless, weightless fluid called *caloric*). In his third experiment he noted that the "total quantity of ice-cold water which with the heat actually generated by friction, and accumulated in $2^h\ 30^m$, might have been heated 180°, or made to boil, = 26.58 lb." He also stated that "the machinery used in the experiment could easily be carried round by the force of one horse." Use this crude data of Rumford to estimate the mechanical equivalent of heat (i.e., the number of ft·lbf per Btu). Take the specific heat of liquid water to be 1.0 Btu/(lbm·R).

115. The mechanical equivalent of heat (i.e., the number of ft·lbf per Btu) was first established accurately by James Prescott Joule (1818–1889) in a long series of experiments carried out between 1849 and 1878. In one of his first experiments the work done by falling weights caused the rotation of a paddle wheel immersed in water. The resulting paddle wheel motion caused an increase in temperature of 0.563 °F in 13.9 lbm of water in an insulated container. Using a specific heat of $c = 1.0$ Btu/(lbm·R), determine the mechanical equivalent of heat from this early data of Joule.

116. Determine the heat generated (in Btu/year) by the brakes of 100 million 3000-lbm automobiles that isothermally brake to a stop on a horizontal surface from 55 mph 10 times per day. Then convert your answer into equivalent barrels of crude oil per year and then into quads per year, where one barrel of crude oil contains 5,800,000 Btu of energy and one quad is defined to be 10^{15} Btu.

117. An insulated vessel contains an unknown amount of ammonia. A 600-W electrical heater is put into the vessel and turned on for 30 min. The heater raises the temperature of the ammonia from 20 to 100 °C in a constant pressure process at 100 kPa. Determine the mass of ammonia in the vessel.

118. Using the general ERB for a closed system, show that under adiabatic, isothermal and aergonic conditions the acceleration of an object falling vertically downward in a vacuum is simply the local acceleration of gravity g.

119. Determine the difference in water temperature between the top and the bottom of a waterfall 100 ft high. Choose as your system 1.0 lbm of water at the top of the falls and follow its change of state as it moves to the bottom of the falls. Assume water to be an incompressible liquid and neglect any heat loss. Also assume a constant water velocity for this process.

120. In days of yore a bow and arrows were an archer's best friend. Determine

a) the maximum velocity of a 0.4 lbm arrow shot horizontally from a bow in which 100 ft·lbf was required to draw back the arrow before releasing, and

b) the maximum height this arrow would reach if aimed vertically.

121. A 5.0-cm-diameter steel sphere initially at 20 °C is to be heated by immersing it in boiling water at 100 °C with a convective heat transfer coefficient of 2000 W/(m^2·K). Determine the time required to raise the bulk temperature of the sphere to 90 °C. The specific heat of the steel is 0.5 kJ/(kg·K) and its density is 7800 kg/m^3.

122. An asteroid enters the earth's atmosphere and descends vertically with a constant velocity of 100 m/s. Determine the rate of change of the asteroid's temperature at the point where its temperature exactly equals the surrounding air temperature. The specific heat of the asteroid is 0.3 kJ/(kg·K).

123. 50,000 kg of saturated liquid water at 20 °C is to be heated in a mass–energy conversion oven in which 10^{-6} kg of mass is converted into pure thermal energy ($Q = mc^2$). Assuming that the water is an incompressible liquid with a specific heat of 4.2 kJ/(kg·K), determine the final temperature of the water. The velocity of light is 2.998×10^8 m/s.

124. A hand grenade contains 1.9 ounces (0.12 lbm) of TNT. Determine the number of hand grenades it would take to produce an explosion equivalent to the Brockton shoe factory boiler explosion discussed in text Example 4.18.

125. The greatest steam explosion in history is thought to have occurred on August 27, 1883, when the volcano Krakatoa in Sunda Strait, Indonesia, erupted and its molten lava vaporized an estimated one cubic mile of sea water. The entire 2600-ft-high mountain was disintegrated and a crater 1000 ft deep was produced. More than 36,000 people were killed, most by the 120-ft tidal wave that was created by the eruption. Assuming that the seawater was simply saturated liquid water at 60 °F, determine the number of tons of TNT that would have the same explosive power as this eruption. For reference, the total military production of explosives for both world wars was equivalent to 32 million tons of TNT.

126. Show that if a pressure vessel filled with a constant specific heat ideal gas ruptures, and if the gas follows a polytropic process during the subsequent depressurization, then the maximum explosive energy of this system can be written as

$$\Gamma_{\max} = p_{\text{initial}}/(k - 1)$$

127. Consider a gaseous star undergoing a gravitational collapse. Assume the star to be a closed system and to be composed of an ideal gas with constant specific heats. The collapse process is given by the relations

$$v/r^3 = \text{constant} \quad \text{and} \quad Tr = \text{constant}$$

where v, T, and r are the specific volume, temperature, and radius of the star.

a) Show that the collapse process is a polytropic process with $n = 4/3$.

b) Beginning with the per unit mass differential form of the first law, find an expression for the star's heat transfer as a function of its specific heats and temperature. Note that the star does p-V work on itself as it collapses.

c) Using the expression found in part b above along with $c_v = 0.2$ Btu/(lbm·R) and $k = 1.4$, calculate the amount of heat transfer per unit mass of star as its temperature changes from 5000 to 10,000 R.

d) Explain the critical condition that exists when the specific heat ratio k takes on the value of 4/3.

Section II Computer Problems

The following computer problems were designed to be completed in BASIC on a microcomputer. They require relatively little programming skill and may be used as part of a weekly homework assignment.

128. Write an interactive computer program that will perform an energy balance on a closed system containing an incompressible substance (either a liquid or a solid). Prompt the user for the following input (in proper units): the heat and work transports of energy, the system volume, the initial temperature of the system, and the density and specific heat of the incompressible material contained in the system. Output to the screen the system mass and final temperature. Allow the user the choice of working in either Engineering English or SI units.

129. Write an interactive computer program that will perform an energy balance on a closed system containing an ideal gas with constant specific heats. Prompt the user for the following input (in proper units): the heat and work transports of energy, the system volume, the initial temperature and pressure of the system, and the constant volume specific heat and gas constant of the gas contained in the system. Output to the screen the system mass and the final pressure and temperature. Allow the user the choice of working in either Engineering English or SI units.

130. Repeat Problem 129, except allow the user to choose the system ideal gas from a screen menu, and omit the prompts for gas properties. Use the data in Appendix C.13 for the properties of the gases in your menu.

131. Write a computer program that will generate enough data to allow you to plot (either manually or with the computer, ask your instructor for his/her preference) the explosive energy contained in a 1000-ft^3 pressure vessel containing compressed air vs.

a) the vessel initial temperature when the initial pressure is held constant at 100 psia, and

b) the vessel initial pressure when the initial temperature is held constant at 80 °F.

c) Create a three-dimensional plot with the explosive energy on the vertical axis and the initial pressure and initial temperature on the horizontal axes.

Assume the final temperature and pressure of the air after the vessel has ruptured are 70 °F and 14.7 psia in each case, and that the air undergoes a polytropic decompression process with $n = 1.25$ when the vessel ruptures. Also assume that the air behaves as a constant specific heat ideal gas with $k = 1.4$.

132. A white dwarf is a spherical mass of gas in outer space. Its radial pressure gradient must always be in equilibrium with its own gravitational force field, or

$$\frac{dp}{dr} = -Gm\rho/r^2$$

where G is the gravitational constant, ρ is the density of the gas at radius r (i.e., $\rho = \rho(r)$), and m is the mass of gas inside a sphere of radius r,

$$m = 4\pi \int_0^r \rho r^2 \, dr$$

During its formation, the gas of a white dwarf obeys the polytropic equation

$$pv^{-5/3} = \alpha = \text{constant}$$

The above relations can be combined to yield a differential equation for the density field $\rho = \rho(r)$ inside a white dwarf of the form

$$\frac{d^2\phi}{dx^2} + \frac{2}{x}\left(\frac{d\phi}{dx}\right) + \phi^{2/3} = 0$$

where $\phi = (\rho/\rho_0)^{2/3}$, $\rho_0 = \rho(r = 0)$, and $x = r/r^*$ where $r^* = 5\alpha/(8\pi G\rho_0{}^{1/3})$.

a) Solve the above differential equation for $\phi(x)$ using a computer-generated numerical solution with the boundary conditions $\phi = 1$ and $d\phi/dx = 0$ at $x = 0$ to show that $\phi(x) = 0$ at $x = 3.6537$.

b) Show that $\phi(x) = 0$ corresponds to the radius R of the white dwarf and that a white dwarf therefore has a mass m given by

$$m = -45.91\rho_0(r^*)^3(d\phi/dx)|_{x=R}$$

Section III Problems

133. Determine an expression for the time rate of change of the total internal energy of a submarine that is

a) not insulated,
b) being propelled by its propeller shaft,
c) taking on ballast water at only one opening in the submarine, and
d) is diving and accelerating.

134. Write the complete energy rate balance (ERB) for an automobile accelerating up a hill and provide a physical interpretation for each term in the balance.

135. Some vile and disgusting chemical is produced in the rigid insulated reactor vessel shown in the drawing. Determine the electrical power required to maintain the process in a steady state, steady flow condition. Neglect any changes in kinetic or potential energy.

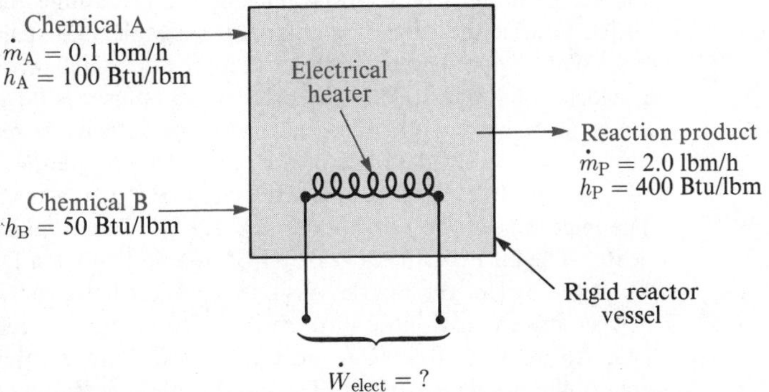

136. Determine the adiabatic change in temperature of a river that aergonically drops 1 m over a waterfall without a change in velocity. The specific heat of the river water is 4.2 kJ/(kg·K).

137. A small hydroelectric power plant discharges 200 ft^3/s of water. If the elevation difference $(Z_{out} - Z_{in})$ between the intake and outlet is 15 ft and the temperature difference $(T_{out} - T_{in})$ is 0.01 °F, determine the mass flow energy transport rate. Assume the inlet and outlet velocities are identical ($c = 1.0$ Btu/(lbm·R) and $\rho = 62.4$ lbm/ft^3).

138. Air flows aergonically at a constant rate of 8.0 lbm/min down a horizontal duct so that its enthalpy remains constant. As the air flows down the duct its velocity increases from 500 to 650 ft/s. Find the heat transfer rate and indicate whether it is to or from the system. Assume steady state operation.

139. A steady state air compressor takes in air at atmospheric pressure and discharges it at 100 psia. The inlet enthalpy is 120 Btu/lbm and the exit enthalpy is 176 Btu/lbm. Heat is transferred out of the compressor to cooling water at the rate of 1600 Btu/min. If the air flow rate through the compressor is 10.0 lbm/min, what horsepower must be supplied to the compressor? Neglect the kinetic and potential energies of the inlet and outlet flowstreams.

140. Refrigerant-12 enters a constant area tube at 100 °F with a quality of 75%. Heat is transferred in a steady flow aergonic process until the R-12 leaves as a saturated liquid at 0 °F. Determine the heat transfer per lbm of R-12 flowing. Neglect any changes in kinetic and potential energies. Assume steady state operation.

141. An architect has designed a 2-mile-high skyscraper. Steam will be used for heating and is to be supplied to the top floor via a vertical pipe. The steam will enter the pipe at the bottom as dry saturated vapor at 30 psia. At the top floor, the pressure is to be 16 psia, and the heat transfer from the steam as it flows up the pipe will be 50 Btu/lbm. What will be the quality of the steam at the top floor?

142. How may watts of power could be recovered by decelerating 0.5 kg/s of air in a ventilating system from 10 m/s to 0.1 m/s before discharging it to the atmosphere?

143. Water initially at 300 psia and 500 °F is expanded isothermally and adiabatically to 14.7 psia in a horizontal steady flow process. In the absence of work modes, determine the change in kinetic energy per pound of water.

144. Refrigerant-12 expands in a steady flow diffuser from 300 psia, 180 °F to 35 psia in an isothermal process. During this process the heat transfer from the R-12 is 3.1 Btu/lbm. Assuming a negligible exit velocity, determine the inlet velocity to the diffuser.

145. A steam whistle is devised by attaching a simple converging nozzle to a steam line. At the inlet to the whistle the pressure is 60 psia, the temperature is 600 °F, and the velocity is 10 ft/s. The steam expands and accelerates horizontally to the outlet where the pressure and temperature are 14.7 psia and 500 °F. Determine the steam velocity at the whistle outlet. Assume the process is adiabatic, aergonic, and steady flow.

146. Water vapor enters a diffuser at a pressure of 0.07 MPa, a temperature of 150 °C, and a velocity of 100 m/s. The inlet area of the diffuser is 0.1 m^2. By removing 288.2 kJ/kg in the form of heat across the duct walls, the velocity is reduced to 1.0 m/s and the pressure is increased to 0.2 MPa at the outlet. Determine the outlet area of the diffuser.

147. Air at 70 °F, 30 psia and a velocity of 3.0 ft/s enters an insulated steady state nozzle. The inlet area of the nozzle is 0.5 ft^2. The nozzle contains an operating 1500-W electrical heater. The air exits the nozzle at 14.7 psia and 300 ft/s. Determine the temperature of the air at the exit of the nozzle. Assume ideal gas behavior with constant specific heats and neglect any changes in flowstream potential energy.

148. Air at 20 °C, 0.5 MPa, and a velocity of 1.0 m/s enters an insulated nozzle. The inlet area of the nozzle is 0.05 m^2. The nozzle contains an operating 500-W electrical resistance heater. The air exits the nozzle at atmospheric pressure and 100 m/s. Assuming ideal gas behavior with constant specific heats, determine the exit temperature.

149. Air at 70 °F and 30 psia enters an insulated nozzle with a mass flow rate of 3.0 lbm/s. The nozzle contains an operating 1000-W electrical resistance heater. The air exits the nozzle at 14.7 psia. The inlet and exit areas of the nozzle are 0.5 and 0.1 ft^2, respectively. Determine the velocity and temperature of the air at the exit of the nozzle. Assume air to be an ideal gas.

150. The adiabatic, aergonic, throttling calorimeter shown in the drawing is a device by which the quality of wet steam flowing in a pipe may be determined. Determine **a)** the enthalpy of the steam in the pipe, and **b)** the quality of the steam in the pipe.

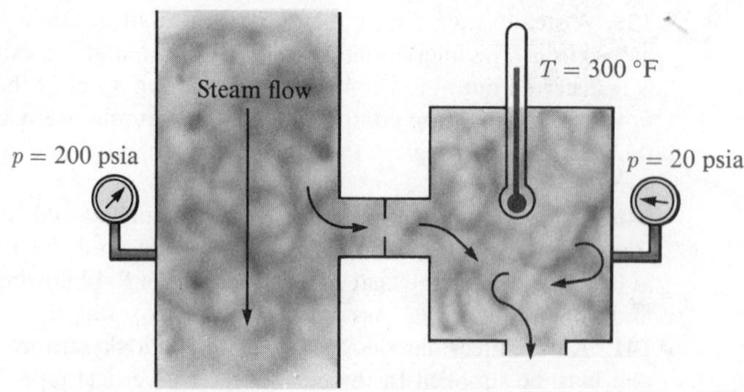

151. Wet steam is throttled adiabatically and aergonically from 800 psia to 5.0 psia and 200 °F. If the inlet and exit velocities and heights are equal, what is the ratio of exit area to inlet area for this device?

152. When the pressure on saturated liquid water is suddenly reduced in an adiabatic aergonic steady flow process, the exit state temperature must also be reduced to reach the new equilibrium state. Consequently, part of the initial liquid is very quickly converted into a saturated vapor at the lower pressure, with the vaporization energy (i.e., heat of vaporization) coming from the remaining liquid. In this way the remaining liquid is cooled to the new (lower) equilibrium temperature. The resulting vapor is called *flash steam* because the liquid appears to "flash" into a vapor as it expands into the low pressure region. Determine the exit temperature and percent flash steam produced as saturated liquid water at 10 MPa is throttled through a partially open valve and discharged into the atmosphere adiabatically, aergonically, and without any change in kinetic or potential energy.

153. Refrigerant-12 is flowing steadily through a refrigerator throttling valve at the rate of 10 lbm/min. At the valve inlet the R-12 is a saturated liquid at 80 °F. At the valve outlet, the pressure is 19.189 psia. If the process can be considered aergonic, adiabatic, and without any change in kinetic or potential energy, find the quality at the valve outlet.

154. The insulated vortex tube shown in the drawing contains no moving mechanical parts, yet it has the ability to separate the inlet air flowstream into hot and cold outlet air flowstreams. Recorded test data are

Inlet pressure, $p_i = 0.69$ MPa gage
Inlet Temperature, $T_i = 20$ °C
Hot side mass flow rate, $\dot{m}_H = 0.136$ kg/min
Cold side mass flow rate, $\dot{m}_C = 0.318$ kg/min

Calculate the cold side temperature, T_C.

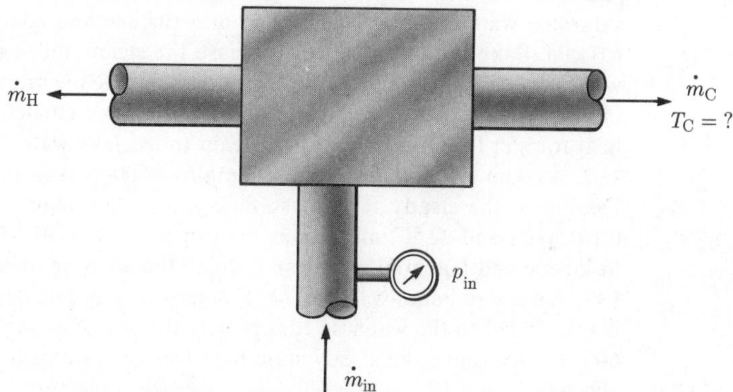

155. Aerosol sprays are commonly used today for such things as hair sets, shaving creams, deodorants, paints, and perfumes. At times various inert gases have been used as the propellant medium for the active chemicals. Consider the design of a new deodorant which uses ammonia as the propellant medium. The spraying process is a simple throttling process (neglect kinetic and potential energy terms). If the can is at 80 °F and 70 psia and it is sprayed into the atmosphere at 15 psia, then **a)** at what temperature does the ammonia spray enter the atmosphere? **b)** Draw this process on an *h-T* diagram and label all the relevant enthalpies and temperatures.

156. Determine the inlet quality and the Joule-Thomson coefficient of wet steam that is throttled from 1.0 to 0.1 MPa and 150 °C.

157. Estimate the Joule-Thomson temperature change that occurs as air is throttled from a pressure of 100 atm and 50 °C to 1.0 atm.

158. Estimate the Joule-Thomson temperature change as carbon dioxide is throttled from a pressure of 60 atm and 0 °C to 1.0 atm.

159. Refrigerant-12 enters a condenser at 30 °F with a quality of 85% at a mass flow rate of 5 lbm/min. What is the smallest diameter tubing that can be used if the velocity of the refrigerant must not exceed 20 ft/s?

160. How much electrical power (in kilowatts) is required to isothermally convert 10 kg/min of water from a saturated liquid to a saturated vapor at 100 °C in an electrically heated and completely insulated electric boiler?

161. The hot and cold water faucets on a bathroom sink have water available at 80 and 15 °C, respectively. When the faucets are opened, the sink drain is also open so that water leaves the sink as fast as it enters. Determine the ratio of hot water to cold water mass flow rates needed to produce a mixture temperature of 30 °C in the sink.

162. A steady state, steady flow, adiabatic, aergonic feedwater heater (see drawing) is used in an electric power plant. It mixes superheated steam with saturated liquid water to produce a low quality outflow. 10 lbm/s of superheated steam at 80 psia and 500 °F is mixed with saturated liquid water at 80 psia. The outlet stream has a quality of 10% at 80 psia. What is the mass flow rate of the saturated liquid water flowstream?

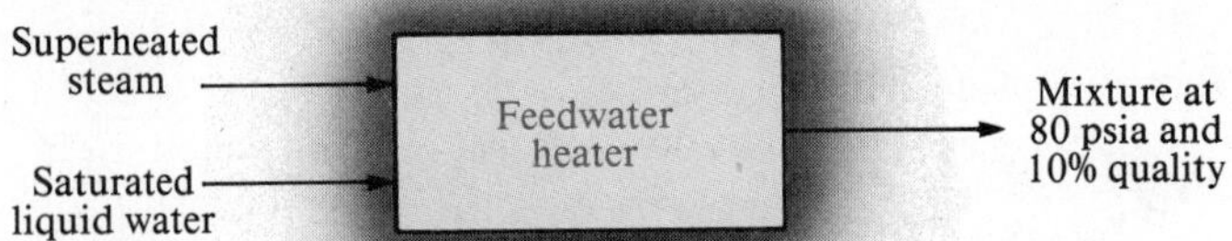

163. An insulated aergonic condenser for a large power plant receives 3×10^6 kg/h of saturated water vapor at 6.0 kPa from a turbine and condenses it to saturated liquid at 6.0 kPa. Lake water is used to condense the steam and it is desired to maintain the inlet water temperature at 4.5 °C and the outlet water temperature at 15.5 °C. **a)** What flow rate of lake water is required for an adiabatic aergonic condenser, and **b)** what is the rate of heat transfer from the condensing steam to the lake water?

164. A commercial slide projector contains a 500-W light bulb. The bulb is to be air cooled. Determine the steady flow mass flow rate of air required if it enters the projector at 0.101 MPa and 22 °C, and leaves the projector at 0.101 MPa and 50 °C (neglect changes in kinetic and potential energies). Assume the air is an ideal gas.

165. Saturated liquid water at 70 °F enters an aergonic device at a rate of 1.0 lbm/s. Heat is transferred to the water so that it exits the device as superheated steam at 100 psia and 600 °F. Determine the steady state heat transfer rate (ignore kinetic and potential energy effects).

166. Liquid water ($\rho = 62.5$ lbm/ft^3) enters one end of a 6-ft-long, 1-in-diameter pipe with a uniform velocity. The entering pressure and velocity are 20 psia and 1.0 ft/s, respectively. Heat is added to the water as it flows down the pipe such that it exits the pipe as a saturated vapor at 14.7 psia. Determine the exit velocity.

167. Saturated liquid mercury at 100 psia enters an electrically heated 1-in-diameter horizontal pipe at a rate of 10 lbm/s with a negligibly small velocity. What is the steady flow heat transfer in Btu/s if the mercury exits the pipe at 80 psia as a saturated vapor with a velocity of 500 ft/s?

168. A straight horizontal constant diameter pipe contains an internal electrical heating coil (a resistance heater) and the outside of the pipe is insulated. Water enters the pipe as a saturated liquid at 0.5 kg/s and 0.2 MPa. How much electrical power must be dissipated in the electrical heater (in kilowatts) in order to produce saturated vapor at 1.0 MPa at the outlet?

169. An engineer wants to make a steady state, steady flow steam-cleaning jet by wrapping an electric heater around a water pipe. Water enters the pipe at 2.0 lbm/min as a slightly compressed liquid at 50 °F and exits the pipe as a jet of saturated vapor at 14.7 psia. If the electric heater is plugged into a standard 110-V ac outlet, how much effective current will it draw? Ignore any kinetic or potential energy effects.

170. A proposed solar collector installation (see drawing) with a frontal area (exposed to the sun) of 50 m^2 combines a thermoelectric generator with the air heating system of a building. The thermoelectric generator produces dc power with an efficiency of 5.0%. Solar radiation provides a net heat transfer rate to the absorber plate of 1000 W/m^2. The incoming air is at 18 °C and to obtain "good" operating efficiency the exit air temperature must be maintained at 30 °C. **a)** How many watts of dc power are produced by the generator, and **b)** what is the required air flow rate?

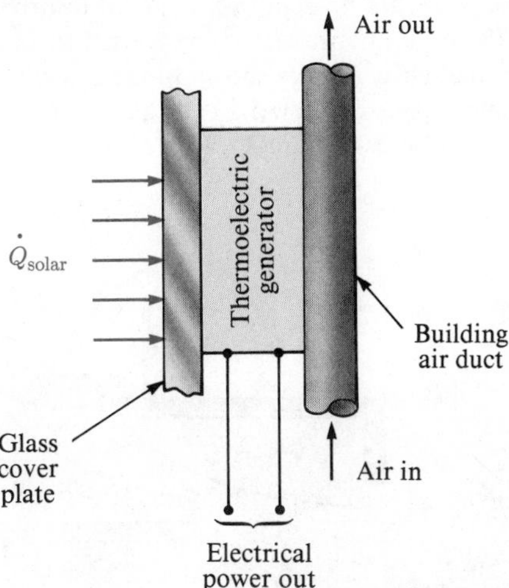

171. Determine the final temperature and the power required to compress 10 ft^3/s of air from 14.7 psia and 80 °F to a state where its specific volume is 2.84 ft^3/lbm in a steady state, steady flow process where $pv^{1.4}$ = constant. Assume ideal gas behavior.

172. Find the power delivered by an adiabatic isenthalpic turbine in which the mass flow rate is 2.0 kg/s and the flow enters at 1667 m/s and leaves at 404 m/s.

173. Liquid nitrogen can be made by a simple adiabatic expansion process through a turbine. 10 lbm/h N_2 enters the turbine at 500 R and 2000 psia, and leaves the turbine at 1 atm as a liquid–vapor mixture. If the turbine produces work at a rate of 1500 Btu/h, what will be the liquid N_2 mass flow rate at the exit of the turbine? Neglect kinetic and potential energy effects.

174. Determine the power required to compress a gas at a rate of 3.0 kg/s in a steady flow process from 0.1 MPa, 25 °C to 0.2 MPa, 60 °C. The specific enthalpy of the gas increases by 34.8 kJ/kg as it passes through the compressor, and the heat loss rate from the compressor is 16.0 kJ/s. Neglect any changes in flow stream kinetic and potential energies.

175. Calculate the power required to compress air in a steady state, steady flow process without change in elevation at a rate of 2.0 kg/s from 0.101 MPa, 40 °C, 10 m/s to 0.3 MPa, 50 °C, 125 m/s. During this process the enthalpy of the air increases by 40.15 kJ/kg while 8.0 kJ/s of heat is lost to the environment.

176. Mercury enters the steady flow, steady state, adiabatic turbine of a starship warp drive system as a saturated vapor at 300 psia, and exits the turbine with a quality of 75% at 1.0 psia. Determine

a) the mass flow rate of mercury required to produce 100 hp of turbine output power, and

b) the inlet flow area if the inlet velocity is 1.0 ft/s.

177. A simple air conditioner can be made by isothermally compressing air at atmospheric conditions of 0.101 MPa and 20 °C to 0.7 MPa and then adiabatically expanding it through a turbine back to its initial pressure. Determine the turbine outlet temperature if the turbine produces 750 W of power at an air flow rate of 0.1 kg/s. Assume ideal gas behavior.

178. The water pump on the engine of an automobile has a mass flow rate of 8.3 lbm/s. The water enters at 0 psig with a velocity of 1.0 ft/s, and leaves at 10 psig with a velocity of 10 ft/s without any change in height or temperature. Assuming that the water is an incompressible liquid with a density of 62.4 lbm/ft^3 and that the pump is adiabatic, determine the power (in horsepower) required to drive the pump.

179. A 20-hp aircraft engine is used to supply air at a rate of 0.982 lbm/s to support the ground effect vehicle shown in the drawing. The vehicle has a support area of 50 ft^2. Estimate the maximum weight that this system can lift. Assume that the environmental temperature and pressure are 80 °F and 14.7 psia respectively.

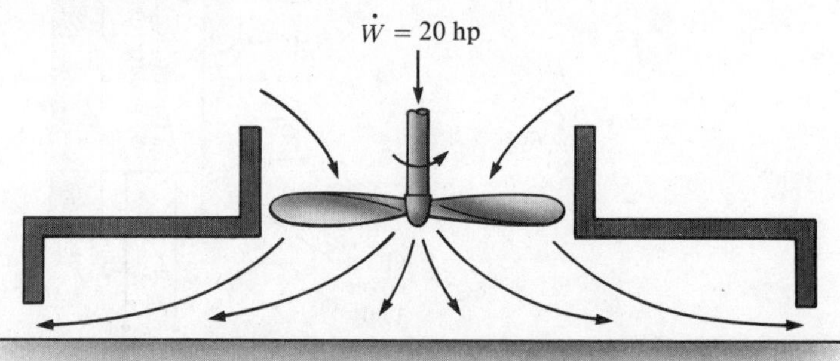

180. Determine the power required to drive a boiler feed pump that isothermally pumps 400 kg/s of saturated liquid water at 30 °C to 8.0 MPa.

181. An adiabatic Refrigerant-12 turbine is mechanically coupled to an adiabatic steam compressor. Saturated R-12 vapor at 100 °F enters the turbine and exits as saturated vapor at −20 °F. The steam enters the compressor as a saturated vapor at 14.7 psia and exits at 1000 psia, 1600 °F. If the steam mass flow rate is 5.0 lbm/s, find the R-12 mass flow rate.

182. 3.0 kg/s of air is compressed in the steady flow, steady state two stage compressor shown schematically in the drawing. Find the interstage temperature (T_2). Assume the air is an ideal gas with constant specific heats.

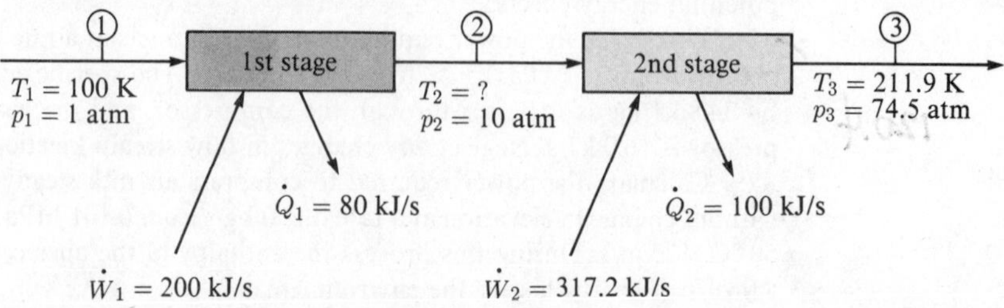

183. In a steady flow process a 1300-hp adiabatic steam turbine is supplied with 10,000 lbm of steam per hour. At the inlet to the turbine the pressure of the steam is 500 psia and its velocity is 100 ft/s. The temperature of the steam leaving the turbine is 60 °F, its quality is 0.87 and its velocity is 700 ft/s. On leaving the turbine, the steam is condensed at constant pressure and exits the condenser as a saturated liquid at 60 °F with negligible velocity. Find the temperature of the steam supplied to the turbine and the heat transfer rate in the condenser.

184. Saturated liquid water at 70 °C enters an aergonic boiler at station 1 in the schematic. The boiler receives heat energy at a rate of 10,000 kJ/s. Superheated steam at 20 MPa and 800 °C leaves the boiler and enters an insulated turbine at station 2. The turbine exhausts to an aerogonic condenser at a pressure of 200 kPa and a quality of 80% at station 3. The condenser cools the water to a saturated liquid at 100 kPa at station 4. Determine **a)** the mass flow rate of water, **b)** the power of the turbine, and **c)** the heat transfer rate of the condenser.

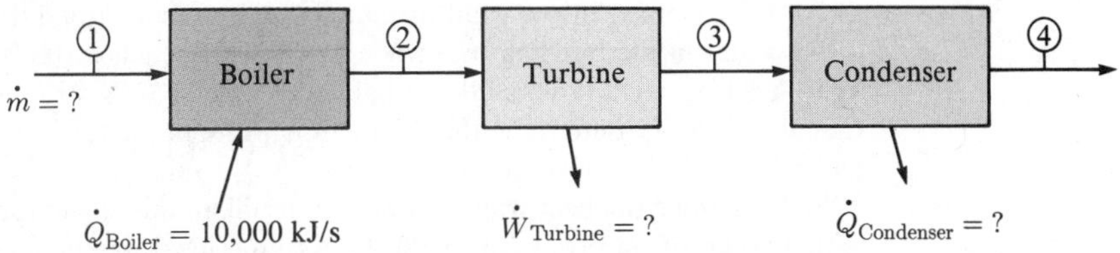

185. 0.5 lbm/s of hydraulic oil (density = 55.6 lbm/ft^3 and specific heat = 0.52 Btu/(lbm·R)) is adiabatically pumped from 14.7 psia to 3014.7 psia with a 10.0-hp gear-type hydraulic pump. Determine the temperature rise in the oil as it passes through the pump.

186. An adiabatic air turbine is used to drive a compressor plus another device as shown in the drawing. Assuming the working fluid (air) to be an ideal gas, find

a) the mass flow rate of the air, and

b) the power required to drive the compressor.

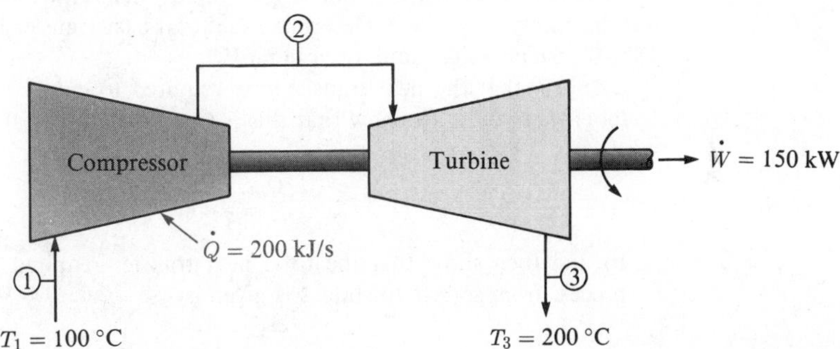

187. It is proposed to construct a power plant on the shores of Lake Gitchee Gumee. To preserve the essential qualities of the lake, a local environmental activist organized the community and passed an ordinance requiring that condenser coolant obtained from the lake be returned to the lake at temperatures no warmer than 5 °F above the temperature at which the water was withdrawn from the lake. Following are some of the design parameters of the proposed plant:

1. Steam flow through condenser: 10,000 lbm/h.

2. Inlet steam conditions: saturated vapor at 1.0 psia.
3. Outlet condensate conditions: saturated liquid at 1.0 psia.
4. External heat loss from condenser: equal to 8% of the energy extracted from the steam during condensation.
5. Lake water has a specific heat of 1.0 Btu/(lbm·R).
Find the required flow rate of coolant from Lake Gitchee Gumee.

188. Determine the air velocity in the $\frac{1}{4}$-in-diameter neck of a balloon required to inflate an initially empty balloon to a diameter of 1.0 ft in 60 s. Assume the density of the air in the balloon remains constant during the inflation process.

189. Explain why the final temperature resulting from the adiabatic filling of a rigid vessel with an ideal gas is independent of the filling pressure (see Eq. 4.144).

190. Incompressible hydraulic oil (density = 880 kg/m^3 and specific heat = 2.1 kJ/(kg·K)) is pumped from a reservoir at 35 °C into a fully extended rigid hydraulic cylinder. Determine the temperature of the oil in the cylinder when its pressure reaches 35 MPa.

191. Incompressible liquid water (density = 62.4 lbm/ft^3 and specific heat = 1.0 Btu/(lbm·R)) at 70 °F is pumped into a rigid insulated hollow bowling ball. Determine the temperature of the water in the bowling ball when its pressure reaches 100,000 psia.

192. A 0.1-m^3 rigid tank is filled adiabatically to 20 MPa with helium. If the helium enters the tank at 20 °C, determine the final temperature in the tank after it is filled. Assume ideal gas behavior with constant specific heats.

193. Determine the heat transfer required to fill an initially empty rigid vessel isothermally with 15.0 kg of pure oxygen at 20 °C. Assume ideal gas behavior with constant specific heats.

194. Determine the heat transfer required to cause a tank initially pressurized with air, to discharge isenthalpically. The initial state inside the tank is $p_1 = 1500$ psia, $T_1 = 100$ °F, $m_1 = 10$ lbm, and the final state is $p_2 = 14.7$ psia and $m_2 = 0.098$ lbm. Assume ideal gas behavior.

195. A rigid tank with a volume of 0.5 m^3 contains superheated steam at 40 MPa and 500 °C. A valve on the tank is suddenly opened and steam is allowed to escape until the pressure in the tank is 1.0 MPa. While the steam is escaping, heat is simultaneously added to the tank in a manner that causes the enthalpy inside the tank to remain constant throughout the emptying process. Determine the total heat transfer required for this process.

196. Consider a rigid tank of volume $\forall$.

a) Show that the heat transfer rate required to empty *or* fill the tank isenthalpically (note that you must show that this is true for both cases) is given by

$$\dot{Q}_{\substack{\text{isenthalpic} \\ \text{empty or fill}}} = -\forall(dp/dt)$$

b) and then show that the total heat transfer required to carry out this isenthalpic process from state 1 to state 2 is given by

$$({}_1Q_2)_{\substack{\text{isenthalpic} \\ \text{empty or fill}}} = \forall(p_1 - p_2)$$

Section III Computer Problems

The following computer problems were designed to be completed in BASIC on a microcomputer. They require relatively little programming skill and may be used as part of a weekly homework assignment.

197. Write an interactive computer program that will determine the output velocity of an incompressible fluid or a constant specific heat ideal gas (allow the user to choose which) flowing through an adiabatic nozzle. Prompt for all the necessary input variables with proper units. Allow the user the choice of working in either Engineering English or SI units.

198. Write an interactive computer program that will determine the output pressure (and temperature in the case of an ideal gas) of an incompressible fluid or constant specific heat ideal gas (allow the user to chose which) from an adiabatic diffuser. Prompt for all the necessary input variables with proper units. Allow the user the choice of working in either Engineering English or SI units.

199. Write an interactive computer program that will determine the temperature of one of the four flowstreams of a heat exchanger having two inlets and two outlets when the mass flow rates and fluid properties of both of the flowstream fluids are known. Assume the fluids do not mix inside the heat exchanger, and allow either flowstream to be an incompressible liquid or a constant specific heat ideal gas at the user's discretion. Prompt for all the necessary input variables with proper units. Allow the user the choice of working in either Engineering English or SI units.

200. Write an interactive computer program that will perform an energy rate balance on a gas turbine engine. Prompt the user for the appropriate gas properties (in the proper units), the turbine's heat loss or gain rate, and the input mass flow rate and the inlet and exit temperatures. Output to the screen the turbine's output power. Assume the gas behaves as a constant specific heat ideal gas, and neglect all kinetic and potential energy terms. Allow the user the choice of working in either Engineering English or SI units.

201. Write an interactive computer program that will perform a steady state energy rate balance on an open system containing an ideal gas with constant specific heats. Prompt the user for all but *one* of the following input quantities (in proper units): the heat and work energy transport rates, the mass flow rate, temperature, velocity and height of each flowstream entering and exiting the system, and the constant pressure specific heat of the gas contained in the system. Calculate the specific enthalpy of the gas with $h = c_p T$, where T is in absolute temperature units. One of the above items will not be supplied by the user and therefore will become the unknown to be determined by the program. Output to the screen all the input variables plus the value of the unknown. Allow the user the choice of working in either Engineering English or SI units.

202. Repeat Problem 201, except allow the user to choose the system ideal gas from a screen menu, and omit the prompts for gas properties. Use the data in Appendix C.13 for the properties of the gases in your menu. Also allow the user to choose which variable is to be the unknown from a screen menu, and then prompt for all the remaining variables. Use the conservation of mass law to determine or check the balance of the mass flows.

Chapter Five The Second Law of Thermodynamics with Applications to Closed and Open Systems

In this chapter we introduce the second law of thermodynamics and an important new thermodynamic property called entropy. The theory is presented first, and then applied to a variety of closed and open systems of engineering interest. Consequently, this chapter has been divided into four distinct sections. In Section I the second law of thermodynamics and its associated entropy balance are presented along with a detailed discussion of the entropy transport mechanisms associated with the energy transports of heat and work. Unlike mass, energy, and momentum, entropy is not conserved. Consequently, the mechanisms of entropy production must be well understood to produce an effective entropy balance equation.

In Section II the focus is on applying the theory presented in Section I to the same steady state closed systems considered in Section I of the previous chapter. Part II ends with a brief discussion of diffusional mixing.

The second law of thermodynamics is expanded upon in Section III to cover open systems. Then appropriate applications are presented dealing with a variety of common open systems of engineering interest such as nozzles, diffusers, throttling devices, heat exchangers, and mixing. Section III ends with a brief discussion of shaft work machines and availability.

Section IV extends the concepts presented in Section III to the more advanced topics of temperature separation, hydraulics, and unsteady state processes.

Chapter Five Section I — The Second Law of Thermodynamics and Entropy Transport and Production Mechanisms

When we discussed the first law of thermodynamics in Chapter 4 it was fairly easy to apply the general balance equations to the energy concept and then to invoke the conservation of energy principle to obtain a workable energy balance equation. *Energy* is a common English word and it is also a well accepted technical term. Everyone has a basic understanding of what the word means, though we would all have a difficult time defining it precisely. The same can be said for the words *force* and *momentum*. They are such familiar words that we easily accept mathematical formulae and logical arguments that are structured around them.[1]

Most people are intrigued by seeing a movie run backward because it produces images of things never observed in the real world. What they do not realize is that they are seeing the effects of the second law of thermodynamics in action. The second law dictates the direction of the *arrow of time*. That is, things will only occur in a certain way in the real world, and by applying the second law to an observation (like the screening of a movie) we can determine whether the event is running forward or backward in time. It is the second law of thermodynamics that prohibits us from actually traveling backward in time. Curiously, it is the only law of nature that has such a restriction. All the other laws of mechanics and

1. This was not always true. During the seventeenth and eighteenth centuries a great controversy raged among the philosophers and mathematicians as to whether mV or mV^2 was the source of the force produced when an object of mass m moving at velocity V was suddenly stopped. This *force of motion* or *living force* (*vis viva* in Latin) controversy was never resolved. Later the term mV became known as *momentum* (from the Latin word for motion), and in 1803 Thomas Young (for whom Young's modulus of elasticity is named) dubbed mV^2 as *energy*. In 1862 it was finally written as $mV^2/2$ and named *kinetic energy* by William Thomson.

thermodynamics are valid regardless of whether time is moving forward or backward. Only the second law of thermodynamics is violated when time is reversed.

At this point we need to introduce a new thermodynamic property that is simply a measure of the amount of *molecular disorder* within a system. The name of this new property is *entropy*. The meaning of this particular name will be explained later, but note that a system that has a high degree of molecular disorder (such as a high temperature gas) has a very high entropy value and, conversely, a system that has a very low degree of molecular disorder (such as a crystalline solid) has a very low entropy value.[2] This new property is very important because entropy is at the core of the second law of thermodynamics.

In the limit, a system that has all of its atoms arranged in some perfectly ordered manner would have an entropy value of zero. This is the substance of the third law of thermodynamics. This law was introduced in 1906 by Walter H. Nernst (1864–1941) and states that the entropy of a pure substance is a constant at absolute zero temperature. In 1911 Max Planck modified this law by setting the entropies of all pure substances equal to zero at absolute zero temperature. This had the effect of normalizing entropy values and thus creating a uniform absolute entropy scale for all substances. Therefore, we can write the following simple mathematical statement of the third law of thermodynamics:

$$\lim_{T \to 0} (\text{entropy of a pure substance}) = 0$$

This law has value in defining the measure of entropy but it does not otherwise contribute to a thermodynamic analysis of an engineering system.

Numerical values for specific entropy are commonly listed in thermodynamic tables along with values for specific volume, specific internal energy, and specific enthalpy. For convenience, most thermodynamic tables are developed around a relative entropy and internal energy scale wherein the values of entropy and internal energy are arbitrarily set equal to zero at a point other than at absolute zero temperature. For example, in the steam tables the specific internal energy and specific entropy of saturated liquid water are set equal to zero at the triple point of water (0.01 °C, 0.6113 kPa or 32.018 °F, 0.0887 psia) and thus the specific internal energies and specific entropies of the less disordered molecular states of water have negative values on this relative scale.

With this simple entropy–disorder relation in mind, we would expect that the entropy of solid water (ice) with its highly ordered molecular structure would be less than that of liquid water with its amorphous molecular structure, which in turn would be less than that of water vapor with its highly random molecular order. This is in fact true, for at the triple point of water (the only point where the solid, liquid, and vapor phases can coexist in equilibrium) the values of the

2. Even though the physical concept of entropy presented here is based on the molecular (or microscopic) behavior of systems, order/disorder phenomenon exist at all levels, macroscopic as well as microscopic. For example, a very messy, disordered room can be said to have a high entropy value.

specific entropies of these phases are

$$(\text{specific entropy})_{\text{solid}} = -1.221 \text{ kJ/(kg·K)} = -0.292 \text{ Btu/(lbm·R)}$$

$$(\text{specific entropy})_{\text{liquid}} = 0.0 \text{ kJ/(kg·K)} = 0.0 \text{ Btu/(lbm·R)}$$

$$(\text{specific entropy})_{\text{vapor}} = 9.157 \text{ kJ/(kg·K)} = 2.187 \text{ Btu/(lbm·R)}$$

and clearly $(\text{entropy})_{\text{solid}} < (\text{entropy})_{\text{liquid}} < (\text{entropy})_{\text{vapor}}$.

Since it always takes an input of energy to create order within a system, it seems reasonable to postulate that a relation exists between the energy transports of a system and its order, or entropy value. Thus, we arrive at the three basic elements of the second law of thermodynamics:

1. The entropy of a system is a measure of the amount of molecular disorder within the system,
2. a system can only produce, not destroy, entropy, and
3. the entropy of a system can be increased or decreased by energy transports across the system boundary.

We begin this chapter by assuming the existence of a disorder-measuring thermodynamic property that we call *entropy*. We will use the symbol S to represent the total entropy (an extensive property), and use $s = S/m$ for the specific entropy (an intensive property).

The Second Law of Thermodynamics

We can use the general balance equation of Chapter 2 to analyze any concept whatsoever. Introducing the total entropy S into balance Eq. 2.11 provides the following total *entropy balance*

$$S_G = S_T + S_P \tag{5.1}$$

where S_G is the gain or loss of total entropy of the system due to the transport of total entropy S_T into or out of the system and the production or destruction of total entropy S_P by the system. A total *entropy rate balance* is easily obtained from Eq. 5.1 by differentiating it with respect to time to give

$$\dot{S}_G = \dot{S}_T + \dot{S}_P \tag{5.2}$$

where the overdot indicates material time differentiation (i.e., $\dot{S} = dS/dt$). The functional abbreviations for the names of these equations are

SB = entropy balance

SRB = entropy rate balance

Unlike energy, mass, and momentum, entropy is usually not conserved in any real process. Processes that have zero entropy production are called *reversible* and are characterized by the fact that they can occur equally well in either the forward or backward direction of time. The thing that makes entropy a unique concept worthy of a thermodynamic law of its own is that entropy is *never destroyed* in any real process. Now, it happens that some processes have very small amounts of entropy production and it will be a useful approximation for these processes to set their entropy production equal to zero.[3] This can be stated in a very succinct mathematical form as

The second law of thermodynamics

$$Sp \geq 0 \tag{5.3}$$

or

$$\dot{S}p \geq 0 \tag{5.4}$$

where the equality sign applies only to a reversible process. Equations 5.1 and 5.2 as modified by Eqs. 5.3 and 5.4 form the mathematical basis for a working form of the entropy balance (SB) and the entropy rate balance (SRB).

At this point we must develop the auxiliary formulae for the entropy transport and production terms before Eqs. 5.1 and 5.2 can be put to any practical use. Unfortunately, this is not an easy task. To understand the concepts of entropy transport and production we must go back to the original nineteenth century classical ideas of Carnot, Clausius, and Thomson (Lord Kelvin), the early developers of this field. When this is completed, we will then bring the subject forward to a modern formulation.

Carnot's Heat Engine

The origins of the second law of thermodynamics lie in the work of a young nineteenth century French Military Engineer named Nicolas Leonard Sadi Carnot[4] (1796–1832). Sadi was the son of one of Napoleon's most successful generals, Lazare Carnot, and was educated at the famous Ecole Polytechnique in Paris. This institution was established in 1794 as an army engineering school and provided a rigorous program of study in chemistry, physics, and mathematics. Between 1794 and 1830 the Ecole Polytechnique had such famous instructors as Lagrange, Fourier, Laplace, Ampere, Cauchy, Coriolis, Poisson, Guy-Lussac, and Poiseuille.

3. In setting the entropy production equal to zero the second law is then made into a conservation law. It is important to remember that entropy is usually not conserved in any real process and that processes that assume zero entropy production are normally only approximations to real world behavior. Reversible processes that inherently have zero entropy production require the existence of a set of active forces called *conservative forces*, and it is felt by some that many intermolecular forces are conservative.

4. Pronounced *car-no*. Many French words have a silent *t* ending. For example, Peugot, Tissot, Monet, ballet, chalet, Chevrolet, and Renault. Sadi was named after the medieval Persian poet Saadi Musharif ed Din, whose poems became popular in France in the late eighteenth century.

After his formal education Carnot chose a career as an army officer. At that time Britain was a powerful military force, primarily as a result of the industrial revolution brought about by the British development of the steam engine. French technology was not developing as fast as Britain's, and in the 1820s Carnot became convinced that France's inadequate utilization of steam power had made it militarily inferior. He began to study the fundamentals of steam engine technology, and in 1824 he published the results of his studies in a small book entitled *Reflections on the Motive Power of Fire* (the French word for *fire* was then a common term for what we call *heat* today).

The essence of the concept of *heat* was a very actively debated scientific topic at the time. In 1789 the great French chemist Antoine Lavoisier (1743–1794) proposed the caloric theory of heat in which heat was presumed to be a colorless, odorless, weightless fluid called *caloric* that could be poured from one object to another. When an object became full of caloric, it was then said to be *saturated* with it. This was the origin of the terms *saturated liquid, saturated vapor*, etc., that we use in thermodynamics today. These terms were introduced into the scientific literature in the early nineteenth century when the caloric theory of heat was popular, and they were never removed when it was later proven that heat was not a fluid. Today they are simply misnomers.

Even during the time of Carnot there were strong attacks against the caloric fluid heat concept. By 1800 the American Benjamin Thompson (Count Rumford, 1753–1814) was able to show that heat could be continuously produced from the mechanical friction of two objects being rubbed together (his famous cannon-boring experiment). From the principal of the conservation of mass, a true fluid can be neither created nor destroyed, so heat could not be a fluid if it could continuously be created in an object by mechanical friction.

The alteration of established scientific dogma is not done easily or quickly, and it was not until the careful and tedious experiments of the English physicist James Prescott Joule (1818–1889) were carried out in the 1840s that the scientific community became firmly convinced that heat was in fact not a fluid after all, and therefore that *caloric* did not really exist. Today when we use the word *heat* in a technical sense we normally mean an *energy transport arising from a temperature difference.*[5] Carnot was trained in the basic principles of hydraulics, pumps, and water wheels at the Ecole Polytechnique. It was clear to him that the power of a steam engine was released as the heat fluid (caloric) fell from the high temperature of the boiler to the lower temperature of the condenser, in much the same way that water falls through a water wheel to produce a mechanical shaft work output. As he stated in his book (the second reference at the end of this chapter),

> According to established principles at the present time, we can compare with sufficient accuracy the motive power of heat to that of a waterfall. The motive power of a waterfall depends on its height and on the quantity of liquid; the motive power of heat depends also on the quantity of caloric used, and on what may be termed, on what in fact we will call, the *height of its fall*, that is to say, the difference of temperature of the bodies between which the exchange of caloric is made.

5. Or, more generally, heat is simply a nonwork, nonmass flow energy transport mechanism.

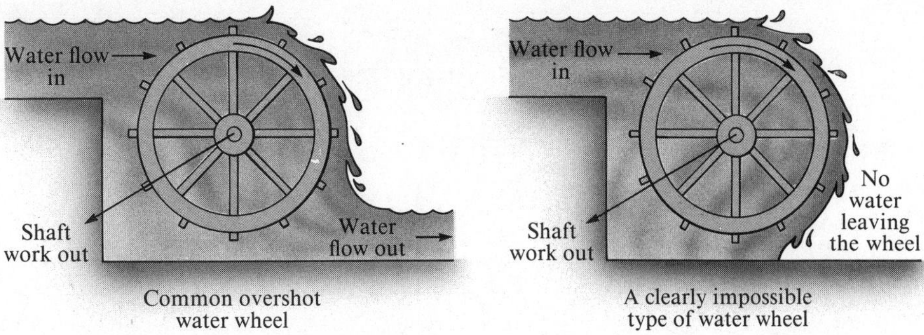

Figure 5.1 Acceptable water wheel operation.

By the 1820s a great deal of work had already been done on the efficiency of water wheels, and the water wheel–steam engine analogy must have seemed to Carnot like a good way to approach the problem of improving steam engine efficiency. Two important conclusions came from his work with this analogy.

First, it is quite obvious that no one could build a water wheel that would produce a continuous work output unless water actually entered and exited the wheel. And if water with a certain kinetic and potential energy entered the wheel, then the same amount of water with a lower energy level must also exit the wheel. In other words, it is impossible to make a water wheel that converts all of the energy of the inlet water into output shaft work. There must also be an outflow of water from the wheel, and this outflow must have some energy. These rather obvious statements are illustrated in Figure 5.1.

Now, if you extend this idea to a steam engine (or any type of heat engine) by replacing the word *water* by the hypothetical heat fluid *caloric*, then it is easy to conclude that when caloric at a certain energy level (temperature) enters a work-producing heat engine, it must also exit the engine at a lower energy level (temperature). This concept was later refined into the following form, known today as the Kelvin-Planck statement of the second law of thermodynamics: *You cannot make a continuously operating heat engine that converts all of its heat input directly into work output* (see Figure 5.2).

The Kelvin-Planck statement is really a direct consequence of the second law of thermodynamics, but it can be used as a somewhat vague formal statement of this law. Its development by recourse to a water wheel analogy is clearly wrong, but the conclusions are nonetheless fortuitously correct. It has many different written forms. For example, another form of the Kelvin-Planck statement is: *It is impossible to build a continuously operating device that will produce a work output while absorbing heat energy from a single thermal reservoir.* A variation on this statement, which is also easily understood from the water wheel analogy, is: *It is impossible to build a continuously operating device that will cause heat energy to be transferred from a low-temperature reservoir to a high-temperature reservoir without the input of work.* This last version is often called the Clausius statement of the second law of thermodynamics.

The second important result of Carnot's work came from his observation that the maximum efficiency of a water wheel was independent of the type of liquid

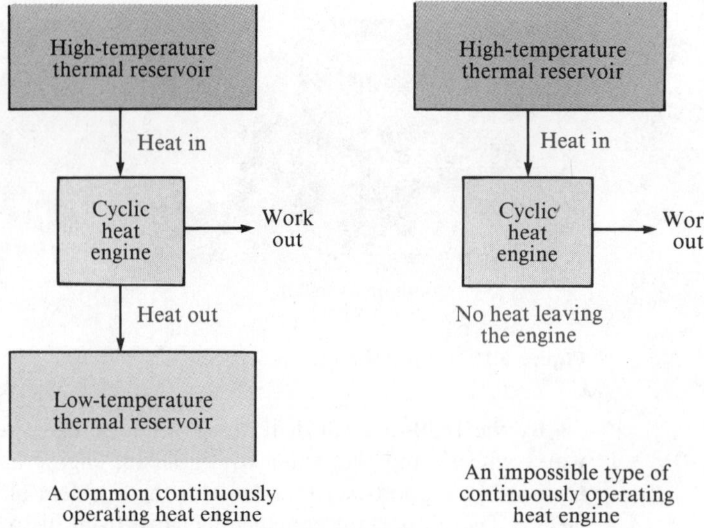

Figure 5.2 Acceptable heat engine operation.

used and depended only on the inlet and outlet flow energies. This led him to the conclusion that

> The motive power of heat is independent of the agents employed to realize it; its quantity is fixed solely by the temperatures of the bodies between which is effected, finally, the transfer of caloric.

Or, the maximum efficiency of a steam engine (or any type of heat engine) is dependent only upon the temperatures of the high- and low-temperature thermal reservoirs of the engine (the boiler and condenser temperatures in the case of a steam engine) and is independent of the working fluid of the engine (water in the case of a steam engine). Of course, to achieve the maximum possible efficiency, the water wheel and the heat engine must be completely *reversible*, i.e., they cannot possess any mechanical friction or other losses of any kind.

The significance of Carnot's conclusions was not recognized until 1850 when Rudolph Clausius (1822–1888) and William Thomson (Lord Kelvin, 1824–1907) worked out a clear formulation of the conservation of energy principle, which was then named the *first* law of thermodynamics. Carnot's first conclusion was then named the *second* law of thermodynamics by Clausius, who also expanded Carnot's energy transformation concepts into a new property he called entropy.[6] Thomson

6. Clausius' German term for Carnot's energy transformation concept was *verwandlungsinhalt*, meaning *transformation content*. Fortunately, in 1865 he chose to formally rename this concept by coining the term *entropy* from the Greeek η τροπή, meaning simply *to change*. Later, there was an unsuccessful attempt to name a total entropy unit, the *clausius*, Cl, after him. It was defined as 1 Cl = 1 kcal/K = 4.186 J/K, but it was not universally accepted. In the chemical and biological literature a specific entropy unit imaginatively named the *entropy unit* (*eu*) has existed for some time now, where 1 eu = 1 kcal/(kgmole·K) = 4.186 kJ/(kgmole·K). However, this unit is not used in engineering today.

then used Carnot's second conclusion regarding maximum (i.e., reversible) engine energy conversion efficiency to develop the concept of an absolute temperature scale.

The Absolute Temperature Scale

In 1848 Thomson used Carnot's conclusion that the efficiency of a heat engine depended only on its thermal reservoir temperatures to develop the concept of an absolute temperature scale. Soon afterward an absolute temperature scale based on the size of the celsius degree (°C) became popular and was given his titled name *kelvin* (*K*) by his admirers.[7] By using Eq. 4.70 we can define the thermal energy conversion efficiency (also called the *thermal efficiency*) η_T of a continuously operating closed system heat engine with a net output work or power as

$$\eta_T = \frac{|W_{out}|_{net}}{Q_{in}} = \frac{|\dot{W}_{out}|_{net}}{\dot{Q}_{in}} \tag{5.5}$$

where absolute values are taken to assure that η_T is always positive. A closed system heat engine can operate continuously only if it operates in a thermodynamic cycle. A system that undergoes a thermodynamic cycle must end up at the same thermodynamic state at the end of the cycle that it started from at the beginning of the cycle. Because the total system energy E is a point function, the closed system first law of thermodynamics energy balance (EB) applied to a cyclic process yields

$$(Q + W)_{cycle} = (E_2 - E_1)_{cycle} = 0 \tag{5.6}$$

Now, from Figure 5.3 we see that the heat input to a cyclic heat engine is

$$(Q)_{cycle} = Q_{in} - |Q_{out}| \tag{5.7}$$

and

$$(W)_{cycle} = |W_{out}| \tag{5.8}$$

where $|Q_{out}|$ and $|W_{out}|$ are the absolute values of these energy flows.

Note that we have introduced the correct *sign* with the absolute value of the symbol in Eqs. 5.7 and 5.8 to indicate the proper flow direction (+ for inflow and − for outflow). Normally we do not introduce the sign convention directly

7. In 1967 the International Bureau of Weights and Measures dropped the prefix "degree" from the SI absolute temperature scale. Thus, we say "100 degrees celsius" (100 °C) equals "373 kelvin" (373 K). Note that we do not capitalize the first letter of a unit whose name is derived from that of a person when the unit's name is written out, but the first letter is capitalized when the unit's name is abbreviated (see Chapter 1). In this text we follow the scheme of omitting the degree symbol with both the kelvin and the rankine absolute temperature scales.

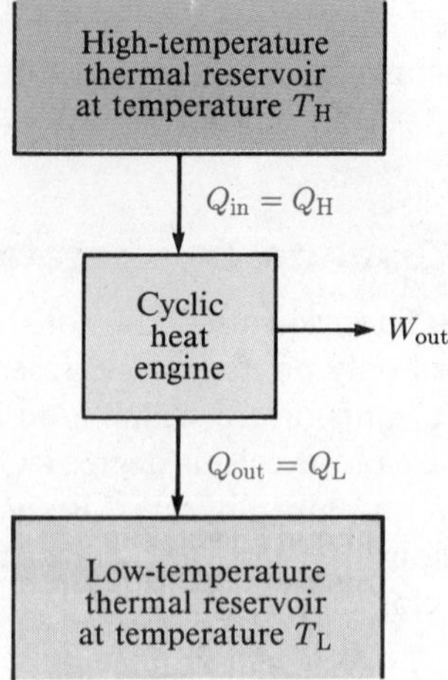

Figure 5.3 Schematic of a cyclic heat engine.

into the equations themselves. The usual custom is to attach the correct flow direction sign to the *number* and not the *symbol*. However, we have changed this notational scheme here to help you understand the operation of closed system heat engines. Later in this chapter we will revert back to the conventional notation scheme for algebraic signs.

Combining Eqs. 5.5 through 5.8 and using the simplified notation shown in Figure 5.3 yields

$$\eta_T = \frac{|W_{out}|_{net}}{Q_{in}} = \frac{(Q_{in} - |Q_{out}|)}{Q_{in}} = 1 - \frac{|Q_{out}|}{Q_{in}} = 1 - \frac{|Q_L|}{Q_H} \tag{5.9}$$

If we now follow Carnot's lead and presume that the thermal efficiency of a reversible heat engine $(\eta_T)_{rev}$ depends only on the absolute temperatures of the thermal reservoirs, then we can write

$$(\eta_T)_{rev} = 1 - \left(\frac{|Q_{out}|}{Q_{in}}\right)_{rev} = 1 - \left(\frac{|Q_L|}{Q_H}\right)_{rev}$$

or

$$1 - (\eta_T)_{rev} = \left(\frac{|Q_L|}{Q_H}\right)_{rev} = f\left(\frac{T_L}{T_H}\right) \tag{5.10}$$

where $f(\ )$ is an unknown function that will eventually be used to define the absolute temperature scale, and the subscripts L and H refer to the low and high-temperature reservoirs, respectively.

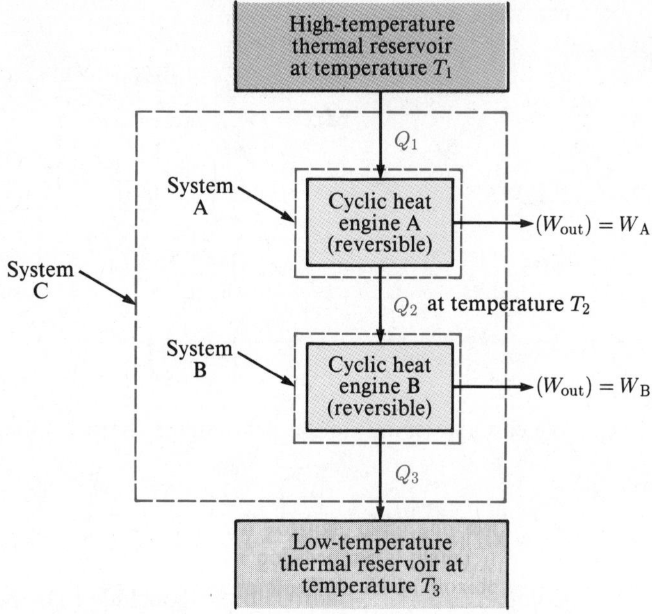

Figure 5.4 Two reversible heat engines connected in series.

Now consider the two reversible heat engines connected in series shown in Figure 5.4. The thermal efficiency of each of the individual reversible heat engines is determined from an analysis of systems A and B individually.

The thermal efficiency of the engine in system A is[8]

$$(\eta_T)_A = \frac{|W_A|}{Q_1} = 1 - \frac{|Q_2|}{Q_1} = 1 - f\left(\frac{T_2}{T_1}\right)$$

and that in system B is

$$(\eta_T)_B = \frac{|W_B|}{Q_2} = 1 - \frac{|Q_3|}{Q_2} = 1 - f\left(\frac{T_3}{T_2}\right)$$

Now, if we include both engines inside the system boundary as in system C of Figure 5.4, then we have $W_C = W_A + W_B$, and utilizing the previous results we

8. Since these engines are defined at the outset to be reversible, the "rev" subscript on the η_T, Q, and W terms in these equations has been dropped for simplicity. This subscript reappears again in the equations at the end of this analysis.

can write

$$(\eta_T)_C = \frac{|W_C|}{Q_1} = \frac{|W_A| + |W_B|}{Q_1} = \frac{(Q_1 - |Q_2|) + (|Q_2| - |Q_3|)}{Q_1}$$

$$= 1 - \frac{|Q_2|}{Q_1} + \left(\frac{|Q_2| - |Q_3|}{|Q_2|}\right)\left(\frac{|Q_2|}{Q_1}\right)$$

$$= 1 - f\left(\frac{T_2}{T_1}\right) + \left[1 - f\left(\frac{T_3}{T_2}\right)\right] f\left(\frac{T_2}{T_1}\right)$$

$$= 1 - f\left(\frac{T_2}{T_1}\right) f\left(\frac{T_3}{T_2}\right) \tag{5.11}$$

We can also compute the heat engine thermal efficiency of system C as

$$(\eta_T)_C = \frac{|W_C|}{Q_1} = \frac{Q_1 - |Q_3|}{Q_1} = 1 - \frac{|Q_3|}{Q_1} = 1 - f\left(\frac{T_3}{T_1}\right) \tag{5.12}$$

Comparing Eqs. 5.11 and 5.12 we conclude that the following functional relation must hold for the unknown temperature function, $f(\ )$

$$f\left(\frac{T_3}{T_1}\right) \equiv f\left(\frac{T_2}{T_1}\right) f\left(\frac{T_3}{T_2}\right) \tag{5.13}$$

Many common functions do not satisfy this equation. For example,

$$\sin\frac{T_3}{T_1} \neq \left(\sin\frac{T_2}{T_1}\right)\sin\frac{T_3}{T_2}$$

$$\log\frac{T_3}{T_1} \neq \left(\log\frac{T_2}{T_1}\right)\log\frac{T_3}{T_2}$$

$$\exp\frac{T_3}{T_1} \neq \left(\exp\frac{T_2}{T_1}\right)\exp\frac{T_3}{T_2}$$

and so forth. However, any simple power function of the form $f(T_3/T_1) = (T_3/T_1)^n$ does satisfy Eq. 5.13 since

$$\left(\frac{T_3}{T_1}\right)^n = \left(\frac{T_2}{T_1}\right)^n \left(\frac{T_3}{T_2}\right)^n$$

The simplest such power function is a linear one ($n = 1$), and this is what Thomson chose to establish his absolute temperature scale. Thus, we will take

$$f\left(\frac{T_3}{T_1}\right) = \frac{T_3}{T_1} = \left(\frac{T_2}{T_1}\right)\left(\frac{T_3}{T_2}\right) = f\left(\frac{T_2}{T_1}\right) f\left(\frac{T_3}{T_2}\right) \tag{5.14}$$

and then Eq. 5.10 becomes

$$\left(\frac{|Q_{\text{out}}|}{Q_{\text{in}}}\right)_{\text{rev}} = \left(\frac{|Q_{\text{L}}|}{Q_{\text{H}}}\right)_{\text{rev}} = \frac{T_{\text{L}}}{T_{\text{H}}} \tag{5.15}$$

It should be noted that Eq. 5.14 is not the only function that accurately defines an absolute temperature scale (but it is the simplest). Many other functions also work. However, they produce nonlinear temperature scales in which the size of the temperature unit is not constant but instead depends upon the temperature level. This might be a useful technique to expand or condense a temperature scale in certain temperature regions, but the additional complexity associated with a nonlinear temperature scale makes it generally unsuitable for common usage.[9]

Now, clearly, the maximum possible thermal energy conversion efficiency of any real irreversible closed system cyclic heat engine is equal to the thermal energy conversion efficiency that the same heat engine would have if it were somehow made to run reversibly. Then, from Eq. 5.9,

$$(\eta_{\text{T}})_{\text{max}} = (\eta_{\text{T}})_{\text{rev}} = (\eta_{\text{T}})_{\text{Carnot}} = 1 - \frac{T_{\text{L}}}{T_{\text{H}}} \tag{5.16}$$

Example 5.1

If a heat engine burns fuel for its thermal energy source and the combustion flame temperature is 4000 °F, determine the maximum possible thermal efficiency of this engine if it exhausts to the environment at 70 °F.

Solution The maximum possible thermal energy conversion efficiency of any heat engine occurs when the engine operates reversibly. Since all reversible engines must have the same thermal energy conversion efficiency when operated between the same high- and low-temperature reservoirs, we can apply the results of the reversible Carnot engine analysis to this problem. Equation 5.16 gives the maximum possible thermal efficiency as

$$(\eta_{\text{T}})_{\text{max}} = (\eta_{\text{T}})_{\text{Carnot}} = 1 - \frac{T_{\text{L}}}{T_{\text{H}}} = 1 - \frac{(70 + 460)\text{ R}}{(4000 + 460)\text{ R}} = 0.881 = 88.1\%$$

The results of Example 5.1 are highly unrealistic since no real heat engine can ever be reversible. The irreversibilities within modern heat engines limit their actual operating thermal energy conversion efficiency to around 30%.

Example 5.2

A coal-fired electrical power plant produces 5.0 MW of electrical power while exhausting 8.0 MW of thermal energy to a nearby river at 10 °C. The power plant requires an input power of 1.0 kW to drive the boiler feed pump.

9. It has been suggested that since many thermal phenomena are inherently nonlinear, the use of a nonlinear (e.g., logarithmic) temperature scale might have some engineering merit.

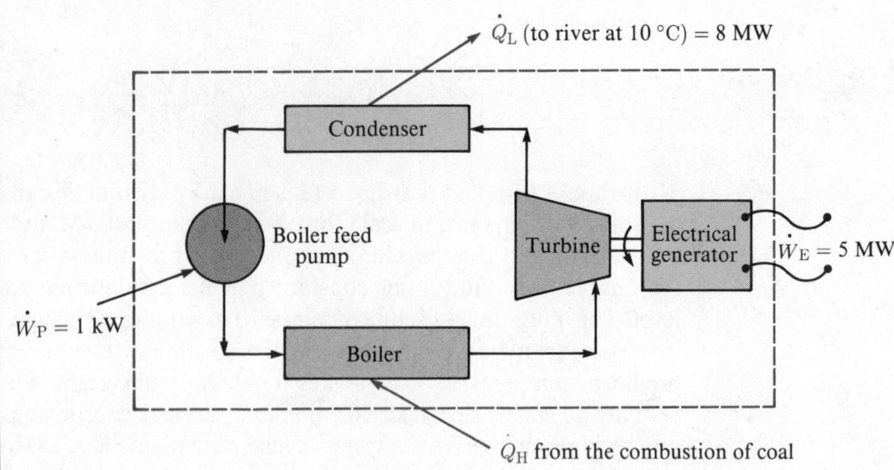

Determine

a) the actual thermal efficiency of the power plant, and

b) the equivalent heat source temperature if the plant operated on a reversible Carnot cycle.

Solution If we construct the system boundary as shown in the sketch the power plant can be considered to be a closed system.

a) The actual thermal efficiency of this system is given by Eq. 5.9 as

$$\eta_T = \frac{|\dot{W}_E + \dot{W}_P|}{\dot{Q}_H} = \frac{\dot{Q}_H - |\dot{Q}_L|}{\dot{Q}_H}$$

and the ERB for the steady state operation of this system is

$$\dot{Q}_H + \dot{Q}_L + \dot{W}_P + \dot{W}_E = 0$$

or

$$\begin{aligned}\dot{Q}_H &= -(\dot{Q}_L + \dot{W}_P + \dot{W}_E)\\ &= -(-8.0\text{ MW} + 0.001\text{ MW} - 5.0\text{ MW})\\ &= 13\text{ MW}\end{aligned}$$

and thus the actual thermal efficiency is

$$\eta_T = \frac{|-5.0\text{ MW} + 0.001\text{ MW}|}{13\text{ MW}} = \frac{13\text{ MW} - 8.0\text{ MW}}{13\text{ MW}} = 0.385$$

$$= 38.5\%$$

b) From Eq. 5.16 we have

$$(\eta_T)_{max} = (\eta_T)_{Carnot} = 1 - \frac{T_L}{T_H} = 0.385$$

so that

$$T_H = \frac{T_L}{1 - 0.385} = \frac{(273 + 10)\text{ K}}{0.615}$$

$$= 460\text{ K} = 187\text{ °C}$$

The calculations of part a are perfectly valid for this power plant since they deal with *actual* input and output energy values. The answer to part b, however, is unrealistically lower than the actual coal flame temperature in the boiler due to the many irreversibilities that exist within a real power plant.

Heat Pumps, Refrigerators, and Air Conditioners

When a heat engine is run thermodynamically backward it becomes a heat pump, a refrigerator or an air conditioner, depending on your point of view. Figure 5.5 shows that when a heat engine is thermodynamically reversed the directions of all the energy flows are reversed. Thus, a work *input* W_{in} will cause a thermal energy transfer Q_L *from* a low-temperature reservoir, and a thermal energy transfer Q_H *to* a high-temperature reservoir. Consequently, the backward-running heat

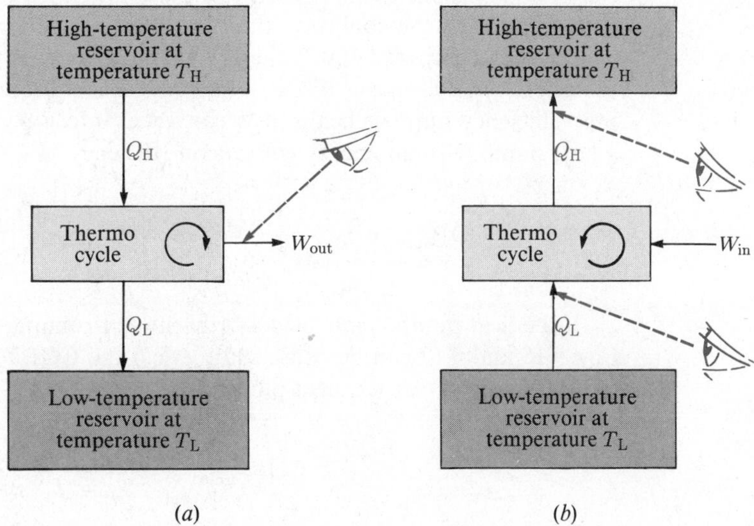

Figure 5.5 (*a*) Heat engine; (*b*) thermodynamically reversed heat engine (heat pump, refrigerator, or air conditioner).

engine appears to "pump" heat from a low-temperature reservoir to a high-temperature reservoir. However, since heat is really a thermal energy transport phenomenon and not a fluid, it is somewhat misleading to refer to it as being "pumped." Yet it is common practice in the heating, ventilating and air conditioning (HVAC) industry to refer to these devices as *heat pumps* when they are used to provide a thermal energy transfer to a warm environment (e.g., a house) from a cold environment (e.g., the outside air).

The *desired energy result* in the operation of a heat pump is heat addition to an already warm environment. Therefore, its energy conversion efficiency can be determined from Eq. 4.70 and an energy balance on the device (see Figure 5.5*b*) as

$$\eta_{\substack{\text{heat}\\\text{pump}}} = \frac{\text{desired energy result}}{\text{required energy input}} = \frac{|Q_H|}{W_{in}} = \frac{|Q_H|}{|Q_H| - Q_L} = \frac{|\dot{Q}_H|}{\dot{W}_{in}} = \frac{|\dot{Q}_H|}{|\dot{Q}_H| - \dot{Q}_L}$$

where, as in the previous section, we have used the absolute values of certain terms to avoid improper or confusing algebraic signs. Under normal operating conditions the numerator in this expression is always greater than the denominator; consequently, the energy conversion efficiency of a heat pump is always greater than 100%. No basic laws are violated here; this is simply the result of the way in which the general efficiency formula (Eq. 4.70) is structured. It is true that in the case of a heat pump you get more thermal energy out of it (the desired result) than work energy put into it. This makes a heat pump much more attractive for domestic heating than, say, a purely resistive electrical heater. Electrical heaters convert all of their input electrical energy directly into thermal energy and therefore have energy conversion efficiencies of 100%, whereas most heat pumps have energy conversion efficiencies far in excess of 100% for the same electrical energy input.

To eliminate the confusion that would arise in the general public by quoting efficiencies in excess of 100%, the HVAC industry uses the less suggestive phrase *coefficient of performance* (COP) to express this concept. The COP is simply the pure efficiency number before it is converted into a percentage (i.e., the COP of a heat pump with an energy conversion efficiency of 450% is 4.5).

$$\text{COP}_{\substack{\text{heat}\\\text{pump}}} = \eta_{\substack{\text{heat}\\\text{pump}}} = \frac{|Q_H|}{W_{in}} = \frac{|Q_H|}{|Q_H| - Q_L} = \frac{|\dot{Q}_H|}{\dot{W}_{in}} = \frac{|\dot{Q}_H|}{|\dot{Q}_H| - \dot{Q}_L} \quad \textbf{(5.17)}$$

If the heat pump is modeled as a backward-running Carnot heat engine, then Eqs. 5.15 and 5.17 can be combined to yield the COP for a "reversible" (i.e., frictionless, etc.), or Carnot, heat pump as

$$\text{COP}_{\substack{\text{Carnot}\\\text{heat pump}}} = \frac{T_H}{T_H - T_L} \quad \textbf{(5.18)}$$

If the removal of heat Q_L from a space is the desired result of a backward-running heat engine, then the engine is called a *refrigerator* when food is stored in the cooled space and an *air conditioner* when people occupy the cooled space.

The energy conversion efficiency of a refrigerator or air conditioner can also be obtained from Eq. 4.70. As in the case of a heat pump, these efficiencies are also normally greater than 100% and they too are commonly represented with the pure number *coefficient of performance* label:

$$\mathrm{COP}_{\substack{\text{refrig. or}\\ \text{air cond.}}} = \eta_{\substack{\text{refrig. or}\\ \text{air cond.}}} = \frac{\text{desired energy result}}{\text{required energy input}}$$

$$= \frac{Q_L}{W_{in}} = \frac{Q_L}{|Q_H| - Q_L} = \frac{\dot{Q}_L}{\dot{W}_{in}} = \frac{\dot{Q}_L}{|\dot{Q}_H| - \dot{Q}_L} \tag{5.19}$$

For a backward-running Carnot (i.e., reversible) heat engine, Eqs. 5.15 and 5.19 can be combined to give the COP for a reversible refrigerator or air conditioner as

$$\mathrm{COP}_{\substack{\text{Carnot}\\ \text{refrig. or}\\ \text{air cond.}}} = \frac{T_L}{T_H - T_L} \tag{5.20}$$

Comparing Eqs. 5.17 and 5.19 we see that

$$\mathrm{COP}_{\text{heat pump}} = \mathrm{COP}_{\substack{\text{refrig. or}\\ \text{air cond.}}} + 1$$

Clausius' Definition of Entropy

Rudolph Clausius extended Thomson's absolute temperature scale work by rearranging Eq. 5.15 to read

$$\frac{(Q_H)_{rev}}{T_H} = \frac{|Q_L|_{rev}}{T_L}$$

and since this applies only to a closed system undergoing a thermodynamic cycle, it can also be written as

$$\sum_{\text{cycle}} \left(\frac{Q}{T}\right) = \frac{(Q_H)_{rev}}{T_H} - \frac{|Q_L|_{rev}}{T_L} = 0$$

If we now take an arbitrary thermodynamic closed system cycle and overlay it with an infinite number of infinitesimal heat engine cycles as shown in Figure 5.6, then we can extend the finite summation process of the previous equation into a cyclic integral. Also, since each of these infinite number of heat engines is now operating over an infinitely small temperature difference, $T_H \approx T_L = T$, and $(Q_H)_{rev} - |Q_L|_{rev} \approx (\bar{d}Q)_{rev}$. Then in the limit, the previous equation becomes

$$\lim_{n\to\infty}\left[\sum_{n_{\text{cycles}}} \left(\frac{Q}{T}\right)\right] = \oint_{\text{cycle}} \left(\frac{\bar{d}Q}{T}\right)_{rev} = 0 \tag{5.21}$$

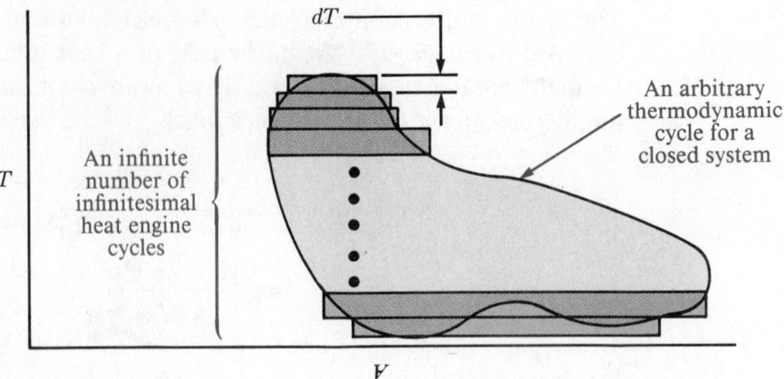

Figure 5.6 An infinite number of infinitesimal heat engine cycles approximating an arbitrary closed system thermodynamic cycle.

The temperature T in this equation is the *absolute* temperature at the point where the heat transfer $\bar{d}Q$ occurs.

Clausius then noted the remarkable result that since by definition,

$$\oint_{\text{cycle}} (\text{any thermodynamic property differential}) = 0$$

then the argument of the integral in Eq. 5.21 *must* define a thermodynamic property! That is,

$$\left(\frac{\bar{d}Q}{T}\right)_{\text{rev}} = \text{differential of some thermodynamic property}$$

But which property? The term $(\bar{d}Q)_{\text{rev}}$ by itself is a path function and thus cannot be a thermodynamic property differential. However, when $(\bar{d}Q)_{\text{rev}}$ is divided by T a property differential results! Clausius realized that he had discovered a new thermodynamic property and he chose to name it *entropy*,[10] and to represent the total entropy of a system by the symbol S, where

$$dS = \left(\frac{\bar{d}Q}{T}\right)_{\text{rev}} \tag{5.22}$$

or

$$S_2 - S_1 = \int_1^2 \left(\frac{\bar{d}Q}{T}\right)_{\text{rev}} \tag{5.23}$$

10. Here is a translation of how Clausius, in 1865, described why he chose the word entropy for the name of his new property. "We might call S the *transformational* content of the body, just as we termed the quantity U the *heat* and *work* content of the body. But since I believe it is better to borrow terms for important quantities from the ancient languages so that they may be adopted unchanged in all modern languages, I propose to call the quantity S the *entropy* of the body, from the Greek word ʽη τροπή, meaning *a transformation*."

or

$$s_2 - s_1 = \frac{S_2 - S_1}{m} = \frac{1}{m}\int_1^2 \left(\frac{đQ}{T}\right)_{\text{rev}} \tag{5.24}$$

Be careful to note that Eqs. 5.22–5.24, which define entropy, are for a *closed system* of fixed mass m only. The effect of mass flow on system entropy will be taken up in a separate section later in this chapter.

The use of a relative temperature scale in a grouping of units can sometimes be confusing. For example, when a temperature unit appears in the denominator of a units grouping it can be written either as °F or R (or °C or K in SI) because only the degree size there is important. Thus, Eq. 5.24 indicates that the units of specific entropy can be written correctly in either of the following forms:

$$s \text{ in Btu/(lbm}\cdot{}^\circ\text{F)} \equiv s \text{ in Btu/(lbm}\cdot\text{R)}$$

or

$$s \text{ in kJ/(kg}\cdot{}^\circ\text{C)} = s \text{ in kJ/(kg}\cdot\text{K)}$$

This does not mean that the °F and R (or °C and K) scales are equal, but only that their *degree sizes* are equal. Therefore, when you have units like Btu/(lbm·°F) you do not have to use any mathematical formula to convert °F to R in order to write this grouping as Btu/(lbm·R). This is a simple but often confusing point.

However, the temperature unit you choose to place in the denominator of a term's units grouping may depend upon how the term is to be used in relation to other temperature terms in the equation. An example of where this occurs is in the use of specific heats. Equation 3.33 is

$$c_v = \left(\frac{\partial u}{\partial T}\right)_v \tag{3.33}$$

where c_v is the constant volume specific heat. Since the temperature appears as an infinitesimal difference in this equation we can use either °F or R (°C or K) temperature units. Therefore, the value of c_v in Btu/(lbm·°F) is the same as its value in Btu/(lbm·R). With c_v in Btu/(lbm·°F) we could use T_2 and T_1 in °F and the temperature unit would cancel, or with c_v given in Btu/(lbm·R) we could use T_2 and T_1 in R and the temperature unit would again cancel. We would get the same answer in each case. However, Eq. 5.24 is an entropy formula in which T stands alone; therefore, temperature must always be in *absolute* unit (R or K) when used in this equation. Now, if we gave you s in say Btu/(lbm·°F) you might be tempted to use T in °F to cancel the temperature unit. This would be incorrect. You would have to recognize that s in Btu/(lbm·°F) has the same numerical value as s in Btu/(lbm·R), and that T *must* be in an absolute temperature unit (R in this case). To eliminate as much confusion as possible, in this text we will always use the absolute temperature unit when it appears in the denominator of a units cluster. In this way you will never be prompted to use the wrong temperature unit in a calculation.

We discussed reversible processes briefly in Chapter 4 and noted that there were few reversible processes in the real world. In fact every heat transport of energy through a finite temperature difference is irreversible. We are able to write Eqs. 5.21 through 5.24 as reversible heat transfers only because we had created a very special situation in which the heat transport of energy was assumed to take place through an infinitesimal temperature difference. But in the real world it would require an infinite amount of time to transport a finite amount of energy by this method. If we try to alter the results of Eq. 5.22 by considering only real irreversible heat transports of energy, we immediately realize that the amount of work done by the cyclic heat engines must be less than in the reversible case. Then, for an actual heat engine,

$$|W_{\text{actual}}| < |W_{\text{reversible}}|$$

and using the first law of thermodynamics we conclude that since the system total energy E is a point function and is therefore independent of whether the process path is reversible or irreversible, then

$$dE = \bar{d}Q_{\text{rev}} + \bar{d}W_{\text{rev}} = \bar{d}Q_{\text{act}} + \bar{d}W_{\text{act}}$$

and dividing by the appropriate absolute temperature and rearranging gives

$$dS = \left(\frac{\bar{d}Q}{T}\right)_{\text{rev}} = \left(\frac{\bar{d}Q}{T}\right)_{\text{act}} + \frac{(\bar{d}W)_{\text{act}} - (\bar{d}W)_{\text{rev}}}{T} \tag{5.25}$$

For a work producing heat engine, $(\bar{d}W)_{\text{act}}$ and $(\bar{d}W)_{\text{rev}}$ are both negative quantities since they represent energy leaving the system, and so Eq. 5.25 can be rearranged to produce

$$dS > \left(\frac{\bar{d}Q}{T}\right)_{\text{act}} \tag{5.26}$$

Equation 5.26 is known as the Clausius inequality. It is Clausius' mathematical form of the second law of thermodynamics for a closed system. Dropping the subscript on the bracketed term and thus allowing it to represent either a reversible or an actual process produces the following somewhat more general mathematical second law expression,

$$dS \geq \left(\frac{\bar{d}Q}{T}\right) \tag{5.27}$$

and

$$\oint_{\text{cycle}} \left(\frac{\bar{d}Q}{T}\right) \leq 0 \tag{5.28}$$

where the equality sign is used for a reversible heat transport of energy.

Numerical Values for Specific Entropy

In Chapter 3 we discussed five different methods for finding numerical values for properties: *thermodynamic equations of state, thermodynamic tables, thermodynamic charts, direct experimental measurements*, and the *formulae of statistical thermodynamics*. These same five methods can be used to find numerical values for the specific entropy. In this section we will focus on the use of *thermodynamic equations of state, tables*, and *charts*.

Energy and entropy are thermodynamic properties and are therefore mathematical point functions. Consequently, the energy and entropy changes of a system depend only on the beginning and ending states of a process, and not on the actual thermodynamic path taken by the process between these states. Therefore, for a closed system we can write the differential energy and entropy balances as

$$(dE)_{\text{rev}} = (dE)_{\text{act}} = dE = (\bar{d}Q)_{\text{rev}} + (\bar{d}W)_{\text{rev}} = (\bar{d}Q)_{\text{act}} + (\bar{d}W)_{\text{act}}$$

and

$$(dS)_{\text{rev}} = (dS)_{\text{act}} = dS = \left(\frac{\bar{d}Q}{T}\right)_{\text{rev}}$$

Combining the "reversible" path parts of these two equations we get

$$(\bar{d}Q)_{\text{rev}} = T\,dS = dE - (\bar{d}W)_{\text{rev}} \tag{5.29}$$

For a stationary differential closed system at a uniform temperature T containing a pure substance that is only subjected to a mechanical moving boundary work mode, Eq. 5.29 becomes

$$T\,dS = dU + p\,d\mathcal{V}$$

and upon dividing through by the system mass m and the absolute temperature T

$$ds = \frac{du}{T} + \frac{p}{T}\,dv \tag{5.30}$$

Since $u = h - pv$, this equation can also be written as

$$ds = \frac{dh}{T} - \frac{v}{T}\,dp \tag{5.31}$$

In Chapter 3 we defined the constant volume and constant pressure specific heats for an incompressible substance as

$$c_v = c_p = c = \frac{du}{dT}$$

Since $v =$ constant and $dv = 0$ for an incompressible material, then Eq. 5.30 becomes

$$(ds)_{\text{incomp.}} = c\left(\frac{dT}{T}\right)$$

or

$$(s_2 - s_1)_{\text{incomp.}} = \int_{T_1}^{T_2} c\left(\frac{dT}{T}\right) \quad \textbf{(5.32)}$$

If the specific heat c is constant over the temperature range from T_1 to T_2, then this equation can be integrated to give

$$(s_2 - s_1)_{\substack{\text{incomp.}\\ \text{constant } c}} = c \ln(T_2/T_1) \quad \textbf{(5.33)}$$

In Chapter 3 we also defined the constant volume and constant pressure specific heats for an ideal gas as

$$c_v = \frac{du}{dT} \quad \textbf{(3.65)}$$

and

$$c_p = \frac{dh}{dT} \quad \textbf{(3.67)}$$

Consequently, we can now write Eqs. 5.30 and 5.31 as

$$(ds)_{\substack{\text{ideal}\\ \text{gas}}} = c_v\left(\frac{dT}{T}\right) + \frac{p}{T}\,dv = c_p\left(\frac{dT}{T}\right) - \frac{v}{T}\,dp$$

Further, for an ideal gas $p/T = R/v$ and $v/T = R/p$, so that this equation can be integrated to give

$$(s_2 - s_1)_{\substack{\text{ideal}\\ \text{gas}}} = \int_1^2 c_v\left(\frac{dT}{T}\right) + R \ln\frac{v_2}{v_1} \quad \textbf{(5.34)}$$

$$= \int_1^2 c_p\left(\frac{dT}{T}\right) - R \ln\frac{p_2}{p_1} \quad \textbf{(5.35)}$$

and if the specific heats are constant over the temperature range from T_1 to T_2, then these equations become

$$(s_2 - s_1)_{\substack{\text{ideal gas}\\ \text{constant}\\ c_p \text{ and } c_v}} = c_v \ln\frac{T_2}{T_1} + R \ln\frac{v_2}{v_1} \quad \textbf{(5.36)}$$

$$= c_p \ln\frac{T_2}{T_1} - R \ln\frac{p_2}{p_1} \quad \textbf{(5.37)}$$

Any process in which entropy remains constant is called an *isentropic* process.[11] If an ideal gas with constant specific heats undergoes an isentropic process, then $s_2 - s_1$ and Eqs. 5.36 and 5.37 give

$$\ln\frac{T_2}{T_1} = -\frac{R}{c_v}\ln\frac{v_2}{v_1} = \frac{R}{c_p}\ln\frac{p_2}{p_1}$$

or

$$\frac{T_2}{T_1} = \left(\frac{v_2}{v_1}\right)^{1-k} = \left(\frac{p_2}{p_1}\right)^{(k-1)/k} \tag{5.38}$$

and

$$p_1v_1^k = p_2v_2^k = \text{constant} \tag{5.39}$$

where

$$k = c_p/c_v \text{ and } R = c_p - c_v \tag{5.40}$$

Consequently, from Eq. 4.27, we see that in the case of an ideal gas with constant specific heats, an isentropic process is the same as a polytropic process with $n = k$.

The above equations for the specific entropy of an incompressible substance and an ideal gas are the only such formulae that will be introduced at this point. Specific entropy equations for more complex substances will be introduced later in the text as they are needed.

The tables and charts in the appendices of this text list specific entropy along with the specific properties v, u, and h. Specific entropy values are obtained from these sources in the same way that any of the other specific properties are obtained. In particular, the quality x of a liquid–vapor mixture is computed using the same type of lever rule relation as was used with v, u, and h, i.e.,

$$x = \frac{v - v_f}{v_{fg}} = \frac{u - u_f}{u_{fg}} = \frac{h - h_f}{h_{fg}} = \frac{s - s_f}{s_{fg}} \tag{5.41}$$

Example 5.3

Determine the change in total entropy of 3.0 lbm of steam at 100 °F and 92% quality when it is heated to 200 psia and 800 °F.

Solution Since we are given two independent properties in each state in this problem we do not need to know how the heating process (i.e., the path) took place. We have a closed system consisting of 3.0 lbm of water for which

State 1 $\xrightarrow{\text{Unknown process path}}$ **State 2**

State 1	State 2
$T_1 = 100\ °\text{F}$	$p_2 = 200$ psia
$x_1 = 0.92$	$T_2 = 800\ °\text{F}$
$s_1 = s_f(100\ °\text{F}) + x_1 s_{fg}(100\ °\text{F})$ $= 0.1296 + 0.92(1.8528)$ $= 1.8342$ Btu/lbm·R	$s_2 = 1.7662$ Btu/lbm·R

11. The term *isentropic* comes from the Greek words for *constant entropy*.

where the specific entropy values have been found in Appendixes C.1*a* and C.3*a*. Then,

$$\begin{aligned} S_2 - S_1 &= m(s_2 - s_1) \\ &= (3.0\ \text{lbm})[(1.7662 - 1.8342)\ \text{Btu/(lbm}\cdot\text{R)}] \\ &= -0.204\ \text{Btu/R} \end{aligned}$$

Figures 5.7*a* and 5.7*b* are *h-s* plots for water. The chart shown in Figure 5.7*a* is called a Mollier diagram after the German engineer Richard Mollier (1863–1935) who developed it in 1904. States 1 and 2 of Example 5.3 are shown on this chart to illustrate its use. The chart shown in Figure 5.7*b* has an oblique coordinate system in which the angle between the *h* and *s* coordinates has been determined by positioning the triple point line horizontally. Figure 5.7*b* is somewhat more revealing than Figure 5.7*a* in that it shows the solid, solid–vapor, compressed liquid, and solid–liquid regions as well as the liquid–vapor and superheated vapor regions. Small charts like these are usually inaccurate for engineering problem solving. Much larger charts are available for use by professional engineers who choose to use this technique.

At this point we must expand the classical concepts presented above so that they fit into the more general balance equations introduced at the beginning of this chapter. We must now look for a set of general entropy transport mechanisms, valid for both open and closed systems, which are consistent with Eq. 5.28 when applied to closed systems.

Entropy Transport and Production Mechanisms

Several conceptual problems occur when Eq. 5.22 is used to define the entropy of a system. First of all, this equation is limited to closed systems only, and at this point we do not know how it must be altered to accommodate open systems. Second, it does not indicate how system entropy may be influenced by work transport of energy, and third, it deals only with largely hypothetical "reversible" processes. The third point is particularly bothersome since all of our auxiliary formulae for heat transfer have been developed from an empirical basis and therefore always give the *actual* rather than the *reversible* heat transport of energy (see Chapter 4).

From the work of Carnot, Thomson, and Clausius discussed earlier in this chapter it seems clear that energy and entropy are related in some way. Therefore, we will investigate the possibility that the energy transport mechanisms of heat, work, and mass flow are also mechanisms for entropy transport and production. First we will investigate heat and work transports and productions of entropy by again restricting our analysis to closed systems. In Chapter 4 we noted that a modern definition of heat transfer was that it is an energy transport mechanism which is neither a work mechanism nor a mass flow mechanism. It is often conveniently viewed as a nonwork, nonmass flow mechanism for transporting internal energy.

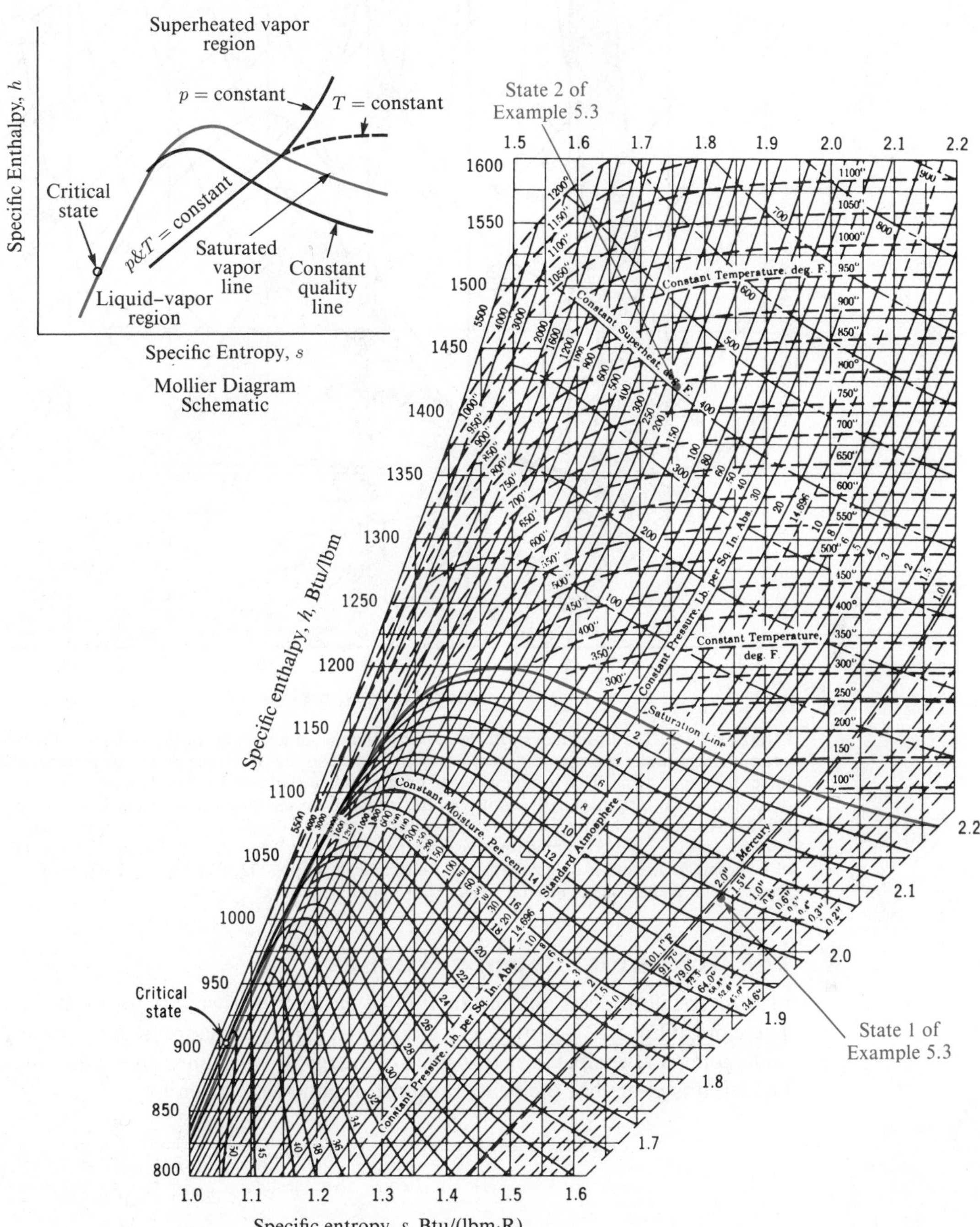

Figure 5.7 (*a*) The Mollier diagram for water, *Sources*: From Joseph H. Keenan and Joseph Keyes, *Thermodynamic Properties of Steam* (New York: Wiley, 1936). Copyright © 1936 John Wiley & Sons. Reprinted by permission of John Wiley & Sons. Also reprinted from William C. Reynolds and Henry C. Perkins, *Engineering Thermodynamics*, 2d ed. (New York: McGraw-Hill, 1977), p. 603 (Table B.2).

1.27 25.45

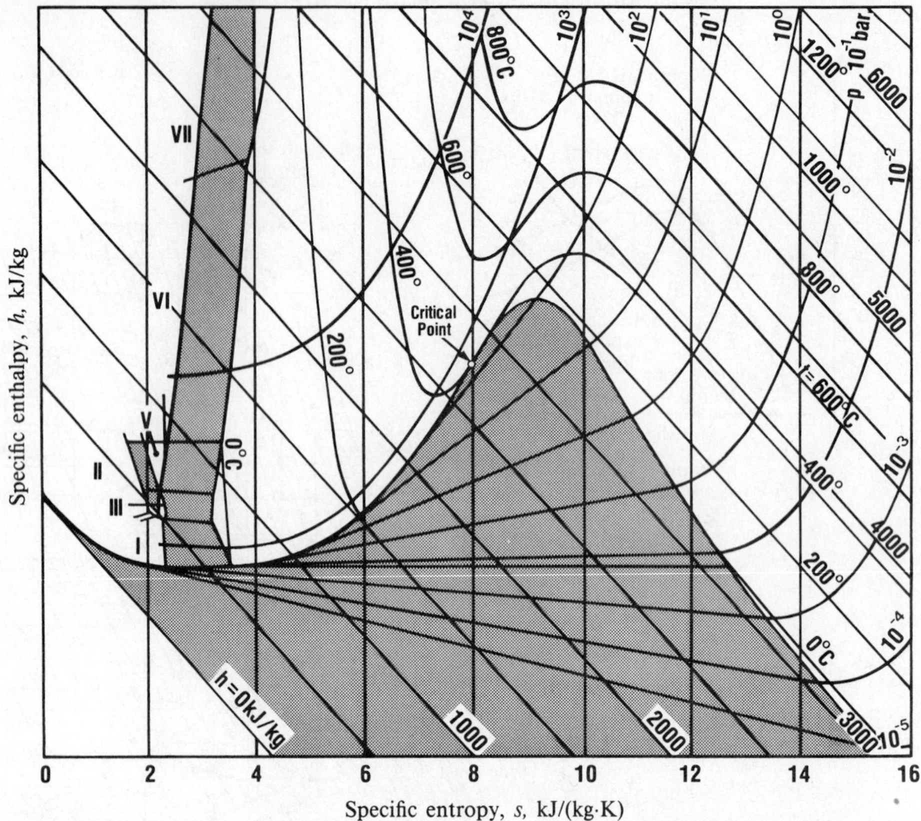

Figure 5.7 (*b*) The Bosnjakovic (Bosh-nja-kovich) diagram for water. In this oblique enthalpy-entropy diagram the coordinate system has been rotated so that the triple point line is horizontal under the vapor dome. This has the effect of expanding the standard Mollier diagram, and was developed in the early twentieth century by the Yugoslavian thermodynamist Fran Bosnjakovic (1902–). A similar technique for expanding cramped property diagrams by plotting with oblique h = constant lines is used in modern psychrometric charts (see Appendix D.6). Adapted by permission of F. Bošnjakovic from F. Bošnjaković, U. Renz, and P. Burow, "Mollier Enthaply, Entropy-Diagram for Water, Steam and Ice," *Tehnička* (Figure 1).

The Differential Entropy Balance

In a reversible process the production of entropy is always zero, by definition. Therefore, if Eq. 5.22 is viewed as a differential entropy balance for a closed system undergoing a reversible heat transport of energy, then, from a differential form of Eq. 5.1, it is clear that the heat transport of entropy is given by

$$(dS_G)_Q = (dS)_Q = (dS_T)_{\underset{Q}{\text{rev}}} + \underbrace{(dS_P)_{\underset{Q}{\text{rev}}}}_{0} = \left(\frac{\bar{d}Q}{T}\right)_{\text{rev}}$$

So, the differential entropy transport due to a hypothetical reversible heat transfer is simply

$$(dS_T)_{\underset{Q}{\text{rev}}} = \left(\frac{\bar{d}Q}{T}\right)_{\text{rev}} \tag{5.42}$$

Unfortunately, the two sides of Eq. 5.42 do not have the same differential form. The left side is the total differential of S_T whereas the right side is a differential divided by an absolute temperature. To integrate this equation over the surface area of the system we will need to know the exact mathematical relationship between Q and the temperature of the boundary T_b at the point where this heat transfer occurs. For a reversible Carnot cycle this relation is very simple since a reversible heat transfer occurs only during an isothermal process, and so T_b must be a constant. In this case Eq. 5.42 can be integrated to give

$$ {}_1(S_T)_2\Big|_{\substack{\text{rev Q and}\\ \text{isothermal}}} = \frac{{}_1Q_2}{T_b}\Bigg|_{\substack{\text{rev Q and}\\ \text{isothermal}}} \tag{5.43} $$

However, Eq. 5.42 cannot be as easily integrated for common nonisothermal heat transfer processes. This problem can be solved by changing the form of Eq. 5.42 by introducing the following mathematical identity

$$ \frac{\bar{d}Q}{T} = d\left(\frac{Q}{T}\right) + \frac{Q}{T^2}\,dT \tag{5.44} $$

Then Eq. 5.42 becomes

$$ (dS_T)_{\substack{\text{rev}\\ \text{Q}}} = d\left(\frac{Q}{T}\right)_{\text{rev}} + \left(\frac{Q}{T^2}\,dT\right)_{\text{rev}} $$

Recall that heat transfer irreversibility is simply due to the heat transport of energy through a finite temperature difference, so that for all reversible heat transfers we must have $dT = 0$, or

$$ \left(\frac{Q}{T^2}\,dT\right)_{\text{rev}} = 0 $$

then

$$ (dS_T)_{\substack{\text{rev}\\ \text{Q}}} = d\left(\frac{Q}{T}\right)_{\text{rev}} \tag{5.45} $$

which, when integrated, produces Eq. 5.43 again.

In an irreversible process the total production of entropy is always positive, by virtue of the second law of thermodynamics. Therefore, Eq. 5.25 can be viewed as an entropy balance equation for a closed system undergoing irreversible heat and work transports of energy. Then,

$$ \begin{aligned} dS &= dS_T + dS_P \\ &= \left(\frac{\bar{d}Q}{T}\right)_{\text{act}} + \frac{(\bar{d}W)_{\text{act}} - (\bar{d}W)_{\text{rev}}}{T} \end{aligned} $$

where $dS_P > 0$ by the second law of thermodynamics. To reconcile the difference between the actual work and the reversible work terms in this equation we use the concept of a work transport energy efficiency, η_W, which was introduced in Chapter 4. For a work absorbing system such as a pump we have

Work absorbing system

$$W_{act} = W_{rev}/\eta_W \tag{4.71}$$

and for a work producing system such as an engine we have

Work producing system

$$W_{act} = \eta_W W_{rev} \tag{4.72}$$

If we define an irreversible work component which is *always* a positive number as

$$W_{irr} = \begin{cases} |(1 - \eta_W)W_{rev}| & \text{for a work producing system} \\ |(1/\eta_W - 1)W_{rev}| & \text{for a work absorbing system} \end{cases} \tag{5.46}$$

then we can write for either a work producing or work absorbing system that

$$W_{act} - W_{rev} = W_{irr}$$

and the entropy balance equation becomes

$$dS = dS_T + dS_P = \left(\frac{\bar{d}Q}{T}\right)_{act} + \left(\frac{\bar{d}W}{T}\right)_{irr} \tag{5.47}$$

We now wish to identify the individual heat and work components of the entropy transport and production terms. For a closed system we may decompose the transport and production terms as follows

$$dS_T = (dS_T)_Q + (dS_T)_W$$

and

$$dS_P = (dS_P)_Q + (dS_P)_W$$

so that

$$dS = (dS_T)_Q + (dS_T)_W + (dS_P)_Q + (dS_P)_W \tag{5.48}$$

Substituting Eq. 5.44 into 5.47 gives

$$dS = d\left(\frac{Q}{T}\right)_{act} + \left(\frac{Q}{T^2}\,dT\right)_{act} + \left(\frac{\bar{d}W}{T}\right)_{irr} \tag{5.49}$$

and comparing Eqs. 5.48 and 5.49 allows us to identify the following terms[12]

$$(dS_T)_Q = d\left(\frac{Q}{T}\right)_{act} \quad \textbf{(5.50)}$$

$$(dS_T)_W = 0 \quad \textbf{(5.51)}$$

$$(dS_P)_Q = \left(\frac{Q}{T^2}\,dT\right)_{act} \quad \textbf{(5.52)}$$

and

$$(dS_P)_W = \left(\frac{\bar{d}W}{T}\right)_{irr} \quad \textbf{(5.53)}$$

Integrating Eq. 5.49 and then differentiating it with respect to time produces an entropy rate balance (SRB) equation for a system as

$$\begin{aligned}\dot{S} = \frac{dS}{dt} &= \frac{d}{dt}\int d\left(\frac{Q}{T}\right)_{act} + \frac{d}{dt}\int\left(\frac{Q}{T^2}\,dT\right)_{act} + \frac{d}{dt}\int\left(\frac{\bar{d}W}{T}\right)_{irr} \\ &= (\dot{S}_T)_Q + (\dot{S}_T)_W + (\dot{S}_P)_Q + (\dot{S}_P)_W \end{aligned} \quad \textbf{(5.54)}$$

so that

$$(\dot{S}_T)_Q = \frac{d}{dt}\int d\left(\frac{Q}{T}\right)_{act} \quad \textbf{(5.55)}$$

$$(\dot{S}_T)_W = 0 \quad \textbf{(5.56)}$$

$$(\dot{S}_P)_Q = \frac{d}{dt}\int\left(\frac{Q}{T^2}\,dT\right)_{act} \quad \textbf{(5.57)}$$

and

$$(\dot{S})_W = \frac{d}{dt}\int\left(\frac{\bar{d}W}{T}\right)_{irr} \quad \textbf{(5.58)}$$

Heat Transport of Entropy

The integration of Eq. 5.50 gives the heat transport of entropy as

$$(S_T)_Q = \int_\Sigma d\left(\frac{Q}{T_b}\right)_{act} = \sum\left(\frac{Q}{T_b}\right)_\Sigma \quad \textbf{(5.59)}$$

---

12. Note that we could also attempt to use the identity of Eq. 5.44 on the irreversible work term and decompose it into $\bar{d}W_{irr}/T = d(W/T)_{irr} + (W_{irr}/T^2)dT$ and then we would be tempted to equate $d(S_T)_W = d(W/T)_{irr}$. This would be incorrect because the irreversible work always occurs *inside* the system boundary and therefore cannot be associated with a transport term that measures quantities crossing the system boundary.

where Σ is the surface area of the system and T_b is the local absolute temperature of the system boundary corresponding to the value of the local heat transfer at the boundary, Q. However, if Q and T_b vary continuously along the boundary, then Eq. 5.59 is not easy to evaluate. To produce a more useful version of this equation, let q be the heat transfer per unit area and let $\dot{q}$ be the heat transfer *rate* per unit area (i.e., the heat "flux"). Then define the heat transport of entropy per unit area as $q/T_b = d(Q/T_b)/dA$ and define the heat transport *rate* of entropy as $\dot{q}/T = d(q/T_b)/(dA\ dt)$ so that Eq. 5.59 becomes

$$(S_T)_Q = \int_\Sigma \left(\frac{q}{T_b}\right)_{act} dA = \int_\Sigma \int_\tau \left(\frac{\dot{q}}{T_b}\right)_{act} dA\ dt \tag{5.60}$$

where τ is the time over which the heat transport occurs. Differentiating this equation with respect to time gives the corresponding rate transport term as

$$(\dot{S}_T)_Q = \int_\Sigma \left(\frac{\dot{q}}{T_b}\right)_{act} dA \tag{5.61}$$

In the simple case where $\dot{q}$ and T_b are constant for time τ over the surface Σ of area A, then Eq. 5.60 reduces to

$$(S_T)_Q = \left(\frac{\dot{q}}{T_b}\right)_{act} (\tau A) = \left(\frac{{}_1Q_2}{T_b}\right)_{act}$$

and Eq. 5.61 reduces to

$$(\dot{S}_T)_Q = \left(\frac{\dot{Q}}{T_b}\right)_{act}$$

Otherwise, the exact relations between $(\dot{q}/T_b)_{act}$, time, and surface area must be known before the integral in Eqs. 5.60 and 5.61 can be evaluated.

Work Mode Transport of Entropy

Integration of Eq. 5.51 for all possible work modes clearly gives

$$(S_T)_W = \text{constant} = 0 \tag{5.62}$$

and from Eq. 5.56 we also have

$$(\dot{S}_T)_W = 0 \tag{5.63}$$

This produces the surprising result that none of the work modes discussed in Chapter 4 will transport entropy into or out of a system. However, as will be shown later, the irreversibilities of these work modes will always contribute to the production of entropy within the system.

Heat Production of Entropy

To integrate Eq. 5.52 properly we define a one-dimensional thermal entropy production rate per unit volume, σ_Q, which is the rate of entropy production per unit volume due to heat transfer, as[13]

$$\frac{d^2(S_P)_Q}{dt\, d\forall} = \frac{d(\dot{S}_P)_Q}{d\forall} = \sigma_Q = -\left[\frac{\dot{q}}{T^2}\left(\frac{dT}{dx}\right)\right]_{act} \quad (5.64)$$

where the minus sign appears because dT/dx will always be negative when $\dot{q}$ is positive. The temperature T in this equation is the local absolute temperature *inside* the system boundary evaluated at the point where the local internal heat flux $\dot{q}$ occurs. It is generally not the same as the local system boundary temperature T_b except in the case of an isothermal system. Equation 5.64 can then be integrated to give

$$d(S_P)_Q = \frac{Q}{T^2}\, dT = -\int_\tau \left[\frac{\dot{q}}{T^2}\left(\frac{dT}{dx}\right)\right]_{act} dt\, d\forall = \int_\tau \sigma_Q\, dt\, d\forall$$

and with a second integration we have

$$(S_P)_Q = -\int_\forall \int_\tau \left[\frac{\dot{q}}{T^2}\left(\frac{dT}{dx}\right)\right]_{act} dt\, d\forall = \int_\forall \int_\tau \sigma_Q\, dt\, d\forall \quad (5.65)$$

Differentiation of Eq. 5.65 yields the production rate term as

$$(\dot{S}_P)_Q = -\int_\forall \left[\frac{\dot{q}}{T^2}\left(\frac{dT}{dx}\right)\right]_{act} d\forall = \int_\forall \sigma_Q\, d\forall \quad (5.66)$$

Example 5.4

Determine an equation for the steady state entropy production rate due to pure heat conduction in an insulated rod connecting a high-temperature (T_1) thermal reservoir with a low-temperature (T_2) thermal reservoir as shown in the following sketch.

---

13. In three-dimensional space this term generalizes to $\sigma_Q = -(\dot{\mathbf{q}}/T^2) \cdot \nabla(T)$, where $\dot{\mathbf{q}}$ is the heat flux vector and $\nabla(\ )$ is the gradient operator. For example, in three-dimensional Cartesian (x, y, z) coordinates σ_Q becomes

$$\sigma_Q = -\frac{1}{T^2}\left(\dot{q}_x \frac{\partial T}{\partial x} + \dot{q}_y \frac{\partial T}{\partial y} + \dot{q}_z \frac{\partial T}{\partial z}\right)$$

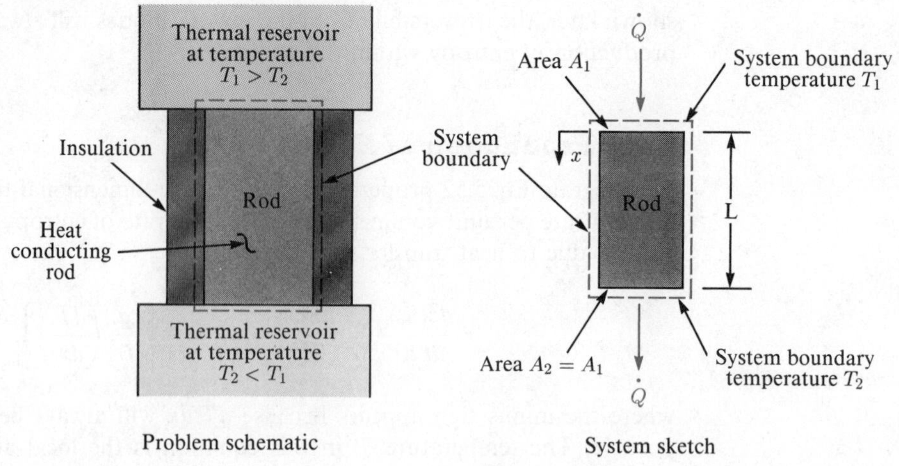

Problem schematic

System sketch

Solution The entropy production rate due to heat transfer is given by Eq. 5.66 as

$$(\dot{S}_P)_Q = -\int_{\forall}\left[\frac{\dot{q}}{T^2}\left(\frac{dT}{dx}\right)\right]_{\text{act}} d\forall$$

For steady state conditions, $\dot{q}$ = constant across areas A_1 and A_2, but $\dot{q} = 0$ on the remaining surfaces of the system boundary. Since $A_1 = A_2 = A$ and $\dot{Q} = \dot{q}A$ is a constant, then using $d\forall = A\,dx$ we can write

$$(\dot{S}_P)_Q = -\int_0^L\left[\frac{\dot{q}}{T^2}\left(\frac{dT}{dx}\right)\right]A\,dx = -\dot{Q}\int_0^L\frac{1}{T^2}\left(\frac{dT}{dx}\right)dx = -\dot{Q}\int_{T_1}^{T_2}\frac{dT}{T^2}$$
$$= \dot{Q}\left(\frac{1}{T_2} - \frac{1}{T_1}\right) = \frac{\dot{Q}}{T_1T_2}(T_1 - T_2) > 0$$

For pure one-dimensional steady state conduction heat transfer Fourier's law (see Eq. 4.75) gives

$$\frac{dT}{dx} = -\frac{T_1 - T_2}{L} = -\frac{\dot{Q}}{k_t A} = \text{constant}$$

or

$$\dot{Q} = k_t A(T_1 - T_2)/L$$

Putting this information into the above entropy production rate formula gives

$$(\dot{S}_P)_Q = \frac{\dot{Q}}{T_1T_2}(T_1 - T_2) = \frac{k_t A}{T_1T_2L}(T_1 - T_2)^2 > 0$$

Notice that in Example 5.4 the entropy production rate becomes zero only when $T_1 = T_2$ (i.e., when $\dot{Q} = 0$), so that a reversible conduction heat transfer is actually impossible. Also note that the larger the temperature difference $T_1 - T_2$ through which a given heat transfer $\dot{Q}$ occurs, the larger the associated heat transfer entropy production rate becomes.

Heat Pipes

The application of basic thermodynamic principles has recently produced a new heat transfer technology. In 1939 the German engineer E. Schmidt demonstrated that a hollow sealed tube filled with a liquid–vapor mixture could transfer several thousand times more thermal energy than could pure conduction in a solid copper rod with the same dimensions as the tube.

Heat applied to the liquid region at the lower end of the tube causes the quality of the mixture in the remainder of the tube to increase. The additional vapor thus produced rises inside the tube and condenses at the cooler end. This condensate

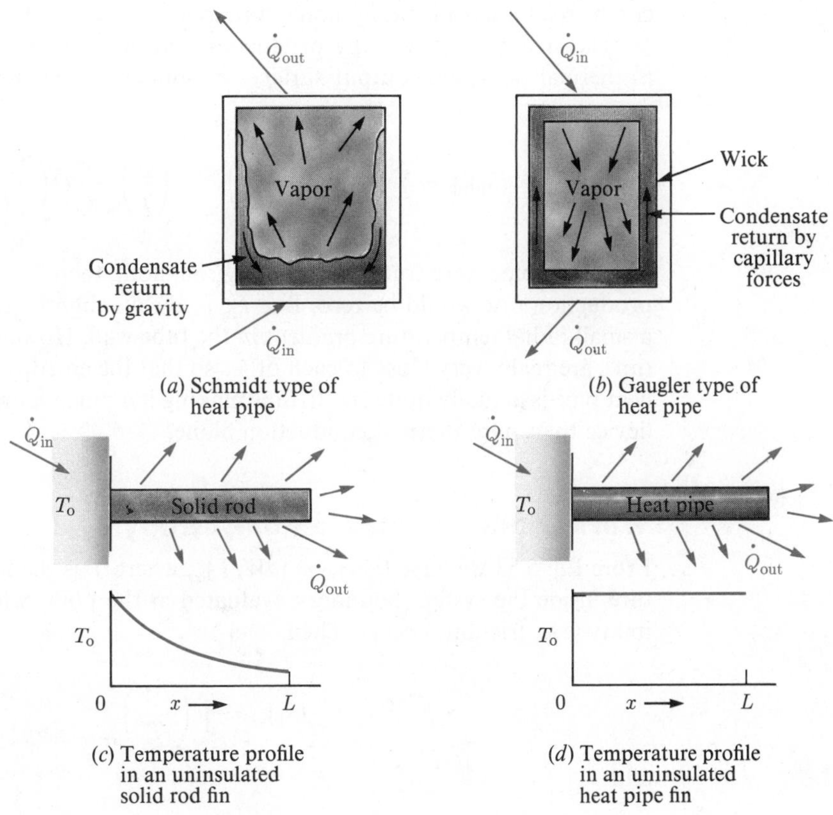

Figure 5.8 Heat pipe construction.

then runs down the inside wall of the tube to replenish the liquid at the lower end. Figure 5.8*a* illustrates this process. A continuous circulation of vapor and condensate occurs when a steady state condition has been reached.

Since vaporization and condensation occur at the same temperature under constant pressure conditions, the entire inside volume of the tube will reach a constant temperature. Pure thermal conduction in a solid rod requires both a radial and an axial temperature gradient (see Figure 5.8*c*) to transport thermal energy. Schmidt's device, however, transports a great deal more thermal energy very efficiently with essentially no temperature gradient (see Figure 5.8*d*).

Since the condensate is returned to the heat source by gravity flow, Schmidt's device must be oriented with the cold end above the hot end. This limitation was overcome by Richard S. Gaugler at the General Motors Research Laboratory in 1942. He incorporated a wick inside the tube which would draw the liquid condensate back to the hot region via capillary forces in the wick, thus allowing the tube to be operated in any orientation (see Figure 5.8*b*). The name *heat pipe* was suggested for this device in 1963 by George M. Grover of the Los Alamos Scientific Laboratory. The first significant application of heat pipe technology occurred in the U.S. space program during the 1960s. It then spread into a wide variety of commercial areas including home furnaces.

The steady state entropy production rate of a closed system heat pipe with isothermal input and output surfaces is obtained from the entropy rate balance as

$$(\dot{S}_P)_{HP} = \sum\left(\frac{\dot{Q}}{T}\right)_{net} = \left(\frac{\dot{Q}}{T}\right)_{out} - \left(\frac{\dot{Q}}{T}\right)_{in} = \dot{Q}\left(\frac{T_{in} - T_{out}}{T_{in}T_{out}}\right) \tag{5.67}$$

If the heat pipe were truly isothermal throughout, then $T_{in} = T_{out}$ and the entropy production rate would be zero. But T_{in} is always slightly greater than T_{out} due to a small radial temperature gradient in the tube wall. However, these two temperatures are really very close to each other so that the entropy production rate of the heat pipe is actually quite small, thus making it a much more efficient heat transfer device than pure thermal conduction alone.

Work Mode Production of Entropy

From Eq. 5.53 we have $(dS_P)_W = (\bar{d}W/T)_{irr}$ where T is the local absolute temperature inside the system boundary evaluated at the point where the work irreversibility (e.g., friction) occurs. Then

$$(S_P)_W = \int\left(\frac{\bar{d}W}{T}\right)_{irr} \tag{5.68}$$

and

$$(\dot{S}_P)_W = \frac{d}{dt}\int\left(\frac{\bar{d}W}{T}\right)_{irr} \tag{5.58}$$

When the system local internal temperature T in Eq. 5.58 is independent of time, then this equation simplifies to

$$(\dot{S}_P)_W = \left(\frac{\dot{W}}{T}\right)_{irr}$$

Thus, only the work mode energy that is dissipated within the system contributes to the entropy production of the system. This dissipated energy has been defined to be the difference between the reversible work (as given by the work mode formula of Chapter 4) and the actual work (for which we have no specific formula except the empirically based efficiency Eq. 5.46). If one has experimentally measured the work efficiency, then W_{irr} can be found from Eq. 5.46. However, to evaluate $(S_P)_W$ or $(\dot{S}_P)_W$ from Eqs. 5.68 or 5.58 we will also need to know the relation between W_{irr} and the local absolute temperature T inside the system at all the points where the irreversibility occurs.

Example 5.5 Determine the entropy production when a measured 42,000 ft·lbf of work are used to compress 1.0 lbm of air (an ideal gas) from 14.7 psia to 50 psia isothermally at 70 °F in a closed system.

Solution Here, $W_{act} = 42{,}000$ ft·lbf. For the isothermal compression of an ideal gas, Eq. 4.28 gives

$$W_{rev} = -\int_1^2 p\, d\mathcal{V} = -p_1\mathcal{V}_1\int_1^2 \frac{d\mathcal{V}}{\mathcal{V}}$$

$$= -p_1\mathcal{V}_1 \ln(\mathcal{V}_2/\mathcal{V}_1) = p_1\mathcal{V}_1 \ln(p_2/p_1)$$

where

$$p_1 = 14.7 \text{ psia} = (14.7 \text{ lbf/in}^2)(144 \text{ in}^2/\text{ft}^2) = 2116.8 \text{ lbf/ft}^2$$

$$\mathcal{V}_1 = \frac{mRT_1}{p_1} = \frac{(1.0 \text{ lbm})[53.34 \text{ ft}\cdot\text{lbf/(lbm}\cdot\text{R)}](460 + 70 \text{ R})}{2116.8 \text{ lbf/ft}^2} = 13.36 \text{ ft}^3$$

Then

$$W_{rev} = (2116.8 \text{ lbf/ft}^2)(13.36 \text{ ft}^3) \ln\frac{50}{14.7} = 34{,}620 \text{ ft}\cdot\text{lbf}$$

Now for an isothermal process, Eq. 5.68 can be integrated to give

$$(S_P)_W = -\int_1^2 \frac{\bar{d}W_{irr}}{T} = \frac{1}{T}\int_1^2 \bar{d}W_{irr}$$

$$= {}_1\left(\frac{W_{irr}}{T}\right)_2$$

Equation 5.59 gives us W_{irr} as

$$W_{irr} = W_{act} - W_{rev} = 42{,}000 - 34{,}620$$
$$= 7380 \text{ ft} \cdot \text{lbf}$$

Therefore,

$$(S_P)_W = \frac{7380 \text{ ft} \cdot \text{lbf}}{460 + 70 \text{ R}} = 13.92 \text{ ft} \cdot \text{lbf/R}$$
$$= (13.92 \text{ ft} \cdot \text{lbf/R})[1 \text{ Btu}/(778 \text{ ft} \cdot \text{lbf})] = 0.0179 \text{ Btu/R}$$

This example illustrates that you *must* know the relation between W_{irr} and T before Eq. 5.68 can be integrated. The simplest possible case occurs if T is a constant throughout the system volume, as in this example.

Note that you must also know the exact relation between Q and T or T_b before Eqs. 5.60, 5.61, 5.65, and 5.66 can be integrated. These relations are often empirically derived auxiliary formulae known as *constitutive equations.* Fourier's law, Newton's law of cooling, and Planck's radiation law are three such constitutive equations discussed in Chapter 4 that relate heat transfer and temperature. However, none of these constitutive equations will produce an easy analytical integration of the entropy transport and production equations.

An alternative approach to evaluating the entropy production due to work mode irreversibilities is to attempt to identify the sources of the irreversibilities and to mathematically model them with appropriate equations. This is normally done by deriving relations for σ_W, the work mode entropy production per unit time per unit volume (or entropy production *rate* per unit volume). Since σ_W has a value at every point within the system, the total entropy production or entropy production rate is determined by integrating σ_W over time and the system volume as

$$(S_P)_W = \int_{\mathcal{V}} \int_{\tau} \sigma_W \, dt \, d\mathcal{V} \tag{5.69}$$

and

$$(\dot{S}_P)_W = \int_{\mathcal{V}} \sigma_W \, d\mathcal{V} \tag{5.70}$$

These results are available for various work mode dissipation mechanisms such as viscous dissipation within a Newtonian fluid, electrical energy resistive dissipation, diffusion of dissimilar chemicals and so on. However, these mathematical models are normally quite complex and therefore only the viscous dissipation and the electrical resistance mechanism models will be introduced at this point. Dissipation resulting from diffusion will be discussed later in this chapter in the section on mass flow production of entropy.

For the one-dimensional flow of a Newtonian fluid with viscosity μ, velocity distribution $V = V(x)$, and local internal absolute temperature T, we have[14]

$$(\sigma_W)_{vis} = \frac{\mu}{T}\left(\frac{dV}{dx}\right)^2$$

Then we can write

$$(S_P)_{\substack{W\\vis}} = \int_\tau \int_{\mathcal{V}} \frac{\mu}{T}\left(\frac{dV}{dx}\right)^2 dt\, d\mathcal{V} \tag{5.71}$$

and

$$(\dot{S}_P)_{\substack{W\\vis}} = \int_{\mathcal{V}} \frac{\mu}{T}\left(\frac{dV}{dx}\right)^2 d\mathcal{V} \tag{5.72}$$

To carry out these integrations we need to know in advance the velocity distribution function $V = V(x)$, and how μ and V depend on the local internal absolute temperature T.

Example 5.6 Determine the entropy production rate per unit volume due to the flow of a lubricating oil ($\mu = 0.1$ N·s/m²) at 30 °C in the hydrostatic bearing shown below. Assume the lubricant is isothermal throughout its volume.

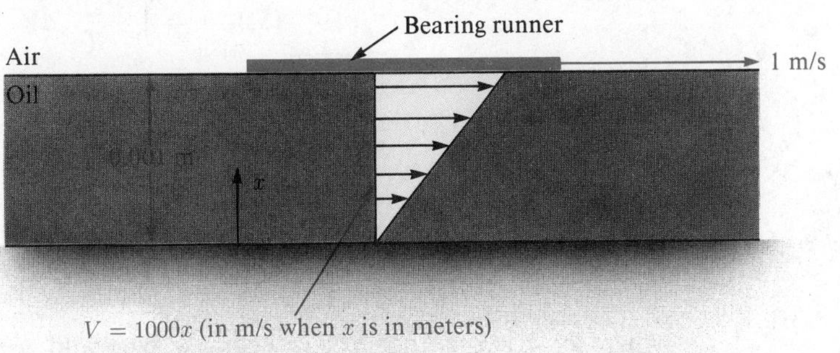

14. In three-dimensional Cartesian (x, y, z) coordinates this generalizes to

$$(\sigma_W)_{vis} = \frac{\mu}{T}\left\{\frac{2}{3}\left[\left(\frac{\partial V_x}{\partial x} - \frac{\partial V_y}{\partial y}\right)^2 + \left(\frac{\partial V_y}{\partial y} - \frac{\partial V_z}{\partial z}\right)^2 + \left(\frac{\partial V_z}{\partial z} - \frac{\partial V_x}{\partial x}\right)^2\right] + \left(\frac{\partial V_x}{\partial y} + \frac{\partial V_y}{\partial x}\right)^2 + \left(\frac{\partial V_y}{\partial z} + \frac{\partial V_z}{\partial y}\right)^2 + \left(\frac{\partial V_z}{\partial x} + \frac{\partial V_x}{\partial z}\right)^2\right\}$$

where V_x, V_y and V_z are the components of the velocity in the x, y, and z directions. In the one-dimensional case discussed here, $V_x = V_z = 0$, and $V_y = V = V(x)$.

Solution In this case, $dV/dx = 1000\ \text{s}^{-1}$ = constant, and since μ, T, and dV/dx are constant here, then Eq. 5.72 can be integrated to give

$$(\dot{S}_P)_{\substack{W\\ \text{vis}}} = \frac{\mu}{T}\left(\frac{dV}{dx}\right)^2 \maltese$$

and

$$\frac{(\dot{S}_P)_{W\text{-vis}}}{\maltese} = \frac{\mu}{T}\left(\frac{dV}{dx}\right)^2 = \frac{(0.1\ \text{N}\cdot\text{s/m}^2)}{(273 + 30\ \text{K})}(1000\ \text{s}^{-1})^2$$

$$= 330.0\ \frac{\text{N}}{\text{m}^2\cdot\text{s}\cdot\text{K}} = 0.33\ \text{kJ/(m}^3\cdot\text{s}\cdot\text{K)}$$

Ohm's law is a simple mathematical model that is used for the resistive dissipation of electrical work mode energy. In this model we have

$$(\sigma_W)_{\text{elect}} = J_e^2 \rho_e / T$$

where $J_e = I/A$ is the electrical current per unit area (i.e., the electrical current flux), $\rho_e = R_e A/L$ is the electrical resistivity, R_e is the total electrical resistance of the conductor, L and A are the length and cross-sectional area of the conductor, and T is the local internal absolute temperature of the conductor. Then Eq. 5.70 gives

$$(\dot{S}_P)_{\substack{W\\ \text{elect}}} = \int_{\maltese} \frac{J_e^2 \rho_e}{T}\, d\maltese \tag{5.73}$$

The electrical current flux J_e is often expressed by the one-dimensional Ohm's law as[15]

$$J_e = -k_e\left(\frac{d\phi}{dx}\right)$$

where $k_e = 1/\rho_e$ is the electrical conductivity and ϕ is the electrical potential (i.e., voltage). The relation between ρ_e and T is shown in Figure 5.9 for various materials.

For the special case of an *isothermal system* with *uniform properties* and a *constant current density*, Eq. 5.73 reduces to

$$(\dot{S}_P)_{\substack{W\\ \text{elect}\\ \text{(special)}}} = J_e^2 \rho_e \maltese / T = (I^2/A^2)\rho_e LA/T = I^2 R_e / T \tag{5.74}$$

15. In three dimensions this becomes $\mathbf{J}_e = -k_e \nabla(\phi)$, where $\nabla(\ )$ is the gradient differential operator.

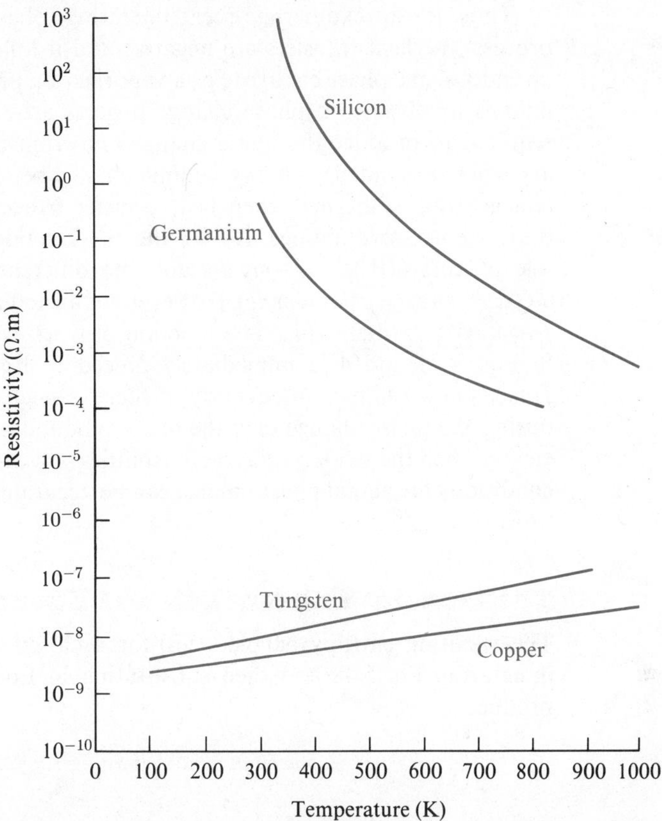

Figure 5.9 The variation of electrical resistivity with temperature. *Source*: Reprinted by permission of the author from Louis H. Lenert, *Semiconductor Physics, Devices, and Circuits* (Columbus, Ohio: (Charles E. Merrill Publishing, 1968), p. 33 (Figure 2-3).

Phase Change Entropy Production

In any process the change in entropy is independent of the actual process path used because entropy is a state property (or a point function). Therefore, we may write $(\Delta S)_{rev} = (\Delta S)_{act}$ or $(\Delta s)_{rev} = (\Delta s)_{act}$ for any process whatsoever. The entropy change produced by an actual process can occasionally be found by assuming that the system has undergone a hypothetical reversible process that is easier to evaluate than the actual irreversible process. As an example of this technique, consider the entropy change and associated entropy production that occurs in a phase change. For a reversible phase change carried out in a closed system we have $(S_P)_{rev} = 0$, and the entropy balance for an isothermal system then gives

$$(S_2 - S_1)_{rev} = (S_2 - S_1)_{act} = (Q/T_b)_{rev} = (Q/T_b)_{act} + (S_P)_{\text{phase change}}$$

or

$$(S_P)_{\text{phase change}} = \frac{Q_{rev} - Q_{act}}{T_b} > 0$$

Thus, for an exothermic (heat liberating) phase change (e.g., a condensation process) the heat transfers are negative and it follows that $|Q_{act}| > |Q_{rev}|$, and for an endothemic phase change (e.g., a vaporization process) $Q_{rev} > Q_{act}$. The irreversibilities involved in a phase change process arise largely from the heat transfer required to produce the phase change and from the mechanical moving boundary work associated with any volume change between the phases. If the real system is truly isothermal, then heat transfer irreversibilities may be allocated to the systems surroundings. As for the work mode irreversibilities, for a reversible process $(\bar{d}W)_{rev} = -mp\,dv$, and the differential energy balance then gives $(\bar{d}Q)_{rev} = m(du + p\,dv) = m(dh)$. However, for an actual irreversible process $(\bar{d}W)_{act} = f(\eta_W)(\bar{d}W)_{rev}$, where $f(\eta_W)$ is a function of work transport energy efficiency given in Eqs. 4.71 and 4.72 immediately preceding Eq. 5.46. Then, $(\bar{d}Q)_{act} = m(du + f(\eta_W)p\,dv) \neq m(dh)$. Consequently, if there is negligible change in system volume during the phase change or if the moving boundary work is carried out very efficiently, then the work mode irreversibilities will also be insignificant. Under these conditions the actual phase change can be accurately approximated as a reversible process.

The General Entropy Balance Equations

The resulting entropy balance (SB) for a closed system of mass m is given by integrating Eq. 5.48 and then substituting in Eqs. 5.60, 5.62, 5.65, and 5.69 to produce

General closed system entropy balance (SB)

$$S_2 - S_1 = m(s_2 - s_1) = \int_\tau \int_\Sigma \left(\frac{\dot{q}}{T_b}\right)_{act} dA\,dt + {}_1(S_P)_2 \tag{5.75}$$

For the simplified case of isothermal boundaries this equation reduces to

Isothermal boundary closed system entropy balance

$$m(s_2 - s_1) = \left(\frac{{}_1Q_2}{T_b}\right)_{act} + {}_1(S_P)_2 \tag{5.76}$$

where in each case

$${}_1(S_P)_2 = \int_\tau \int_V \left\{-\left[\frac{\dot{q}}{T^2}\left(\frac{dT}{dx}\right)\right] + \sigma_W\right\} dV\,dt$$

For an open system, Eqs. 5.54, 5.56, 5.61, 5.66, 5.70, and 5.74 produce

General open system entropy rate balance (SRB)

$$\int \left(\frac{\dot{q}}{T_b}\right)_{act} dA + \sum_{\text{inlet}} \dot{m}s - \sum_{\text{outlet}} \dot{m}s + \dot{S}_P = \dot{S}_{\text{system}} \tag{5.77}$$

and for the simplified case of isothermal boundaries this equation reduces to

Isothermal boundary open system entropy rate balance

$$\left(\frac{\dot{Q}}{T_b}\right)_{act} + \sum_{\text{inlet}} \dot{m}s - \sum_{\text{outlet}} \dot{m}s + \dot{S}_P = \dot{S}_{\text{system}} \tag{5.78}$$

In each case the formula for the entropy production rate is given by

$$\dot{S}_P = \int_{\forall} \sigma \, d\forall > 0 \tag{5.79}$$

where σ is the total entropy production rate density (EPRD) for the system, given by

$$\sigma = \sigma_Q + (\sigma_W)_{vis.} + (\sigma_W)_{elect.} + (\sigma_m)_{diff.} + \cdots$$

whose individual formulae were discussed in Section I of this chapter.

In the next section of this chapter we apply the general energy and entropy balance equations to a variety of closed system problems. In addition, we calculate the entropy production rate in various example problems to gain a feel for the magnitude of this quantity.

Chapter Five Section II — Second Law Closed System Applications

Sections II and III of this chapter provide closed and open system applications of the second law of thermodynamics in the same way that Sections II and III of Chapter 4 dealt with closed and open system applications of the first law of thermodynamics. In Section II of this chapter we present a series of applications of the closed system entropy balance and entropy production equations developed in Section I. This material is organized into two major subdivisions: applications involving reversible processes and applications involving irreversible processes. Because the second law is seldom used alone, most of these examples will also involve the application of the energy balance.

Our discussion of the applications involving reversible processes is similar to the way the second law is treated in many classical thermodynamics textbooks. Restricting consideration to reversible processes significantly simplifies the analysis because the entropy production is zero and the second law is reduced to a simple conservation of entropy law. However, few real processes are truly reversible, so that any analysis that requires (or specifies) that a reversible process be assumed to get a solution will always be somewhat in error. It should be remembered that a "reversible" process is just an idealization (a model) of some real irreversible process much in the same way that we often model complex real gas behavior with the simple ideal gas equation of state. On the other hand, the study of reversible processes does provide an easy introduction to the use of the second law and the entropy balance equations, and they are accurate approximations to real processes in systems that have low entropy production values.

The section dealing with purely irreversible processes will begin by expanding the closed system energy balance (first law) examples presented in Section II of Chapter 4 to include an entropy balance (second law) analysis. In these examples we will be concerned mainly with determining the amount of entropy production for a process by calculating it from the closed system entropy balance. We call this the *indirect method* for determining entropy production. If we instead calculate the amount of entropy production for a process from its defining equations (e.g., Eqs. 5.65 and 5.69) then we are using the *direct method* for determining the entropy production. The following entropy production formulae correspond to these definitions.

Closed System Indirect Method

1. The entropy produced by a change of state is given by Eq. 5.75 as

$$_1(S_P)_2 = m(s_2 - s_1) - \int_\tau \int_\Sigma \left(\frac{\dot{q}}{T_b}\right)_{act} dA\, dt \tag{5.80}$$

2. The entropy production *rate* of a closed system is given by differentiating Eq. 5.80 with respect to time, or

$$\dot{S}_P = \dot{S} - \int_\Sigma \left(\frac{\dot{q}}{T_b}\right)_{act} dA \tag{5.81}$$

where T_b is the local system boundary temperature evaluated at the point where $\dot{q}$ crosses the system boundary Σ.

Closed System Direct Method

1. The entropy produced by a change of state is given by

$$_1(S_P)_2 = \int_1^2 \left[\left(\frac{Q}{T^2}\, dT\right)_{act} + \left(\frac{\bar{d}W}{T}\right)_{irr}\right] = \int_\tau \int_V \left[\left(-\frac{\dot{q}}{T^2}\frac{dT}{dx}\right) + \sigma_W\right] dV\, dt \tag{5.82}$$

2. The entropy production *rate* of a closed system is given by

$$\dot{S}_P = \int_V \left\{\left[-\frac{\dot{q}}{T^2}\left(\frac{dT}{dx}\right)\right] + \sigma_W\right\} dV \tag{5.83}$$

where $\sigma_W = (\sigma_W)_{viscous} + (\sigma_W)_{electrical} + (\sigma_W)_{diffusion} + \cdots$ and T is the local temperature inside the system volume evaluated at the point where the heat transfer and work irreversibilities occur.

Both the direct and the indirect methods will give accurate answers for entropy production if applied correctly. Which method you choose to solve a particular problem depends entirely on the type of information given to you in the problem statement (usually only one of the two methods will work for a given problem scenario). The indirect method requires detailed temperature and heat flow information evaluated at the *boundary* of the system plus specific information about changes in system entropy, whereas the direct method requires detailed information about temperature, heat flow, and work mode irreversibilities spread throughout the *interior* of the system. The examples presented in this section of the chapter will illustrate the use of both of these methods.

Lastly, before we begin the example problems, keep in mind the basic reason why the evaluation of entropy production is important. The entropy production is a measure of the "losses" within the system, so the larger the entropy production, the more inefficient the system is at carrying out its function. We will continually be looking for ways to minimize a system's entropy production and thus improve its overall operating efficiency.

Systems Undergoing Reversible Processes

In any reversible process

$$\dot{S}_P = {}_1(S_P)_2 = 0$$

and the closed system entropy balance (SB) given in Eq. 5.75 reduces to

$$S_2 - S_1 = m(s_2 - s_1) = \int_\tau \int_\Sigma \left(\frac{\dot{q}}{T_b}\right)_{rev} dA\, dt \tag{5.84}$$

where $\dot{q}$ is the heat flux, T_b is the system boundary absolute temperature, A is the system boundary area, and τ is the time required to change from state 1 to state 2. The closed system entropy rate balance (SRB) is obtained from this equation by differentiating it with respect to time as[16]

$$\frac{dS}{dt} = \dot{S} = m\dot{s} = \int_\Sigma \left(\frac{\dot{q}}{T_b}\right)_{rev} dA \tag{5.85}$$

For the case of constant heat flux and isothermal system boundaries (i.e., $\dot{q}$ and T_b both constant) Eqs. 5.84 and 5.85 reduce to

$$S_2 - S_1 = m(s_2 - s_1) = \left(\frac{{}_1Q_2}{T_b}\right)_{rev} \tag{5.86}$$

and

$$\dot{S} = m\dot{s} = \left(\frac{\dot{Q}}{T_b}\right)_{rev} \tag{5.87}$$

where ${}_1Q_2$ and $\dot{Q}$ are the total heat transfer and total heat transfer rate, respectively, and T_b is again the absolute temperature of the system boundary (assumed isothermal here).

If the system boundary temperature is not constant, then the exact analytical dependence of $\dot{q}$ on system boundary temperature T_b, system boundary area A, and process time t must be known before the integrals in Eqs. 5.84 and 5.85 can

16. Recall that the system mass m is always constant in a closed system.

be evaluated. This information must be provided in the problem statement (or determined by measurement or hypothesis in the case of real engineering situations).

Example 5.7

2.0 kg of water undergoes a reversible isothermal expansion in a piston–cylinder apparatus from a saturated liquid at 50 °C to a superheated vapor at 50 °C and 5.0 kPa. Determine the heat and work transports of energy for this process.

Solution The unknowns here are ${}_1Q_2$ and ${}_1W_2$ and the system is the water inside the cylinder (a closed system).

State 1	$\xrightarrow[\text{isothermal}]{\text{Reversible and}}$	State 2
$T_1 = 50\ °C$		$T_2 = T_1 = 50\ °C$
$x_1 = 0$		$p_2 = 5.0\ kPa$

The basic equations here are the EB,

$${}_1Q_2 + {}_1W_2 = m(u_2 - u_1) + \underbrace{KE_2 - KE_1 + PE_2 - PE_1}_{0 \text{ (assume the system is stationary)}}$$

and the SB,

$$m(s_2 - s_1) = \int_\tau \int_\Sigma \left(\frac{\dot{q}}{T_b}\right)_{rev} dA\, dt$$

Since this process is isothermal, the system boundary absolute temperature T_b is a constant and

$$\int_\tau \int_\Sigma \left(\frac{\dot{q}}{T_b}\right)_{rev} dA\, dt = \left(\frac{{}_1Q_2}{T_b}\right)_{rev}$$

and the SB reduces to

$$m(s_2 - s_1) = \left(\frac{{}_1Q_2}{T_b}\right)_{rev}$$

We know that the work mode involved in this system is of the moving boundary type ($-\int p\, dV$), but we do not know the p-V relation for the process. Therefore, we cannot evaluate ${}_1W_2$ directly from its auxiliary equation. However, we can solve for ${}_1Q_2$ from the SB, and then we can find ${}_1W_2$ from the EB.

$${}_1Q_2 = mT_b(s_2 - s_1)$$

and

$${}_1W_2 = m(u_2 - u_1) - {}_1Q_2$$

Here,

$$s_1 = s_f(50\ °\text{C}) = 0.7036\ \text{kJ/(kg} \cdot \text{K)}$$

$$s_2 = 8.4982\ \text{kJ/(kg} \cdot \text{K)}$$

and

$$u_1 = u_f(50\ °\text{C}) = 209.3\ \text{kJ/kg}$$

$$u_2 = 2444.7\ \text{kJ/kg}$$

so that

$$\begin{aligned} {}_1Q_2 &= (2.0\ \text{kg})(273 + 50\ \text{K})[8.4982 - 0.7036\ \text{kJ/(kg} \cdot \text{K)}] \\ &= 5035.3\ \text{kJ} \end{aligned}$$

and

$$\begin{aligned} {}_1W_2 &= (2.0\ \text{kg})(2444.7 - 209.3\ \text{kJ/kg}) - 5035.3\ \text{kJ} \\ &= -564.5\ \text{kJ} \end{aligned}$$

In this example we had to deduce certain things based on information that was not explicitly given in the problem statement. This is a common engineering situation and it requires the use of common sense assumptions that often come from practice and experience. In this problem, for example, you had to know that the piston would move and thus would do moving boundary mechanical work.

Example 5.8 The solar power plant shown below utilizes the thermal energy of the sun to drive a heat engine. Solar collectors with a surface temperature of 200 °F absorb 100,000 Btu/h of solar energy and deliver it to the heat engine. The heat engine

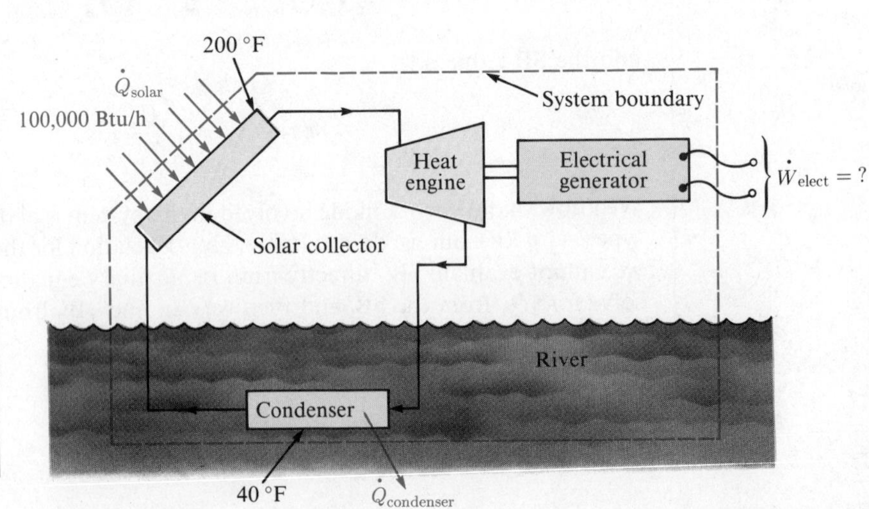

rejects heat to a condenser in a river at 40 °F. What is the maximum steady state electrical power (in kW) that can be produced by this power plant?

Solution Here the unknown is $(\dot{W}_{\text{electrical}})_{\text{max}}$, and the system is the entire power plant as shown in the schematic. You must now realize that a system like this will produce maximum work output when the internal losses (friction, etc.) are a minimum, and the absolute maximum occurs when the system is reversible. Therefore, what we wish to find here is $(\dot{W}_{\text{electrical}})_{\text{rev}}$.

Since there are no clearly defined system states given in the problem statement, and since all the given values are rate values, we recognize that this problem requires a *rate analysis.* The ERB for this system is

$$\dot{Q}_{\text{net}} + \dot{W}_{\text{net}} = \underbrace{m\dot{u}}_{\substack{0 \\ \text{(steady} \\ \text{state)}}} + \underbrace{\dot{\text{KE}} + \dot{\text{PE}}}_{\substack{0 \\ \text{(assume the system} \\ \text{is stationary)}}}$$

or

$$(\dot{W}_{\text{electrical}})_{\text{rev}} = \dot{W}_{\text{net}} = -\dot{Q}_{\text{net}}$$
$$= -(\dot{Q}_{\text{solar}} - |\dot{Q}|_{\text{condenser}})$$

Note that there are two heat transfer surfaces in this system (the solar collector and the condenser), each at different isothermal temperatures, and one work mode (electrical). The SRB for this system is

$$\dot{S} = \underbrace{m\dot{s}}_{\substack{0 \\ \text{(steady} \\ \text{state)}}} = \int_{\Sigma} \left(\frac{\dot{q}}{T_{\text{b}}}\right)_{\text{rev}} dA + \underbrace{\dot{S}_{\text{P}}}_{\substack{0 \\ \text{(reversible} \\ \text{system)}}}$$

Since the heat transfer surfaces are all isothermal and

$$\Sigma = \Sigma_{\text{collector}} + \Sigma_{\text{condenser}} + \Sigma_{\text{no heat transfer}}$$

then we can set

$$\int_{\Sigma} \left(\frac{\dot{q}}{T_{\text{b}}}\right) dA = \int_{\Sigma_{\text{collector}}} \left(\frac{\dot{q}}{T_{\text{b}}}\right) dA + \int_{\Sigma_{\text{condenser}}} \left(\frac{\dot{q}}{T_{\text{b}}}\right) dA = \frac{\dot{Q}_{\text{solar}}}{T_{\text{collector}}} - \left|\frac{\dot{Q}_{\text{condenser}}}{T_{\text{river}}}\right|$$

Therefore,

$$|\dot{Q}_{\text{condenser}}| = \dot{Q}_{\text{solar}} \left(\frac{T_{\text{river}}}{T_{\text{collector}}}\right)$$

and the ERB becomes

$$(\dot{W}_{\text{electrical}})_{\text{rev}} = -\dot{Q}_{\text{solar}}\left(1 - \frac{T_{\text{river}}}{T_{\text{collector}}}\right)$$

$$= -(100{,}000 \text{ Btu/h})\left(1 - \frac{40 + 460}{200 + 460}\right)$$

$$= -(24{,}200 \text{ Btu/h})\left(\frac{1 \text{ kW}}{3412 \text{ Btu/h}}\right)$$

$$= -7.09 \text{ kW}$$

The negative sign indicates that the electrical power is *out of* the system.

This example could also have been solved by using the Carnot heat engine efficiency (which is defined only for a reversible system) and the definition of the absolute temperature scale given in Eq. 5.15.

Example 5.9 Determine an expression for the minimum isothermal system boundary temperature required by the second law of thermodynamics as an incompressible material is heated or cooled from a temperature T_1 to a temperature T_2 in a closed system with a constant heat flux.

Solution Here we are asked to derive a formula for the minimum value of an isothermal boundary temperature, $(T_b)_{\min} = ?$ The system is closed and made up exclusively of an incompressible material (solid or liquid). The EB for this system is

$${}_1Q_2 + {}_1W_2 = m(u_2 - u_1) + \underbrace{\text{KE}_2 - \text{KE}_1 + \text{PE}_2 - \text{PE}_1}_{0 \text{ (assume the system is stationary)}}$$

For an incompressible substance, $V = \text{constant}$, so $dV = 0$, and ${}_1W_2 = -\int_1^2 p\, dV = 0$. Since no other work modes are mentioned in the problem statement we will assume that there are none. The resulting EB is then

$${}_1Q_2 = m(u_2 - u_1)$$

The SB for this system is

$$m(s_2 - s_1) = \int_\tau \int_\Sigma \left(\frac{\dot{q}}{T_b}\right) dA\, dt + {}_1(S_P)_2$$

which for a constant heat flux ($\dot{q}$) and isothermal boundaries reduce to

$$m(s_2 - s_1) = \frac{{}_1Q_2}{T_b} + {}_1(S_P)_2$$

Combining the EB and the SB we get

$$T_b = \frac{m(u_2 - u_1)}{m(s_2 - s_1) - {}_1(S_P)_2}$$

Now, since ${}_1(S_P)_2 \geq 0$, then clearly T_b will be a *minimum* when ${}_1(S_P)_2 = 0$ (a reversible process). Therefore,

$$(T_b)_{\text{minimum}} = \frac{u_2 - u_1}{s_2 - s_1}$$

For an incompressible material, $u_2 - u_1 = c(T_2 - T_1)$ and $s_2 - s_1 = c \ln(T_2/T_1)$ (see Eqs. 3.61 and 5.33). Then

$$(T_b)_{\text{minimum}} = \frac{T_2 - T_1}{\ln(T_2/T_1)}$$

This is the required final formula.

Note that $T_2 < (T_b)_{\text{min}} < T_1$ in the above example. This means that the isothermal boundary temperature $(T_b)_{\text{min}}$ cannot be the same as the constantly changing system bulk temperature. Therefore, to change the temperature of an incompressible substance by a heat transfer process from an external source *without* producing entropy (i.e., reversibly), the system must be constructed with a well-defined boundary that is somehow maintained isothermal at the temperature given by the above formula. This would cause all of the entropy generated by the heat transfer process to be produced outside the system.

Example 5.10 Show that a reversible adiabatic process carried out in a closed system results in the system having a constant entropy. That is, that a closed system reversible adiabatic process is also isentropic.

Solution Here we begin with just the SB and note that

$$m(s_2 - s_1) = \underbrace{\int_\tau \int_\Sigma \left(\frac{\dot{q}}{T_b}\right) dA\, dt}_{0 \text{ (adiabatic)}} + \underbrace{{}_1(S_P)_2}_{0 \text{ (reversibile)}} = 0$$

and therefore $s_2 = s_1$ and we have a constant entropy or isentropic process. Similarly, the SRB gives

$$\dot{S} = \underbrace{\int_\Sigma \left(\frac{\dot{q}}{T_b}\right) dA}_{0 \text{ (adiabatic)}} + \underbrace{\dot{S}_P}_{0 \text{ (reversible)}} = 0$$

and therefore S (and, of course, s) is again constant.

Isentropic processes are an important new category that we will add to our list of *constant* property processes (isothermal, isobaric, isochoric, and isenthalpic). Note from the above example that all reversible adiabatic closed system processes are isentropic, but not all isentropic processes are necessarily reversible and adiabatic. A heat loss from a system results in an entropy loss for that system, and if this entropy loss exactly balances the entropy production for the process the system is undergoing, then the process will also be isentropic without being either reversible or adiabatic.

Systems Undergoing Irreversible Processes

We will begin our treatment of irreversible processes by extending Examples 4.12 through 4.17 of Chapter 4 by using the SB or SRB in their analysis to obtain additional results from the problem. To do this effectively we will have to add some information to these problem statements in the way of additional unknowns or additional data. When additional wording has been added to these problem statements it will appear in bold type so that you can clearly see what changes have been made. Also, the analysis in these examples will contain less commentary as they are designed to be straightforward applications.

Example 5.11 (a continuation of Example 4.12, pg. 141)

A sealed rigid container whose volume is 1.0 m^3 contains 2.0 kg of liquid water plus water vapor at 20 °C. The container is heated until the temperature inside is 95 °C. Determine

a) the quality in the container when the water is 20 °C,

b) the quality in the container when the water is at 95 °C,

c) the heat transport of energy required to raise the temperature of the contents from 20 to 95 °C, **and**

d) the entropy production that occurs if the boundary of the tank is maintained isothermal at 100 °C during the heat transfer process by condensing steam at atmospheric pressure on the outside of the tank.

Solution The unknowns are **a)** x_1, **b)** x_2, **c)** ${}_1Q_2$, and **d)** ${}_1(S_P)_2$. The system is the water and is therefore closed, and

State 1	$\xrightarrow[v_2 = v_1]{\text{Isochoric}}$	State 2
$T_1 = 20$ °C		$T_2 = 95$ °C
$v_1 = 0.5$ m^3/kg		$v_2 = v_1 = 0.5$ m^3/kg

The answers to a), b), and c) can be found in Example 4.12:

a) $x_1 = 0.863\%$

b) $x_2 = 25.19\%$

c) ${}_1Q_2 = 1647$ kJ

The answer to part d is obtained from the SB or the indirect method (we do not have the detailed information about the interior of the system required to use the direct method). Equation 5.83 for an isothermal boundary becomes

$${}_1(S_P)_2 = m(s_2 - s_1) = \frac{{}_1Q_2}{T_b}$$

where

$$s_1 = s_{f1} + x_1 s_{fg1}$$
$$= 0.2965 + (0.00863)(8.3715) = 0.3687 \text{ kJ/(kg} \cdot \text{K)}$$

and

$$s_2 = s_{f2} + x_2 s_{fg2}$$
$$= 1.2503 + (0.2519)(6.1664) = 2.8036 \text{ kJ/(kg} \cdot \text{K)}$$

Then

$${}_1(S_p)_2 = (2.0 \text{ kg})[2.8036 - 0.3687 \text{ kJ/(kg} \cdot \text{K)}] - \frac{1647 \text{ kJ}}{100 + 273 \text{ K}}$$
$$= 0.4543 \text{ kJ/K} = 454.3 \text{ J/K}$$

Notice that the process described in this example also has a minimum isothermal system boundary temperature, like that described in Example 5.9. In this case,

$$(T_b)_{\text{minimum}} = \frac{{}_1Q_2}{m(s_2 - s_1)} = 338.2 \text{ K} = 65.2 \text{ °C}$$

Any attempt to carry out this process at an isothermal system boundary temperature lower than 62.5 °C (say, by radiation) would fail because it would violate the second law by requiring a negative entropy production.[17]

17. Note that cooling the tank from 95 °C back to 20 °C again with an isothermal boundary would reverse all the signs in the entropy production calculation so that ${}_2(S_P)_1 = {}_1(S_P)_2$. This cooling process would therefore require an isothermal boundary temperature *less* than 65.2 °C to satisfy the second law.

Example 5.12 (a continuation of Example 4.13, pg. 144)

An incandescent light bulb is a simple electrical device. Using the energy rate balance **and the entropy rate balance** on a light bulb determine

a) the heat transfer rate of an illuminated 100-W incandescent light bulb in a room,

b) the rate of change of its internal energy if this bulb were put into a small sealed insulated box.

c) the value of the entropy production rate for part a if the bulb has an isothermal surface temperature of 110 °C, and

d) an expression for the entropy production rate as a function of time for part b.

Solution Here the unknowns are **a)** $\dot{Q}$, **b)** $\dot{U}$, **c)** $\dot{S}_P$ for part a, and **d)** an expression for $\dot{S}_P$ as a function of time for part b. The system is the light bulb itself, and apparently we do not need to know any specific system properties to solve this problem.

The answers for parts a and b can be found in Example 4.13 as

$$\textbf{a)}\quad \dot{Q} = -100 \text{ W}$$

$$\textbf{b)}\quad \dot{U} = 100 \text{ W}$$

The answer to part c can be obtained by the indirect method of the SRB. From Eq. 5.81 we have

$$\dot{S}_P = \dot{S} - \frac{d}{dt}\int_\Sigma \left(\frac{\bar{d}Q}{T_b}\right)_{\text{act}}$$

Since we are given that the surface temperature of the bulb is isothermal, then

$$\frac{d}{dt}\int_\Sigma \left(\frac{\bar{d}Q}{T_b}\right) = \frac{1}{T_b}\frac{d}{dt}\int_\Sigma \bar{d}Q = \frac{\dot{Q}}{T_b}$$

and

$$\dot{S}_P = \dot{S} - \frac{\dot{Q}}{T_b}$$

In part a we have steady state operation so $\dot{S} = 0$, then the answer to part c is

$$\dot{S}_P = -\frac{\dot{Q}}{T_b} = \frac{100 \text{ W}}{(273 + 110 \text{ K})} = 0.261 \text{ W/K}$$

The solution to part d is obtained by recognizing that in part b the bulb is insulated, so $\dot{Q} = 0$, then

$$\dot{S}_P = \dot{S}$$

The surface and internal temperatures of the bulb are not constant here. If we recognize that most of the mass of the bulb is made up of incompressible material (glass and tungsten wire), then we can write

$$m(s - s_{ref}) = c \ln(T/T_{ref}) = c \ln(T) - c \ln(T_{ref})$$

where s_{ref} and T_{ref} are values chosen at some arbitrary reference state. Then,

$$\dot{S} = m\dot{s} = \frac{mc}{T}\left(\frac{dT}{dt}\right) = \frac{mc}{T}(\dot{T})$$

Similarily, we can write

$$m(u - u_{ref}) = c(T - T_{ref})$$

so that

$$\dot{U} = m\dot{u} = mc\left(\frac{dT}{dt}\right) = mc(\dot{T})$$

Therefore,

$$\dot{S} = \frac{\dot{U}}{T} = \dot{S}_P$$

The temperature in this equation is the mean temperature of the bulb and can be evaluated from the answer to part b where we found that $\dot{U} = 100$ W. Therefore,

$$\dot{T} = \frac{dT}{dt} = \frac{\dot{U}}{mc} = \text{constant}$$

and integration of this equation gives

$$T = \frac{\dot{U}}{mc}t + T_o$$

where T_o is the bulb temperature immediately before the insulation is applied. Thus, the answer to part d is

$$\dot{S}_P = \frac{\dot{U}}{\dfrac{\dot{U}t}{mc} + T_o} = \frac{mc}{t + \dfrac{mcT_o}{\dot{U}}}$$

Since $\dot{U} = 100$ W, and m, c, and T_o are all constant measurable quantities, it is clear from this result that $\dot{S}_P$ will slowly decay to zero as time t goes to infinity.

Note, however, that the bulb temperature increases linearly with time, therefore the bulb will overheat and burn out rather quickly.

Example 5.13 (a continuation of Example 4.14, pg. 146)

A basic vapor cycle power plant consists of the following four parts:

a) the boiler where high-pressure vapor is produced,

b) the turbine where energy is removed from the high-pressure vapor as shaft work,

c) the condenser where the low-pressure vapor leaving the turbine is condensed into a liquid, and

d) the boiler feed pump that pumps the condensed liquid back into the high-pressure boiler for reheating.

In such a power plant the boiler receives 950,000 Btu/h from the burning fuel, and the condenser rejects 600,000 Btu/h to the environment. The boiler feed pump requires 30-hp input, which it receives directly from the turbine. Assuming that the turbine, pump, and connecting pipes are all insulated, determine the net power of the turbine **and the rate of entropy production of the plant if the boiler temperature is 500 °F and the condenser temperature is 40 °F.**

Solution The unknowns here are $(\dot{W}_T)_{net}$ and $\dot{S}_P$ for the entire power plant. Therefore, the system is the entire power plant. Since we do not have many specific details on the internal operation of the plant, the thermodynamic properties within the power plant are apparently not needed in the solution.

The net turbine work output was determined in Example 4.14 to be

$$(\dot{W}_T)_{net} = -137.5 \text{ hp}$$

The answer to the second part of this problem can be obtained by the indirect method from Eq. 5.81 as

$$\dot{S}_P = \dot{S} - \frac{d}{dt}\int_\Sigma \left(\frac{\bar{d}Q}{T_b}\right)_{act}$$

The surface area of our system can be divided into three major parts: The boiler's surface area, the condenser's surface area, and all the remaining surface area. Thus, we can write

$$\Sigma = \Sigma_{boiler} + \Sigma_{condenser} + \Sigma_{remainder}$$

Now, both the boiling and the condensing processes are isothermal phase changes, and since no heat transfer occurs at any other point in the system we can write

$$\frac{d}{dt}\int_\Sigma \frac{\bar{d}Q}{T_b} = \frac{d}{dt}\left(\int_{\Sigma boiler} \frac{\bar{d}Q}{T_b} + \int_{\Sigma condenser} \frac{\bar{d}Q}{T_b} + \int_{\Sigma remainder} \frac{\bar{d}Q}{T_b}\right)$$

where

$$\frac{d}{dt}\int_{\Sigma_{\text{boiler}}} \frac{\bar{d}Q}{T_b} = \frac{\dot{Q}_{\text{boiler}}}{T_{\text{boiler}}}$$

$$\frac{d}{dt}\int_{\Sigma_{\text{condenser}}} \frac{\bar{d}Q}{T_b} = \frac{\dot{Q}_{\text{condenser}}}{T_{\text{condenser}}}$$

and

$$\frac{d}{dt}\int_{\Sigma_{\text{remainder}}} \frac{\bar{d}Q}{T_b} = 0 \quad \text{(no heat transfer across the remaining surface area)}$$

Then we have

$$\dot{S}_P = \dot{S} - \frac{\dot{Q}_{\text{boiler}}}{T_{\text{boiler}}} - \frac{\dot{Q}_{\text{condenser}}}{T_{\text{condenser}}}$$

and for steady state operation ($\dot{S} = 0$) this reduces to

$$\begin{aligned}\dot{S}_P &= -\left(\frac{\dot{Q}_{\text{boiler}}}{T_{\text{boiler}}} + \frac{\dot{Q}_{\text{condenser}}}{T_{\text{condenser}}}\right)\\ &= -\left(\frac{950{,}000}{500 + 460} + \frac{-600{,}000}{40 + 460}\right) \text{Btu/(h·R)} = 210 \text{ Btu/(h·R)}\end{aligned}$$

Note that the actual thermal efficiency of this power plant is given by Eq. 5.9 as

$$(\eta_T)_{\text{act}} = 1 - \frac{|\dot{Q}_{\text{out}}|}{\dot{Q}_{\text{in}}} = 1 - \frac{600{,}000}{950{,}000} = 0.368 = 36.8\%$$

whereas its theoretical reversible (Carnot) efficiency is given by Eq. 5.16 as

$$(\eta_T)_{\text{rev}} = 1 - \frac{T_{\text{condenser}}}{T_{\text{boiler}}} = 1 - \frac{40 + 460}{500 + 460} = 0.479 = 47.9\%$$

Thus, the actual efficiency is less than the theoretical maximum (reversible) efficiency as it should be.

Example 5.14 (a continuation of Example 4.15, pg. 148)

A food processor has a cutting/mixing blade driven by a 0.25-hp electric motor. The machine is initially filled with 1.0 quart of water at 60 °F, 14.7 psia. It is then turned on at full speed for 10 min. Assuming the entire machine is insulated and that the mixing takes place at constant pressure, determine the temperature of the water **and the amount of entropy produced** when the machine is turned off.

Solution The unknowns here are T_2 and ${}_1(S_P)_2$. The system is the water in the food processor, which we will assume to be an incompressible material. The data of the water are as follows

State 1	$\xrightarrow[\text{mixing}]{\text{Isobaric}}$	State 2
$p_1 = 14.7$ psia		$p_2 = p_1 = 14.7$ psia
$T_1 = 60$ °F		

The solution to the first part of this problem is given in Example 4.15 as

$$T_2 = 111\ °\text{F}$$

The solution to the second part will be determined by the indirect (entropy balance) method. Equation 5.80 gives

$${}_1(S_P)_2 = m(s_2 - s_1) - \underbrace{\int_\Sigma \left(\frac{dQ}{T_b}\right)}_{0 \quad \text{(insulated system)}}$$

and for an incompressible substance,

$$s_2 - s_1 = c \ln \frac{T_2}{T_1}$$

so that

$${}_1(S_P)_2 = mc \ln \frac{T_2}{T_1}$$

or

$${}_1(S_P)_2 = (2.085\ \text{lbm})[1.0\ \text{Btu/(lbm}\cdot\text{R)}] \ln \frac{111 + 460}{60 + 460}$$

$$= 0.195\ \text{Btu/R}$$

If we wished to know the entropy production *rate* for this example our analysis and results would be the same as that for part b of Example 5.12. The entropy production rate would not be constant in time, but would decrease as the water became hotter. Since it was stated that the food processor is insulated, eventually enough mixing energy would be converted into internal (thermal) energy to cause the water to completely vaporize, whereupon the assumption of an incompressible fluid would no longer apply.

Example 5.15 (a continuation of Example 4.16, pg. 150)

0.1 lbm of Refrigerant-12 initially at 180 °F and 100 psia in a cylinder with a movable piston undergoes the following two-part process. First, the refrigerant is expanded adiabatically to 30 psia and 120 °F, and then it is isobarically compressed to half its initial volume. Determine

a) the work transport of energy during the adiabatic expansion,
b) the heat transport of energy during the isobaric compression,
c) the final temperature at the end of the isobaric compression, **and**
d) the total entropy production for both processes if the heat transport of energy and the boundary temperature are related by the formula $Q = KT_b$, where $K = 5.0$ Btu/R.

Solution The unknowns here are **a)** ${}_1W_2$, **b)** ${}_2Q_3$, **c)** T_3, and **d)** ${}_1(S_P)_3$. The system is just the R-12, and the state variables are as follows

State 1	$\xrightarrow[\text{expansion}]{\text{Adiabatic}}$	State 2	$\xrightarrow[\text{compression}]{\text{Isobaric}}$	State 3
$p_1 = 100$ psia		$p_2 = 30$ psia		$p_3 = p_2 = 30$ psia
$T_1 = 180$ °F		$T_2 = 120$ °F		$v_3 = v_1/2$
$v_1 = 0.52291$ ft³/lbm		$v_2 = 1.6600$ ft³/lbm		$v_3 = 0.2615$ ft³/lbm
$h_1 = 102.257$ Btu/lbm		$h_2 = 94.843$ Btu/lbm		$x_3 = 0.1941$
$s_1 = 0.19262$ Btu/(lbm·R)		$s_2 = 0.19918$ Btu/(lbm·R)		$s_3 = 0.05227$ Btu/(lbm·R)

The solutions to the first three parts of this problem are given in Example 4.16 as

a) ${}_1W_2 = -0.695$ Btu

b) ${}_2Q_3 = -7.082$ Btu

c) $T_3 = 11.04$ °F

The solution to part d can be determined by the indirect (entropy balance) method as follows. From Eq. 5.80 we have

$$
{}_1(S_P)_2 = m(s_2 - s_1) - \underbrace{\int_\Sigma \left(\frac{đQ}{T_b}\right)_{\text{act}}}_{0 \text{ (adiabatic process)}}
$$

From Appendix C.8*a* we find that

$$s_1 = 0.19262 \text{ Btu/(lbm·R)}$$

and

$$s_2 = 0.19918 \text{ Btu/(lbm·R)}$$

Therefore,

$$ {}_1(S_p)_2 = (0.1 \text{ lbm})[0.19918 - 0.19262 \text{ Btu/(lbm} \cdot \text{R)}] = 6.56 \times 10^{-4} \text{ Btu/R} $$
$$ = (6.56 \times 10^{-4} \text{ Btu/R})(778 \text{ ft} \cdot \text{lbf/Btu}) = 0.510 \text{ ft} \cdot \text{lbf/R} $$

Similarly,

$$ {}_2(S_P)_3 = m(s_3 - s_2) - \int_\Sigma \frac{\bar{d}Q}{T_b} $$

In this process we are given that $Q = KT_b$, where $K = 5.0$ Btu/R. Therefore, $\bar{d}Q = K(dT_b)$, and

$$ \int_\Sigma \frac{\bar{d}Q}{T_b} = \int_{T_{b2}}^{T_{b3}} K\left(\frac{dT_b}{T_b}\right) = K \ln \frac{T_{b3}}{T_{b2}} $$

Therefore,

$$ {}_2(S_P)_3 = m(s_3 - s_2) - K \ln \frac{T_{b3}}{T_{b2}} $$

Now, $s_3 = s_{f3} + x_3 s_{fg3}$, and interpolating in Appendix C.7*a* at 30 psia we get

$$ s_{f3} = 0.02442 \text{ Btu/(lbm} \cdot \text{R)} $$

$$ s_{fg3} = 0.14347 \text{ Btu/(lbm} \cdot \text{R)} $$

Then,

$$ s_3 = 0.02442 + (0.1941)(0.14347) = 0.05227 \text{ Btu/(lbm} \cdot \text{R)} $$

and

$$ {}_2(S_P)_3 = (0.1 \text{ lbm})[0.05227 - 0.19918 \text{ Btu/(lbm} \cdot \text{R)}] $$
$$ - (5.0 \text{ Btu/R}) \ln \frac{11.04 + 460}{120 + 460} = 1.026 \text{ Btu/R} $$

Finally, the entropy production for the entire process is given by

$$ {}_1(S_P)_3 = {}_1(S_P)_2 + {}_2(S_P)_3 = 6.56 \times 10^{-4} + 1.026 = 1.027 \text{ Btu/R} $$

In the above example a special $Q = Q(T_b)$ relation was introduced that is similar to that used to describe convection heat transfer processes (see, for example, Eq. 4.79). These relations are often called *thermal constitutive equations*, and are mathematical models developed to describe specific heat transfer mechanisms.

Example 5.16 (a continuation of Example 4.17, pg. 153)

The muffler bearing of a 1923 Detroit Electric automobile consists of a one-foot-diameter rigid hollow steel sphere of negligible wall thickness. During its fabrication the bearing undergoes a heat treating operation in which it is initially filled with helium at 20 psia and 200 °F, and then is plunged into cold water at 50 °F for 5 s. The convective heat transfer coefficient of the sphere in the water is 2.0 Btu/(h·ft^2·R). Neglecting any changes in kinetic or potential energy, and assuming the helium behaves as an ideal gas, determine

a) the final temperature of the helium,
b) the change in total internal energy of the helium, **and**
c) the total entropy production of the helium.

Solution The unknowns here are, after 5 s have passed, **a)** T_2, **b)** $U_2 - U_1$, and **c)** ${}_1(S_P)_2$ for the helium. The system here is the helium, and the solutions to the first two parts of this problem can be found in Example 4.17 as

a) $T_2 = 70.7$ °F, and

b) $U_2 - U_1 = 0.569$ Btu

The solution to part c can be found again by the indirect (entropy balance) method as follows. From Eq. 5.80 we have

$${}_1(S_P)_2 = m(s_2 - s_1) - \int_\Sigma \left(\frac{đQ}{T}\right)_{\text{act}}$$

We can assume that helium behaves as an ideal gas, then since $v_2 = v_1 =$ constant, we can use Eq. 5.36 to produce

$$\begin{aligned} s_2 - s_1 &= c_v \ln \frac{T_2}{T_1} + R \ln \frac{v_2}{v_1} \\ &= [0.74 \text{ Btu/(lbm·R)}] \ln \frac{70.7 + 460}{200 + 460} + 0 \\ &= -0.161 \text{ Btu/(lbm·R)} \end{aligned}$$

and from Example 4.17 we have

$$\dot{Q} = -hA(T_s - T_\infty) = \frac{đQ}{dt}$$

so

$$đQ = -hA(T_s - T_\infty)\, dt$$

and

$$\frac{đQ}{T_b} = \frac{đQ}{T_\infty} = -hA[(T_s - T_\infty)/T_\infty]\, dt$$

where we have set $T_b = T_\infty$ (i.e., we have put the system boundary slightly outside the sphere itself). Also, in Example 4.17 we discovered that

$$T_s = T_\infty + (T_1 - T_\infty)\exp\left(-\frac{hAt}{mc_v}\right)$$

where $T_1 = T_s$ evaluated at $t = 0$. Then

$$\int_\Sigma \left(\frac{\bar{d}Q}{T_b}\right)_{act} = -hA\int_0^{5s}\left(\frac{T_s - T_\infty}{T_\infty}\right)dt$$

$$= mc_v\left(\frac{T_1 - T_\infty}{T_\infty}\right)\left[\exp\left(-\frac{hAt}{mc_v}\right)\Big|_0^{5s}\right]$$

Now, from Example 4.17 we have the following numerical values,

$$m = 5.92 \times 10^{-3}\ \text{lbm}$$

$$c_v = 0.744\ \text{Btu/lbm R}$$

$$T_1 = 200\ °\text{F} = 600\ \text{R}$$

$$T_\infty = 50\ °\text{F} = 510\ \text{R}$$

and $hA/(mc_v) = 1427\ \text{h}^{-1} = 0.3964\ \text{s}^{-1}$. Substituting these values into the integration result above gives

$$\int_\Sigma \left(\frac{\bar{d}Q}{T_b}\right)_{act} = -1.12 \times 10^{-3}\ \text{Btu/R}$$

and then

$$_1(S_P)_2 = (5.92 \times 10^{-3}\ \text{lbm})[-0.161\ \text{Btu/(lbm}\cdot\text{R)}] + 1.12 \times 10^{-3}\ \text{Btu/R}$$

$$= 1.67 \times 10^{-4}\ \text{Btu/R}$$

$$= (1.67 \times 10^{-4}\ \text{Btu/R})(778\ \text{ft}\cdot\text{lbf/Btu}) = 0.130\ \text{ft}\cdot\text{lbf/R}$$

The next three examples illustrate the use of the direct method of determining the entropy production. This method is usually more difficult than the entropy balance (indirect) method because it requires detailed information about *local* property values (i.e., properties at each point inside the system boundary) and the integration of Eq. 5.85 or 5.86 is often quite difficult. The formulae for the work mode entropy production per unit time per unit volume (σ_W) are given in Section I of this chapter for viscous and electrical work mode irreversibilities.

Example 5.17 The heat transfer rate from a very long fin of constant cross section is given by

$$\dot{Q} = \sqrt{hPk_tA}(T_f - T_\infty)$$

where h is the convective heat transfer coefficient, P is the perimeter of the fin in a plane normal to its axis, k_t is the thermal conductivity of the fin, and A is the cross-sectional area of the fin (again in a plane normal to its axis). T_∞ is the temperature of the fin's surrounding (measured far from the fin itself) and T_f is the temperature of the foot (or base) of the fin. The temperature profile along the fin is given by

$$T(x) = T_\infty + (T_f - T_\infty)e^{-mx}$$

where

$$m = \left(\frac{hP}{k_tA}\right)^{1/2}$$

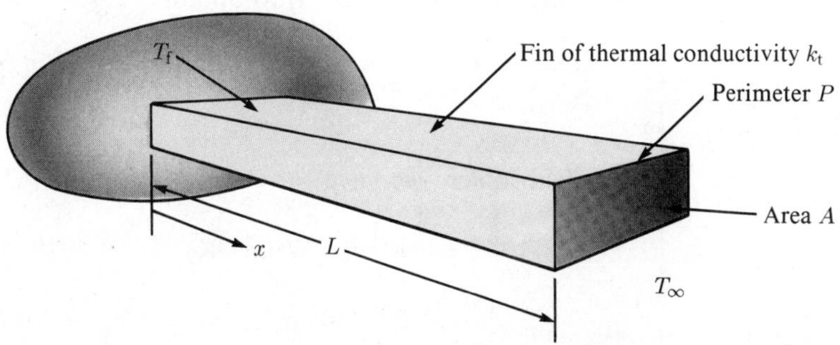

The fin is attached to an engine whose surface temperature is 95 °C. Determine the entropy production rate for the fin if it is a very long square aluminum fin 0.01 m on a side in air at 20 °C. The thermal conductivity of aluminum is 204 W/(m·K) and the convective heat transfer coefficient of the fin is 3.5 W/(m²·K).

Solution Since there is no work mode entropy production here, Eq. 5.66 will be used to find the fins entropy production rate by the direct method (note that we do not have enough information to use the more convenient indirect entropy balance method here) as

$$\dot{S}_P = (\dot{S}_P)_Q = -\int_{\mathcal{V}} \left[\frac{\dot{q}}{T^2}\left(\frac{dT}{dx}\right)\right]_{\text{act}} d\mathcal{V}$$

Since this is a one-dimensional heat transfer problem, we can substitute $A\,dx$ for $d\mathcal{V}$. Then,

$$(\dot{S}_P)_Q = -\int_0^L \left[\frac{\dot{q}}{T^2}\left(\frac{dT}{dx}\right)\right] A\,dx = \int_0^\infty \left[\frac{k_tA}{T^2}\left(\frac{dT}{dx}\right)^2\right] dx$$

where we have used Fourier's law, $\dot{q} = -k_t(dT/dx)$, and have let $L \to \infty$ for a very long fin. We can differentiate the fin's temperature profile given above to obtain

$$\frac{dT}{dx} = -m(T_f - T_\infty)e^{-mx}$$

then

$$k_t\left(\frac{A}{T^2}\right)\left(\frac{dT}{dx}\right)^2 = \frac{\sqrt{hPk_tA}(m)(T_f - T)^2 e^{-2mx}}{[T_\infty + (T_f - T_\infty)e^{-mx}]^2}$$

and

$$(S_P)_Q = m(T_f - T_\infty)^2\sqrt{hPk_tA}\int_0^\infty \frac{e^{-2mx}\,dx}{[T_\infty + (T_f - T_\infty)e^{-mx}]^2}$$

This expression can be integrated by using a table of integrals and a change of variables (e.g., let $y = e^{-mx}$) to obtain

$$(\dot{S}_P)_Q = \sqrt{hPk_tA}\left(\ln\frac{T_f}{T_\infty} + \frac{T_\infty}{T_f} - 1\right)$$

In this problem we have

$$h = 3.5\ \text{W/(m}^2\cdot\text{K)} \qquad A = 10^{-4}\ \text{m}^2$$

$$P = 0.04\ \text{m} \qquad T_\infty = 20\ ^\circ\text{C} = 293\ \text{K}$$

$$k_t = 204\ \text{W/(m}\cdot\text{K)} \qquad T_f = 95\ ^\circ\text{C} = 368\ \text{K}$$

Then,

$$\dot{S}_P = (\dot{S}_P)_Q$$

$$= \sqrt{[3.5\ \text{W/(m}^2\cdot\text{K)}](0.04\ \text{m})[204\ \text{W/(m}\cdot\text{K)}](10^{-4}\ \text{m}^2)}\left(\ln\frac{368}{293} + \frac{293}{368} - 1\right)$$

$$= 0.0013\ \text{W/K}$$

Note that the entropy production rate in this example is quite small. This is due to the fact that the fin temperature $T(x)$ is quite close to the environmental temperature T_∞ over most of the length of the fin. Entropy production due to heat transfer is always minimized when the temperature difference producing the heat transfer is minimal. Check for yourself to see that $(\dot{S}_P)_Q$ becomes zero in the above formula when $T_f = T_\infty$. The maximum entropy production rate occurs when the temperature difference is a maximum. This occurs in this example when $T_\infty = 0$ K or when $T_f = \infty$. In this case

$$(\dot{S}_P)_{max} = \lim_{T_\infty \to 0} \dot{S}_P = \lim_{T_f \to \infty} \dot{S}_P = \infty$$

Example 5.18 The velocity profile in the steady isothermal laminar flow of an incompressible Newtonian fluid contained between concentric cylinders in which the inner cylinder is rotating and the outer cylinder is stationary is given by

$$V = \frac{\omega R_1^2}{R_2^2 - R_1^2}\left(\frac{R_2^2}{x} - x\right) \qquad \text{for } R_1 \le x \le R_2$$

where ω is the angular velocity of the inner cylinder, and x is measured radially outward.

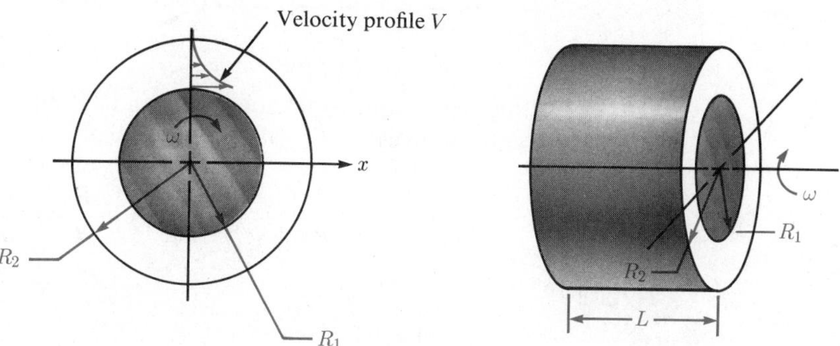

Determine the rate of entropy production due to laminar viscous losses for engine oil at 20 °C in the gap between cylinders of radii 0.050 and 0.051 m when the inner cylinder is rotating at 1000 rev/min. The viscosity of the oil is 0.8 N·s/m^2 and the length of the cylinder is 0.100 m.

Solution Here we will use Eq. 5.72 for the viscous dissipation of mechanical work. By differentiating the velocity formula given above we get

$$\frac{dV}{dx} = -\frac{\omega R_1^2}{R_2^2 - R_1^2}\left(\frac{R_2^2}{x^2} + 1\right)$$

and then

$$(\sigma_W)_{vis} = \frac{\mu}{T}\left(\frac{dV}{dx}\right)^2 = \frac{\omega^2 R_1^4 \mu}{(R_2^2 - R_1^2)^2 T}\left(\frac{R_2^2}{x^2} + 1\right)^2$$

Equation 5.70 gives the entropy production rate for viscous effects as

$$(\dot{S}_P)_{\substack{W\\vis}} = \int_{\mathcal{V}} (\sigma_W)_{vis}\, d\mathcal{V}$$

For the differential volume element $d\mathcal{V}$ we will use the volume of an annulus of thickness dx, or $d\mathcal{V} = 2\pi L x\, dx$.

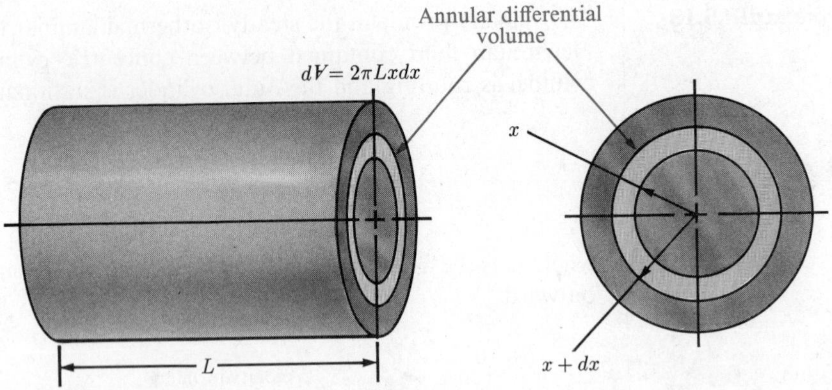

Putting these expressions for $(\sigma_W)_{vis}$ and dV into Eq. 5.70 and carrying out the integration gives

$$(\dot{S}_P)_{\substack{W\\vis}} = \frac{2\pi L\omega^2 R_1^4 \mu}{(R_2^2 - R_1^2)^2 T}\left(2R_2^2 \ln\frac{R_2}{R_1} + \frac{R_2^4}{2R_1^2} - \frac{R_1^2}{2}\right)$$

where

$$\mu = 0.8 \text{ N}\cdot\text{s/m}^2$$

$$L = 0.100 \text{ m}$$

$$\omega = \left(1000 \frac{\text{rev}}{\text{min}}\right)\left(\frac{2\pi \text{ rad}}{\text{rev}}\right)\left(\frac{1 \text{ min}}{60 \text{ s}}\right) = 104.7 \text{ rad/s}$$

$$R_1 = 0.050 \text{ m}$$

$$R_2 = 0.051 \text{ m, and}$$

$$T = 20\ ^\circ\text{C} = 293 \text{ K}$$

Substituting these values into the above formula gives

$$(\dot{S}_P)_{\substack{W\\vis}} = 2.37 \text{ W/K}$$

In this example we have a reasonably high entropy production rate. This is due to the very small gap between the cylinders and the high viscosity of the engine oil. Check for yourself to see that $(\dot{S}_P)_{W\,vis} \to 0$ as R_2 becomes much larger than R_1, or as $\mu \to 0$. Conversely, check to see that $(\dot{S}_P)_{W\,vis} \to \infty$ as $R_1 \to R_2$, or as $\mu \to \infty$.

Example 5.19 An electrical circuit board contains a variety of digital logic elements. When operating, the board draws 10 mA at 5.0 V dc and it has a steady state surface temperature of 30 °C. Estimate the entropy production rate of the circuit board.

Solution Since nearly all the electrical energy entering the circuit board is being converted into heat we could calculate the entropy production rate of the board from its heat loss characteristics (convective heat transfer coefficient, surface temperature, environmental temperature, surface area, etc.); however, none of this information is supplied in the problem statement. We could also calculate the entropy production rate for electrical work mode dissipation directly from Eq. 5.73 if we knew how the current density J_e, electrical resistivity ρ_e, and local internal temperature T were distributed throughout the circuit board. But we do not know this information either. However, the problem statement asks for only an estimate of the entropy production rate, and we can obtain this from the special electrical work mode dissipation Eq. 5.74 if we lump all the components on the board into one uniform, isothermal, constant current density system. From Ohm's law, $\phi = IR_e$, we can write Eq. 5.74 as

$$(\dot{S}_P)_W = \frac{I^2 R_e}{T} = \frac{\phi I}{T} = \frac{(5.0 \text{ V})(10 \times 10^{-3} \text{ A})}{30 + 273 \text{ K}}$$

$$= 1.65 \times 10^{-4} \text{ W/K}$$

This is only a lumped parameter estimate of the entropy production rate for this system. The actual entropy production rate will be somewhat larger due to the nonuniform distribution of entropy producing electrical components within the system volume.

Diffusional Mixing

Here we wish to use the indirect method to analyze the entropy production that results from a simple diffusion type of mixing processes. Consider the rigid insulated container shown in Figure 5.10. It contains the same substance on both sides

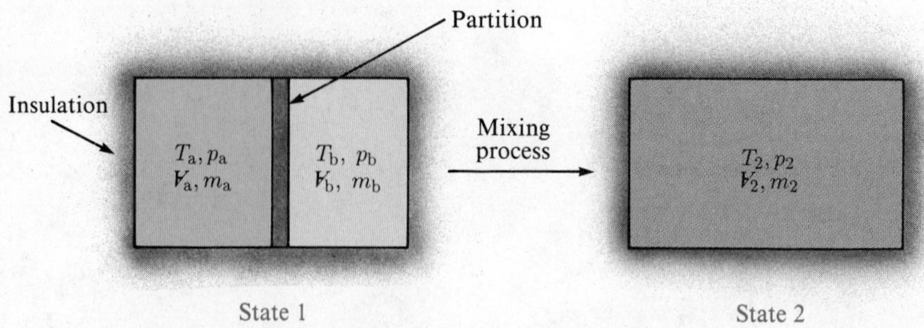

Figure 5.10 Mixing of single-species substances.

of the partition, but generally at different pressures, temperatures, and amounts. When the partition is removed the material in the chambers mixes by diffusion, resulting in a final temperature T_2 and final pressure p_2. We are interested in the amount of entropy produced by this mixing process.

The EB for this system gives

$$\underbrace{{}_1Q_2}_{\substack{0\\\text{(adiabatic)}}} + \underbrace{{}_1W_2}_{0\ \text{(aergonic)}} = U_2 - U_1 + \underbrace{\mathrm{KE}_2 - \mathrm{KE}_1 + \mathrm{PE}_2 - \mathrm{PE}_1}_{0\ \text{(stationary system)}}$$

or

$$U_2 = m_2 u_2 = U_1 = m_a u_a + m_b u_b$$

or

$$u_2 = \frac{m_a u_a + m_b u_b}{m_a + m_b} = u_b + y(u_a - u_b) \tag{5.88}$$

where

$$y = \frac{m_a}{m_a + m_b}$$

and

$$1 - y = \frac{m_b}{m_a + m_b}$$

The SB gives

$${}_1(S_P)_2 = S_2 - S_1 - \underbrace{\frac{{}_1Q_2}{T_b}}_{\substack{0\\\text{(adiabatic)}}}$$

or

$$_1(S_P)_2 = m_2 s_2 - m_a s_a - m_b s_b$$
$$= (m_a + m_b)[s_2 - s_b + y(s_b - s_a)] \quad \textbf{(5.89)}$$

When the chambers contain identical ideal gases, then Eqs. 3.37 and 5.88 give

$$u_2 - u_b = c_v(T_2 - T_b) = yc_v(T_a - T_b)$$

or

$$T_2 = T_b + y(T_a - T_b) \quad \textbf{(5.90)}$$

and Eqs. 5.37 and 5.89 give

$$_1(S_P)_2 = (m_a + m_b)\left[c_p \ln\frac{T_2}{T_b} - R\ln\frac{p_2}{p_b} + y\left(c_p \ln\frac{T_b}{T_a} - R\ln\frac{p_b}{p_a}\right)\right]$$

or

$$_1(S_P)_2 = (m_a + m_b)\{c_p \ln[(T_2/T_b)(T_b/T_a)^y] - R\ln[(p_2/p_b)(p_b/p_a)^y]\}$$

and inserting Eq. 5.90 for T_2 gives

$$_1(S_P)_2 = (m_a + m_b)\{c_p \ln[(1 + y(T_a/T_b - 1))(T_b/T_a)^y]$$
$$- R\ln[(p_2/p_b)(p_b/p_a)^y]\} \geq 0 \quad \textbf{(5.91)}$$

When the chambers contain identical incompressible liquids, then Eqs. 3.61, 5.88, and 5.89 can be combined to yield

$$_1(S_P)_2 = (m_a + m_b)c\ln[(1 + y(T_a/T_b - 1))(T_b/T_a)^y] \geq 0 \quad \textbf{(5.92)}$$

The actual mixing process need not have the same two-chamber geometry shown in Figure 5.10, as illustrated by the following example.

Example 5.20

Determine the entropy produced when 3.0 g of cream at 10 °C are added adiabatically and without stirring to 200 g of hot coffee at 80 °C. Assume both the coffee and the cream have the properties of pure water.

Solution Let a = cream and b = coffee. Then $y = \frac{3}{203} = 0.0148$. Assuming both the coffee and the cream are incompressible liquids with a specific heat of water, $c = 4186$ J/(kg·K), Eq. 5.92 then gives

$$_1(S_P)_2 = (0.203 \text{ kg})[4186 \text{ J/(kg·K)}]\ln\left[\left(1 + 0.0148\left(\frac{10+273}{80+273} - 1\right)\right)\right.$$
$$\left.\times\left(\frac{80+273}{10+273}\right)^{0.0148}\right]$$
$$= 0.285 \text{ J/K}$$

Note that this example does not include the entropy production due to the heat transfer required to cool the mixture down to a drinkable temperature.

Equations 5.91 and 5.92 show that the amount of entropy production in this type of mixing process depends on the amounts mixed and their initial states. The larger the property differences between the initial states, the larger entropy production will be upon mixing. That is, the farther the initial states are from the final equilibrium state, the larger the associated entropy production will be. This is a general characteristic of the second law.

Chapter Five Section III Second Law Open System Applications

Section III of this chapter is an extension of Section III of Chapter 4, except here we demonstrate the use of both the first and second laws of thermodynamics to analyze open systems. As in Section II of this chapter we will have two different types of system processes to consider, reversible and irreversible. A reversible process is easier to analyze because its entropy production is always equal to zero. However, reversible process models are often unrealistic in actual engineering applications because they require that the system have no losses (i.e., no friction or no heat transfer through a finite temperature difference, etc.). On the other hand, irreversible process models are very realistic because they take into account all the losses within the system, but they are often very difficult to analyze because of the complex entropy production terms that must be evaluated. We are therefore faced with the choice of carrying out a quick but possibly inaccurate analysis based upon hypothetical reversible processes, or of carrying out a more complex but accurate analysis based upon real irreversible processes. The material presented in Section III of this chapter focuses primarily on the latter by utilizing the appropriate entropy production formulae developed in Section I of this chapter.

Since we have not yet considered the impact of flowstreams on the general entropy balance, we must now introduce the mass flow transport and production of entropy characteristic of open systems.

Mass Flow Transport of Entropy

Mass flow transport of entropy occurs every time mass crosses the system boundary. Every element of mass dm is assumed to be in local equilibrium and thus has a well-defined specific entropy s. Therefore, dm transports an amount of entropy

sdm when it crosses a system boundary, and we can set

$$(dS_T)_m = s\,dm$$

and

$$(S_T)_m = \int s\,dm$$

This equation can also be written as

$$(S_T)_m = \int s\,dm = \int s\left(\frac{dm}{dt}\right)dt = \int \dot{m}s\,dt$$

where $\dot{m}$ is the mass flow rate crossing the system boundary. Differentiation of this equation with respect to time yields the mass transport rate term as

$$(\dot{S}_T)_m = \dot{m}s$$

Unlike heat and work transports of entropy, it is customary in mass flow transport to write a more explicit formula for the *net* mass flow entropy transport rate as

$$[(\dot{S}_T)_m]_{net} = \sum_{in} \dot{m}s - \sum_{out} \dot{m}s \tag{5.93}$$

where the summations are over all inlet and outlet flowstreams (the flowstreams will normally be pipes or ducts which convey mass into or out of the system).

Mass Flow Production of Entropy

Mass flow entropy production is due to mass flow that occurs *inside* the system. There is no entropy production due solely to mass crossing the system boundary because it is an imaginary boundary of zero thickness. There are two main sources for this type of internal mass flow entropy production

1. viscous dissipation, and
2. diffusion of dissimilar chemical species.

The first of these is really a work mode entropy production mechanism because viscous dissipation has already been treated in Eqs. 5.71 and 5.72. Consequently, the only mass flow entropy production mechanism we will consider here is that due to the diffusion of dissimilar chemical species.

One-dimensional diffusion of n dissimilar chemical species can be treated by introducing a mass flow entropy production per unit time per unit volume due to diffusion as[18]

$$\sigma_m = (\sigma_m)_{diff} = -\sum_{i=1}^{n-1} \dot{J}_{ix}\left[\frac{d}{dx}\left(\frac{\hat{\mu}_i}{T}\right)\right] \quad \textbf{(5.94)}$$

where $\dot{J}_{ix}$ is the mass flux (mass flow per unit area per unit time) of chemical species i in the x direction, $\hat{\mu}_i$ is the chemical potential (on a mass rather than a molar basis) of chemical species i, and T is the local internal absolute temperature. Since only $n - 1$ of the n chemical species are independent (the conservation of mass law provides an independent equation relating all n species), then the species summation needs to run only from 1 to $n - 1$.

For an *isothermal* mixture of *ideal gases*, many experiments have shown that

$$\hat{\mu}_i = R_i T \ln \rho_i + \text{constant}$$

where R_i is the gas constant and $\rho_i = m_i/V$ is the mass concentration (i.e. density) of gas i in the mixture. Then

$$\frac{d\hat{\mu}_i}{dx} = \frac{R_i T}{\rho_i}\left(\frac{d\rho_i}{dx}\right) \quad \textbf{(5.95)}$$

and

$$\frac{d}{dx}\left(\frac{\hat{\mu}_i}{T}\right) = \frac{R_i}{\rho_i}\left(\frac{d\rho_i}{dx}\right) = \frac{R_i}{w_i}\left(\frac{dw_i}{dx}\right)$$

where $w_i = \rho_i/\rho$ is the mass fraction of gas i. In the case of a *binary* mixture with ideal gas species A and B the mass flux term is often modeled with the one-dimensional form of Fick's first law,[19]

$$\dot{J}_{Ax} = \rho D_{AB}\left(\frac{dw_A}{dx}\right) = -\dot{J}_{Bx} = \rho D_{BA}\left(\frac{dw_B}{dx}\right) \quad \textbf{(5.96)}$$

where $\rho = \rho_A + \rho_B$ is the mass density of the mixture and $D_{AB} = D_{BA}$ is the diffusivity coefficient. Table 5.1 lists the diffusivity coefficients for various binary gas mixtures.

---

18. In three-dimensional space this is generalized to

$$\sigma_m = (\sigma_m)_{diff} = -\sum_{i=1}^{n-1} \dot{\mathbf{J}}_i \cdot \nabla\left(\frac{\hat{\mu}_i}{T}\right)$$

where $\dot{\mathbf{J}}_i$ is the mass flux vector of chemical species i, $\hat{\mu}_i$ is the chemical potential of chemical species i, T is the local absolute temperature, and $\nabla(\ )$ is the gradient operator.

19. Here $\mathbf{j}_A = \rho_A(\mathbf{V}_A - \mathbf{V})$ is the mass flux relative to the mass average velocity, $\mathbf{V} = w_A\mathbf{V}_A + w_B\mathbf{V}_B$.

Table 5.1 Diffusion coefficients for some binary gas mixtures at atmospheric pressure and 0 °C*

Components A–B	Diffusion coefficient (m^2/s) $D_{AB} = D_{BA}$
Acetone–air	1.09×10^{-5}
CO_2–N_2O	0.96×10^{-5}
CO_2–O_2	1.39×10^{-5}
CO_2–CH_4	1.53×10^{-5}
CO_2–H_2	5.50×10^{-5}
CO_2–air	1.38×10^{-5}
H_2–air	6.11×10^{-5}
O_2–air	1.78×10^{-5}
H_2O–air	2.20×10^{-5}

* For ideal gases, the diffusion coefficient at temperature T and pressure p may be estimated from $D_{AB}(p, T) \approx [D_{AB}(1 \text{ atm}, 0\text{ °C})](1/p)(T/273)^{3/2}$ where T is in K and p is in atmospheres. Abstracted from J. H. Perry, *Chemical Engineers Handbook*, 4th ed., New York: McGraw-Hill, 1963. Used with permission.

Substituting Eqs. 5.95 and 5.96 into 5.94 gives (for an isothermal, isobaric, binary mixture of ideal gases)

$$(\sigma_m)_{diff} = \rho D_{AB} R_A \left(\frac{dw_A}{dx}\right)^2 \Big/ w_A = \rho D_{BA} R_B \left(\frac{dw_B}{dx}\right)^2 \Big/ w_B$$

Then,

$$(\dot{S}_P)_{diff} = \rho D_{AB} R_A \int_{\mathcal{V}} \frac{1}{w_A}\left(\frac{dw_A}{dx}\right)^2 d\mathcal{V} \tag{5.97}$$

To continue this analysis further the mass fraction function, $w_A = w_A(x)$, must be known. This is illustrated in the following example problem.

Example 5.21 A chemical reaction at a solid wall is used to remove carbon dioxide (CO_2) from air as shown in the schematic below. The CO_2 must diffuse through a 2.0- stagnant gas mixture layer where its mass fraction varies linearly as

$$w_{CO_2} = (w^{\delta}_{CO_2} - w^{\circ}_{CO_2})(x/\delta) + w^{\circ}_{CO_2} \qquad \text{for } 0 \le x < \delta$$

and

$$w_{CO_2} = w^{\delta}_{CO_2} \qquad \text{for } x \ge \delta$$

Determine the entropy production rate per unit wall area due to the diffusion of CO_2 through the stagnant layer if the binary mixture of CO_2 and air is isothermal at 0 °C, isobaric at 1 atm pressure, and the gases are ideal.

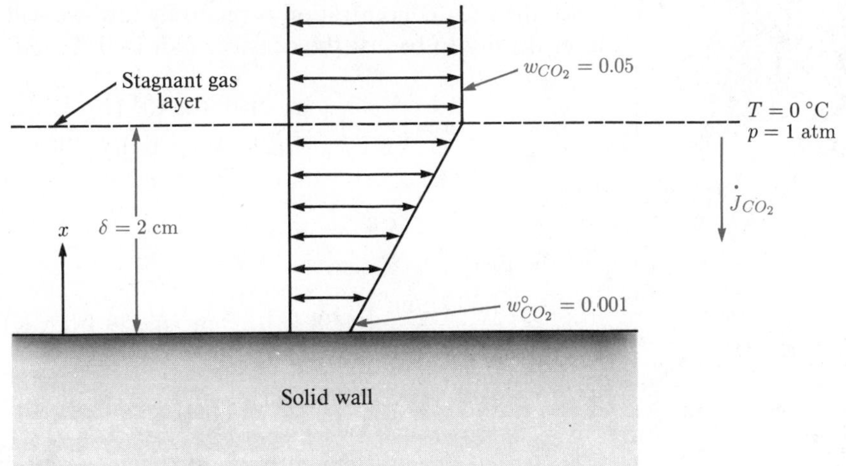

Solution From the linear mass fraction profile given above we find that

$$\frac{dw_{CO_2}}{dx} = (w^\delta_{CO_2} - w^\circ_{CO_2})/\delta$$

then, in the stagnant gas layer,

$$(\sigma_m)_{diff} = \frac{\rho(D_{CO_2\text{–}air})(R_{CO_2})[w^\delta_{CO_2} - w^\circ_{CO_2})/\delta]^2}{(w^\delta_{CO_2} - w^\circ_{CO_2})(x/\delta) + w^\circ_{CO_2}}$$

and from Eq. 5.97 we can determine the total entropy production rate as

$$(\dot{S}_P)_{diff} = \rho(D_{CO_2\text{–}air})(R_{CO_2}) \int_0^\delta (\sigma_m)_{diff}(A_{wall})\, dx$$

where we have used $d\mathcal{V} = (A_{wall})\, dx$. Substituting the expression for $(\sigma_m)_{diff}$ into this equation and carrying out the integration gives the entropy production rate per unit wall area as

$$(\dot{S}_P/A_{wall})_{diff} = (\rho/\delta)(D_{CO_2\text{–}air})(R_{CO_2})(w^\delta_{CO_2} - w^\circ_{CO_2}) \ln \frac{w^\delta_{CO_2}}{w^\circ_{CO_2}}$$

The data for this problem are

$$\delta = 0.02 \text{ m}$$

$$D_{CO_2\text{–}air} = 1.38 \times 10^{-5} \text{ m}^2/\text{s (from Table 5.1)}$$

$$R_{CO_2} = 189 \text{ J/(kg}\cdot\text{K)}$$

$$w^\delta_{CO_2} = 0.05$$

$$w^\circ_{CO_2} = 0.001$$

Since the CO_2 concentration is relatively low, we will take the mean stagnant layer density to be just the density of air at 0 °C and 1 atm pressure, or

$$\rho = \left(\frac{p}{RT}\right)_{\text{air}} = \frac{101.3 \times 10^3 \text{ N/m}^2}{[286 \text{ J/(kg·K)}](273 \text{ K})} = 1.30 \text{ kg/m}^3$$

Then,

$$(\dot{S}_P/A_{\text{wall}})_{\text{diff}}$$
$$= \left(\frac{1.30 \text{ kg/m}^3}{0.02 \text{ m}}\right)(1.38 \times 10^{-5} \text{ m}^2/\text{s})[189 \text{ J/(kg·K)}](0.05 - 0.001) \ln \frac{0.05}{0.001}$$
$$= 0.032 \text{ W/(m}^2\text{·K)}$$

The general open system entropy rate balance was given in Eq. 5.77 as

General open system entropy rate balance (SRB)

$$\int_\Sigma \left(\frac{\dot{q}}{T_b}\right)_{\text{act}} dA + \sum_{\text{inlet}} \dot{m}s - \sum_{\text{outlet}} \dot{m}s + \dot{S}_P = \dot{S}_{\text{system}} \qquad \textbf{(5.77)}$$

and when the system boundaries are isothermal this equation reduces to Eq. 5.78

Isothermal boundary open system entropy rate balance

$$\dot{S} = \left(\frac{\dot{Q}}{T_b}\right)_{\text{act}} + \sum_{\text{in}} \dot{m}s - \sum_{\text{out}} \dot{m}s + \dot{S}_p \qquad \textbf{(5.78)}$$

In each case the formula for the direct determination of the entropy production rate $\dot{S}_P$ is given by Eq. 5.79 as

$$\dot{S}_P = \int_V \sigma \, dV > 0 \qquad \textbf{(5.79)}$$

where σ is the total entropy production rate density (EPRD) for the system, given by

$$\sigma = \sigma_Q + (\sigma_W)_{\text{vis.}} + (\sigma_W)_{\text{elect.}} + (\sigma_m)_{\text{diff.}} + \cdots$$

whose individual formulae were given earlier in this chapter.[20]

20. In Section III of this chapter we assume that the processes of interest are truly irreversible, so that we will write $\dot{S}_P > 0$ rather than the less restrictive form $\dot{S}_P \geq 0$.

Since the use of Eq. 5.79 for the direct determination of $\dot{S}_P$ is often quite difficult, most of the example problems presented in this chapter will use the indirect entropy rate balance, Eq. 5.77, to determine $\dot{S}_P$. When this is done the SRB can only be used to generate values for $\dot{S}_P$, and nothing else. This is the major disadvantage of the indirect method, since if we could easily determine $\dot{S}_P$ from the auxiliary Eq. 5.79 we could then use the SRB to determine other important information about the system. However, the determination of $\dot{S}_P$ (by either method) is not a useless exercise. Entropy production rate values provide us with a measure of how well or how poorly a system is operating. Large $\dot{S}_P$ values may indicate excessive losses within a particular system or a particularly inefficient mode of operation. Some of the examples in this chapter will explore the possibility of reducing $\dot{S}_P$ values through alternative realistic processes which produce the same system operating goals. These analyses will lead to methods of increasing the overall system efficiency (and thus reduce operating costs) by using processes which dissipate less useful energy as "losses."

In Section III of Chapter 4 we introduced the modified energy balance (MEB) and the modified energy rate balance (MERB) so that we would not have to continually deal with the complex general open system first law formula. These formulae were designed to work only for steady state, steady flow, single-inlet, single-outlet systems, but the conditions were found to fit most of the applications we were interested in analyzing. When one or more of these four conditions did not exist in a particular problem, we carried out the analysis by reverting to the complete, accurate, general energy rate balance equation.

The general SRB given in Eq. 5.77 is not as mathematically complex as the general ERB given in Eq. 4.90, but we will still find it convenient to develop similar modified entropy balance and modified entropy rate balance formula. Therefore, we define the symbolism

MSB = modified entropy balance

MSRB = modified entropy rate balance

The MSB and MSRB formulae will require the four conditions used in the MEB and MERB formulae plus one more condition. In the SRB, the steady state condition requires that

Steady state

$$\dot{S}_{\text{system}} = \left(\frac{dS}{dt}\right)_{\text{system}} = 0 \tag{5.98}$$

and the steady flow condition requires that

Steady flow

$$\sum_{\text{inlet}} \dot{m} = \sum_{\text{outlet}} \dot{m} \tag{5.99}$$

and finally, the steady flow, single-inlet, single-outlet condition requires that

$$\sum_{\text{inlet}} \dot{m} = \sum_{\text{outlet}} \dot{m} = \dot{m} \tag{5.100}$$

In addition to these four conditions we add the fifth condition of *isothermal boundaries* at all points along the system boundary where heat transport of energy occurs. Under this condition the entropy transport term due to the heat transport of energy becomes

$$\int_{\Sigma} \left(\frac{\dot{q}}{T_b}\right)_{\text{act}} dA = \sum_{\Sigma} \left(\frac{\dot{Q}}{T_b}\right)_{\text{act}} = \frac{\dot{Q}}{T_b} \tag{5.101}$$

In this equation the simplified notation $\dot{Q}/T_b$ is used to describe the *net* (or total) value of the "actual" $\dot{Q}/T_b$ summed over the entire system boundary Σ. This simplification was also used in the EB and ERB equations where Q, W, $\dot{Q}$, and $\dot{W}$ were used to represent their net (or total) values (e.g., see Eq. 4.91). The "act" subscript and the summation sign have been dropped in the last term of Eq. 5.101 to simplify the notation, but they must always be considered to be present. Under these five restrictive conditions the general open system entropy rate balance of Eq. 5.77 becomes the *modified entropy rate balance* (MSRB) defined as

$$\frac{\dot{Q}}{T_b} + \dot{m}(s_{\text{in}} - s_{\text{out}}) + \dot{S}_P = 0 \tag{5.102}$$

Multiplying this equation through by dt and integrating over time from system state 1 to state 2 gives the open system *modified entropy balance* (MSB) equation as

$$\frac{{}_1Q_2}{T_b} + \int_1^2 \dot{m}(s_{\text{in}} - s_{\text{out}})\, dt + {}_1(S_P)_2 = 0 \tag{5.103}$$

Nozzles, Diffusers, and Throttles

In Section III of Chapter 4 we saw that nozzles, diffusers, and throttling devices are normally steady state, steady flow, single-inlet, single-outlet open systems with approximately constant surface temperature, and that they may or may not be adiabatic. Therefore, Eq. 5.102 can be applied to all three of these types of open systems. Solving Eq. 5.102 for $\dot{S}_P$ gives

1. for *adiabatic* nozzles, diffusers, and throttling devices,

$$\dot{S}_P = \dot{m}(s_{\text{out}} - s_{\text{in}}) > 0 \tag{5.104}$$

2. for *isothermal surface* nozzles, diffusers, and throttling devices

$$\dot{S}_P = \dot{m}(s_{out} - s_{in}) - \frac{\dot{Q}}{T_b} > 0 \tag{5.105}$$

where the second law condition that $\dot{S}_P > 0$ has been added.

If the fluid flowing through these systems is incompressible and has a constant specific heat c, then from Section I of this chapter we have

$$s_{out} - s_{in} = c \ln \frac{T_{out}}{T_{in}} \tag{5.33}$$

Equations 5.104 and 5.105 then become

$$\dot{S}_P \Big|_{\substack{\text{adiabatic} \\ \text{incompressible} \\ \text{fluid}}} = \dot{m}c \ln \frac{T_{out}}{T_{in}} > 0 \tag{5.106}$$

and

$$\dot{S}_P \Big|_{\substack{\text{incompressible} \\ \text{fluid}}} = \dot{m}c \ln \frac{T_{out}}{T_{in}} - \frac{\dot{Q}}{T_b} > 0 \tag{5.107}$$

Equation 5.106 shows us that the outlet temperature must always be greater than the inlet temperature for an insulated (adiabatic) open system with an incompressible fluid. This is because all the dissipation due to the irreversibilities within the system simply goes into increasing the temperature of an incompressible fluid.

Nozzles, diffusers, and throttling devices are all physically small (i.e., $Z_{out} \approx Z_{in}$) aergonic systems, so their modified energy rate balance becomes

$$\dot{Q} = \dot{m}\left(h_{out} - h_{in} + \frac{V_{out}^2 - V_{in}^2}{2g_c}\right) \tag{5.108}$$

and for constant specific heat incompressible fluids we have

$$h_{out} - h_{in} = c(T_{out} - T_{in}) + v(p_{out} - p_{in}) \tag{4.108}$$

Combining Eqs. 5.107, 5.108, and 4.108 gives the combined nonadiabatic first and second law relation for an incompressible fluid with a constant specific heat as

$$\dot{S}_P \Big|_{\substack{\text{incompressible} \\ \text{fluid}}} = \dot{m}\left[c \ln \frac{T_{out}}{T_{in}} - \frac{c(T_{out} - T_{in})}{T_b} - \frac{v(p_{out} - p_{in})}{T_b} - \frac{V_{out}^2 - V_{in}^2}{2g_c T_b}\right] \tag{5.109}$$

Notice that Eq. 5.109 is now written completely in terms of directly measurable physical quantities (m, c, T, v, p, and V).

Similarly, if the fluid flowing through these devices is an ideal gas with constant specific heats c_p and c_v, then from Section I of this chapter we have

$$s_{out} - s_{in} = c_v \ln \frac{T_{out}}{T_{in}} + R \ln \frac{v_{out}}{v_{in}} \tag{5.36}$$

$$= c_p \ln \frac{T_{out}}{T_{in}} - R \ln \frac{p_{out}}{p_{in}} \tag{5.37}$$

and from Chapter 4 we have

$$h_{out} - h_{in} = c_p(T_{out} - T_{in}) \tag{4.113}$$

Combining Eqs. 5.104 and 5.37 gives the adiabatic MSRB for an ideal gas with constant specific heats as

$$\dot{S}_P\Big|_{\substack{\text{adiabatic}\\ \text{ideal gas}}} = \dot{m}\left(c_p \ln \frac{T_{out}}{T_{in}} - R \ln \frac{p_{out}}{p_{in}}\right) > 0 \tag{5.110}$$

In the case of diffusers $p_{out} > p_{in}$ and Eq. 5.110 requires that $T_{out} > T_{in}$, as in the case of incompressible fluid flow. However, for nozzles and throttling devices $p_{out} < p_{in}$ and then T_{out} can be either greater or less than T_{in} depending on the value of the Joule-Thomson coefficient (see Eq. 4.123). Combining Eqs. 5.105, 5.108, 5.37, and 4.113 gives the combined nonadiabatic first and second law relation for an ideal gas with constant specific heats as

$$\dot{S}_P\Big|_{\text{ideal gas}} = \dot{m}\left(c_p \ln \frac{T_{out}}{T_{in}} - R \ln \frac{p_{out}}{p_{in}} - c_p \frac{T_{out} - T_{in}}{T_b} - \frac{V_{out}^2 - V_{in}^2}{2g_c T_b}\right) > 0 \tag{5.111}$$

Finally, if the fluid flowing through these devices is neither an incompressible fluid nor an ideal gas, then Eqs. 5.105 and 5.108 can still be combined and rearranged to give a combined non-adiabatic first and second law relation of the form

$$\dot{S}_P = -\frac{\dot{m}}{T_b}\left[(h_{out} - T_b s_{out}) - (h_{in} - T_b s_{in}) + \frac{V_{out}^2 - V_{in}^2}{2g_c}\right] > 0 \tag{5.112}$$

Example 5.22 Determine the rate of entropy production as 0.2 lbm/s of liquid water at 50 °F, 95 psia flows through the nozzle on the end of a garden hose and exits at 14.7 psia. The inlet and outlet diameters of the nozzle are 1.0 and 0.25 in, respectively. Assume that the flow through the nozzle is too fast to allow a significant heat transfer to occur.

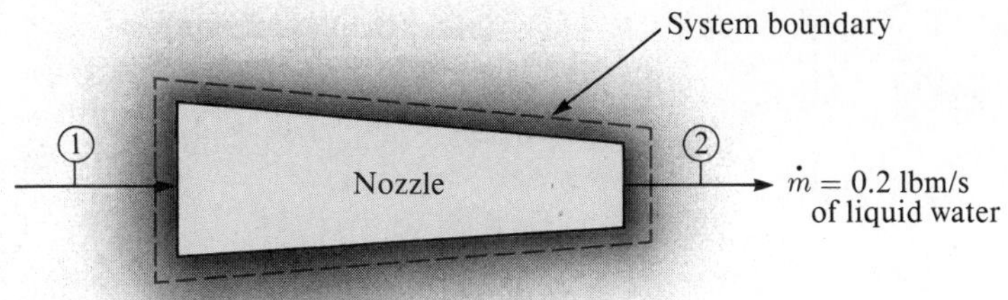

Solution

Station 1	$\xrightarrow[\text{process}]{\text{Nozzle}}$	Station 2
$p_1 = 95$ psia		$p_2 = 14.7$ psia
$T_1 = 50$ °F		

Unknown: $\dot{S}_P = ?$

The MERB for this system is

$$\underset{0}{\dot{Q}} + \underset{0}{\dot{W}} + \dot{m}[h_1 - h_2 + (V_1^2 - V_2^2)/2g_c + \underbrace{g(Z_1 - Z_2)/g_c}_{0}] = 0$$

Assuming liquid water is incompressible with a constant specific heat under these conditions and using the incompressible liquid auxiliary equation for enthalpy (Eq. 4.108) allows the MERB above to be written as

$$h_2 - h_1 = c(T_2 - T_1) + v(p_2 - p_1) = (V_1^2 - V_2^2)/2g_c$$

or

$$T_2 = T_1 + \frac{v}{c}(p_1 - p_2) - \frac{(V_2^2 - V_1^2)}{2cg_c}$$

Where $v = v_f$ (at 50 °F) = 0.01602 ft³/lbm (from Appendix C.1*a*). From the data given in the problem statement we can compute V_1 and V_2 as

$$V_1 = \frac{\dot{m}}{\rho A_1} = \frac{4\dot{m}v}{\pi D_1^2} = \frac{4(0.2\text{ lbm/s})(0.01602\text{ ft}^3/\text{lbm})(144\text{ in}^2/\text{ft}^2)}{\pi(1.0\text{ in})^2}$$
$$= 0.59\text{ ft/s}$$

and

$$V_2 = \frac{4\dot{m}v}{\pi D_2^2} = V_1\left(\frac{D_1}{D_2}\right)^2 = (0.59)\left(\frac{1.0}{0.25}\right)^2 = 9.4\text{ ft/s}$$

Then

$$T_2 = (460 + 50\ \text{R}) + (0.01602\ \text{ft}^3/\text{lbm})\left[\frac{(95 - 14.7\ \text{lbf/in}^2)(144\ \text{in}^2/\text{ft}^2)}{[1.0\ \text{Btu/(lbm}\cdot\text{R)}](778\ \text{ft}\cdot\text{lbf/Btu})}\right]$$

$$- [(9.4)^2 - (0.59)^2\ \text{ft}^2/\text{s}^2]$$

$$\div \{(2)[1.0\ \text{Btu/(lbm}\cdot\text{R)}][32.2\ \text{lbm}\cdot\text{ft/(lbf}\cdot\text{s}^2)](778\ \text{ft}\cdot\text{lbf/Btu})\}$$

$$= 510 + 0.24 - 0.002 = 510.2\ \text{R}$$

and using Eq. 5.106 gives

$$\dot{S}_P = \dot{m}c \ln \frac{T_2}{T_1} = (0.2\ \text{lbm/s})[1.0\ \text{Btu/(lbm}\cdot\text{R)}] \ln \frac{510.2}{510.0}$$

$$= [7.84 \times 10^{-5}\ \text{Btu/(s}\cdot\text{R)}](778\ \text{ft}\cdot\text{lbf/Btu}) = 0.061\ \text{ft}\cdot\text{lbf/(s}\cdot\text{R)}$$

Notice that the kinetic energy terms in the above example provided a negligible contribution to the exit temperature and that the vast majority of the entropy production resulted from the pressure loss across the nozzle. The increase in velocity across the nozzle as converted pressure energy does decrease the entropy production rate slightly (but only by less than 1% in this case). Therefore, this nozzle is quite inefficient at converting pressure energy into kinetic energy. Its efficiency could be improved, however, by making the nozzle outlet diameter smaller so that the outlet velocity was substantially increased.

Example 5.23 0.8 kg/s of argon flows at 93 m/s through an insulated diffuser from 97 kPa, 80 °C to 101.3 kPa. Assuming the argon to be an ideal gas with constant specific heats, determine the rate of entropy production within the diffuser.

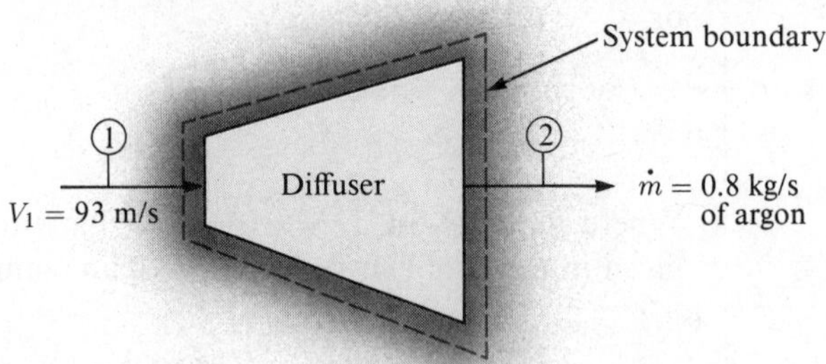

Solution

Station 1	$\xrightarrow[\text{process}]{\text{Diffuser}}$	Station 2
$p_1 = 97$ kPa		$p_2 = 101.3$ kPa
$T_1 = 80$ °C		

Unknown: $\dot{S}_P = ?$

The MERB for this system is

$$\dot{Q} + \dot{W} = 0 = \dot{m}\left(h_2 - h_1 + \frac{V_2^2 - V_1^2}{2g_c}\right)$$

Assuming $V_2 \approx 0$ and using the ideal gas auxiliary formula (Eq. 4.113) with data for argon from Appendix C.13*b* we find that

$$T_2 = T_1 + \frac{V_1^2}{2g_c c_p} = (80 + 273\text{ K}) + \frac{(93\text{ m/s})^2}{2(1)[523\text{ J/(kg}\cdot\text{K)}]}$$

$$= 353 + 8.27 = 361.27\text{ K}$$

Then Eq. 5.110 gives

$$\dot{S}_P = (0.8\text{ kg/s})\left[[523\text{ J/(kg}\cdot\text{K)}]\ln\frac{361.27}{353} - [208\text{ J/(kg}\cdot\text{K)}]\ln\frac{101.3}{97}\right]$$

$$= 2.47\text{ J/K}$$

In this example, both the pressure and the temperature of the gas increased as it passed through the diffuser.

Example 5.24 0.1 lbm/s of Refrigerant-12 is throttled across the expansion valve in a refrigeration unit. The R-12 enters the valve as a saturated liquid at 100 °F and exits at 20 °F with a quality of 53%. If the inlet and exit velocities are equal, determine

a) the entropy production rate inside the valve if the valve is *not* insulated and has an isothermal external surface temperature of 60 °F,

b) the entropy production rate inside the valve if it *is* insulated and assuming it has the same inlet conditions and exit temperature as stated above, and

c) the percent decrease in the entropy production rate of part a brought about by adding the insulation in part b.

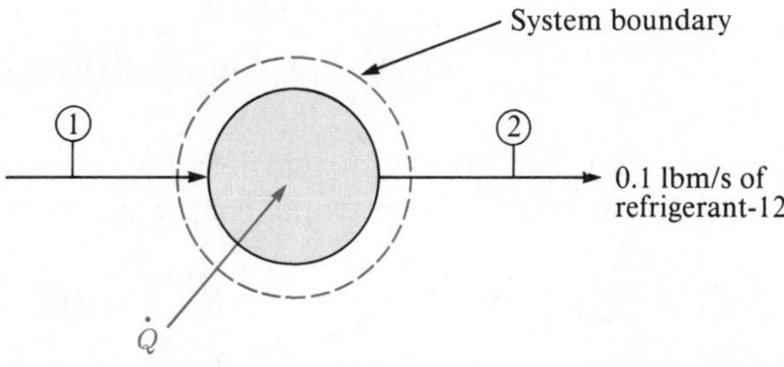

Solution Unknowns: $(\dot{S}_P)_{\text{uninsulated}}$, $(\dot{S}_P)_{\text{insulated}}$, and the % decrease in $\dot{S}_P$ due to the insulation.

Station 1 $\xrightarrow[\text{process}]{\text{Throttling}}$	**Station 2**
$x_1 = 0$	$x_2 = 0.53$ (only in part a)
$T_1 = 100\ °\text{F}$	$T_2 = 20\ °\text{F}$

a) The MERB for this aergonic device with negligible change in kinetic and potential energy is

$$\dot{Q} + 0 = \dot{m}(h_2 - h_1 + 0)$$

and from Appendix C.7*a* for R-12 we find

$$h_1 = h_f(100\ °\text{F}) = 31.100\ \text{Btu/lbm}$$

$$s_1 = s_f(100\ °\text{F}) = 0.06323\ \text{Btu/(lbm·R)}$$

and

$$h_2 = h_f(20\ °\text{F}) + x_2 h_{fg}(20\ °\text{F})$$
$$= 12.863 + (0.53)(66.522) = 48.120\ \text{Btu/lbm}$$

$$s_2 = s_f(20\ °\text{F}) + x_2 s_{fg}(20\ °\text{F})$$
$$= 0.02852 + (0.53)(0.13867) = 0.10202\ \text{Btu/(lbm·R)}$$

Then the MERB gives

$$\dot{Q} = (0.1\ \text{lbm/s})(48.120 - 31.100\ \text{Btu/lbm}) = 1.70\ \text{Btu/s}$$

and Eq. 5.105 gives

$$\dot{S}_P = (0.1\ \text{lbm/s})[0.10202 - 0.06323\ \text{Btu/(lbm·R)}] - \left(\frac{1.70\ \text{Btu/s}}{60 + 460\ \text{R}}\right) = 6.1 \times 10^{-4}\ \text{Btu/(s·R)}$$
$$= [6.1 \times 10^{-4}\ \text{Btu/(s·R)}](778\ \text{ft·lbf/Btu}) = 0.47\ \text{ft·lbf/(s·R)}$$

b) The MERB for this device as an adiabatic, aergonic, negligible change in kinetic and potential energy system is

$$0 + 0 = \dot{m}(h_2 - h_1 + 0)$$

or

$$h_2 = h_1$$

Now station 2 is fixed by the pair of properties

$$T_2 = 20\ ^\circ\text{F}$$

and $h_2 = h_1 = 31.100$ Btu/lbm. Consequently the quality at station 2 cannot be 53%, but is instead

$$x_2 = \frac{h_2 - h_{f2}}{h_{fg2}} = \frac{31.100 - 12.863}{66.522} = 0.2741 = 27.41\%$$

and then

$$s_2 = 0.02852 + 0.2741(0.13867) = 0.06653\ \text{Btu/(lbm}\cdot\text{R)}$$

Then, with $\dot{Q} = 0$, Eq. 5.105 gives

$$\begin{aligned}\dot{S}_P &= (0.1\ \text{lbm/s})[0.06653 - 0.06323\ \text{Btu/(lbm}\cdot\text{R)}]\\ &= [3.3 \times 10^{-4}\ \text{Btu/(s}\cdot\text{R)}](778\ \text{ft}\cdot\text{lbf/Btu})\\ &= 0.26\ \text{ft}\cdot\text{lbf/(s}\cdot\text{R)}\end{aligned}$$

c) The percentage decrease in $\dot{S}_P$ brought about by adding the insulation is

$$\frac{6.1 \times 10^{-4} - 3.3 \times 10^{-4}}{6.1 \times 10^{-4}} \times 100 = 46\%$$

Note that there was a substantial decrease in the entropy production rate of Example 5.24 due to simply insulating the valve. This resulted from the elimination of the entropy generated by the heat transfer present in the uninsulated valve.

Heat Exchangers

Heat exchangers were discussed briefly in the energy balance examples of Section III of Chapter 4. This section expands the earlier material on this subject by introducing some of the basic concepts of heat exchanger design and analysis. Heat exchangers are normally classified as either *parallel flow*, *counter flow*, or *cross flow*, as shown in Figure 5.11. If both fluids flow in the same direction it is said to be a parallel flow heat exchanger; if they flow in opposite directions, it is said to be a counter flow heat exchanger; and if they flow at right angles to each other it is said to be a cross flow heat exchanger.

The two most common types of heat exchangers are *shell and tube* and *plate and tube*. The simplest type of shell and tube heat exchanger is the double-pipe system shown in Figures 5.11*a* and *b*. Figure 5.11*c* illustrates a simple plate and tube geometry. The efficiency of a shell and tube heat exchanger can be improved

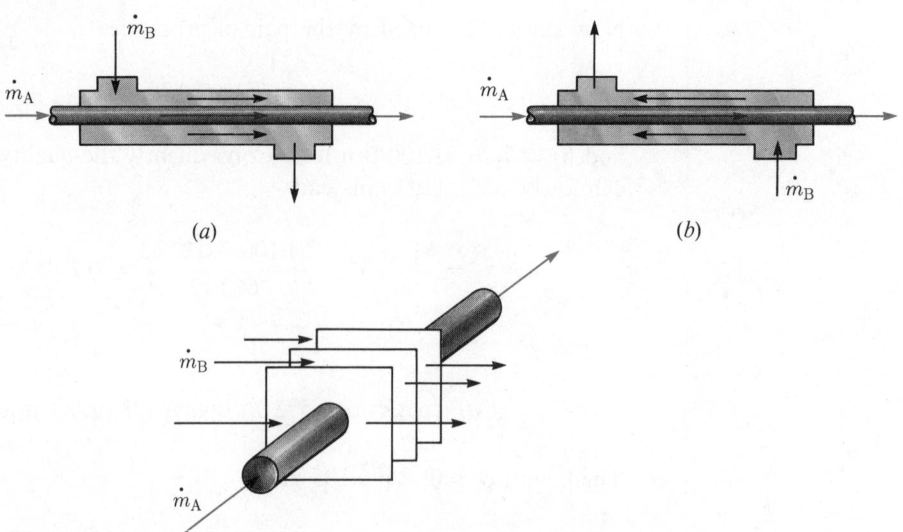

Figure 5.11 Single-tube, single-pass heat exchanger geometries: (*a*) parallel flow; (*b*) counter flow; (*c*) cross flow.

by using multiple tubes and multiple passes as shown in Figure 5.12. Figure 5.13 illustrates a typical commercial multiple tube heat exchanger.

The temperature profiles inside single-tube, single-pass heat exchangers are shown in Figure 5.14. In the parallel flow arrangement the outlet temperature of the cold flowstream can never exceed the outlet temperature of the hot flowstream. However, in the counter flow arrangement this situation can occur and consequently the required surface area to produce a given amount of heat transfer is less in the counter flow as compared to the parallel flow configuration.

In heat exchanger design, the basic formula used to determine the internal heat transfer rate is

$$\dot{Q}\Big|_{\substack{\text{heat}\\\text{exchanger}\\\text{(internal)}}} = UA(\Delta T)_{\text{LMTD}} \tag{5.113}$$

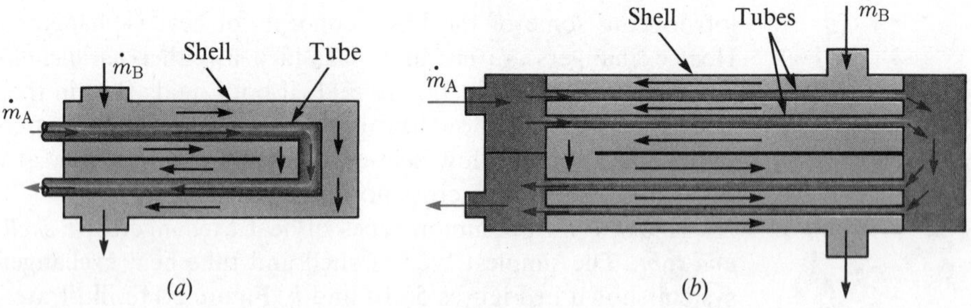

Figure 5.12 Multiple-tube, multiple-pass heat exchanger geometries: (*a*) Single tube, double pass, parallel flow; (*b*) double tube, double pass, counter flow.

Figure 5.13 A cutaway of a single-pass shell and tube heat exchanger. Photo courtesy Modine Manufacturing Company. Used with permission.

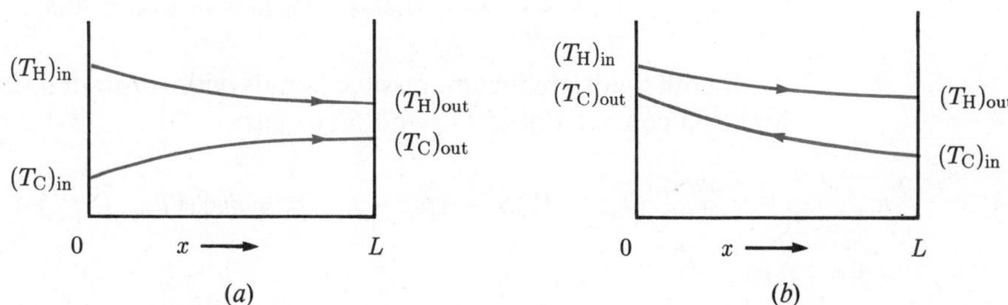

Figure 5.14 Temperature profiles inside single-tube, single-pass heat exchangers: (*a*) parallel flow; (*b*) counter flow.

Table 5.2 **Typical ranges for the overall heat transfer coefficient (U)**

Fluids used	Btu/(h·ft²·R)	W/(m²·K)
Water and		
Water	200–250	1140–1420
Gasoline	60–100	340–570
Fuel oil	15–25	85–140
Compressed air	10–30	57–170
Steam and		
Water (liquid)	250–400	1420–2270
Fuel oil (light)	60–90	340–510
Fuel oil (heavy)	15–25	85–140
Compressed air	5–50	28–280
Kerosene and		
Water	25–50	140–280
Oil	20–35	110–200

where U is the overall heat transfer coefficient (see Table 5.2), A is the total internal heat transfer area, and $(\Delta T)_{\text{LMTD}}$ is the *log mean temperature difference*, defined for a single-tube, single-pass heat exchanger as

$$(\Delta T)_{\text{LMTD}} = \frac{(T_{\text{H}} - T_{\text{C}})|_{x=L} - (T_{\text{H}} - T_{\text{C}})|_{x=0}}{\ln[T_{\text{H}} - T_{\text{C}})|_{x=L}/(T_{\text{H}} - T_{\text{C}})|_{x=0}]} \tag{5.114}$$

Heat exchangers are normally two fluid aergonic devices with dual inlets and dual outlets. If the entire heat exchanger is taken as the system, it is normally adiabatic (the main heat transfer takes place inside the heat exchanger, not across its external boundary) and the MERB for negligible change in kinetic and potential energy reduces to (see Eq. 4.126)

$$\dot{m}_{\text{H}}(h_{\text{in}} - h_{\text{out}})_{\text{H}} = \dot{m}_{\text{C}}(h_{\text{out}} - h_{\text{in}})_{\text{C}} \tag{5.115}$$

and the MSRB for this system yields

$$\dot{S}_{\text{P}} = \dot{m}_{\text{H}}(s_{\text{out}} - s_{\text{in}})_{\text{H}} + \dot{m}_{\text{C}}(s_{\text{out}} - s_{\text{in}})_{\text{C}} \tag{5.116}$$

If both fluids are incompressible liquids with constant specific heats, Eqs. 4.108 and 5.33 convert Eqs. 5.115 and 5.116 into

$$\dot{m}_{\text{H}}[c(T_{\text{in}} - T_{\text{out}}) + v(p_{\text{in}} - p_{\text{out}})]_{\text{H}} = \dot{m}_{\text{C}}[c(T_{\text{out}} - T_{\text{in}}) + v(p_{\text{out}} - p_{\text{in}})]_{\text{C}}$$

and

$$\dot{S}_{\text{P}} = \dot{m}_{\text{H}}c_{\text{H}} \ln\left(\frac{T_{\text{out}}}{T_{\text{in}}}\right)_{\text{H}} + \dot{m}_{\text{C}}c_{\text{C}} \ln\left(\frac{T_{\text{out}}}{T_{\text{in}}}\right)_{\text{C}} \tag{5.117}$$

And if both fluids are ideal gases with constant specific heats, then Eqs. 4.113 and 5.37 give

$$\dot{m}_H(c_p)_H(T_{in} - T_{out})_H = \dot{m}_C(c_p)_C(T_{out} - T_{in})_C$$

and

$$\dot{S}_P = \dot{m}_H\left[(c_p)_H \ln\left(\frac{T_{out}}{T_{in}}\right)_H - R_H \ln\left(\frac{p_{out}}{p_{in}}\right)_H\right] + \dot{m}_C\left[(c_p)_C \ln\left(\frac{T_{out}}{T_{in}}\right)_C - R_C \ln\left(\frac{p_{out}}{p_{in}}\right)_C\right] \quad \textbf{(5.118)}$$

Example 5.25 A single-tube, single-pass heat exchanger is used to cool a compressed air flow of 0.2 kg/s from 90 to 75 °C. The cooling fluid is liquid water that enters the heat exchanger at 20 °C and leaves at 40 °C. If the overall heat transfer coefficient is 140 W/(m^2·K) and all flowstreams have negligible pressure drop, determine the required heat exchanger area and the entropy production rate for

a) parallel flow, and
b) counter flow.

Assume the compressed air behaves as an ideal gas with constant specific heats.

Solution The heat exchanger area, from Eq. 5.113, is

$$A = \frac{\dot{Q}}{U(\Delta T)_{LMTD}}$$

where the log mean temperature difference has a different value for the parallel and for the counter flow arrangements. From Eq. 5.114 we have

a) Parallel flow

$$(\Delta T)_{LMTD} = \frac{(75 - 40) - (90 - 20)}{\ln \dfrac{75 - 40}{90 - 20}} = 50.5 \text{ K}$$

b) Counter flow

$$(\Delta T)_{LMTD} = \frac{(75 - 20) - (90 - 40)}{\ln \dfrac{75 - 20}{90 - 40}} = 52.5 \text{ K}$$

For each case the heat transfer rate $\dot{Q}$ is obtained by applying the MERB to only the air flowstream. Then, using the ideal gas assumption and the fact that the value of $\dot{Q}$ must be positive for use in Eq. 5.113,

$$\dot{Q} = |\dot{m}_{air}(h_{out} - h_{in})_{air}| = |\dot{m}_{air}(c_p)_{air}(T_{out} - T_{in})_{air}|$$
$$= |(0.2 \text{ kg/s})[1004 \text{ J/(kg·k)}](75 - 90 \text{ K})| = |-3012 \text{ J/s}| = 3012 \text{ J/s}$$

and then the corresponding heat exchanger areas are

$$A_{\substack{\text{parallel}\\\text{flow}}} = \frac{3012\ \text{J/s}}{[140\ \text{W/(m}^2\cdot\text{K)}](50.5\ \text{K})} = 0.426\ \text{m}^2$$

and

$$A_{\substack{\text{counter}\\\text{flow}}} = \frac{3012\ \text{J/s}}{[140\ \text{W/(m}^2\cdot\text{K)}](52.5\ \text{K})} = 0.410\ \text{m}^2$$

Also, in this case, one of the heat transfer fluids is an ideal gas and one is an incompressible liquid. Combining Eqs. 5.33 and 5.37 into Eq. 5.116 with the condition $(p_{in})_{air} = (p_{out})_{air}$ (i.e., a negligible pressure drop gives

$$\dot{S}_P = \dot{m}_{air}(c_p)_{air} \ln\left(\frac{T_{out}}{T_{in}}\right)_{air} + \dot{m}_{water}c_{water} \ln\left(\frac{T_{out}}{T_{in}}\right)_{water}$$

Now, $\dot{m}_{air}$ is given and $\dot{m}_{water}$ can be found from the MERB by combining Eqs. 4.108 with $(p_{in})_{water} = (p_{out})_{water}$ and Eq. 4.113 with Eq. 5.115 as

$$\dot{m}_{water} = \dot{m}_{air}\{[(c_p)_{air}/c_{water}](T_{in} - T_{out})_{air}/(T_{out} - T_{in})_{water}\}$$

Our calculations begin with this last equation,

$$\dot{m}_{water} = (0.2\ \text{kg/s})\left[\frac{1.004\ \text{kJ/(kg}\cdot\text{K)}}{4.186\ \text{kJ/(kg}\cdot\text{K)}}\right]\left[\frac{(90 - 75\ \text{K})}{(40 - 20\ \text{K})}\right] = 0.036\ \text{kg/s}$$

Then the entropy production rate equation gives

$$\dot{S}_P = (0.2\ \text{kg/s})[1004\ \text{J/(kg}\cdot\text{K)}] \ln \frac{75 + 273}{90 + 273}$$

$$+ (0.036\ \text{kg/s})[4186\ \text{J/(kg}\cdot\text{K)}] \ln \frac{40 + 273}{20 + 273} = 1.48\ \text{J/K}$$

Notice that the entropy production rate in the previous example was independent of whether the heat exchanger was parallel or counter flow since the same amount of heat transfer occurred in each case. We would see a difference if we had included the effect of the viscous pressure drop in the entropy production rate equation. The counter flow arrangement requires less heat transfer area and would therefore produce a smaller pressure drop than would the parallel flow arrangement. Then the counter flow heat exchanger would have a smaller entropy production rate than would a parallel flow heat exchanger with the same $\dot{Q}$, $U(\Delta T)_H$, and $(\Delta T)_C$ values.

Mixing

A *mixer* is not necessarily adiabatic nor aergonic and it normally has two or more inlet flowstreams but only one outlet flowstream. Often mixers are used simply to mix different chemical species to produce a final product. When all the entering fluids have the same composition but are at different temperatures, then the mixer becomes a type of simple heat exchanger.

Consider the dual-inlet, single-exit mixer shown in Figure 5.15. The steady state, steady flow ERB (neglecting any change in kinetic and potential energy) is

$$\dot{Q} + \dot{W} + \dot{m}_1 h_1 + \dot{m}_2 h_2 - \dot{m}_3 h_3 = 0$$

and the similar MRB is

$$\dot{m}_1 + \dot{m}_2 - \dot{m}_3 = 0$$

Combining these two equations and introducing the mass fraction y as

$$\dot{m}_1/\dot{m}_3 = y \tag{5.119}$$

or

$$\dot{m}_2/\dot{m}_3 = 1 - y$$

where y is always bound by $0 \leq y \leq 1$, gives

$$\dot{Q} + \dot{W} + \dot{m}_3[y(h_1 - h_2) + (h_2 - h_3)] = 0$$

Similarly, the appropriate SRB for an isothermal system boundary is

$$(\dot{S}_P)_{\text{mixing}} = \dot{m}_3 s_3 - \dot{m}_1 s_1 - \dot{m}_2 s_2 - \frac{\dot{Q}}{T_b}$$

$$= \dot{m}_3[y(s_2 - s_1) + (s_3 - s_2)] - \frac{\dot{Q}}{T_b}$$

Many mixing systems use the inlet flowstreams to induce mixing and thus tend to be isobaric (i.e., $p_1 = p_2 = p_3$).[21] To simplify the above results somewhat, consider the adiabatic, aergonic, isobaric mixing of two flowstreams of the same material, but at different temperatures. Then the above formulae reduce to

$$y(h_1 - h_2) + (h_2 - h_3) = 0 \tag{5.120}$$

and

$$(\dot{S}_P)_{\text{mixing}} = \dot{m}_3[y(s_2 - s_1) + (s_3 - s_2)] > 0 \tag{5.121}$$

21. Isobaric mixing also requires negligible viscous friction losses.

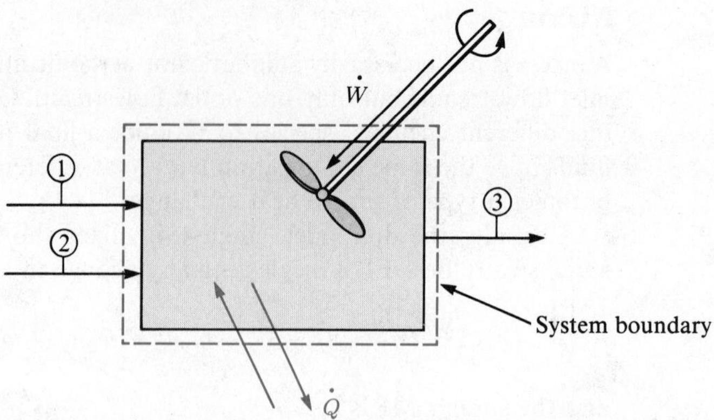

Figure 5.15 A simple mixing system.

If these materials are identical incompressible liquids with negligible mixer pressure loss or identical ideal gases with constant specific heats, then Eqs. 4.108 and 5.33 or Eqs. 4.113 and 5.37 can be used to give

$$y(T_1 - T_2) + T_2 - T_3 = 0 \tag{5.122}$$

and

$$(\dot{S}_P)_{\text{mixing}} = \dot{m}_3 c \left(y \ln \frac{T_2}{T_1} + \ln \frac{T_3}{T_2} \right) \tag{5.123}$$

where $c = c_p$ in the case of ideal gases. Combining these two equations by eliminating T_3 gives

$$(\dot{S}_P)_{\text{mixing}} = \dot{m}_3 c \ln \left\{ \left[1 + y\left(\frac{T_1}{T_2} - 1 \right) \right] \left(\frac{T_1}{T_2} \right)^{-y} \right\} \tag{5.124}$$

For a given T_1/T_2 ratio, there is a critical mass fraction (y_c) which will produce a *maximum* rate of entropy production.[22] The critical mass fraction can be found from Eq. 5.124 by setting $d\dot{S}_P/dy = 0$ and solving for $y = y_c$. The result is

$$y_c = \frac{(1 - T_1/T_2) + \ln(T_1/T_2)}{(1 - T_1/T_2)\ln(T_1/T_2)} \tag{5.125}$$

which gives

$$(\dot{S}_P)_{\substack{\text{mixing} \\ \text{(max)}}} = \dot{m}_3 c \ln \left\{ \left[1 + y_c\left(\frac{T_1}{T_2} - 1 \right) \right] \left(\frac{T_1}{T_2} \right)^{-y_c} \right\} \tag{5.126}$$

22. It is a maximum because $d^2\dot{S}_P/dy^2 < 0$ when evaluated at $y = y_c$. Also, the minimum value of $\dot{S}_P$ is always zero, which occurs here when $T_1 = T_2$.

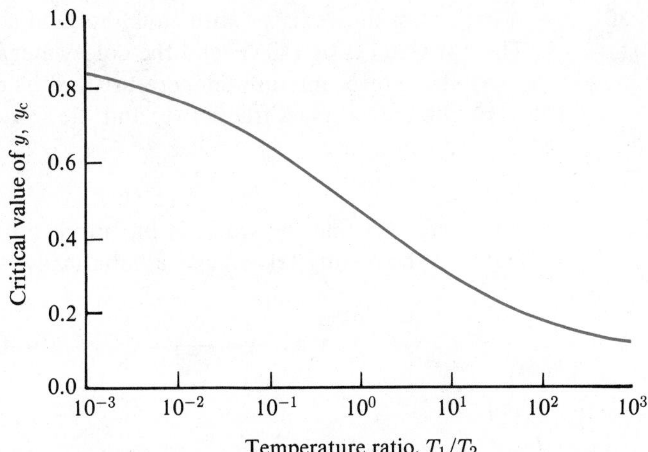

Figure 5.16 The critical mass fraction required to produce a maximum entropy production rate in adiabatic, aergonic, isobaric (i.e., viscousless) mixing of identical incompressible liquids or ideal gases with constant specific heats (note that $y_c = 1.0$ at $T_1/T_2 = 0$, and $y_c \to 0$ as $T_1/T_2 \to \infty$).

Figure 5.16 shows the variation in y_c with the absolute temperature ratio T_1/T_2, and Figure 5.17 shows the resulting $(\dot{S}_P)_{\text{mixing (max)}}$ vs. T_1/T_2 relation.

Note that y_c is limited by its definition to be less than or equal to 1 in Figure 5.16, and that in Figure 5.17 it is impossible to have a mixer whose entropy production rate falls in the region *above* the curve shown.

Finally, the analysis of the adiabatic, aergonic, isobaric (i.e., viscousless) mixing of identical ideal gases with constant specific heats will produce formulae identical to Eqs. 5.124, 5.125, and 5.126 except c will be replaced with the constant pressure specific heat c_p.

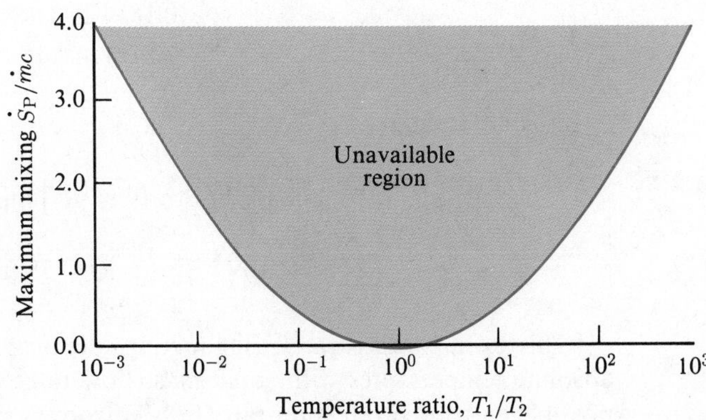

Figure 5.17 The maximum entropy production rate vs. temperature ratio for a simple mixing process.

Example 5.26 A bathroom shower is set with equal hot and cold mass flow rates of 0.3 lbm/s. The hot water is at 140 °F and the cold water is 50 °F. Determine

a) the shower mixture temperature and its entropy production rate, and

b) the critical mass fraction y_c and the value of the maximum entropy production rate.

Solution Assume the water is incompressible with a constant specific heat and that the mixing takes place adiabatically, aergonically, and isobarically.

$$\textbf{a)}\quad y = \frac{\dot{m}_H}{\dot{m}_M} = 0.5 \qquad \text{(from Eq. 5.119)}$$

and

$$\frac{T_1}{T_2} = \frac{T_H}{T_C} = \frac{140 + 460}{50 + 460} = 1.18$$

Then from Eq. 5.122 we have

$$\begin{aligned} T_3 = T_M &= T_C + y(T_H - T_C) \\ &= 50 + 0.5(140 - 50) = 95\ °\text{F} \end{aligned}$$

and from Eq. 5.124 we have (using $\dot{m}_3 = \dot{m}_M = \dot{m}_H + \dot{m}_C = 0.6$ lbm/s)

$$\begin{aligned} (\dot{S}_P)_{\text{mixing}} &= (0.6\ \text{lbm/s})[1.0\ \text{Btu/(lbm}\cdot\text{R)}]\ \ln[(1 + 0.5(0.18))(1.18)^{-0.5}] \\ &= [2.051 \times 10^{-3}\ \text{Btu/(s}\cdot\text{R)}](778\ \text{ft}\cdot\text{lbf/Btu}) \\ &= 1.596\ \text{ft}\cdot\text{lbf/(s}\cdot\text{R)} \end{aligned}$$

b) From Eq. 5.125 we have

$$y_c = \frac{-0.18 + \ln 1.18}{(-0.18)\ln 1.18} = 0.486$$

Then, from Eq. 5.126,

$$\begin{aligned} (\dot{S}_P)_{\substack{\text{mixing} \\ \text{(max)}}} &= (0.6\ \text{lbm/s})[1.0\ \text{Btu/(lbm}\cdot\text{R)}]\ \ln[(1 + 0.486(0.18))(1.18)^{-0.486} \\ &= [2.056 \times 10^{-3}\ \text{Btu/(s}\cdot\text{R)}](778\ \text{ft}\cdot\text{lbf/Btu}) = 1.600\ \text{ft}\cdot\text{lbf/(s}\cdot\text{R)} \end{aligned}$$

This example illustrates that mixing identical materials at almost the same absolute temperatures with equal mass flow rates produces nearly the maximum possible entropy production rate. Less entropy is produced if the mixing fraction is either $y < 0.5$ or $y > 0.5$ when $T_1 \approx T_2$.

Shaft Work Machines and Availability

A shaft work machine was defined in Section III of Chapter 4 as any device that has work (or power) input or output through a rotating or reciprocating shaft. These devices are normally steady state, steady flow, single-inlet, single-outlet systems and their resulting MERB is

$$\dot{Q} + \dot{W} = \dot{m}[h_2 - h_1 + (V_2^2 - V_1^2)/2g_c + (g/g_c)(Z_2 - Z_1)] \quad \textbf{(4.132)}$$

and assuming an isothermal system boundary the MSRB is

$$\dot{Q}/T_b + \dot{m}(s_1 - s_2) + \dot{S}_P = 0$$

or

$$\dot{Q} = \dot{m}T_b(s_2 - s_1) - T_b\dot{S}_P$$

Using this expression for $\dot{Q}$ in the above MERB and solving for $\dot{W}$ produces

$$\dot{W} = \dot{m}[(h_2 - T_b s_2) - (h_1 - T_b s_1) + (V_2^2 - V_1^2)/2g_c + (g/g_c)(Z_2 - Z_1)] + T_b\dot{S}_P \quad \textbf{(5.127)}$$

Shaft work machines that *produce* work are normally surrounded by an environment that is at a lower energy level than the working fluid inside the machine. If we denote the properties of the machine's working fluid evaluated at the pressure and temperature of the surroundings with a subscript "o," then we can express the amount of energy in the machine's working fluid which is available to do work in terms of a thermodynamic *availability function A* as

$$A = H - T_o S - (H_o - T_o S_o) + m(V^2/2g_c + gZ/g_c)$$

and

$$a = A/m = (h - T_o s) - (h_o - T_o s_o) + V^2/2g_c + gZ/g_c$$
$$= (h - h_o) - T_o(s - s_o) + V^2/2g_c + gZ/g_c \quad \textbf{(5.128)}$$

where a is called the *specific availability function*, and where we have set $V_o = Z_o = 0$.[23] If the system boundary is now chosen so that it is at the environmental temperature, i.e., $T_b = T_o$, then Eq. 5.127 can be written in terms of the specific availability function a as

$$\dot{W}_{\text{actual}} = \dot{m}(a_2 - a_1) + T_o\dot{S}_P \quad \textbf{(5.129)}$$

23. Although the concept of available energy has been discussed in the thermodynamic literature since the time of Thomson, it was not formalized into an availability function until 1941 by Joseph Keenan (1900–1977). Note that when the kinetic and potential energy terms are negligible, then $A = G - G_{\min}$, where $G = H - TS$ is the Gibbs function which is introduced in Chapter 6.

For a reversible process, $\dot{S}_P = 0$, and Eq. 5.129 gives

$$\dot{W}_{rev} = \dot{m}(a_2 - a_1) \tag{5.130}$$

and since, from Section I of this chapter,

$$\dot{W}_{actual} = \dot{W}_{rev} + \dot{W}_{irr}$$

then by comparing these last three equations we see that

$$\dot{W}_{irr} = T_o\dot{S}_P$$

The work transport energy efficiency η_w was defined in Chapter 4 for a work producing system as

$$\eta_W = \frac{\dot{W}_{act}}{\dot{W}_{rev}} \tag{4.72}$$

and inserting Eqs. 5.129 and 5.130 gives[24]

$$\eta_W = 1 + \frac{T_o\dot{S}_P}{\dot{m}(a_2 - a_1)} \tag{5.131}$$

Example 5.27 Determine the maximum (reversible) power that could be produced by expanding 0.5 kg/s of steam at 8.0 MPa, 300 °C to a saturated vapor at 100 °C. Neglect any kinetic and potential energy effects. The environment is at 20 °C and standard atmospheric pressure.

Solution For this open system we have the following general data:

Station 1	$\xrightarrow{\text{Expansion}}$	Station 2	Environment
$p_1 = 8.0$ MPa		$x_2 = 1.0$	$T = 20$ °C
$T_1 = 300$ °C		$T_2 = 100$ °C	$p = 101.3$ kPa

The states at both stations and the environment are thus fixed, and we can then calculate the specific availability functions at those conditions from Eq. 5.128 as

$$\begin{aligned} a_1 &= h_1 - h_o - T_o(s_1 - s_o) \\ &= 2785.0 - 83.9 - (20 + 273)(5.7914 - 0.2965) = 1091.1 \text{ kJ/kg} \end{aligned}$$

24. Note that for work-producing machines (engines, turbines, etc.) a_2 will be less than a_1 so that η_W will be less than 1.0.

and

$$a_2 = h_2 - h_o - T_o(s_2 - s_o)$$
$$= 2676.0 - 83.9 - (20 + 273)(7.3557 - 0.2965) = 523.8 \text{ kJ/kg}$$

Then

$$\dot{W}_{rev} = \dot{m}(a_2 - a_1) = (0.5 \text{ kg/s})(523.8 - 1091.1 \text{ kJ/kg}) = -283.7 \text{ kW}$$

In these equations we have used $h_o = h_f(20\ °\text{C})$ and $s_o = s_f(20\ °\text{C})$. However, this had no effect on our final answer since both h_o and s_o cancel out in the final formula,

$$\dot{W}_{rev} = \dot{m}(a_2 - a_1) = \dot{m}[h_2 - h_1 - T_o(s_2 - s_1)]$$

The availability function does not provide any new information for either the energy or the entropy balance equations. It simply provides a way of looking at energy flows by referencing them to a standard state, the local environment. It is possible to show that the maximum power output from a work-producing machine is obtained when its discharge is at the local environmental pressure and temperature. Therefore, any discharge flow that is not at these conditions wastes available energy. However, from a practical point of view the economics of the free market makes it impossible to design and manufacture machines whose exhausts are always in equilibrium with their local environment.

Chapter Five Section IV Advanced Topics

The following three sections use the second law in analyzing several advanced topics in modern engineering thermodynamics. They are included here to provide the student with an exposure to a second law analysis of complex systems typical of modern engineering technology.

Temperature Separation

A *vortex tube* is a thermal or temperature separation device for gases. The input is a single stream of pressurized gas and the vortex tube separates this flow into a high-temperature outlet flowstream and a low-temperature outlet flowstream. Figure 5.18 illustrates the operation of this simple device.

The vortex tube contains no moving parts other than the gas. The inlet flow enters the separation chamber tangentially, and in the swirling operation the gaseous core along the chamber centerline becomes extremely cold while the gas near the chamber wall becomes quite hot. The core gas exits through one tube while the wall gas exits through the other, thus producing flowstream temperature (or thermal) separation.

This remarkable phenomenon was discovered by Georges Joseph Ranque and was first described in a French patent in 1931.[25] In 1933 Ranque presented a paper to the Societe Francaise de Physique on this device, and nothing more was heard about it until 1945 when a vortex tube was found by an American and British investigation team at the end of World War II in the laboratory of Rudolph Hilsch at the University of Erlangen, Germany. Hilsch had begun research on the

25. In 1932 he applied for a U.S. patent, which was awarded March 27, 1934 (U.S. Patent number 1,952,281).

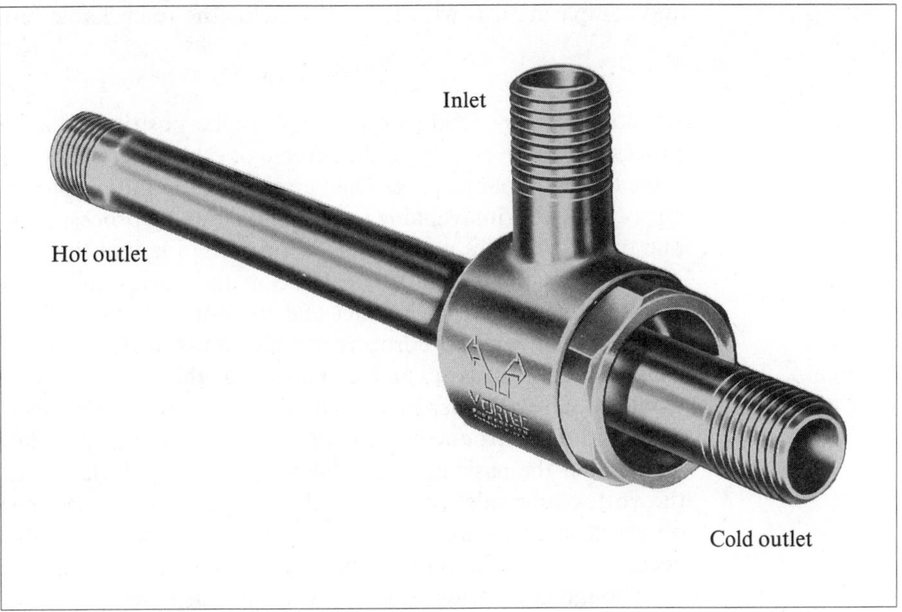

Figure 5.18 A typical vortex tube. Courtesy of Vortec Corporation. Used with permission.

vortex tube in 1944 after reading Ranque's paper, and he published his results in Germany in 1946 and in the United States in 1947. Since then, interest in the vortex tube has remained high, and it is now frequently used in industry for inexpensive localized cooling applications. It is not entirely clear why the inlet stream separates into hot and cold regions inside the vortex chamber. It is currently thought that acoustical "streaming" produces the temperature separation effect. However, this effect may actually turn out to be another example of a *coupled phenomena* like the thermoelectric, photoelectric, and piezoelectric phenomena discussed briefly in Section I of Chapter 4.

Applying the ERB to the adiabatic and aergonic vortex tube shown in Figure 5.18 and assuming ideal gas behavior with constant specific heats yields

$$y(T_1 - T_2) + T_2 - T_3 = 0$$

in which we have introduced the mass fraction y defined by Eq. 5.119. Note that this result is exactly the same as Eq. 5.122, which was developed for the mixing operation. Thus, the first law of thermodynamics is insensitive as to whether the fluids are being mixed or separated. It yields the same result in either case.

However, application of the SRB to the same system produces

$$(\dot{S}_P)_{\text{vortex tube}} = \dot{m}_3[y(s_1 - s_2) + s_2 - s_3] > 0 \tag{5.132}$$

and comparing this with Eq. 5.121 yields the remarkable result that

$$(\dot{S}_P)_{\text{vortex tube}} = -(\dot{S}_P)_{\text{mixing}} \tag{5.133}$$

yet both entropy production rates must be positive! This means that these two processes cannot simply be the reverse of each other. They cannot both follow the same thermodynamic path. The vortex tube separation phenomena must occur by a process that is unavailable to the simple mixing process and vice versa, otherwise one of these devices would violate the second law of thermodynamics.

To produce temperature separation the vortex tube must have a significant pressure drop between the inlet and the outlet flowstreams. It will not work isobarically. This pressure drop is not necessary in the mixing operation. Mixing is usually nearly isobaric, and emulation of the vortex tube separation operation would require a higher mixer outlet pressure than inlet pressure. This cannot be done without introducing heat or work energy transport into the system, which would alter the basic nature of the simple mixing device. Therefore, it is clear that the vortex tube inlet pressure is the source of the energy needed to produce the observed temperature separation. It is also the source of the entropy generation needed to allow Eq. 5.133 to be valid, as shown in Example 5.28 below.

Though the vortex tube is not an isobaric device, its two exit pressures are essentially equal (i.e., $p_1 \approx p_2$). Combining this condition with Eq. 5.37 for ideal gases, and substituting the result into Eq. 5.132 gives

$$(\dot{S}_P)_{\text{vortex tube}} = \dot{m}_3 \left[c_p \ln \frac{(T_1/T_2)^y}{1 + y(T_1/T_2 - 1)} + R \ln \frac{p_3}{p_2} \right] \tag{5.134}$$

Example 5.28 The Vortec Corporation manufactures a vortex tube to provide hot and cold air from a standard compressed air system. For an equally split mass flow rate ($y = 0.5$) the table below lists the hot and cold outlet temperatures for various inlet pressures when the inlet temperature is 70 °F. Assuming the exit pressure is atmospheric, determine the entropy production rate per unit mass flow rate for each pressure shown and plot the results.

Inlet pressure		Outlet temperatures		
(psig)	(psia)	T_{Hot}(°F)	T_{Cold}(°F)	$\frac{T_H(°F) + 460}{T_C(°F) + 460}$
0	14.7	70.0	70.0	1.000
20	34.7	119.0	19.5	1.209
40	54.7	141.0	−3.0	1.315
60	74.7	150.0	−14.0	1.368
80	94.7	156.0	−22.0	1.406
100	114.7	161.0	−29.0	1.441
120	134.7	164.0	−34.0	1.465
140	154.7	166.0	−39.0	1.487

Solution Using Eq. 5.134 for air with $R = 0.0685$ Btu/(lbm·R), $c_p =$ 0.24 Btu/(lbm·R), and $y = 0.5$ to calculate $\dot{S}_P/\dot{m}_3$ gives the following results. At 20 psig = 34.7 psia,

$$(\dot{S}_P/\dot{m}_3)_{\substack{\text{vortex}\\ \text{tube}}} = [0.24 \text{ Btu/(lbm}\cdot\text{R)}] \ln \frac{(1.209)^{0.5}}{1 + 0.5(0.209)}$$

$$+ [0.0685 \text{ Btu/(lbm}\cdot\text{R)}] \ln \frac{34.7}{14.7}$$

$$= -0.0011 + 0.0588 = 0.0577 \text{ Btu/(lbm}\cdot\text{R)}$$

Notice that the first term (which corresponds to isobaric separation) in this calculation is negative while the second term resulting from the pressure loss is positive and dominant. Thus, if the vortex tube were required to be isobaric it could not work because to do so would violate the second law of thermodynamics. However, isobaric mixing is possible because then the lead term in this equation would be positive and the second term would be zero. The remaining results are

Inlet pressure psig	T_1/T_2	$\dot{S}_P/\dot{m}_3$ Btu/(lbm·R)
0	1.000	0.0000
20	1.209	0.0578
40	1.315	0.0878
60	1.368	0.1084
80	1.406	0.1241
100	1.441	0.1367
120	1.465	0.1474
140	1.487	0.1565

These values are plotted below.

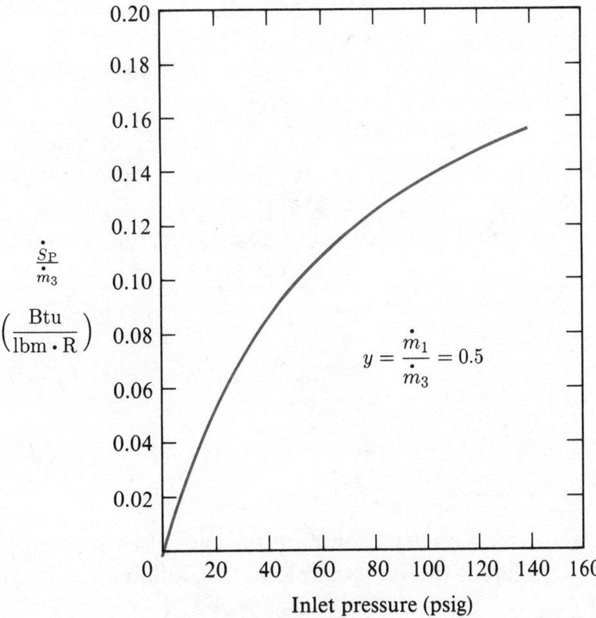

Hydrodynamic Flow Systems

A variety of hydrodynamic flow situations can be effectively analyzed with the entropy rate balance. Consider a steady state, steady flow, single-inlet, single-outlet system. The MERB for this system using the definition of enthalpy, $h = u + pv$, and the definition of density, $\rho = 1/v$, can be written as

$$\begin{aligned}\dot{Q} + \dot{W} &= \dot{m}[u_2 - u_1 + (p/\rho)_2 - (p/\rho)_1 \\ &\quad + (V_2^2 - V_1^2)/2g_c + (g/g_c)(Z_2 - Z_1)] \\ &= \dot{m}\{u_2 - u_1 - (g/g_c)[{}_1(h_L)_2]\}\end{aligned}$$

where, using $\gamma = \rho g$ (the specific weight),

$${}_1(h_L)_2 = (pg_c/\gamma)_1 - (pg_c/\gamma)_2 + (V_1^2 - V_2^2)/2g + Z_1 - Z_2 \qquad \textbf{(5.135)}$$

is the *head loss* between the inlet station 1 and the exit station 2. In fluid mechanics texts Eq. 5.135 is known as the Bernoulli equation, named after the Swiss mathematician and hydrodynamist Daniel Bernoulli (1700–1782). The MSRB for this system is

$$\dot{S}_P = \dot{m}(s_2 - s_1) - \dot{Q}/T_b$$

If the flowing fluid is a constant specific heat incompressible liquid, then

$$\rho_1 = \rho_2 = \text{constant}$$

$$u_2 - u_1 = c(T_2 - T_1)$$

$$s_2 - s_1 = c \ln \frac{T_2}{T_1}$$

and if it is a constant specific heat ideal gas, then

$$\rho = p/(RT) = 1/v$$

$$u_2 - u_1 = c_v(T_2 - T_1)$$

$$s_2 - s_1 = c_p \ln \frac{T_2}{T_1} - R \ln \frac{p_2}{p_1}$$

Now let's compare the rate of entropy production for two cases (i.e., two different thermodynamic paths), adiabatic flow and isothermal flow.

Case 1: SS, SF, SI/SO, aergonic, adiabatic flow.[26]

a) Incompressible, constant specific heat liquids.

In this case the MERB gives

$$T_2 = T_1 + g[{}_1(h_L)_2]/(cg_c)$$

and the MSRB gives

$$(\dot{S}_P)\Big|_{\substack{\text{incomp.}\\ \text{liquid.}\\ \text{(adiabatic)}}} = \dot{m}c \ln\{1 + g[{}_1(h_L)_2]/(cg_c T_1)\} \tag{5.136}$$

b) Ideal gases with constant specific heats.

In this case the MERB gives

$$T_2 = T_1 + g[{}_1(h_L)_2]/(c_v g_c)$$

and the MSRB gives

$$(\dot{S}_P)\Big|_{\substack{\text{ideal}\\ \text{gas}\\ \text{(adiabatic)}}} = \dot{m}c_p \ln[1 + g[{}_1(h_L)_2]/(c_v g_c T_1)] - \dot{m}R \ln \frac{p_2}{p_1} \tag{5.137}$$

Case 2: SS, SF, SI/SO aergonic, isothermal flow.

a) Incompressible, constant specific heat liquids.

In this case the MERB gives

$$\dot{Q} = -\dot{m}g[{}_1(h_L)_2]/g_c$$

and the MSRB gives

$$(\dot{S}_P)\Big|_{\substack{\text{incomp.}\\ \text{liquid}\\ \text{(isothermal)}}} = \dot{m}g[{}_1(h_L)_2]/(T_b g_c) \tag{5.138}$$

b) Ideal gases with constant specific heats.

In this case the MERB again gives

$$\dot{Q} = -\dot{m}g[{}_1(h_L)_2]/g_c$$

---

26. Recall that these terms mean that we are assuming that the flow is steady state (SS) and steady flow (SF), that the flow has a single inlet and a single outlet (SI/SO), and that there is no work (aergonic) or heat transfer (adiabatic).

and the MSRB gives

$$(\dot{S}_{\text{P}})\Big|_{\substack{\text{ideal}\\ \text{gas}\\ \text{(isothermal)}}} = \dot{m}g[{}_1(h_{\text{L}})_2]/(T_{\text{b}}g_{\text{c}}) - \dot{m}R \ln \frac{p_2}{p_1} \tag{5.139}$$

The question is, which process, adiabatic or isothermal, is the most efficient by producing less entropy. For the incompressible liquids we must compare Eqs. 5.136 and 5.138. Using a series expansion for the logarithm we find that for all $x > 0$, $\ln(1 + x) < x$, so that for $T_{\text{b}} = T_1$, we have

$$c \ln\{1 + g[{}_1(h_{\text{L}})_2]/(cg_{\text{c}}T_1)\} < g[{}_1(h_{\text{L}})_2]/(T_1 g_{\text{c}})$$

Table 5.3 Hydraulic flow systems[a]

System	Heat Loss Formula
Flow in a straight pipe 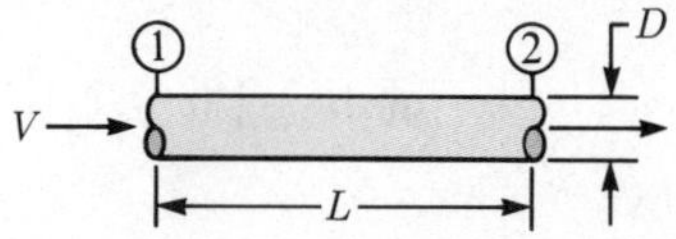	${}_1(h_L)_2 = f(L/D)(V^2/2g)$, where f is the Darcy-Weisbach friction factor.
Flow through valves, fittings, etc. ("minor losses") 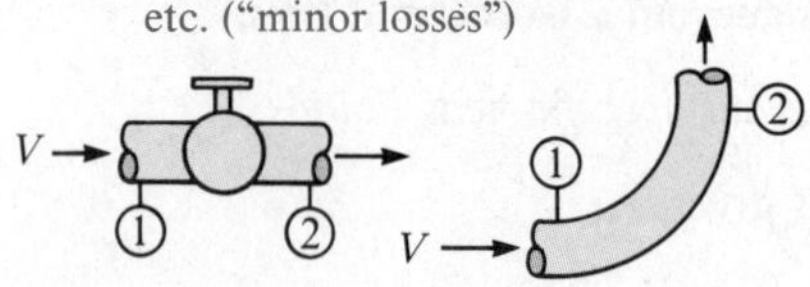	${}_1(h_L)_2 = K_{\text{M}}(V^2/2g)$, where K_{M} is the minor loss coefficient.
Flow through sudden contractions or expansions 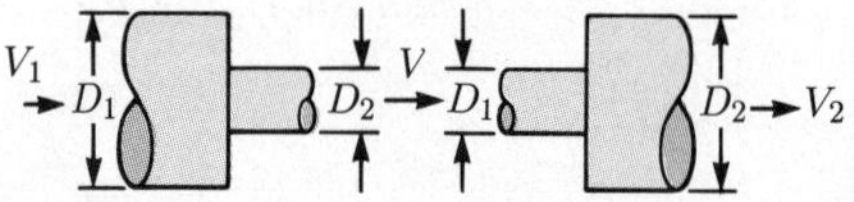	$[{}_1(h_L)_2]_{\text{contraction}} = K_{\text{C}}(V^2/2g)$, where K_{C} is the contraction coefficient and V is the largest velocity (see sketch). Also $[{}_1(h_L)_2]_{\text{Expansion}} = (1 - D_1^2/D_2^2)^2(V^2/2g)$.
Flow through a hydraulic jump 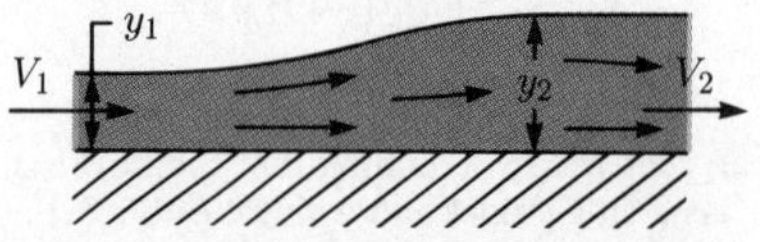	${}_1(h_L)_2 = (y_2 - y_1)^3/(4y_1y_2)$, where $y_2 - y_1$ is the jump height.

[a] Values for the coefficients f, K_{M}, and K_{C} can be found in standard fluid mechanics textbooks.

and consequently

$$(\dot{S}_P)\Big|_{\substack{\text{incomp.}\\\text{liquid}\\\text{(adiabatic)}}} < (\dot{S}_P)\Big|_{\substack{\text{incomp.}\\\text{liquid}\\\text{(isothermal)}}}$$

Similarly, for the ideal gases we compare Eqs. 5.137 and 5.139 and again find that

$$(\dot{S}_P)\Big|_{\substack{\text{ideal}\\\text{gas}\\\text{(adiabatic)}}} < (\dot{S}_P)\Big|_{\substack{\text{ideal}\\\text{gas}\\\text{(isothermal)}}}$$

In both of these cases the adiabatic process produces less entropy. This will always be true in this type of comparison because an adiabatic system eliminates the entropy production due to heat transfer across the system boudary.

Combining the MERB and the MSRB equations for any type of material produces a general formula for the entropy production rate inside a steady state, steady flow, single-inlet, single-outlet system with an isothermal boundary as

$$\dot{S}_P = \dot{m}\{s_2 - s_1 + [(g/g_c)[{}_1(h_L)_2] - u_2 + u_1]/T_b\} \quad \textbf{(5.140)}$$

Table 5.3 shows typical head loss formulations for a few common hydrodynamic flow situations. With these formulae the entropy production rates can be calculated for many different hydraulic or pneumatic flow systems.

The hydraulic jump is a very effective phenomenon for dissipating energy. It commonly appears at the end of chutes or spillways to dissipate the kinetic energy of the flow. It is also an effective mixing process due to the violent dissipative agitation that takes place. The following example illustrates the entropy production rate in a hydraulic jump.

Example 5.29

500 lbm/s of water at 50 °F flows down a spillway onto a horizontal floor. A hydraulic jump 1.8 ft high appears at the bottom of the spillway. The jump has an inlet velocity of 8.0 ft/s and an inlet height of 1.0 ft. Determine the energy dissipation rate and entropy production rate.

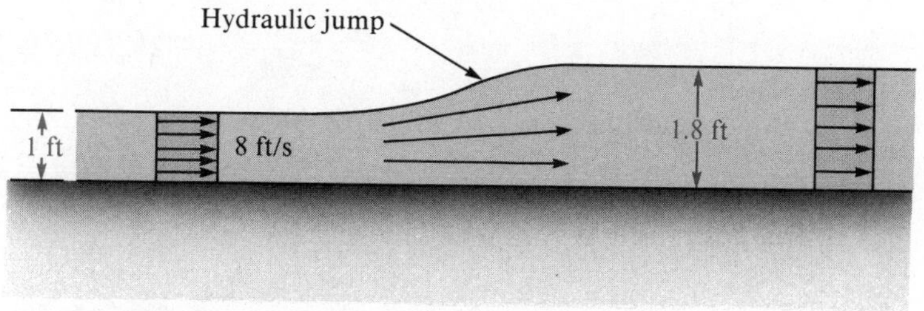

Solution From the formula in Table 5.3 we get

$${}_1(h_L)_2 = (1.8 - 1.0)^3/(4(1.0)(1.8)) = 0.0711\text{ ft}$$

and

$$\dot{m}(g/g_c)[_1(h_L)_2] = (500\ \text{lbm/s})\{(32.2\ \text{ft/s}^2)/[32.2\ \text{lbm}\cdot\text{ft}/(\text{lbf}\cdot\text{s}^2)]\}(0.0711\ \text{ft})$$
$$= (35.55\ \text{ft}\cdot\text{lbf/s})/(778\ \text{ft}\cdot\text{lbf/Btu}) = 0.0457\ \text{Btu/s}$$

Assuming the flow to be incompressible and adiabatic, the entropy production rate is given by Eq. 5.132 as

$$\dot{S}_P = (500\ \text{lbm/s})[1.0\ \text{Btu}/(\text{lbm}\cdot\text{R})] \times \ln\left[1 + \frac{(32.2\ \text{ft/s}^2)(0.0711\ \text{ft})}{\left(1.0\dfrac{\text{Btu}}{\text{lbm}\cdot\text{R}}\right)\left(32.2\dfrac{\text{lbm}\cdot\text{ft}}{\text{lbf}\cdot\text{s}^2}\right)(50 + 460\ \text{R})}\right]$$
$$= 0.0697\ \text{Btu}/(\text{s}\cdot\text{R})$$

The next example illustrates the use of the more complex direct method of determining the entropy production rate in a simple laminar hydrodynamic flow situation.

Example 5.30 The velocity profile in the steady isothermal laminar flow of an incompressible Newtonian fluid in a horizontal circular tube of radius R is given by

$$V = V_m[1 - (x/R)^2]$$

where V_m is the maximum (i.e., centerline) velocity of the fluid, and x is the radial coordinate measured from the centerline of the tube.

Determine the rate of entropy production due to laminar viscous losses in water at 20 °C flowing in a 2.5-cm-diameter pipe with a centerline velocity of 0.5 m/s. The viscosity of the water is 10.1×10^{-3} kg/(m·s) and the length of the pipe is 10 m.

Solution Here we will use Eq. 5.72 for the viscous dissipation of pumping work. By differentiating the velocity formula given above we get

$$\frac{dV}{dx} = -2V_m(x/R^2)$$

and then

$$(\sigma_W)_{vis} = \frac{\mu}{T}\left(\frac{dV}{dx}\right)^2 = \frac{4\mu V_m^2 x^2}{R^4 T}$$

Now

$$(\dot{S}_P)_{\substack{W\\vis}} = \int_{\Psi} (\sigma_W)_{vis}\, d\Psi$$

and for the differential volume element $d\Psi$ we will use the volume of an annulus of thickness dx, or $d\Psi = 2\pi L x\, dx$

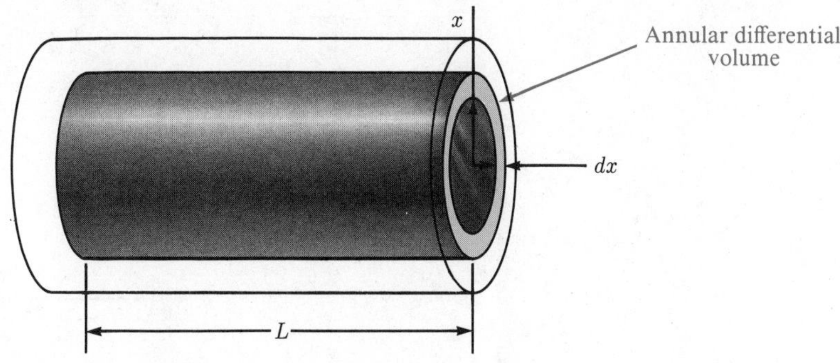

Then Eq. 5.72 gives

$$(\dot{S}_P)_{\substack{W\\vis}} = \frac{8\pi\mu L V_m^2}{R^4 T}\int_0^R x^3\,dx = \frac{2\pi\mu L V_m^2}{T}$$

For this problem,

$$\mu = 10.1 \times 10^{-3}\ \text{kg/(m}\cdot\text{s)}$$

$$L = 10\ \text{m}$$

$$V_m = 0.5\ \text{m/s}$$

$$T = 20\ ^\circ\text{C} = 293\ \text{K}$$

then

$$(\dot{S}_P)_{\substack{W\\wis}} = \frac{2\pi[10.1 \times 10^{-3}\ \text{kg/(m}\cdot\text{s)}](10\ \text{m})(0.5\ \text{m/s})^2}{293\ \text{K}}$$

$$= 5.4 \times 10^{-4}\ \text{W/K}$$

In the above example we again have a very low entropy production rate. This is due, in this case, to the fact that laminar flow is a very energy efficient type of flow. Turbulent flow (which will occur spontaneously here at higher flow velocities) is much more dissipative and consequently is a much less energy efficient flow.

Unsteady State Processes

In Section III of Chapter 4 we analyzed the energy transport requirements in the emptying and the filling of a rigid container. In this section we perform an entropy analysis of the filling of a rigid container and determine whether it is more efficient to fill it adiabatically or isothermally.

The ERB analysis of the adiabatic aergonic system shown in Figure 5.19 was done in Section III of Chapter 4. The result was

$$u_2 = h_{in} \tag{4.142}$$

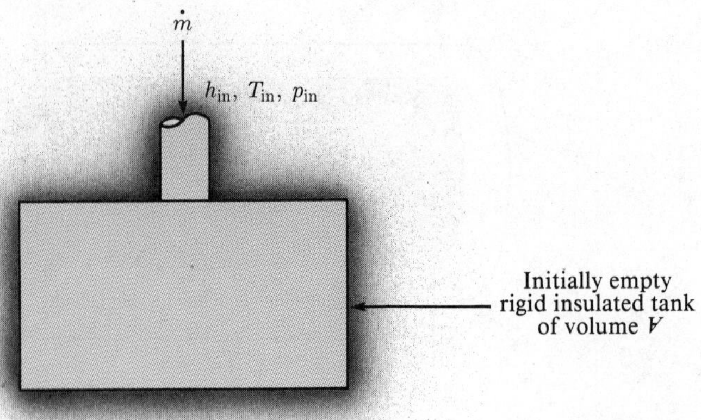

Figure 5.19 The filling of an insulated rigid container.

and in the case of an incompressible, constant specific heat liquid this meant that the final temperature T_2 was

$$T_2 = T_{in} + (v/c)p_{in} \tag{4.143}$$

and for an ideal gas with constant specific heats it meant that

$$T_2 = (c_p/c_v)T_{in} = kT_{in} \tag{4.144}$$

The entropy rate balance for this unsteady state system is

$$\dot{S} = \frac{dS}{dt} = \underbrace{\frac{\dot{Q}}{T_b}}_{0 \text{ (insulated)}} + \dot{m}s_{in} + \dot{S}_P$$

Integrating this equation from its initial empty state 1 to its final filled state 2 with s_{in} equal to a constant and then solving for the entropy production gives

$${}_1(S_P)_2 = S_2 - S_1 - (m_2 - m_1)s_{in} = m_2 s_2 - m_1 s_1 - (m_2 - m_1)s_{in}$$

Now, for simplicity, assume that the container was initially evacuated, then $m_1 = 0$ and

$${}_1(S_P)_2 = m_2(s_2 - s_{in}) \tag{5.141}$$

Then Eqs. 5.33, 5.37, and 5.141 give

$${}_1(S_P)_2\Big|_{\substack{\text{incomp.}\\ \text{liquid}\\ \text{(adiabatic)}}} = m_2 c \ln\frac{T_2}{T_{in}} = m_2 c \ln\left[1 + \frac{(pv)_{in}}{cT_{in}}\right] \tag{5.142}$$

and

$$ {}_1(S_P)_2\Big|_{\substack{\text{ideal}\\ \text{gas}\\ \text{(adiabatic)}}} = m_2 c_p \ln \frac{T_2}{T_{in}} - m_2 R \ln \frac{p_2}{p_{in}} = m_2 c_p \ln k \tag{5.143} $$

where, for the ideal gas case, $m_2 = p_2 \text{V}_2/(RT_2) = p_2 \text{V}/(kRT_{in})$, where V is the volume of the container, and where we have used $p_2 = p_{in}$.

A similar ERB on the same system except now uninsulated and kept isothermal at $T_1 = T_{in} = T_2$ gives

$$ \dot{Q} + \dot{m}_{in} h_{in} = \frac{d}{dt}(\text{mu}) $$

and multiplying this equation by dt and integrating gives

$$ {}_1Q_2 + (m_2 - m_1) h_{in} = m_2 u_2 - m_1 u_1 $$

again setting $m_1 = 0$ for an initially evacuated container produces

$$ u_2 = h_{in} + \frac{{}_1Q_2}{m_2} = u_{in} + (pv)_{in} + \frac{{}_1Q_2}{m_2} \tag{5.144} $$

For an incompressible isothermal liquid this reduces to

$$ u_2 - u_{in} = c(T_2 - T_{in}) = (pv)_{in} + \frac{{}_1Q_2}{m_2} = 0 $$

or

$$ {}_1Q_2 = -m_2 (pv)_{in} \tag{5.145} $$

and for an isothermal ideal gas it becomes

$$ {}_1Q_2 = -m_2 R T_{in} = -m_2 c_v T_{in}(k - 1) \tag{5.146} $$

The integrated entropy rate balance for this system with both s_{in} and T_b constant is

$$ {}_1(S_P)_2 = m_2 s_2 - m_1 s_1 - (m_2 - m_1) s_{in} - \frac{{}_1Q_2}{T_b} $$

and when $m_1 = 0$ this becomes

$$ {}_1(S_P)_2 = m_2(s_2 - s_{in}) - \frac{{}_1Q_2}{T_b} \tag{5.147} $$

For an isothermal incompressible liquid with $T_2 = T_{in} = T_b = T$, Eqs. 5.33, 5.145, and 5.147 give

$$ {}_1(S_P)_2\Big|_{\substack{\text{incomp.}\\ \text{liquid}\\ \text{(isothermal)}}} = m_2(pv)_{in}/T \tag{5.148} $$

and for an isothermal ideal gas with $p_2 = p_{in}$ and $T_2 = T_{in} = T_b = T$,

$$ {}_1(S_P)_2\Big|_{\substack{\text{ideal}\\ \text{gas}\\ \text{(isothermal)}}} = m_2c_v(k-1) = m_2R = p_2V/T \tag{5.149} $$

where $R = c_p - c_v = c_v(c_p/c_v - 1) = c_v(k-1)$ and $m_2 = p_2V/(RT)$.

Now, comparing Eqs. 5.142 and 5.148 for filling the container with the same amount of an incompressible liquid (i.e., m_2 is the same in each case) we see that since $\ln(1 + x) < x$ for all $x > 0$, then

$$ {}_1(S_P)_2\Big|_{\substack{\text{incomp.}\\ \text{liquid}\\ \text{(adiabatic)}}} < {}_1(S_P)_2\Big|_{\substack{\text{incomp.}\\ \text{liquid}\\ \text{(isothermal)}}} \quad \text{(for adding the same amount of mass in each case)} \tag{5.150} $$

but upon comparing Eqs. 5.143 and 5.149 for ideal gases we find that we cannot add the same amount of mass in each case because

$$ (m_2)\Big|_{\substack{\text{adiabatic}\\ \text{filling}}} = p_2V/(RT_2) = p_2V/(kRT_{in}) = (m_2)/k\Big|_{\substack{\text{isothermal}\\ \text{filling}}} \tag{5.151} $$

But since

$$ k\left(\frac{R}{c_p}\right) = \frac{c_p - c_v}{c_v} = k - 1 $$

and also since the series expansion for the logarithm of k for $0 < k < 2$ is

$$ \ln k = (k-1) - (k-1)^2/2 + (k-1)^3/3 - \cdots $$

then clearly $kR/c_p > \ln k$, which produces the following result when the tanks are filled to the same pressure (but not with the same amount of mass),

$$ {}_1(S_P)_2\Big|_{\substack{\text{ideal}\\ \text{gas}\\ \text{(adiabatic)}}} < {}_1(S_P)_2\Big|_{\substack{\text{ideal}\\ \text{gas}\\ \text{(isothermal)}}} \tag{5.152} $$

In the dissipative hydraulic flows studied earlier in this chapter we found that less entropy was produced in both incompressible and ideal gas systems if the flows were carried out adiabatically as opposed to isothermally. The analysis above shows that this is also true in the filling of a rigid vessel. Note, however, that these two filling processes will not normally produce the same final system state.[27] A complete entropy production analysis would have to include any additional processes required to reduce both systems to the same final state (e.g., see Problem 193 at the end of this chapter).

Example 5.31 A 3.0-ft^3 rigid container is filled with oxygen entering at 70 °F to a final pressure of 2000 psia. Assuming the container is initially evacuated and that the oxygen behaves as an ideal gas with constant specific heats, determine the amount of entropy produced when the container is filled

a) adiabatically by insulating it, and
b) isothermally by submerging it in a water bath at 70 °F while filling.

Solution From Appendix C.13*a* we find for oxygen $c_p = 0.219$ Btu/(lbm·R), $R = 48.29$ ft·lbf/(lbm·R), $k = 1.39$. The final temperature after filling adiabatically is given by Eq. 4.144 as

$$T_2 = kT_{\text{in}} = 1.39(70 + 460\text{ R}) = 736.7\text{ R} = 276.7\text{ °F}$$

The final mass of oxygen in the container can be found from the ideal gas equation of state as

$$(m_2)\Big|_{\substack{\text{isothermal}\\\text{filling}}} = \frac{p_2 V_2}{RT_2} = \frac{(2000\text{ lbf/in}^2)(144\text{ in}^2/\text{ft}^2)(3.0\text{ ft}^3)}{[48.29\text{ ft}\cdot\text{lbf/(lbm}\cdot\text{R)}](70 + 460\text{ R})} = 33.76\text{ lbm}$$

and

$$(m_2)\Big|_{\substack{\text{adiabatic}\\\text{filling}}} = (m_2)/k\Big|_{\substack{\text{isothermal}\\\text{filling}}} = (33.76\text{ lbm})/1.39 = 24.29\text{ lbm}$$

a) From Eq. 5.143 for an adiabatic filling operation we have

$$\begin{aligned}({}_1(S_P)_2)_{\text{adiabatic}} &= m_2 c_p \ln k \\ &= (24.29\text{ lbm})[0.219\text{ Btu/(lbm}\cdot\text{R)}]\ln(1.39) \\ &= 1.752\text{ Btu/R}\end{aligned}$$

27. For example, adiabatic filling will clearly produce a higher final temperature than will isothermal filling when starting from the same initial temperature.

b) From Eq. 5.149 for an isothermal filling operation we have

$$({}_1(S_P)_2)_{\text{isothermal}} = m_2 R$$
$$= (33.76 \text{ lbm}) \frac{48.29 \text{ ft}\cdot\text{lbf/(lbm}\cdot\text{R)}}{778 \text{ ft}\cdot\text{lbf/Btu}}$$
$$= 2.095 \text{ Btu/R}$$

which is about 20% more than the entropy produced in part a.

Equations 5.143, 5.149, and 5.151 can be combined to give

$$\left[\frac{({}_1(S_P)_2)_{\text{isothermal}}}{({}_1(S_P)_2)_{\text{adiabatic}}}\right]_{\substack{\text{ideal}\\\text{gas}}} = \frac{k-1}{\ln k} \tag{5.153}$$

which is greater than 1.0 for $k > 1.0$. This relation is plotted in Figure 5.20 for $1 \le k \le 2$. However, the specific entropy production ratio on a per unit mass of charge basis (i.e., as ${}_1(S_P)_2/m_2 = {}_1(s_P)_2$) is

$$\left[\frac{({}_1(s_P)_2)_{\text{isothermal}}}{({}_1(s_P)_2)_{\text{adiabatic}}}\right]_{\substack{\text{ideal}\\\text{gas}}} = \frac{k-1}{k \ln k} \tag{5.154}$$

which is less than 1.0 for $k > 1.0$ because the two processes do not take on the same total charge of gas (see Eq. 5.151).

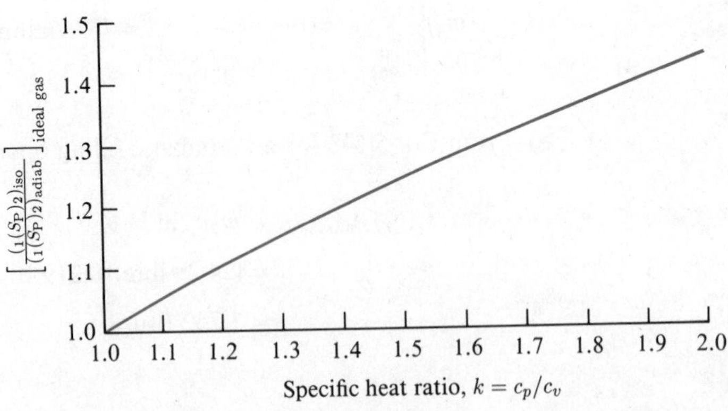

Figure 5.20 Entropy production ratio for filling an initially evacuated container with an ideal gas.

Summary

In this chapter we have dealt with the fundamentals of the second law of thermodynamics for nonequilibrium systems. This law introduced the new thermodynamic property *entropy* which is usually *not* conserved in any real process. The second law of thermodynamics states that entropy must always be *produced* in any irreversible process; however, a positive entropy production does not mean that the net system entropy must necessarily increase because entropy may be transported out of a system faster than it is produced within the system, therefore *the entropy level of the entire system can either increase or decrease in any real process.*

In Section II of this chapter we investigated closed system applications of the second law of thermodynamics for both reversible and irreversible processes. In so doing we have expanded the first law examples given in Section II of Chapter 4 to include an entropy balance analysis. Since entropy production is a direct consequence of system losses that lead to diminished operating efficiency, many of the examples in this chapter focused on determining the entropy production or its rate to gain further insight into the causes of system inefficiency. This was done by using either the auxiliary entropy production equations (the direct method) or an appropriate entropy balance equation (the indirect method).

In Sections III and IV of this chapter we used the second law of thermodynamics in the analysis of open systems. We used the entropy balance to determine the entropy production rates for a variety of common engineering devices (nozzles, diffusers, throttles, heat exchangers, etc.). We also looked at how different processes that achieve the same end states affect the amount of entropy produced by the system during those processes. This allows us to choose the process or method of changing the state that will be the least dissipative and consequently will be the most efficient. Determining processes that minimize the entropy production will produce economic and productivity rewards to the user.

We also introduced a new thermodynamic property, availability, which is an effective way of referencing the system energy level to a local environmental base.

Selected References

Bejan, A. *Entropy Generation Through Heat and Fluid Flow.* New York: Wiley, 1982.

Carnot, S. *Reflections on the Motive Power of Fire* (*and other papers on the Second Law of Thermodynamics by E. Clapeyron and R. Clausius*), E. Mendoza (Ed.). New York: Dover, 1960.

Chi, S. W. *Heat Pipe Theory and Practice: A Sourcebook.* New York: Hemisphere, 1976.

DeGroot, S. R. *Thermodynamics of Irreversible Processes.* Amsterdam: North-Holland, 1963.

Dunn, P. D., and Reay, D. A. *Heat Pipes*, 3d ed., New York: Pergamon, 1982.

Haase, R. *Thermodynamics of Irreversible Processes.* Reading, Mass.: Addison-Wesley, 1969.

Moran, M. J. *Availability Analysis: A Guide to Efficient Energy Use.* Englewood Cliffs, NJ: Prentice-Hall, 1982.

Prigogine, I. *Introduction to Thermodynamics of Irreversible Processes.* New York: Interscience, 1955.

Prigogine, I. *Introduction to Thermodynamics of Irreversible Processes,* 3d ed. New York: Interscience, 1967, pp. 65–70.

Reynolds, W. C., and Perkins, H. C. *Engineering Thermodynamics,* 2d ed. New York: McGraw-Hill, 1977.

Rysselberghe, P. V. *Thermodynamics of Irreversible Processes.* New York: Blaisdell, 1963.

Van Wylen, G., and Sonntag, R. E. *Fundamentals of Classical Thermodynamics,* 3d ed. New York: Wiley, 1986.

Wood, B. D. *Applications of Thermodynamics,* 2d ed. Reading, Mass.: Addison-Wesley, 1982.

Woods, L. C. *The Thermodynamics of Fluid Systems.* Oxford: Clarendon, 1975.

Yao, Y. L. *Irreversible Thermodynamics.* New York: Van Nostrand Reinhold, 1981.

Chapter Five Problems

Problems for Section I

The first ten problems below are designed to review some basic thermodynamic concepts of this and earlier chapters. They may have more than one correct answer.

1. A closed system becomes an open system when
- **a)** there is no heat transfer to energy
- **b)** there is no work transfer of energy
- **c)** there is no mass flow
- **d)** there is no entropy production
- **e)** there is no kinetic or potential energy
- **f)** none of the above

2. Which of the following are *intensive* properties
- **a)** pressure **b)** temperature **c)** volume
- **d)** mass **e)** quality **f)** power

3. The entropy change of a closed system will be zero for which of the following processes
- **a)** adiabatic **b)** isothermal **c)** isentropic
- **d)** isenthalpic **e)** aergonic **f)** reversible

4. An insulated rigid container is divided into two compartments separated by a partition. One compartment contains air at 100 °F and 14.7 psia, the other compartment contains air at 50 °F and 14.7 psia. When the dividing partition is removed, the total internal energy of the system
- **a)** increases **b)** decreases
- **c)** does not change **d)** is converted into entropy
- **e)** is converted into temperature **f)** is converted into heat

5. A rigid container contains air (an ideal gas), at 70 °F and 14.7 psia. If the air is heated to 510 °F, its pressure will
- **a)** increase **b)** decrease
- **c)** not change **d)** cause moving boundary work to occur
- **e)** causes polytropic work to occur **f)** be converted into thermal energy

6. A constant velocity throttling process
- **a)** is reversible **b)** is isothermal
- **c)** is isentropic **d)** is isenthalpic
- **e)** is aergonic **f)** does not exist in the real world

7. Heat and work are both
a) intensive properties **b)** extensive properties
c) process path dependent **d)** zero for an ideal gas
e) zero for an adiabatic process **f)** zero for an aergonic process

8. An ideal gas must satisfy
a) $pv^n = \text{constant}$ **b)** $u = u(T)$ **c)** $s = \text{constant}$
d) $p_2/p_1 = v_1/v_2$ **e)** $pv = nRT$ **f)** $pv = mRT$

9. In a steady flow *irreversible* process, the total entropy of a system
a) always increases **b)** always decreases
c) always remains constant **d)** can increase, decrease or remain constant
e) cannot decrease **f)** cannot remain constant

10. To determine the maximum possible work that a heat engine could produce one must assume
a) no entropy is produced by the engine
b) no heat energy is discharged to the environment
c) no mechanical friction occurs anywhere in the engine
d) no chemical reactions occur anywhere in the engine
e) no irreversibilities occur anywhere within the engine
f) no heat transfer occurs to or from the engine

11. a) Write either the Clausius or the Kelvin-Planck word statements of the second law of thermodynamics,
b) write an accurate mathematical equation for the second law, and
c) given any process, how can you determine whether it is physically possible?

12. An inventor claims to have developed an engine that operates on a cycle that consists of two reversible adiabatic processes and one reversible isothermal heat addition process (see diagram). Explain whether this engine violates either the first or second laws of thermodynamics. (*Hint*: Recall that the net work for the process is the area enclosed on the p-$\forall$ diagram.)

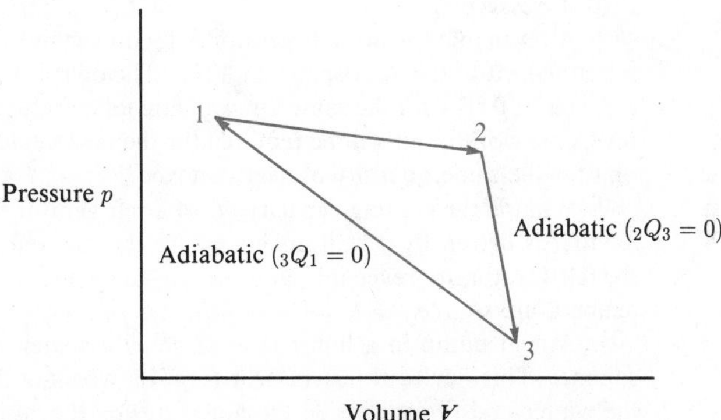

13. If the human body is modeled as a heat engine with its heat source at body temperature, what is its maximum (reversible or Carnot) efficiency when the ambient temperature is 70 °F?

14. An engine that operates on a reversible Carnot cycle transfers 4.0 kW of heat from a reservoir at 1000 K. Heat is then rejected to the atmosphere at 300 K. What is the thermal efficiency and the power output of this engine?

15. Determine whether each of the following functions could be used to define an absolute temperature scale:

a) $f(x) = \cos x$ **b)** $f(x) = \tan x$

c) $f(x) = x^4$ **d)** $f(x) = 1 + x$

16. A closed system undergoes a cycle consisting of the following four processes:

Process 1. 10 kJ of heat are added to the system and 20 kJ of work are done by the system.
Process 2. The system energy increases by 30 kJ adiabatically.
Process 3. 10 kJ of work are done on the system while the system gains 50 kJ of energy.
Process 4. The system does 40 kJ of work while returning to its initial state.

a) Complete the following table (all values in kJ)

Process	${}_iQ_j$	${}_iW_j$	$E_i - E_j$
1			
2			
3			
4			
Totals			

b) Find the thermal efficiency of this cycle.

17. It is proposed to heat a house using a Carnot heat pump. The heat loss from the house is 50,000 J/s. The house is to be maintained at 25 °C while the outside air is at −10 °C. What should be the coefficient of performance of the heat pump selected, and what would be the minimum horsepower of the motor required to drive the heat pump?

18. A reversible Carnot refrigerator is to be used to remove 400 Btu/h from a region at −60 °F and discharge heat to the atmosphere at 40 °F. The reversible Carnot refrigerator is to be driven by a reversible heat engine operating between thermal reservoirs at 1040 and 40 °F. How much heat must be supplied to the reversible Carnot heat engine from the 1040 °F reservoir?

19. A reversible Carnot refrigerator is used to maintain food in a refrigerator at 40 °F by rejecting heat to the atmosphere at 80 °F. The owner wishes to convert the refrigerator into a freezer at 0 °F with the same atmospheric temperature of 80 °F. What percent increase in reversible work input will be required for the new freezer unit over the existing refrigerated unit for the same quantity of heat removed?

20. What is the cooling capacity Q_L of a refrigerator with a coefficient of performance of 3.0 that is driven by a heat engine whose thermal efficiency is 50%. Both the engine and the refrigerator are reversible, and the engine receives 600 kW of heat energy from its high-temperature source.

21. A heat pump in a home is to serve as a heater in winter and an air conditioner in summer. This device transfers heat from its working fluid to air inside the house during the winter and to air outside the house during the summer. The design conditions (worst case) are as follows:

Winter	Summer
$T_{\text{house}} = 70\ °\text{F}$	$T_{\text{house}} = 70\ °\text{F}$
$T_{\text{outside}} = 20\ °\text{F}$	$T_{\text{outside}} = 100\ °\text{F}$
$\dot{Q}_{\text{house}} = -50{,}000\ \text{Btu/h}$	$\dot{Q}_{\text{house}} = +30{,}000\ \text{Btu/h}$

Use the reversible Carnot cycle to determine the minimum power required to drive the heat pump.

22. The air inside a garage is to be heated using a heat pump driven by a 500-W electric motor. The outside air is at a temperature of −20 °C and provides the low-temperature heat source for the heat pump. The heat loss from the garage to the outside through the walls and roof is 12,500 kJ/h. If the heat pump operates on a reversible cycle, what is the highest temperature that can be maintained in the garage?

23. A heat pump, with the elements shown in the schematic below, is to be used to heat a home. On a given day, the evaporator receives heat at 30 °F and the condenser rejects heat at 70 °F. The required heat transfer rate from the condenser to the home is 50,000 Btu/h.

a) If the heat pump is operated reversibly, what is the rate of work transfer of energy to the compressor?

b) Express this compressor work rate in kilowatts and calculate the cost per 24-h day if electricity is purchased at 10 cents/(kW·h).

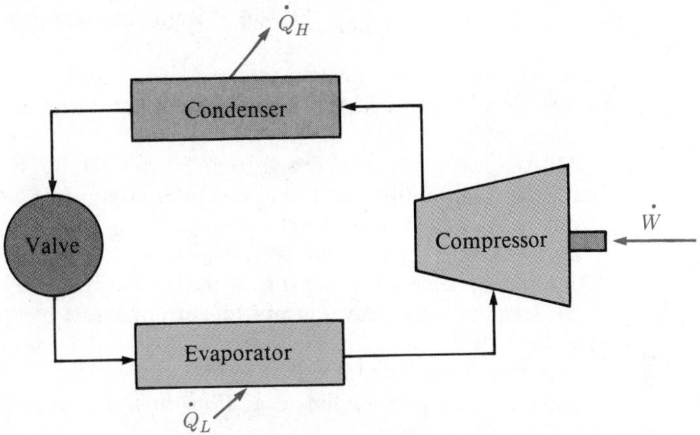

24. An automobile air conditioner removes 7500 Btu/h from the vehicle's interior. Determine the amount of engine horsepower required to drive the air conditioner if it has a coefficient of performance of 2.5.

25. A thermodynamic cycle using water is shown on the *T-s* diagram below. Calculate the coefficient of performance for this cycle using the equation

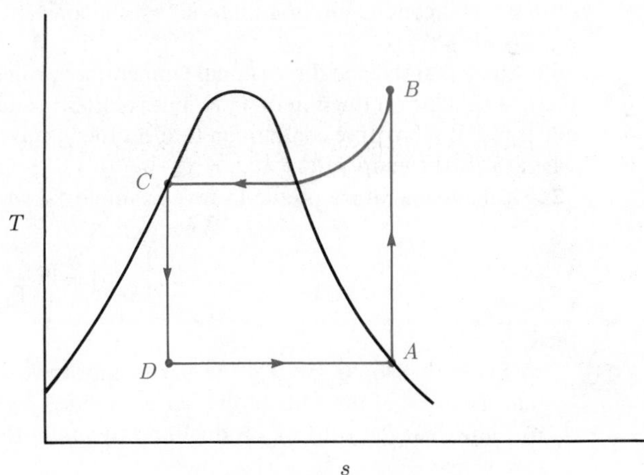

$$\text{COP} = \frac{h_A - h_D}{(h_B - h_C) - (h_A - h_D)}$$

State A	State B	State C	State D
$x_A = 1.0$	$p_B = 300$ psia	$x_C = 0.0$	$p_D = 9$ psia
$p_A = 9$ psia			

The processes are

A → B = isentropic compression,

B → C = isobaric expansion,

C → D = isentropic expansion,

D → A = isothermal compression.

26. Determine the change in total entropy of 3.0 kg of incompressible liquid water with a specific heat of 4.2 kJ/(kg·K) as it is heated at atmospheric pressure from 20 °C to its boiling point.

27. An ideal gas is compressed from 1.0 atm and 40 °F to 3.0 atm and 540 °F. For this gas, $c_p = 0.28$ Btu/(lbm·R) and $c_v = 0.13$ Btu/(lbm·R). Calculate the change in specific entropy of this gas for this process.

28. Determine the rate of heat transport of entropy through an isothermal boundary at 50 °C when the heat transfer rate at the boundary is 350 kJ/min.

29. Determine the heat transport of entropy into a pan of boiling water at 100 °C which has been sitting on a kitchen stove for 30 min. During this time 0.3 kg of water is converted from a saturated liquid to a saturated vapor.

30. If the heat entropy flux at a 2.7 m² boundary is given by

$$\dot{q}/T_b = 500t + 243$$

in W/(m²·K) where t is in seconds, determine the total heat transport of entropy across this boundary during the time period from $t = 0$ to $t = 60$ s.

31. If the thermal entropy production rate per unit volume is constant at 0.315 W/(m³·K) throughout a 0.5 m³ system, determine the system's rate of heat production of entropy.

32. Show that the one-dimensional thermal entropy production rate per unit volume for pure thermal conduction in a material with a constant thermal conductivity k_t is given by $\sigma_Q = (k_t/T^2)(dT/dx)^2$.

33. Show that the one-dimensional temperature profile inside a system that has a constant thermal entropy production rate per unit volume σ_Q and a constant thermal conductivity k_t, and is restricted to pure conduction heat transfer, is given by $T = T_o \exp[(\sigma_Q/k_t)^{1/2}(x - x_o)]$, where T_o is the temperature at $x = x_o$.

34. If the temperature profile in text Example 5.4 was given by

$$T = T_1\left[\exp\left(\frac{x}{L}\ln\frac{T_2}{T_1}\right)\right]$$

then

a) Show that for $\dot{Q}_{in} = \dot{Q}_{out}$ the bar cannot have a constant cross-sectional area, and that the areas of the ends of the bar are related by $A_2 = A_1(T_1/T_2)$.

b) Show that the entropy production rate under these circumstances is given by

$$(\dot{S}_P)_Q = \left(\frac{k_t A_1}{L}\right)\left(\frac{T_1}{T_2} - 1\right)\ln\frac{T_1}{T_2}$$

c) Show that the entropy production rate of part b above is greater than that obtained with the linear temperature profile used in text Example 5.4 when $A = A_1$.

35. A stainless steel heat pipe ($k_1 = 30$ W/(m·K)) has an isothermal external surface temperature of 130 °C when its heat transfer rate is 1000 W. The surface area and wall thickness are 0.001 m^2 and 0.001 m, respectively. Determine the heat pipe's entropy production rate.

36. If 0.101 g of water (liquid plus vapor) at 0.01 MPa absolute are put into a heat pipe 0.005 m i.d. and 1.0 m long, determine the temperature at which the heat pipe phenomena ceases to operate due to the complete vaporization of the water.

37. Determine the work mode **a)** entropy transport rate and **b)** entropy production rate as 100 hp is continuously dissipated in a mechanical brake operating isothermally at 300 °F.

38. Determine the work mode entropy production as a 300-kg steel block slides 10 m down a 60° incline. The coefficient of friction between the block and the incline is 0.1, and the bulk mean temperature of the sliding surface is 50 °C.

39. A mechanical gearbox at a uniform temperature of 160 °F receives 150 hp at the input shaft and transmits 145 hp out the output shaft. Determine its work mode **a)** entropy transport rate and **b)** entropy production rate.

40. Determine the work mode entropy production as 0.5 m^3 of air is compressed adiabatically from 200 kPa, 20 °C to 0.1 m^3 in a piston–cylinder apparatus with a mechanical efficiency of 85%. Assume constant specific heat ideal gas behavior.

41. The velocity profile for the steady laminar flow of an incompressible Newtonian fluid in a horizontal circular pipe is

$$V = V_m[1 - (x/R)^2]$$

where V_m is the centerline ($x = 0$) velocity, R is the pipe radius and x is the radial coordinate measured from the centerline.

a) Determine the position in this flow where the entropy production rate per unit volume is a minimum.

b) Determine the position in this flow where the entropy production rate per unit volume is a maximum.

c) Comment on how you can minimize the total entropy production rate for this flow.

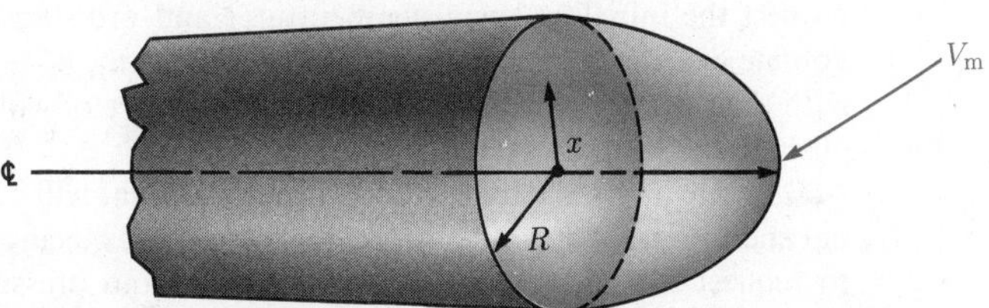

42. The viscous work entropy production rate per unit volume in three-dimensional Cartesian coordinates is

$$(\sigma_W)_{vis} = \frac{\mu}{T}\left\{\frac{2}{3}\left[\left(\frac{\partial V_x}{\partial x} - \frac{\partial V_y}{\partial y}\right)^2 + \left(\frac{\partial V_y}{\partial y} - \frac{\partial V_z}{\partial z}\right)^2 + \left(\frac{\partial V_z}{\partial z} - \frac{\partial V_x}{\partial x}\right)^2\right]\right.$$
$$\left. + \left(\frac{\partial V_x}{\partial y} + \frac{\partial V_y}{\partial x}\right)^2 + \left(\frac{\partial V_y}{\partial z} + \frac{\partial V_z}{\partial y}\right)^2 + \left(\frac{\partial V_z}{\partial x} + \frac{\partial V_x}{\partial z}\right)^2\right\}$$

Show that this can be written as

$$(\sigma_W)_{vis} = \frac{\mu}{T}\left\{-\frac{2}{3}\left(\frac{\partial V_x}{\partial x}+\frac{\partial V_y}{\partial y}+\frac{\partial V_z}{\partial z}\right)^2 + 2\left[\left(\frac{\partial V_x}{\partial x}\right)^2+\left(\frac{\partial V_y}{\partial y}\right)^2+\left(\frac{\partial V_z}{\partial z}\right)^2\right]\right.$$
$$\left. + \left(\frac{\partial V_x}{\partial y}+\frac{\partial V_y}{\partial x}\right)^2 + \left(\frac{\partial V_y}{\partial z}+\frac{\partial V_z}{\partial y}\right)^2 + \left(\frac{\partial V_z}{\partial x}+\frac{\partial V_x}{\partial z}\right)^2\right\}$$

43. Show that the three-dimensional Cartesian coordinate viscous work entropy production rate per unit volume given in Problem 42 reduces to the following for two-dimensional incompressible flow:

$$(\sigma_W)_{vis} = \frac{\mu}{T}\left(\frac{\partial V_x}{\partial y}+\frac{\partial V_y}{\partial x}\right)^2$$

$\left(\textit{Hint}: \text{For incompressible fluids, } \frac{\partial V_x}{\partial x}+\frac{\partial V_y}{\partial y}+\frac{\partial V_z}{\partial z} = 0.\right)$

44. Determine the entropy production rate of a 10,000-Ω electrical resistor that draws a constant 10 mA of current. The temperature of the resistor is constant throughout its volume at 35 °C.

Section I Computer Problems

The following computer programming assignments are designed to be carried out on any personal computer using BASIC as the programming language. They are meant to be exercises in input/output screen formatting and manipulation of some of the basic formulae of this section of Chapter 5. They may be used as part of a weekly homework assignment.

45. Write an interactive computer program that will allow the user to input *any* temperature (i.e., value plus unit symbol) in either the relative or absolute Engineering English or SI units system at the keyboard and then convert this input into *all* of the following temperatures and output them to the screen: °C, °F, R, and K.

46. Write an interactive computer program that will compute the change in specific internal energy, enthalpy, and entropy for an incompressible material. Use screen prompts to request the initial and final temperatures and pressures, the specific heat, and the specific volume or density of the material. Output $u_2 - u_1$, $h_2 - h_1$, and $s_2 - s_1$ to the screen along with their proper units. Allow the user the choice of working in either the Engineering English or the SI units system.

47. Write an interactive computer program that will compute the change in specific internal energy, enthalpy, and entropy for a constant specific heat ideal gas. Use screen prompts to request the initial and final temperatures and pressures or specific volumes (allow the user the choice of which to input), the specific heats and gas constant. Output $u_2 - u_1$, $h_2 - h_1$, and $s_2 - s_1$ to the screen along with their proper units. Allow the user the choice of working in either the Engineering English or the SI units system.

48. Repeat Problem 47 except allow the user to choose a gas from a menu. Have all the specific heats and gas constants for the gases resident in your program. Good screen graphics and etiquette are important here.

49. Write an interactive computer program that will output the heat production rate $(\dot{S}_P)_Q$ of entropy due to steady state one-dimensional thermal conduction. Utilize Fourier's law of conduction, and use screen prompts to request the user to input the appropriate temperatures, thermal conductivity, cross-sectional area, and length in the proper units. Allow the user the choice of working in either the Engineering English or the SI units system.

50. Write an interactive computer program that will output the work mode entropy production rate $(\dot{S}_P)_W$ due to the viscous dissipation in the steady one-dimensional flow of a Newtonian fluid in a circular pipe with the velocity profile given in Problem 41. Use screen prompts to request the user to input the fluid's viscosity, density, and mass flow rate, and the appropriate pipe dimensions in proper units. Allow the user the choice of working in either the Engineering English or the SI units system.

51. Write an interactive computer program that will output the electrical work mode entropy production rate $(\dot{S}_P)_W$ due to resistive dissipation in an isothermal system with uniform properties and a constant current density. Use screen prompts to request the user to input the appropriate variables in proper units. Allow the user the choice of working in either the Engineering English or the SI units system.

52. Since Figure 5.9 is a semilogarithmic plot, the straight line for copper there has an equation of the form $\rho_e = A(e^{BT})$. Estimate the coefficients A and B for copper from this figure and write an interactive computer program that will output the electrical work mode entropy production rate $(\dot{S}_P)_W$ due to the temperature dependent resistive dissipation in an isothermal copper wire. Use screen prompts to request the user to input the appropriate variables in proper units. Allow the user the choice of working in either the Engineering English or the SI units system.

Problems for Section II

53. Air contained in a cylinder fitted with a piston initially at 2.0 MPa and 2000 °C expands to 0.2 MPa in an isentropic process. Assuming the air behaves as a constant specific heat ideal gas, determine the following

a) the final temperature,
b) the change in specific internal energy,
c) the change in specific enthalpy,
d) the change in specific entropy, and
e) the work done per lbm of air during the expansion.

54. A constant specific heat ideal gas has a gas constant of 42.92 ft·lbf/(lbm·R) and a constant pressure specific heat of 0.200 Btu/(lbm·R). Determine the heat transferred and the change of total entropy if 9.0 lbm of this gas is heated from 40 to 340 °F in a rigid container.

55. A reversible Carnot heat engine has 1.0 lbm of air as the working fluid. Heat is received at 740 °F and rejected at 40 °F. At the beginning of the heat addition process the pressure is 100 psia, and during this process the volume triples. Calculate the net cycle work per lbm of air. Assume the air behaves as a constant specific heat ideal gas.

56. A 1.0-ft^3 glass bottle is initially evacuated and then has 1.000 g of water added that eventually comes to equilibrium at 70 °F. The pressure in the bottle is then increased by 11.1668 psia during a reversible adiabatic compression. **a)** What is the work done during compression? **b)** What is the entropy production for the compression?

57. 3.0 lbm of Refrigerant-12 (*not* an ideal gas) is compressed adiabatically in a closed piston–cylinder device from 5 psia, 220 °F to 200 psia, 340 °F.

a) Determine the work for this process, and
b) Show whether or not this process violates the second law of thermodynamics.

58. An engineer claims to be able to compress 0.1 kg of water vapor at 200 °C and 0.1 MPa in a piston–cylinder arrangement in an isothermal *and* adiabatic process. The engineer claims that the final volume is 6.1% of the initial volume. Determine

a) the final temperature and pressure, and
b) the work required.
c) Show whether the process is thermodynamically possible.

59. An inventive engineer claims to have designed a mechanochemical single stroke closed system that will compress 10 lbm of air isothermally from 14.7 psia, 100 °F to 200 psia while inputting 500 Btu of mechanochemical compression work. Assuming constant specific heat ideal gas behavior,

a) what heat transfer is required for this process to occur, and

b) does this process violate the second law of thermodynamics?

60. Saturated liquid water at 8.58 MPa undergoes a reversible isothermal process in a cylinder until the pressure reaches 0.1 MPa. Calcuate the heat transfer and work per kg of water for this process. Show the process on a *T-s* diagram. Neglect any changes in kinetic and potential energies.

61. Air is compressed in a steady state reversible adiabatic process from 25 °C and 0.15 MPa to 1.7 MPa. Determine the change of specific enthalpy in this process and find the density of the exit air. Assume the air behaves as an ideal gas with constant specific heats. Neglect any changes in kinetic and potential energies.

62. One cubic meter of hydrogen (a constant specific heat ideal gas) expands from an initial pressure of 0.5 MPa to a final pressure of 0.1 MPa. The gas temperature before expansion is 27 °C.

a) Determine the final temperature if the process is isentropic,

b) determine the final temperature if the process is polytropic with $n = 1.30$, and

c) calculate the heat transfer required for the polytropic case.

63. 2.0 lbm of saturated water vapor at 247.1 psia undergoes a reversible isothermal expansion until the pressure reaches 20 psia. Determine the heat transfer and the work done for this process. The system boundary temperature is the same as the process temperature.

64. Consider a fixed mass of a constant specific heat ideal gas in a piston–cylinder device undergoing a compression process for which $p\mathcal{V}^n =$ constant (a polytropic process). Show that the work done per unit mass of gas in such a process is given by $(p_2v_2 - p_1v_1)/(n - 1)$ if $n \neq 1$. If the process is isentropic, show that this reduces to $c_v(T_2 - T_1)$.

65. 0.13 kg of a constant specific heat ideal gas is compressed in a closed system from 1.0 atm and 40 °C to 11.39 atm in an isothermal process. For this gas, $c_p = 523$ J/(kg·K), $c_v = 315$ J/(kg·K) and $R = 208$ J/(kg·K). For this process, determine

a) the work required,

b) the resulting heat transfer, and

c) the amount of entropy produced.

d) Explain whether this process violates the second law of thermodynamics.

66. Show that a constant specific heat ideal gas undergoing a constant heat flux polytropic process ($pv^n =$ constant with $n \neq 1$), has a limiting isothermal system boundary temperature corresponding to a reversible process given by

$$(T_b)_{rev} = \frac{T_2 - T_1}{\ln(T_2/T_1)}$$

(*Hint*: Recall that ${}_1W_2 = mR(T_2 - T_1)/(n - 1)$ for such a polytropic process with an ideal gas.)

67. A 20-ft^3 tank contains air at 100 psia, 100 °F. A valve on the tank is opened and the pressure in the tank drops to 20 psia. If the air that remains in the tank is considered to be a closed system undergoing a reversible adiabatic process, calculate the final mass of air in the tank. Assume constant specific heat ideal gas behavior, and neglect any changes in kinetic and potential energies.

68. A pressure vessel contains ammonia at a pressure of 100 psia and a temperature of 100 °F. A valve at the top of the vessel is opened allowing vapor to escape. Assume that at any instant the ammonia that remains in the vessel has undergone an isentropic process. When the ammonia remaining in the vessel becomes a saturated vapor, the valve is closed. The mass of ammonia in the vessel at this moment is 2.00 lbm. Find the mass of ammonia that escaped into the surroundings. Neglect any changes in kinetic and potential energies.

69. A 2.0-m^3 tank contains air at 0.2 MPa and 35 °C. A valve on the tank is opened and the pressure in the tank drops to 0.1 MPa. If the process is isentropic, calculate the final mass of air in the tank. Assume the air behaves as a constant specific heat ideal gas. Neglect any changes in kinetic and potential energies.

70. A 58-ft^3 tank contains air at 30 psia and 100 °F. A valve on the tank is opened and the pressure in the tank drops to 10 psia. If the air that remains in the tank has gone through an adiabatic polytropic process with $n = 1.33$, calculate the final mass of air in the tank and the entropy production that has occurred in this mass. Assume the air behaves as a constant specific heat ideal gas, and neglect any changes in kinetic and potential energies.

71. An operating gear box (transmission) has 200 hp at its input shaft while 190 hp are delivered to the output shaft. The gear box has a steady state surface temperature of 140 °F. Determine the rate of entropy production by the gear box.

72. A gear box (transmission) operating at steady state, receives 100 kW of power from an engine and delivers 97 kW to the output shaft. If the surface of the gear box is at a uniform temperature of 50 °C and the surrounding temperature is 20 °C, what is the rate of entropy production?

73. Determine the amount of entropy produced in the process described in Problem 73 at the end of Chapter 4 when both the specific internal energy and the specific entropy of the water has returned to its initial value.

74. Determine the amount of entropy produced in the process described in Problem 75 at the end of Chapter 4. Assume that the system boundary temperature is the same as its bulk isothermal temperature.

75. Determine the amount of entropy produced in the process described in Problem 76 at the end of Chapter 4 if the 500 Btu heat transfer occurred across an isothermal system boundary at 250 °F.

76. Determine the amount of entropy produced in the process described in Problem 80 at the end of Chapter 4 if the work transport is 90% of the magnitude of the heat transport. Assume that the system boundary temperature is the same as its bulk isothermal temperature.

77. Determine the amount of entropy produced in the process described in Problem 85 at the end of Chapter 4. Assume the human body is a steady state closed system with an isothermal surface temperature of 36 °C during the exercise process.

78. Determine the amount of entropy produced during the adiabatic expansion process described in Problem 89 at the end of Chapter 4. Discuss the difficulty encountered in determining the entropy production during the final isobaric compression process.

79. 1.0 lbm of saturated water vapor at 212 °F is condensed in a closed, nonrigid system to saturated liquid at 212 °F in a constant pressure process by a heat transfer across a system boundary with a constant temperature of 80 °F. What is the total entropy production for this process?

80. A rigid container encloses 150 lbm of air at 15 psia and 500 R. We wish to increase the temperature to 540 R. Assuming constant specific heat ideal gas behavior,

a) determine the energy input to the air for such a change of state, and

b) determine the entropy production if this change of state is accomplished by using a constant system boundary temperature of 300 °F.

81. A sealed kitchen pressure cooker whose volume is 1.0 ft^3 contains 2.2 lbm of saturated water (liquid plus vapor) at 14.7 psia. The pressure cooker is then heated until its internal pressure reaches 20 psia. Determine

a) the work done during the process,

b) the heat transfer during the process, and

c) the entropy produced during the process if the inner surface of the pressure cooker is constant at 250 °F.

82. A closed sealed rigid container is filled with 0.05833 ft^3 of liquid water and 0.94167 ft^3 of water vapor in equilibrium at 1.0 psia.

a) What is the quality in the vessel at this state?

The vessel is then heated until its contents become a saturated vapor.

b) What are the temperature and pressure in the vessel at this state?

If the heating process described above was done irreversibly,

c) determine the total entropy produced for this process if the surface temperature of the vessel is maintained constant at 300 °F.

83. Determine the entropy produced as a 4.0-g, 80 °C lead bullet traveling at 900 m/s impacts a perfectly rigid surface aergonically and adiabatically. The specific heat of lead at the mean temperature of the bullet is 167 J/(kg·K).

84. Determine the minimum isothermal system boundary temperature required by the second law as a 1500-kg iron ingot is heated from 20 to 1000 °C. Assume the ingot is incompressible.

85. In the twenty-first century the earth will be terrorized by Zandar the Wombat, an asexual rebel engineer from the planet Q-dot. Earth's only hope for survival lies in your ability to determine the entropy production rate of Zandar. To do this, you cleverly trick Zandar into completely wrapping himself with insulation and holding his breath. You then quickly measure his body temperature and find that it is increasing at a constant rate of 2.0 °C per minute. Zandar weighs 981 N and has the thermodynamic properties of water. Determine Zandar's entropy production rate when his body temperature reaches 50 °C.

86. The surface temperature of a 100-W incandescent light bulb is 60 °C. The surface temperature of a 20-W fluorescent tube producing the same amount of light as the 100-W incandescent light bulb is 30 °C. Determine the steady state entropy production rate of each light source and comment on which is the most efficient.

87. Rework text Example 5.16 by setting $T_b = T_s$. Using the formula for T_s given in the example, show that

$$\frac{\bar{d}Q}{T_b} = -\frac{hA\,dt}{1 + T_\infty e^{\alpha t}/(T_1 - T_\infty)}$$

where $\alpha = hA/(mc_v)$. Integrate this from $t = 0$ to 5 s and combine it with the $m(s_2 - s_1)$ result from the example to get ${}_1(S_P)_2$ under this condition. What is the significance of this result?

88. Determine the entropy production and total entropy change for an aergonic closed system in which the temperature increases from $T_1 = 70$ °F to $T_2 = 200$ °F for the cases where the heat transfer varies with the system absolute temperature according to the relations

a) $Q = K_1 T$ (convection), and

b) $Q = K_2 T^4$ (radiation)

where $K_1 = 3.0$ Btu/R and $K_2 = 3.0 \times 10^{-4}$ Btu/R^4. The system boundary is maintained isothermal at 212 °F.

89. Determine the entropy production rate due to conduction heat transfer inside a system having a volume of 3.0 ft^3 and a thermal conductivity of 105 Btu/(h·ft·R) that contains the following temperature profile.

$$T = 300.0[\exp(x/3.0)]$$

where T is in R and x is in feet.

90. Using Eq. 5.64, show that the entropy production rate per unit volume due to heat transfer (σ_Q) is a constant if the temperature distribution due to conduction heat transfer is given by

$$T = C_1[\exp(C_2 x)]$$

where C_1 and C_2 are constants. (*Hint*: Use Fourier's law of heat conduction to eliminate the $\dot{q}$ term.)

91. The temperature distribution due to conduction heat transfer inside a flat plate with an internal heat generation is given by

$$T = T_o + (T_s - T_o)(x/L)^2$$

where T_s is the surface ($x = L$) and T_o is the centerline ($x = 0$) temperature. Determine a formula for the entropy production rate ($\dot{S}_P$) for this system.

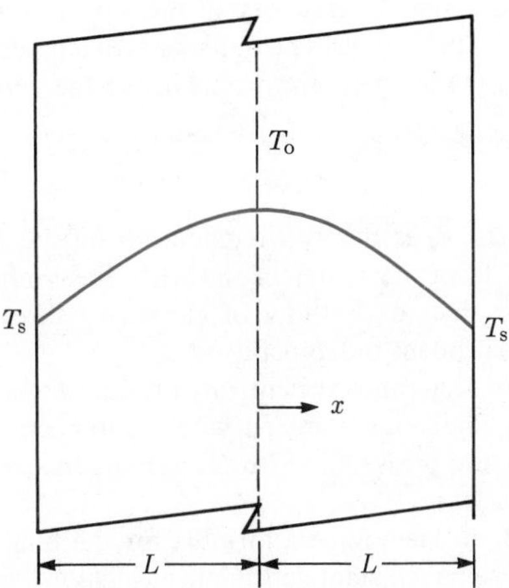

92. Example 5.18 in the text dealt with the velocity profile in a liquid contained in the gap between two concentric cylinders of radii R_1 and $R_2 > R_1$ in which the inner cylinder is rotating with an angular velocity ω and the outer cylinder is stationary. If this gap is very small, the velocity profile can be approximated by the linear relation

$$V = R_1\omega(R_2 - x)/(R_2 - R_1)$$

where $R_2 \gg (R_2 - R_1)$ and x is measured radially outward from the center of the inner cylinder. Using the data given in text Example 5.18, determine the entropy production rate using this simpler velocity profile and compare your answer to that given in Example 5.18 for the more complex nonlinear velocity profile.

93. Text Example 5.18 deals with the entropy production rate in the flow between concentric rotating cylinders in which the outer cylinder was stationary and the inner cylinder rotated with a constant angular velocity ω. If, instead, we allow both cylinders to rotate in the same direction with constant angular velocities ω_2 at the outer cylinder and ω_1 at the inner, then the velocity profile in the gap between the cylinders becomes

$$V = [(\omega_2 R_2^2 - \omega_1 R_1^2)x - (\omega_2 - \omega_1)(R_1^2 R_2^2)/x]/(R_2^2 - R_1^2)$$

Find the expression for the entropy production rate due to viscous effects in the fluid of viscosity μ contained between these rotating cylinders of radii R_1 and $R_2 > R_1$ and length L. Assume the fluid is maintained isothermal at temperature T.

94. A *dipstick heater* is an electrical resistance heater that is plugged into a regular 110-V ac outlet and then inserted into the dipstick tube of an automobile engine. Its purpose is to keep the engine oil warm during the winter when the car is not in use, thus allowing the engine to start easier. Determine the entropy produced during an 8-h period by a 100-W steady state dipstick heater whose surface is isothermal at 90 °C.

95. The potential difference across the tungsten filament operating at 2400 °C in a cathode ray vacuum tube is 25,000 V. The filament is a small disk 0.002 m in diameter and 0.0001 m thick having a resistivity of $6 \times 10^{-4}\ \Omega\cdot\text{m}$. Assuming all the voltage drop occurs uniformly across the thickness of the disk, determine its entropy production rate.

96. A current of 100 A is passed through a 6.0-ft-long stainless steel wire 0.1 in in diameter. The electrical resistivity of the wire is $1.97 \times 10^{-5}\ \Omega\cdot\text{in}$, and its thermal conducitivity is 12.5 Btu/(h·ft·R). The outer surface temperature of the wire is maintained constant at 300 °F and the temperature profile inside the wire is given by

$$T = T_w + \rho_e J_e^2 (R^2 - x^2)/(4k_t)$$

where T_w is the wall temperature of the wire, R is its radius, and x is measured radially out from the center of the wire. Determine the total entropy production rate within the wire due to the flow of electricity through it. Assume all the physical properties are independent of temperature.

97. Determine the entropy produced when 3.0 lbm of carbon dioxide at 70 °F and 30 psia are adiabatically mixed with 7.0 lbm of carbon dioxide at 100 °F and 15 psia. The final mixture pressure is 17 psia. Assume the carbon dioxide behaves as a constant specific heat ideal gas.

98. **a)** Determine a formula for the final pressure (p_2) that results when two volumes of the same constant specific heat ideal gas initially at p_a, T_a and p_b, T_b are mixed isentropically. **b)** Does this mixture pressure represent an upper or lower bound when this mixing is done adiabatically but not isentropically?

99. Determine the entropy produced as 0.005 lbm of human saliva at 98.6 °F is adiabatically mixed with 0.003 lbm of human saliva at 103.2 °F in a passionate and infectious kiss. The specific heat of the saliva is 0.95 Btu/(lbm·R).

100. Determine the entropy produced as 10 kg of liquid water at 10 °C is adiabatically mixed with 20 kg of liquid water at 80 °C. The specific heat of the water is 4.2 kJ/(kg·K).

101. Here is the complete classical coffee and cream problem. Which of the following processes produces less entropy

a) mixing cream with hot coffee and then letting the mixture cool to the drinking temperature, or

b) letting the coffee cool to a temperature such that when the cream is added the mixture will be at the drinking temperature?

Do not ignore the cooling heat transfer entropy production.

Design Problems for Section II

The following are elementary open-ended design problems. The objective is to carry out a preliminary thermal design as indicated. A detailed design with working drawings is not expected unless otherwise specified. These problems do not have specific answers, so each student's design will be unique.

102. Carry out a preliminary thermodynamic design of a system that will heat 20 kg of liquid water from 20 to 80 °C in 15 min at atmospheric pressure in a closed vessel. Use an electrical heating system and determine the electrical power and current requirements (assume standard line voltage values). Include a means of relieving any pressure buildup, and discuss safety considerations.

103. Carry out a preliminary thermodynamic design of a single piston–cylinder apparatus that will produce 25 hp as it moves through a mechanical cycle in 10 s. The piston is to be drawn into the cylinder by condensing steam that enters the apparatus as a saturated vapor at 212 °F. No work is done during the return stroke of the piston, during which time a fresh charge of steam is drawn into the apparatus. Continuous motion of this type can be accomplished through the use of a flywheel.

104. Carry out a preliminary thermodynamic design of a system that will mix by only diffusive processes 5 kg of gaseous CO_2 with 10 kg of air in a maximum of 6 min in a closed rigid vessel. Specify the vessel material, size, and internal geometry, and discuss any relevant safety considerations.

Computer Problems for Section II

The following computer problems are designed to be completed in BASIC on a microcomputer.

105. Write an interactive computer program that will determine the power output from a reversible solar power plant similar to that discussed in text Example 5.8. Have the user input all of the relevant variables (in proper units), and output the net reversible electrical power produced. At your instructor's discretion, add screen graphics depicting a diagram of the power plant and the input and output variables. Allow the user the choice of working in either Engineering English or SI units.

106. Write an interactive computer program that will perform an energy *and* entropy balance on a closed system with an isothermal boundary. The system contains an incompressible substance (either a liquid or a solid) that is undergoing an irreversible process. Prompt the user for the following input (in proper units): the heat and work transports of energy, the system volume, the initial internal temperature and the isothermal boundary temperature of the system, and the density and specific heat of the incompressible material contained in the system. Output to the screen the system mass, final temperature, and entropy production. Note that if the entropy production becomes negative (an impossible physical situation), then the system boundary temperature was not properly specified. Check for this possibility and prompt the user for another boundary temperature if it occurs. Allow the user the choice of working in either Engineering English or SI units.

107. Write an interactive computer program that will perform an energy *and* an entropy balance on a closed system with an isothermal boundary. The system contains an ideal gas with constant specific heats that is undergoing an irreversible process. Prompt the user for the following input (in proper units): the heat and work transports of energy, the system volume, the initial temperature and pressure of the system, and the constant volume specific heat and gas constant of the gas contained in the system. Output to the screen the system mass, the final pressure and temperature, and the entropy production for the process. Check to make sure the entropy production is positive and prompt the user for corrected input if it is not. Allow the user the choice of working in either Engineering English or SI units.

108. Repeat Problem 107 above, except allow the user to choose the system ideal gas from a screen menu, and omit the prompts for gas properties. Use the data in Appendix C.13 for the properties of the gases in your menu.

109. Write a computer program that will allow you to plot (either on the computer or manually) the entropy production rate due to the heat transfer from the fin in text Example 5.17 vs. the base temperature of the fin T_f. Allow the T_f to range from 20 to 200 °C. Keep all the remaining variables constant.

110. The temperature profile for the fin discussed in text Example 5.17 was for a "very long" (i.e., infinite) fin. A more accurate equation for a finite fin of length L is

$$T(x) = T_\infty + (T_f - T_\infty)\left\{\frac{\cosh[m(L-x)] + [h/(mk)]\sinh[m(L-x)]}{\cosh(mL) + [h/(mk)]\sinh(mL)}\right\}$$

where the remaining variables are defined in Example 5.17. Using this temperature profile, rework Example 5.17 and Problem 109 above to produce a new plot of entropy production rate vs. fin base temperature (you may wish to use a numerical integration technique here). Which has the smaller entropy production rate, the infinite fin or the finite fin?

111. In text Example 5.18 the fluid in the gap between the cylinders was maintained isothermal. If, instead, the outer and inner cylinder surfaces are maintained isothermal at temperatures T_2 and T_1, respectively, and the gap between the cylinders is very small, then the fluid in the gap will not be isothermal but will have temperature and velocity profiles given by

$$T(x) = T_1 + (T_2 - T_1)[1 + \text{Br}/2)][1 - (x - R_1)/t](x - R_1)/t$$

$$V(x) = R_1\omega(R_2 - x)/t$$

where $t = R_2 - R_1$ and Br is the dimensionless Brinkman number,[28]

$$\text{Br} = \mu R_1^2\omega^2/[k_t(T_2 - T_1)]$$

Rework text Example 5.18 using these temperature and velocity profiles with $T_1 = 40$ °C, $T_2 = 20$ °C, and $k_t = 0.13$ W/(m·K). Use the values given in Example 5.18 for the remaining variables. Since the resulting integrals involve a considerable amount of algebraic manipulation, you may wish to use a numerical integration technique.

Problems for Section III

112. Using a linear mass fraction profile similar (but with a different slope) to that of text Example 5.21, compute the mass flux and entropy production rate per unit area of water evaporating from a wet wall where the mass fraction of water is 0.003, through a 1.0-cm

28. The Brinkman number is named after H. C. Brinkman who solved the equations for the flow of a fluid with viscous heat generation in a circular tube in 1951. This dimensionless number is approximately the ratio of the viscous heat generation rate to the rate of conduction heat transfer due to the imposed temperature difference, $T_2 - T_1$. Note that there will be a maximum in the temperature profile between the two cylinders if $|\text{Br}| > 2$.

stagnant air–water vapor mixture at 5 °C and standard atmospheric pressure. The water vapor mass fraction at the top of the stagnant layer is 10^{-4}.

113. The mass fraction profile that results from the gaseous diffusion of a checimal species B across a stagnant layer of thickness δ of a mixture of gases A and B is often modeled as

$$w_A = w_A^\circ (w_A^\delta / w_A^\circ)^{x/\delta} \qquad \text{for } 0 \le x \le \delta$$

where w_A° is the value of w_A at $x = 0$, and w_A^δ is the value of w_A at $x = \delta$. For this profile determine

a) the mass flux (from Fick's first law) at any distance x from the surface,

b) the formula for the local entropy production rate density due to diffusion within the stagnant layer, and

c) the formula for the total entropy production rate per unit area normal to the diffusion flux.

114. Evaluate part c of Problem 113 for water vapor diffusing through a stagnant air–water vapor mixture 0.01 m thick at standard atmospheric pressure and 0 °C. The water vapor mass fraction at the top of the stagnant layer ($x = \delta$) is 10^{-4}, and at the bottom of the layer it is 0.003.

115. Evaluate part c of Problem 113 for the same gases and conditions used in text Example 5.21. Compare your result with that of Example 5.21 and explain any major differences.

116. Binary radial diffusion through an isothermal stagnant spherical gas layer around a liquid droplet is often modeled by the following mass fraction profile

$$w_B = 1 - w_A = w_{B1}(w_{B2}/w_{B1})^\alpha \qquad \text{for } r_1 \le x \le r_2$$

where $\alpha = \left(\frac{1}{r_1} - \frac{1}{x}\right) \Big/ \left(\frac{1}{r_1} - \frac{1}{r_2}\right)$ and w_{B1} and w_{B2} are the values of w_B at $x = r_1$ and at $x = r_2$. For this system, determine

a) the formula for the mass flux of A through the layer,

b) the formula for the local entropy production rate density in the layer, and

c) the formula for the total entropy production rate within the layer.

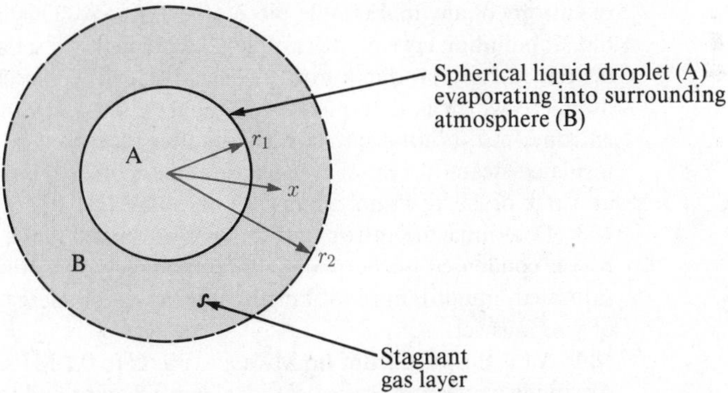

117. An inventor reports that he has a refrigeration compressor that receives saturated Refrigerant-12 vapor at 0 °F and delivers it at 150 psia and 120 °F. The compression process is adiabatic. Show whether or not this process violates the second law of thermodynamics.

118. A steam power plant operates on the simple reversible thermodynamic cycle shown below.

a) What is its thermal efficiency?

b) What is the steam mass flow rate in this system?

c) What would its thermal efficiency be if it were operated on a Carnot cycle?

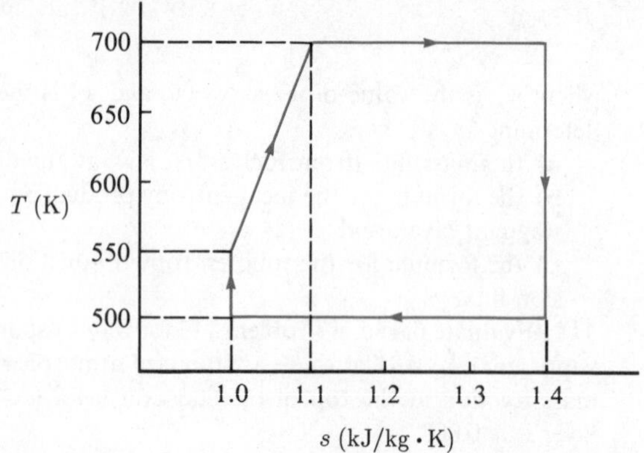

119. A steam turbine is limited to a maximum inlet temperature of 800 °C. The exhaust pressure is 0.01 MPa and the moisture in the turbine exhaust is not to exceed 9.0%.

a) What is the maximum allowable turbine inlet pressure if the flow is adiabatic and reversible?

b) What is the maximum power output per unit mass flow rate?

120. A steam turbine receives steam at 1.0 MPa and 700 °C and exhausts at 0.1 MPa. If the turbine can be considered to operate as a steady flow, reversible, adiabatic machine, what is the work done per pound of steam flowing? Neglect any changes in kinetic or potential energy.

121. Saturated mercury vapor enters a steady flow turbine of a high-pressure auxiliary power system at 600 psia and emerges as a mixture of liquid and vapor at a pressure of 1.0 psia. What must be the flow rate if the power output is to be 10 kW? Assume the turbine is reversible and adiabatic, and neglect any changes in kinetic or potential energy.

122. In the year 2238 there will be a law that will require certain limits on the production of entropy of any marketable piece of technology. This law will be similar in nature to the old air pollution laws of the twentieth century. It will set an upper limit of 0.001 kJ/(kg·K·s) on the entropy production rate density (which will become known simply as the EPRD number), which is determined by dividing the entire mass of the device generating the entropy into its total entropy production rate. Determine the steady state EPRD of an insulated steam turbine that has a total mass of 2000 kg, takes in steam at 3.5 MPa, 400 °C at a rate of 2.0 kg/s and exhausts it at 5.0 kPa, 90.0% quality.

123. Determine the entropy production rate as 5.0 lbm/s of saturated water vapor at 14.696 psia is condensed isothermally and aergonically in a steady flow, steady state process to a saturated liquid. Ignore all kinetic and potential energy changes. Explain the significance of your answer.

124. Air is throttled from 1.0 MPa and 30 °C to 0.1 MPa in a steady flow adiabatic process. Assuming constant specific heat ideal gas behavior and ignoring any changes in kinetic and potential energy, determine

a) the change in flow stream entropy, and

b) the entropy produced per kg of air flowing.

125. Determine the nozzle outlet diameter in text Example 5.22 required to increase the nozzle efficiency by decreasing the entropy production rate by 25%.

126. Determine the final temperature and the entropy production per unit mass of air at 1.0 MPa, 25 °C, and 2 m/s that expands adiabatically through a horizontal nozzle to 0.1 MPa and 100 m/s. Assume constant specific heat ideal gas behavior and ignore any changes in kinetic and potential energy.

127. Refrigerant-12 enters an insulated nozzle at 25 psia, 80 °F, and 10 ft/s. The flow accelerates and reaches 15 psia and 60 °F just before it exits the nozzle. The process is adiabatic and steady flow.

a) What is the exit velocity?

b) Is the flow reversible or irreversible?

128. Air is expanded in an insulated horizontal nozzle from 100 psia, 100 °F to 26 psia, 70 °F. Neglecting the inlet velocity and any change in potential energy determine **a)** the outlet velocity and **b)** the entropy production rate per unit mass flowing. Assume the air behaves as an ideal gas with constant specific heats.

129. 40 MPa, 800 °C steam expands through a heated nozzle to 0.1 MPa and 90% quality at a rate of 100 kg/h. Neglect the inlet velocity and any change in potential energy, and take the entropy production rate to be 10% of the magnitude of the entropy transport due to heat transfer. Determine

a) the entropy production rate if the surface temperature of the nozzle is 450 °C,

b) the exit velocity, and

c) the exit area of the nozzle.

130. Refrigerant-12 flows steadily through an adiabatic throttling valve. At the inlet to the valve the fluid is a saturated liquid at 110 °F. At the valve outlet the pressure is 19.189 psia. Neglecting any changes in kinetic and potential energy, determine

a) the quality of the fluid at the valve outlet, and

b) the entropy production per pound of R-12 flowing through the valve.

131. Carbon dioxide (CO_2) at 50 MPa and 207 °C is expanded isothermally through an uninsulated nozzle to 1.5 MPa in a steady state, steady flow process. Assuming the CO_2 to be a constant specific heat ideal gas, determine

a) the heat transfer rate of the nozzle per kg of CO_2 flowing, and

b) the change in kinetic energy of the CO_2 across the nozzle per lbm of CO_2 flowing.

There is no change in potential energy across the nozzle, and the surface temperature of the nozzle is 307 °C. The entropy production rate magnitude in this problem can be taken to be 10% of the absolute value of the heat transfer rate.

132. Refrigerant-12 is throttled irreversibly through an insulated horizontal constant diameter tube. Saturated liquid R-12 enters the tube at 80 °F, and exits the tube at 10 °F.

a) What is the increase in entropy per lbm of R-12 flowing through the tube?

b) What is the entropy production rate per unit mass flow rate of R-12?

c) Show the initial and final states on a *T-s* diagram.

d) Determine the average Joule-Thomson coefficient for this process.

133. Saturated liquid Refrigerant-12 is expanded irreversibly in a refrigerator expansion valve from 100 to 0 °F. Determine **a)** the entropy of the R-12 after the expansion and **b)** the entropy production rate of the expansion process per unit mass flow rate. Assume the process is adiabatic and aergonic, and neglect any changes in kinetic and potential energy.

134. A steady state desuperheater (a type of mixing heat exchanger) adiabatically mixes superheated vapor and liquid with the properties shown below. Complete vaporization of the liquid reduces the enthalpy of the vapor to $h = 1390$ kJ/kg at the exit of the desuperheater. Compute the rate of entropy production in the desuperheater.

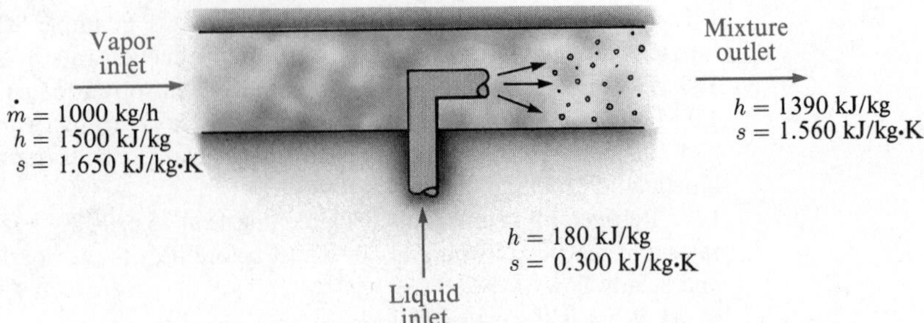

135. A solar concentrating heat exchanger system directs sunlight onto a long straight pipe. The pipe receives 153.616 Btu/h per foot of length. If water enters the pipe at 50 lbm/h as saturated liquid at 300 °F and is heated isothermally so that it leaves as vapor at 20 psia, then

a) how long is the pipe for steady state, steady flow conditions, and
b) what is the rate of entropy production.
c) Show whether this system violates the second law of thermodynamics.

136. Consider a simple constant pressure boiler (heat exchanger) which converts 3.0 kg/min of saturated liquid water at 1.0 atm pressure into saturated vapor at 1.0 atm in a steady state, steady flow, single-inlet, single-outlet process.

a) What is the heat transfer rate into the boiler?
b) What is the entropy production rate inside the boiler?

137. A brilliant young engineering student has just invented a new chrome-plated digital heat exchanger which has water flowing through it at 14.41 kg/s. At the inlet the water is a saturated vapor at 200 °C. The water passes isothermally through the heat exchanger while it absorbs heat from the environment. At the outlet the pressure is 1.0 MPa. Determine **a)** the heat transfer rate, and **b)** the entropy production rate. **c)** Show whether this device violates the second law of thermodynamics. Assume that the system boundary temperature is isothermal at 200 °C.

138. A contact feedwater heat exchanger for heating the water going into a boiler operates on the principle of mixing steam with liquid water. For the steady flow adiabatic process shown below calculate

a) the rate of change of entropy of the entire heater, and
b) the rate of entropy production inside the heater.

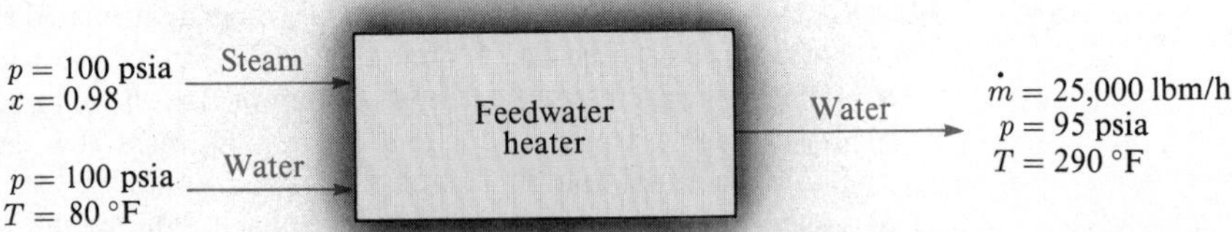

139. As an engineering consultant you are asked to review a design proposal in which an electric resistance heater is to be used in conjunction with a precision air bearing. The heater uses 100 W of electrical power and the air bearing has a constant surface temperature of 160 °F. The heater is well insulated on the outside and air enters the bearing at 40 °F, 35 psia and exists at 80 °F, 40 psia. The bearing is a steady flow, steady state device with an air flow rate of 35.55 lbm/h. Determine

a) whether this device violates the first law of thermodynamics, and
b) whether this device violates the second law of thermodynamics.

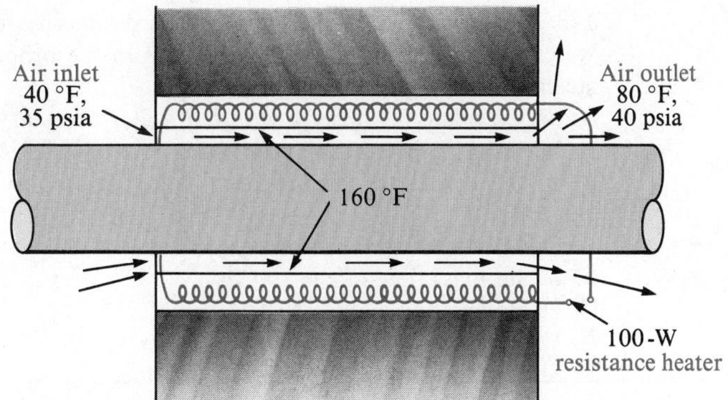

140. A slide projector contains a 500-W light bulb that is cooled by an internal fan that blows room air across the bulb at a rate of 1.0 kg/min. If the equilibrium surface temperature of the bulb is 350 °C and the inlet temperature (the room air) is at 20 °C, then determine **a)** the outlet temperature of the cooling air and **b)** the rate of entropy production by the projector. Assume the air is an ideal gas with constant specific heats and that it undergoes an aergonic process.

141. Determine the total entropy production rate for the heat exchanger shown below. In addition to the air–water heat transfer within the heat exchanger, the air also losses an unknown amount of heat to the surroundings while the water receives an additional 10 Btu/s from the surroundings. Assume the internal air–water interface is isothermal at 100 °F and that the outer surface of the heat exchanger is isothermal at 70 °F.

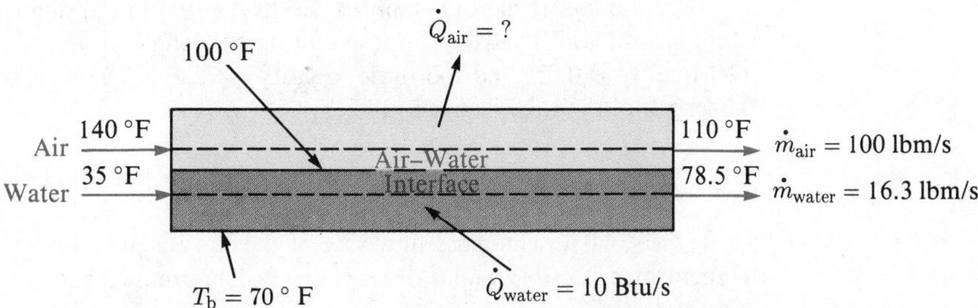

142. A new Yo Yo Dyne propulsion system has three flowstreams as shown below. It mixes 0.5 kg/s of saturated water vapor at 100 °C with 0.2 kg/s of saturated liquid water at 100 °C in a steady flow, steady state, isobaric process. This system is cheaply made and uninsulated, and consequently it loses heat at the rate of 75 kJ/s to the surroundings. Assuming the system boundary temperature is isothermal at 100 °C, determine

a) the quality of the outlet mixture, and

b) the entropy production rate of the system.

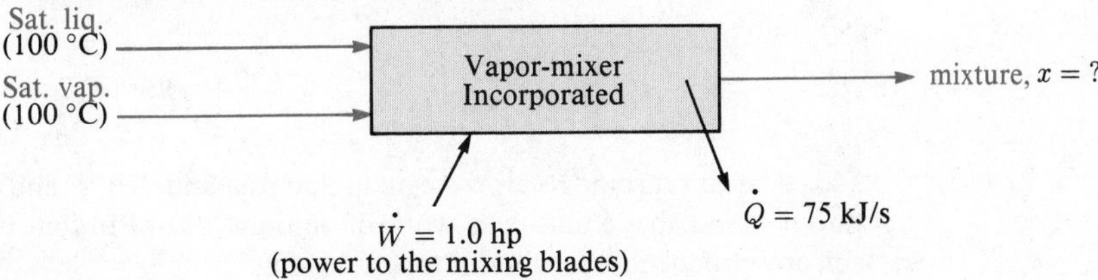

2257

143. In a steady flow adiabatic aergonic desuperheater (a kind of mixing heat exchanger), water is sprayed into superheated steam in the proper amount to cause the superheated steam to become saturated.

a) Calculate the mass flow rate of water necessary for desuperheating.
b) What is the entropy production rate of this system?
c) Show whether this process violates the second law of thermodynamics.

Given:

- Steam mass flow rate = 200 kg/h
- Steam entering state = 10.0 MPa, 600 °C
- Water entering state = 10.0 MPa, 100 °C
- Steam outlet state = 10.0 MPa, saturated vapor.

144. A steady state, steady flow steam mixer consists of a box with two inlet pipes and one outlet pipe. One of the inlet pipes carries saturated water vapor at 50 lbm/s and 20 psia. The other inlet pipe carries saturated liquid water at 10 lbm/s and 20 psia. The mixing process is isobaric. In addition, 9602 Btu/s of heat is added to the box by heat transfer from an external source. The surface temperature of the box is isothermal at 300 °F and no work is done on or by the mixing box. Determine

a) the quality (or temperature if superheated) of the exit flow, and
b) the rate of entropy production inside the mixing box.

145. You are now a world famous energy researcher and have been commissioned by the National Entropy Foundation (NEF) to determine the effect of vapor generation on the entropy production rate in a two-phase mixture. Your experiment consists of a steady state closed loop flow system in which a liquid–vapor mixture of Refrigerant-12 flows through a test section consisting of a stainless steel tube 0.319 in in diameter and 4.0 ft long. There is a constant wall heat flux imposed along the length of the tube of 450 Btu/(h·ft^2). The inlet quality is 0.0% and the outlet quality is 72.6%. The wall surface temperature along the length of the tube is given in °F by

$$T_w = 199.28 - 0.007217(x) + 0.39449(x^2)$$

for $0 \leq x \leq 4.0$ ft. The mass flow rate of the R-12 is 1000 lbm/h, and the inlet and outlet temperatures are 10 °F and 0 °F respectively. Determine the total entropy production rate in the test section.

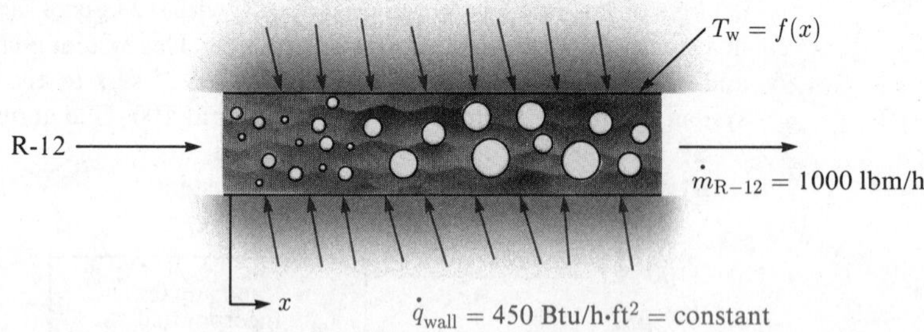

146. A steam turbine receives steam at 250 psia and 900 °F and exhausts it at 20 psia. The turbine is adiabatic and does work of amount 190.4 Btu/lbm of steam flowing. Find the entropy production per lbm of steam flowing.

147. What mass flow rate is required to produce 75 kW from a steam turbine with inlet conditions of 2.0 MPa, 900 °C and exit conditions of 0.1 MPa, 200 °C, if the turbine is reversible but not adiabatic? The heat transfer from the turbine occurs at a surface temperature of 50 °C. Neglect any changes in kinetic and potential energy.

148. Calculate the isentropic efficiency of a continuous flow adiabatic compressor that compresses 20 lbm/min of a constant specific heat ideal gas. The test data for this compressor are: Inlet state = 1.0 atm and 25 °C; outlet state = 1.0 MPa and 350 °C. $c_p = 1.0$ kJ/(kg·K), $R = 0.25$ kJ/(kg·K). The isentropic efficiency of a compressor is defined as

$$\eta_W = \frac{\dot{W}_{\text{isentropic compression}}}{\dot{W}_{\text{actual compression}}}$$

149. A steady flow, steady state air compressor handles 4000 ft^3/min measured at the intake state of 14.1 psia, 30 °F and a velocity of 70 ft/s. The discharge is at 45 psia and has a velocity of 280 ft/s. Both the inlet and exit stations are located 4 ft above the floor. Determine the discharge temperature and the power required to drive the compressor using the specific availability function relative to the environmental temperature of 80 °F for

a) a reversible adiabatic process, and

b) an irreversible adiabatic process with a compressor work transport efficiency of 80%.

150. Determine the work required to compress 15 kg/min of superheated steam in an uninsulated reversible compressor from 0.15 MPa, 600 °C to 1.5 MPa, 500 °C in a steady state, steady flow process. Neglect any changes in kinetic and potential energy. Use the availability function approach and calculate the specific availability at the inlet and exit if the environmental temperature is 20 °C. Choose the reference state to be saturated liquid at the environmental temperature.

151. An adiabatic, steady flow compressor is designed to compress superheated steam at a rate of 50 lbm/min. At the inlet to the compressor the state is: 100 psia and 400 °F, and at the compressor exit the state is: 200 psia and 600 °F. Neglecting any kinetic or potential energy effects, calculate

a) the power required to drive the compressor, and

b) the rate of entropy production of the compressor.

152. A steady flow air compressor takes in 5.0 kg/min of atmospheric air at 101.3 kPa and 20 °C and delivers it at an exit pressure of 1.0 MPa. The air can be considered an ideal gas with constant specific heats. Potential and kinetic energy effects are negligible. If the process is not reversible, but is adiabatic and polytropic with a polytropic exponent of $n = 1.47$, calculate

a) the power required to drive the compressor,

b) the entropy production rate of the compressor, and

c) the entrance and exit specific availability functions if the environmental temperature and pressure are 20 °C and 101.3 kPa.

153. An uninsulated irreversible steam engine whose surface temperature is 200 °F produces 50 hp with a steam mass flow rate of 15 lbm/min. The inlet steam is at 400 °F, 100 psia and it exits at 14.7 psia, 90% quality. Determine **a)** the rate of heat loss from the engine, **b)** its entropy production rate, and **c)** its entrance and exit specific availability functions based on an environmental temperature of 80 °F (use saturated liquid at the environmental temperature as the reference state).

154. A design for a turbine has been proposed involving the adiabatic, steady flow of steam through the turbine. Saturated vapor at 300 °C enters the turbine and the steam leaves at 0.2 MPa with a quality of 95%. **a)** Draw a *T-s* diagram for the turbine. **b)** Determine the work and entropy production per kilogram of steam flowing through the turbine. **c)** If the atmospheric temperature is 25 °C, determine the entrance and exit specific availability functions. Neglect any kinetic and potential energy effects, and take the reference state to be saturated liquid at the environmental temperature.

155. An uninsulated warp drive steam engine on a Romulan battle cruiser has a surface temperature of 200 °F. It produces 50 hp with a steam mass flow rate of 150 lbm/min. The inlet steam is at 400 °F, 100 psia, and it exits at 16.0 psia, 90% quality. Determine

a) the heat transfer rate from the engine, and

b) the entropy production rate of the engine.

c) Show whether the Romulans have discovered how to build steam engines that violate the second law of thermodynamics.

156. Steam enters a turbine at 1.5 MPa and 700 °C and exits the turbine at 0.2 MPa and 400 °C. The process is steady flow, steady state, and adiabatic. The environmental temperature and pressure are 35 °C and 0.1013 MPa. Determine the following on the basis of a steam flow rate of 6.3 kg/s:

a) the entropy production rate of the turbine,

b) the turbine's entrance and exit specific availability functions,

c) the work transport energy efficiency of the turbine, and

d) the turbine's actual output power.

157. Steam at 400 psia and 50% quality is heated in a steady flow isobaric heat exchanger until it becomes a saturated vapor. It is then expanded adiabatically through a turbine to 1.0 psia and 98% quality. This is followed by isobaric cooling to a saturated liquid in a second heat exchanger and then adiabatic compression to the initial state. Determine

a) the *net* output work, and

b) the entropy production rate per lbm of steam flowing in this system.

158. Through a clerical error our purchasing department has ordered a finely crafted but mysterious device from a foreign manufacturer. The manuals are all in a foreign language, and the only intelligible information is in the form of some numbers printed next to the extrance/exit ports and the rotating shaft. The 10-kW rating on the shaft may mean either a work input or a work output. Determine

a) the flow direction, *a* to *b* or *b* to *a*,

b) the mass flow rate, and

c) the entropy production rate of the device.

Assume a steady state, adiabatic device and that the working substance is H_2O. Assume also that the kinetic and potential energies of outlet and inlet flow streams are negligible.

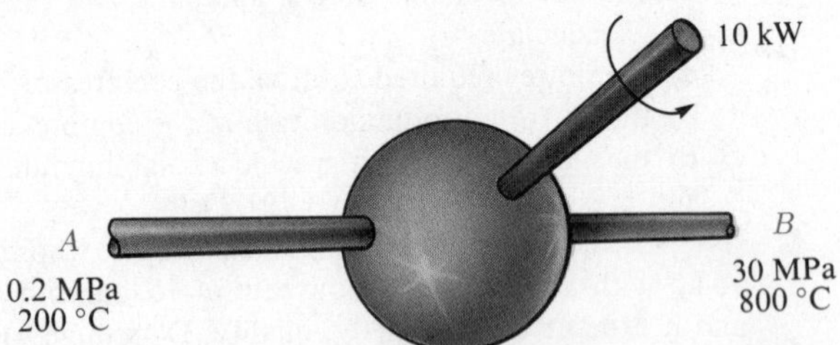

159. An irreversible steady state, steady flow steam turbine that has no thermal insulatiion has an isothermal surface temperature of 100 °F. It operates with a steam mass flow rate of 15 lbm/s. The turbine inlet is at 300 psia, 1200 °F and the exit is at 14.7 psia, 300 °F. If the turbine's entropy production rate is 0.5 Btu/(s·R), then determine

a) the turbine's heat transfer rate, and

b) the turbine's work rate (power).

160. A dog food manufacturer wishes to carry out the canning and sterilization process of a new pet food product at 100 °C, 0.01 MPa. After crawling around in the rafters of the plant an engineer finds a 1.6 MPa wet steam line. A pipe is then run from this line to the canning area, where it produces 1.4 MPa steam with 2% moisture. Now, instead of just throttling down to the 0.01 MPa state needed and wasting all that energy, the engineer decides to drop the pressure through a small adiabatic steam turbine.

a) What steam mass flow rate must be used to obtain 1.0 hp from the turbine?
b) What will be the turbine's entropy production rate under these conditions?

161. A nuclear reactor heats a fluid for the steady flow power plant shown below. The mass flow rate is 10 lbm/s. Determine

a) the horsepower input to the adiabatic pump,
b) the entropy production rate in the insulated reactor, and
c) the entropy production rate in the insulated turbine.

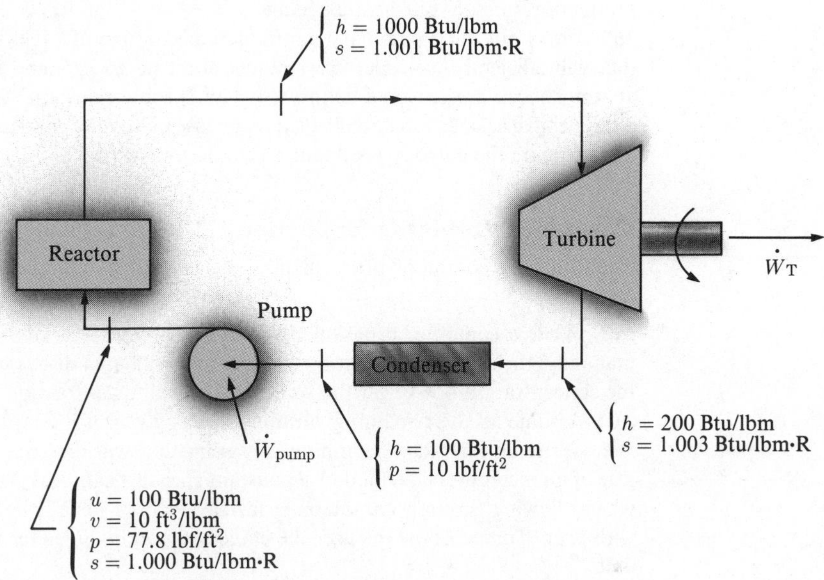

Design Problems for Section III

The following are elementary open-ended design problems. The objective is to carry out a preliminary thermal design as indicated. A detailed design with working drawings is not expected unless otherwise specified. These problems do not have specific answers, so each student's design will be unique.

162. A liquid will *cavitate* when the local pressure drops below the saturation pressure and the liquid begins to vaporize, or boil. The cavitation process is the formation of these vapor bubbles. Carry out the preliminary thermodynamic design of a closed loop apparatus that will illustrate this phenomenon by having a liquid pumped through a transparent nozzle wherein the pressure drops below the local saturation pressure and the vapor bubbles become visible. Choose a suitable liquid and provide an engineering sketch containing all the major dimensions and materials of your system. Estimate the pump size and power required, and the entropy production rate of your nozzle.

163. The Engine Test Facility at the Arnold Air Force Base in Tennessee requires a test cell 48 ft in diameter and 85 ft long with an air flow rate of 4300 ft^3/s at atmospheric pressure and temperature. Carry out the preliminary thermodynamic design of a compressor–nozzle system that will meet these requirements. The compressor inlet is at atmospheric conditions, and the inlet temperature of the nozzle must be 70 °F (this means an intercooling system must be used). Determine the horsepower required to drive the compressor, the nozzle outlet temperature and the entropy production rate of your nozzle. Assume the compression process is polytropic with $n = 1.3$, and that the pressure loss through the nozzle is 15% of the inlet pressure.

164. The Aeropropulsion System Test Facility at the Arnold Air Force Base in Tennessee requires a heat exchanger capable of cooling 2750 lbm/s of gas turbine exhaust from 3500 to 80 °F before discharging it to the atmosphere. Carry out a preliminary thermodynamic design of a suitable heat exchanger using water as the second fluid. Determine the amount of cooling water needed and recommend an appropriate source. Also determine the entropy production rate of your heat exchanger.

165. Carry out the preliminary thermodynamic design of a fuel-mixing valve for a furnace that will efficiently mix inlet flowstreams of air at 2.5 kg/s and methane at 0.5 kg/s, both at atmospheric pressure and temperature, and produce one outlet flowstream. Assume these gases behave as constant specific heat ideal gases. Provide a dimensioned engineering sketch and estimate the entropy production rate of your valve.

Computer Problems for Section III

The following computer problems are designed to be completed in BASIC on a microcomputer.

166. Write a computer program that will allow you to plot (either with the computer or manually) the entropy production rate per unit wall area discussed in text Example 5.21 vs. the concentration of CO_2 at the wall. Let the wall mass fraction of CO_2 range from 0.0 to 0.05. Assume all the remaining variables are as given in Example 5.21.

167. Write an interactive computer program that will determine the entropy production rate of an incompressible fluid or a constant specific heat ideal gas (allow the user to choose which) flowing through an adiabatic nozzle. Prompt for all the necessary input variables with proper units. Allow the user the choice of working in either Engineering English or SI units.

168. Write an interactive computer program that will determine the entropy production rate of an incompressible fluid or constant specific heat ideal gas (allow the user to choose which) from an adiabatic diffuser. Prompt for all the necessary input variables with proper units. Allow the user the choice of working in either Engineering English or SI units.

169. Write an interactive computer program that will determine the entropy production inside a heat exchanger having two inlets and two outlets when the mass flow rates, temperatures, and fluid properties of both of the flowstream fluids are known. Assume the fluids do not mix inside the heat exchanger, and allow either flowstream to be an incompressible liquid or a constant specific heat ideal gas at the user's discretion. Prompt for all the necessary input variables with proper units. Allow the user the choice of working in either Engineering English or SI units.

170. Write an interactive computer program that will perform an energy rate balance on a gas turbine engine. Prompt the user for the appropriate gas properties (in the proper units), the turbine's heat loss or gain rate, and the input mass flow rate and the inlet and exit temperatures. Output to the screen the turbine's output power. Assume the gas behaves as a constant specific heat ideal gas, and neglect all kinetic and potential energy terms. Allow the user the choice of working in either Engineering English or SI units.

171. Write an interactive computer program that will perform a steady state energy *and* entropy rate balance on an open system with an isothermal boundary. The system contains an ideal gas with constant specific heats that is undergoing an irreversible process. Prompt the user for all but *two* of the following input values (in proper units): the heat and work energy transport rates, the entropy production rate, the mass flow rate, all relevant temperatures and pressures, velocity and height of each flowstream entering and exiting the system, and the constant pressure specific heat of the gas contained in the system. Use a suitable reference state for the specific enthalpy and entropy calculations. Two of the above items will not be supplied by the user and therefore will become the unknown to be determined by the program. Output to the screen all the input variables plus the values of the unknowns. Allow the user the choice of working in either Engineering English or SI units.

172. Repeat Problem 171 above, except allow the user to choose the system ideal gas from a screen menu, and omit the prompts for gas properties. Use the data in Appendix C.13 for the properties of the gases in your menu. Also allow the user to choose which variable is to be the unknown from a screen menu, and then prompt for all the remaining variables. Use the conservation of mass law to determine or check the balance of the mass flows.

Problems for Section IV (Advanced Topics)

173. The sales literature for the device shown below claims that the outlet temperature is slightly higher than the inlet temperature due to the presence of the vortex tube.

a) Assuming the vortex tube and the rest of the system is isentropic, determine the outlet temperature (T_4) from the data given in the schematic.

b) Explain how the temperature rise claimed by the manufacturer could in fact exist.

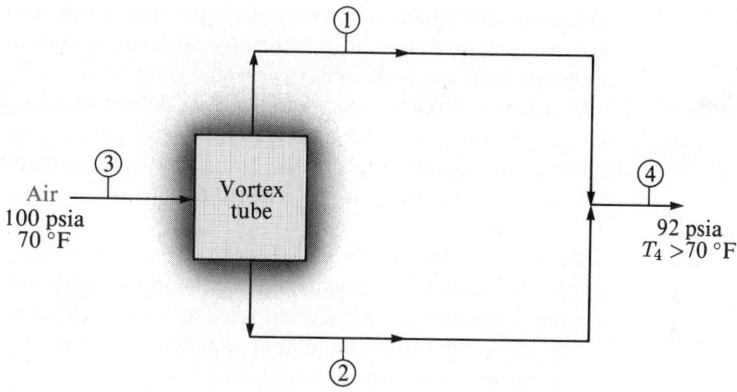

174. Determine the entropy production rate as 0.05 kg/s of air flows through a vortex tube from an inlet pressure of 1.0 MPa. Both hot and cold side exit pressures are 101.3 kPa, and the hot side temperature is 50 °C while the cold side temperature is −40 °C. Two-thirds of the inlet mass flow rate passes through the hot side exit. Assume constant specific heat ideal gas behavior and neglect any changes in kinetic and potential energy.

175. Using Eqs. 5.132, 5.120 and 5.33, discuss the possibility of having a temperature separation occur in a constant specific heat incompressible liquid flowing through a vortex tube.[29]

---

29. This effect was predicted and later experimentally verified as a result of preparing this text problem. See R. T. Balmer, Pressure-driven Ranque-Hilsch temperature separation in liquids, ASME *Journal of Fluids Engineering*, 161–164 (June 1988).

176. A company claims to be able to manufacture a vortex tube using air that reaches −250 °F cold side and +250 °F hot side (both at atmospheric pressure) with an inlet pressure of 20 psig and a hot side mass flow fraction of 50%. Does their vortex tube violate the second law of thermodynamics? Assume constant specific heat ideal gas behavior and neglect any changes in kinetic and potential energy.

177. Determine the maximum possible hot side exit temperature in a vortex tube using air when the cold side temperature is 0 °C, the hot side mass flow fraction is 50%, the inlet pressure is 0.8 MPa, and both exits are at atmospheric pressure. Assume constant specific heat ideal gas behavior and neglect any changes in kinetic and potential energy.

178. Determine the heat transfer rate and the entropy production rate for the steady state, steady flow of water flowing through a straight horizontal 1.0-in-inside-diameter pipe 10 ft long at a rate of 5.0 ft^3/min. The Darcy-Weisbach friction factor for this flow is 0.032. The flow is isothermal at 75 °F, and the mass density of the water is 62.26 lbm/ft^3.

179. Determine the entropy production rate and heat transfer in a newly designed valve with 1.1 kg/s of an incompressible hydraulic oil flowing through it. The minor loss coefficient of the valve is 26.3, and the inlet and outlet oil temperatures are 53 and 49 °C, respectively. The surface temperature of the valve is constant at 46 °C. The flow velocity through the valve is constant at 3.0 m/s, and the specific heat of the oil is 1.13 kJ/(kg·K).

180. A valve in an air handling system has a mass flow rate of 2.9 kg/min and a minor loss coefficient of 11.56. The valve inlet temperature is 20 °C and the valve is insulated. The inlet and exit pressures of the valve are 1.66 and 0.3 MPa, respectively. The air velocity through the valve is 2.7 m/s. Assuming air to be an ideal gas with constant specific heats, determine the exit temperature and entropy production rate of the valve.

181. Air enters a sudden contraction in a pipe at a rate of 0.3 lbm/s. The contraction coefficient is 0.47, the exit temperature is 156 °F and the exit diameter is 2.0 in. The pipe is insulated. The pressure across the contraction drops from 185 to 50 psia. Determine the entrance temperature and the entropy production rate of the contraction. Assume the air to be an ideal gas with constant specific heats.

182. Liquid mercury enters an insulated sudden expansion with a velocity of 1.15 m/s at 20 °C. The inlet and exit areas are 0.001 and 0.01 m^2, respectively. Assuming the flow is incompressible and adiabatic, determine the exit temperature and the entropy production rate of the expansion. The specific heat and density of the mercury are 0.1394 kJ/(kg·K) and 13,579 kg/m^3.

183. It is required to dissipate 3.3 kJ/s of water flow energy in a spillway with a hydraulic jump. 1000 kg/s of water enters at 15 °C and a depth of 0.5 m. The water passes through the jump fast enough to be considered adiabatic. Determine

a) the required hydraulic jump depth, $y_2 - y_1$ (see Table 5.3),
b) the exit water temperature, and
c) the entropy production rate of the hydraulic jump.

184. 0.73 kg/s of oil at 1.2 MPa and 20 °C enters a system at 8 m/s and exits the system at 0.8 MPa, 40 °C, and 4 m/s. The exit is 4 m below the inlet. The specific weight of the oil is 6000 N/m^3, which is a constant throughout the system. The specific heat of the oil is constant at 1.21 kJ/(kg·K). Determine **a)** the heat transfer rate and **b)** the entropy production rate of this system if its boundary temperature is maintained constant at 40 °C.

185. Determine the entropy production rate for the isothermal steady laminar flow of a constant specific heat incompressible power law non-Newtonian fluid in a horizontal circular tube of radius R whose velocity profile is given by

$$V = V_m[1 - (x/R)^{(n+1)/n}]$$

where V_m is the maximum (i.e., centerline) velocity, x is the radial coordinate measured from the tube's centerline, and n is the power law exponent (a positive constant). Sketch a plot of $\dot{S}_P$ vs. n and determine the value of n that minimizes $\dot{S}_P$.

186. The steady laminar flow of a constant specific heat incompressible Newtonian fluid through a horizontal circular tube of radius R has a velocity profile given by

$$V = V_m[1 - (x/R)^2]$$

where V_m is the maximum (i.e., centerline) velocity and x is the radial coordinate measured from the tube's centerline. If there is a uniform heat flux $\dot{q}_s$ at the tube wall, then the temperature profile within the fluid (neglecting axial conduction) is given by

$$T = T_o + (\dot{q}_s R/k_t)[\alpha - (x/R)^2 + 0.25(x/R)^4] \quad \textbf{(1)}$$

where T_o and α are constants, and k_t is the thermal conductivity of the fluid.

a) Combine the heat transfer and viscous work entropy production rates per unit volume to show that the total entropy production rate per unit volume for this system is given by

$$\sigma = \frac{4\mu V_m^2 x^2}{R^4 T} + \frac{1}{k_t}\left\{\frac{\dot{q}_s}{T}[2x/R - (x/R)^3]\right\}^2 \quad \textbf{(2)}$$

b) Comment on the integration of σ over the system volume. Remember that the T in Eq. 2 is given by Eq. 1, and that in a polar cylindrical coordinate system, $d\mathcal{V} = 2\pi Lx\, dx$. Carry out the integration analytically if you can.

c) What factors in Eq. 2 can be manipulated to minimize $\dot{S}_P$?

187. The velocity and temperature profiles that are established in the free convection of a fluid contained between two flat parallel vertical walls maintained at different isothermal temperatures T_1 and T_2 are

$$V = \rho\beta g b^2(T_2 - T_1)(x/b)[(x/b)^2 - 1]/12\mu$$

and

$$T = (T_1 + T_2)/2 - (T_2 - T_1)(x/2b)$$

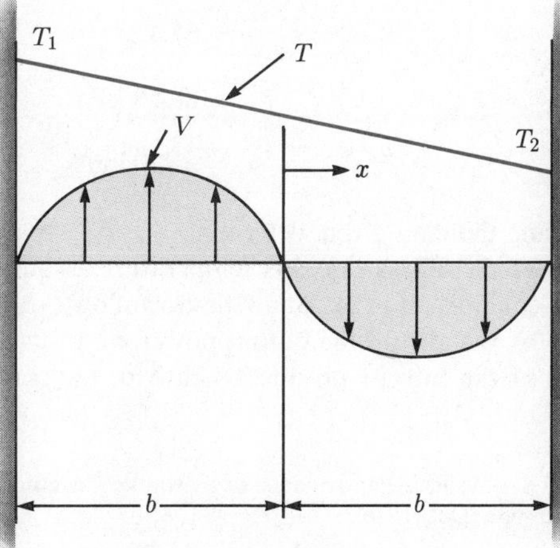

where x is measured from the centerline between the plates, β is the coefficient of volume expansion, ρ is the density and $2b$ is the distance between the plates. Determine a formula for the entropy production rate per unit depth and length of this flow due to viscous effects.

188. The figure below is a schematic of a novel hydraulic air compressor built in Michigan in 1906 at the Victoria Copper Mining Company and operated unitl 1921. This plant used the power of falling water from the Ontonagon River to produce high-pressure air without having any moving mechanical parts. The falling water compressed entrained air bubbles which were then separated from the water in a large underground separation tank. The efficiency of this system is defined to be

$$\eta = \frac{\text{rate of energy removed from the compressed air}}{\text{net hydraulic power of the water}} = \frac{\dot{m}_a(h_2 - h_3)_a}{\dot{m}_w(gH/g_c)}$$

where the "a" subscript refers to the air and the "w" subscript refers to the water.

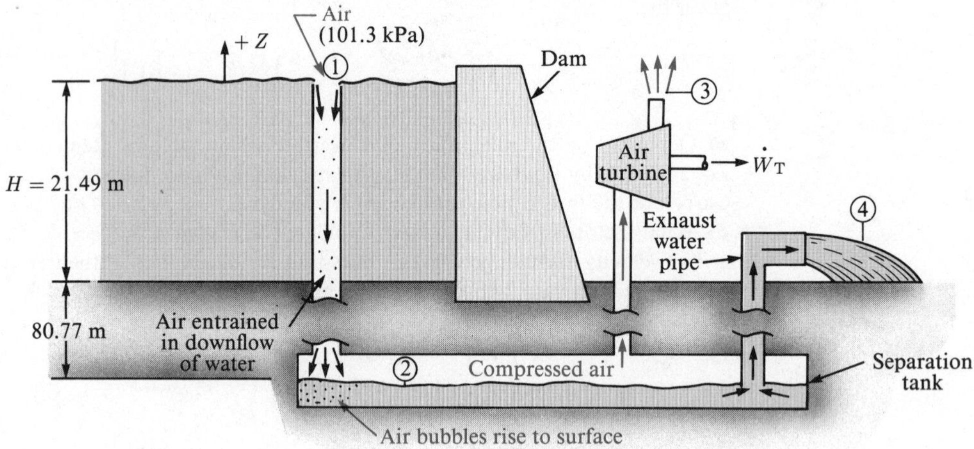

Data for the Victoria hydraulic air compressor[30]

$\eta = 57.4\%$	$\dot{m}_w = 6119.1$ kg/s
$p_{2a} = 882.6$ kPa	$T_{1a} = T_{1w} = 20$ °C
$\dot{m}_a = 5.430$ kg/s	$H = 21.49$ m

Using the data given, determine

a) the separation tank temperature assuming the air and water are in constant thermal equilibrium in an adiabatic downflow,

b) the air turbine output power, and

c) the entropy production rate for the compressor assuming it is completely adiabatic.

30. See W. Rice Performance of hydraulic gas compressors, ASME *Journal of Fluids Engineering* 645–653 (Dec. 1976).

In your analysis assume air to be a constant specific heat ideal gas and water to be an incompressible liquid. Neglect any changes in kinetic energy of the air and the water. Note that the air turbine discharges to the atmosphere, so

$$p_3 = p_{atm} = 101.3 \text{ kPa}.$$

189. A bottle of beer is emptied reversibly and adiabatically at a rate of 0.1 kg/s. What is the rate of change of entropy of the contents of the beer bottle if the properties of the beer are

$$h = 53 \text{ kJ/kg} \qquad T = 10.0\text{ °C}$$

$$p = 0.1013 \text{ MPa} \qquad s = 1.000 \text{ kJ/(kg·K)}$$

and the entropy production rate is 0.01 kJ/(s·K).

190. Helium at 70 °F enters a 3.0-ft^3 rigid tank that is filled to a final pressure of 2200 psia. Assuming the tank is initially evacuated and that the helium behaves as an ideal gas with constant specific heats, determine the amount of entropy produced when the tank is filled

a) adiabatically, and

b) isothermally at 70 °F.

191. Plot the isothermal to adiabatic entropy production ratio for filling an initially evacuated container with equal amounts of an incompressible liquid vs. the dimensionless ratio $pv/(cT)$ as this ratio ranges from 0 to 10.

192. A 0.037 m^3 hydraulic cylinder is filled with 30 kg of oil (an incompressible liquid) from a supply at 20 °C and 50 MPa. The specific heat of the oil is 1.83 kJ/(kg·K). Determine

a) the entropy produced if the cylinder is filled isothermally at 20 °C, and

b) the final temperature and the entropy produced if the cylinder is filled adiabatically.

193. Eq. 5.150 shows that filling a rigid container adiabatically with an incompressible liquid produces less entropy than filling it isothermally. However, an adiabatic filling process will produce a temperature rise in the vessel (see Eq. 4.143) such that $T_{final} = T_2 > T_{initial} = T_1$.

a) Develop a formula for the additional entropy produced when the rigid container adiabatically filled with an incompressible liquid is cooled back to the initial temperature by submerging it into a large isothermal bath at temperature T_1.

b) Compare the total entropy produced by the adiabatic filling plus the cooling process described in part a with that produced during an isothermal filling process at temperature T_1.

Design Problems for Section IV

194. Carry out the preliminary thermodynamic design of a system that uses a vortex tube to cool a full body suit for a fire fighter. The suit must be able to reject up to 1200 Btu/h, and this cooling rate must be easily adjustable by the wearer. Use the data given in text Example 5.28 or from appropriate industrial literature.

195. Carry out the preliminary thermodynamic design of a system that uses a vortex tube to heat a skin-tight suit for an underwater diver by bleeding off part of the air supply to the diver. The suit must be able to supply 800 Btu/h, and this heating rate must be easily adjustable by the diver. Use the data given in text Example 5.28 or from appropriate industrial literature.

196. Carry out the preliminary thermodynamic design of a hydraulic system that will deliver 60 °F water at a rate of 150 gallons per minute through a manual valve (gate, globe, ball, etc., your choice) and a piping system to a reservoir. The piping system will require 1500 ft of straight pipe, eight 90° elbows, and one sudden expansion entrance at the reservoir. Use only standard sizes of schedule 40 galvanized iron pipe and fittings, and consult a price catalog from a local pipe and fitting supplier to minimize the ratio of material cost to entropy production rate. You will find the appropriate values of minor loss coefficients, friction factors, etc., in an engineering fluid mechanics textbook. The computer program suggested in Problem 200 will be of value in the design process.
197. Carry out the preliminary thermodynamic design of a system that will isothermally fill an initially evacuated rigid cylindrical tank with air at 20 °C to 20.0 MPa with a minimum amount of entropy production. The tank is 0.25 m in diameter and 1.5 m high. Assume the air behaves as a constant specific heat ideal gas. Discuss the technology and the economics of how the tank will be maintained isothermal during the filling process. Note that there will be entropy production in the pipes and valves used to connect the tank to the air supply.
198. The Von Karman Gas Dynamics Facility at the Arnold Air Force Base in Tennessee has need of a blow-down wind tunnel which is to be supplied from tank containing compressed air initially at 1000 psia and 70 °F. The wind tunnel is to be at the end of a nozzle attached to the tank, and must be 8 ft in diameter and have a velocity of 10,000 ft/s at 2000 R. The tank must be of sufficient size to sustain these wind tunnel conditions for a minimum of 30 min of testing. Carry out the preliminary thermodynamic design of such a facility and estimate the size of the storage tank required, the power required to compress the air in filling the tank if it must be done overnight (i.e., in 8 h). Determine the entropy production associated with both the filling and the emptying of the tank if both are done isothermally.

Computer Problems for Section IV

The following computer problems are designed to be completed in BASIC on a microcomputer.

199. Curve fit the hot and cold outlet temperature data given in text Example 5.28 vs. the inlet absolute pressure. Then write an interactive computer program that will return these outlet temperatures plus the COP of this device when it is used as a Carnot heat pump and when it is used as a Carnot refrigerator or air conditioner when the user inputs the inlet pressure. Use this program to generate enough data to plot (either on the computer or manually) the values of these two COPs vs. the inlet absolute pressure.
200. Write an interactive computer program that will output the entropy production rate for the steady state, steady aergonic isothermal flow of an incompressible liquid through the series of hydraulic systems illustrated in Table 5.3. Prompt the user for the appropriate input values ($\dot{m}$, T_b, f, L, D, K_M, K_C, etc.) in proper units.
201. Write an interactive computer program that will output the entropy production rate for the filling of an initially evacuated rigid vessel with an incompressible liquid or an ideal gas (allow the user to choose which) when the vessel is filled either adiabatically or isothermally (again allow the user to choose). Prompt the user for all the required input information in proper units. Allow the user to work in either Engineering English or SI units.

Chapter Six Generalized Thermodynamic Property Relations

In Chapter 3 we discussed some of the basic relations used in determining numerical values for thermodynamic properties. The values of all the thermodynamic properties that are not directly measurable (e.g., u, h, s) must be determined from the values of the properties that are measurable (e.g., p, v, T). For elementary materials such as incompressible substances and ideal gases, simple equations of state provide these relations. More complex materials require sophisticated equations of state plus a general knowledge of various mathematical property interrelations to be able to evaluate their thermodynamic properties. In this chapter we build upon the equations of state introduced in Chapter 3 and formulate various new property interrelations whose results can be used for real materials. We further explain how to obtain numerical values for real as well as ideal substances based upon experimental measurements for only a few thermodynamic properties. Later, in Chapter 12, we complete this subject by showing how thermodynamic property values can be estimated when only the basic molecular structure of the material is known and experimental measurements of thermodynamic properties are not available.

To begin this chapter we will round out our list of thermodynamic properties by introducing two new properties, the Helmholtz and Gibbs functions. We will then move on to develop a series of general mathematical relations among all the thermodynamic properties. We end this chapter by using the principle of corresponding states to develop a set of generalized thermodynamic property charts that are valid for many real gases.

Two New Properties: Helmholtz and Gibbs Functions

If we consider a stationary closed system containing a pure substance subjected only to a moving boundary mechanical work mode, then the combined energy and entropy balance is given by Eq. 5.30 as

$$du = T\,ds - p\,dv \tag{6.1}$$

Since any two independent properties will fix the thermodynamic state of a pure substance subjected to only one work mode (see Section I of Chapter 4), we can take the two independent properties here to be s and v, or

$$u = u(s, v)$$

The total differential of this composite function, then, has the form

$$du = \left(\frac{\partial u}{\partial s}\right)_v ds + \left(\frac{\partial u}{\partial v}\right)_s dv \tag{6.2}$$

Comparing Eqs. 6.1 and 6.2 we see that

$$T = \left(\frac{\partial u}{\partial s}\right)_v \tag{6.3}$$

and

$$p = -\left(\frac{\partial u}{\partial v}\right)_s \tag{6.4}$$

For this same system we can also write, from Eq. 5.31, that

$$dh = T\,ds + v\,dp \tag{6.5}$$

and in this case we take the two independent properties to be s and p so that

$$h = h(s, p)$$

whose total differential is

$$dh = \left(\frac{\partial h}{\partial s}\right)_p ds + \left(\frac{\partial h}{\partial p}\right)_s dp \tag{6.6}$$

Upon comparing Eqs. 6.5 and 6.6 we see that

$$T = \left(\frac{\partial h}{\partial s}\right)_p \tag{6.7}$$

and

$$v = \left(\frac{\partial h}{\partial p}\right)_s \tag{6.8}$$

We now introduce two new thermodynamic properties. The first is the total Helmholtz function F, named after the German physicist and physiologist Hermann Ludwig Ferdinand Von Helmholtz (1821–1894), defined as

$$F = U - TS$$

Dividing by the system mass gives the specific Helmholtz function f as

$$f = u - Ts \tag{6.9}$$

Differentiating this equation gives

$$df = du - T\,ds - s\,dT$$

but from Eq. 6.1 we have

$$du - T\,ds = -p\,dv$$

so that

$$df = -p\,dv - s\,dT \tag{6.10}$$

If we presume the existence of a functional relation of the form

$$f = f(v, T)$$

then its total differential is

$$df = \left(\frac{\partial f}{\partial v}\right)_T dv + \left(\frac{\partial f}{\partial T}\right)_v dT \tag{6.11}$$

and upon comparing Eqs. 6.10 and 6.11 we see that

$$p = -\left(\frac{\partial f}{\partial v}\right)_T \tag{6.12}$$

and

$$s = -\left(\frac{\partial f}{\partial T}\right)_v \tag{6.13}$$

The second new thermodynamic function is the total Gibbs function G, named after the American physicist Josiah Willard Gibbs (1839–1903), defined as

$$G = H - TS$$

Dividing by the system mass gives the specific Gibbs function g as

$$g = h - Ts \tag{6.14}$$

Differentiating Eq. 6.14 gives

$$dg = dh - T\,ds - s\,dT$$

but from Eq. 6.5 we have

$$dh = T\,ds + v\,dp$$

so that

$$dg = v\,dp - s\,dT \tag{6.15}$$

If we presume a functional relation of the form

$$g = g(p, T)$$

then its total differential is

$$dg = \left(\frac{\partial g}{\partial p}\right)_T dp + \left(\frac{\partial g}{\partial T}\right)_p dT \tag{6.16}$$

and comparing Eqs. 6.15 and 6.16 gives

$$v = \left(\frac{\partial g}{\partial p}\right)_T \tag{6.17}$$

and

$$s = -\left(\frac{\partial g}{\partial T}\right)_p \tag{6.18}$$

Table 6.1 summarizes these results. The importance of this set of partial differential equations lies in the fact that they relate easily measurable properties (p, v, T) to nonmeasurable properties (u, h, s, f, and g). Therefore, accurate p, v, T data on any pure substance can be used to generate information about u, h, s, f, and g for that substance.

Table 6.1 Summary of thermodynamic property relations

$$T = \left(\frac{\partial u}{\partial s}\right)_v = \left(\frac{\partial h}{\partial s}\right)_p$$

$$v = \left(\frac{\partial h}{\partial p}\right)_s = \left(\frac{\partial g}{\partial p}\right)_T$$

$$p = -\left(\frac{\partial u}{\partial v}\right)_s = -\left(\frac{\partial f}{\partial v}\right)_T$$

$$s = -\left(\frac{\partial f}{\partial T}\right)_v = -\left(\frac{\partial g}{\partial T}\right)_p$$

The Gibbs Phase Equilibrium Condition

Both the pressure and the temperature must be constant when the liquid and vapor phases of a pure substance are in equilibrium with each other. Under these conditions Eq. 6.16 gives $dg = 0$, and since $g = g_f + xg_{fg}$, we can then write

$$dg = dg_f + x\,dg_{fg} + g_{fg}\,dx = 0$$

Again Eq. 6.15 can be used to evaluate $dg_f = dg_{fg} = 0$. Since x can vary during the phase equilibrium, dx cannot be zero. Therefore, we are forced to conclude from the above equation that $g_{fg} = 0$ at phase equilibrium, or $g_f = g_g$. Using the definition of the Gibbs function, Eq. 6.14, we see that at phase equilibrium

$$g_f = g_g = h_f - (T_{sat})s_f = h_g - (T_{sat})s_g$$

or

$$h_g - h_f = h_{fg} = (T_{sat})(s_g - s_f) = (T_{sat})s_{fg}$$

or

$$s_{fg} = h_{fg}/T_{sat} \tag{6.19}$$

The Maxwell Equations

Two sets of equations were named after the Scottish physicist James Clerk Maxwell (1831–1879): the electromagnetic field equations, and the thermodynamic property equations. The thermodynamic Maxwell equations allow additional numerical information to be obtained about the nonmeasurable properties u, h, s from accurately measured p, v, T data.

Consider an arbitrarily continuous function of the form

$$z = z(x, y)$$

Then we can write its total differential as

$$\begin{aligned} dz &= \left(\frac{\partial z}{\partial x}\right)_y dx + \left(\frac{\partial z}{\partial y}\right)_x dy \\ &= M\,dx + N\,dy \end{aligned} \tag{6.20}$$

where we have set

$$M = \left(\frac{\partial z}{\partial x}\right)_y \quad \text{and} \quad N = \left(\frac{\partial z}{\partial y}\right)_x$$

If we now differentiate M with respect to y while holding x constant and differentiate N with respect to x while holding y constant we get

$$\left(\frac{\partial M}{\partial y}\right)_x = \frac{\partial^2 z}{\partial y\,\partial x} \quad \text{and} \quad \left(\frac{\partial N}{\partial x}\right)_y = \frac{\partial^2 z}{\partial x\,\partial y}$$

Since we require $z(x, y)$ to be a continuous function, it follows that

$$\frac{\partial^2 z}{\partial y\,\partial x} = \frac{\partial^2 z}{\partial x\,\partial y}$$

or that

$$\left(\frac{\partial M}{\partial y}\right)_x \equiv \left(\frac{\partial N}{\partial x}\right)_y \tag{6.21}$$

Recall that the thermodynamic state of any pure substance is fixed by any pair of independent intensive thermodynamic properties of that substance. That is, any property of a pure substance can be written as a function of any other two independent properties of that substance. Consequently, if x and y are such independent properties, then z will also be a property provided that Eq. 6.21 is satisfied. For example, suppose for some pure substance we have the relation $dz = p\,dv + v^2\,dp$. Then, $M = p$ and $N = v^2$, and

$$\left(\frac{\partial M}{\partial y}\right)_x = \left(\frac{\partial p}{\partial p}\right)_v = 1$$

and

$$\left(\frac{\partial N}{\partial x}\right)_y = \left(\frac{\partial (v^2)}{\partial v}\right)_p = 2v \neq \left(\frac{\partial M}{\partial y}\right)_x$$

and since Eq. 6.21 is not satisfied by these functions of M and N, then this particular z function cannot be a thermodynamic property.

If we now look at our four basic property relationships as being differential equations of the form of Eq. 6.20,

$$du = T\,ds - p\,dv \tag{6.1}$$

$$dh = T\,ds + v\,dp \tag{6.5}$$

$$df = -p\,dv - s\,dT \tag{6.10}$$

$$dg = v\,dp - s\,dT \tag{6.15}$$

then Eq. 6.21 must be valid for these equations since we already know that all of these functions are thermodynamic properties. Applying Eq. 6.21 to each of these equations yields a new set of equations, known as the Maxwell thermodynamic equations

$$\left(\frac{\partial T}{\partial v}\right)_s = -\left(\frac{\partial p}{\partial s}\right)_v \tag{6.22}$$

$$\left(\frac{\partial T}{\partial p}\right)_s = \left(\frac{\partial v}{\partial s}\right)_p \tag{6.23}$$

$$\left(\frac{\partial p}{\partial T}\right)_v = \left(\frac{\partial s}{\partial v}\right)_T \tag{6.24}$$

$$\left(\frac{\partial v}{\partial T}\right)_p = -\left(\frac{\partial s}{\partial p}\right)_T \tag{6.25}$$

These relations will be used later in this chapter to provide property information from experimental p, v, T data. The following example shows that the form of these equations depends upon the type of reversible work mode present in the system.

Example 6.1

The equation of state for a nonlinear elastic material is given by

$$F = KT(L/L_o - 1)^2$$

where F is the stretching force, L is the stretched length, L_o is the initial length, K is the elastic constant, and T is the absolute temperature of the material. Then

a) determine the Maxwell equations for this material,

b) show that the internal energy of this material is a function of temperature only, and

c) determine the heat transfer required when this material is stretched isothermally and reversibly from $L_o = 0.07$ m to $L = 0.2$ m at $T = 20$ °C when $K = 0.150$ N/K.

Solution

a) Since the reversible work mode involved in the stretching process is

$$(\bar{d}W)_{\text{rev}} = F\,dL$$

the Maxwell equations for this material can be easily obtained from those derived in the text by replacing p by $-F$ and v by $L/m = \ell$, the *specific length* of the material. Then Eqs. 6.22 to 6.25 become

$$\left(\frac{\partial T}{\partial \ell}\right)_s = \left(\frac{\partial F}{\partial s}\right)_\ell$$

$$\left(\frac{\partial T}{\partial F}\right)_s = -\left(\frac{\partial \ell}{\partial s}\right)_F$$

$$\left(\frac{\partial F}{\partial T}\right)_\ell = -\left(\frac{\partial s}{\partial \ell}\right)_T$$

and

$$\left(\frac{\partial \ell}{\partial T}\right)_F = \left(\frac{\partial s}{\partial F}\right)_T$$

b) The combined energy and entropy balance for this material is

$$du = T\,ds + F\,d\ell$$

so that

$$\left(\frac{\partial u}{\partial \ell}\right)_T = T\left(\frac{\partial s}{\partial \ell}\right)_T + F$$

From the third Maxwell equation for this substance listed in part a above and from the given equation of state we have

$$\left(\frac{\partial s}{\partial \ell}\right)_T = -\left(\frac{\partial F}{\partial T}\right)_\ell$$

$$= -\,K(L/L_o - 1)^2$$

and

$$T\left(\frac{\partial s}{\partial \ell}\right)_T = -\,KT(L/L_o - 1)^2 = -F$$

Therefore,

$$\left(\frac{\partial u}{\partial \ell}\right)_T = -\,F + F = 0$$

That is, u does not depend on ℓ and therefore u must be a function of T only.
c) A closed system energy balance applied to this material for an isothermal process gives

$$
\begin{aligned}
{}_1Q_2 &= -\,{}_1W_2 = -\int_{L_o}^{L} F\,dL \\
&= -KT\int_{L_o}^{L} (L/L_o - 1)^2\,dL \\
&= -KTL_o(L/L_o - 1)^3/3 \\
&= -\,(0.150\text{ N/K})(293\text{ K})(0.07\text{ m})\left(\frac{0.20}{0.07} - 1\right)^3\Big/3
\end{aligned}
$$

$${}_1Q_2 = -\,6.57\text{ N}\cdot\text{m}$$

Consequently, there is a heat transfer out of the system equal in magnitude to the work input.

The Clapeyron Equation

Benoit Pierre Emile Clapeyron (1799–1864) was a French mining engineer and a contemporary of Carnot who, in the 1830s, took an interest in studying the physical behavior of gases and vapors. He was able to derive a relation for the enthalpy change of the liquid to vapor phase transition (h_{fg}) in terms of pressure, temperature, and specific volume, thus providing one of the first equations for calculating a property that is not directly measurable in terms of properties that are directly measurable. Today this relation is most easily derived from one of the Maxwell equations, Eq. 6.24. For an isothermal phase change from a saturated liquid to a saturated vapor, the pressure and temperature are independent of volume. Then Eq. 6.24 becomes

$$\left(\frac{\partial p}{\partial T}\right)_v = \left(\frac{dp}{dT}\right)_{sat} = \frac{s_g - s_f}{v_g - v_f} = s_{fg}/v_{fg}$$

and using Eq. 6.19 we obtain the Clapeyron equation as[1]

$$\left(\frac{dp}{dT}\right)_{sat} = h_{fg}/(T_{sat}v_{fg}) \tag{6.26}$$

For most substances $v_g \gg v_f$, so we can approximate $v_{fg} \approx v_g$. Also, for vapors at very low pressures the saturated vapor curve can be accurately approximated by the ideal gas equation of state, so we can write $v_g = RT_{sat}/p$. Then Eq. 6.26 becomes

$$\left(\frac{dp}{dT}\right)_{sat} = ph_{fg}/(RT_{sat}^2)$$

or

$$\left(\frac{dp}{p}\right)_{sat} = [h_{fg}/(RT_{sat}^2)]dT_{sat} \tag{6.27}$$

This equation is often called the Clapeyron–Clausius equation. For small pressure and temperature changes h_{fg} can be assumed to be constant and then Eq. 6.27 can be integrated from a reference state to any other state to give

$$\ln(p/p_o)_{sat} = (h_{fg}/R)\frac{T_{sat} - T_o}{T_{sat}T_o} \tag{6.28a}$$

1. The Clapeyron equation is valid for any type of phase change in a simple substance. For example, if we let the i subscript denote the solid phase, then for melting we can write

$$\left(\frac{dp}{dT}\right)_{\substack{\text{solid-}\\\text{liquid}\\\text{saturation}}} = h_{if}/(T_{sat}v_{if})$$

and for sublimation,

$$\left(\frac{dp}{dT}\right)_{\substack{\text{solid-}\\\text{vapor}\\\text{saturation}}} = h_{ig}/(T_{sat}v_{ig})$$

or

$$p_{sat} = p_o \exp\left[(h_{fg}/R)\frac{T_{sat} - T_o}{T_{sat}T_o}\right] \qquad \textbf{(6.28b)}$$

Where p_o and T_o are reference state values. An exponential relation between p_{sat} and T_{sat} fits experimental data quite well for most substances at low pressure.

Example 6.2

In 1849 William Rankine proposed the following relation between the saturation pressure and saturation temperature of water

$$\ln p_{sat} = 14.05 - \frac{6289.78}{T_{sat}} - \frac{913{,}998.92}{T_{sat}^2}$$

where p_{sat} is in psia, and T_{sat} is the temperature in °F + 461.2 (at that time −461.2 °F was Rankine's best estimate of absolute zero temperature). Determine h_{fg} at 212 °F from the Rankine equation and compare the result with that listed in the steam tables in the Appendix.

Solution The Rankine equation does not have the same form as Eq. 6.28*a*, so it must have a temperature dependent h_{fg}. In this case we must use Eq. 6.27. Differentiating Rankine's equation we obtain

$$\left(\frac{1}{p}\frac{dp}{dT}\right)_{sat} = \frac{6289.78}{T_{sat}^2} + \frac{1{,}827{,}997.8}{T_{sat}^3}$$

then using Eq. 6.27 we get

$$h_{fg} = \left[\frac{RT^2}{p}\left(\frac{dp}{dT}\right)\right]_{sat} = R(6289.78 + 1{,}827{,}997.8/T_{sat})$$

From Appendix C.13*a* we find $R = 85.78$ ft·lbf/(lbm·R) = 0.1102 Btu/(lbm·R). Then, at 212 °F,

$$h_{fg}(212\ °F) = [6289.78\ R + (1{,}827{,}997.8\ R^2)/(461.2 + 212\ R)] \times [0.1102\ Btu/(lbm \cdot R)] = 992.37\ Btu/lbm$$

Appendix C.1*a* gives $h_{fg}(212\ °F) = 970.4$ Btu/lbm. Thus, the value obtained from Rankine's equation is in error by only +2.26%.

Additional Property Relations

For a simple substance any two independent intensive properties fix its thermodynamic state. Consider the specific internal energy described by a function of temperature and specific volume. We can write this as $u = u(T, v)$. Differentiating this function we get

$$du = \left(\frac{\partial u}{\partial T}\right)_v dT + \left(\frac{\partial u}{\partial v}\right)_T dv$$

From Eq. 6.1 we can write

$$\left(\frac{\partial u}{\partial v}\right)_T = T\left(\frac{\partial s}{\partial v}\right)_T - p$$

and using the Maxwell Eq. 6.24 this becomes

$$\left(\frac{\partial u}{\partial v}\right)_T = T\left(\frac{\partial p}{\partial T}\right)_v - p$$

In Chapter 3 we introduced the constant volume specific heat c_v as

$$c_v = \left(\frac{\partial u}{\partial T}\right)_v \tag{3.33}$$

and our equation for the total differential du then becomes

$$du = c_v\, dT + \left[T\left(\frac{\partial p}{\partial T}\right)_v - p\right] dv \tag{6.29}$$

Therefore, the change in specific internal energy for any simple substance can be determined by integrating Eq. 6.29,

$$u_2 - u_1 = \int_{T_1}^{T_2} c_v\, dT + \int_{v_1}^{v_2} \left[T\left(\frac{\partial p}{\partial T}\right)_v - p\right] dv \tag{6.30}$$

Notice that Eq. 6.30 is cast completely in terms of the measurable quantities p, v, T, and c_v.

Similarly, we can consider the specific enthalpy to be given by a continuous function of temperature and pressure, $h = h(T, p)$. Then its total differential is

$$dh = \left(\frac{\partial h}{\partial T}\right)_p dT + \left(\frac{\partial h}{\partial p}\right)_T dp$$

In Chapter 3 we introduced the constant pressure specific heat c_p as

$$c_p = \left(\frac{\partial h}{\partial T}\right)_p \tag{3.42}$$

Introducing the definition of specific enthalpy into Eq. 6.1 gives

$$du = dh - p\,dv - v\,dp = T\,ds - p\,dv$$

or

$$dh = T\,ds + v\,dp \tag{6.31}$$

and from this equation we can deduce that

$$\left(\frac{\partial h}{\partial p}\right)_T = T\left(\frac{\partial s}{\partial p}\right)_T + v$$

Using the Maxwell Eq. 6.25 we get

$$\left(\frac{\partial h}{\partial p}\right)_T = -T\left(\frac{\partial v}{\partial T}\right)_p$$

and our total differential dh then becomes

$$dh = c_p\,dT + \left[v - T\left(\frac{\partial v}{\partial T}\right)_p\right]dp \tag{6.32}$$

The change in specific enthalpy for any simple substance is then given by

$$h_2 - h_1 = \int_{T_1}^{T_2} c_p\,dT + \int_{p_1}^{p_2}\left[v - T\left(\frac{\partial v}{\partial T}\right)_p\right]dp \tag{6.33}$$

Again we have an equation cast completely in terms of the measurable quantities, p, v, T, and c_p. Also note that Eqs. 6.30 and 6.33 are related by the fact that $h_2 - h_1 = u_2 - u_1 + p_2v_2 - p_1v_1$.

Finally, we can carry out the same type of analysis for the specific entropy of a simple substance. If we let $s = s(T, v)$, then

$$ds = \left(\frac{\partial s}{\partial T}\right)_v dT + \left(\frac{\partial s}{\partial v}\right)_T dv$$

From Eqs. 6.1 and 3.33 we can deduce that

$$\left(\frac{\partial s}{\partial T}\right)_v = \left(\frac{1}{T}\right)\left(\frac{\partial u}{\partial T}\right)_v = \frac{c_v}{T}$$

and using the Maxwell Eq. 6.24 we can write the total differential ds as

$$ds = \left(\frac{c_v}{T}\right)dT + \left(\frac{\partial p}{\partial T}\right)_v dv \tag{6.34}$$

Integrating this gives a relation for the change in specific entropy of a pure substance based completely upon measurable quantities,

$$s_2 - s_1 = \int_{T_1}^{T_2} \frac{c_v}{T}\,dT + \int_{v_1}^{v_2} \left(\frac{\partial p}{\partial T}\right)_v dv \tag{6.35}$$

By assuming $s = s(T, p)$ we can also show that (see Problem 27 at the end of this chapter)

$$ds = \frac{c_p}{T}\,dT - \left(\frac{\partial v}{\partial T}\right)_p dp \tag{6.36}$$

and

$$s_2 - s_1 = \int_{T_1}^{T_2} \frac{c_p}{T}\,dT - \int_{p_1}^{p_2} \left(\frac{\partial v}{\partial T}\right)_p dp \tag{6.37}$$

Example 6.3

In Chapter 3 an equation of state developed in 1903 by Pierre Berthelot (1827–1907) was briefly discussed. Using this equation of state, develop equations based on measurable properties for the changes in **a)** specific internal energy, **b)** specific enthalpy and **c)** specific entropy for an isothermal process.

Solution The Berthelot equation is given in Eq. 3.72 as

$$p(v - b) = RT - a(v - b)/(Tv^2)$$

where a and b are constants. Solving this equation for p gives

$$p = RT/(v - b) - a/(Tv^2)$$

a) The change in specific internal energy is given by Eq. 6.30, for which we need

$$\left(\frac{\partial p}{\partial T}\right)_v = R/(v - b) + a/(T^2v^2)$$

Then, for an isothermal process ($T_1 = T_2$), Eq. 6.30 gives

$$(u_2 - u_1)_T = \int_{v_1}^{v_2} [RT/(v - b) + a/(Tv^2) - RT/(v - b) + a/(Tv^2)]\,dv$$

$$= -(2a/T)(1/v_2 - 1/v_1) = 2a(v_2 - v_1)/(Tv_1v_2)$$

b) To find the change in specific enthalpy we could use Eq. 6.33. However, to evaluate this equation we need to be able to determine the relation $(\partial v/\partial T)_p$. Since the Berthelot equation is not readily solvable for $v = v(T, p)$, we choose instead to use the simpler approach utilizing only the definition of specific enthalpy, $h = u + pv$. Then,

$$(h_2 - h_1)_T = (u_2 - u_1)_T + p_2v_2 - p_1v_1 = \frac{2a(v_2 - v_1)}{Tv_1v_2} + p_2v_2 - p_1v_1$$

$$= \frac{a(v_2 - v_1)}{Tv_1v_2} + RT\left(\frac{v_2}{v_2 - b} - \frac{v_1}{v_1 - b}\right)$$

c) Finally, since we have already evaluated the relation $(\partial p/\partial T)_v$, we choose to use Eq. 6.35 for the isothermal specific entropy relation:

$$(s_2 - s_1)_T = \int_{v_1}^{v_2} \left(\frac{\partial p}{\partial T}\right)_v dv$$

$$= \int_{v_1}^{v_2} [R/(v - b) + a/(T^2v^2)]\, dv$$

$$= R \ln[(v_2 - b)/(v_1 - b)] + a(v_2 - v_1)/(T^2v_1v_2)$$

Note that for an ideal gas undergoing an isothermal process,

$$(u_2 - u_1)_T = (h_2 - h_1)_T = 0 \quad \text{and} \quad (s_2 - s_1)_T = R \ln(v_2/v_1)$$

Therefore, the equations developed in Example 6.3 can be considered to be Berthelot corrections to ideal gas behavior.

Equation 6.34 has the same $M\,dx + N\,dy$ form as Eq. 6.20, so that we can utilize Eq. 6.21 to produce the property relation

$$\left[\frac{\partial(c_v/T)}{\partial v}\right]_T = \left[\frac{\partial}{\partial T}\left(\frac{\partial p}{\partial T}\right)_v\right]_v$$

or

$$\left(\frac{\partial c_v}{\partial v}\right)_T = T\left(\frac{\partial^2 p}{\partial T^2}\right)_v \tag{6.38}$$

Similarly, Eq. 6.36 has the same $M\,dx + N\,dy$ form and application of Eq. 6.21 to it gives

$$\left[\frac{\partial(c_p/T)}{\partial p}\right]_T = -\left[\frac{\partial}{\partial T}\left(\frac{\partial v}{\partial T}\right)_p\right]_p$$

or

$$\left(\frac{\partial c_p}{\partial p}\right)_T = -T\left(\frac{\partial^2 v}{\partial T^2}\right)_p \tag{6.39}$$

Both Eqs. 6.38 and 6.39 give specific heat information from measurable p, v, T properties.

Example 6.4 Using the Berthelot equation of state given in Example 6.3, determine an equation for the isothermal variation in the constant volume specific heat with volume change.

Solution From Eq. 6.38 we have what we seek,

$$\left(\frac{\partial c_v}{\partial v}\right)_T = T\left(\frac{\partial^2 p}{\partial T^2}\right)_v$$

and from Example 6.3, the Berthelot equation of state can be written as

$$p = \frac{RT}{v - b} - \frac{a}{Tv^2}$$

so that

$$\left(\frac{\partial p}{\partial T}\right)_v = \frac{R}{v - b} + \frac{a}{T^2 v^2}$$

and

$$\left(\frac{\partial^2 p}{\partial T^2}\right)_v = -\frac{2a}{T^3 v^2}$$

then

$$\left(\frac{\partial c_v}{\partial v}\right)_T = -\frac{2a}{T^2 v^2}$$

and to find an explicit $c_v = c_v(T, v)$ equation, the above equation can be integrated from a reference state specific volume v_o to give

$$c_v = -\frac{2a}{T^2}\int_{v_o}^{v}\frac{dv}{v^2} = 2a(v_o - v)/(T^2 v_o v) > 0$$

Note that c_v is independent of v only in the case of an ideal gas ($a = b = 0$ in the Berthelot equation of state).

Finally, if Eqs. 6.34 and 6.36 are set equal to each other,

$$\left(\frac{c_v}{T}\right) dT + \left(\frac{\partial p}{\partial T}\right)_v dv = \left(\frac{c_p}{T}\right) dT - \left(\frac{\partial v}{\partial T}\right)_p dp$$

and if we solve for dT,

$$dT = \left(\frac{T}{c_p - c_v}\right)\left(\frac{\partial v}{\partial T}\right)_p dp + \left(\frac{T}{c_p - c_v}\right)\left(\frac{\partial p}{\partial T}\right)_v dv$$

Then, writing the general relation $T = T(p, v)$ and differentiating it we get

$$dT = \left(\frac{\partial T}{\partial p}\right)_v dp + \left(\frac{\partial T}{\partial v}\right)_p dv$$

and by comparing coefficients of dp and dv in these two equations it is clear that

$$\left(\frac{\partial T}{\partial p}\right)_v = \left(\frac{T}{c_p - c_v}\right)\left(\frac{\partial v}{\partial T}\right)_p$$

and

$$\left(\frac{\partial T}{\partial v}\right)_p = \left(\frac{T}{c_p - c_v}\right)\left(\frac{\partial p}{\partial T}\right)_v$$

or

$$c_p - c_v = T\left(\frac{\partial v}{\partial T}\right)_p\left(\frac{\partial p}{\partial T}\right)_v = T\left(\frac{\partial p}{\partial T}\right)_v\left(\frac{\partial v}{\partial T}\right)_p$$

Using Eq. 3.15 we can write

$$\left(\frac{\partial p}{\partial T}\right)_v = -\left(\frac{\partial v}{\partial T}\right)_p\left(\frac{\partial p}{\partial v}\right)_T$$

which, when substituted into the previous equation yields

$$c_p - c_v = -T\left(\frac{\partial v}{\partial T}\right)_p^2\left(\frac{\partial p}{\partial v}\right)_T \tag{6.40}$$

In Chapter 3 we defined the isobaric coefficient of volume expansion β as

$$\beta = \frac{1}{v}\left(\frac{\partial v}{\partial T}\right)_p \tag{3.20}$$

and the isothermal coefficient of compressibility κ as

$$\kappa = -\frac{1}{v}\left(\frac{\partial v}{\partial p}\right)_T \tag{3.21}$$

Substituting these two relations into Eq. 6.40 gives the final result,

$$c_p - c_v = T\beta^2 v/\kappa \tag{6.41}$$

This equation reveals several important results. First of all, $c_p = c_v$ for all simple substances at absolute zero temperature. Second, since $\beta^2/\kappa = 0$ for incompressible materials, then $c_p = c_v$ for all incompressible materials. In this case the p and v subscripts are normally dropped and we write $c_p = c_v = c$ for all incompressible materials. Finally, since T, β, v, and κ are always positive, then $c_p \geq c_v$ for all simple substances.

Example 6.5 Using the data in Table 3.2, determine the difference between c_p and c_v for saturated liquid water at 20 °C.

Solution From Table 3.2, for water, we find that

$$\beta = 0.207 \times 10^{-6}\ \text{K}^{-1}$$

$$\kappa = 45.9 \times 10^{-11}\ \text{m}^2/\text{N}$$

and from Appendix C.1*b* we find that

$$v = v_f(20\ °\text{C}) = 0.001002\ \text{m}^3/\text{kg}$$

Then from Eq. 6.41, we have

$$c_p - c_v = \frac{(293\ \text{K})(0.207 \times 10^{-6}\ \text{K}^{-1})^2(0.001002\ \text{m}^3/\text{kg})}{45.9 \times 10^{-11}\ \text{m}\cdot\text{s}^2/\text{kg}}$$

$$= 2.74 \times 10^{-5}\ \text{J/(kg}\cdot\text{K)} = 2.74 \times 10^{-8}\ \text{kJ/(kg}\cdot\text{K)}$$

In most applications this difference is clearly negligible since the value of c_p for liquid water at STP is 4.18 kJ/(kg·K).

Constructing Tables and Charts

The construction of thermodynamic tables and charts like the ones in the appendix of this text require, first of all, that a great deal of accurate experimental p, v, T, and c_v (or c_p) data be obtained. These data are then reduced to mathematical equations through curve-fitting techniques. The resultant mathematical equations are then used to derive equations for u, h, and s using the thermodynamic property relations discussed above. One of the simplest methods for generating saturation and superheat tables is carried out as follows.

A) the following four data sets must be developed from appropriate experiments:

Data Set 1. saturation temperature and saturation pressure, (T_{sat}, p_{sat});
Data Set 2. pressure, specific volume, and temperature in the superheated vapor region and along the saturated vapor curve, (p, v, T);
Data Set 3. saturated liquid specific volume (or density) and saturation temperature, (v_f, T_{sat}); and
Data Set 4. low- (or zero) pressure constant volume specific heat and temperature in the superheated vapor region and along the saturated vapor curve[2], (c_v°, T).

2. The superscript ° is used to denote the fact that the c_v values are measured at (essentially) zero pressure.

B) Once these four data sets have been obtained a mathematical equation is curve fit to each of them to obtain four mathematical equations of the form:

Curve fit 1. $p_{sat} = p_{sat}(T_{sat})$ **(6.42*a*)**

Curve fit 2. $p = p(v, T)$ (for superheated and saturated vapor) **(6.42*b*)**

Curve fit 3. $v_f = v_f(T_{sat})$ **(6.42*c*)**

Curve fit 4. $c_v^\circ = c_v^\circ(T)$ (for superheated and saturated vapor) **(6.42*d*)**

C) A very low-pressure reference state (p_o, v_o, T_o) is chosen such that $(c_v)_o = c_v^\circ$, and then Eqs. 6.30, 3.39, and 6.35 are used to calculate values for u, h, and s relative to this reference state as

$$u = u_o + \int_{T_o}^{T} c_v^\circ \, dT + \int_{v_o}^{v} \left[T\left(\frac{\partial p}{\partial T}\right)_v - p \right] dv \tag{6.43}$$

$$h = u + pv \tag{3.39}$$

and

$$s = s_o + \int_{T_o}^{T} \left(\frac{c_v^\circ}{T}\right) dT + \int_{v_o}^{v} \left(\frac{\partial p}{\partial T}\right)_v dv \tag{6.44}$$

where u_o and s_o are the internal energy and entropy values of the reference state. Note that these reference state properties will always cancel out in a typical internal energy change $(u_2 - u_1)$ or entropy change $(s_2 - s_1)$ calculation, so their values can be arbitrarily chosen and need not be made known to the user of the table or chart. Typically u_o and s_o are chosen so as to make h_f and s_f zero at the reference temperature T_o, and T_o is often taken to be the triple point temperature (see, for example, the first row of values for water in Appendix C.1*a*) because the triple point is a well-defined and easily reproducible reference state. Therefore, u_o and s_o are seldom chosen to be zero themselves.

The generation of the tables can now be carried out as follows:

Saturation Tables A temperature entry saturation table can be constructed as follows:

1. A temperature $T = T_{sat}$ is chosen at which the properties are to be determined.
2. From the $p_{sat} = p_{sat}(T_{sat})$ curve fit formula (Eq. 6.42*a*), $(dp/dt)_{sat}$ is determined and then u_g, h_g, and s_g values are determined at this T_{sat} value from Eqs. 6.43, 3.39, and 6.44.
3. Then the $p = p(v, T)$ curve fit formula (Eq. 6.42*b*), which must be valid for saturated vapor as well as superheated vapor, is used to calculate v_g at the T_{sat} value.

4. Then Eq. 6.42*c* is used to calculate $v_{fg} = v_g - v_f$ at the T_{sat} value.
5. The remaining saturated liquid properties are determined from the Clapeyron and Gibbs Eqs. 6.26 and 6.19 as follows:

$$h_f = h_g - h_{fg} = h_g - T(v_{fg})\left(\frac{dp}{dT}\right)_{sat} \tag{6.45}$$

$$u_f = u_g - u_{fg} = u_g - (h_{fg} - p_{sat}v_{fg}) \tag{6.46}$$

and

$$s_f = s_g - s_{fg} = s_g - h_{fg}/T_{sat} \tag{6.47}$$

This sequence of operations is repeated for a variety of T_{sat} values, and the compilation of all these results gives a temperature entry saturation table like Appendix C.1*a* or C.1*b*.

Beginning the calculation sequence with a $p = p_{sat}$ value and then calculating the corresponding T_{sat} value from Eq. 6.42*a* and continuing as described above will produce a pressure entry saturation table like Appendix C.2*a* or C.2*b*.

Superheated Vapor Tables Superheated vapor tables are somewhat easier to construct.

1. Begin by choosing a pair of pressure–temperature (p, T) values and then calculate the corresponding specific volume v from Eq. 6.42*b*.
2. Values are then calculated for u, h, and s from Eqs. 6.43, 3.39, and 6.44 by utilizing $(\partial p/\partial T)_v$ determined from Eq. 6.42*b*.

The compilation of v, u, h, and s for each set of p and T values chosen forms a superheated vapor table like Appendix C.3*a* or C.3*b*.

Many tables do not list both u and h values since these properties are simply related to each other through $h = u + pv$. Therefore, if only one is listed in a table (it is usually h), the other can be easily calculated.

Thermodynamic Charts When accurate values for p, T, v, u, h, and s have been determined for the construction of saturated and superheated property tables it is a relatively simple task to plot these values to form thermodynamic charts. Two-dimensional plots only allow two independent properties to be plotted, and the remaining properties have to be added to the plot as parametric families of lines representing constant property values (isotherms, isobars, etc.). For example, the Mollier diagram (see Figure 5.7*a*) has h and s as coordinate axes. This means that all the remaining property information must be displayed as families of lines of constant p, constant T, constant v, and so forth.

Because of the large number of variables to choose from and the lack of any standard thermodynamic chart format, the charts found in the appendix of this text have many different coordinate axes (*h-s*, *T-s*, *p-h*, *p-v*, *v-u*, etc.).

Although all thermodynamic tables and charts up to about 1950 were generated from manual calculations, the use of a modern digital computer can substantially reduce the amount of human labor involved. Most of the required software programming is straightforward, simply by following the steps outlined above. However, one aspect of this process that is not so obvious involves solving Eq. 6.42*b* for v when p and T are known. These equations are often so algebraically complex that v cannot be determined explicitly in terms of p and T. The next section discusses a simple technique for determining v once p, T, and Eq. 6.42*b* are known.

The Newton-Raphson Technique

Most equations of state for the superheated and saturated vapor regions are correlations of the form shown in Eq. 6.42*b*. These equations are often very complex (sometimes containing 30 or more terms) and it is normally impossible to solve them algebraically for the specific volume as a function of pressure and temperature. Consequently, thermodynamic correlations are usually set up with v and T as the independent (entry) variables and p as the dependent variable. But if you wish to use p and T as the independent variables, then a way must be found to calculate v from Eq. 6.42*b* when p and T values are known. This is usually done with some type of trial and error method. One of the simplest of these methods is the highly effective Newton-Raphson technique.

Let v be the unknown specific volume corresponding to pressure p and temperature T such that Eq. 6.42*b* is satisfied. Now let $v^* \neq v$ be a trial guess for the unknown value of v. The pressure p^* that corresponds to the values of v^* and T can be determined from Eq. 6.42*b* as

$$p^* = p(v^*, T)$$

We now use Taylor's series to expand the function $p(v, T)$ along an isotherm from the point (v, T) to the point (v^*, T), as follows:

$$p = p(v, T) = p(v^*, T) + \left(\frac{\partial p}{\partial v}\right)\bigg|_{T,v^*} dv + \frac{1}{2!}\left(\frac{\partial^2 p}{\partial v^2}\right)\bigg|_{T,v^*} (dv)^2 + \cdots$$

Now, if v^* is close enough to v we can truncate this series after the second term and approximate $dv \approx v - v^*$. This gives

$$p \approx p(v^*, T) + \left(\frac{\partial p}{\partial v}\right)\bigg|_{T,v^*} (v - v^*) = p^* + \left(\frac{\partial p}{\partial v}\right)\bigg|_{T,v^*} (v - v^*)$$

Solving for v gives

$$v \approx v^* + \frac{p - p(v^*, T)}{\left(\frac{\partial p}{\partial v}\right)\Big|_{T,v^*}} = v^* + \frac{p - p^*}{\left(\frac{\partial p}{\partial v}\right)\Big|_{T,v^*}}$$

Now, let $p - p^* = \text{PE}$, the pressure error. Then this equation becomes

$$v \approx v^* + \text{PE} \Big/ \left(\frac{\partial p}{\partial v}\right)\Big|_{T,v^*} \tag{6.48}$$

On a single trial we will probably not guess v^* close enough to v for Eq. 6.48 to be an accurate estimate of v, but it will be closer to v than was our guess v^*. So, if we use the value of v calculated from Eq. 6.48 as a new guess and continue to iterate in this fashion we will be able to make the pressure error $p - p^*$ as small as we wish. Thus, through repeated use, Eq. 6.48 will converge to the correct value of v for the given p and T values.

This method of determining v is called the Newton-Raphson technique. The convergence is rather quick with relatively few iterations required. Consequently, the initial value chosen for v^* is not too important. For example, we could always take the value of v^* to be 1.0 for the first guess. However, a better initial guess occurs when the ideal gas equation is used to calculate the first v^* value from the given p and T values, i.e.,

$$v^* \text{ (initial guess)} = RT/p$$

This technique is fast and simple enough to be run on a personal computer. This is illustrated in the following example problem.

Example 6.6

Write a BASIC language computer program to determine the specific volume from the van der Waals equation of state (Eq. 3.70) when the pressure and temperature are known. Use the Newton-Raphson technique.

Solution From Chapter 3, Eq. 3.70, the van der Waals equation of state is

$$p = RT/(v - b) - a/v^2 = p(v, T)$$

Rearranging this equation we find that it is cubic in v,

$$v^3 - (b + RT/p)v^2 + av/p - ab/p = 0$$

Since there are algebraic techniques available to solve this equation, we can use its algebraic solution to check the accuracy of the Newton-Raphson technique. Differentiating the original van der Waals equation and evaluating it at T and v^* gives

$$\left(\frac{\partial p}{\partial v}\right)\Big|_{T,v^*} = 2a/(v^*)^3 - RT/(v^* - b)^2$$

and then Eq. 6.48 gives

$$v \approx v^* + (p - p^*)/[2a/(v^*)^3 - RT/(v^* - b)^2]$$

where

$$p^* = RT/(v^* - b) - a/(v^*)^2$$

The following BASIC language program illustrates how these equations are used to find v when p, T, a, b, and R are known. Values for a, b, and R for various gases can be found in Appendix C.15.

```
10   REM: ***** VAN DER WAALS PROGRAM *****
20   PRINT "THIS PROGRAM CALCULATES THE SPECIFIC VOLUME FROM
     THE VAN DER WAALS EQN. OF STATE USING THE NEWTON-RAPHSON
     TECHNIQUE AND COMPARES THESE RESULTS WITH THE EXACT
     SOLUTION."
30   PRINT : INPUT "THE NAME OF THE GAS = ";A$
40   PRINT : PRINT "INPUT THE VAN DER WAALS CONSTANTS:"
50   PRINT : INPUT "A(IN KNM^4/KG^2) = ";A
60   PRINT : INPUT "B(IN M^3/KG) = ";B
70   PRINT : INPUT "THE GAS CONSTANT R(IN KJ/KG.K) = ";R
80   PRINT : PRINT "INPUT THE PRESSURE AND TEMPERATURE:"
90   PRINT : INPUT "P(IN KN/M^2) = ";P
100  PRINT : INPUT "T(IN K) = ";T
110  PRINT : PRINT "INPUT THE ALLOWABLE % ERROR IN THE
     VAN DER WAALS MODEL."
120  INPUT "THE ALLOWABLE % ERROR IN P = ";EPS
130  REM : COMPUTE THE INITIAL GUESS FOR THE SPECIFIC VOLUME
     FROM THE IDEAL GAS LAW.
140  VS = R * T / P
150  REM : SET THE ITERATION COUNTER:
160  K = 1
170  REM : CALCULATE P STAR:
180  PS = R * T / (VS - B) - A / (VS ^ 2)
190  REM : CALCULATE THE % ERROR IN PRESSURE:
200  PE = ((P - PS) / P) * 100
210  REM : COMPARE THE CALCULATED % ERROR WITH THE ALLOWABLE
     % ERROR:
220  IF ABS (PE) < EPS GOTO 290
230  REM : USE THE NEWTON-RAPHSON TECHNIQUE NOW.
240  VS = VS + (P - PS) / ((2 * A / (VS ^ 3)) -
     (R * T / (VS - B) ^ 2))
250  REM : INDEX COUNTER:
260  K = K + 1
270  REM: BEGIN ITERATIONS:
280  GOTO 170
290  REM : THE NEWTON-RAPHSON SOLUTION IS FINISHED, NOW SOLVE
     THE CUBIC VAN DER WAALS EQUATION ALGEBRAICALLY (SEE
     STANDARD MATH TEXT).
300  REM : DEFINE VARIABLES IN ALGEBRAIC SOLUTION:
310  C = - (B + R * T / P)
320  D = A / P
330  E = - A * B / P
340  F = D - (C ^ 2) / 3
350  G = 2 * (C ^ 3) / 27 - C * D / 3 + E
360  H = (G ^ 2) / 4 + (F ^ 3) / 27
370  KK = - G / 2 + H ^ 0.5
380  L = - G / 2 - H ^ 0.5
390  VA = KK ^ 0.33333 + L ^ 0.33333 - C / 3
```

```
400  ER = INT (((VA - VS) / VA)* 10000) / 100
410  REM : PRINT FINAL RESULTS:
420  PRINT : PRINT "THE SPECIFIC VOLUME OF ";A$;" HAS CONVERGED
     TO ";VS;" M^3/KG AFTER ";K;" ITERATIONS."
430  PRINT : PRINT "THE ALGEBRAIC SOLUTION OF THE VAN DER
     WAALS EQUATION YIELDS A SPECIFIC VOLUME OF ";VA;" M^3/KG.
440  PRINT : PRINT : PRINT "THE ERROR IN SPECIFIC VOLUME
     RESULTING FROM USING THE NEWTON-RAPHSON TECHNIQUE IS:
     ";ER;"%"
450  REM : RERUN OPTION:
460  PRINT : PRINT "DO YOU WISH TO CONTINUE WITH ANOTHER SET
     OF P AND T VALUES (Y OR N)?"
470  INPUT B$
480  IF B$ = "Y" GOTO 80
490  IF B$ < > "N"  GOTO 460
500  PRINT : PRINT : PRINT "THIS PROGRAM HAS ENDED!": END
```

PROGRAM RESULTS

```
THIS PROGRAM CALCULATES THE SPECIFIC
VOLUME FROM THE VAN DER WAALS EQN. OF
STATE USING THE NEWTON-RAPHSON TECHNIQUE
AND COMPARES THESE RESULTS WITH THE
EXACT SOLUTION.

THE NAME OF THE GAS = WATER VAPOR

INPUT THE VAN DER WAALS CONSTANTS:

A(IN KNM^4/KG^2) = 1.704

B(IN M^3/KG) = 0.00169

THE GAS CONSTANT R(IN KJ/KG.K) = 0.461

INPUT THE PRESSURE AND TEMPERATURE:

P(IN KN/M^2) = 10000

T(IN K) = 673

INPUT THE ALLOWABLE % ERROR IN THE VAN
DER WAALS MODEL:

THE ALLOWABLE % ERROR IN P = 1.0

THE SPECIFIC VOLUME OF WATER VAPOR HAS
CONVERGED TO .0267371129 M^3/KG AFTER 3
ITERATIONS.

THE ALGEBRAIC SOLUTION OF THE VAN DER
WAALS EQUATION YIELDS A SPECIFIC VOLUME
OF .0267478028 M^3/KG.

THE ERROR IN SPECIFIC VOLUME RESULTING
FROM USING THE NEWTON-RAPHSON TECHNIQUE
IS: .03%

DO YOU WISH TO CONTINUE WITH ANOTHER SET
OF P AND T VALUES (Y OR N)?  ?N

THIS PROGRAM HAS ENDED!
```

Appendix C.3*b* gives the specific volume of water vapor at 10 MPa, 400 °C (673 K) as 0.02641 m^3/kg. Note that this is only about 1.3% lower than the value calculated above using the van der Waals equation of state.

The Gas Tables

When the concept of an ideal gas was introduced in Chapter 3 it was noted that ideal gases generally do not have constant specific heats. Therefore, one of the simplest steps one can take to make the ideal gas equations more accurate is to take into account their temperature dependent specific heats. This is what is done for you in the gas tables in Appendix C.16.

The specific internal energy and enthalpy values listed in the gas tables were determined from an integration of Eqs. 3.36 and 3.45 by incorporating an accurate specific heat vs. temperature data curve fit as

$$u = u_o + \int_{T_o}^{T} c_v \, dT$$

and

$$h = h_o + \int_{T_o}^{T} c_p \, dT$$

where u_o, h_o, and T_o are the arbitrarily chosen reference state values, all of which are set equal to zero in these tables.

Since the ideal gas specific entropy depends on more than just temperature, it is not listed in these tables. However, the temperature dependent part of the specific entropy is listed as the ϕ function, where

$$\phi = \int_{T_o}^{T} (c_p/T) \, dT \tag{6.49}$$

and from Eq. 5.35 we have

$$\begin{aligned} s &= s_o + \int_{T_o}^{T} (c_p/T) \, dT - R \ln(p/p_o) \\ &= s_o + \phi - R \ln(p/p_o) \end{aligned} \tag{5.35}$$

In the gas tables, s_o and T_o are both arbitrarily set equal to zero, and p_o is set equal to 1 atm. As always, the arbitrarily chosen reference states for u, h, and s cancel out when we calculate the changes $u_2 - u_1$, $h_2 - h_1$, and $s_2 - s_1$. Such changes are calculated directly from values taken from the gas tables for u and h, but the change in entropy is given by Eq. 5.35 and 6.49 as

$$s_2 - s_1 = \phi_2 - \phi_1 - R \ln(p_2/p_1) \tag{6.50}$$

For an isentropic process, $s_2 = s_1$, and Eq. 6.50 then gives

$$(\phi_2 - \phi_1)/R = \ln(p_2/p_1) = \ln \frac{p_2 p_o}{p_1 p_o} = \ln(p_{r2}/p_{r1})$$

where p_r is the *relative pressure* defined as

$$p_r = p/p_o = \exp(\phi/R)$$

and consequently

$$p_2/p_1 = p_{r2}/p_{r1} \tag{6.51}$$

Equation 5.34 expresses the specific entropy in terms of temperature and specific volume as

$$s_2 - s_1 = \int_{T_1}^{T_2} (c_v/T)\, dT + R \ln(v_2/v_1) \tag{5.34}$$

Again, for an isentropic process, $s_2 = s_1$, and

$$-\frac{1}{R}\int_{T_1}^{T_2} (c_v/T)\, dT = \ln(v_2/v_1) = \ln\frac{v_2 v_o}{v_1 v_o} = \ln(v_{r2}/v_{r1})$$

where v_r is the *relative volume* defined as

$$v_r = v/v_o = \exp\left[-\frac{1}{R}\int_{T_o}^{T} (c_v/T)\, dT\right]$$

and consequently

$$v_2/v_1 = v_{r2}/v_{r1} \tag{6.52}$$

The p_r and v_r columns of the gas tables are to be used *only for isentropic processes*, and their values are to be used *only in Eqs. 6.51 and 6.52.*

Example 6.7

A diesel engine has a compression ratio of 19.2 to 1. Air at 60 °F and 14.7 psia is drawn into the engine during the intake stroke and is compressed isentropically during the compression stroke. Determine the final temperature and pressure of the air at the end of the compression stroke, and the work required per lbm of air present.

Solution The piston–cylinder arrangement of a diesel engine forms a closed system for the air being compressed. The unknowns are T_2, p_2, and ${}_1W_2/m$. The energy balance for this system (neglecting any changes in the potential and kinetic energies of the air) is

$${}_1Q_2 + {}_1W_2 = m(u_2 - u_1)$$

Now, ${}_1Q_2 = 0$ (isentropic processes are also adiabatic), so

$${}_1W_2/m = u_2 - u_1$$

The gas tables will be used for the thermodynamic properties of air here since they are more accurate than the standard constant specific heat ideal gas equations. From Appendix C.16*a* we find that at 60 °F = 520 R,

$$u_1 = 88.62 \text{ Btu/lbm}$$

$$p_{r1} = 1.2147$$

and

$$v_{r1} = 158.58$$

For a compression ratio of 19.2 to 1, $v_2/v_1 = 1/19.2$. Then, from Eq. 6.52,

$$v_{r2} = v_{r1}(v_2/v_1) = 158.58/19.2 = 8.26$$

Scanning down the v_r column in Appendix C.16*a* we find that $v_r = 8.26$ at about

$$T_2 = 1600 \text{ R} = 1140 \text{ °F}$$

$$u_2 = 286.06 \text{ Btu/lbm}$$

and

$$p_{r2} = 71.73$$

Then, from Eq. 6.51,

$$p_2 = p_1(p_{r2}/p_{r1}) = (14.7 \text{ psia})(71.73/1.2147) = 868.1 \text{ psia}$$

Finally, from the energy balance above,

$${}_1W_2/m = u_2 - u_1 = 286.06 - 88.62 = 197.44 \text{ Btu/lbm}$$

This problem could have been solved using the constant specific heat ideal gas isentropic process equations of Eq. 5.38. Then, using $k = 1.4$ for air, we obtain

$$T_2 = T_1(v_2/v_1)^{1-k} = (460 + 60 \text{ R})(1/19.2)^{-0.4} = 1695.6 \text{ R} = 1235.6 \text{ °F}$$

which is about 6% higher than the gas tables value. Also, again from Eq. 5.38,

$$p_2 = p_1(v_2/v_1)^{-k} = (14.7 \text{ psia})(1/19.2)^{-1.4} = 920.3 \text{ psia}$$

which is also about 6% higher than the gas tables value. Finally, using a constant

$c_v = 0.170$ Btu/(lbm·R) for air, the work per unit mass becomes

$$\begin{aligned} {}_1W_2/m &= u_2 - u_1 = c_v(T_2 - T_1) \\ &= [0.170\ \text{Btu/(lbm·R)}](1695.6 - 520\ \text{R}) \\ &= 199.8\ \text{Btu/lbm} \end{aligned}$$

which is higher than the value obtained from the gas tables by only about 1%.

Generalized Charts

In 1880 the Dutch physicist Johannes Diederik van der Waals reasoned that if the *p-v-T* equation of state could be nondimensionalized, then all gases might be found to fit the same dimensionless *p-v-T* equation. Further, he noted that since every substance has a vapor dome, and every vapor dome has a unique critical point (its peak), then perhaps the critical point properties (p_c, T_c, and v_c) could be used to create a dimensionless equation of state. He defined the dimensionless variables *reduced pressure* p_R, *reduced temperature* T_R, and *reduced specific volume* v_R as[3]

$$p_R = p/p_c \qquad T_R = T/T_c \qquad v_R = v/v_c$$

Then he hypothesized that $p_R = p_R(v_R, T_R)$ would define a generalized dimensionless equation of state that would be valid for all substances. Today this hypothesis is called van der Waals' *law of corresponding states*, but unfortunately it has been found to be valid only for materials with similar molecular structures.

In 1883 van der Waals introduced his now classical equation of state

$$p = RT/(v - b) - a/v^2 \qquad \textbf{(3.70)}$$

in which the constants a and b are corrections for intermolecular forces and molecular volume, respectively. This is a cubic equation in v (see Example 6.6) and has isotherms shaped as shown in Figure 6.1. For given p and $T < T_c$ values there are three real roots of this equation. One root corresponds to v_f, another corresponds to v_g and the third is a meaningless root between v_f and v_g.

van der Waals noted that the critical temperature isotherm seemed to have an inflection point at the critical point. If this were generally true, then all equations of state would have to obey the mathematical constraints of an inflection point, or

$$\left(\frac{\partial p}{\partial v}\right)\bigg|_{T_c, v_c} = \left(\frac{\partial^2 p}{\partial v^2}\right)\bigg|_{T_c, v_c} = 0$$

3. Note that the *reduced* properties p_R and v_R are not the same as the *relative* properties p_r and v_r introduced in the previous section.

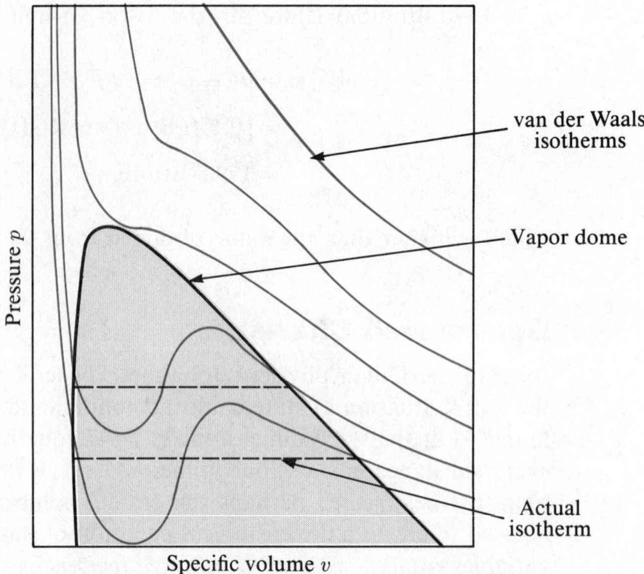

Figure 6.1 A schematic of van der Waals isotherms near the vapor dome.

Applying these conditions to the van der Waals equation yields

$$\left(\frac{\partial p}{\partial v}\right)\bigg|_{T_c, v_c} = RT_c/(v_c - b)^2 + 2a/v_c^3 = 0$$

and

$$\left(\frac{\partial^2 p}{\partial v^2}\right)\bigg|_{T_c, v_c} = 2RT_c/(v_c - b)^3 - 6a/v_c^4 = 0$$

and solving these two equations simultaneously for a and b while using Eq. 3.70 evaluated at the critical point gives

$$a = 9RT_c v_c/8 = \frac{27}{64}\left(\frac{R^2T_c^2}{p_c}\right)$$

and

$$b = v_c/3 = \frac{RT_c}{8p_c}$$

Thus, if the van der Waals equation accurately represented universal material behavior, the constants a and b could be determined from a single experimental measurement at the critical point.

Substituting the above formula for a and b back into the van der Waals equation and dividing both sides by p_c gives

$$p/p_c = p_R = 8T_R/(3v_R - 1) - 3/v_R^3$$

which was the type of dimensionless equation of state that he was seeking. Unfortunately, the molecular interactions in real substances are more complex than the elementary corrections used in the van der Waals equation, so it does not work well over large pressure and temperature ranges.

A serious flaw in van der Waals' law of corresponding states was that it broke down at low pressures where ideal gas behavior was expected. Further, his equation of state (Eq. 3.70) has the curious property that (from the equation for b above) the ratio $p_c v_c/(RT_c) = 3/8 = 0.375$, whereas for an ideal gas $pv/(RT)$ was always equal to unity. This similarity led many researchers to investigate $pv/(RT)$ data, and this grouping is now called the *compressibility factor* Z, defined in Chapter 3 as

$$Z = pv/(RT) \quad \textbf{(3.76)}$$

The van der Waals equation predicts that

$$Z_c = p_c v_c/(RT_c) = 0.375$$

but many experiments on a large number of substances have shown that

$$0.23 \leq Z_c \leq 0.375$$

and so Z_c is not the same for all substances. Though many tried to correlate Z with p or T for various substances, it was not until 1939 that H. C. Weber correlated Z with p_R and T_R and thus produced the first generalized compressibility chart of the form $Z = Z(p_R, T_R)$. There was, however, a problem with this chart in that lines of constant reduced specific volume could not be added because the v_R data were inconsistent. In 1946 Gouq-Jen Su solved this problem by choosing the product $v_R Z_c$ as a "pseudo" reduced specific volume v'_R, defined as

$$v'_R = v_R Z_c = (v/v_c)Z_c = v/v'_c \quad \textbf{(3.79)}$$

where a new critical state specific volume v'_c has been defined as

$$v'_c = v_c/Z_c = RT_c/p_c$$

This change produced a much better correlation of the experimental data and lines of constant v'_R could be accurately added to the chart. The resulting $Z = Z(p_R, T_R, v'_R)$ plot is now called the generalized compressibility chart and is shown in Figures 3.12*a*, *b* and 3.13 of Chapter 3.

Though the van der Waals equation is not very accurate as a universal equation of state, Su's modified compressibility factor formulation as an approximate approach to the law of corresponding states has found universal acceptance within the engineering community.[4] Compressibility factor data can be used to estimate the specific enthalpy and entropy pressure dependence of substances as follows. Integrating the specific enthalpy total differential given in Eq. 6.32 from a reference state at p_o, v_o, T_o, and h_o to any other state at p, v, T, and h gives

$$h = h_o + \int_{T_o}^{T} c_p\, dT + \int_{p_o}^{p} \left[v - T\left(\frac{\partial v}{\partial T}\right)_p \right] dp$$

Then arbitrarily choosing h_o, T_o, and p_o to be zero gives

$$h = \int_0^T c_p\, dT + \int_0^p \left[v - T\left(\frac{\partial v}{\partial T}\right)_p \right] dp$$

$$= h^* + \int_0^p \left[v - T\left(\frac{\partial v}{\partial T}\right)_p \right] dp \tag{6.53}$$

where h^* is the ideal gas specific enthalpy defined earlier in the discussion of the gas tables. From Eq. 3.76 we can write

$$v = ZRT/p$$

so that

$$\left(\frac{\partial v}{\partial T}\right)_p = ZR/p + (RT/p)(\partial Z/\partial T)_p \tag{6.54}$$

Then,

$$v - T\left(\frac{\partial v}{\partial T}\right)_p = ZRT/p - ZRT/p - (RT^2/p)(\partial Z/\partial T)_p$$

$$= -(RT^2/p)(\partial Z/\partial T)_p$$

and Eq. 6.53 becomes

$$h = h^* - R\int_0^p (T^2/p)(\partial Z/\partial T)_p\, dp$$

Nondimensionalizing this equation with $T = T_c T_R$ and $p = p_c p_R$, and rearranging it gives

$$(h^* - h)/T_c = R\int_0^{p_R} (T_R^2/p_R)(\partial Z/\partial T_R)_{p_R}\, dp_R \tag{6.55}$$

Equation 6.55 still depends upon the substance under consideration because the value of R is substance dependent. This dependence can be removed by dividing

4. More accurate equations of state such as the Beattie-Bridgeman and Redlich-Kwong that have a wider range of application were briefly discussed in Chapter 3.

both sides of Eq. 6.55 by the molecular mass M, and thus converting it into molar units

$$(\bar{h}^* - \bar{h})/T_c = \mathscr{R} \int_0^{p_R} (T_R^2/p_R)(\partial Z/\partial T_R)_{p_R}\, dp_R \tag{6.56}$$

where $\bar{h}^* = h^*/M$ is the ideal gas molar enthalpy, $\bar{h} = h/M$ is the real substance molar enthalpy, and $\mathscr{R} = R/M$ is the universal gas constant. Using compressibility factor data, Eq. 6.56 has been integrated and the results are shown in Figure 6.2.

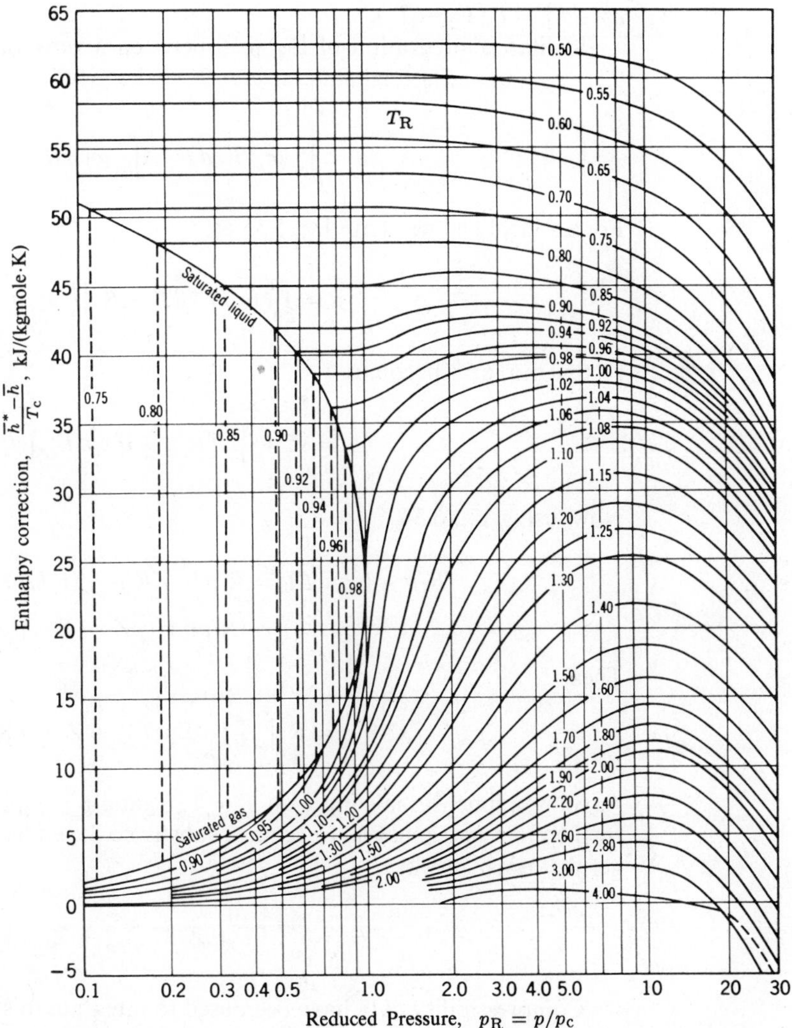

Figure 6.2 Generalized chart for enthalpy correction. *Note*: To convert this figure to SI units use the factor 1 Btu/(lbmole·R) = 4.1865 kJ/(kgmole·K). *Source*: Gordon J. Van Wylen and Richard E. Sonntag, *Fundamentals of Classical Thermodynamics*, 2d ed. (New York: Wiley, 1973), p. 709 (Figure A.9). Copyright © 1973 John Wiley & Sons. Reprinted by permission of John Wiley & Sons.

To find the change in specific enthalpy between states 1 and 2 using this figure, values of p_R and T_R are calculated and values of $(\bar{h}^* - \bar{h})/T_c$ are then read from the figure. The change in specific enthalpy between states 1 and 2 is then determined from

$$h_2 - h_1 = (h_2^* - h_1^*) - \left[\left(\frac{\bar{h}^* - \bar{h}}{T_c}\right)_2 - \left(\frac{\bar{h}^* - \bar{h}}{T_c}\right)_1\right]\left(\frac{T_c}{M}\right) \tag{6.57}$$

where $h_2^* - h_1^*$ is determined from the gas tables (Appendix C.16*c*), or by assuming constant specific heats over the temperature range from T_1 to T_2 and using $h_2^* - h_1^* = c_p(T_2 - T_1)$.

Similarly, integration of Eq. 6.36 between a zero value reference state ($p_o = T_o = s_o = 0$) and a final state at p, v, T, and s gives

$$s = \int_0^T (c_p/T)\,dT - \int_0^p (\partial v/\partial T)_p\,dp \tag{6.58}$$

For an ideal gas we write Eq. 5.35 as

$$s = \int_0^T (c_p/T)\,dT - R\int_0^p dp/p$$

so that Eq. 6.58 becomes

$$s = s^* + \int_0^p [R/p - (\partial v/\partial T)_p]\,dp$$

Now, using Eq. 6.54,

$$\begin{aligned} R/p - (\partial v/\partial T)_p &= R/p - ZR/p - (RT/p)(\partial Z/\partial T)_p \\ &= (R/p)[1 - Z - T(\partial Z/\partial T)_p] \end{aligned}$$

Then,

$$s^* - s = R\int_0^p [T(\partial Z/\partial T)_p + Z - 1](dp/p)$$

Again nondimensionalizing with $T = T_c T_R$ and $p = p_c p_R$, and dividing both sides by the molecular mass M to remove substance dependence from the equation, we get the molar results

$$\bar{s}^* - \bar{s} = \mathcal{R}\int_0^{p_R} [T_R(\partial Z/\partial T_R)_{p_R} + Z - 1](dp_R/p_R) \tag{6.59}$$

Compressibility data have been used to integrate this equation, and the results are shown in Figure 6.3. To find the change in specific entropy between states 1 and 2 using this figure, calculate the values of p_R and T_R and then obtain values for $\bar{s}^* - \bar{s}$ from the figure. Then compute

$$s_2 - s_1 = (s_2^* - s_1^*) - [(\bar{s}^* - \bar{s})_2 - (\bar{s}^* - \bar{s})_1](1/M) \tag{6.60}$$

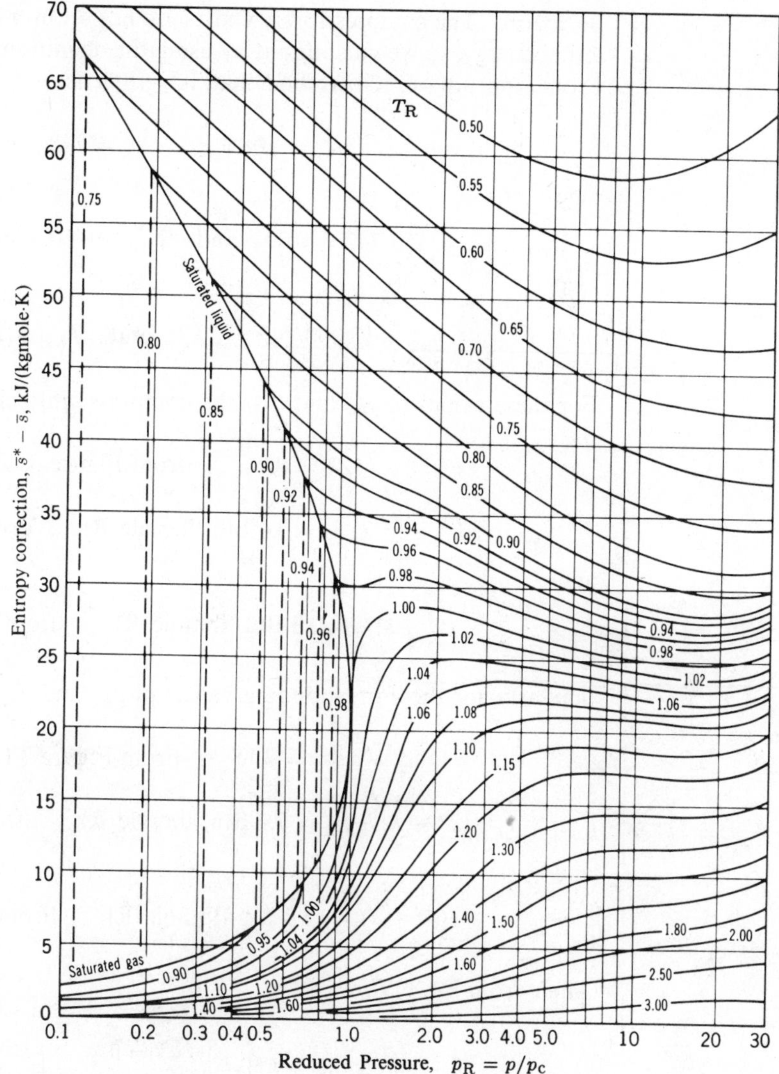

Figure 6.3 Generalized chart for the entropy correction. *Note*: To convert this figure to SI units use the factor 1 Btu/(lbmole·R = 4.1865 kJ/(kgmole·K). *Source*: Gordon J. Van Wylen and Richard E. Sonntag, *Fundamentals of Classical Thermodynamics*, 2d ed. (New York: Wiley, 1973), p. 711 (Figure A.11). Copyright © 1973 John Wiley & Sons. Reprinted by permission of John Wiley & Sons.

where $s_2^* - s_1^* = \phi_2 - \phi_1 - R\ln(p_2/p_1)$ from the gas tables, or by assuming constant specific heats over the temperature range from T_1 to T_2 and using $s_2^* - s_1^* = c_p \ln(T_2/T_1) - R\ln(p_2/p_1)$.

Example 6.8 Using the compressibility charts, determine the change in specific internal energy, specific enthalpy, and specific entropy of ethylene (C_2H_4)when it is compressed isothermally from 150 psia and 80 °F to 15,000 psia.

Solution The compressibility charts are not set up in terms of the specific internal energy, so we must find it by using the definition of enthalpy, $u = h - pv$. From Appendix C.12*a* we find that, for ethylene,

$$T_c = 508.3 \text{ R} \qquad p_c = 742 \text{ psia}$$

then

$$p_{R1} = 150/742 = 0.20 \quad \text{and} \quad T_{R1} = (460 + 80)/508.3 = 1.06$$

and

$$p_{R2} = 15{,}000/742 = 20.2 \quad \text{and} \quad T_{R2} = T_{R1} = 1.06$$

For these values of p_{R1} and T_{R1} the compressibility charts give

$$Z_1 = 0.94 \qquad \text{(from Figure 3.12}a\text{)}$$

$$[(\bar{h}^* - \bar{h})/T_c]_1 = 0.4 \text{ Btu/(lbmole·R)} \qquad \text{(from Figure 6.2)}$$

and

$$(\bar{s}^* - \bar{s})_1 = 0.3 \text{ Btu/(lbmole·R)} \qquad \text{(from Figure 6.3).}$$

Similarly, for the corresponding values of p_{R2} and T_{R2} we find that

$$Z_2 = 2.15 \qquad \text{(from Figure 3.13)}$$

$$[(\bar{h}^* - \bar{h})/T_c]_2 = 7.4 \text{ Btu/(lbmole·R)} \qquad \text{(from Figure 6.2)}$$

and

$$(\bar{s}^* - \bar{s})_2 = 5.3 \text{ Btu/(lbmole·R)} \qquad \text{(from Figure 6.3)}$$

Then, from Eq. 6.57, we have

$$h_2 - h_1 = (h_2^* - h_1^*) - \left[\left(\frac{\bar{h}^* - \bar{h}}{T_c}\right)_2 - \left(\frac{\bar{h}^* - \bar{h}}{T_c}\right)_1\right]\left(\frac{T_c}{M}\right)$$

where $h_2^* - h_1^* = \int_{T_1}^{T_2} c_p\, dT = 0$ for an isothermal process $(T_1 = T_2)$, and $M = 28.05$ lbm/lbmole.

Then,

$$\begin{aligned} h_2 - h_1 &= 0 - [(7.4 - 0.4) \text{ Btu/(lbmole·R)}](508.3 \text{ R})/(28.05 \text{ lbm/lbmole}) \\ &= -126.8 \text{ Btu/lbm} \end{aligned}$$

Next,

$$u_2 - u_1 = h_2 - h_1 - (p_2 v_2 - p_1 v_1)$$

where

$$v_1 = Z_1 R T_1 / p_1$$

and

$$R = \mathscr{R}/M = [1545.35 \text{ ft·lbf/(lbmole·R)}]/(28.05 \text{ lbm/lbmole})$$
$$= 55.09 \text{ ft·lbf/(lbm·R)}$$

Then,

$$v_1 = (0.94)[55.09 \text{ ft·lbf/(lbm·R)}](460 + 80 \text{ R})/[(150 \text{ lbf/in}^2)(144 \text{ in}^2/\text{ft}^2)]$$
$$= 1.295 \text{ ft}^3/\text{lbm}$$

Similarly,

$$v_2 = Z_2 R T_2 / p_2$$
$$= (2.15)[55.09 \text{ ft·lbf/(lbm·R)}](540 \text{ R})/[(15{,}000 \text{ lbf/in}^2)(144 \text{ in}^2/\text{ft}^2)]$$
$$= 0.030 \text{ ft}^3/\text{lbm}$$

Then,

$$u_2 - u_1 = -126.8 \text{ Btu/lbm} - [(15{,}000 \text{ lbf/in}^2)(144 \text{ in}^2/\text{ft}^2)(0.030 \text{ ft}^3/\text{lbm})$$
$$- (150 \text{ lbf/in}^2)(144 \text{ in}^2/\text{ft}^2)(1.295 \text{ ft}^3/\text{lbm})][1 \text{ Btu/(778 ft·lbf)}]$$
$$= -174.1 \text{ Btu/lbm}$$

Finally, from Eq. 6.60, we have

$$s_2 - s_1 = (s_2^* - s_1^*) - [(\bar{s}^* - \bar{s})_2 - (\bar{s}^* - \bar{s})_1](1/M)$$

where

$$s_2^* - s_1^* = \int_{T_1}^{T_2 = T_1} (c_p/T)\, dT - R \ln(p_2/p_1)$$
$$= 0 - \left[\frac{55.09 \text{ ft·lbf/(lbm·R)}}{778 \text{ ft·lbf/Btu}}\right] \ln\left(\frac{15{,}000}{150}\right)$$
$$= -0.3261 \text{ Btu/(lbm·R)}$$

Then,

$$s_2 - s_1 = -0.3261 \text{ Btu/(lbm·R)} - \left[\frac{5.3 - 0.3 \text{ Btu/(lbmole·R)}}{28.05 \text{ lbm/lbmole}}\right]$$
$$= -0.5044 \text{ Btu/(lbm·R)}$$

Steam Gas

One of the most unforgivable mistakes that a thermodynamics student can make is to use the ideal gas equations to calculate the values of the properties u, h, and s of superheated steam. Yet we will do just that in the next chapter when we discuss the thermodynamics of water vapor and air mixtures (i.e., humidity). Where did this great academic fear of steam as an ideal gas come from, and is it really justified?

When the term *steam vapor* was introduced into engineering jargon in the nineteenth century it originally meant only visible, or "wet" steam. That is, steam whose state was far enough under the vapor dome to contain tiny visible fog like liquid water droplets (sometimes called *water dust*). As soon as the steam became a saturated or superheated vapor, it became invisible to the naked eye and was called *steam gas*, and for a long time its properties were actually calculated from the ideal gas equations. By the end of the nineteenth century it had become clear to thermodynamicists that the ideal gas equations did not accurately describe the behavior of high-pressure steam, and during the first half of the twentieth century considerable effort was devoted toward developing new empirical equations for steam properties over the full range of pressures and temperatures of industrial interest. However, these empirical equations were generally too complex and time-consuming for ordinary engineering work, so they were used instead to generate elaborate saturation and superheated steam tables that were accurate to within 1% or less over their full range. Those tables could be used easily and quickly by working engineers with at most a simple linear interpolation required between table entries. These tables were widely distributed and were continuously improved through a series of annual International Conferences on the Properties of Steam that began in 1929. Today the full steam tables have small pressure and temperature increment listings and fill an entire book.

To provide engineering students with a working knowledge of these new tables a condensed version was appended to all thermodynamics textbooks.[5] Authors and professors attempted to encourage the use of these tables and to discourage the use of ideal gas equations for steam by extending the definition of a vapor to include any state near the vapor dome and below the critical point (see, for example, Figures 3.1 and 3.3 of Chapter 3). Under this definition superheated steam was now a vapor, not a gas, and it would be unforgivable for a student to apply ideal gas equations to a vapor. For many years this subterfuge was successful. But growing student computer literacy and the availability of complex software containing all the equations necessary to generate accurate steam properties will eventually make the use of printed tables obsolete. Yet there remains the nagging question of whether or not the ideal gas equations can be used to describe the thermodynamic properties of steam with reasonable accuracy in low-pressure or high-temperature situations. If so, then engineering students could write relatively

5. At some universities it was common for the professor to require students to buy a copy of the full steam tables as well as a thermodynamics textbook.

simple computer programs to solve challenging thermodynamic steam (or any other "vapor") problems without using elaborate software for generating property values.

There is no record of who first took interest in measuring the p-v-T properties of steam, but the development of the steam engine and the associated Industrial Revolution it produced created a strong practical need for such information. By 1683 Samuel Morland (1625–1695) is said to have acquired data on the pressure and temperature of saturated steam near atmospheric pressure. In 1662 Robert Boyle (1627–1691) developed the equation $p\forall$ = constant for isothermal "elastic fluids" (i.e., compressible gases) and this equation was used over 100 years later for steam by James Watt (1736–1819) in his improved steam engine patent of 1782. In about 1787 Jacques Charles (1746–1823) developed the equation for isobaric gas behavior, $\forall/T$ = constant, and soon thereafter the laws of Boyle and Charles were combined into the ideal gas equation that we have today, $p\forall = mRT$.[6]

The combined Boyle-Charles ideal gas equation continued to be used for steam engine design until the end of the nineteenth century when engines were operating at sufficiently high pressures and temperatures as to render the equation noticeably inaccurate.

In the 1840s the French scientist Henri Victor Regnault (1810–1878) was sponsored by his government to carry out a series of precise measurements of the saturation properties of various substances, including water. He found that the Boyle-Charles ideal gas equation was only approximately true for real substances. By 1847 he had correlated his experimental results for the saturation pressure and temperature of steam with the formula given in Problem 86 at the end of this chapter. Regnault's data was considered to be an accurate authoritative source for over 60 years and many others made mathematical correlations from it. By the end of the nineteenth century many steam tables based upon various correlations of increasing complexity of Regnault's data had become available for engineering use. Yet it was the pragmatic Scottish engineer William John Macquorn Rankine (1820–1872) in his *Manual of the Steam Engine and Other Prime Movers*,[7] who noted that:

> Steam attains a condition which is sensibly that of a perfect gas, by means of a very moderate extent of superheating; and it may be inferred that the formulae for the relations between heat and work which are accurate for steam-gas are not materially erroneous for actual superheated steam; while they possess the practical advantage of great simplicity.

6. Boyle's law was independently discovered in 1676 by Edme Mariotte (1620–1684), and is sometimes known as Mariotte's law. Also, Charles' law was independently discovered in 1802 by Joseph Louis Gay-Lussac (1778–1850) and is sometimes known as Gay-Lussac's law. Carnot, Clapeyron, and many others were using the ideal gas equation in the form $pv = R(T + A)$ where T was in °C and $A = 273$ °C was then an empirical constant. Later, in 1848, William Thomson (Lord Kelvin) recognized that -273 °C corresponded to absolute zero temperature.

7. This book has the honor of being the first comprehensive engineering thermodynamics textook. It was first printed in 1859 and went through 17 editions.

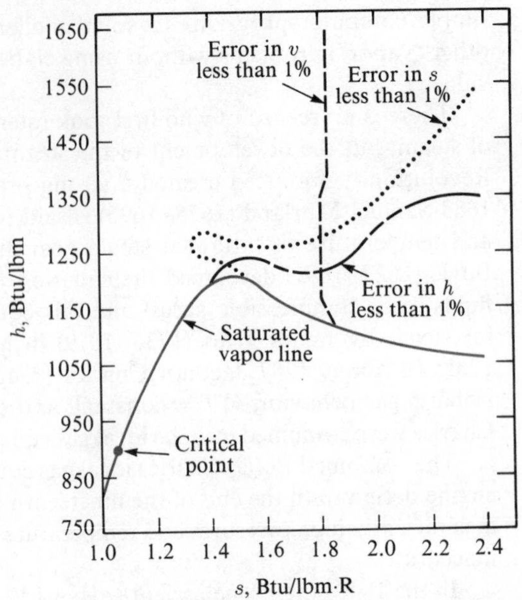

Figure 6.4 The ideal gas equations are accurate to 1% or less in the regions to the *right* of the dashed and dotted lines shown on this Mollier diagram.

The concept of a region of steam ideal gas behavior is illustrated in Figure 6.4. This figure is a Mollier diagram that shows the regions in which the equations $v_g = RT_{sat}/p_{sat}$, $v = RT/p$, $h = h_g + c_p(T - T_{sat})$ and $s = s_g + c_p \ln(T/T_{sat}) - R \ln(p/p_{sat})$ are accurate to within about 1% or less of the actual steam table values (where h_g and s_g are evaluated at T_{sat}). The use of these ideal gas equations for steam in the regions shown will produce errors of only a few percent in an analysis, which is often quite acceptable for many engineering thermodynamic applications. The reader can easily define the regions shown in Figure 6.4 by using the above equations and a steam table. A personal computer greatly speeds up the required calculations.

Example 6.9

1 lbm of superheated steam at 1 psia and 200 °F is mixed adiabatically and aergonically with 5 lbm of superheated steam at 5 psia and 400 °F in a closed rigid system. Determine the final temperature and pressure.

Solution The unknowns here are T_2 and p_2, and since this is a closed system the energy balance (neglecting any changes in system kinetic and potential energy) is

$$\underset{\substack{0 \\ \text{(adiabatic)}}}{{}_1Q_2} + \underset{\substack{0 \text{ (aergonic)}}}{{}_1W_2} = m(u_2 - u_1) = U_2 - U_1$$

or

$$U_2 = U_1$$

or

$$u_2 = u_1 = U_1/m_1 = (m_A u_A + m_B u_B)/(m_A + m_B)$$

Also, for a closed rigid system the total volume and mass are constant, so

$$v_2 = v_1 = (m_A v_A + m_B v_B)/(m_A + m_B)$$

This problem is very difficult to solve using the steam tables or the Mollier diagram. It requires the construction of lines of constant u and constant v for various combinations of pressure and temperature, and then finding the intersection of the $u = u_1 = u_2$ and $v = v_1 = v_2$ lines. However, the steam states given in the problem statement fall within the ideal gas region of Figure 6.4, so we can solve this problem with reasonable accuracy by using the ideal gas equations of state. Since the reference state values ultimately cancel out here, we can simplify the algebra by taking $T_o = 0$ R and $u_o = 0$ Btu/lbm, then we can write $u_A = c_v T_A$, $u_B = c_v T_B$, and $u_2 = c_v T_2$. Also, from the Boyle-Charles ideal gas equation we have that $v_A = RT_A/p_A$, $v_B = RT_B/p_B$, and $v_2 = RT_2/p_2$. Then,

$$u_2 = c_v T_2 = u_1 = c_v(m_A T_A + m_B T_B)/(m_A + m_B)$$

or

$$T_2 = (m_A T_A + m_B T_B)/(m_A + m_B)$$

and

$$v_2 = RT_2/p_2 = R(m_A T_A/p_A + m_B T_B/p_B)/(m_A + m_B)$$

or

$$p_2 = (m_A + m_B)T_2/(m_A T_A/p_A + m_B T_B/p_B)$$

For the values given in the problem statement we get

$$T_2 = [(1\text{ lbm})(660\text{ R}) + (5\text{ lbm})(860\text{ R})]/(6\text{ lbm}) = 826.7\text{ R} = 366.7\text{ °F}$$

and

$$p_2 = (6\text{ lbm})(826.7\text{ R})/[(1\text{ lbm})(660\text{ R})/(1\text{ psia}) + (5\text{ lbm})(860\text{ R})/(5\text{ psia})]$$
$$= 3.26\text{ psia}$$

Summary

In this chapter we discussed a series of generalized thermodynamic property relations. We also introduced two new thermodynamic properties, the Helmholtz and Gibbs functions, and developed a series of differential property relations known as the Maxwell thermodynamic property equations. The Clapeyron equation, Gibbs phase equilibrium equation, and a series of differential relations for the non-measurable u, h, s properties cast in terms of the measurable p, v, T properties allowed us to develop a general procedure for constructing thermodynamic tables and charts.

The Newton-Raphson technique was discussed in terms of using simple BASIC language computer programs to generate numerical values for thermodynamic properties of real substances. Then the gas tables and the generalized charts were discussed as approximate methods for dealing with real gas behavior.

In the concluding section of this chapter the history and philosophy of modeling steam with the ideal gas equations was discussed. It is seen that this is a reasonably accurate approximation for saturated vapor at low pressure and for superheated vapor (steam gas) at low pressure or high temperature.

Selected References

Look, D. C., Jr., and Sauer, H. J., Jr. *Thermodynamics.* Monterey, CA: Brooks Cole, 1982.

Karlekar, B. V. *Thermodynamics for Engineers.* Englewood Cliffs, NJ: Prentice Hall, 1983.

Rankine, W. J. M. *A Manual of the Steam Engine and Other Prime Movers*, 16th ed. London: Griffin, 1906.

Regnault, H. V. *Memoires de L'Academie Royle des Sciences de L'Institut de France.* Paris: Didot Freres, 1847.

Reynolds, W. C. *Thermodynamic Properties in SI.* Palo Alto, CA: Stanford University, Department of Mechanical Engineering, 1979.

Reynolds, W. C., and Perkins, H. C. *Engineering Thermodynamics*, 2d ed. New York: McGraw-Hill, 1977.

Van Wylen, G. J., and Sonntag, R. E. *Fundamentals of Classical Thermodynamics*, 3d ed. New York: Wiley, 1986.

Wark, K. *Thermodynamics*, 5th ed. New York: McGraw-Hill, 1988.

Chapter Six Problems

1. Calculate the specific Gibbs and Helmholtz functions of saturated water vapor at 100 °C.

2. You are given an unknown material whose boiling point at atmospheric pressure is 50 °F. You are also given the following property values at this pressure and temperature: $s_f = 0.31$ Btu/(lbm·R), $s_g = 1.76$ Btu/(lbm·R), and $h_g = 940$ Btu/lbm. Calculate the following quantities for this material at this state **a)** h_{fg}, **b)** h_f, **c)** g_f, and **d)** g_g.

3. Using Eq. 6.5 and the definition of specific enthalpy, $h = u + pv$, show that

$$c_p = \left(\frac{\partial h}{\partial T}\right)_p = T\left(\frac{\partial s}{\partial T}\right)_p$$

4. Beginning with Eq. 6.1 show that

$$\frac{c_v}{T} = \left(\frac{\partial s}{\partial T}\right)_v = -\left(\frac{\partial^2 f}{\partial T^2}\right)_v$$

5. Beginning with Eq. 6.5 show that

$$\frac{c_p}{T} = \left(\frac{\partial s}{\partial T}\right)_p = -\left(\frac{\partial^2 g}{\partial T^2}\right)_p$$

6. Using Eq. 6.1 show that another definition of thermodynamic pressure is

$$p = T\left(\frac{\partial s}{\partial v}\right)_u$$

7. Using Eqs. 6.15 and 6.19 and the Gibbs phase equilibrium conditions, show that

$$\left(\frac{dp}{dT}\right)_{sat} = \frac{s_{fg}}{v_{fg}} = \frac{h_{fg}}{T_{sat}v_{fg}}$$

8. Calculate s_{fg} for water at 100 °C using the Gibbs phase equilibrium conditions and compare it with the value listed in the steam tables.

9. Using the h_{fg} data from the steam tables at $p_{sat} = 14.7$, 100, 200, and 300 psia, calculate the value of s_{fg} at these temperatures from the Gibb's phase equilibrium condition and compare your results with the s_{fg} values listed in the steam tables.

10. Determine whether or not any of the following are properties

a) $dM = \frac{7}{3}u^3 s\, du + \frac{1}{2}u^2 s^3\, ds$
b) $dN = (h/T)\, dT + \ln(1/T)\, dh$
c) $X = \int [(p/2)\, ds - (s/2)\, dp]$
d) $Y = \int (v\, dp)$

11. Beginning with Eq. 6.1 and the condition that $s = s(u, v)$, show that for an ideal gas,

$$\left(\frac{\partial T}{\partial v}\right)_u = 0$$

and thus that $T = T(u)$ or $u = u(T)$ only.

12. Beginning with Eq. 6.1, and by using the appropriate Maxwell equation show that

$$\left(\frac{\partial u}{\partial v}\right)_T = T\left(\frac{\partial p}{\partial T}\right)_v - p$$

13. Using the results of Problem 12 show that it can be further reduced to

a) $\left(\frac{\partial u}{\partial v}\right)_T = T^2\left[\frac{\partial(p/T)}{\partial T}\right]_v$ **b)** $\left(\frac{\partial u}{\partial v}\right)_T = -\left[\frac{\partial(p/T)}{\partial(1/T)}\right]_v$

14. Beginning with Eq. 6.5 and by using the appropriate Maxwell equation show that

$$\left(\frac{\partial h}{\partial p}\right)_T = -T\left(\frac{\partial v}{\partial T}\right)_p + v$$

15. Using the results of Problem 14 show that it can be further reduced to

a) $\left(\frac{\partial h}{\partial p}\right)_T = -T^2\left[\frac{\partial(v/T)}{\partial T}\right]_p$ **b)** $\left(\frac{\partial h}{\partial p}\right)_T = \left[\frac{\partial(v/T)}{\partial(1/T)}\right]_p$

16. Let the isentropic exponent k for an arbitrary substance be defined by the process pv^k = constant.

a) Show that $k = -(v/p)(\partial p/\partial v)_s$.

b) Using Eqs. 6.34 and 6.36 and the classical definition of an isentropic process (s = constant) along with the appropriate Maxwell equations, show that a) above reduces to $k = -(v/p)(\partial p/\partial v)_T(c_p/c_v)$.

c) Show that for an ideal gas b) above reduces to $k = c_p/c_v$.

17. An empirical equation of state has been proposed of the form

$$pv = RT + pA(T) + p^2B(T)$$

where $A(T)$ and $B(T)$ are empirically determined functions of temperature. Beginning with Eq. 6.1, and using the appropriate Maxwell thermodynamic property equation, show that for this material

$$\left(\frac{\partial u}{\partial p}\right)_T = -T\frac{dA}{dT} - p\left(B + T\frac{dB}{dT}\right)$$

18. A simple magnetic substance has the following differential equation of state

$$du = T\,ds + \mu_o v\mathbf{H}\cdot d\mathbf{M}$$

where $\mathbf{H}$ is the strength of the applied magnetic field, $\mathbf{M}$ is the magnetization vector, and μ_o is the magnetic permeability of free space (a constant). For this substance show that the thermodynamic temperature is defined by

$$T = \left(\frac{\partial u}{\partial s}\right)_{\mathbf{M}}$$

and that the Maxwell equation analogous to Eq. 6.22 is

$$\left(\frac{\partial T}{\partial \mathbf{M}}\right)_s = \left(\frac{\partial \mu_o v\mathbf{H}}{\partial s}\right)_{\mathbf{M}}$$

19. A system involves both reversible expansion work ($-\int p\,dv$) and reversible electrochemical work ($\int \phi\,dq$, where ϕ is the voltage and q is the charge per unit mass). For such a system its specific enthalpy is now defined as $h = u + pv - \phi q$.

a) Find an expression for the differential change in specific Gibbs free energy, dg, in terms of p, v, s, T, ϕ, and q.

b) Find the Maxwell equation $(\partial q/\partial T)_{p,\phi} = ?$.

20. Estimate h_{fg} for water at 10 °C using Eq. 6.26 and compare your answer with the steam table value.

21. Estimate v_{fg} for water at 10 °C using Eq. 6.26 and compare your answer with the steam table value.

22. Using the triple point of water (0.01 °C, 611.3 Pa) as a reference state, estimate the saturation pressure of ice in equilibrium with water vapor at −20 °C if $h_{ig} = 2834.8$ kJ/kg is a constant over this range.

23. If saturated solid ice at −10°C is subjected to an isothermal compression process to 200 MPa, will it melt? Use the triple point (0.01 °C, 611.3 Pa) as the reference state, where $h_{if} = -333.41$ kJ/kg and $v_{if} = 9.08 \times 10^{-5}$ m^3/kg. Sketch this process on a p-T diagram.

24. At very low pressures a substance has a saturation curve given by $p_{sat} = \exp(A_1 - A_2/T_{sat})$ where A_1 and A_2 are constants. Show that h_{fg} is constant for this substance.

25. At very low pressures the saturation curve for a particular substance is given by $p_{sat} = \exp[A_1 + A_2/T_{sat} + A_3(\ln T_{sat})]$ where A_1, A_2, and A_3 are constants. Show that h_{fg} varies linearly with T_{sat} for this substance.

26. Using Eq. 6.32

a) Show that the Joule-Thomson coefficient defined by Eq. 4.123 can be written as

$$\mu_J = (\partial T/\partial p)_h = [T(\partial v/\partial T)_p - v]/c_p$$

b) Use this result to evaluate the Joule-Thomson coefficient for an ideal gas.

27. Assuming $s = s(T, p)$ for a simple substance, derive Eqs. 6.36 and 6.37 of this chapter.

28. The following equation of state has been proposed for a gas

$$pv = RT + A/T - B/T^2$$

where A and B are constants. Beginning with this equation develop equations based upon the measurable properties p, v, and T for the property changes $u - u_o$, $h - h_o$, and $s - s_o$, where u_o, h_o, and s_o are reference state properties at p_o, v_o, and T_o.

29. Develop an equation based upon measurable properties p, v, and T for the property changes $u_2 - u_1$, $h_2 - h_1$, and $s_2 - s_1$ of a van der Waals gas with constant specific heats. The van der Waals equation of state, Eq. 3.70, can be written as $p = RT/(v - b) - a/v^2$ where a and b are constants.

30. Develop equations based upon measurable properties p, v, and T for the isothermal property changes $(u_2 - u_1)_T$, $(h_2 - h_1)_T$, and $(s_2 - s_1)_T$ of a Dieterici gas (see Eq. 3.71).

31. Develop equations based upon measurable properties p, v, and T for the isothermal property changes $(u_2 - u_1)_T$, $(h_2 - h_1)_T$, and $(s_2 - s_1)_T$ of a Beattie-Bridgeman gas (see Eq. 3.73).

32. Develop equations based upon measurable properties p, v, and T for the isothermal property changes $(u_2 - u_1)_T$, $(h_2 - h_1)_T$, and $(s_2 - s_1)_T$ of a Redlich-Kwong gas (see Eq. 3.74).

33. Determine $(\partial c_v/\partial v)_T$ for a Redlich-Kwong gas (see Eq. 3.74) and integrate this to find the function $c_v = c_v(T, v, v_o)$, where v_o is a reference state specific volume.

34. Using Eq. 6.41 calculate the difference between c_p and c_v for **a)** copper at 300 °C, **b)** mercury at 20 °C, **c)** glycerin at 20 °C. Use Tables 3.1 and 3.2 for compressibility values. The densities at 20 °C are $\rho_{Cu} = 8954\ \text{kg/m}^3$, $\rho_{Hg} = 13{,}579\ \text{kg/m}^3$, and $\rho_{glyc} = 1264\ \text{kg/m}^3$.

35. Determine $(\partial c_v/\partial v)_T$ for a van der Waals gas (see Eq. 3.70).

36. Determine $(\partial c_v/\partial v)_T$ for a Beattie-Bridgeman gas (see Eq. 3.73) and integrate this to find the function $c_v = c_v(T, v, v_o)$, where v_o is a reference state specific volume.

37. Saturated mercury vapor has an equation of state of the form

$$p_{sat} = \left(\frac{RT}{v}\right)_{sat} - \left(\frac{T}{v^2}\right)_{sat} \exp(A_1 + A_2/T_{sat} + A_3 \ln T_{sat})$$

where A_1, A_2, and A_3 are constants. The constant volume specific heat c_v is also constant for this material. Determine equations that will allow u_g, h_g, and s_g to be calculated relative to a reference state at p_o, v_o, u_o, and s_o in terms of the measurable quantities p, v, and T.

38. Verify the computer results for the actual specific volume determined in Example 6.6 by algebraically solving the cubic van der Waals equation for v by hand. Then compute the percent error in v between your calculated value and the Newton-Raphson technique result given in Example 6.6.

39. Develop a Newton-Raphson technique to solve an equation of state for T when p and v are known.

40. Modify the Newton-Raphson technique to solve for T rather than v and determine the temperature of superheated ammonia at 2.0 MPa, 0.0824 m^3/kg by using the Beattie-Bridgeman equation of state (see Eq. 3.73). Iterate by hand (or computer) until the pressure error, $p^* - p$ is less than 1% of p.

41. A standard spark ignition piston–cylinder automobile engine has a compression ratio of 8.6 to 1, and the intake air is at 0.1 MPa, 17 °C. For an isentropic compression process, use the gas tables (Appendix C.16*b*) to determine

a) the work required per unit mass of air compressed,
b) the temperature at the end of the compression stroke, and
c) the pressure at the end of the compression stroke.

42. Air enters an isentropic steady flow axial compressor at 14.7 psia and 60 °F, and exits at 197 psia. Determine the exhaust temperature and the input power per unit mass flow rate. Use Appendix C.16*a* in your solution.

43. An engineer claims to have designed an uninsulated diffuser that will expand 3.0 kg/s of air from 1.0 MPa, 37 °C to 0.1 MPa, 17 °C. The inlet and exit air velocities are 80 and 5.0 m/s, respectively. Use the gas tables (Appendix C.16*b*) to determine the heat transfer rate and entropy production rate for the diffuser if the average wall temperature is 27 °C. Will the diffuser work as designed?

44. Determine the final pressure, temperature, and required work per unit mass when 1.0 m^3 of air is isentropically compressed from 0.15 MPa, 300 K to 0.1 m^3 using

a) constant specific heat ideal gas equations, and
b) the gas tables for air (Appendix C.16*b*).

45. An insulated axial flow air compressor for a gas turbine engine is being tested in a laboratory. The inlet conditions are 0.09 MPa, −3 °C and the outlet is at 0.286 MPa, 217 °C. Use the gas tables to determine the ratio of the power input for an isentropic process to the actual adiabatic power input. This ratio is defined to be the compressor's *isentropic efficiency*.

46. An insulated air compressor with an isentropic efficiency of 78% (see Problem 45) compresses air from 0.1 MPa, 290 K to 10 MPa. Use the gas tables to determine the power required per unit mass flow rate and the exit air temperature.

47. Use the gas tables (Appendix C.16*a*) to determine the final temperature and the minimum possible power required to compress 3.0 lbm/s of air from 14.7 psia, 40 °F to 10 atm in a steady flow adiabatic process.

48. Air is compressed in an adiabatic steady flow process from 0.081 MPa to 2.5 MPa, 400 K with an isentropic efficiency (see Problem 45) of 85%. Use the gas tables to determine

a) the power required per unit mass flow rate,
b) the actual inlet temperature, and
c) the entropy production rate per unit mass flow rate.

49. An uninsulated piston-type air compressor operates in a steady flow process from 0.1 MPa, 300 K to 2.0 MPa, 540 K. Use the gas tables to determine per unit mass flow rate,

a) the power required, and
b) the heat transfer rate

when the entropy production rate per unit mass flow rate is 0.5380 kJ/(kg·K) and the mean cylinder external wall temperature is 432 K.

50. 700 ft·lbf is used to compress 0.45 lbm of air isothermally in a closed piston–cylinder apparatus from 14.7 psia, 70 °F to 2000 psia. Assuming ideal gas behavior,

a) is this process possible?

b) If not, what is the maximum possible compression pressure that could be reached with this process?

51. Determine the compressibility factor for methane at 20 MPa and 0 °C.

52. 200 lbm of carbon dioxide is to be put into a rigid 3.0 ft^3 tank at 87.5 °C. Use the compressibility factor to determine the final pressure.

53. Determine the ratio of v_c'/v_c for the following substances:

a) water vapor, **b)** nitrogen,

c) propane, and **d)** methane.

54. Using the generalized charts, determine the sum of the heat transfer rate and power required to isothermally compress 0.3 kg/s of hydrogen in a steady flow process from 2.0 to 20 atm at 50 K. Is it possible to carry out this process adiabatically?

55. Using the generalized charts, determine the entropy change as 0.73 kg of carbon monoxide is expanded from 35 MPa to 0.1 MPa in an isothermal process at 100 K.

56. Compare the specific volumes of water vapor obtained from the steam tables to those obtained from the compressibility factor charts (Figures 3.12 and 3.13) at the following states

a) 14.7 psia, 300 °F,

b) 6000 psia, 1000 °F,

c) 8000 psia, 2000 °F.

57. Compare the values of $h_2 - h_1$ and $s_2 - s_1$ for water vapor obtained from **a)** the gas tables (Appendix C.16*c*) and **b)** the generalized charts (Figures 6.2 and 6.3) with those obtained from the steam tables for the following conditions: 14.7 psia, 300 °F (state 1) and 6000 psia, 1000 °F (state 2).

58. Use the generalized charts to calculate the heat transfer rate required to cool 6.0 lbm/s of argon gas from 500 °F, 2000 psia to 300 °F in a steady flow constant pressure heat exchanger. Assume the specific heats of argon are constant over this temperature range.

59. Methane is throttled adiabatically with negligible velocity change from 1500 psia, 70 °F to atmospheric pressure. Assuming constant specific heats and using the generalized charts, determine the exit temperature.

60. Carbon dioxide is throttled adiabatically with negligible velocity change from 2500 psia, 800 R to atmospheric pressure. Use the generalized charts to determine the exit temperature by

a) assuming constant specific heats, and

b) using the gas tables (Appendix C.16*c*).

61. Helium in an external storage tank on a spacecraft is expanded through an isentropic attitude control nozzle with a negligible inlet velocity from 2.0 MPa, 10 K to 0.01 MPa. Assuming constant specific heats and using the generalized charts, determine the exit temperature and velocity.

62. Sulfur dioxide with a negligible inlet velocity is expanded through an isentropic nozzle from 20 MPa, 500 K to 0.2 MPa in a chemical processing unit. Assuming constant specific heats and using the generalized charts, determine the exit temperature and velocity.

63. Hydrogen is cooled in an isobaric heat exchanger from 5000 to 527 R at 20 psia. The heat transfer occurs across an isothermal wall at 500 R inside the heat exchanger. Use the generalized charts to determine the hydrogen's heat transfer and entropy production rates per unit mass flow rate.

64. Use the generalized charts to determine the changes in specific enthalpy and specific entropy of nitrogen as it undergoes an isobaric cooling process from 2000 to 1000 R at 14.7 psia by assuming

a) constant specific heats, and
b) temperature dependent specific heats.
c) Compute the percentage difference between the results of a and b.

65. According to Dalton's law of partial pressures, the partial pressure exerted by the water vapor in a mixture of air and water vapor is equal to the pressure the water vapor would exert if it alone occupied the total volume of the mixture. If 1.0 m^3 of humid air at 20 °C contains 10.3 g of water vapor, determine

a) the partial pressure of the water vapor,
b) the maximum partial pressure of water vapor at this temperature,
c) the ratio of the answer in a to that of b (this ratio is called the *relative humidity* of the air).

66. Steam is throttled from 100 psia, 500 °F to 14.7 psia in an isenthalpic process. Determine the change in specific entropy and the exit temperature of the steam by using

a) ideal gas equations, and
b) the steam tables.
c) Compute the percent error in assuming ideal gas behavior.

67. In the warp drive system of an intergalactic spacecraft, 13 kg/s of water vapor is reversibly and isothermally expanded from 500 to 125 Pa at 100 °C. Determine the heat transfer rate and the power produced. Assume ideal gas behavior.

68. Water vapor is heated from 300 to 400 °F in a steady flow isobaric process. Determine the percent error in calculating the heat transfer rate per unit mass flow rate by using the ideal gas equations for system pressures of **a)** 20 psia, **b)** 2 psia, and **c)** 0.2 psia.

69. Saturated water vapor at 10 kPa is expanded reversibly and isentropically in a steady flow process in a door knob heat treating plant to 5.0 kPa. Determine the final temperature, the heat transfer rate, and the power produced per unit mass flow rate. Assume the steam is an ideal gas.

Design Problems

The following are open ended design problems. The objective is to carry out a preliminary thermal design as indicated. A detailed design with working drawings is not expected unless otherwise specified. These problems do not have specific answers, so each student's design will be unique.

70. Design a system to liquefy nitrogen by repeatedly expanding it until it reaches the saturation temperature. (*Hint*: Consult your library about the Linde gas liquefaction process.)

71. Design a system to cut ice into various two-dimensional shapes by using localized pressure to produce a phase change and thus locally "melting" out the desired shape. (*Suggestion*: Try a high-pressure "cookie-cutter" technique.)

72. Design a fire extinguisher system that will expand liquid carbon dioxide under a suitable pressure at ambient temperature (which can vary by ± 50 °C) and produce a fine spray of solid carbon dioxide particles at high velocity and low temperature.

73. Design a 3.0-ft^3 cylindrical tank that will safely contain oxygen gas at 2500 psia under ambient temperature conditions (which can vary by ± 100 °F). (*Suggestion*: Consult the ASME Pressure Vessel Design Codes in your library.)

74. Design an experiment that will illustrate and accurately measure the difference in p-v-T behavior between water vapor and a suitable ideal gas (such as air) over the temperature range from 0 to 150 °C.

Computer Problems

The following computer programming assignments were designed to be carried out on any personal computer using BASIC as the programming language. They are meant to be exercises in input/output screen formatting and manipulation of some of the basic formulae of this chapter. They may be used as part of a weekly homework assignment.

75. Modify the van der Waals program given in Example 6.6 to create data from which you can plot (by hand or by computer) for water vapor the percent error in v due to the Newton-Raphson technique vs. the percent error in p along the $T = 700$ K isotherm. Note that the allowable error must now be treated as an input variable.

76. Modify the program given in Example 6.6 to provide the user with a menu choice of the following working options:

a) output p when T and v are input,
b) output v when p and T are input, and
c) output T when p and v are input.

77. Modify the program given in Example 6.6 to allow the user to choose the gas from a menu. The program must contain all the van der Waals constants for all the gases listed in the menu plus the option of the user inputing constants for gases not listed in the menu.

78. Plot a minimum of 100 points along the $T = 500$ R isotherm on p-v coordinates for air using

a) the ideal gas equation of state, and
b) the Clausius equation of state (use the van der Waals value for b).

79. Plot a minimum of 100 points along the $T = 500$ R isotherm on p-v coordinates for hydrogen using

a) the ideal gas equation of state, and
b) the van der Waals equation of state.

80. Plot a minimum of 100 points along the $T = 500$ R isotherm on p-v coordinates for methane using

a) the ideal gas equation of state, and
b) the Beattie-Bridgeman equation of state.

81. Using the steam tables as a guide, find the regions on a Mollier diagram and/or a p-v diagram where the ideal gas equations with constant specific heats are accurate to within $\pm 1\%$ for

a) specific volume v, **b)** enthalpy h, and **c)** entropy s.

82. Expand Problem 81 by adding temperature-dependent ideal gas specific heats.

83. Expand Problem 81 by using the van der Waals equation of state in place of the ideal gas equation of state.

84. Write an interactive BASIC language computer program for ammonia using the Beattie-Bridgeman equation of state to produce the following results from responses to appropriate screen prompts

a) output p when v and T are input,
b) output T when p and v are input, and
c) output v when p and T are input.

85. Write an interactive BASIC language computer program that will replace the gas tables, Appendices C.16a and C.16b. Do this in two steps:

a) First write a program that will return u, h, ϕ, p_r, and v_r when T is input by assuming constant specific heats, and
b) modify the program developed in step a above to include the temperature dependent specific heats given in Appendix C.14.

86. The purpose of this assignment is to investigate the accuracy of several historically important p-T relations for saturated water vapor. Using the tables in the back of the book as a source for accurate saturation p-T data, calculate, tabulate, and plot the percent error in saturation pressure for each of the following cases by using % error = (CP – TP)/TP, where CP is the calculated saturation pressure and TP is the saturation pressure found in the steam tables.

a) By 1847 Henri Regnault had developed an equation from his experimental p_{sat}-T_{sat} results for saturated steam. It was valid in the range of -33 to 232°C, and had the form

$$\log_{10} p_{sat} = A - BD^n - CE^n$$

where p_{sat} is in mm Hg and

$$A = 6.2640348 \qquad \log_{10} D = 9.994049292 - 10$$

$$\log_{10} B = 0.1397743 \qquad \log_{10} E = 9.998343862 - 10$$

$$\log_{10} C = 0.6924351 \qquad n = T_{sat} + 20 \quad \text{where } T_{sat} \text{ is in °C}$$

Make your % error calculations every 20 °C between 20 and 220 °C.

b) In 1849 Williams Rankine fit his own equation to Regnault's data and came up with the following relation:

$$\log_{10} p_{sat} = A - B/T_{sat} - C/T_{sat}^2$$

where p_{sat} is in psia and $T_{sat} = T_{sat}(\text{in °F}) + 461.2$ (-461.2 °F was Rankine's best estimate of absolute zero), and

$$A = 6.1007 \qquad \log_{10} B = 3.43642 \qquad \log_{10} C = 5.59873$$

Make your % error calculations here at 20 °F intervals between 40 and 700 °F.

c) By 1899 very careful p_{sat}-T_{sat} measurements had been made and K. Thiesen curve fit these data to the following equation

$$(T_{sat} + 459.6) \log_{10} p_{sat} = 5.409(T_{sat} - 212) - (8.71 \times 10^{-10})[(689 - T_{sat})^4 - (477)^4]$$

where p_{sat} is in atmospheres and T_{sat} is in °F. Make your % error calculations here at intervals of 20 °F between 20 and 700 °F.

d) By 1915 G. A. Goodenough had developed the following more complex equation which he claimed fit steam quite well over the entire range from 32 °F to the critical point (705 °F).

$$\log_{10} p_{sat} = A - B/T_{sat} - C \log_{10} T_{sat} - DT_{sat} + ET_{sat}^2 - F$$

where $F = 0.0002\{10 - 10[(T_{sat} - 829.6)/100]^2 + [(T_{sat} - 829.6)/100]^4\}$. Here p_{sat} is in psia, T_{sat} is in R, and

$$A = 10.5688080 \qquad \log_{10} D = 7.6088020 - 10$$

$$\log_{10} B = 3.6881209 \qquad \log_{10} E = 4.1463000 - 10$$

$$C = 0.0155$$

Make your % error calculations at any convenient temperature interval between 32 and 705 °F. *Note*: The use of base 10 logarithms in the above equations is the way these equations were originally written, and it has been continued here for historical accuracy.

87. Equations 6.42 for mercury are given by (see the fifth reference at the end of this chapter)

1. $\ln p_{sat} = 23.6321 - 7042.6208/T_{sat} - 0.1207(\ln T_{sat}) - 58{,}060.290/T_{sat}^2$

2. $p = RT/v - (T/v^2)\exp[10.3338 - 312.0954/T - 2.0795(\ln T)]$

3. $v_f = [12{,}813.6070 - 2.4531(T_{sat} - 600) - 0.000267(T_{sat} - 600)^2]^{-1}$

4. $c_v^\circ = 62.168$ J/(kg·K) = constant

where p and p_{sat} are in Pa, T and T_{sat} are in K, and v and V_f are in m^3/kg, and R = 41.4453 J/(kg·K). Write a computer program that will return v, u, h, and s values when p and T are input. Make sure your program checks to see what region (saturated or superheated) your input data are in. Use reference states of $T_o = 400$ K, $u_o = 285.336$ kJ/kg, and $s_o = 0.5580$ kJ/(kg·K). Typical results are $p = 1.89$ MPa, $T = 850$ K, $v_f = 8.21 \times 10^{-5}$ m^3/kg, $v_g = 0.01822$ m^3/kg, $h_f = 61.81$ kJ/kg, $h_g = 346.36$ kJ/kg, $s_f = 0.1014$ kJ/(kg·K), and $s_g = 0.4370$ kJ/(kg·K). *Note*: More ambitious programs can now be produced by adding subroutines that will return the remaining properties when any pair of independent properties (T-s, p-h, etc.) are input.

Chapter Seven Homogeneous Nonreacting Mixtures of Gases and Vapors

In this chapter we deal with the problem of generating thermodynamic properties for homogeneous mixtures of gases and vapors that are not involved in chemical reactions. Properties of chemically reacting mixtures are discussed in Chapter 9.

The technique employed here is basically very simple. The mixture is considered to be a unique substance with unique thermodynamic properties. Because thermodynamic equations of state are always homogeneous functions of the first degree (even for an arbitrary homogeneous mixture), then the value of any *specific* property of the mixture turns out to be simply the mass weighted sum of the related *partial* properties of all the species present in the mixture. Thus, the specific properties of the mixture can be calculated directly if one knows **a)** the composition of the mixture and **b)** the partial properties of all the components present in the mixture.

We will also need either a thermodynamic table, a thermodynamic chart, or an equation of state for the mixture to be able to have access to all its thermodynamic properties. Since the number of possible mixtures is infinite, it is impractical to create general thermodynamic property tables or charts for anything but the most common mixtures (such as air; see, for example, Appendix C.16*a*), or mixtures of important industrial value (such as air and water vapor because the thermodynamics of this mixture is an essential part of the heating, ventilating, and air conditioning (HVAC) industry; see Appendicies D.6*a* and *b*). Normally, mixture equations of state are used to determine the numerical values of the thermodynamic properties of a mixture.

Thermodynamic Properties of Mixtures

Unfortunately, there is no single measure of mixture composition. A mixture composition will often be given simply as a percentage, but the percentage will have been calculated on a mass (or weight) basis,[1] a molar basis, a volume basis, or a pressure basis and its numerical value depends upon which basis was used. This ambiguity leads us to define four different composition percentages or fraction measures.

Consider a homogeneous mixture made up of N distinct chemical species, each of which has a unique molecular mass M_i. Let the mass of each chemical species present in the mixture be m_i. Then the mass balance gives the total mass of the mixture m_m as

$$m_m = m_1 + m_2 + \cdots + m_N = \sum_{i=1}^{N} m_i \tag{7.1}$$

The corresponding number of moles n_i of chemical species i can be determined from Eq. 1.12 as

$$n_i = m_i/M_i \tag{1.12}$$

and because the mole unit is just another measure of mass, the total number of moles of mixture n_m is simply

$$n_m = n_1 + n_2 + \cdots + n_N = \sum_{i=1}^{N} n_i \tag{7.2}$$

With these two different mass measures we can define two different mass-based composition fractions as

a) The *mass fraction* w_i of chemical species i in the mixture is

$$w_i = m_i/m_m \tag{7.3}$$

and

b) the *mole fraction*, x_i, of chemical species i in the mixture is

$$x_i = n_i/n_m \tag{7.4}$$

With the exception of system mass, the extensive properties of a system are not generally conserved in any thermodynamic process, so that their mixture values are not normally equal to the sum of their constituent values. However, extensive properties are mathematically homogeneous functions of the first degree.[2] For example, the total volume $\mathcal{V}_m$ of a homogeneous mixture can be written as a function of the mixture total pressure p_m, mixture temperature T_m, and the composi-

1. This is also sometimes called a *gravimetric* basis.

2. See, for example, J. Kestin, *A Course in Thermodynamics*. Vol. 1, New York: McGraw-Hill Hemisphere, 1979, pp. 326–327.

tion of the mixture $m_1, m_2, \ldots, m_N$ as

$$\mathcal{V}_{\mathrm{m}} = \mathcal{V}_{\mathrm{m}}(p_{\mathrm{m}}, T_{\mathrm{m}}, m_1, \ldots, m_N)$$

and when the total pressure and temperature are constant this must also be a homogeneous function of the first degree, and must therefore obey the relation

$$\lambda \mathcal{V}_{\mathrm{m}} = \mathcal{V}_{\mathrm{m}}(p_{\mathrm{m}}, T_{\mathrm{m}}, \lambda m_1, \ldots, \lambda m_N)$$

where λ is an arbitrary variable. Differentiating this equation with respect to λ while holding the pressure and temperature constant gives

$$\mathcal{V}_{\mathrm{m}}\big|_{p_m, T_m} = \left(\frac{\partial \mathcal{V}_{\mathrm{m}}}{\partial m_1}\right) m_1 + \cdots + \left(\frac{\partial \mathcal{V}_{\mathrm{m}}}{\partial m_N}\right) m_N = \sum_{i=1}^{N} m_i \hat{v}_i \tag{7.5a}$$

where

$$\hat{v}_i = \left(\frac{\partial \mathcal{V}_{\mathrm{m}}}{\partial m_i}\right)_{p_{\mathrm{m}}, T_{\mathrm{m}}, m_j} \tag{7.6a}$$

is defined to be the *partial specific volume* of species i in the mixture. Similarly, the rest of the extensive properties of the mixture can be written in terms of their specific partial properties as

$$U_{\mathrm{m}} = \sum_{i=1}^{N} m_i \hat{u}_i \tag{7.5b}$$

$$H_{\mathrm{m}} = \sum_{i=1}^{N} m_i \hat{h}_i \tag{7.5c}$$

$$S_{\mathrm{m}} = \sum_{i=1}^{N} m_i \hat{s}_i \tag{7.5d}$$

where the partial specific internal energy $\hat{u}_i$, the partial specific enthalpy $\hat{h}_i$, and the partial specific entropy $\hat{s}_i$ are defined as

$$\hat{u}_i = \left(\frac{\partial U_{\mathrm{m}}}{\partial m_i}\right)_{p_{\mathrm{m}}, T_{\mathrm{m}}, m_j} \tag{7.6b}$$

$$\hat{h}_i = \left(\frac{\partial H_{\mathrm{m}}}{\partial m_i}\right)_{p_{\mathrm{m}}, T_{\mathrm{m}}, m_j} \tag{7.6c}$$

$$\hat{s}_i = \left(\frac{\partial S_{\mathrm{m}}}{\partial m_i}\right)_{p_{\mathrm{m}}, T_{\mathrm{m}}, m_j} \tag{7.6d}$$

Dividing both sides of Eqs. 7.5*a* through 7.5*d* by the mixture mass m_m gives the corresponding *specific properties* of the entire mixture as

$$v_m = V_m/m_m = \sum_{i=1}^{N} w_i \hat{v}_i \tag{7.7a}$$

$$u_m = U_m/m_m = \sum_{i=1}^{N} w_i \hat{u}_i \tag{7.7b}$$

$$h_m = H_m/m_m = \sum_{i=1}^{N} w_i \hat{h}_i \tag{7.7c}$$

and

$$s_m = S_m/m_m = \sum_{i=1}^{N} w_i \hat{s}_i \tag{7.7d}$$

On a molar basis, similar mixture molar partial properties and mixture molar specific properties are defined as

$$\hat{\bar{v}}_i = \left(\frac{\partial V_m}{\partial n_i}\right)_{p_m, T_m, n_j} \tag{7.8a}$$

$$\hat{\bar{u}}_i = \left(\frac{\partial U_m}{\partial n_i}\right)_{p_m, T_m, n_j} \tag{7.8b}$$

$$\hat{\bar{h}}_i = \left(\frac{\partial H_m}{\partial n_i}\right)_{p_m, T_m, n_j} \tag{7.8c}$$

$$\hat{\bar{s}}_i = \left(\frac{\partial S_m}{\partial n_i}\right)_{p_m, T_m, n_j} \tag{7.8d}$$

and

$$\bar{v}_m = \sum_{i=1}^{N} x_i \hat{\bar{v}}_i \tag{7.9a}$$

$$\bar{u}_m = \sum_{i=1}^{N} x_i \hat{\bar{u}}_i \tag{7.9b}$$

$$\bar{h}_m = \sum_{i=1}^{N} x_i \hat{\bar{h}}_i \tag{7.9c}$$

$$\bar{s}_m = \sum_{i=1}^{N} x_i \hat{\bar{s}}_i \tag{7.9d}$$

Finally, the constant volume specific heat of the mixture $c_{v\text{m}}$ can be determined from Eqs. 3.33 and 7.7*b* as

$$c_{v\text{m}} = \left(\frac{\partial u_\text{m}}{\partial T_\text{m}}\right)_{v\text{m}} = \sum_{i=1}^{N} w_i \left(\frac{\partial \hat{u}_i}{\partial T_\text{m}}\right)_{v\text{m}} = \sum_{i=1}^{N} w_i \hat{c}_{vi} \tag{7.7e}$$

and Eqs. 3.42 and 7.7*c* give the constant pressure specific heat of the mixture $c_{p\text{m}}$ as

$$c_{p\text{m}} = \left(\frac{\partial h_\text{m}}{\partial T_\text{m}}\right)_{p\text{m}} = \sum_{i=1}^{N} w_i \left(\frac{\partial \hat{h}_i}{\partial T_\text{m}}\right)_{p\text{m}} = \sum_{i=1}^{N} w_i \hat{c}_{pi} \tag{7.7f}$$

where the partial specific heats of chemical species *i* are defined as

$$\hat{c}_{vi} = \left(\frac{\partial \hat{u}_i}{\partial T_\text{m}}\right)_{v\text{m}} \tag{7.6e}$$

$$\hat{c}_{pi} = \left(\frac{\partial \hat{h}_i}{\partial T_\text{m}}\right)_{p\text{m}} \tag{7.6f}$$

On a molar basis these equations become

$$\bar{c}_{v\text{m}} = \sum_{i=1}^{N} x_i \hat{\bar{c}}_{vi} \tag{7.9e}$$

$$\bar{c}_{p\text{m}} = \sum_{i=1}^{N} x_i \hat{\bar{c}}_{pi} \tag{7.9f}$$

where

$$\hat{\bar{c}}_{vi} = \left(\frac{\partial \hat{\bar{u}}_i}{\partial T_\text{m}}\right)_{v\text{m}} \tag{7.8e}$$

and

$$\hat{\bar{c}}_{pi} = \left(\frac{\partial \hat{\bar{h}}_i}{\partial T_\text{m}}\right)_{p\text{m}} \tag{7.8f}$$

Equation 7.5*a* leads us to the third common composition measure, used mainly with gases:

c) the *volume fraction* ψ_i of chemical species *i* in the mixture is

$$\psi_i = V_i / V_\text{m} \tag{7.10}$$

where $V_i = m_i \hat{v}_i = n_i \hat{\bar{v}}_i$ is the partial volume of chemical species *i* in the mixture.

The mass, mole, and volume fractions all have the characteristic that they always sum to unity,

$$\sum_{i=1}^{N} w_i = \sum_{i=1}^{N} x_i = \sum_{i=1}^{N} \psi_i = 1.0 \tag{7.11}$$

and therefore when either w_i, x_i, or ψ_i is multiplied by 100 it represents the *percentage* of chemical species i present on a *mass, molar*, or *volume* basis respectively. Note, however, that w_i and ψ_i do not have the same numerical values and therefore *the percentage analysis of the composition depends upon which fractional base was used in its determination.*

If we consider the mixture to be a unique substance then we can compute its equivalent molecular mass M_m from Eqs. 7.1, 1.13, and 7.4 as

$$M_m = m_m/n_m = \left(\sum_{i=1}^{N} m_i\right)\Big/ n_m = \sum_{i=1}^{N} n_i M_i/n_m$$

$$= \sum_{i=1}^{N} x_i M_i \tag{7.12}$$

or by using Eqs. 7.2, 1.13, and 7.3 as

$$M_m = m_m/n_m = m_m\Big/\left(\sum_{i=1}^{N} m_i/M_i\right) = 1\Big/\left(\sum_{i=1}^{N} (m_i/m_m)/M_i\right)$$

$$= 1\Big/\left(\sum_{i=1}^{N} w_i/M_i\right) \tag{7.13}$$

Using Eqs. 7.12 and 7.13 we can now easily convert back and forth between mass and mole fractions with

$$w_i = m_i/m_m = n_i M_i/(n_m M_m) = x_i(M_i/M_m) \tag{7.14a}$$

and

$$x_i = n_i/n_m = w_i(M_m/M_i) \tag{7.14b}$$

Lastly, if the mixture is a gas or a vapor, we can determine its equivalent gas constant R_m from the universal gas constant $\mathcal{R}$ and Eq. 7.12 or 7.13 as

$$R_m = \mathcal{R}/M_m \tag{7.15}$$

At this point we have developed general formulae for determining the values of thermodynamic properties and other important characteristics of mixtures of substances in their solid, liquid, vapor, or gaseous states. Before we can continue we need to know how these mixture thermodynamic properties are related to each other. Since the number of possible mixture compositions is infinite, the construction of thermodynamic tables and charts is impractical except for very common mixtures such as the mixture of gases we call "air," and air–water vapor mixtures.

In this text we will restrict our attention to simple equations of state such as those for ideal and real gases discussed in Chapter 6.

Mixtures of Ideal Gases

A mixture of ideal gases is normally considered to behave as a unique ideal gas with an equivalent molecular mass M_m and gas constant R_m given by Eq. 7.12 or 7.13 and 7.15. This is illustrated in the following example.

Example 7.1

The molar composition of air that is normally used to determine the thermodynamic properties of air at standard temperature and pressure is

Component	Molar %
Nitrogen	78.09
Oxygen	20.95
Argon	0.93
CO_2 and trace gases	0.03
TOTAL	100.00%

Determine the equivalent molecular mass and gas constant for this mixture, and determine the composition of air on a mass (or weight) basis.

Solution Since we are given the molar composition for air we can find its equivalent molecular weight from Eq. 7.12. Assuming argon and carbon dioxide are the only minor components present, and utilizing Appendix C.13*a* for the values of the molecular masses, Eq. 7.12 gives

$$M_{air} = \sum_{i=1}^{4} x_i M_i = 0.7809(28.02) + 0.2095(32.00)$$

$$+ 0.0093(39.94) + 0.0003(44.01)$$

$$= 28.97 \text{ kg/kgmole}$$

and then Eq. 7.15 gives the equivalent gas constant as

$$R_{air} = \mathscr{R}/M_{air} = \frac{8.3143 \text{ kJ/(kgmole}\cdot\text{K)}}{28.97 \text{ kg/kgmole}} = 0.287 \text{ kJ/(kg}\cdot\text{K)}$$

which agree with the values given in Appendix C.13*b*. Equation 7.14*a* can be used to determine the corresponding mass or weight fraction composition as

$$w_{N_2} = x_{N_2}(M_{N_2}/M_{air}) = 0.7809(28.02/28.97) = 0.7553 \quad \text{(or 75.53\% by mass)}$$

$$w_{O_2} = 0.2095(32.00/28.97) = 0.2314 \quad \text{(or 23.14\% by mass)}$$

$$w_{Ar} = 0.0093(39.94/28.97) = 0.0128 \quad \text{(or 1.28\% by mass)}$$

and

$$w_{CO_2} = 0.0003(44.01/28.97) = 0.00046 \quad \text{(or 0.046\% by mass)}$$

Ideal gas mixtures that are themselves ideal obey all of the ideal gas equations of state:

$$p_m \mathcal{V}_m = m_m R_m T_m \tag{7.16a}$$

$$u_{m2} - u_{m1} = \int_{T_{m1}}^{T_{m2}} c_{vm}\, dT_m \tag{7.16b}$$

$$h_{m2} - h_{m1} = \int_{T_{m1}}^{T_{m2}} c_{pm}\, dT_m \tag{7.16c}$$

and

$$s_{m2} - s_{m1} = \int_{T_{m1}}^{T_{m2}} (c_{vm}/T_m)\, dT_m + R_m \ln(v_{m2}/v_{m1}) \tag{7.16d}$$

$$= \int_{T_{m1}}^{T_{m2}} (c_{pm}/T_m)\, dT_m - R_m \ln(p_{m2}/p_{m1}) \tag{7.16e}$$

where p_m and T_m are the mixture pressure and temperature, respectively. If the mixture can be considered to have constant specific heats then Eqs. 7.6*b* through 7.6*e* reduce to

$$u_{m2} - u_{m1} = c_{vm}(T_{m2} - T_{m1}) \tag{7.16f}$$

$$h_{m2} - h_{m1} = c_{pm}(T_{m2} - T_{m1}) \tag{7.16g}$$

$$s_{m2} - s_{m1} = c_{vm} \ln(T_{m2}/T_{m1}) + R_m \ln(v_{m2}/v_{m1}) \tag{7.16h}$$

$$= c_{pm} \ln(T_{m2}/T_{m1}) - R_m \ln(p_{m2}/p_{m1}) \tag{7.16i}$$

From Eqs. 7.3, 7.13, 7.15, and 7.16*a* we find that for a mixture of ideal gases,

$$\begin{aligned}\mathcal{V}_m &= m_m R_m T_m/p_m = m_m(\mathcal{R}/M_m)(T_m/p_m)\\ &= m_m \mathcal{R}\left(\sum_{i=1}^{N} w_i/M_i\right)(T_m/p_m)\\ &= (\mathcal{R}T_m/p_m)\sum_{i=1}^{N} m_i/M_i\end{aligned}$$

Then Eq. 7.6*a* can be used to find

$$\begin{aligned}\hat{v}_i &= \left(\frac{\partial \mathcal{V}_m}{\partial m_i}\right)_{p_m, T_m, m_j} = \left(\frac{\mathcal{R}}{M_i}\right)(T_m/p_m)\\ &= R_i T_m/p_m = v_i\end{aligned} \tag{7.17}$$

where v_i is the specific volume of gas i at the pressure and temperature of the mixture. Similarly, using the appropriate equations for the partial specific internal energy, enthalpy, and entropy, we can show that for a mixture of ideal gases with constant specific heats,

$$\hat{u}_i = c_{vi}(T_m - T_o) + u_o = u_i \tag{7.18a}$$

$$\hat{h}_i = c_{pi}(T_m - T_o) + h_o = h_i \tag{7.18b}$$

and

$$\hat{s}_i = c_{pi} \ln(T_m/T_o) - R_i \ln(p_m/p_o) = s_i \tag{7.18c}$$

where T_o, p_o, u_o, h_o, and s_o are arbitrary reference state values. Also, from Eqs. 7.6*e*, 7.6*f*, 7.18*a*, and 7.18*b* it is easy to show that

$$\hat{c}_{vi} = c_{vi} \tag{7.18d}$$

and

$$\hat{c}_{pi} = c_{pi} \tag{7.18e}$$

The above relations were also discovered experimentally in the nineteenth century and are now known as the Gibbs-Dalton and Amagat laws. In 1801 John Dalton (1766–1844) carried out a series of experiments which lead him to conclude that the total pressure p_m of a mixture of ideal gases was equal to the sum of the *partial pressures* of the individual component gases in the mixture, where

the partial pressure p_i of gas i in a mixture of ideal gases is the pressure gas i would exert if it alone occupied the volume of the mixture at the temperature of the mixture.

This can be written mathematically as *Dalton's law* of partial pressures:

$$p_m = \sum_{i=1}^{N} p_i \tag{7.19}$$

where

$$p_i = m_i R_i T_m / V_m \tag{7.20}$$

Later, Emile Amagat (1841–1915) discovered experimentally that the total volume V_m of a mixture of ideal gases was equal to the sum of the *partial volumes* V_i of the individual component gases in the mixture, where

the partial volume V_i of gas i in a mixture of ideal gases is the volume gas i would occupy if it alone was at the pressure and temperature of the mixture.

This can be written mathematically as *Amagat's law* of partial volumes:

$$V_m = \sum_{i=1}^{N} V_i \tag{7.21}$$

where

$$V_i = m_i R_i T_m / p_m \qquad (\text{or } v_i = R_i T_m / p_m) \tag{7.17}$$

Finally, the thermodynamic description of a mixture of ideal gases was completed through the work of Josiah Willard Gibbs (1838–1903) by generalizing Dalton's law to define all the partial properties (except volume) of the components in the mixture to be equal to the values that those properties would have if each component gas alone occupied the volume of the mixture at the temperature of the mixture and at the partial pressure of that component. The Gibbs-Dalton ideal gas mixture law presumes that there are no molecular interactions between the components of the mixture because each component is presumed to behave as though the other components were not present. Under this assumption all the extensive properties of a mixture of ideal gases are conserved, and the mixture value of any extensive property can be determined by summing the contributions made by each gas present in the mixture. Therefore, for ideal gases only,

$$\not{V}_{\mathrm{m}} = \sum_{i=1}^{N} \not{V}_i = \sum_{i=1}^{N} m_i v_i \tag{7.22a}$$

$$U_{\mathrm{m}} = \sum_{i=1}^{N} U_i = \sum_{i=1}^{N} m_i u_i \tag{7.22b}$$

$$H_{\mathrm{m}} = \sum_{i=1}^{N} H_i = \sum_{i=1}^{N} m_i h_i \tag{7.22c}$$

and

$$S_{\mathrm{m}} = \sum_{i=1}^{N} S_i = \sum_{i=1}^{N} m_i s_i \tag{7.22d}$$

Equations 7.7*a*–7.7*f* then give the specific properties of a mixture of N ideal gases as

$$v_{\mathrm{m}} = \sum_{i=1}^{N} w_i v_i \tag{7.23a}$$

$$u_{\mathrm{m}} = \sum_{i=1}^{N} w_i u_i \tag{7.23b}$$

$$h_{\mathrm{m}} = \sum_{i=1}^{N} w_i h_i \tag{7.23c}$$

$$s_{\mathrm{m}} = \sum_{i=1}^{N} w_i s_i \tag{7.23d}$$

$$c_{v\mathrm{m}} = \sum_{i=1}^{N} w_i c_{vi} \tag{7.23e}$$

$$c_{p\mathrm{m}} = \sum_{i=1}^{N} w_i c_{pi} \tag{7.23f}$$

and on a molar basis, Eqs. 7.9*a*–7.9*f* become

$$\bar{v}_m = \sum_{i=1}^{N} x_i \bar{v}_i \tag{7.24a}$$

$$\bar{u}_m = \sum_{i=1}^{N} x_i \bar{u}_i \tag{7.24b}$$

$$\bar{h}_m = \sum_{i=1}^{N} x_i \bar{h}_i \tag{7.24c}$$

$$\bar{s}_m = \sum_{i=1}^{N} x_i \bar{s}_i \tag{7.24d}$$

$$\bar{c}_{vm} = \sum_{i=1}^{N} x_i \bar{c}_{vi} \tag{7.24e}$$

$$\bar{c}_{pm} = \sum_{i=1}^{N} x_i \bar{c}_{pi} \tag{7.24f}$$

Because of the form of Dalton's law, we have reached our fourth composition fraction:

d) the *partial pressure ratio* (or pressure fraction) π_i of chemical species i in the mixture is $\pi_i = p_i/p_m$.

Note that since the partial pressure ratio also sums to unity it too can be used as a percent composition measure when multiplied by 100.

The mass fraction w_i, the mole fraction x_i, the volume fraction ψ_i, and the pressure fraction π_i make four different composition measures that can be used to describe a mixture. However, for ideal gases there is a simple relation between these four quantities. From Eqs. 7.20 and 7.17 we can write the pressure and volume fractions as

$$\pi_i = \frac{p_i}{p_m} = \frac{m_i R_i T_m/\mathcal{V}_m}{m_m R_m T_m/\mathcal{V}_m} = w_i R_i/R_m = w_i M_m/M_i = n_i/n_m = x_i$$

and

$$\psi_i = \frac{\mathcal{V}_i}{\mathcal{V}_m} = \frac{m_i R_i T_m/p_m}{m_m R_m T_m/p_m} = w_i R_i/R_m = w_i M_m/M_i = n_i/n_m = x_i$$

Consequently, for a mixture of ideal gases we have

$$p_i/p_m = \pi_i = \mathcal{V}_i/\mathcal{V}_m = \psi_i = n_i/n_m = x_i = w_i M_m/M_i \tag{7.25}$$

which relates all four composition measures. Thus, the pressure fraction, volume fraction, and mole fraction are all equal, and differ from the mass fraction by only a molecular mass ratio.

Example 7.2

Though oxygen is necessary to sustain life, breathing oxygen at elevated pressure has toxic effects. It causes changes in lung tissue and affects the liver and brain. Acute oxygen poisoning at high pressures can cause convulsions that can lead to death (even at atmospheric pressure pure oxygen can be breathed safely for only two hours). Oxygen poisoning at elevated environmental pressure can be avoided by maintaining the oxygen partial pressure equal to that of atmospheric air at standard temperature and pressure (STP). Also, since atmospheric nitrogen is very soluble in blood and body tissue, rapid depressurization will cause nitrogen bubbles to form in the blood and tissue (nitrogen embolism) producing a condition commonly called "the bends."

Divers going to great depths in the sea are able to circumvent this problem somewhat by breathing a compressed helium–oxygen mixture in which the oxygen partial pressure is adjusted so that it is always equal to its value in atmospheric air at STP. Helium, being much less soluble in body tissue than nitrogen, decreases the time required for depressurization when the diver returns to the surface.

The engineering problem that we must solve is stated as follows:

a) For a deep water diver, determine the proper helium–oxygen breathing mixture composition for a dive to 100 m below the surface of the water where the pressure is 0.98 MN/m^2. Give your answer in mole, volume, and mass fractions.

b) Determine the effective gas constant, the specific heats, and the specific heat ratio for this mixture.

Assume helium and oxygen behave as ideal gases with constant specific heats.

Solution

a) From Example 7.1 and Eq. 7.25 we find that the partial pressure of oxygen in air at STP is

$$p_{O_2} = x_{O_2} p_m = 0.2095(0.1013\ \mathrm{MN/m^2})$$
$$= 0.0212\ \mathrm{MN/m^2}$$

Therefore, at a total pressure in 100 m of water of 0.98 MN/m^2, this same partial pressure requires a mole and volume fraction of oxygen of only

$$x_{O_2} = \psi_{O_2} = \pi_{O_2} = p_{O_2}/p_m = 0.0212/0.98 = 0.0216$$

and from Eq. 7.11 the helium mole and volume fractions are

$$x_{He} = \psi_{He} = 1 - x_{O_2} = 0.9784$$

The equivalent mass fractions are given by Eq. 7.14*a* where the mixture equivalent molecular mass can be computed from Eq. 7.12 as

$$\begin{aligned} M_m &= x_{O_2}M_{O_2} + x_{He}M_{He} \\ &= 0.0216(32.00) + 0.9784(4.003) \\ &= 4.61 \text{ kg/kgmole} \end{aligned}$$

then,

$$\begin{aligned} w_{O_2} &= x_{O_2}(M_{O_2}/M_m) \\ &= 0.0216(32.00/4.61) = 0.1499 \end{aligned}$$

and

$$w_{He} = 1 - w_{O_2} = 0.8501$$

Thus, the required oxygen concentration is only 2.16% on a volume or molar basis, but it is 14.99% on a mass or weight basis.

b) The mixture equivalent gas constant can be computed from Eq. 7.15 as

$$R_m = \mathscr{R}/M_m = \frac{8.3143 \text{ kJ/(kgmole}\cdot\text{K)}}{4.61 \text{ kg/kgmole}} = 1.804 \text{ kJ/(kg}\cdot\text{K)}$$

and the mixture specific heats can be determined from Eqs. 7.23*e* and 7.23*f* and Appendix C.13*b* as

$$\begin{aligned} c_{vm} &= w_{O_2}c_{vO_2} + w_{He}c_{vHe} \\ &= 0.1499(0.657) + 0.8501(3.123) \\ &= 2.753 \text{ kJ/(kg}\cdot\text{K)} \end{aligned}$$

and

$$\begin{aligned} c_{pm} &= w_{O_2}c_{pO_2} + w_{He}c_{pHe} \\ &= 0.1499(0.917) + 0.8501(5.200) \\ &= 4.558 \text{ kJ/(kg}\cdot\text{K)} \end{aligned}$$

Finally, the specific heat ratio of the mixture is

$$k_m = c_{pm}/c_{vm} = \frac{4.558}{2.753} = 1.656$$

(Note that $k_m \neq \sum w_i k_i$ because of its definition as a ratio.)

Ideal gas mixture equations are used to produce property values in thermodynamic problems just as though the mixture was a single unique gas. This is illustrated in the next example.

Example 7.3 Determine the power per unit mass flow rate required to isentropically compress the helium–oxygen mixture described in Example 7.2 from atmospheric pressure (0.1013 MN/m^2) and 20 °C to 0.98 MN/m^2 in a steady flow, steady state process. Assume the mixture has constant specific heats.

Solution The unknown here is the power per unit mass flow rate $\dot{W}/\dot{m}_m$. Since this is an open system, the energy rate balance for a steady state, steady flow, single-inlet, single-outlet system is (neglecting kinetic and potential energy effects)

ERB (SS, SF, SI/SO)

$$\dot{Q} + \dot{W} + \dot{m}_m(h_{m1} - h_{m2}) = 0$$

and since an isentropic process is normally also adiabatic, then

$$\dot{W}/\dot{m}_m = h_{m2} - h_{m1} = c_{pm}(T_{m2} - T_{m1})$$

For an ideal gas in an isentropic process, Eq. 5.38 gives

$$T_{m2} = T_{m1}(p_{m2}/p_{m1})^{(k_m - 1)/k_m}$$

and using the results of Example 7.2 this gives

$$T_{m2} = (20 + 273 \text{ K})(0.98/0.1013)^{0.656/1.656} = 718 \text{ K} = 447 \text{ °C}$$

Then,

$$\dot{W}/\dot{m}_m = c_{pm}(T_{m2} - T_{m1}) = [4.558 \text{ kJ/(kg·K)}](718 - 293 \text{ K})$$
$$= 1937 \text{ kJ/kg}$$

Note that an equivalent aergonic heat transfer of -1937 kJ/kg would be required to cool the compressed mixture in Example 7.3 back to 20 °C again.

Psychrometrics

Psychrometrics is the study of *atmospheric air*, which is a mixture of pure air and water vapor at atmospheric pressure.[3] The pure air portion of an air–water vapor mixture is commonly called *dry air*; consequently, atmospheric air is said to consist of a mixture of dry air and water vapor. Both the air and the water vapor in this mixture are treated as ideal gases (even though we say "water vapor" and not "water gas"). This particular mixture of ideal gases is important because of its meteorological and environmental comfort implications.

3. The term *psychrometer* is from the Greek *psychros* (cold) and *meter* (measure).

To begin this discussion we define two new composition measures for the amount of water vapor present in the mixture. Both of these measures are a type of *humidity*, as shown below.[4]

a) The *relative humidity* ϕ is the ratio of the actual partial pressure of the water vapor present in the mixture to the saturation pressure of the water vapor at the temperature of the mixture, or

$$\phi = p_w/p_{sat} \tag{7.26}$$

The value of p_{sat} can be found in Appendix C.1 at the temperature of the mixture. Since $0 \leq \phi \leq 1$, the relative humidity is normally reported as a percentage. This is the common meteorological humidity measure.

b) The *humidity ratio* ω is the ratio of the mass of water vapor present in the mixture divided by the mass of dry air present in the mixture, or

$$\omega = m_w/m_a \tag{7.27}$$

where $m_m = m_a + m_w$, and $p_m = p_a + p_w =$ atmospheric pressure.

Assuming ideal gas behavior for both the air and water vapor we can write $m_w = p_w V_m/(R_w T_m)$ and $m_a = p_a V_m/(R_a T_m)$, then

$$\begin{aligned} \omega &= p_w R_a/(p_a R_w) = p_w M_w/(p_a M_a) \\ &= (18.016/28.97)(p_w/p_a) \\ &= 0.622(p_w/p_a) = 0.622[p_w/(p_m - p_w)] \end{aligned} \tag{7.28}$$

From Eq. 7.26 we find that $p_w = \phi p_{sat}$, and substituting this into Eq. 7.28 provides a formula that relates the two humidity measures

$$\omega = 0.622(\phi p_{sat}/p_a) = 0.622[\phi p_{sat}/(p_m - \phi p_{sat})] \tag{7.29}$$

A colorful term from the meteorological profession is the *dew point* temperature T_{DP}, which is the temperature at which liquid water (dew) will condense out of the atmosphere at constant atmospheric pressure (and consequently at constant water vapor partial pressure):

$$T_{DP} = T_{sat}(\text{evaluated at } p_w) \tag{7.30}$$

If the partial pressure of the water vapor (p_w) is known, then the dew point temperature can be found in Appendix C.2. Figure 7.1 illustrates these concepts on a pressure-specific volume schematic.

4. Since neither of these two humidity measures corresponds to any of the four composition measures previously discussed, this brings the number of different composition measures used in this chapter to six.

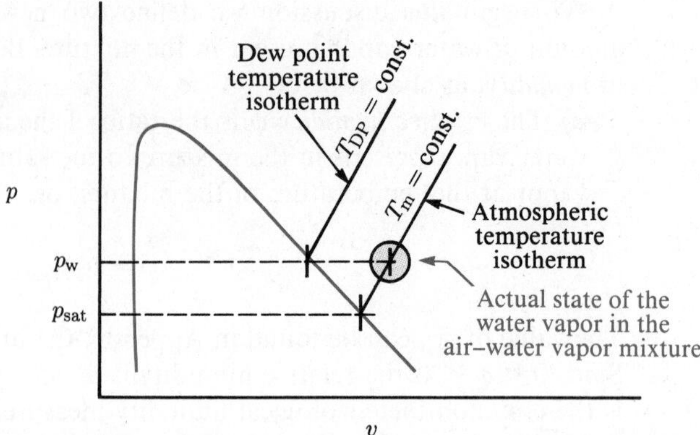

Figure 7.1 Schematic illustrating the partial pressure and dew point temperature of a mixture of water vapor and dray air.

Example 7.4

On a particular day the weather forecast states that the relative humidity is 56.8% when the atmospheric temperature and pressure are 25 °C and 0.1013 MPa, respectively. Determine:

a) the partial pressure of the water vapor in the atmosphere,
b) the humidity ratio of the atmosphere, and
c) the dew point temperature of the atmosphere.

Solution

a) From Appendix C.1*b* we find that

$$p_{sat}(25\ °C) = 0.003169\ \text{MPa}$$

and then from Eq. 7.26 we can calculate the partial pressure of the water vapor present in the mixture as

$$p_w = \phi p_{sat} = 0.568(0.003169\ \text{MPa})$$
$$= 0.0018\ \text{MPa} = 1.8\ \text{kPa}$$

b) From Dalton's law for partial pressure we can find the partial pressure of the dry air in the mixture as

$$p_a = p_m - p_w = 101.3 - 1.8 = 99.5\ \text{kPa}$$

then Eq. 7.28 gives the humidity ratio ω as

$$\omega = 0.622(p_w/p_a) = 0.622(1.8/99.5)$$
$$= 0.0113\ \text{kg } H_2O \text{ per kg of dry air}$$

Note that since the value of ω is not constrained to lie between zero and one, it is not reported as a percentage.

c) Using Eq. 7.30 and Appendix C.2*b* we find the dew point temperature to be

$$T_{\text{DP}} = T_{\text{sat}}(0.0018 \text{ MPa}) = 15.8\ ^\circ\text{C}$$

The steady state, steady flow, isothermal boundary, energy and entropy rate balances for a mixture of dry air and water vapor with negligible flowstream kinetic and potential energies can be written either on an unmixed *component* basis as

$$\dot{Q} + \dot{W} + \dot{m}_{\text{a}}(h_1 - h_2)_{\text{a}} + \dot{m}_{\text{w}}(h_1 - h_2)_{\text{w}} = 0 \tag{7.31a}$$

and

$$\dot{Q}/T_{\text{b}} + \dot{m}_{\text{a}}(s_1 - s_2)_{\text{a}} + \dot{m}_{\text{w}}(s_1 - s_2)_{\text{w}} + \dot{S}_p = 0 \tag{7.31b}$$

or on a premixed *mixture* basis as

$$\dot{Q} + \dot{W} + \dot{m}_{\text{m}}(h_1 - h_2)_{\text{m}} = 0 \tag{7.32a}$$

and

$$\dot{Q}/T_{\text{b}} + \dot{m}_{\text{m}}(s_1 - s_2)_{\text{m}} + \dot{S}_p = 0 \tag{7.32b}$$

where the mixture enthalpy and entropy changes are given by

$$(h_1 - h_2)_{\text{m}} = w_{\text{a}}(h_1 - h_2)_{\text{a}} + w_{\text{w}}(h_1 - h_2)_{\text{w}}$$

and

$$(s_1 - s_2)_{\text{m}} = w_{\text{a}}(s_1 - s_2)_{\text{a}} + w_{\text{w}}(s_1 - s_2)_{\text{w}}$$

In these formula h_{a} is found in the gas tables (Appendix C.16), h_{w} is found in the superheated steam tables, and w_{a} and w_{w} are the mass fractions of the dry air and water vapor. However, since psychrometrics involves only a two-component mixture, there is no particular advantage to using the complicated premixed *mixture* formula. Therefore, we will confine our attention to the simpler unmixed *component* form illustrated in Eqs. 7.31*a* and 7.31*b*.

The Adiabatic Saturator

Evaporative humidification processes normally occur without external heat transfer and are therefore adiabatic. If the outlet of an evaporative humidifier is saturated with water vapor ($\phi = 100\%$), then the device is known as an *adiabatic saturator*. A simple adiabatic saturator is shown in Figure 7.2. It consists of an inlet air–water vapor flowstream at temperature T_1, a liquid makeup water flow stream at temperature T_2, and an outlet air–water vapor flow stream. If the unit

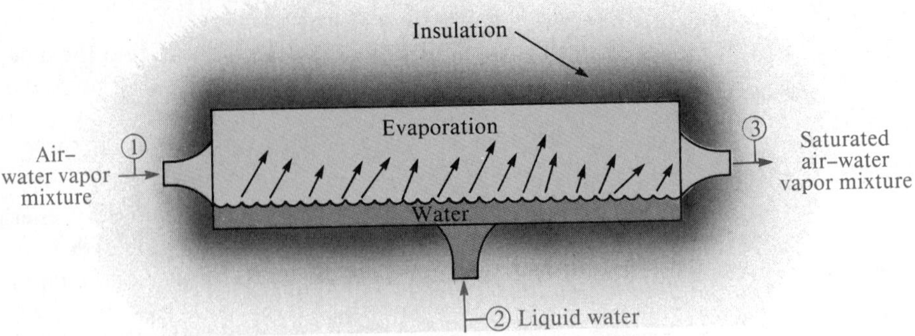

Figure 7.2 Schematic of an adiabatic saturator.

is insulated and made long enough, the outlet flow stream will be saturated with water vapor and the temperature T_3 of the outlet flow stream is then called the *adiabatic-saturation* temperature.

Since this device is adiabatic and aergonic, its steady state, steady flow energy rate balance (ERB) reduces to (neglecting changes in flowstream kinetic and potential energy)

$$\dot{m}_{a1}h_{a1} + \dot{m}_{w1}h_{w1} + \dot{m}_{w2}h_{w2} - \dot{m}_{a3}h_{a3} - \dot{m}_{w3}h_{w3} = 0$$

where we have chosen to separate the contributions from the air and water components according to Eq. 7.31*a*. From the conservation of mass, $\dot{m}_{a1} = \dot{m}_{a3} = \dot{m}_a$ and $\dot{m}_{w2} = \dot{m}_{w3} - \dot{m}_{w1}$. Then the ERB becomes

$$\dot{m}_a(h_{a1} - h_{a3}) + (\dot{m}_{w3} - \dot{m}_{w1})h_{w2} + \dot{m}_{w1}h_{w1} - \dot{m}_{w3}h_{w3} = 0$$

or

$$\dot{m}_a(h_{a1} - h_{a3}) + \dot{m}_{w1}(h_{w1} - h_{w2}) + \dot{m}_{w3}(h_{w2} - h_{w3}) = 0$$

Dividing by $\dot{m}_a$ and then introducing the humidity ratios $\omega_1 = \dot{m}_{w1}/\dot{m}_a$ and $\omega_3 = \dot{m}_{w3}/\dot{m}_a$, and then solving for ω_1 gives

$$\omega_1 = \frac{(h_{a3} - h_{a1}) + \omega_3(h_{w3} - h_{w2})}{h_{w1} - h_{w2}} \tag{7.33}$$

Since we can treat the air here as an ideal gas, and assuming $T_3 = T_2$, then

$$h_{a3} - h_{a1} = c_{pa}(T_3 - T_1) = c_{pa}(T_2 - T_1)$$

and since the liquid makeup water is only a slightly compressed liquid, we can write

$$h_{w2} \approx h_f(T_2) = h_{f2}$$

Finally, since the outlet state contains saturated water vapor at the adiabatic-saturation temperature, $T_3 = T_2$, then

$$h_{w3} = h_g(T_3) = h_g(T_2) = h_{g2}$$

The water vapor in the inlet region is superheated. A quick check of the Mollier diagram (Figure 5.7*a*) reveals that the isotherms in the low-pressure super-heated region are very nearly horizontal. Therefore the enthalpy of water vapor in this region depends only on temperature, so we can take

$$h_{w1} = h_g(T_1) = h_{g1}$$

Then Eq. 7.33 becomes

$$\omega_1 = \frac{c_{pa}(T_2 - T_1) + \omega_3(h_{fg2})}{h_{g1} - h_{f2}} \tag{7.34}$$

Thus by simply measuring the inlet temperature T_1 and the outlet adiabatic-saturation temperature $T_2 = T_3$, we can calculate ω_1 directly from Eq. 7.34. However, an adiabatic saturator must be extremely long to obtain 100% relative humidity at the outlet. This difficulty is overcome by the sling psychrometer discussed below.

The Sling Psychrometer

Figure 7.3 illustrates a simple device for determining air humidity called a *sling psychrometer*. It contains two thermometers, one of which is covered with a wick saturated with ambient temperature liquid water. These two thermometers are called *dry bulb* and *wet bulb*, respectively. When the sling psychrometer is spun rapidly in the air, the evaporation of the water from the wick causes the wet bulb thermometer to read lower than the dry bulb thermometer. After the psychrometer

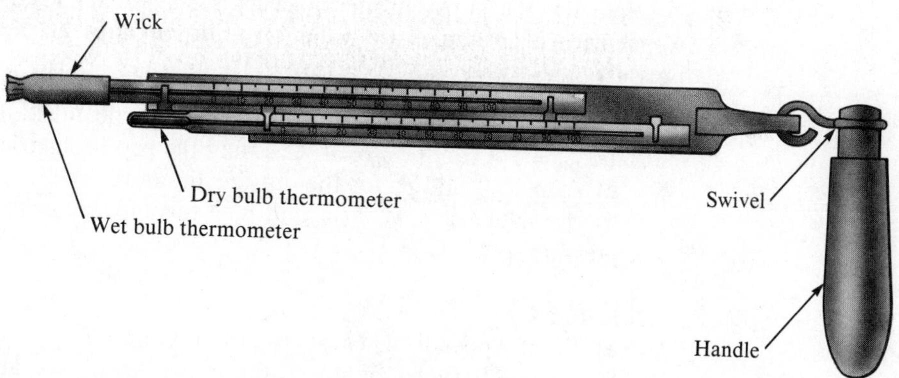

Figure 7.3 Schematic of a sling psychrometer.

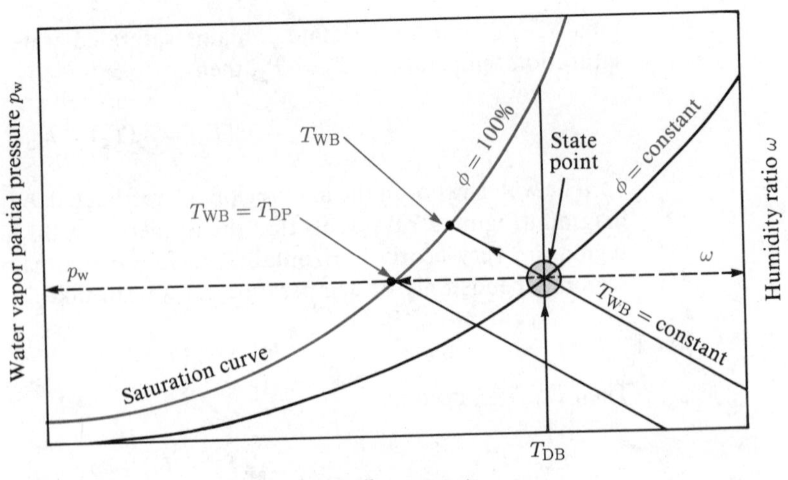

Figure 7.4 Schematic of the elements of a psychrometric chart. The intersection of the dry bulb and wet bulb constant temperature lines determine the state of the water vapor in the system, from which T_{DP}, p_w, ϕ, and ω can then be found.

has been spun long enough for the thermometers to reach equilibrium temperatures, the unit is stopped and the two thermometers are quickly read. A psychrometric chart (or table) is then used to convert the dry bulb temperature T_{DB} and the wet bulb temperature T_{WB} into humidity information. The wet bulb temperature is approximately equal to the adiabatic-saturation temperature, so $T_{WB} \approx T_2 = T_3$ in Eq. 7.34.

Figure 7.4 illustrates the major characteristics of a psychrometric chart. Larger charts of professional engineering quality can be found in Appendixes D.6*a* and *b*. Note that the dry bulb temperature is just the temperature registered on any ordinary thermometer, and also that the psychrometric chart is just part of the *p-T* diagram for saturated and superheated water vapor in the low-pressure region. When the mixture is saturated with water vapor ($\phi = 100\%$), then no water can evaporate from the wet bulb wick and $T_{WB} = T_{DB} = T_{DP}$.

Note also that a psychrometric chart is drawn for a fixed total pressure, thus Appendixes D.6*a* and *b* are valid only for mixtures at one atmosphere total pressure.

Example 7.5

Wet and dry bulb temperature measurements made outside on a cold day reveal that $T_{DB} = 5$ °C and $T_{WB} = 4$ °C. Using the psychrometric chart, determine

a) ϕ, ω, T_{DP}, and p_w for the outside air, and

b) the values of ϕ, ω, T_{WB}, and p_w if this mixture is heated at constant pressure to 25 °C.

Solution

a) From Appendix D.6*b* at $T_{DB1} = 5$ °C and $T_{WB1} = 4$ °C we read: $\phi_1 = 80\%$, $\omega_1 = 0.004$ kg of water vapor per kg of dry air, $T_{DP1} = 2$ °C and $p_{w1} = 700$ N/m^2.

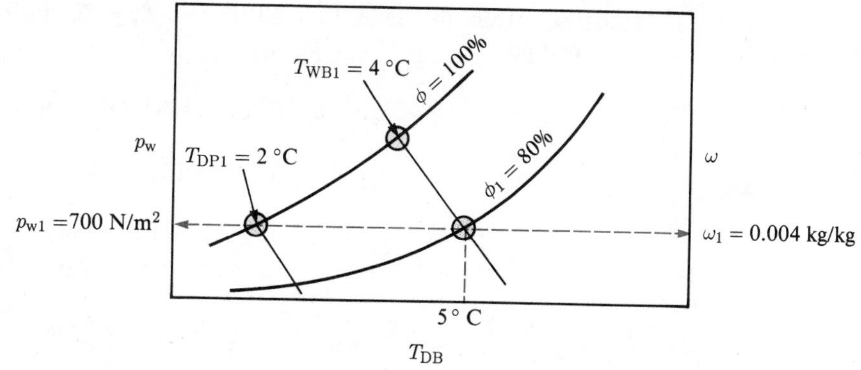

b) Now the mixture is heated at constant pressure until its dry bulb temperature increases to 25 °C. Note that when the temperature is stated without a modifier (i.e., "wet" or "dry") we presume it is the ordinary, or dry bulb temperature. Then Appendix D.6*b* gives $\phi_2 \approx 20\%$, $\omega_2 = \omega_1$, $T_{WB2} = 13$ °C, $T_{DP2} = T_{DP1}$, and $p_{w2} = p_{w1}$.

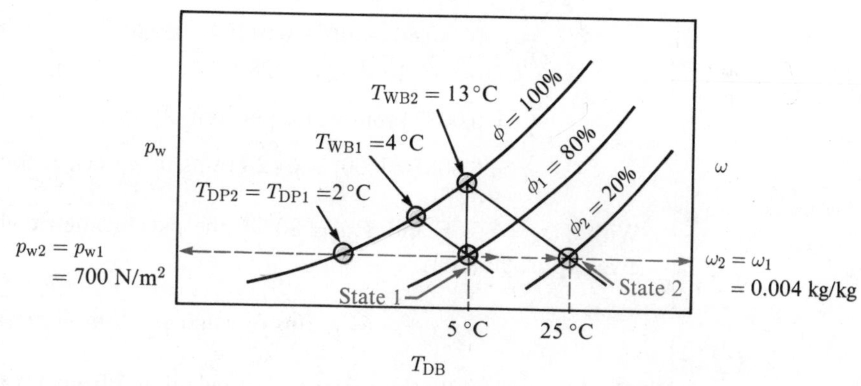

Notice that under these conditions the relative humidity and the wet and dry bulb temperatures change, but none of the other characteristics change. This is because the amount of water vapor and the amount of air present have not changed.

If a sling psychrometer is spun such that the air velocity over the wick is greater than 3 m/s, then the wet bulb temperature will be essentially equal to the adiabatic saturation temperature T_2 in Eq. 7.34. The following example illustrates this point.

Example 7.6 The wet and dry bulb temperatures measured in a dormitory room are 60 and 70 °F, respectively, when the barometric pressure is 14.7 psia. Assuming that the wet bulb temperature is equal to the adiabatic saturation temperature T_2, use Eq. 7.34 to find the humidity ratio (ω) in the room and compare your answer with that obtained from the psychrometric chart, Appendix D.6*a*.

Solution Here we have $T_2 = 60\ °\mathrm{F}$ and $T_1 = 70\ °\mathrm{F}$. Then, from Appendix C.1*a* we find

$$h_{g1} = h_g(70\ °\mathrm{F}) = 1092.0\ \mathrm{Btu/lbm}$$

$$h_{fg2} = h_{fg}(60\ °\mathrm{F}) = 1059.6\ \mathrm{Btu/lbm}$$

$$h_{f2} = h_f(60\ °\mathrm{F}) = 28.1\ \mathrm{Btu/lbm}$$

and

$$p_{w3} = p_{sat}(60\ °\mathrm{F}) = 0.2563\ \mathrm{psia}$$

Then Eq. 7.28 gives

$$\begin{aligned}\omega_3 &= 0.622(0.2563)/(14.7 - 0.2563)\\ &= 0.01104\ \text{lbm water per lbm of dry air}\end{aligned}$$

and from Eq. 7.34 we get

$$\begin{aligned}\omega_1 &= \frac{0.240(60 - 70) + 0.01104(1059.6)}{1092.0 - 28.1}\\ &= 0.00874\ \text{lbm water per lbm of dry air}\\ &= 0.00874(7000) = 61.2\ \text{grains of water per lbm of dry air}^5\end{aligned}$$

With $T_{WB} = 60\ °\mathrm{F}$ and $T_{DB} = 70\ °\mathrm{F}$, the psychrometric chart, Appendix D.6*a*, gives approximately

$$\omega_1 = 61\ \text{grains of water per lbm of dry air}$$

which is essentially the same as that calculated from Eq. 7.34 above.

Equation 7.34 gives essentially the same values as obtained from the psychrometric chart, but the chart is much easier and quicker to use.

Air Conditioning

Complete air conditioning involves producing an environment with desired pressure, temperature, humidity, purity, and circulation characteristics. In this section we are concerned only with altering the temperature and the humidity in typical air conditioning applications.

5. The *grain* is the smallest of the ancient Egyptian measures of weight (see Chapter 1), and originally represented the average weight of a grain of barley corn. Today it is still used in some engineering fields (e.g., in the heating, ventilating, and air conditioning field) as a mass unit, with 7000 grains = 1 lbm.

Humans are essentially isothermal open systems with complex temperature regulating mechanisms. The body temperature (98.6 °F, 37 °C) is normally above the surrounding environmental temperature so that the excess heat generated by the irreversibilities inside the body can be removed by normal convection, conduction, and radiation heat transfer mechanisms. During periods of physical stress or high environmental temperature the body produces a surface layer of water, called perspiration, whose evaporation into the atmosphere helps cool the body. This is one of the body's primary temperature-regulating mechanisms. When the relative humidity of the surrounding atmosphere is high, the evaporation of body perspiration is low and the body automatically tries to minimize its internal heat generation resulting in the person feeling lethargic and becoming inactive. Because the sensation of human comfort is so subjective, attempts to define a "comfortable" atmosphere have met with only limited success. Tests have shown that a relative humidity below 15% produces a dried (or *parched*) condition of the membranes in the mouth, nose, and lungs, and an increased susceptibility to disease germs. However, a relative humidity above 70% causes an accumulation of moisture in the clothing, and a general "sticky" or "muggy" feeling. For best health and comfort conditions it has been found that the relative humidity should range from 40 to 50% during cold winter weather, and from 50 to 60% during warm summer weather.

In Example 7.5 we saw how winter air is severely dehumidified if it is simply heated up to room temperature. Water vapor must be added to bring its humidity up into the 40 to 50% relative humidity range. This can easily be done by blowing the heated air across a moist surface, as shown in Figure 7.5. This is the technique used in a common room humidifier.

The humidification process 2–3 shown in Figure 7.5 is also an example of evaporative cooling. When unsaturated air is brought into contact with liquid water at the same (dry bulb) temperature, some of the water will evaporate (thus cooling the mixture) and the resulting air water vapor mixture will move upward along the T_{WB} = constant line, as shown in Figure 7.5*b*. The minimum dry bulb temperature that can be produced by evaporative cooling occurs when the outlet

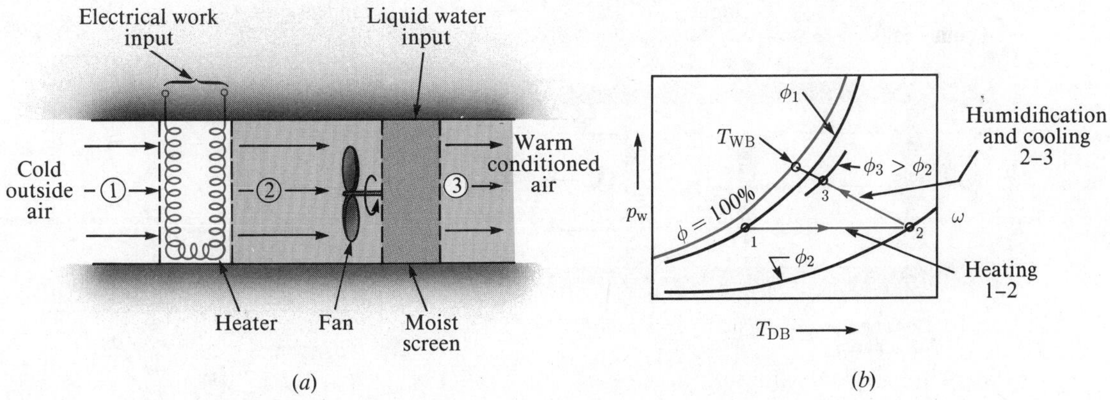

Figure 7.5 Temperature and humidity conditioning of cold winter air.

air becomes saturated with water vapor ($\phi = 100\%$), then $T_{DB} = T_{WB}$. This concept is illustrated in the following examples.

Example 7.7 Determine the minimum outlet temperature that could be realized by using evaporation of liquid water to rehumidify the heated air of part b of Example 7.5.

Solution The minimum temperature associated with the evaporation process is the wet bulb temperature that corresponds to the mixture's dry bulb temperature. For part b of Example 7.5 this was

$$(T_{DB})_{min} = T_{WB} = 13\ °C$$

Example 7.8 Desert air at 110 °F and 10% relative humidity is to be cooled and humidified by using evaporative cooling only. Determine the minimum outlet mixture temperature and its relative humidity.

Solution This is the same type of problem as Example 7.7. The minimum outlet temperature in this case is the wet bulb temperature corresponding to a dry bulb temperature of 110 °F and 10% relative humidity. From Appendix D.6*a* we find that this is approximately

$$(T_{DB})_{min} = T_{WB} = 69\ °F$$

and, of course, the relative humidity at this new dry bulb temperature will be 100%.

Hot humid air can be easily cooled and dehumidified by cooling it to below its dew point (saturation) temperature, condensing out some of the water, and then

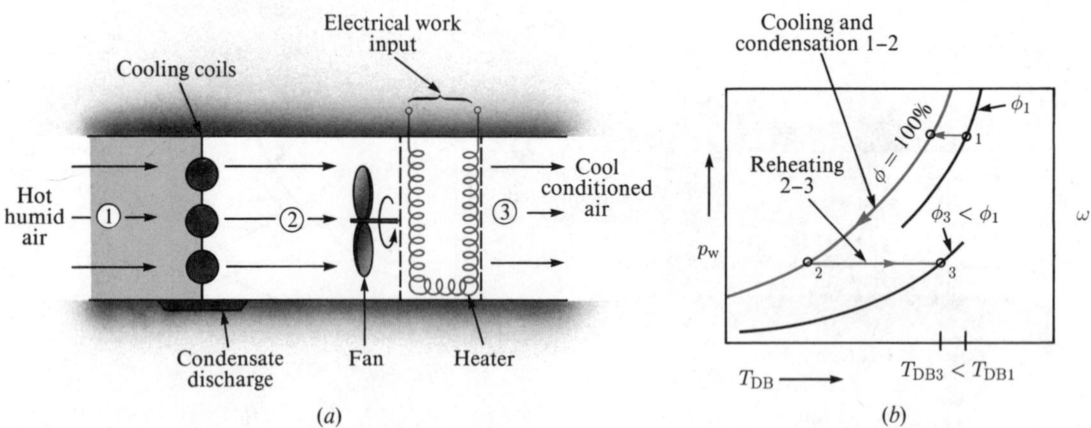

Figure 7.6 Dehumidification by cooling, condensing and reheating again.

reheating the remaining air–water vapor mixture back up to the desired temperature. This is illustrated in Figure 7.6. The water in the cooling section will condense at various temperatures, but it is assumed to exit the system at temperature T_2 in Figure 7.6.

Psychrometric Enthalpies

The psychrometric chart also contains enthalpy information that is useful in energy balance calculations. Though water vapor may be added or removed from the mixture by an air conditioning system, the mass flow rate of the dry air component is usually constant throughout the system. This makes it convenient to define the mixture's specific enthalpy on a *per unit mass of dry air* basis, rather than on a per unit mass of mixture basis. Specific enthalpies so constructed will be referred to as *psychrometric enthalpies* and will be denoted by $h^{\#}$ to distinguish them from the ordinary form of the specific enthalpy. Thus, the specific psychrometric enthalpy is defined as

$$h^{\#} = H_m/m_a \tag{7.35}$$

whereas the ordinary mixture specific enthalpy is defined as

$$h_m = H_m/m_m$$

Note that since $H_m = m_a h^{\#} = m_m h_m = (m_a + m_w)h_m$, then we have

$$h^{\#} = (1 + \omega)h_m$$

Further, since

$$H_m = H_a + H_w = m_a h_a + m_w h_w$$

then,

$$H_m/m_a = h^{\#} = h_a + (m_w/m_a)h_w = h_a + \omega h_w$$

Values of $h^{\#}$ are given on the psychrometric charts in Appendix D.6.[6]

Using the psychrometric enthalpy values in the energy rate balance on the adiabatic saturator (see Figure 7.2) gives

$$\dot{m}_a h_1^{\#} + \dot{m}_{w2} h_{w2} - \dot{m}_a h_3^{\#} = 0$$

or

$$h_1^{\#} + \omega_2 h_{w2} = h_3^{\#}$$

6. Note that h_a has a zero reference state at 0 °F (not 0 R) in D.6*a* and 0 °C in D.6*b* with the h_w value coming from the appropriate steam table in each case. Recall that the choice of a reference state is arbitrary so long as property differences are used in the calculations.

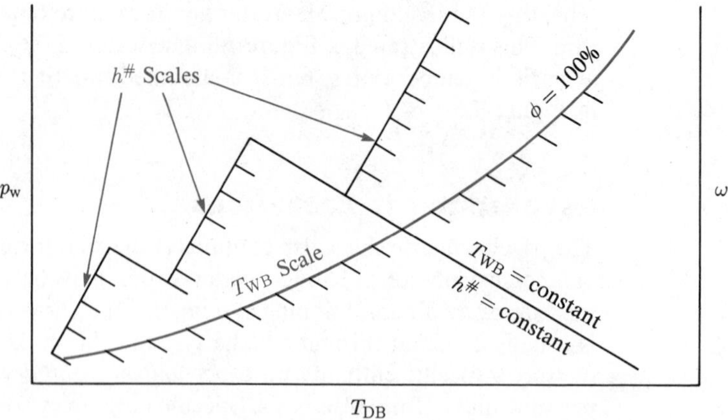

Figure 7.7 Reading the psychrometric enthalpy from the psychrometric chart.

Typically, $\omega_2 h_{w2} \ll h_1^\#$ so that we obtain $h_1^\# \approx h_3^\#$, and since both h_a and h_w depend only on temperature at low pressures, lines of constant $h^\#$ are parallel to lines of constant T_{WB}, as shown in Figure 7.7.

Example 7.9

Determine the heat transfer per kg of dry air required to heat the air in Example 7.5 from 5 to 25 °C.

Solution Using the data from Example 7.5, we find from Appendix D.6*b* that the psychrometric enthalpies are

$$\text{at } T_{DB1} = 5\ °\text{C}: \quad T_{WB1} = 4\ °\text{C} \quad \text{and} \quad h_1^\# = 17\ \text{kJ/(kg dry air)}$$

and

$$\text{at } T_{DB2} = 25\ °\text{C}: \quad T_{WB2} = 13\ °\text{C} \quad \text{and} \quad h_2^\# = 36\ \text{kJ/(kg dry air)}$$

Then the energy rate balance for aergonic heating gives

$$\dot{Q}/\dot{m}_a = h_2^\# - h_1^\# = 36 - 17 = 19\ \text{kJ/(kg dry air)}$$

The following example illustrates the processes of dehumidification in an air conditioning application.

Example 7.10

Moist air at atmospheric pressure and 25 °C with a relative humidity of 80% is to be cooled and dehumidified to 20 °C with a relative humidity of 40%. On a per unit mass of dry air basis determine **a)** the amount of water to be removed, **b)** the cooling heat transfer rate, and **c)** the reheating heat transfer rate.

Solution The schematic for this process is the same as Figure 7.6. From the psychrometric chart (Appendix D.6*b*) we can find the following information

State 1	State 2	State 3
$T_{DB1} = 25\ °C$	$T_{WB2} = 6\ °C$	$T_{DB3} = 20\ °C$
$\phi_1 = 80\%$	$\phi_2 = 100\%$	$\phi_3 = 40\%$
$h_1^\# = 67$ kJ/(kg da)	$h_2^\# = 21$ kJ/(kg da)	$h_3^\# = 35$ kJ/(kg da)
$\omega_1 = 0.0160$ kg H_2O/(kg da)	$\omega_2 = 0.0056$ kg H_2O/(kg da)	$\omega_3 = \omega_2$

a) The amount of water removed per unit mass of dry air is then

$$\omega_1 - \omega_2 = 0.0160 - 0.0056 = 0.0104 \text{ kg H}_2\text{O/(kg dry air)}$$

b) The amount of cooling required per unit mass of dry air is given by an energy rate balance on the cooling section as

$$\begin{aligned}\dot{Q}_{\text{cooling}}/\dot{m}_{\text{dry air}} &= h_2^\# - h_1^\# + (\omega_1 - \omega_2)h_f(T_2)\\ &= 21 - 67 + 0.0104(25.2) = -45.7 \text{ kJ/(kg dry air)}\end{aligned}$$

c) The reheating heat transfer rate is given by an energy rate balance on the reheating section as

$$\dot{Q}_{\text{reheating}}/\dot{m}_{\text{dry air}} = h_3^\# - h_2^\# = 35 - 21 = 14 \text{ kJ/(kg dry air)}$$

Another common air conditioning design problem where the psychrometric chart is put to good use is in the mixing of two or more wet air streams. This normally involves determining how to mix the inlet airstreams to produce a desired output conditional airstream or predicting the outlet airstream properties when all the inlet airstream properties are known.

The conservation of mass equation for water when wet airstreams 1 and 2 are adiabatically and aergonically mixed to form wet airstream 3 is

$$\dot{m}_{w3} = \dot{m}_{w1} + \dot{m}_{w2}$$

or

$$\dot{m}_{w3} = \dot{m}_{a3}\omega_3 = \dot{m}_{a1}\omega_1 + \dot{m}_{a2}\omega_2$$

or

$$\omega_3 = (\dot{m}_{a1}/\dot{m}_{a3})\omega_1 + (\dot{m}_{a2}/\dot{m}_{a3})\omega_2 \quad \textbf{(7.36)}$$

From the energy rate balance applied to this process we get

$$\underbrace{\dot{Q} + \dot{W}}_{0} + \dot{m}_{a1}h_1^\# + \dot{m}_{a2}h_2^\# - \dot{m}_{a3}h_3^\# = 0$$

or

$$h_3^\# = (\dot{m}_{a1}/\dot{m}_{a3})h_1^\# + (\dot{m}_{a2}/\dot{m}_{a3})h_2^\# \tag{7.37}$$

If the states of the inlet flow streams are known, then Eqs. 7.36 and 7.37 allow the calculation of two independent thermodynamic properties (ω_3 and $h_3^\#$) that fix the state of the outlet flow stream. The following example illustrates this type of problem.

Example 7.11 2000 ft^3/min of air at 14.7 psia, 50 °F, $\phi = 80\%$ is adiabatically and aergonically mixed with 1000 ft^3/min of air at 14.7 psia, 100 °F, and $\phi = 40\%$. Determine the dry bulb temperature and the relative humidity of the outlet mixture.

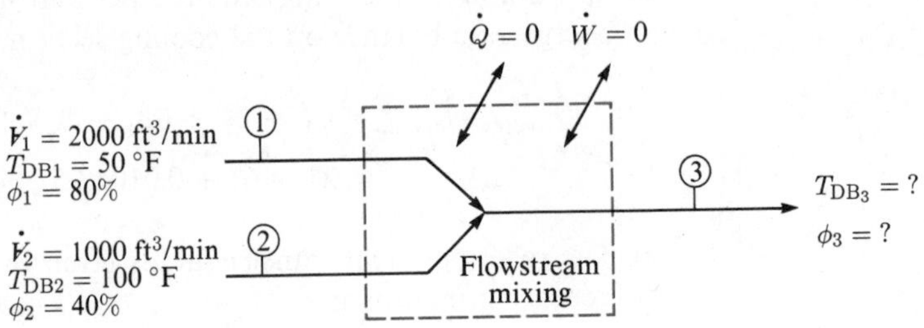

Solution At 50 °F, $p_{w1} = \phi_1 p_{sat}(50\text{ °F}) = 0.8(0.178) = 0.142$ psia. Then,

$$\begin{aligned} v_{a1} &= R_a T_m / p_{a1} \\ &= [53.34\text{ ft}\cdot\text{lbf/(lbm}\cdot\text{R)}](460 + 50\text{ R})/[(14.7 - 0.142\text{ lbf/in}^2)(144\text{ in}^2/\text{ft}^2)] \\ &= 12.98\text{ ft}^3/\text{(lbm dry air)} \end{aligned}$$

Similarly,

$$p_{w2} = \phi_2 p_{sat}(100\text{ °F}) = 0.4(0.9503) = 0.380\text{ psia}$$

and

$$\begin{aligned} v_{a2} &= 53.34(460 + 100)/[(14.7 - 0.38)(144)] \\ &= 14.49\text{ ft}^3/\text{(lbm dry air)} \end{aligned}$$

Also, since $\dot{m}_a = \dot{V}_a / v_a$, then,

$$\begin{aligned} \dot{m}_{a1} &= (2000\text{ ft}^3/\text{min})/[12.98\text{ ft}^3/\text{(lbm dry air)}] \\ &= 154\text{ lbm dry air/min} \end{aligned}$$

$$\dot{m}_{a2} = 1000/14.49 = 69\text{ lbm dry air/min}$$

and using the conservation of mass applied to the air,

$$\dot{m}_{a3} = \dot{m}_{a1} + \dot{m}_{a2} = 154 + 69$$
$$= 223 \text{ lbm dry air/min}$$

Then from the psychrometric chart (Appendix D.6*a*) we find

$$\omega_1 = [44 \text{ grains of water vapor/(lbm dry air)}]/(7000 \text{ grains/lbm})$$
$$= 0.0063 \text{ lbm water vapor/(lbm dry air)}$$

$$\omega_2 = 115/7000$$
$$= 0.0164 \text{ lbm water vapor/(lbm dry air)}$$

$$h_1^{\#} = 19 \text{ Btu/(lbm dry air)}$$

$$h_2^{\#} = 42 \text{ Btu/(lbm dry air)}$$

From the water conservation of mass equation, Eq. 7.36, we can now calculate

$$\omega_3 = (154/223)(0.0063) + (69/223)(0.0164)$$
$$= 0.0094 \text{ lbm water vapor/(lbm dry air)}$$
$$= 0.0094(7000) = 65.8 \text{ grains of water vapor/(lbm dry air)}$$

and the resulting energy rate balance equation, Eq. 7.37, gives

$$h_3^{\#} = (154/223)(19) + (69/223)(42)$$
$$= 26.1 \text{ Btu/(lbm dry air)}$$

From the point of the intersection of the lines $\omega = 65.8$ grains/(lbm dry air) = constant and $h^{\#} = 26.1$ Btu/(lbm dry air) = constant on the psychrometric chart we can then read from this chart that

$$T_{DB} = 63\ ^\circ\text{F} \qquad T_{WB} = 59\ ^\circ\text{F} \qquad \phi = 75\% \quad \text{and} \quad T_{DP} = 56\ ^\circ\text{F}$$

Mixtures of Real Gases

If the components of an ideal gas mixture interact in any way or if one or more of the gases is not ideal, the resulting mixture will not be ideal and will not obey the Gibbs-Dalton and Amagat laws. Then its partial properties must be determined from accurate pressure, volume, temperature, and specific heat data by the techniques discussed in the previous chapter.

Though Amagat's law, Eqs. 7.17 and 7.21, may not hold for a mixture of real gases, the definition of partial specific volumes, Eqs. 7.5*a* and 7.6*a*, is always valid. The difference is that for real gases,

$$\hat{v}_i = (\partial \forall_m/\partial m_i)_{p_m, T_m, m_j} \neq v_i = R_i T_m/p_m$$

For a binary mixture of gases A and B, $\hat{v}_A$ and $\hat{v}_B$ can be determined at any composition from experimental data of v_m vs. w_A as shown in Figure 7.8.

When p, v, T, and c_v data on the gas mixture of interest are not available, engineering approximations can be obtained by combining either Dalton's or Amagat's law with the simplified compressibility factor equation of state $p\forall = ZmRT$. For example, using Dalton's law

$$p_m = \sum_{i=1}^{N} p_{Di} = Z_{Dm} m_m R_m T_m/\forall_m \quad \textbf{(7.38)}$$

where p_{Di} is the Dalton compressibility factor partial pressure defined by

$$p_{Di} = Z_{Di} m_i R_i T_m/\forall_m \quad \textbf{(7.39)}$$

and Z_{Di} and Z_{Dm} are the Dalton species i and mixture compressibility factors, respectively. Substituting the latter equation into the former and solving for Z_{Dm} gives

$$Z_{Dm} = \sum_{i=1}^{N} (w_i M_m/M_i) Z_{Di} = \sum_{i=1}^{N} x_i Z_{Di} \quad \textbf{(7.40)}$$

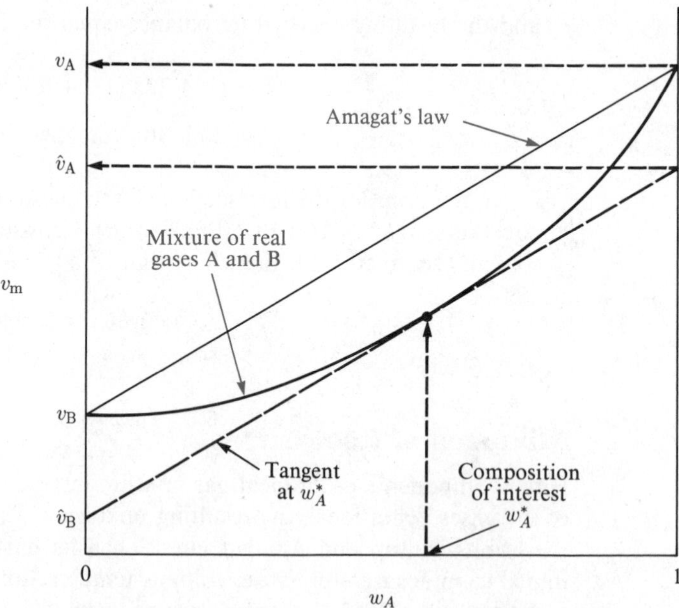

Figure 7.8 Determining $\hat{v}_A$ and $\hat{v}_B$ at $w_A = w_A^*$ from real gas data by the method of tangents.

For each gas i, the Dalton Z_{Di} compressibility factor is determined from the compressibility charts (Figures 3.12 and 3.13 of Chapter 3) by using the reduced temperature T_{Ri} and reduced pseudo specific volume v'_{Ri} for gas i at the temperature and volume of the mixture, or

$$T_{Ri} = T_m/T_{ci}$$

$$\begin{aligned} v'_{Ri} &= v_{Di}p_{ci}/(R_iT_{ci}) \\ &= (\forall_m/m_i)(m_m/m_m)(p_{ci})/(R_iT_{ci}) = (v_m/w_i)[p_{ci}/(R_iT_{ci})] \\ &= (\forall_m/n_i)(n_m/n_m)(p_{ci})/(\mathscr{R}T_{ci}) = (\bar{v}_m/x_i)[p_{ci}/(\mathscr{R}T_{ci})] \end{aligned}$$

where $v_{Di} = \forall_m/m_i$ is the Dalton specific volume of gas i, $v_m = \forall_m/m_m$, and $\bar{v}_m = \forall_m/n_m$ are the mixture mass and molar specific volumes, respectively. Note that we cannot use the reduced pressure $p_{Ri} = p_{Di}/p_{ci}$ in this case because $p_{Di} = Z_{Di}m_iR_iT_m/\forall_m$, and Z_{Di} is not usually known in advance.

Alternatively, we could use Amagat's Law and incorporate a real gas compressibility factor as

$$\forall_m = \sum_{i=1}^{N} \forall_{Ai} = Z_{Am}m_mR_mT_m/p_m \tag{7.41}$$

where $\forall_{Ai}$ is the Amagat compressibility factor partial volume defined by

$$\forall_{Ai} = Z_{Ai}m_iR_iT_m/p_m \tag{7.42}$$

and Z_{Ai} and Z_{Am} are Amagat species i and mixture compressibility factors, respectively. Substituting the latter equation into the former gives

$$Z_{Am} = \sum_{i=1}^{N} (w_iM_m/M_i)Z_{Ai} = \sum_{i=1}^{N} x_iZ_{Ai} \tag{7.43}$$

In this case, for each gas i the Amagat Z_{Ai} compressibility factor is determined from the compressibility charts by using the reduced temperature T_{Ri} and reduced pressure p_{Ri} for gas i at the temperature and pressure of the mixture, or

$$p_{Ri} = p_m/p_{ci} \quad \text{and} \quad T_{Ri} = T_m/T_{ci}$$

Note that we cannot use the reduced pseudo specific volume $v'_{Ri} = v_{Ai}p_m/(R_iT_m)$ in this case because the Amagat specific volume is given by $v_{Ai} = \forall_{Ai}/m_i = Z_{Ai}R_iT_m/p_m$, and Z_{Ai} is not usually known in advance.

It should be clear from the above formulae that $Z_{Di} \neq Z_{Ai}$; therefore, the resultant Dalton and Amagat mixture compressibility factors also will not in general be equal, or $Z_{Dm} \neq Z_{Am}$.

Dalton's law for mixtures of real gases (Eq. 7.38) is based on the premise that each gas in the mixture acts as though it alone occupied the entire volume of the mixture at the temperature of the mixture. Therefore, the gases are assumed not to interact in any manner. We do not find this to be true experimentally except at very low pressures or at very high temperatures.

Amagat's law for mixtures of real gases (Eqs. 7.41), on the other hand, incorporates the resultant mixture pressure and therefore automatically takes gas molecular interactions into account. Consequently, it tends to be more accurate than Dalton's law at high pressures and low temperatures.

A third method of incorporating the compressibility factor charts into predicting the behavior of real gas mixtures involves defining a *pseudo critical pressure* and a *pseudo critical temperature* for the mixture as

$$p_{\mathrm{cm}} = \sum_{i=1}^{N} x_i p_{\mathrm{c}i} \tag{7.44}$$

and

$$T_{\mathrm{cm}} = \sum_{i=1}^{N} x_i T_{\mathrm{c}i} \tag{7.45}$$

This was introduced by W. B. Kay in 1936 and is now known as Kay's law. The reduced pressure and temperature of the mixture can then be computed from

$$p_{\mathrm{Rm}} = p_{\mathrm{m}}/p_{\mathrm{cm}} \quad \text{and} \quad T_{\mathrm{Rm}} = T_{\mathrm{m}}/T_{\mathrm{cm}}$$

and these values are used to find the mixture's compressibility factor, called the Kay's compressibility factor Z_{Km}, directly from the compressibility charts. This compressibility factor is then used in the normal way, as, for example, in the equation $p_{\mathrm{m}}\mathcal{V}_{\mathrm{m}} = Z_{\mathrm{Km}} m_{\mathrm{m}} R_{\mathrm{m}} T_{\mathrm{m}}$, where $R_{\mathrm{m}} = \mathcal{R}/M_{\mathrm{m}}$.

Note that, in general, $Z_{\mathrm{Dm}} \neq Z_{\mathrm{Am}} \neq Z_{\mathrm{Km}}$. Which one of these three is the most accurate in a specific instance depends upon the molecular characteristics and the thermodynamic state of the gas under consideration. A demonstration of the accuracy of these three different methods of modeling real gas behavior is provided in the following examples.

Example 7.12 Determine the critical pressure and temperature for air using Kay's law. Use the composition information for air given in Example 7.1.

Solution Using Eqs. 7.44 and 7.45, the composition data given in Example 7.1 and the critical point data given in Appendix C.12*b* give

$$\begin{aligned}(p_{\mathrm{c}})_{\mathrm{air}} &= x_{\mathrm{N_2}}(p_{\mathrm{c}})_{\mathrm{N_2}} + x_{\mathrm{O_2}}(p_{\mathrm{c}})_{\mathrm{O_2}} + x_{\mathrm{Ar}}(p_{\mathrm{c}})_{\mathrm{Ar}} + x_{\mathrm{CO_2}}(p_{\mathrm{c}})_{\mathrm{CO_2}}\\ &= 0.7809(3.39) + 0.2095(5.08) + 0.0093(4.86) + 0.0003(7.39)\\ &= 3.76\ \mathrm{MPa}\end{aligned}$$

and

$$\begin{aligned}(T_{\mathrm{c}})_{\mathrm{air}} &= x_{\mathrm{N_2}}(T_{\mathrm{c}})_{\mathrm{N_2}} + x_{\mathrm{O_2}}(T_{\mathrm{c}})_{\mathrm{O_2}} + x_{\mathrm{Ar}}(T_{\mathrm{c}})_{\mathrm{Ar}} + x_{\mathrm{CO_2}}(T_{\mathrm{c}})_{\mathrm{CO_2}}\\ &= 0.7809(126.2) + 0.2095(154.8) + 0.0093(151) + 0.0003(304.2)\\ &= 132.5\ \mathrm{K}\end{aligned}$$

These values agree quite well with the values of 3.774 MPa and 132.4 K for air given in Appendix C.12*b*.

Example 7.13 The molar specific volume of a mixture of 30% nitrogen and 70% methane (on a molar basis) at 1500 psia and -100 °F was measured and found to be 1.315 ft³/lbmole. Calculate the molar specific volume of this mixture under these conditions using

a) ideal gas mixture behavior,
b) the Dalton compressibility factor,
c) the Amagat compressibility factor,
d) Kay's law

and compute the percent error in each case.

Solution

a) For ideal gas mixture behavior,

$$\bar{v}_m = \mathscr{R}T_m/p_m = \frac{[1545.35\ \text{ft}\cdot\text{lbf/(lbmole}\cdot\text{R)}](460 - 100\ \text{R})}{(1500\ \text{lbf/in}^2)(144\ \text{in}^2/\text{ft}^2)}$$

$$= 2.576\ \text{ft}^3/\text{lbmole}$$

and

$$\%\ \text{error} = \left(\frac{2.576 - 1.315}{1.315}\right)(100)$$

$$= 95.9\%\ \text{(high)}$$

b) From Appendix C.12*a* we find

$$(p_c)_{N_2} = 492\ \text{psia}$$

$$(T_c)_{N_2} = 227.1\ \text{R}$$

and

$$(p_c)_{CH_4} = 673\ \text{psia}$$

$$(T_c)_{CH_4} = 343.9\ \text{R}$$

Since the mixture specific volume is the unknown here, it must be determined by a trial and error method using the reduced pseudo specific volume v'_{Ri}, which as was shown earlier can be written in a variety of forms, for example, as

$$v'_{Ri} = \bar{v}_m p_{ci}/(x_i \mathscr{R} T_{ci})$$

We will assume values for $\bar{v}_m$, find $(Z_D)_{N_2}$, $(Z_D)_{CH_4}$, and Z_{Dm}, and then check the assumption with $\bar{v}_m = Z_{Dm}\mathscr{R}T_m/p_m$. Assume $\bar{v}_m = 1.51$ ft³/lbmole, then

$$(v'_R)_{N_2} = \frac{(1.51)(492)(144)}{(0.3)(1545.35)(227.1)} = 1.016$$

and

$$(v'_R)_{CH_4} = \frac{(1.51)(673)(144)}{(0.7)(1545.35)(343.9)} = 0.393$$

Then

$$(T_R)_{N_2} = (460 - 100)/227.1 = 1.59$$

and

$$(T_R)_{CH_4} = (460 - 100)/343.9 = 1.05$$

From Figure 3.12*b* in Chapter 3 we find that for these values

$$(Z_D)_{N_2} = 0.91 \quad \text{and} \quad (Z_D)_{CH_4} = 0.39$$

Then from Eq. 7.40 we have

$$Z_{Dm} = 0.3(0.91) + 0.7(0.39) = 0.59$$

Now checking the $\bar{v}_m$ assumption,

$$\bar{v}_m = Z_{Dm}\mathscr{R}T_m/p_m = \frac{0.59(1545.35)(460 - 100)}{(1500)(144)}$$
$$= 1.52 \text{ ft}^3/\text{lbmole}$$

which is close enough to our original assumption. Then,

$$\% \text{ error} = \left(\frac{1.52 - 1.315}{1.315}\right)(100) = 15.6\% \text{ (high)}$$

c) Using the Amagat compressibility factor method we use

$$(p_R)_{N_2} = p_m/(p_c)_{N_2} = \frac{1500}{492} = 3.05$$

$$(T_R)_{N_2} = T_m/(T_c)_{N_2} = (460 - 100)/227.1 = 1.59$$

$$(p_R)_{CH_4} = \frac{1500}{673} = 2.23$$

$$(T_R)_{CH_4} = (460 - 100)/343.9 = 1.05$$

Using these values in Figure 3.12*b* of Chapter 3 we find that

$$(Z_A)_{N_2} = 0.84 \quad \text{and} \quad (Z_A)_{CH_4} = 0.35$$

then Eq. 7.43 gives

$$Z_{Am} = 0.3(0.84) + 0.7(0.35)$$
$$= 0.50$$

and

$$\bar{v}_m = Z_{Am}\mathcal{R}T_m/p_m = \frac{0.50(1545.35)(460 - 100)}{1500(144)}$$
$$= 1.288 \text{ ft}^3/\text{lbmole}$$

or an error of

$$\left(\frac{1.288 - 1.315}{1.315}\right)(100) = -2.1\% \text{ (low)}$$

d) Using Kay's law, Eqs. 7.44 and 7.45, we get

$$p_{cm} = 0.3(492) + 0.7(673)$$
$$= 619 \text{ psia}$$

and

$$T_{cm} = 0.3(227.1) + 0.7(343.9)$$
$$= 308.9 \text{ R}$$

then,

$$p_{Rm} = 1500/619 = 2.42$$

and

$$T_{Rm} = (460 - 100)/308.9$$
$$= 1.17$$

For these reduced values Figure 3.12*b* of Chapter 3 gives $Z_{Km} = 0.51$. Then the mixture molar specific volume is

$$\bar{v}_m = Z_{Km}\mathcal{R}T_m/p_m = \frac{0.51(1545.35)(460 - 100)}{1500(144)}$$
$$= 1.314 \text{ ft}^3/\text{lbmole}$$

which has a negligible error from the measured value of 1.315 ft^3/lbmole.

Summary

In this chapter we have dealt with the problem of generating thermodynamic properties for homogeneous nonreacting mixtures. Because of their engineering value we have focused our analysis on gases and vapors, but the theory extending beyond Eq. 7.15 can be easily modified to cover mixtures of liquids and solids.

We have found that if the mixture components and ultimately the mixture itself behave as an ideal gas, then all extensive properties are additive and the partial specific properties reduce to the component specific properties. This produces simple working equations for all the intensive properties (v, u, h, and s) of the mixture.

Last, we combined Dalton's and Amagat's laws with the compressibility factor technique to produce methods for dealing with the p-v-T mixture properties of real gases and vapors.

Selected References

Balzhiser, R. E., Samuels, M. R., and Eliassen, J. D. *Chemical Engineering Thermodynamics.* Englewood Cliffs, NJ: Prentice-Hall, 1972.

Holman, J. P. *Thermodynamics*, 3d ed. New York: McGraw-Hill, 1980.

Kestin, J. *A Course in Thermodynamics* Vol. 1. New York: Hemisphere/McGraw-Hill, 1979.

Reynolds, W. C., and Perkins, H. C. *Engineering Thermodynamics*, 2d ed. New York: McGraw-Hill, 1977.

Rizzi, E. A. *Designing and Estimating for Heating, Ventilating, and Air Conditioning.* New York: Van Nostrand Reinhold, 1980.

Van Wylen, G. J., and Sonntag, R. E. *Fundamentals of Classical Thermodynamics*, 3d ed. New York: Wiley, 1986.

Wark, K. *Thermodynamics*, 5th ed. New York: McGraw-Hill, 1988.

Chapter Seven Problems

1. 1 kg of CH_4, 6.3 kg of O_2, and 13.18 kg of N_2 are combined to form a gas mixture. Find the molecular mass of the mixture.

2. Ammonia gas is flowing in a tube whose cross sectional area is 1.0 ft^2. The density of the ammonia is 0.1 lbm/ft^3. At some point in the system CO_2 is added at a rate of 0.001 lbm/h in a steady flow process. At a point further downstream a detector indicates that the concentration of CO_2 on a mass basis is 0.001%. Determine the inlet velocity of the ammonia.

3. Following is the gravimetric analysis of a gaseous mixture:

Constituent	% by mass
N_2	60
CO_2	22
CO	11
O_2	7

Find the mole fractions of the components in the mixture.

4. If the amount of helium produced by the large scale liquefaction of air is 1.3 lbm per 100 tons of air, determine the mass, mole, and volume fractions of helium in air. Assume air is a mixture of ideal gases.

5. A mixture of air and water vapor at 20 °C and 0.1013 MPa has a relative humidity of 100%. Using the information given in Example 7.1, determine

a) the molar composition,

b) the effective molecular mass,

c) the mass concentration, and

d) the effective gas constant of this mixture whose components are nitrogen, oxygen, water vapor, argon, and carbon dioxide.

6. A gas bulb of volume 0.1 ft^3 contains hydrogen at a pressure of 10 psia and a temperature of 50 °C. Nitrogen is introduced into the bulb such that the final pressure is 20 psia and the final temperature is 80 °F. Find the mole fraction and the mass fraction of the hydrogen in the final state.

7. Using Eqs. 7.12, 7.13, and 7.15 show that the equivalent gas constant of a mixture R_m can be determined directly from the mass and mole fraction compositions (w_i and x_i) and the species gas constants ($R_i = \mathscr{R}/M_i$) as

a) $R_m = \sum w_i R_i$ **b)** $R_m = \dfrac{1}{\sum (x_i/R_i)}$

8. A mixture of ideal gases at a total pressure of 40 psia and 70 °F contains 0.6 lbm of hydrogen (H_2) and 4.8 lbm of oxygen (O_2). Determine

a) the mole fraction of the hydrogen in the mixture,

b) the equivalent molecular mass of the mixture, and

c) the total volume occupied by the mixture under the conditions stated.

9. a) How many kg of nitrogen must be mixed with 5.0 kg of carbon dioxide to produce an ideal gas mixture that is 50% by volume of each component?

b) For the resulting mixture of part a, determine the mixture molecular mass (M_m), gas constant (R_m), and the partial pressure of the nitrogen if that of the carbon dioxide is 0.07 MPa.

10. A furnace exhaust stack is instrumented so that a sample of the stack gas can be analyzed for composition. The analysis gives the following volume fractions: 70% N_2, 20% CO_2, 8.0% CO, 1.0% Ar, and 1.0% H_2O.

a) What is the effective molecular mass of the stack gas?

b) Calculate the mass fraction of each of the gases.

c) If the measured pressure in the stack is 15.0 psia, what is the partial pressure of the carbon monoxide?

11. 10 kg of nitrogen (N_2) is mixed with 0.5 kg of a highly toxic unknown gas. The resulting mixture occupies a volume of 2.0 m^3 at 0.8 MPa and 65 °C. Both gases and the mixture are ideal gases. Determine

a) the molecular mass of the unknown gas and

b) the volume fraction of each gas present in the mixture.

12. On board a starship a demented alien creature has released a mixture of ideal gases made up of 4.0 lbm of molecular oxygen (O_2) and 6 lbm of an unknown and possibly toxic gas. Before the gas mixture was released you noticed that its original container had a volume of 10 ft^3, and that at 150 °F it had a pressure of 114.31 psia. As a line officer engineer, the captain asks you for your assessment of the situation. Is the gas lethal? To draw a proper conclusion you must determine

a) the molecular mass of the unknown gas,

b) the probable name of this gas, and

c) the volume fraction of each gas present in the mixture.

13. The measured molecular masses of many naturally occurring chemical elements differ appreciably from integer values due to the presence of isotopes of the element in the test sample. Commercially available neon has a measured molecular mass of 20.183. The gas is known to be a mixture of two isotopes whose molecular masses are 20.0 and 22.0. Determine the mole and mass fractions of each of the neon isotopes present in commercial neon.

14. One ft^3 of steam at 300 °F and 14.7 psia is mixed with 3.0 ft^3 of methane at 80 °F and 14.7 psia. Assuming ideal gas behavior for both of these substances determine

a) the mass fractions,
b) the mole fractions,
c) the pressure fractions, and
d) both the constant pressure and constant volume specific heats of the mixture.

15. A rigid insulated tank is divided into two compartments by a partition. Initially 5.6 lbm of nitrogen is introduced into one compartment at a pressure of 30 psia and a temperature of 140 °F. At the same time 13.2 lbm of carbon dioxide is introduced into the other compartment at a pressure of 15 psia and a temperature of 60 °F. The partition is then removed and the gases are allowed to mix. Assuming ideal gas behavior, find the pressure in the tank after the mixing.

16. A perfect gas mixture consists of 3.0 kg of nitrogen (N_2) and 5.0 kg of carbon dioxide (CO_2) at a pressure of 1.0 MPa and a temperature of 30 °C. If the mixture is heated at constant pressure to 40 °C, find the work and the heat transfer required for this process.

17. 2.0 kg/min of hydrogen at 5.0 °C and 1.0 atm is continuously aergonically mixed with 1.0 kg/min of nitrogen at 30 °C and 1.0 atm. The mixture leaves the mixing chamber at 60 °C and 0.8 atm. Find the heat transfer rate and indicate whether it is into or out of the mixture.

18. On planet 3M4G6 in the subsystem Zeta-12 the atmosphere consists of a binary mixture of sewer gas (methane) and an unknown gas, called "Esh-nugim Marookee Moo" by the local mush foot natives. An extremely accurate spectral scan reveals that the mass fraction to mole fraction ratio for methane is 0.9341875, and that the mole fraction of methane is 0.4281377. Determine the name of the unknown gas (in English).

19. Methane, ethane, and propane, all ideal gases, are mixed together in equal parts by mass to create a new "super" fuel gas. Then it is adiabatically compressed from 40 °F to 1.75 ft^3 at 300 psia, 80 °F. Determine the work required.

20. A chemical processing facility produces exhaust gases (46% N_2, 43% CO_2, and 11% SO_2 by volume) at a total pressure of 0.32 MPa at 1000 °C. It is proposed that energy be recovered from this gas by expanding it through a turbine to atmospheric pressure. Assuming ideal gas behavior, determine the maximum possible power output per unit mass flow rate for this system.

21. Two parts of molecular hydrogen gas are mixed with one part of molecular oxygen gas (on a molar basis) at 2.0 MPa, 0 °C and then expanded through a reversible nozzle from a negligible inlet velocity to 292 m/s at the entrance to the combustion zone of a rocket engine. Through a preheating process in the nozzle, the gas mixture receives 1325.5 kJ per kg of mixture of heat at 500 °C. Determine the exit pressure of the gas mixture. Assume ideal gas behavior.

22. A diving experiment is to be performed with a mixture of helium and air at a total pressure of 50 psia. The composition must be such that the partial pressure of oxygen in the compressed mixture is the same as that in air at STP. Assuming a closed system and ideal gas behavior, determine

a) the work required to isentropically compress 2.7 lbm of the mixture from 14.7 psia, 70 °F to 50 psia, and
b) the heat transfer required to aergonically cool the compressed mixture back to 70 °F again.

23. Acetylene and oxygen are drawn from pressurized storage tanks and mixed together in an oxy-acetylene torch in a ratio of 5 parts of oxygen per one part acetylene on a volume basis. This mixture flows reversibly through the torch from 0.14 MPa, 20 °C, to atmospheric pressure at 173 °C, at which point it is ignited by the flame. The mean surface temperature of the torch is 30 °C, and it uses 0.1 m^3/s of oxygen at STP (0.101325 MPa, 20 °C). Assuming ideal gas behavior, determine the work and heat transfer rates.

24. 18 m^3/s of methane are mixed with 10 m^3/s of isobutane in a test of a new furnace gas. The mixture is preheated before being ignited by passing it through an adiabatic isobaric heat exchanger. The second fluid in the heat exchanger is condensing steam at 200 °C flowing at 8.3 kg/s. The steam enters as a saturated vapor and exits with a quality of 21%. The gas mixture enters at 20 °C and exits at 150 °C. Determine the entropy production rate of the heat exchanger.

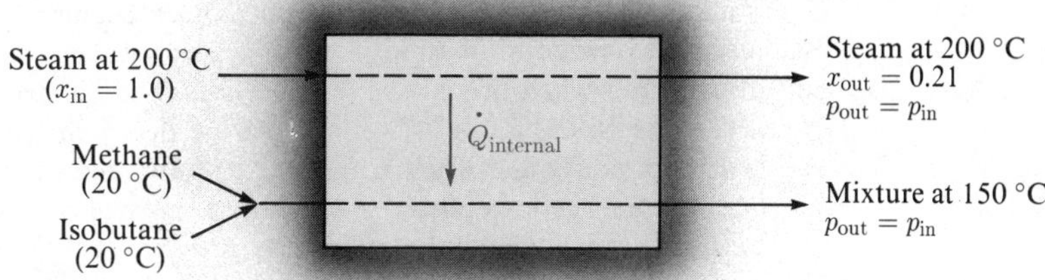

25. Air at 0.1013 MPa and 50 °C is saturated with water vapor. It is to be aergonically heated to 80 °C in a steady flow isobaric process by putting it in contact with an isothermal reservoir at 100 °C. Determine the heat transfer and entropy production rates per unit mass flow rate if

a) the presence of the water vapor is ignored, and

b) the presence of the water vapor is considered (as an ideal gas).

c) Determine the percent error in answer a due to the effect of the water vapor.

26. The combustion of 1 mole of octane, C_8H_{18}, will yield 8 moles of CO_2, 9 moles of H_2O, and 47 moles of N_2. The exhaust gases at 811.11 K, 0.1723 MPa from a spark ignition engine are to be expanded through a turbocharger used to compress the incoming air charge to the engine. The incoming air is at 20 °C and atmospheric pressure, and the turbocharger turbine exhausts to the atmosphere. Find the compressor's isentropic outlet temperature T_{2s} and its isentropic power input per unit mass flow rate $(\dot{W}_C/\dot{m})_s$.

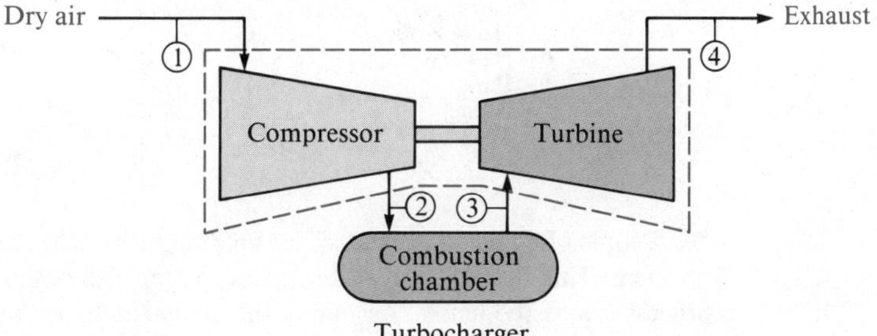

Turbocharger

27. A pneumatic motor in a highly explosive environment uses a mixture of the ideal gases argon and helium in equal parts on a mass basis. The motor has inlet conditions of 150 psia at 500 R and an exit pressure of 14.7 psia. If the motor must produce 3.0 hp of output power while operating in a steady state, steady flow, reversible, and adiabatic manner, then

a) what is the exit temperature of the gas mixture, and

b) what mass flow rate of the mixture is required?

28. An insulated gas turbine is attached to the exhaust stack of an oil fired boiler in a power plant. The pressure and temperature at the inlet to the turbine are 0.5 MPa absolute, 1000 °C and the exit pressure is atmospheric. The exhaust gas analysis by volume is 12% CO_2, 2.0% CO, 4.0% O_2, and 82% N_2. What is the maximum possible power output from this turbine per kg of exhaust gas flowing through it? Assume that the exhaust gas is an ideal gas and ignore all kinetic and potential energy effects.

29. An air–water vapor mixture at 14.7 psia, 100 °F, and 40.4% relative humidity is contained in a 10 ft^3 closed tank. The tank is cooled until the water just begins to condense. Determine the temperature at which condensation begins.

30. When the dew point of atmospheric air is between 60 and 70 °F the weather is said to be "humid," and when it is above 70 °F it is said to be "tropical." If the partial pressure of water vapor in the air is 0.40 psia when the dry bulb temperature is 80 °F, determine the relative humidity and whether the weather is humid or tropical.

31. The volume fractions of the gases in the atmosphere of Mars measured at the surface of the planet where the total atmospheric pressure is 0.112 psia was found by the early Viking I mission to be 95% CO_2, 2.5% N_2, 2.0% Ar, 0.4% O_2, and 0.1% H_2O. Determine

a) the partial pressure of the water vapor in the Martian atmosphere,

b) the mass fractions of all the gases in the Martian atmosphere, and

c) the specific humidity of the Martian atmosphere (consider the Martian dry "air" to be everything in its atmosphere except the water vapor).

32. An engineer at a party is handed a cold glass of beverage with ice in it. The engineer estimates the outside temperature of the glass to be 35 °F and the room temperature to be 70 °F. What is the relative humidity in the room when moisture just begins to condense on the outside of the glass?

33. The following list of cities includes representative wet and dry bulb temperatures. Use the psychrometric chart to determine their corresponding relative humidity, humidity ratio, dew point temperature, and water vapor partial pressure.

City	T_{WB}	T_{DB}	ϕ	ω	T_{DP}	p_w
Berlin	21 °C	32 °C				
Chicago	75 °F	97 °F				
Hong Kong	28 °C	33 °C				
New York City	75 °F	93 °F				
Paris	20 °C	31 °C				
Rome	23 °C	36 °C				
Tokyo	79 °F	92 °F				

34. People often clean eyeglasses by holding them near their mouths and exhaling heavily on them. This usually causes the lenses to "fog"; the moisture is then wiped off, and this process cleans the lenses. Assuming the air in the lungs has a relative humidity of 75% at a dry bulb temperature of 100 °F, determine the maximum temperature of the glasses that will just cause moisture droplets (i.e., "fog") to form when cleaned in this manner.

35. Seven thousand cubic meters per minute of air at 28 °C and 0.1013 MPa with a relative humidity of 60% is to be cooled at constant total pressure to its dew point temperature. Determine the required heat transfer rate and indicate its direction.

36. Two hundred cubic meters per minute of air with a dry bulb temperature of 7 °C and a wet bulb temperature of 5 °C is continuously mixed with 500 m^3/min of air with a dry bulb temperature of 32 °C and a relative humidity of 60%. The mixing chamber is at atmospheric pressure and is electrically heated with a power consumption of 3.0 kW. For the resulting mixture determine **a)** the dry bulb temperature, **b)** the wet bulb temperature, **c)** the dew point temperature, and **d)** the relative humidity.

37. Thirty cubic feet per minute of air with a dry bulb temperature of 90 °F and a relative humidity of 80% is to be cooled and dehumidified to a dry bulb temperature of 65 °F and a relative humidity of 50%. Determine **a)** the wet bulb temperature of the air before dehumidification, **b)** the dew point temperature of the air after dehumidification, **c)** the amount of moisture removed during the dehumidification process, and **d)** the amount of heat removed during the cooling part of the dehumidification process.

38. A room containing 275 m^3 of air at 1.0 atm pressure is to be humidified. The initial conditions are $T_{DB} = 24$ °C and $\phi = 10\%$, and the final conditions are $T_{DB} = 20$ °C and $\phi = 50\%$. Determine the mass of water that must be added to the room air.

39. One thousand cubic feet per hour of moist air at atmospheric pressure, 80 °F and 70% relative humidity is to be cooled to 50 °F at constant total pressure. Find whether or not this can be done without the removal of water from the air. If it cannot, determine the minimun amount of water that must be removed in lbm/h.

40. A classroom contains 6000 ft^3 of air–water vapor mixture at 1 atm total pressure. The dry bulb temperature is 70 °F and the wet bulb temperature is 65 °F. Assuming a closed constant total pressure system, determine the following:

a) the relative humidity,
b) the partial pressure of the water vapor,
c) the dew point, and
d) the amount of water that must be added to or removed from the air in the room to achieve 40% relative humidity at the same dry bulb temperature.

41. An unknown amount of Refrigerant-11 is spilled on the floor in a closed room and it evaporates into previously dry air. To determine the relative amount of R-11 in the air, an engineer measures the wet and dry bulb temperatures using a sling psychrometer with the wet bulb wick soaked with R-11 and finds them to be 17 and 24 °C, respectively. The barometric pressure in the room is 0.101 MPa. Using the following data for R-11, determine the humidity ratio of the R-11 in the air.

$p_{sat}(17\ °C) = 0.078$ MPa $\qquad M = 137.4$ kg/kgmole

$h_g(24\ °C) = 262.9$ kJ/kg $\qquad h_f(24\ °C) = 82.6$ kJ/kg

$h_g(17\ °C) = 259.4$ kJ/kg $\qquad h_f(17\ °C) = 76.6$ kJ/kg

42. 10,000 ft^3/h of moist air at 14.7 psia and 75 °F is to be cooled to 45 °F at constant total pressure. Find the amount (lbm/h) of water condensed if the mole fraction of water in the inlet mixture is 0.026.

43. Atmospheric air can be dehumidified by cooling the air at constant total pressure until the moisture condenses out. Suppose that air with a humidity ratio of 0.005 kg water per kg of dry air must be achieved by cooling incoming atmospheric air with a dry bulb temperature of 25 °C and a wet bulb temperature of 20 °C.

a) To what temperature must the incoming air–water vapor mixture be cooled to achieve a humidity ratio of 0.005 kg water per kg dry air?
b) How much water must be removed per kg of dry air to achieve this state?

44. Outside atmospheric air with a dry bulb temperature of 90 °F and a wet bulb temperature of 85 °F is to be passed through an air conditioning device so that it enters a house at 71 °F and 40% relative humidity. The process consists of two steps. First the air passes over a cooling coil where it is cooled below its dew point temperature and the water condenses out until the desired humidity ratio is reached. Then the air is passed over a reheating coil until its temperature reaches 71 °F. Determine

a) the amount of water removed per pound of dry air passing through the device,
b) the heat removed by the cooling coil in Btu/(lbm dry air), and
c) the heat added by the reheating coil in Btu/(lbm dry air).

45. 100 kg of atmospheric air (whose composition is given in text Example 7.1) is cooled in a 0.5 m^3 constant volume container to 200 K. Determine the mixture pressure using Dalton's compressibility factor. Compare this result with that obtained by assuming ideal gas (i.e., $Z_m = 1.0$) behavior.

46. Show that the ratio of the Amagat specific volume, $v_{Ai} = V_{Ai}/m_i$, to the Dalton specific volume, $v_{Di} = V_m/m_i$, of gas i can be written as

$$\frac{v_{Ai}}{v_{Di}} = \frac{Z_{Ai} p_{Di}}{Z_{Di} p_m}$$

47. Atmospheric air, whose composition is given in text Example 7.1, is compressed to 1000 atm at 0 °C. Determine the density of the compressed air using Amagat's compressibility factor and compare this result with that obtained by assuming ideal gas (i.e., $Z_m = 1.0$) behavior.

48. In normal psychrometric analysis at or below atmospheric pressure both the air and the water vapor are treated as ideal gases. However, at high pressures this assumption is no longer valid. Determine the relative humidity (ϕ) that results when 10 g of water are added to 1.0 kg of dry air at a total pressure of 10 MPa at 350 °C. Assume Amagat's compressibility factor is valid here and compare your result with that obtained by assuming ideal gas behavior.

49. 0.5 m^3 of a mixture of 35% acetylene (C_2H_2), 25% oxygen (O_2), 20% hydrogen (H_2), and 20% sulfur dioxide (SO_2) on a mass basis is to be adiabatically compressed in a piston–cylinder arrangement from 1 atm, 20 °C to 100 atm and 300 °C.

a) Using Kay's law, find the final volume of the mixture.
b) Assuming constant specific heats, determine the work required per unit mass of mixture.

50. A mixture of 80% methane and 20% ethane on a molar basis is contained in an insulated 1.0-m^3 tank at 3.0 MPa and 50 °C. An automatic flow control valve opens causing the tank pressure to drop quickly to 2.0 MPa before it closes again.

a) Calculate the mass that escaped from the tank using Kay's law.
b) Determine the equilibrium tank temperature when the control valve closes assuming that the gas remaining in the tank underwent a reversible process.

51. 6.0 kg of hydrogen gas (H_2) is mixed with 28 kg of nitrogen gas (N_2) and then compressed to 40.53 MN/m^2 at 300 °C. At this state the specific volume of the mixture was measured and found to be 0.0160 m^3/kg. Determine the specific volume of this state as predicted by each of the following models and calculate the percent deviation from the measured value.

a) Ideal gas model,
b) Dalton's law compressibility factor,
c) Amagat's law compressibility factor, and
d) Kay's law.

52. Determine the total mixture volume when one kgmole each of hydrogen (H_2) and helium (He) gases are mixed at 15 atm and 40 K using

a) Dalton s law compressibility factor,
b) Amagat's law compressibility factor, and
c) Kay's law.
d) Which of the three results above do you believe is the most accurate, and why?

Design Problems

The following are open ended design problems. The objective is to carry out a preliminary thermal design as indicated. A detailed design with working drawings is not expected unless otherwise specified. These problems do not have specific answers, so each student's design will be unique.

53. Design an electrically driven sling psychrometer that will produce the wet and dry bulb temperatures on digital readouts. The finished product must cost less than 30 h of minimum wage pay and be battery powered. If possible, fabricate and test your design. (*Suggestion*: Try designing around inexpensive "off the shelf" components.)

54. Design an apparatus to measure the dew point of an air sample based upon the cooling of a mirrored surface until it fogs. If possible, build and test this apparatus. (*Suggestion*: Consider thermoelectric cooling of a polished metal plate.)

55. Design a system to remove the respiration carbon dioxide from inside a spacecraft and replace it with oxygen. Use a living quarters volume of 10 m^3 with the crew generating a maximum of 0.02 m^3/s of CO_2. Assume the mixture enters your system at 30 °C and exits it at 20 °C. Maintain the same oxygen partial pressure in your mixture as that in atmospheric air at STP.

56. Design a system to remove the respiration carbon dioxide from inside a submarine and replace it with oxygen. The air volume of the submarine is 1000 m^3, and the crew can generate a maximum of 1.3 m^3/s of CO_2. The submarine must be able to achieve a depth of 300 m. Assume the air mixture enters your system at 30 °C and exits at 20 °C. Maintain the oxygen partial pressure at all times in your mixture equal to that in atmospheric air at STP.

57. Cooling towers are large evaporative cooling systems that can be used to transfer heat from warm water to the atmosphere by evaporation of the water to be cooled.

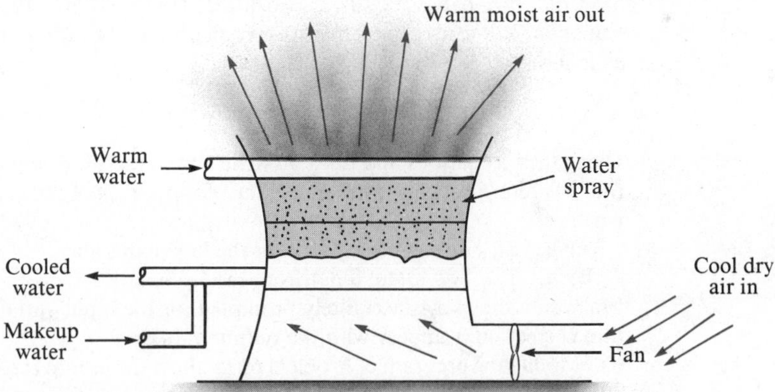

Prepare a preliminary design for a cooling tower that will cool 30,000 kg/s of water from 40 to 30 °C. Atmospheric air enters at 20 ± 10 °C with a relative humidity of 45 ± 15%.

Establish the overall physical dimensions of the cooling tower, air flow rate, water pumping power, fan power (if forced convection is used), makeup water requirements, air exit conditions, and so forth.

Computer Problems

The following open-ended computer problems are designed to be done on a personal computer using BASIC language programming.

58. Write an interactive computer program that will return all four ideal gas mixture composition fractions when any one composition fraction is input for an arbitrary mixture of ideal gases. Use screen prompts to request from the user the values of the gas constant, molecular masses, number of gases in the mixture, and anything else you will need to make the appropriate calculations. Format the screen output in a neat and informative manner. Make sure the user is accurately prompted for the input variables in the proper units, and that correct units appear with the output values.

59. Create a simple interactive computer version of the gas tables (Appendix C.16) for an arbitrary mixture of ideal gases with constant specific heats. Have the user input the composition (on a mass, molar, or volume basis), specific heats (in proper units), and temperature from the keyboard in response to screen prompts. Output in a properly formatted manner the values of u, h, ϕ, p_r, and v_r with correct units. Use reference levels of $h_o = \phi_o = 0$ at $T_o = 300$ K and $p_o = 1.0$ atm.

60. Modify computer Problem 59 by adding the mixture pressure to the list of keyboard input variables and output the specific entropy s instead of ϕ. Use $s_o = \phi_o = 0$ at $T_o = 300$ K and $p_o = 1.0$ atm.

61. Create an accurate expanded version of the gas tables (Appendix C.16) for an arbitrary mixture of ideal gases with temperature dependent specific heats. Allow the user to choose the gases in the mixture from those you list in a screen menu. Have the user input the composition (on a mass, molar, or volume basis), the pressure, and the temperature from the keyboard in response to properly formatted screen prompts. Output in a properly formatted manner the values of u, h, s, p_r, and v_r with correct units. Use reference levels of $h_o = s_o = 0$ at $T_o = 300$ K and $p_o = 1.0$ atm.

62. The saturation pressure curve for ammonia (NH_3) can be approximated with $p_{sat} = \exp[A - B/T_{DB} - C(\ln T_{DB}) - D(T_{DB}) + E(T_{DB}^2)]$ where p_{sat} is in psia, T_{DB} is in R and $A = 58.88706$, $B = 7.58730 \times 10^3$, $C = 6.40125$, $D = 9.55176 \times 10^{-4}$ and $E = 3.39860 \times 10^{-6}$. Equation 7.28 can be modified to give the humidity ratio ω of an air–ammonia mixture as follows:

$$\omega = (M_{NH_3}/M_a)[p_{NH_3}/(p_m - p_{NH_3})] = 0.588[p_{NH_3}/(p_m - p_{NH_3})]$$

Using these equations and Eq. 7.26 write an interactive computer program in English units that will return properly formatted values for p_m, T_{DB}, ϕ, and ω for an air–ammonia mixture when

a) p_m, T_{DB}, and ϕ are input from the keyboard, and

b) p_m, T_{DB}, and ω are input from the keyboard.

Make sure the user is accurately prompted for the input variables in the proper units, and that correct units appear with the output values.

63. Modify the program of Problem 62 to allow the user to separately choose either English or Metric (SI) units for the input and the output values.

64. Expand Problem 62 by using the Newton-Raphson technique discussed in Chapter 6 to find the dew point temperature from the saturation pressure evaluated at the partial pressure of ammonia (see Eq. 7.30). Then add T_{DP} to your output list.

65. Using Eqs. 7.26 and 7.28 and the four equations listed below[7] write an interactive computer program in metric (SI) units that will replace the psychrometric chart of Appendix D.6. Prompt the user for keyboard input of atmospheric pressure p_m, atmospheric temperature T_{DB}, and either the relative humidity ϕ or the humidity ratio ω. Return to the screen properly formatted values (with units) for p_m, T_{DB}, T_{DP}, ω, ϕ, $h^{\#}$, and v_a.

1. $p_{sat} = 0.1 \exp[14.4351 - 5333.3/(T_{DB} + 273.15)]$ for $0 \leq T_{DB} \leq 38$ °C

2. $T_{DP} = 5333.3/[14.4351 - \ln(p_w/0.1)] - 273.15$ for $0 \leq T_{DP} \leq 38$ °C

3. $h^{\#} = 1.005(T_{DB}) + \omega[2501.7 + 1.82(T_{DB})]$

4. $v_a = (0.286 \times 10^{-3})(T_{DB} + 273.15)/(p_m - p_w)$

where p_{sat}, p_m, and p_w are in MPa, T_{DB} and T_{DP} are in °C, $h^{\#}$ is in kJ/(kg dry air), and v_a is in m^3/(kg dry air).

66. Modify the program of Problem 65 to allow the user to separately choose either metric (SI) or English units for the input and the output values.

67. Expand Problem 65 above by adding Eq. 7.34 to your program. In Eq. 7.34 let $\omega_1 = \omega$, $T_1 = T_{DB}$, $T_2 = T_{WB}$, and use $c_{pa} = 1.005$ kJ/(kg·K). Also, use[8]

1. $h_{g1} = 2501.7 + 1.82(T_{DB})$

2. $h_{f2} = 4.194(T_{WB})$

3. $h_{fg2} = 2501.7 - 2.374(T_{WB})$

4. $\omega_3 = 0.622 p_{sat}/(p_m - p_{sat})$

where h_{g1}, h_{f2}, and h_{fg2} are in kJ/kg, T is in °C, and p_{sat} is evaluated at T_{WB} and is obtained from Eq. 1 in Problem 65 by replacing T_{DB} with T_{WB}. The wet bulb temperature can now be used as an input parameter. Prompt for inputs of p_m, T_{DB}, and either T_{WB}, ϕ or ω. Return to the screen properly formatted values (with appropriate units) of p_m, T_{DB}, T_{WB}, T_{DP}, ω, ϕ, $h^{\#}$, and v_a.

---

7. and 8. These equations are from P. E. Liley, Approximations for the thermodynamic properties of air and steam useful in psychrometric calculations. *Merchanical Engineering News* 17(4), 19–20 (1980).

Chapter Eight Heat Engine Power and Refrigeration Cycles

The material in this chapter embodies the heart and soul of applied thermodynamics. Because of the human and cultural impact this technology has had on society, it was decided to present this material chronologically to provide a historical framework for its study. It is important that engineers today develop an understanding of the relative effect the technology they create can have on society. Therefore, the normally dry technical aspects of this enormously powerful technology have been augmented with a small amount of relevant humanistic information with the hope of giving it some interesting perspective.

Section I deals with heat engine power cycles and their associated technology. Were it not for this technology the industrial revolution that began in the mid eighteenth century would not have taken place, and the world would be a much different place today. This section begins with basic definitions regarding engines, machines, and heat, and ends with a discussion of modern power plant technology.

Section II is concerned with refrigeration cycles, which are often just backward-running heat engine cycles. This technology has also had an important impact on our culture. Since the thrust and scope of refrigeration systems is somewhat less involved than that of the heat engine, it requires proportionally less discussion.

Chapter Eight Section I Vapor and Gas Power Cycles

To fully understand the technical meaning of the phrase *heat engine* one must first understand what the term *engine* implies, why there are different kinds of engines, and how to distinguish between them. The English words *engine* and *ingenious* are both derived from the same Latin root word *ingenerare*, meaning *to create*. About A.D. 200 Tertullian[1] referred to a military battering ram in Latin as an *ingenium* or product of genius, and soon thereafter the word *ingen* was used in Latin to describe all military machines (catapults, assault towers, etc.). Ingen then became assimilated into English as *engine*, and early English speaking machine designers were known as *engine-ers*, and later as *engineers*.[2]

Until the mid nineteenth century the terms *engine* and *machine* were used interchangeably. These devices were normally driven by either animal, wind, or water power and would be referred to as animal (or horse) engines, wind (or air) engines, or water (or hydraulic) engines, respectively. Also, from the medieval period through the eighteenth century an ingenious machine was commonly called a *gin* (a contraction applicable to either *ingen* or *engine*).[3]

Thus the term engine has a much broader historical meaning than normally realized. The vast number of different engines (machines) that were developed dur-

1. Quintus Septimius Florens Tertullianus (ca. A.D. 150–230) was an early Christian author who helped establish Latin (rather than Greek) as the language of Christianity. He coined many new Latin words and phrases as he wrote about the moral and practical problems facing the early Christians of his time (proper dress, military service, marriage and divorce, arts, theater, etc.).

2. In modern French and German an engineer is an *ingenieur*, and in modern Italian it is *ingegnere*. The English term *machine* is from the Greek *μαση*ν, meaning a device consisting of interrelated parts with separate functions. Strictly speaking, then, an engine is more than just a machine. It is an *ingenious* machine.

3. The alcoholic beverage, gin (a spirit distilled from grain and originally flavored with the juice of juniper berries), is a contraction of the word *geneva* which comes from the Latin *juniperus*.

Table 8.1 Some typical heat engine characteristics

Heat sources	Heat sinks	Working fluids	Work output prime movers	Cycle types	Functions
Combustion	Atmosphere	Vapor	Reciprocating (piston–cylinder)	Power	Transportation
Nuclear	Oceans, lakes	Gas	Turbine	Refrigeration	Generate electricity
Atmosphere	Rivers		Rocket (thrustor)	Heat pump	Heating and cooling
Ocean	Groundwater		Solid state (e.g., thermo-electric)		

ing this period are usually classified today either *generally* according to their source of power (animal, wind, water, etc.) or *specifically* according to their function. In 1773 Eli Whitney (1765–1825) built an ingenious machine for removing the seeds from cotton. His cotton engine became known as a *cotton gin*, and it changed the economy of the South by bringing it prosperity. A calculating engine would be a machine whose function was to make calculations (e.g., an adding machine), whereas a pneumatic engine would be an engine whose source of power was air pressure. A *heat engine* is any machine whose source of power is heat (fire, steam, solar, etc.), and whose specific function is undefined (i.e., it simply produces work that can be mechanical, electrical, chemical, etc., in nature). Initially, heat engines simply produced mechanical work that was used directly (e.g., in manufacturing) or else they were connected to other engines. For example, they were often connected to pumping engines (pumps) to move water, and later to electrical engines (generators) to generate electricity. Most heat engines use either a vapor or a gas as the internal energy transfer medium (even a thermoelectric device can be thought of as transporting energy via an internal electron gas). Typical heat engine characteristics are shown in Table 8.1.

We call the device that actually produces the heat engines output work the *prime mover*. A prime mover can be a reciprocating piston–cylinder steam engine, a steam turbine, an internal combustion engine, and so forth. Figure 8.1 illustrates these terms.

It is common to use the words engine and prime mover interchangeably when referring to reciprocating piston–cylinder devices. We will follow this custom in this textbook when no confusion is likely to occur.

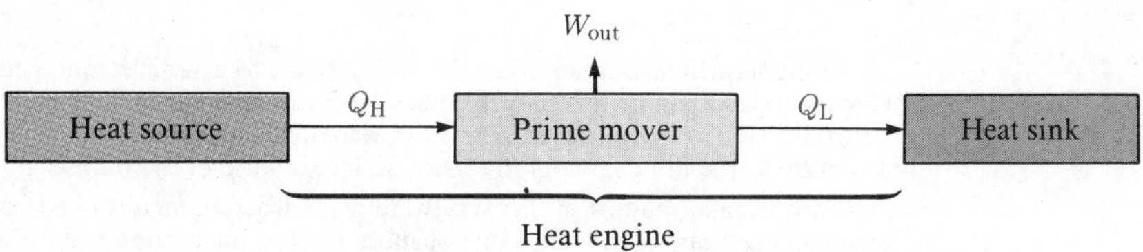

Figure 8.1 Heat engine terminology.

The reason heat engines are so important to the study of thermodynamics is that the history of heat engine technology is essentially the history of the Industrial Revolution. The heat engine whose prime mover was the reciprocating piston steam engine was the first large-scale source of portable mechanical power. It was a source of power that did not depend upon wind or river, and could therefore be located anywhere. The heat engine is still the primary source of power for travel and electricity today, and it is likely to remain so for the foreseeable future. Because of the enormous impact that heat engine technology has had and continues to have on the course of humanity, a brief review of its development is in order.

The Evolution of Steam Power

Heat engine steam power technology began in 1698 when Thomas Savery (1650–1715) was granted a patent by King William III of England for "an engine for raising water by the impellant force of fire." Savery's machine was designed to pump water from flooded English mines, and he called it a *fire engine* because it drew its power from the fire under the boiler rather than from horses or wind.[4] Its only moving mechanical parts were hand operated valves and automatic check valves. It drew water by suction when a partial vacuum was created as steam condensed inside a pumping chamber. This engine and its operation are shown in Figure 8.2.

Savery's engine could not draw water from a depth of more than about 20 ft (6.1 m) and it was somewhat dangerous because of the relatively high boiler pressure required to push the water out through the discharge pipe. Boiler technology had not advanced beyond that of the brewing industry then in existence and many boiler explosions are known to have occurred. Nonetheless, Savery's engine was an enormous economic success. It used fire to pump water, which was something that no other engine could do, and it was the first technologically successful heat engine. In spite of its large size and rather primitive use of steam, its simplicity made it a popular means of pumping water through short distances. Engines of this design were in continuous use in England until 1830.

By 1712 Thomas Newcomen (1663–1729), an English blacksmith, had devised a better steam engine that could pump water from very great depths while simultaneously eliminating the need for a high boiler pressure. His engine and a schematic of its operation is shown in Figure 8.3. He introduced a piston–cylinder arrangement in place of Savery's pumping chamber, with the piston attached to one end of a walking beam[5] and a positive displacement piston–cylinder pump

4. In modern English the phrase *fire engine* refers to a vehicle equipped to extinguish large fires. However, the origin of this phrase comes from the fact that all early fire extinguishing vehicles used a steam-driven water pump which was powered by a fire in the boiler. Thus, their pump was driven by a true fire engine in the sense of Savery's use of the phrase.

5. Early Roman pumps of this type were made wherein men walked back and forth across a long balance beam attached to one or more pumps, their combined weight causing enough imbalance to drive the pumps (a sort of teeter-totter pump). This type of human powered balance beam then became known as a *walking beam*.

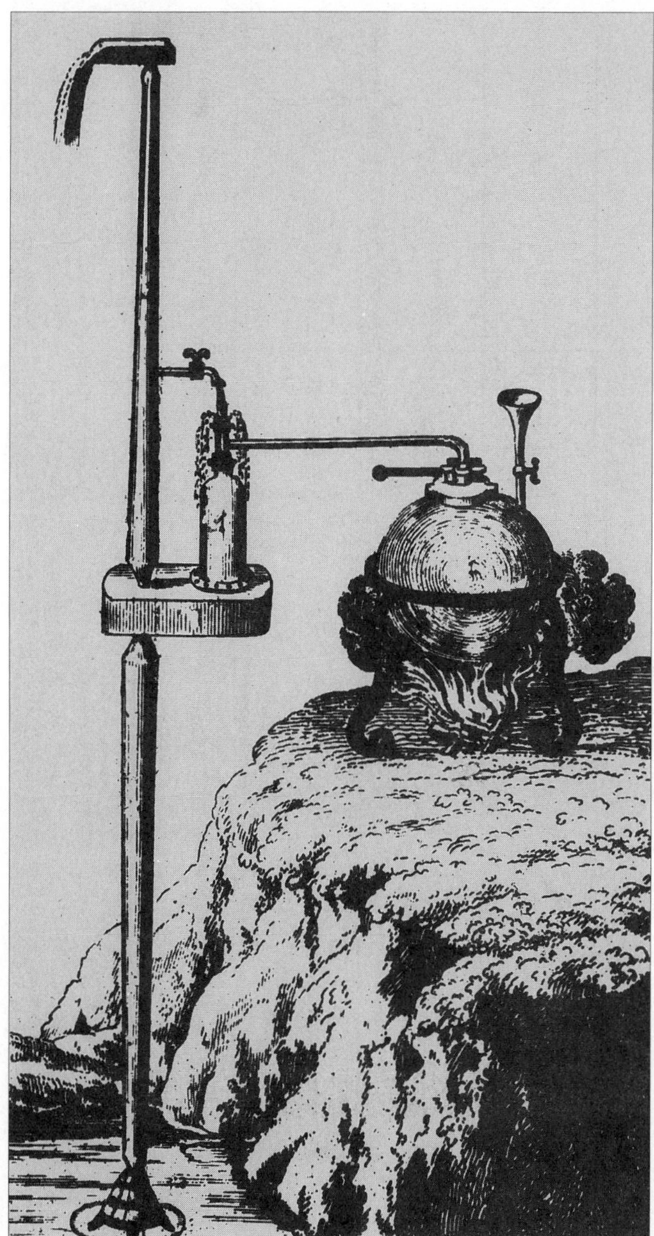

Figure 8.2 (*a*) Savery's fire engine (1698).

located deep in the mine attached to the other end of the walking beam. The pump end was counterweighted so as to hold the driving piston at the top of its stroke. When low-pressure (3 to 5 psig) steam was introduced under the driving piston and then condensed by using a cold water spray, the resulting partial vacuum allowed atmospheric pressure to push the driving piston down (thus charging the

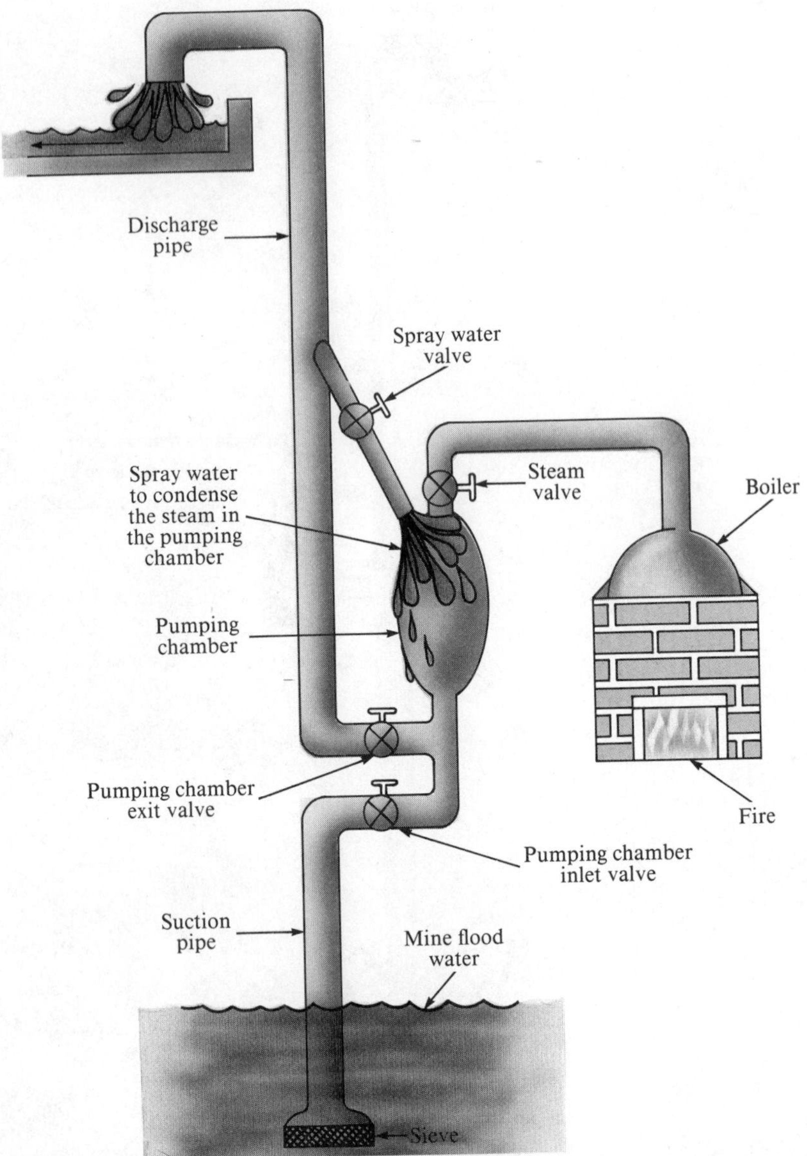

Figure 8.2 (*b*) A schematic of the operation of Savery's fire engine. Steam was generated in the boiler at 100–150 psig. To operate the engine, the manual control valve was opened to fill the pumping chamber with steam. This valve was then closed and cold water was allowed to flow over the outside of the pumping chamber, causing the steam inside to condense and form a partial vacuum. Atmospheric pressure (acting on the surface of the mine water) then forced the water from the flooded mine up through the suction pipe and into the pumping chamber. Opening the manual valve again allowed steam from the boiler to force this water out through the vertical discharge pipe. A skilled operator could run this engine at about five cycles per minute.

Figure 8.3 (*a*) The Newcomen steam engine near Dudley Castle, Staffordshire, 1712 (from an engraving by R. Barney, 1719).

pump with water). Venting the driving piston to the atmosphere allowed the counterweight to drop, thus pumping the water. These engines typically ran at a speed of about ten cycles per minute.

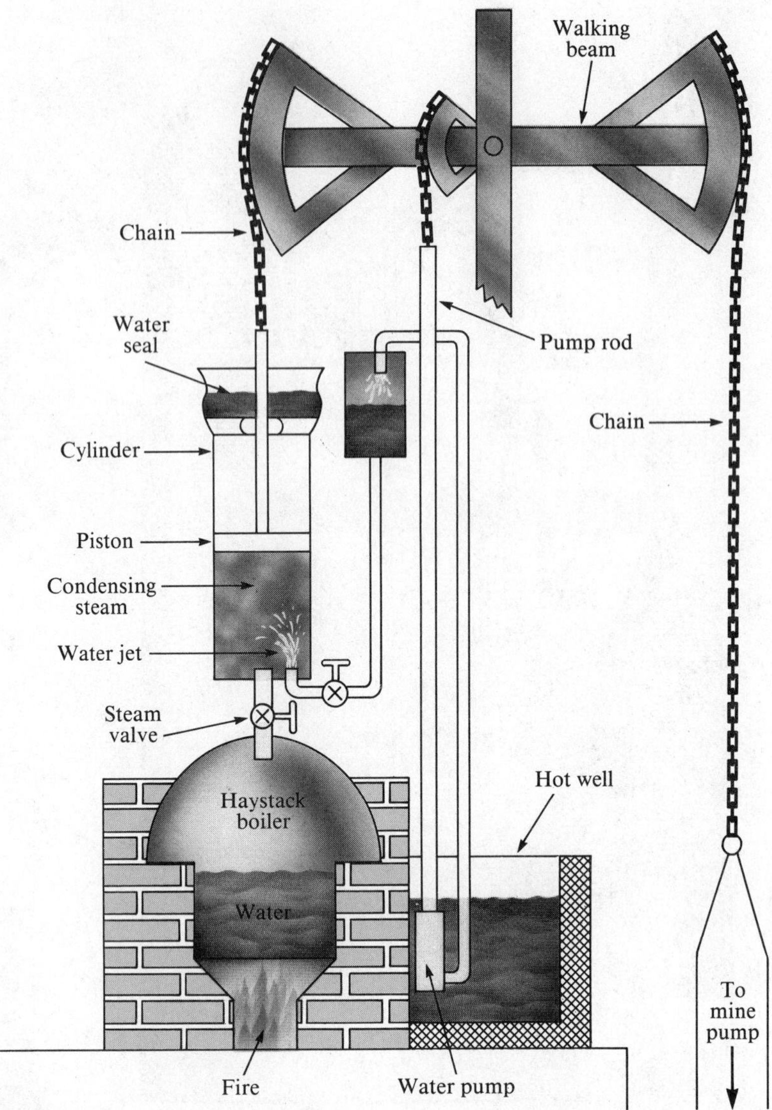

Figure 8.3 (*b*) A schematic of the operation of Newcomen's steam engine. When the cylinder has been filled with steam the driving piston rises and the weight of the pump rod forces a stroke on the pump (not shown) at the bottom of the mine shaft. The steam valve is then closed and the injection water valve opened. The cold water jet condenses the steam in the cylinder, producing a partial vacuum. Atmospheric pressure (acting on the top of the driving piston) forces the driving piston down, and the walking beam lifts the pump rod and makes the engine ready for another pumping cycle.

Since both the Savery and Newcomen engines depended upon creating a partial vacuum by condensing steam and then using atmospheric pressure to cause the necessary motion, they are called *atmospheric* engines. Also, since both engines alternately heated and cooled large metal chambers (Savery's pumping chamber and Newcomen's piston–cylinder) during each cycle of operation, they both had very low thermal efficiencies (a fraction of one percent). But since the concept of thermal efficiency had not yet been developed their poor thermal performance went undetected. However, as the technology advanced and more engines came into use it became clear to their owners that they required an enormous amount of fuel (wood or coal) to keep them operating.

By the late 1760s John Smeaton (1724–1792)[6] had undertaken a study of the fuel efficiencies of a number of England's Newcomen steam engines. He called his measure of fuel efficiency the *duty* of the engine and he defined it as follows

> The *duty* of a pumping engine is equal to the number of pounds of water that are raised one foot in height by the engine's pump when one 84-pound bushel of coal is burned in the boiler.

Because Smeaton's efficiency (duty) was applied to the total energy conversion process from chemical input (coal) to work output (water pumped), it constituted a measure of the overall system efficiency that included the boiler and pump efficiencies as well as the efficiency of the piston–cylinder operation. By assuming the average energy content of coal to be 13,000 Btu per pound we can easily convert Smeaton's duty measurements into overall thermal efficiencies. One 84-lbm bushel (bu) of coal contains (13,000 Btu/lbm)(84 lbm/bu)(778 ft·lbf/Btu) = 8.5×10^8 ft·lbf of energy. Defining thermal efficiency η_T as the ratio of net output (pounds of water raised one foot) to net input (ft·lbf of energy of coal consumed), we obtain (in percent)

$$\eta_T \text{ (in \%)} = \frac{\text{duty}}{8.5 \times 10^8} \times 100 \qquad \textbf{(8.1)}$$

For example, in 1765 Smeaton built a small Newcomen engine with a 10-in (0.25-m) diameter piston having a 38-in (0.97-m) stroke and found that it raised 2,919,000 lbf of water one foot high when one 84-lbm bushel of coal was consumed in the boiler. Therefore, it had a duty of 2,919,000 which corresponds to an overall thermal efficiency of

$$\eta_T = \frac{2{,}919{,}000}{8.5 \times 10^8} \times 100 = 0.34\%$$

For the next five years Smeaton collected duty measurements for over thirty different Newcomen pumping engines and found they had an average duty of

---

6. John Smeaton was a successful English engineer and in about 1750 he introduced the name *civil engineer* for any nonmilitary engineer (*civil* being simply a contraction of the word *civilian*). In 1771 he started the British Institution of Civil Engineers (the world's first professional engineering society). This was followed by the founding of the British Institution of Mechanical Engineers in 1847 by George Stephenson (1781–1848). In America, the American Society of Civil Engineers (ASCE) was founded in 1852. This was followed by the American Institute of Mining Engineers (AIME) in 1871, the American Society of Mechanical Engineers (ASME) in 1880, the American Institute of Electrical Engineers (AIEE) in 1884, the Society of Automotive Engineers (SAE) in 1904, American Institute of Chemical Engineers (AIChE) in 1908, and many others.

5,590,000, which corresponds to an average overall thermal efficiency of 0.65%. With these results he was able to conclude that large diameter pistons with short strokes made the most efficient engines. Using this result and improved cylinder boring techniques (necessary to reduce piston leakage) he was able to build an engine with a 52-in (1.32-m) diameter piston and a 7-ft (2.13-m) stroke in 1772 that had a duty of 9,450,000 and an overall thermal efficiency of 1.11%. Thus, he was able to produce an engine with *double* the efficiency of the average Newcomen engine simply by using his experimental observations to optimize its design.

In 1764 James Watt (1736–1819), a young Scottish machinist at the College of Glasgow, was given the job of repairing a classroom teaching scale model of a Newcomen engine. The engine wasn't actually broken. Its problem was that it consumed so much steam that its boiler was emptied after only a few cycles of operation and consequently it soon stopped running. Watt discovered that this was due to the alternate heating and cooling of the piston–cylinder unit during the condensation and reheat portions of each cycle. Part of the thermal energy contained in the steam had to be used to reheat the piston and cylinder after the condensation process was brought about by the cold water jet. This energy therefore became unavailable for doing mechanical work. The small size of the scale model engine had magnified this effect to the point where the engine was so inefficient that it would run for only a few cycles before using up all the steam available in the boiler.[7] Several months later he realized that if the steam was condensed not *inside* the piston–cylinder unit, but *outside* of it in a separate condenser chamber, then the piston and cylinder could be continuously kept at the high temperature of the steam. Then the piston–cylinder unit would not have to be reheated during each cycle of the engine and the steam consumption would be greatly reduced. With this simple observation was born one of the most significant technological innovations of the eighteenth century, the separate steam condenser.

With the addition of a condenser unit the efficiency of a full-size Newcomen engine was increased severalfold. This meant that these engines could be reduced in size somewhat (most Newcomen engines at that time were as big as a two-story house) and adapted to other uses beside pumping water out of flooded mines. The smaller Watt engines provided the medium-scale power sources necessary to bring about the onset of centralized manufacturing, which was the beginning of the Industrial Revolution. Figure 8.4 schematically shows how a separate condenser was added to a standard Newcomen pumping engine.

In 1775 Watt entered into a business partnership with the British industrialist Matthew Boulton (1728–1809) for the purpose of manufacturing his version of the external condenser Newcomen engine. Boulton provided the financial support (and consequently took two-thirds of the patent rights) and Watt was responsible for the engineering and manufacturing activities. The Boulton and Watt company was very successful and manufactured steam engines for many years, including the

7. Heat engine scale models magnify thermal inefficiencies that arise from convective heat loss from the engine's surface to the atmosphere. Since the surface area to volume ratio of a given geometric shape always *increases* as the physical dimensions of the shape *decrease*, small heat engine models are inherently much less efficient than their full-scale counterparts.

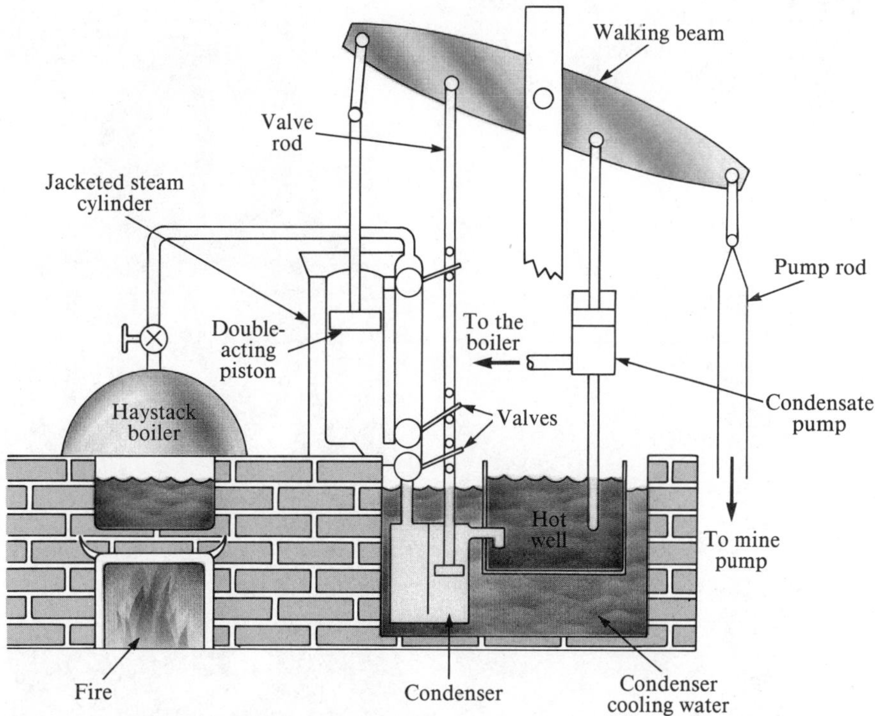

Figure 8.4 Watt's condenser added to a Newcomen pumping engine. Automatic valves alternately admit steam from the boiler to the proper side of a double-acting piston inside a steam jacketed cylinder and then into a separate condenser unit.

engine used in 1807 by Robert Fulton (1765–1815) on the first American steamboat, the Clermont. Over the years Watt made many important technological advances including automatic controls (the centrifugal governor), safety devices (the pressure gage), and efficiency improvements (the double-acting cylinder).[8]

By 1800 Watt's improvements had increased the thermal efficiency of a full-size Newcomen steam engine by about a factor of four. But even then the overall

8. The term *horsepower* had been introduced by Savery as a measure of how many horses driving a mechanical pump were replaced by his fire engine. However, as a unit of power measurement it lacked a precise definition until Watt carried out experiments in about 1780 to determine how much power an average horse could deliver on a continuous basis. He then multiplied this value by a factor of *two* to ensure that when he sold engines rated at a given horsepower the purchasers would have no complaints as to their performance. Using this technique he finally arrived at the figure of 33,000 ft·lbf/min as his horsepower definition. In addition to his conservative two-horse horsepower definition some other equivalences that Watt felt were valid are

$$1 \text{ horsepower} = 2 \text{ average horses} = 3 \text{ powerful oxen} = 12 \text{ men working cranks}$$
$$= 396 \text{ gallons of water falling 10 feet in 1 minute.}$$

Much later the electrical unit of power was named after him, 1 watt = 1 volt·ampere (and 1 hp = 746 watts).

Figure 8.5 An inverted vertical expansion steam engine built in New England in the mid 1860s. First used at the Jos. Schlitz Brewing Company in Milwaukee as a pumping engine. *Source*: Courtesy of the Milwaukee Public Museum, Milwaukee, Wisconsin.

thermal efficiency was only around 4 or 5%. This was to be the upper limit of atmospheric engine thermal efficiency because they were soon to be replaced by a new technological breakthrough: the high-pressure, expansion steam engine.[9]

Before the early nineteenth century high-pressure steam (anything over about 10 psig) was considered extremely dangerous. Explosions of the primitive boilers of Savery's time had caused much damage and loss of life, and had traumatized steam engine manufacturers. But new boiler materials and manufacturing and testing techniques in the early 1800s allowed operational steam pressures many

9. It has been estimated that the upper limit of the thermal efficiency of the reciprocating atmospheric steam engine, using the technology available in 1915, was less than 15%.

times the single atmosphere of pressure available to Watt's engines. One hundred-psig engines were common by 1840, and 200 psig was in use by 1880. High-pressure engine technology brought another quantum leap in thermal efficiency, another factor of three, from Watt's 4 to 5% in 1800 to 12 to 15% by 1850.

High-pressure engines used the pressure of the steam to *push* the piston by expanding against it, rather than having atmospheric pressure push the piston into a vacuum as the atmospheric engines had done. Thus, they were known as *expansion* engines (see, for example, Figure 8.5). By the 1820s high-pressure engines were sufficiently efficient that Watt's condenser unit was no longer considered to be essential, and consequently the steam was often exhausted from the cylinder directly into the atmosphere. The condenser always increased the engine's thermal efficiency somewhat, but if the piston–cylinder was not cooled during each cycle (as it was in the Newcomen atmospheric engines but not in the newer expansion engines) this effect was minimal.[10] The elimination of the condenser and its attendant pump simplified the engine's construction and further reduced its cost and size with only a small loss in thermal efficiency. At this point the steam engine was finally small enough to become truly portable and its application to locomotion on land (railroads) and water (steamboats) produced new transportation technologies that changed the face of the world.

The Carnot Cycle

In Chapter 5 we discussed how the young French military engineer Sadi Carnot (1796–1832) came to understand the rudiments of heat engine theory in the 1820s by using a water wheel analogy. His theory was based on the caloric (or fluid) theory of heat, and he believed that heat passed through a heat engine undiminished (like water passes through a water wheel undiminished), and that in so doing the heat engine could perform work. Today we know that this is incorrect. The heat flow through an engine is diminished (i.e.,reduced) by its conversion into work. Carnot's ideas were so revolutionary that they were largely ignored. Soon after Carnot's death from scarlet fever, Emile Clapeyron (1799–1864) in 1834 strengthened Carnot's ideas by using more precise mathematical derivations. From Carnot's description of a reversible heat engine Clapeyron constructed its thermodynamic cycle. He deduced that it must be composed of two isothermal processes and two reversible adiabatic processes. Using the pressure–volume steam engine indicator diagram format common at that time,[11] he deduced the cycle shape

10. However, steam condensers are still used on modern steam-driven electrical power plants to increase their overall thermal efficiency.

11. In an effort to continue to improve the performance of his steam engines, Watt wanted to know how the pressure varied with piston position inside the cylinder as the engine was running. About 1790 he developed an ingenious device for this purpose that he called a *steam engine indicator*. This device drew the actual pressure–volume diagram of the steam inside the cylinder as the engine was running. Such p-V diagrams soon became known as *indicator diagrams*, and the area enclosed by these diagrams represented the reversible work produced inside the engine. Thus, it was only natural for a physicist like Clapeyron to choose the indicator pressure–volume diagram graphical format to develop and test his analytical model of a reversible heat engine cycle based on Carnot's ideas.

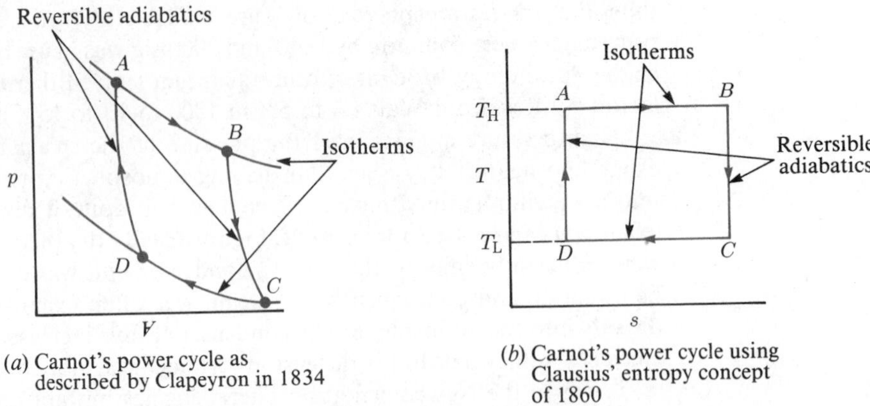

Figure 8.6 (*a*) Carnot's power cycle as described by Clapeyron in 1834. (*b*) Carnot's power cycle using Clausius' entropy concept of 1860.

shown in Figure 8.6*a*.[12] This cycle is still known as Carnot's cycle today, but, because it is defined to be a reversible cycle, no heat engine can ever be made to operate using it. The Carnot cycle is important because **1)** it was the first heat engine cycle ever to be properly conceptualized, and **2)** because no other heat engine, reversible or irreversible, can ever be more efficient than a Carnot cycle heat engine (though even a reversible heat engine *may* be less efficient), thus it can be used as a bench-mark, or standard for comparison, for gaging both real and reversible (ideal) heat engine performance.

When Rudolph Clausius (1822–1888) formalized the second law of thermodynamics and defined entropy in 1860, Carnot's reversible adiabatic processes then became an isentropic process, and the Carnot cycle was defined by two $T =$ constant processes and two $s =$ constant processes. The Carnot cycle then took on its characteristic rectangular shape on a *T-s* diagram, as shown in Figure 8.6*b*.

In Chapter 5 we also discussed how Carnot's ideas led to the development of the Kelvin absolute temperature scale, and finally to an expression for the thermal efficiency of a reversible heat engine (see Eq. 5.16), which we call in this chapter the *Carnot thermal efficiency*,

$$(\eta_T)_{\text{Carnot}} = 1 - T_L/T_H \qquad \textbf{(5.16)}$$

where T_H and T_L are the absolute isothermal temperatures of the high-temperature heat addition and low-temperature heat rejection reservoirs, respectively.

The Newcomen and Rankine Cycles

In the period from 1850 to 1880 the subject of thermodynamics was formally developed. One of its early practical goals was to provide a scientific foundation

12. The reversible Carnot *p-V* cycle diagram was chosen as the logo for the Mechanical Engineering Honor Society, Π Τ Σ (Pi Tau Sigma).

for the empirical steam technology that had by then grown to dominate the economy of the western world. By 1850 it had been determined that heat was a form of energy, and by 1860 the first and second laws of thermodynamics had been accurately formulated by Clausius, Kelvin, Joule, and others. But it was the Scottish engineer William John Macquorn Rankine (1820–1872) who first worked out the thermodynamic cycle for the adiabatic cylinder steam engine.[13] Because Rankine was the first person to understand how this type of steam engine worked thermodynamically, the thermodynamic cycle for adiabatic cylinder engines was named after him (rather than, say, the person who originally developed the engine itself). Thus the Watt, Evans, Corliss, and all the other adiabatic cylinder thermodynamic vapor cycles are known simply as the *Rankine cycle* today.

The Savery and Newcomen engines do not operate with adiabatic cylinders and therefore do not operate on a Rankine cycle. Since the atmospheric engines of Savery and Newcomen were obsolete by the time Rankine began his investigations, their thermodynamic cycles were never completely analyzed. Both the Savery and Newcomen engines operated on the same thermodynamic cycle, a cycle that we will call the *Newcomen cycle* in this text. Newcomen's name has been chosen as the cycle name because his engine was the first commercially successful reciprocating piston engine and because it had the greatest impact on bringing about the Industrial Revolution. The difference between the Newcomen and Rankine cycles can be seen by comparing Figures 8.7*a* and *b*.

Though the Newcomen cycle is obsolete and the Rankine cycle is still in common use, it is difficult to separate the early development of these two important prime mover thermodynamic cycles. Consequently, we will carry out an analysis of the thermal efficiency of each of these cycles, but then we will focus only on the further development of the Rankine cycle throughout the remainder of this chapter.

The Rankine cycle is a thermodynamic representation of a high-pressure or expansion type of steam engine cycle and, because of the shape of the T-s saturation curve for water, the ideal or reversible Rankine cycle without superheat is very close to the (reversible) Carnot cycle. The difference between these cycles is shown in Figure 8.7*c*. Because it is very difficult to efficiently pump wet vapor back into the boiler, the vapor is completely condensed into a liquid in the condenser and then, using a common liquid pump, it is pumped into the boiler as a compressed liquid. The Rankine cycle boiler feed pump only raises the pressure of the liquid condensate to that of the boiler (state 4), leaving its temperature nearly (or exactly if the condensate is incompressible and the pump isentropic) equal to that of the condenser (state 3). The Carnot cycle boiler feed pump, on the other hand, must raise the pressure of the liquid condensate to a very high pressure so that it enters the boiler at the boiler temperature.

---

13. An adiabatic cylinder steam engine is any expansion engine or any atmospheric engine with an external condenser. Rankine's work on this subject was published in his classic *Manual of the Steam Engine and Other Prime Movers*, first published in 1859. This text went through 17 editions, and was in print for over 50 years. It is considered to be the first comprehensive engineering thermodynamics textbook.

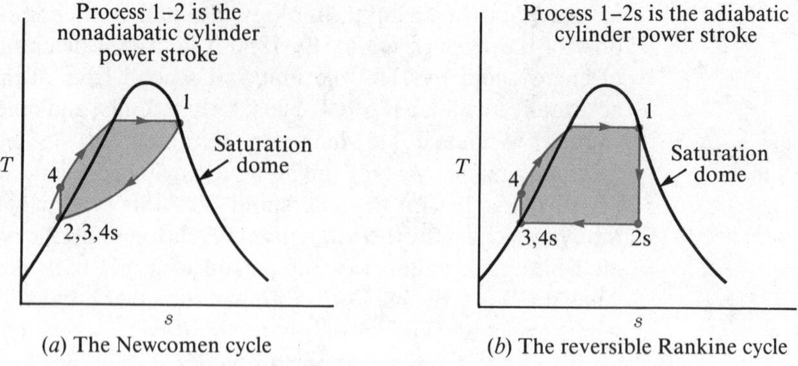

(*a*) The Newcomen cycle (*b*) The reversible Rankine cycle

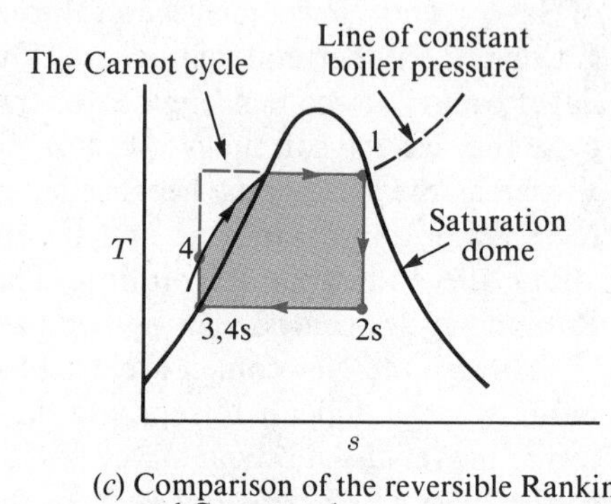

(*c*) Comparison of the reversible Rankine and Carnot cycles

Figure 8.7 The Newcomen, Rankine, and Carnot cycles.

The thermal efficiency η_T of a heat engine was defined in Eq. 5.5 as

$$\eta_T = \frac{\text{net work output}}{\text{total heat input}}$$

$$= \frac{\text{engine work output} - \text{pump work input}}{\text{boiler heat input}} \tag{5.5}$$

Consider first the atmospheric engine of the Savery or Newcomen type which does not have an external condenser (see Figure 8.8*a*). An energy rate balance on the steady state boiler, the condensate pump, and the piston–cylinder prime mover (neglecting any changes in flowstream kinetic or potential energy) gives

Heat transport rate into the boiler $= \dot{Q}_B = \dot{m}(h_1 - h_4)$

Power into the condensate pump $= |\dot{W}_{\text{pump}}| = \dot{m}(h_4 - h_3)$

Power out of the piston–cylinder prime mover $= |\dot{W}_{\text{pm}}| = \dot{m}(h_1 - h_2) - |\dot{Q}_{\text{pm}}|$

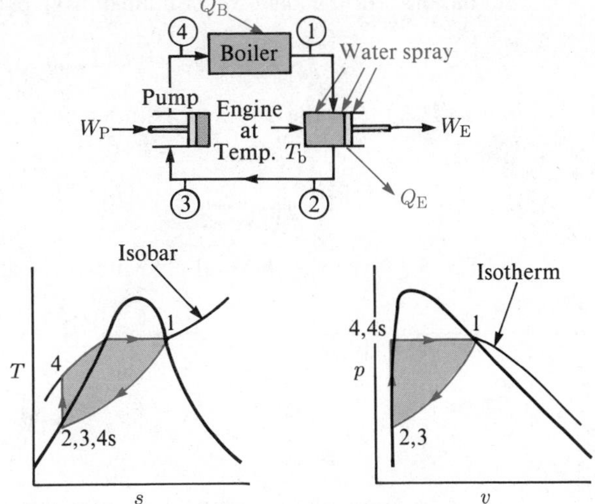

(*a*) Atmospheric engine without an external condenser (Newcomen cycle)

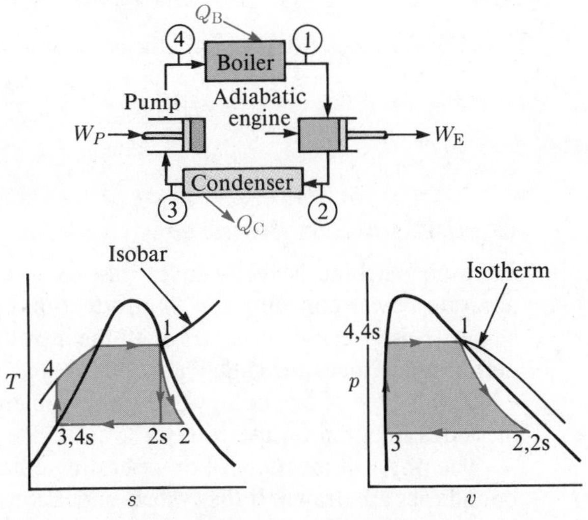

(*b*) Atmospheric engine with an external condenser (Rankine cycle)

Figure 8.8 Reciprocating heat engines operating on Newcomen and Rankine cycles.

where $\dot{Q}_{pm}$ is the heat removed from the piston–cylinder engine (prime mover) by the cold water spray (which causes the steam inside the cylinder to condense). Since a large heat transfer from the cylinder is necessary for this engine to operate, it cannot reasonably be modeled as an isentropic device. However, it can be modeled as a reversible heat transfer process, in which case the steady state entropy rate balance on the piston–cylinder unit gives

$$\dot{Q}_{\text{pm}} = \dot{m}(T_{\text{wall}})_{\text{avg}}(s_2 - s_1)$$

where $(T_{\text{wall}})_{\text{avg}}$ is the average cylinder wall absolute temperature. Then we can write

$$|\dot{W}_{\text{pm}}|_{\substack{\text{reversible}\\ \text{Newcomen}}} = \dot{m}[h_1 - h_2 - (T_{\text{wall}})_{\text{avg}}(s_1 - s_2)]$$

and Eq. 5.5 gives the thermal efficiency of a reversible Newcomen engine as[14]

$$(\eta_T)_{\substack{\text{reversible}\\ \text{Newcomen}}} = \frac{|\dot{W}_{\text{pm}}| - |\dot{W}_{\text{p}}|}{\dot{Q}_{\text{B}}} = \frac{h_1 - h_2 - (T_{\text{wall}})_{\text{avg}}(s_1 - s_2) - (h_4 - h_3)}{h_1 - h_4} \tag{8.2}$$

For an atmospheric engine with an external condenser (e.g., a Watt engine) or a high-pressure expansion engine, the cylinder can be assumed to be insulated and therefore it will operate on a Rankine cycle. Then the prime mover output becomes

$$|\dot{W}_{\text{pm}}|_{\text{Rankine}} = \dot{m}(h_1 - h_2)$$

and Eq. 5.5 gives the thermal efficiency of a Rankine cycle heat engine as

$$(\eta_T)_{\text{Rankine}} = \frac{|\dot{W}_{\text{pm}}| - |\dot{W}_{\text{p}}|}{\dot{Q}_{\text{B}}} = \frac{h_1 - h_2 - (h_4 - h_3)}{h_1 - h_4} \tag{8.3}$$

Operating Efficiencies

Since no machine is really reversible, we need to develop a method of making accurate power consumption or production calculations for real irreversible machines. This is usually done through the introduction of an empirically determined performance measure called an operating *efficiency*. Because of the manner in which this type of technology evolved, there are several different types of efficiency measures in common use today.

The physical meaning of an operating efficiency depends on where the system boundaries are drawn. If the system under consideration consists of only the working fluid, then this efficiency represents the effect of the irreversibilities that occur only within the working fluid. However, if the system under consideration consists of the entire work-producing or work-absorbing machine (including the working fluid), then this efficiency represents the effect of the irreversibilities within the working fluid as well as those within the machine itself (such as bearing friction, etc.). To be effective an operating efficiency should apply to a system consisting of the device plus the working fluid it contains.

14. Note that the thermal efficiency equation requires that a positive engine *output* work be used, and since the sign convention used in the ERB assumes positive work is *into* the system, we have had to use the magnitude $|\dot{W}_{\text{pm}}|$ in Eqs. 8.2 and 8.3 for the positive output work rate of the engine.

The first important measure of the performance of any device is the work transport energy efficiency η_W, which was defined in Chapter 4 as the ratio of the actual work to the reversible work for a work-producing device, or the ratio of the reversible work to the actual work for a work-absorbing device. This efficiency compares the actual performance of a device with that which would occur if the device were reversible (but not adiabatic), and it is commonly known as the *reversible efficiency* of the device. However, in mechanical devices the source of the internal irreversibilities is primarily mechanical friction. Consequently, it is customary to refer to the reversible efficiency of a mechanical device as simply the *mechanical efficiency* of the device, and to use the notation η_m instead of η_W. The mechanical efficiency of work-producing and work-absorbing devices is defined mathematically in Table 8.2.

Next we define the *isentropic efficiency* η_s as the ratio of the actual work to the isentropic work for a work-producing device, or the ratio of the isentropic work to the actual work for a work-absorbing device. It is similar to the work transport energy efficiency η_W, defined in Chapter 4, but whereas η_W was based on comparing the actual performance of the device with that which would occur if the device were reversible, the isentropic efficiency η_s is based on comparing the actual performance of the device with that which would occur if the device were adiabatic as well as reversible (i.e., isentropic). Since most prime movers and pumps are thermally insulated, *we will always assume that they are adiabatic when their heat loss is not given.* The isentropic efficiency of work-producing and work-absorbing devices is defined mathematically in Table 8.2.

It is also possible to define a *relative efficiency* (or *efficiency ratio*) η_r for these devices which relates the mechanical and isentropic efficiencies. For a work-producing device the relative efficiency is defined as the ratio of the reversible work to the isentropic work, and for a work-absorbing device it is defined as the inverse of that for a work-producing device (see Table 8.2). Then we can write $\eta_s = \eta_m \eta_r$ for either a work-producing or a work-absorbing device. Notice that if a device is insulated and is therefore adiabatic, then $\eta_s = \eta_m$ and $\eta_r = 1.0$.

The terms *shaft* and *brake* are also commonly used to describe the *actual* work or power produced or absorbed by a device.[15] These terms are all interchangeable, but, for clarity, the term *actual* will be most often used throughout this chapter. Further, the terms *reversible* and *indicated* are synonymous because the reversible work or power produced inside a device can be determined from *p-V* data provided by an indicator diagram (see footnote 11), and therefore we can write $\dot{W}_{\text{reversible}} = \dot{W}_{\text{indicated}}$. Consequently, for a work-producing device we can always write

$$\dot{W}_{\text{actual}} = \dot{W}_{\text{shaft}} = \dot{W}_{\text{brake}} = (\eta_s)(\dot{W}_{\text{isentropic}}) = (\eta_m)(\dot{W}_{\text{reversible}})$$

and for a work absorbing device we can always write

$$\dot{W}_{\text{actual}} = \dot{W}_{\text{shaft}} = \dot{W}_{\text{brake}} = (\dot{W}_{\text{isentropic}})/(\eta_s) = (\dot{W}_{\text{reversible}})/(\eta_m)$$

15. The term *brake* is a descriptive term that comes from an early method of measuring the power output of machines using a friction band brake dynamometer called a *Prony brake.* It was named after Baron Gaspard Clair Francois Marie Riche de Prony (1755–1839) and was developed in the 1830s to measure the power output of water wheels and steam engines.

Table 8.2 Definitions of some common efficiencies

Mechanical efficiency

$$(\eta_m)_{\substack{\text{work}\\\text{producing}\\\text{device}}} = \frac{W_{\text{actual}}}{W_{\text{reversible}}} = \frac{\dot{W}_{\text{actual}}}{\dot{W}_{\text{reversible}}}$$

$$(\eta_m)_{\substack{\text{work}\\\text{absorbing}\\\text{device}}} = \frac{W_{\text{reversible}}}{W_{\text{actual}}} = \frac{\dot{W}_{\text{reversible}}}{\dot{W}_{\text{actual}}}$$

Isentropic efficiency

$$(\eta_s)_{\substack{\text{work}\\\text{producing}\\\text{device}}} = \frac{W_{\text{actual}}}{W_{\text{isentropic}}} = \frac{\dot{W}_{\text{actual}}}{\dot{W}_{\text{isentropic}}}$$

$$(\eta_s)_{\substack{\text{work}\\\text{absorbing}\\\text{device}}} = \frac{W_{\text{isentropic}}}{W_{\text{actual}}} = \frac{\dot{W}_{\text{isentropic}}}{\dot{W}_{\text{actual}}}$$

Relative efficiency

$$(\eta_r)_{\substack{\text{work}\\\text{producing}\\\text{device}}} = \frac{W_{\text{reversible}}}{W_{\text{isentropic}}} = \frac{\dot{W}_{\text{reversible}}}{\dot{W}_{\text{isentropic}}}$$

$$(\eta_r)_{\substack{\text{work}\\\text{absorbing}\\\text{device}}} = \frac{W_{\text{isentropic}}}{W_{\text{reversible}}} = \frac{\dot{W}_{\text{isentropic}}}{\dot{W}_{\text{reversible}}}$$

Thermal efficiency

$$(\eta_T)_{\text{isentropic}} = \frac{|\dot{W}_{\text{out}}|_{\text{isentropic}}}{\dot{Q}_{\text{in}}}$$

$$(\eta_T)_{\text{reversible}} = (\eta_T)_{\text{indicated}} = \frac{|\dot{W}_{\text{out}}|_{\text{reversible}}}{\dot{Q}_{\text{in}}}$$

$$(\eta_T)_{\text{actual}} = (\eta_T)_{\text{brake}} = \frac{|\dot{W}_{\text{out}}|_{\text{actual}}}{\dot{Q}_{\text{in}}} = \frac{|\dot{W}_{\text{out}}|_{\text{brake}}}{\dot{Q}_{\text{in}}}$$

where $|\dot{W}_{\text{out}}|$ represents the magnitude of the *net* power output in each case.

Furthermore, we will now have to deal with three different types of thermal efficiencies for work-producing or work-absorbing systems: isentropic, reversible (or indicated), and actual (or brake). These thermal efficiencies are all defined mathematically in Table 8.2.

Using these definitions, the isentropic efficiency of the adiabatic piston-cylinder work-producing prime mover of the heat engine shown in Figure 8.8*b* would be

$$(\eta_s)_{\substack{\text{prime}\\\text{mover}}} = (\eta_s)_{\text{pm}} = \frac{(h_1 - h_2)_{\text{actual}}}{(h_1 - h_2)_{\text{isentropic}}} = \frac{h_1 - h_2}{h_1 - h_{2s}} \tag{8.4a}$$

or

$$h_1 - h_2 = (h_1 - h_2)_{\text{actual}} = (h_1 - h_{2s})(\eta_s)_{\text{pm}} \tag{8.4b}$$

where h_{2s} is determined from p_2 (but not T_2) and the condition $s_{2s} = s_1$, as shown in Figure 8.8*b*. Similarly the isentropic efficiency of the adiabatic work-absorbing condensate pump in the heat engine shown in Figure 8.8*b* would be

$$(\eta_s)_{pump} = (\eta_s)_p = \frac{(h_4 - h_3)_{isentropic}}{(h_4 - h_3)_{actual}} = \frac{h_{4s} - h_3}{h_4 - h_3} \tag{8.5}$$

where h_{4s} is determined from p_4 (but *not* T_4) and the condition $s_{4s} = s_3$, as shown in Figure 8.8*b*. If the fluid being pumped is an incompressible liquid (v = constant) with a constant specific heat c, then Eq. 5.33 of Chapter 5 clearly shows that any isentropic process that it undergoes must also be isothermal. That is, $T_{4s} = T_3$ and consequently $u_{4s} = u_3$. Then, for $v_{4s} = v_4 = v_3$ and $p_{4s} = p_4$[16]

$$\begin{aligned} h_{4s} - h_3 &= u_{4s} - u_3 + p_{4s}v_{4s} - p_3v_3 \\ &= c(T_{4s} - T_3) + v_3(p_{4s} - p_3) \\ &= v_3(p_4 - p_3) \end{aligned} \tag{8.6}$$

Equation 8.5 can now be written as

$$(\eta_s)_{\substack{\text{incompressible}\\ \text{liquid}\\ \text{pump}}} = \frac{v_3(p_4 - p_3)}{h_4 - h_3} = \frac{v_3(p_4 - p_3)}{c(T_4 - T_3) + v_3(p_4 - p_3)} \tag{8.7a}$$

or

$$h_4 - h_3 = (h_4 - h_3)_{actual} = v_3(p_4 - p_3)/(\eta_s)_p \tag{8.7b}$$

Substituting Eq. 8.7*b* into the Newcomen cycle thermal efficiency, Eq. 8.2, gives[17]

$$(\eta_T)_{\substack{\text{reversible}\\ \text{Newcomen}}} = \frac{h_1 - h_2 - (T_{wall})_{avg}(s_1 - s_2) - v_3(p_4 - p_3)/(\eta_s)_p}{h_1 - h_3 - v_3(p_4 - p_3)/(\eta_s)_p} \tag{8.8a}$$

and the maximum possible Newcomen cycle thermal efficiency occurs when the condensate pump is isentropic, $(\eta_s)_p = 1.0$, or

$$(\eta_T)_{\substack{\text{maximum}\\ \text{Newcomen}}} = \frac{h_1 - h_2 - (T_{wall})_{avg}(s_1 - s_2) - v_3(p_4 - p_3)}{h_1 - h_3 - v_3(p_4 - p_3)} \tag{8.8b}$$

Similarly, using Eqs. 8.4*b* and 8.7*b* in the Rankine cycle thermal efficiency, Eq. 8.3, gives

$$(\eta_T)_{Rankine} = \frac{(h_1 - h_{2s})(\eta_s)_{pm} - v_3(p_4 - p_3)/(\eta_s)_p}{h_1 - h_3 - v_3(p_4 - p_3)/(\eta_s)_p} \tag{8.9a}$$

---

16. Note that for an isentropic pump points 3 and 4s coincide on a T-s diagram but not on a p-v diagram (see Figure 8.8*b*).

17. Note that since the prime mover of a Newcomen engine cannot possibly be adiabatic and therefore cannot be modeled as an isentropic device, then $h_1 - h_2 \neq (h_1 - h_{2s})(\eta_s)_{pm}$ in Eq. 8.8*a*.

where $(\eta_s)_{pm}$ is the isentropic efficiency of the prime mover. The maximum possible Rankine cycle thermal efficiency occurs when both the prime mover and the condensate pump are isentropic, $(\eta_s)_{pm} = (\eta_s)_p = 1.0$, or[18]

$$(\eta_T)_{\substack{\text{maximum}\\ \text{Rankine}}} = (\eta_T)_{\substack{\text{isentropic}\\ \text{Rankine}}} = \frac{h_1 - h_{2s} - v_3(p_4 - p_3)}{h_1 - h_3 - v_3(p_4 - p_3)} \tag{8.9b}$$

Example 8.1

A typical Newcomen atmospheric steam engine of 1750 without an external condenser had a boiler pressure of 14.7 psia and an average cylinder condensation pressure of 8.0 psia. Determine the maximum possible thermal efficiency of this engine assuming it operates on **a)** a Carnot cycle, and **b)** a Newcomen cycle with an average cylinder wall temperature of 200 °F.

Solution

a) A Carnot cycle is defined to be a reversible cycle, so it will automatically represent the maximum possible thermal efficiency for this cycle. Equation 5.16 gives the Carnot efficiency as

$$(\eta_T)_{\text{Carnot}} = 1 - T_L/T_H$$

where

$$T_H = T_{sat}(14.7 \text{ psia}) = 212 \text{ °F} = 672 \text{ R}$$

and

$$T_L = T_{sat}(8.0 \text{ psia}) = 182.8 \text{ °F} = 642.8 \text{ R}$$

Then,

$$(\eta_T)_{\text{Carnot}} = 1 - 642.8/672 = 0.0435 = 4.35\%$$

b) The maximum possible Newcomen cycle thermal efficiency will occur when the piston–cylinder unit is reversible and the condensate pump is isentropic. Then, from Eq. 8.8*b*,

$$(\eta_T)_{\substack{\text{maximum}\\ \text{Newcomen}}} = \frac{h_1 - h_2 - (T_{\text{wall}})_{\text{avg}}(s_1 - s_2) - v_3(p_4 - p_3)}{h_1 - h_3 - v_3(p_4 - p_3)}$$

18. We use the phrase *isentropic Rankine cycle thermal efficiency* here to denote that the prime mover and the condensate pump are both isentropic (i.e., reversible *and* adiabatic). Clearly, the entire cycle is not isentropic since there are thermal irreversibilities associated with reheating the cold condensate returned to the hot boiler. This notation is necessary to distinguish between *reversible* Rankine cycles in which the prime movers and pumps are modeled as reversible but are not adiabatic, and those Rankine cycles in which these items are modeled as both reversible and adiabatic (i.e., isentropic). This same notation will be used in referring to other power and refrigeration cycles that contain isentropic components.

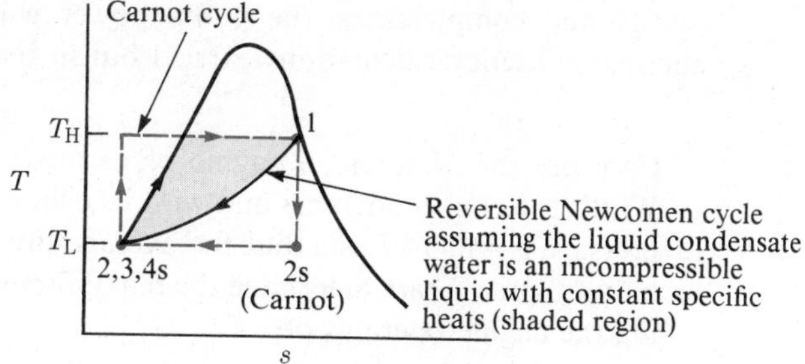

where, from Appendix C.2*a*, we find

$$v_3 = v_f(8.0 \text{ psia}) = 0.01653 \text{ ft}^3/\text{lbm}$$

$$h_1 = h_g(14.7 \text{ psia}) = 1150.5 \text{ Btu/lbm}$$

$$h_2 = h_3 = h_f(8.0 \text{ psia}) = 150.8 \text{ Btu/lbm}$$

$$h_4 = h_f(14.7 \text{ psia}) = 180.1 \text{ Btu/lbm}$$

and

$$s_1 = s_g(14.7 \text{ psia}) = 1.7569 \text{ Btu/(lbm}\cdot\text{R)}$$

$$s_2 = s_f(8.0 \text{ psia}) = 0.2676 \text{ Btu/(lbm}\cdot\text{R)}$$

Then, with $(T_{\text{wall}})_{\text{avg}} = 200\ °\text{F} = 660$ R, Eq. 8.8*b* gives

$$(\eta_T)_{\substack{\text{maximum}\\ \text{Newcomen}}} = \frac{1150.5 - 150.8 - 660(1.7569 - 0.2676) - 0.01653(14.7 - 8.0)(144/778)}{1150.5 - 150.8 - 0.01653(14.7 - 8.0)(144/778)}$$

$$= 0.0167 = 1.67\%$$

The thermal efficiency calculated in part b of the previous example was for a reversible Newcomen engine, and thus was impossible to achieve with a real Newcomen engine. Considering the mechanical and thermal inefficiencies of these relatively crude engines it is easy to see why their actual operating thermal efficiencies were in the range of 1% or less. Also note that the ratio of pump power to engine power in this example was only

$$|\dot{W}_p/\dot{W}_{pm}| = \frac{0.1653(14.7 - 8.0)(144/778)}{1150.5 - 150.8 - 660(1.7569 - 0.2676)} = 0.00123 = 0.123\%$$

and consequently the pump input power could be safely neglected in comparison to the engine output power in the thermal efficiency calculation. Even so, for clarity and completeness, the pump power will be included in all subsequent thermal efficiency calculations carried out in the examples given in this chapter.

Example 8.2

Consider the Newcomen engine of Example 8.1 now retrofitted with one of Watt's external condensers and with its cylinder thermally insulated. The boiler pressure is still 14.7 psia, but the average pressure in the external condenser is only 4.0 psia. Again determine the maximum possible thermal efficiency assuming the engine operates on

a) a Carnot cycle, and

b) a Rankine cycle.

c) Determine the percentage increase in these efficiencies due to the addition of the Watt external condenser and the insulation on the cylinder.

Solution

a) Here we have

$$T_H = T_{sat}(14.7 \text{ psia}) = 212\ °\text{F} = 672 \text{ R}$$

and

$$T_L = T_{sat}(4.0 \text{ psia}) = 152.9\ °\text{F} = 612.9 \text{ R}$$

Then Eq. 5.16 gives

$$(\eta_T)_{Carnot} = 1 - T_L/T_H = 1 - 612.9/672 = 0.0879$$
$$= 8.79\%$$

b) Using Eq. 8.9*b* for the efficiency of an isentropic Rankine cycle we have

$$v_3 = v_f(4.0 \text{ psia}) = 0.01636 \text{ ft}^3/\text{lbm}$$

$$h_1 = h_g(14.7 \text{ psia}) = 1150.5 \text{ Btu/lbm}$$

$$h_3 = h_f(4.0 \text{ psia}) = 120.9 \text{ Btu/lbm}$$

and

$$x_{2s} = \frac{s_2 - s_{f2}}{s_{fg2}} = \frac{s_1 - s_{f2}}{s_{fg2}} = \frac{1.7569 - 0.2198}{1.6428} = 0.9357$$

Then,

$$h_{2s} = h_f(4.0 \text{ psia}) + x_{2s}h_{fg}(4.0 \text{ psia})$$
$$= 120.9 + (0.9357)(1006.4)$$
$$= 1062.5 \text{ Btu/lbm}$$

and Eq. 8.9*b* gives

$$(\eta_T)_{\text{isentropic}} = \frac{1150.5 - 1062.5 - 0.01636(14.7 - 4.0)(144/778)}{1150.5 - 120.5 - 0.01636(14.7 - 4.0)(144/778)}$$

$$= 0.0854 = 8.54\%$$

c) The effect of Watt's condenser was to increase the equivalent Carnot cycle thermal efficiency by

$$\frac{8.79 - 4.35}{4.35} \times 100 = 102\%$$

and to increase the maximum Newcomen cycle thermal efficiency by

$$\frac{8.54 - 1.67}{1.67} \times 100 = 411\%$$

Thus, by simply lowering the average condensation pressure by only 4.0 psi, Watt effectively *quadrupled* the theoretical thermal efficiency of the ideal (i.e., reversible) Newcomen engine. The actual engine, however, had large inherent irreversibilities, primarily due to mechanical friction, leakage around the piston, and uncontrolled heat loss from the boiler and cylinder surfaces. Watt continued to improve the engine's performance with such innovations as double-acting cylinders, better seals and valving, and automatic speed control so that by 1800 his engines were actually about four times more efficient than the earlier Newcomen engines.[19]

The move to high-pressure expansion steam engines after 1800 by other innovators led to much higher thermal efficiencies. For example, the Carnot and isentropic Rankine cycle thermal efficiencies for an expansion engine using dry saturated steam from a boiler at 100 psia and utilizing a condenser at 1.0 psia are 28.7 and 26.1%, respectively. This was much higher than Watt could ever hope to achieve with his atmospheric engine.

The actual thermal efficiencies achieved by these early engines were naturally considerably less than that predicted through an isentropic analysis. Figure 8.9 illustrates the growth of both the actual and the isentropic efficiencies for the past three centuries.

19. Since the early steam engines were very large and expensive, the firm of Boulton & Watt devised a creative marketing scheme based upon the superior thermal efficiency of their engine. They let the purchaser pay for his engine by giving the company one-third of the value of the fuel saved with the new engine as compared with the fuel consumption of a standard Newcomen engine of the same size.

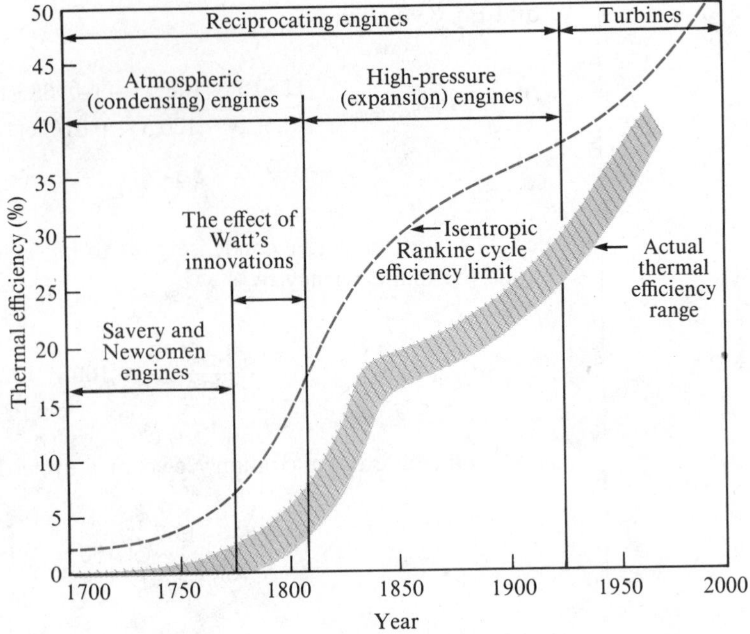

Figure 8.9 A chronology of steam engine thermal efficiency, 1700–2000.

The Rankine Cycle with Superheat

Between 1850 and 1890 a variety of mechanical complexities were added to the reciprocating steam engine to improve its thermal efficiency. For example, the cylinders were often staged in series so that the steam was first expanded in a high-pressure cylinder and then exhausted to lower-pressure cylinder stages.[20] Two-stage (duplex) expansion was introduced in 1811, three-stage (triplex) in 1871, and four-stage (quadruplex) in 1875.

By 1880 it was recognized that initially dry saturated steam became wet when condensation occurred during the expansion stroke of the piston (process 1 to 2 in Figure 8.7*b*). The water droplets thus formed inside the cylinder tended to cool it slightly and they promoted corrosion. This meant that the cylinder walls were being alternately cooled and heated (as in the original Newcomen engine) slightly with each cycle of the engine, and this reduced the engine's thermal efficiency. However, if the steam entered the cylinder in a superheated state, then the amount of moisture produced during the expansion stroke was greatly reduced or eliminated altogether.[21]

20. Series staging of an engine's cylinders with the steam expanding only partially in each stage was then called *compounding*.

21. Originally the term *surcharging* was used to denote the use of superheated steam. This term has since been replaced by the more direct term *superheating*.

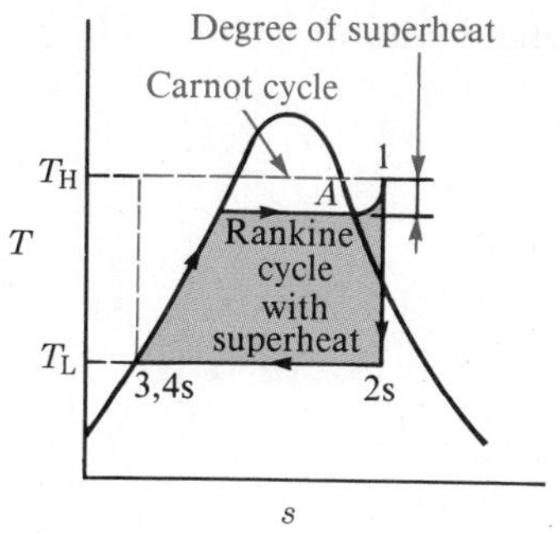

(*a*) The temperature-entropy diagram for the Carnot and Rankine cycles with superheat

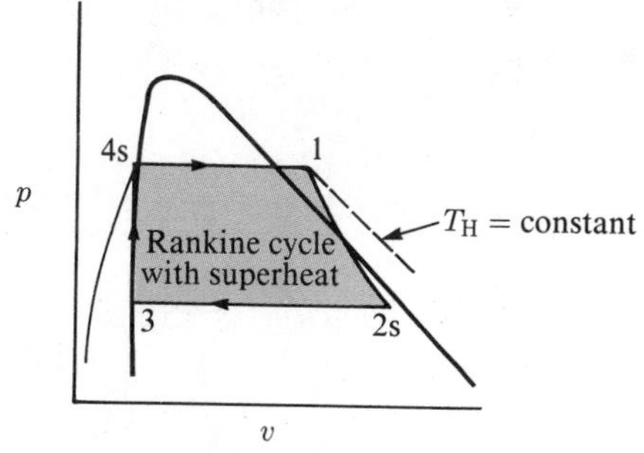

(*b*) The pressure-volume diagram for the Carnot and Rankine cycles with superheat

Figure 8.10 A comparison between the Carnot cycle and the isentropic Rankine cycle with superheat.

Superheating the steam at the entrance to the cylinder alters the equivalent Carnot cycle by raising T_H to the superheating temperature and consequently increases the equivalent Carnot efficiency considerably. This in turn makes the Rankine cycle appear less desirable by comparison, as shown in Figure 8.10. But all vapor cycle heat engines operate on the Rankine cycle, and using the Carnot cycle for engineering comparison purposes is purely academic. A more realistic comparison would be between the *isentropic* Rankine cycle and the *real* Rankine cycle.

The *degree of superheat* is defined to be the difference between the actual superheated vapor temperature and the saturation temperature at the pressure of the superheated vapor, i.e.,

$$\left\{\begin{matrix}\text{Degree of superheat of} \\ \text{superheated vapor at} \\ \text{temperature of } T \text{ and} \\ \text{pressue } p\end{matrix}\right\} = T - T_{\text{sat}}(p) \tag{8.10}$$

For example, in Figure 8.10*a* the degree of superheat is $T_1 - T_A$. The degree of superheat that can be used in any particular heat engine design is limited only by the engine's ability to resist high temperatures. This has lead to the industrial development and use of high-temperature alloys and ceramics for critical heat engine components.

Example 8.3

A Rankine cycle steam engine with superheat has a boiler outlet state of 100 psia, 500 °F, and a condenser pressure of 1 psia. Determine

a) the degree of superheat.
b) the equivalent Carnot cycle efficiency, and
c) the isentropic Rankine cycle efficiency.

Solution The system sketch is shown below.

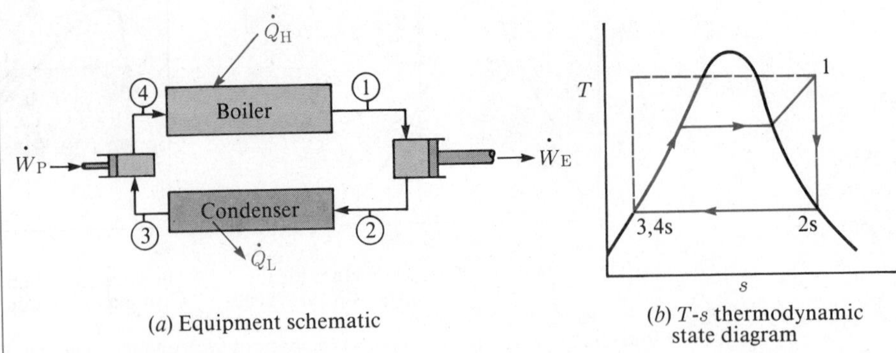

(*a*) Equipment schematic

(*b*) *T-s* thermodynamic state diagram

The thermodynamic states of the steam at the four monitoring points shown in the equipment schematic are

Station 1

$p_1 = 100$ psia
$T_1 = 500\ °\text{F}$

$h_1 = 1279.1$ Btu/lbm
$s_1 = 1.7087$ Btu/(lbm·R)

Station 2s

$p_{2s} = p_2 = 1.0$ psia
$s_{2s} = s_1 = 1.7087$ Btu/(lbm·R)

$x_{2s} = 0.8540$
$h_{2s} = 954.4$ Btu/lbm

Station 3

$p_3 = 1.0$ psia
$x_3 = 0.0$

$h_3 = h_f = 69.7$ Btu/lbm
$s_3 = s_f = 0.1326$ Btu/(lbm·R)

Station 4s

$p_{4s} = p_4 = 100$ psia
$s_{4s} = s_3 = 0.1326$ Btu/(lbm·R)

$h_{4s} = 70.0$ Btu/lbm

where we have calculated the following items

$$v_3 = v_f(1.0\text{ psia}) = 0.01614\ \text{ft}^3/\text{lbm}$$

$$x_{2s} = (s_2 - s_{f2})/s_{fg2} = (s_1 - s_{f2})/s_{fg2}$$
$$= (1.7087 - 0.1326)/1.8455 = 0.8540$$

$$h_{2s} = h_{f2} + x_{2s}h_{fg2} = 69.7 + (0.8540)(1036.0)$$
$$= 954.4\ \text{Btu/lbm}$$

$$h_{4s} = h_3 + v_3(p_4 - p_3) = 69.7 + (0.01614)(100 - 1.0)(144/778)$$
$$= 70.0\ \text{Btu/lbm}$$

a) The degree of superheat is determined from Appendix C.2*a* and Eq. 8.10 as and Eq. 8.10 as

$$\text{degree of superheat} = 500 - T_{\text{sat}}(100 \text{ psia})$$
$$= 500 - 327.8 = 172.2\ ^\circ\text{F}$$

b) Here the highest temperature in the cycle is $T_H = 500 + 460 = 960$ R, and the lowest temperature in the cycle is $T_L = T_{\text{sat}}(1.0 \text{ psia}) = 101.7 + 460 = 561.7$ R. Then Eq. 5.16 gives the Carnot efficiency as

$$(\eta_T)_{\text{Carnot}} = 1 - 561.7/960 = 0.415 = 41.5\%$$

c) Equation 8.9*b* is used to determine the isentropic Rankine cycle thermal efficiency as

$$(\eta_T)_{\substack{\text{isentropic}\\ \text{Rankine}}} = \frac{1279.1 - 954.4 - (0.01614)(100 - 1.0)(144/778)}{1279.1 - 69.7 - (0.01614)(100 - 1.0)(144/778)}$$
$$= 0.268 = 26.8\%$$

Initially, the purpose of superheating the vapor was simply to eliminate or at least reduce the amount of moisture in the engine's low-pressure stages. However, at the higher boiler pressures and temperatures of the twentieth century, the effect of superheating the steam can add as many as 5 percentage points to the isentropic Rankine cycle thermal efficiency.

The Rankine Cycle with Regeneration

A *regeneration* process in a system is a feedback process whereby energy is transferred internally from one part of a system to a different part of the system for the purpose of improving the system's overall energy conversion efficiency. This internal transport of energy within a system is called regeneration, and the associated equipment is called a regenerator. In the case of heat engines, regeneration usually involves utilizing otherwise waste exhaust thermal energy to preheat fluid in another part of the same system. More specifically, in the case of the Rankine cycle heat engine a certain percentage of the vapor passing through the prime mover is removed and used to preheat the boiler feedwater to a temperature between the condenser outlet temperature and the boiler outlet temperature. This serves to significantly reduce the thermal irreversibility that occurs when relatively cold condenser outlet water is pumped back into a much hotter boiler. Thus, by reducing a major irreversibility of the cycle, the overall thermal efficiency of the cycle is increased.

Regenerative feedwater heating is shown schematically in Figure 8.11. These regenerators are simply heat exchangers. There are two common types: **a)** *open*

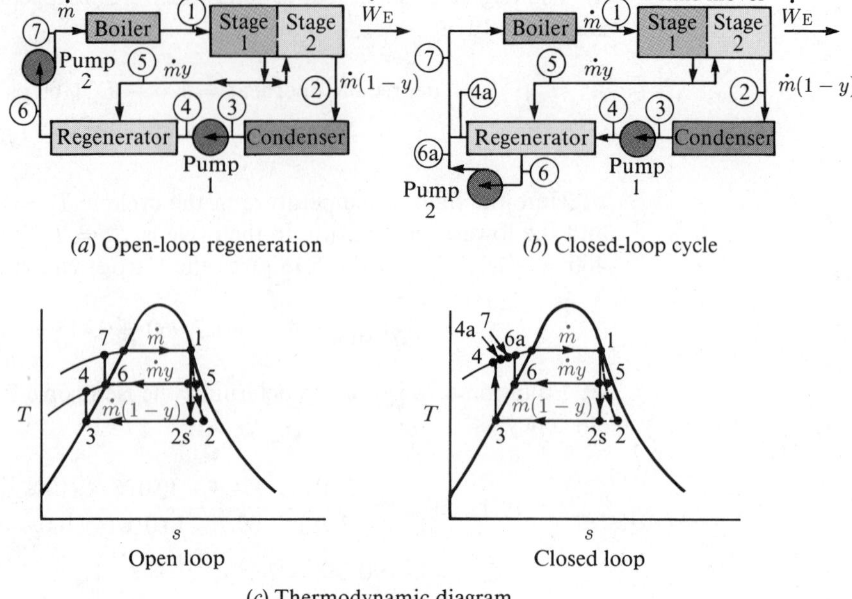

Figure 8.11 The Rankine cycle with regeneration.

loop (or direct contact) heat exchangers in which the regeneration vapor mixes directly with the boiler feedwater, and **b)** *closed loop* heat exchangers in which the regeneration vapor and the boiler feedwater do not mix until after the regeneration vapor has been condensed into a liquid.

As an example of regeneration thermodynamics, consider the open loop regenerative feedwater heater shown in Figure 8.11*a*. These units were normally adiabatic (all the heat transfer occurs internally) and aergonic. A steady state, steady flow mass and energy rate balance (neglecting any changes in potential or kinetic energy) on the regenerator yields

$$\dot{m}_4 + \dot{m}_5 - \dot{m}_6 = 0$$

and

$$\dot{m}_4 h_4 + \dot{m}_5 h_5 - \dot{m}_6 h_6 = 0$$

Combining these two equations so as to eliminate $\dot{m}_4$ gives

$$h_6 = (1 - y)h_4 + yh_5$$

where we have used $y = \dot{m}_5/\dot{m}_6 = \dot{m}_5/\dot{m}_1$ as the mass fraction of regeneration vapor extracted from the prime mover. Solving for y produces

$$y = (h_6 - h_4)/(h_5 - h_4) \tag{8.11}$$

This equation allows us to calculate the mass fraction of vapor that must be removed from the prime mover and added to the open loop regenerator to achieve a desired saturated liquid state at station 6. There is an optimum value of y that will maximize the system's thermal efficiency. Due to the complexity of the system, this optimum can be found only by trial and error methods. The determination of the optimum value of y for a given system is a good computer problem when accurate computerized thermodynamic tables are available.

The thermal efficiency of either regeneration system shown in Figure 8.11 is

$$(\eta_T)_{\substack{\text{Ranking cycle}\\ \text{with one regenerator}}} = \frac{(h_1 - h_5) + (1-y)[(h_5 - h_2) - (h_4 - h_3)] - \dot{W}_{p2}/\dot{m}}{h_1 - h_7} \tag{8.12}$$

$$= \frac{(h_1 - h_{5s})(\eta_s)_{pm1} + (1-y)[(h_5 - h_{2s})(\eta_s)_{pm2} - (h_{4s} - h_3)/(\eta_s)_{p1}] - \dot{W}_{p2}/\dot{m}}{h_1 - h_7}$$

where the power per unit mass flow rate required to drive boiler feed pump 2 is given by

$$\left(\frac{\dot{W}_{p2}}{\dot{m}}\right) = \begin{cases} (h_{7s} - h_6)/(\eta_s)_{p2} & \text{for open loop regeneration} \\ y(h_{6as} - h_6)/(\eta_s)_{p2} & \text{for closed loop regeneration} \end{cases}$$

Example 8.4

A two-stage steam prime mover (either reciprocating or turbine) receives dry saturated steam at 200 psia. It has an interstage pressure of 80 psia and a condenser pressure of 1.0 psia. Determine

a) the isentropic Rankine cycle thermal efficiency of the system without regeneration present,

b) the mass fraction of regeneration steam required to produce saturated liquid water at 80 psia at the exit of an open loop regenerator, and

c) the isentropic Rankine cycle thermal efficiency of the system with an open loop boiler feedwater regenerator at 80 psia.

Solution

a) Before boiler feedwater regeneration is added, the configuration of the isentropic Rankine cycle system is as follows,

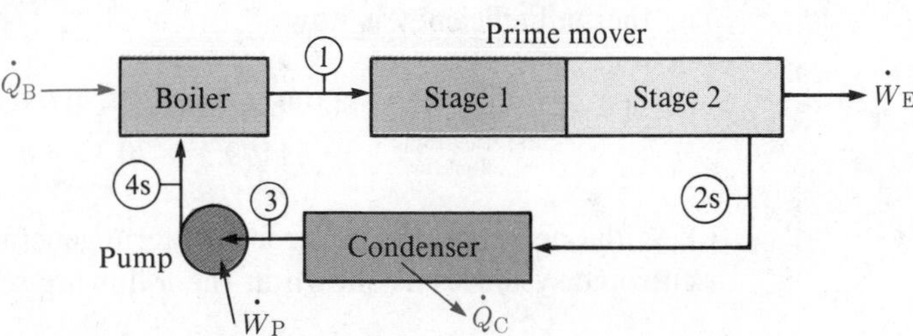

and its thermal efficiency is

$$(\eta_T)_{\substack{\text{isentropic}\\ \text{Rankine}}} = \frac{(h_1 - h_{2s}) - (h_{4s} - h_3)}{(h_1 - h_{4s})}$$

where, assuming an incompressible liquid condensate, Eq. 8.6 gives

$$h_{4s} = h_3 + v_3(p_4 - p_3)$$

and

$$v_3 = v_4(1.0 \text{ psia}) = 0.01614 \text{ ft}^3/\text{lbm}$$

The monitoring station data are as follows

Station 1

$p_1 = 200$ psia
$x_1 = 1.0$

$h_1 = 1199.3$ Btu/lbm
$s_1 = 1.5466$ Btu/(lbm·R)

Station 2s

$p_{2s} = p_2 = 1.0$ psia
$s_{2s} = s_1 = 1.5466$ Btu/(lbm·R)

$h_{2s} = 863.5$ Btu/lbm

Station 3

$p_3 = 1.0$ psia
$x_3 = 0.0$

$h_3 = 69.7$ Btu/lbm
$s_3 = 0.1326$ Btu/(lbm·R)

Station 4s

$p_{4s} = p_4 = 200$ psia
$s_{4s} = s_3 = 0.1326$ Btu/(lbm·R)

$$\begin{aligned} h_{4s} &= h_3 + v_3(p_4 - p_3) \\ &= 69.7 + (0.01614)(200 - 1.0)(144/778) \\ &= 69.7 + 0.6 = 70.3 \text{ Btu/lbm} \end{aligned}$$

where at station 2s we have used

$$x_{2s} = \frac{s_{2s} - s_{f2}}{s_{fg2}} = \frac{s_1 - s_{f2}}{s_{fg2}} = \frac{1.5466 - 0.1326}{1.8455} = 0.7662$$

then

$$h_{2s} = 69.7 + (0.7662)(1036.0) = 863.5 \text{ Btu/lbm}$$

The thermal efficiency is now

$$(\eta_T)_{\substack{\text{isentropic}\\ \text{Rankine}}} = \frac{1199.3 - 863.5 - 0.6}{1199.3 - 70.3} = 0.297 = 29.7\%$$

b) With one open-loop boiler feedwater regenerator the configuration of the isentropic system is as shown in the following schematic.

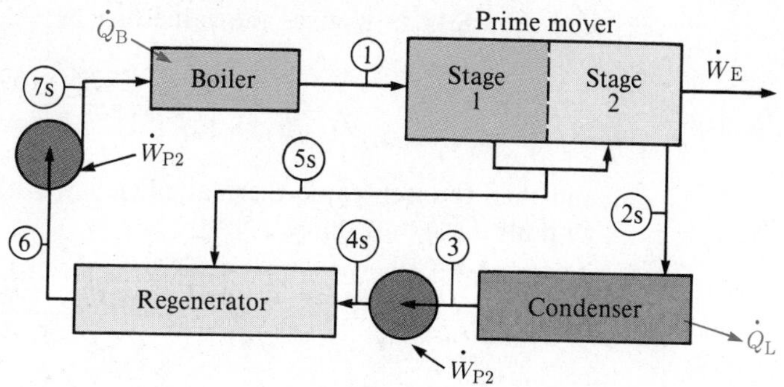

The properties at monitoring stations 1, 2, and 3 are the same as they were in part a, but pump 1 only brings the condensate pressure up to 80 psia (to match the vapor inlet pressure), and pump 2 brings the pressure the rest of the way up from 80 to 200 psia. Then,

$$v_3 = v_f(1.0 \text{ psia}) = 0.01614 \text{ ft}^3/\text{lbm}$$

and

$$v_6 = v_f(80 \text{ psia}) = 0.01757 \text{ ft}^3/\text{lbm}$$

The additional monitoring station data needed are

Station 4s

$p_{4s} = p_4 = 80$ psia
$s_{4s} = s_3 = 0.1326$ Btu/(lbm·R)

$$h_{4s} = h_3 + v_3(p_4 - p_3) = 69.7 + (0.01614)(80 - 1.0)(144/778) = 69.7 + 0.2 = 69.9 \text{ Btu/lbm}$$

Station 5s

$p_{5s} = p_5 = 80$ psia
$s_{5s} = s_1 = 1.5466$ Btu/(lbm·R)

$h_{5s} = 1125.7$ Btu/lbm

Station 6

$p_6 = 80$ psia
$x_6 = 0.0$

$h_6 = 282.2$ Btu/lbm
$s_6 = 0.4535$ Btu/(lbm·R)

Station 7s

$p_{7s} = p_7 = 200$ psia
$s_{7s} = s_6 = 0.4535$ Btu/(lbm·R)

$$h_{7s} = h_6 + v_6(p_7 - p_6) = 282.2 + (0.01757)(200 - 80)(144/778) = 282.2 + 0.4 = 282.6 \text{ Btu/lbm}$$

where at station 5s we have used

$$x_{5s} = (1.5466 - 0.4535)/1.1681 = 0.9358$$

and

$$h_{5s} = 282.2 + (0.9358)(901.4) = 1125.7 \text{ Btu/lbm}$$

Equation 8.11 now gives the value of y as

$$y = \frac{h_6 - h_{4s}}{h_{5s} - h_{4s}} = \frac{282.6 - 69.9}{1125.7 - 69.9} = 0.20$$

and then the isentropic thermal efficiency of the cycle is given by Eq. 8.12 with all the $\eta_s = 1.0$ as

$$(\eta_T)_{\text{isentropic}} = \frac{(h_1 - h_{5s}) + (1 - y)[(h_{5s} - h_{2s}) - (h_{4s} - h_3)] - (h_{7s} - h_6)}{h_1 - h_{7s}}$$

Rankine cycle with one regenerator

$$= \frac{(1199.3 - 1125.7) + (0.8)[(1125.7 - 863.5) - (69.9 - 69.7)] - (282.6 - 282.2)}{1199.3 - 282.6}$$

$$= 0.308 = 30.8\%$$

Note that the effect of a single regeneration unit in the previous example was to increase the thermal efficiency by only 1.1%. The extra expense of the regenerators and the additional pumps cannot be economically justified unless the system is large enough to make such a small thermal efficiency increment produce a significant savings in fuel costs.

This type of Rankine cycle regeneration was first seriously proposed in 1890, and was first implemented in 1898 with a four-stage quadruple expansion (quadruplex) reciprocating piston–cylinder steam engine. This system achieved an actual thermal efficiency of 22.8%, which was remarkably high for its day. After about 1910 the production of large reciprocating piston–cylinder steam engines decreased rapidly. They were being replaced by a new prime mover technology, the steam turbine. Consequently, regeneration was temporarily discontinued until about 1920, at which point the steam turbine had been established as the preferred prime mover for large stationary power plants. After 1920, regeneration became standard practice in the design of large vapor cycle turbine prime mover power plants.

The Steam Turbine

By the end of the nineteenth century the large, slow-speed reciprocating piston–cylinder steam engine had reached its upper limit in size and complexity.[22] Mean-

22. When the maximum practical piston speed had been reached in reciprocating steam engine design, the only way to increase the work output further was to increase the physical size of the engine. The largest reciprocating steam engine ever built in the United States was constructed in 1891 by the E. P. Allis Company (renamed the Allis Chalmers Company in 1901) of Milwaukee, Wisconsin. It was installed as a pumping engine at the Chapin mine in Iron Mountain, Michigan, in 1892. A duplex steeple compound condensing engine with high-pressure cylinders 50 in (4.17 ft) in diameter and low-pressure cylinders 100 in (8.33 ft) in diameter (both with strokes of 10 ft), it was 54 ft high and 75 ft long, weighed 725 tons, and had a flywheel 40 ft in diameter. At its maximum speed of 10 rpm it could produce over 1200 hp.

while, a new heat engine prime mover technology was quickly being developed: the steam turbine.[23]

A turbine is a prime mover in which mechanical rotating shaft work is produced by a steady flow of fluid through the system. The output work is produced by changing the *momentum* of the working fluid as it passes through the system (the turbine). Reciprocating prime mover output work, on the other hand, is produced by changing the *pressure* of a fixed mass of working fluid within the system (the piston–cylinder apparatus).

There are two basic types of turbine designs: *impulse* and *reaction*.[24] In the impulse turbine high-velocity fluid jets from stationary nozzles impinge on a set of blades on a rotor. The impulse force generated by the momentum change of the fluid passing through these blades causes the rotor to spin rapidly, like blowing on a pinwheel. In a reaction turbine the rotation is caused by a reaction force generated by the momentum change of the fluid accelerating through nozzles that are attached to the rotor itself (like the nozzles on a lawn sprinkler). The nozzles in a rotor type reaction turbine are not the same as the simple axisymmetric cylindrical jet producing nozzles of the impulse turbine. Instead, they are two-dimensional nozzle-like channels formed in the passage between the blades of each row. The characteristics of impulse and reaction turbines are shown in Figure 8.12.

It can be easily shown from the momentum balance equations of fluid mechanics that the maximum energy conversion efficiency of an impulse turbine occurs when the fluid enters the rotor blades parallel to the direction of motion of the blades

---

23. The word *turbine* was coined in 1822 from the Latin root word *turbo*, for *that which spins*. When it was coined it was applied only to water wheels (as in hydraulic or water turbines).

24. Both the impulse and reaction turbine concepts date from antiquity. The paddle-type water wheels developed in Italy in about 70 B.C. (and used throughout the world, well into the twentieth century A.D.) were of the impulse type. Also, in the first century A.D., a Greek known today only as Heron (or, in Latin, Hero) of Alexandria (Egypt) devised a simple reaction steam turbine (called an aeolipile) in which a hollow copper sphere was made to rotate by steam jetting out of four nozzles mounted perpendicular to the axis of rotation (see the schematic below). No practical use was then made of this device. However, it was known to James Watt and his contemporaries because they experimented with steam driven reaction turbines of the Heron type and still found them impractical in their time due to the extremely high rotational speeds required to make them efficient enough to be competitive with existing reciprocating steam engine technology.

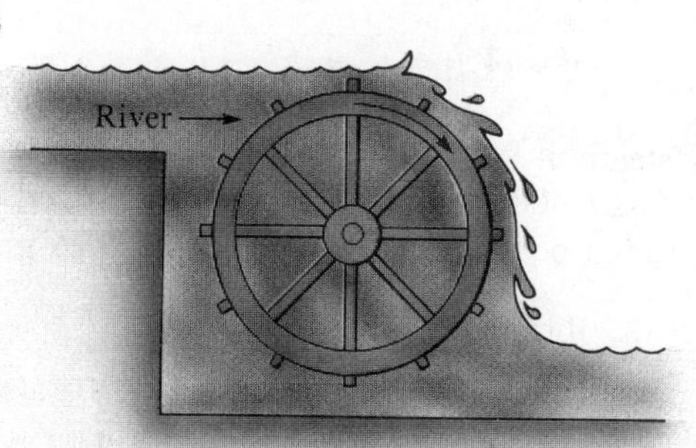

Roman paddlewheel
Impulse turbine (ca. 70 B.C.)

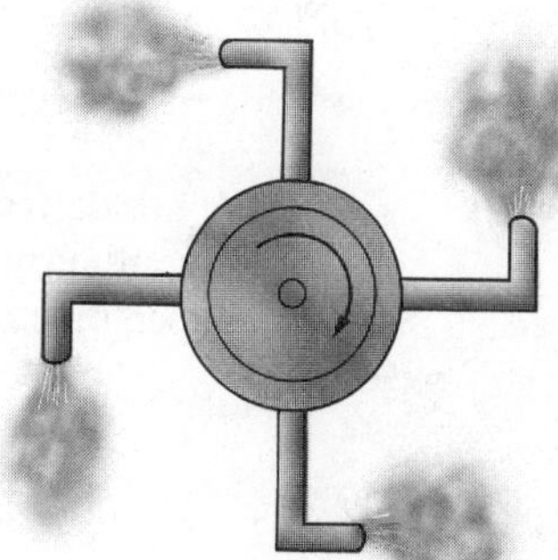

Heron's reaction steam turbine
(ca. 1st century A.D.)

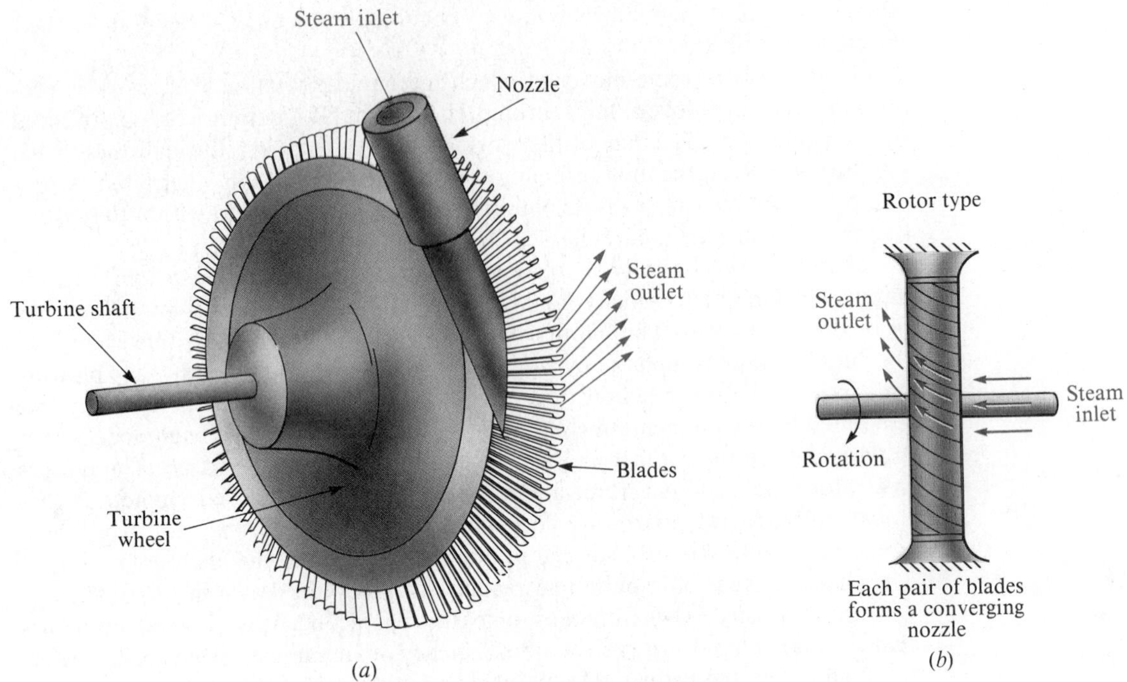

Figure 8.12 Characteristics of (*a*) impulse and (*b*) reaction turbines.

and with a velocity equal to exactly twice the blade average velocity, and that this efficiency drops off quickly when these conditions are deviated from. Similarly, it can be shown that a reaction turbine has a maximum energy conversion efficiency when the fluid enters the rotor blades parallel to the direction of motion of the blades and with a velocity exactly equal to the blade average velocity. The effect of the turbine's nozzles is to convert static pressure energy into dynamic kinetic energy whose momentum can then be manipulated by the turbine's geometry to drive the rotor. Nozzles were analyzed in Chapter 4, and the outlet velocity of an adiabatic nozzle with a negligible inlet velocity is given by Eq. 4.105 as

$$V_{\text{out}} = \sqrt{2g_c(h_{\text{in}} - h_{\text{out}})} \tag{4.105}$$

A nozzle receiving steam at 200 psia, 700 °F and exhausting to 1.0 psia will have an enthalpy drop of, say, 400 Btu/lbm. The resulting nozzle outlet velocity will be supersonic and can then be calculated from Eq. 4.105 as

$$\begin{aligned} V_{\text{out}} &= \{2[32.2 \text{ lbm}\cdot\text{ft}/(\text{lbf}\cdot\text{s}^2)](400 \text{ Btu/lbm})(778 \text{ ft}\cdot\text{lbf/Btu})\}^{1/2} \\ &\approx 4500 \text{ ft/s} \end{aligned}$$

Then, a reaction turbine operating at its most efficient speed would require a blade average velocity of about 4500 ft/s. If we assume a mean rotor radius of 1.0 ft,

then the angular velocity of the rotor at its most efficient operating speed is 4500 radians per second, or about 43,000 rpm. This is an extremely high rotational speed and is very dangerous due to the high centrifugal stresses and the high bearing loads produced by unbalanced forces. Also, few auxiliary turbine driven devices (e.g., an electrical generator) could be made to operate at these speeds. Therein was the major problem with early turbine development. How could they be slowed down while still maintaining their good energy conversion and thermal efficiencies?

This problem remained unsolved until the end of the nineteenth century when it was discovered that certain types of turbine *staging* would significantly decrease the turbines operating speed while maintaining its energy conversion efficiency. The region between stationary nozzles in an impulse turbine is referred to as an *impulse stage*. It was discovered that the effect of adding two extra rows of blades, one stationary and one moving, to each stage of an impulse turbine reduced its most efficient operating speed by about a factor of two. In a reaction turbine, every other row of blades is stationary, and the combination of a stationary row and a moving row forms a *reaction stage* of the turbine. Large reaction turbines typically have 30 to 100 or more stages, whereas impulse turbines normally have less than 10 stages.

In 1883 the Swedish engineer Carl Gustaf Patrik DeLaval (1845–1913) built and ran the first practical single-stage impulse steam turbine. It had a mean rotor diameter of 3 in (0.076 m) and produced about 1.5 hp with a shaft speed of 40,000 rpm. In 1889 he discovered that if the pressure ratio across his stationary nozzles was less than about 0.55, he could increase the nozzle exit velocity to supersonic speeds if he made the nozzles with a converging–diverging internal profile.[25] The high shaft velocity of the DeLaval impulse turbine required a gearbox to reduce the output rotational speed to a usable value. Since high-speed gear reduction is very inefficient, it became necessary to find other ways of reducing the turbine's speed effectively. The addition of multiple stages of fixed nozzles and moving blades to the same shaft of a DeLaval impulse turbine was first carried out by the Frenchman Auguste Camille Edmond Rateau (1863–1930) in 1898. By having a sufficient number of these stages in series he was able to reduce the efficient rotating speed enough to allow electrical generators to be driven directly from the output shaft. Also, in 1898 the American engineer Charles Gordon Curtis (1860–1953) introduced multiple sets of stationary and moving blade rows downstream from a single stationary nozzle. This technique exposed each set of moving

25. It will be shown in Chapter 10 that supersonic flow will occur in a converging–diverging nozzle when the pressure ratio across the nozzle is less than $[2/(k+1)]^{k/(k-1)}$, which is about 0.55 for superheated steam ($k \approx 1.3$).

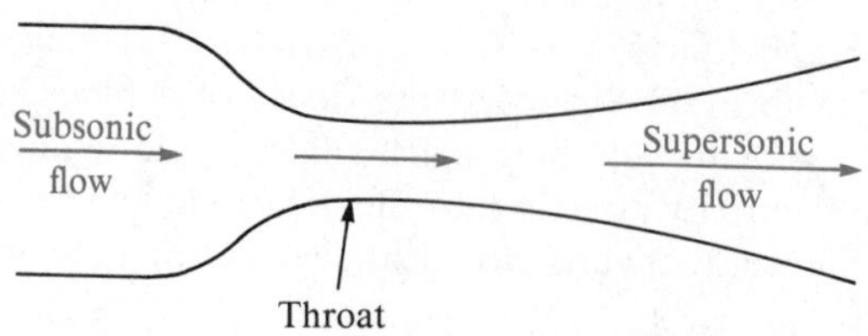

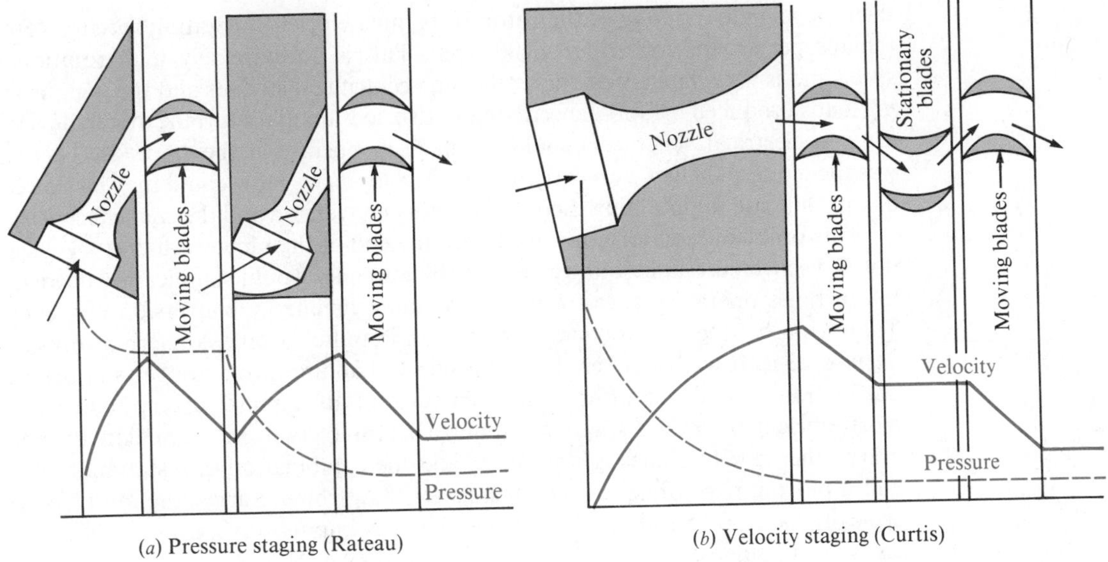

(*a*) Pressure staging (Rateau)

(*b*) Velocity staging (Curtis)

Figure 8.13 Pressure (Rateau) and velocity (Curtis) staging in the DeLaval impulse turbine.

vanes to a different mean velocity, and also had the effect of slowing down an impulse turbine while maintaining its energy conversion efficiency. Rateau staging exposes each row of moving blades to nearly constant pressure, and this is usually called *pressure compounding*, or *pressure staging*. Curtis staging exposes each row of stationary blades to nearly constant velocity, and this is usually called *velocity compounding*, or *velocity staging*. Figure 8.13 illustrates these impulse turbine staging concepts.

The practice of putting several different constant pressure stages in series in a reaction turbine was introduced in 1884 by the Englishman Charles Algernon Parsons (1854–1931). His first turbine had 14 stages (14 pairs of stationary and moving blade rows) and produced about 10 hp at 18,000 rpm. This was still too fast for direct coupling to the existing electrical generators, so Parsons designed a new high-speed generator that could be driven directly by his turbine.

By the early twentieth century the pressure and velocity staged DeLaval impulse turbine and the multiple pressure staged Parsons reaction turbine became nearly equal rivals in terms of cost and efficiency. There was a lot at stake at this point in time because electrical power generation was just coming into existence, and it was clear that it had the potential for creating a second Industrial Revolution based on electricity rather than steam.

Thomas Alva Edison's (1847–1931) development of a practical electric light bulb in 1879 opened the doors of a remarkable new technology, electricity. To make his light bulb marketable he had to develop and produce a means of putting electricity directly into the home. He had to conceive and build an entire electrical power plant and electrical distribution network. This he did, and in 1882 he opened

the Pearl Street power station in New York City, the first such station in the world. By 1890 several electrical power stations were in place in major cities across the United States, and they were rapidly growing in size and complexity. Initially, reciprocating steam engines drove the electrical generators, but it became clear rather quickly that this type of prime mover was not going to be able to meet the needs of this growing industry for very long. Reciprocating steam engines were too slow, too large, and too unreliable to carry the burden. The steam turbine was cultivated as a viable replacement prime mover.

By 1900 the Westinghouse Electric Company was manufacturing multistage reaction steam turbines of the Parson's type for the electrical power generation industry, and the General Electric Company was developing an impulse turbine of the DeLaval type with Curtis velocity staging for the same market.

Thus, the search for a suitable prime mover for large-scale electrical generators was the motivation that led to the successful commercial development of the steam turbine. Though early steam turbines were actually less energy efficient than their reciprocating counterparts, their potential for improvement was enormous. In addition, they were about *ten times smaller* than a reciprocating engine with the same power output. Also, even very large steam turbines could be made to run efficiently at generator speeds (1800 or 3600 rpm), they were quiet and they required little maintenance. It was for these reasons, not the reasons of improved thermal or mechanical efficiency, that by 1920 the steam turbine had replaced virtually all large-scale reciprocating steam engines.[26]

The Rankine Cycle with Reheat

By 1920 boiler technology had advanced to the point where steam at 650 °F, 250 psia was generally available. In the early 1920s the regenerative process, initially developed in the late 1890s to improve the thermal efficiency of reciprocating steam engines, was reintroduced as a means of improving steam turbine power plant thermal efficiency. Regeneration using steam turbine prime movers required that steam be extracted from between one or more of the turbine stages and used to preheat the boiler feedwater. During the 1920s boiler technology continued to increase rapidly and by 1930 steam was commonly supplied at 725 °F and 550 psia. This lead to the commercial use of steam *reheat*, in which steam is extracted from the outlet of a turbine stage, returned to the boiler to be reheated, and then brought back to the inlet of the next turbine stage for further expansion.[27] This prevents excessive moisture levels from occurring in the low-pressure stages and it also has the effect of slightly increasing the thermal efficiency of the cycle. A simple power plant utilizing reheat (but no regeneration) is shown schematically in Figure 8.14.

26. By 1960 virtually all small- and medium-scale reciprocating steam engines had been replaced by electric motors or internal combustion engines.

27. After its introduction in the mid 1920s, reheat technology became unpopular during the depression due to technical and economic difficulties. Single reheat cycles were again introduced in the 1940s and double reheat cycles were introduced in the 1950s.

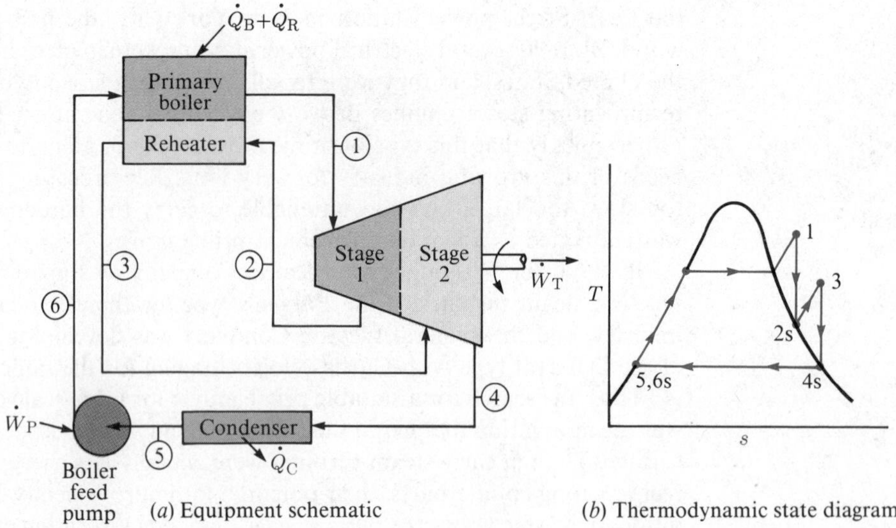

Figure 8.14 A Rankine cycle power plant with reheat.

The thermal efficiency of the Rankine cycle power plant with reheat shown in Figure 8.14 can be computed from the general thermal efficiency definition as

$$(\eta_T)_{\substack{\text{Rankine}\\ \text{cycle with}\\ \text{one reheat unit}}} = \frac{|\dot{W}_{pm}| - |\dot{W}_p|}{\dot{Q}_B + \dot{Q}_R} = \frac{(h_1 - h_2) + (h_3 - h_4) - (h_6 - h_5)}{(h_1 - h_6) + (h_3 - h_2)}$$

and if the liquid condensate is considered to be incompressible, then Eq. 8.7*b* can be used to give

$$(\eta_T)_{\substack{\text{Rankine}\\ \text{cycle with}\\ \text{one reheat unit}}} = \frac{(h_1 - h_2) + (h_3 - h_4) - v_5(p_6 - p_5)/(\eta_s)_p}{(h_1 - h_6) + (h_3 - h_2)}$$

where $(\eta_s)_p$ is the isentropic efficiency of the boiler feed pump. Using Eq. 8.4*a* we can introduce the isentropic efficiencies of the two turbine stages $(\eta_s)_{pm1}$ and $(\eta_s)_{pm2}$ as

$$(\eta_s)_{pm1} = \frac{h_1 - h_2}{h_1 - h_{2s}} \tag{8.13}$$

and

$$(\eta_s)_{pm2} = \frac{h_3 - h_4}{h_3 - h_{4s}} \tag{8.14}$$

Finally, the thermal efficiency of the cycle can be written as

$$(\eta_T)_{\substack{\text{Rankine}\\ \text{cycle with}\\ \text{one reheat unit}}} = \frac{(h_1 - h_{2s})(\eta_s)_{pm1} + (h_3 - h_{4s})(\eta_s)_{pm2} - v_5(p_6 - p_5)/(\eta_s)_p}{(h_1 - h_6) + (h_3 - h_2)} \quad \textbf{(8.15)}$$

where the values of h_2 and h_6 in the denominator of this equation are calculated from Eqs. 8.13 and 8.7*b* as

$$h_2 = h_1 - (h_1 - h_{2s})(\eta_s)_{pm1} \quad \textbf{(8.16)}$$

and

$$h_6 = h_5 + v_5(p_6 - p_5)/(\eta_s)_p \quad \textbf{(8.17)}$$

Example 8.5

The First Rankine cycle steam turbine prime mover with reheat used in the United States was at the Crawford Avenue power station of the Commonwealth Edison Company of Chicago, Illinois, which went into operation in September 1924. The primary steam was at 700 °F, 600 psia, with reheat to 700 °F at 100 psia. The isentropic efficiencies of the first and second turbine stages and of the boiler feed pump were 84, 80, and 61%, respectively. The condenser pressure was 1.0 psia with saturated liquid being produced at its outlet.

Determine

a) the isentropic Rankine cycle thermal efficiency of the plant with reheat, and

b) the isentropic Rankine cycle thermal efficiency of the plant without reheat (assume a turbine isentropic efficiency of 82% for this calculation).

Solution

a) Using the notation of Figure 8.14, the monitoring station data for this problem are

Station 1	Station 2s
$p_1 = 600$ psia	$p_{2s} = p_2 = 100$ psia
$T_1 = 700$ °F	$s_{2s} = s_1 = 1.5874$ Btu/(lbm·R)
$h_1 = 1350.6$ Btu/lbm	$x_{2s} = 0.9856$
$s_1 = 1.5874$ Btu/(lbm·R)	$h_{2s} = 1175.0$ Btu/lbm

Station 3	Station 4s
$p_3 = p_{2s} = 100$ psia	$p_{4s} = p_4 = 1.0$ psia
$T_3 = 700$ °F	$s_{4s} = s_3 = 1.8035$ Btu/(lbm·R)
$h_3 = 1379.2$ Btu/lbm	$x_{4s} = 0.9054$
$s_3 = 1.8035$ Btu/(lbm·R)	$h_{4s} = 1007.7$ Btu/lbm

Station 5	**Station 6s**
$p_5 = 1.0$ psia	$p_{6s} = p_6 = 600$ psia
$x_5 = 0.0$	$s_{6s} = s_5 = 0.1326$ Btu/(lbm·R)
$h_5 = 69.7$ Btu/lbm	$h_6 = 72.5$ Btu/lbm
$s_5 = 0.1326$ Btu/(lbm·R)	

where the following calculations have been used

$$x_{2s} = \frac{s_{2s} - s_{f2}}{s_{fg2}} = \frac{s_1 - s_{f2}}{s_{fg2}} = \frac{1.5874 - 0.4745}{1.1291} = 0.9856$$

Then,

$$h_{2s} = h_{f2} + x_{2s}(h_{fg2}) = 298.6 + (0.9856)(889.2) = 1175.0 \text{ Btu/lbm}$$

$$x_{4s} = \frac{s_3 - s_{f4}}{s_{fg4}} = \frac{1.8035 - 0.1326}{1.8455} = 0.9054$$

and then,

$$h_{4s} = h_{f4} + x_{4s}(h_{fg4}) = 69.7 + (0.9054)(1036.0) = 1007.7 \text{ Btu/lbm}$$

Since $v_5 = v_f(1.0 \text{ psia}) = 0.01614 \text{ ft}^3\text{/lbm}$, Eqs. 8.16 and 8.17 can now be used to give

$$h_2 = 1350.6 - (0.84)(1350.6 - 1175.0) = 1203.1 \text{ Btu/lbm}$$

and

$$h_6 = 69.7 + (0.01614)(600 - 1.0)(144/778)/(0.61)$$
$$= 69.7 + 2.9 = 72.6 \text{ Btu/lbm}$$

Then, finally, Eq. 8.15 yields

$$\eta_T = \frac{(1350.6 - 1175.0)(0.84) + (1379.2 - 1007.7)(0.80) - 2.9}{(1350.6 - 72.6) + (1379.2 - 1203.1)}$$
$$= 0.304 = 30.4\%$$

b) Here we will remove the reheat loop by simply eliminating the pipes with monitoring stations 2 and 3 in Figure 8.14. The power plant's thermal efficiency becomes

$$\eta_T = \frac{(h_1 - h_{4s})(\eta_s)_{pm} - (h_{6s} - h_5)/(\eta_s)_p}{h_1 - h_6}$$

where all the enthalpy values are the same as they were in part a except for h_{4s}. Here, $s_{4s} = s_1$, and

$$x_{4s} = \frac{s_1 - s_{f4}}{s_{fg4}} = \frac{1.5874 - 0.1326}{1.8455} = 0.7883$$

so

$$h_{4s} = 69.7 + (0.7883)(1036.0) = 886.4 \text{ Btu/lbm}$$

Then,

$$\eta_T = \frac{(1350.6 - 886.4)(0.82) - 2.9}{1350.6 - 72.6} = 0.296 = 29.6\%$$

Note that the interstage reheating used in this example only increased the isentropic Rankine cycle thermal efficiency by 0.8%. However, it had the much more important effect of reducing the moisture content at the turbine exit. Wet steam with a moisture content of more than 8 to 10% can produce serious blade erosion problems in the low-pressure region of a turbine. The effect of reheating in this example kept the exit moisture level within this range, whereas without reheating part b of the example shows that the exit moisture level would have been (1 – 0.7883)(100) = 21.2%, which is much too high.

Modern Steam Power Plants

In the years since the 1930s the advancements in boiler technology have been as dramatic as those in turbine technology.[28] Turbine inlet pressures and temperatures continued to increase over the years mainly due to significant improvements in high-temperature strength properties of various metal alloys. The simultaneous use of superheat, reheat, and regeneration, along with improved turbine isentropic and mechanical efficiencies at higher turbine inlet temperatures and pressures allowed actual operating power station thermal efficiencies to reach percentages in the low 40s by the 1980s (see Figure 8.8). In the 1930s, the turbine–generator unit output reached 200 MW, and by the 1970s it had reached 1000 MW. Figure 8.15 shows the Wisconsin Electric Power Company's Pleasant Prairie Power Plant which went into operation in 1985.

28. Between 1898 and 1902 there were 1600 boiler explosions in the United States in which 1184 people were killed. On March 10, 1905, a boiler explosion in a shoe factory in Brockton, MA, killed 58 people and injured an additional 117 people, and on December 6, 1906, a similar explosion occurred in a shoe factory in Lynn, MA. As a result of the ensuing public outcry, the state of Massachusetts enacted the first legal code of rules for the construction of steam boilers in 1907. From 1908 to 1910 Ohio and various other states enacted similar legislation, but because no two states had exactly the same code, boiler manufacturers had great difficulty in satisfying all the varying and occasionally conflicting rules. In 1911 the American Society of Mechanical Engineers (ASME) joined with the boiler manufacturers to formulate a set of uniform standards for the design and construction of safe boilers. The first edition of the resulting ASME Boiler and Pressure Vessel Code was produced in 1914, and by the 1930s many advancements in boiler technology had been made. An updated and modernized version of this code is used throughout industry today.

Figure 8.15 Wisconsin Electric Power Company Pleasant Prairie Power Plant. Used with permission. *Source*: Courtesy of the Wisconsin Electric Power Company.

Modern power plant performance can be expressed in four different ways.

1. The actual thermal efficiency $(\eta_T)_{actual}$, where

$$(\eta_T)_{actual} = (|\dot{W}_{out}|_{net}/\dot{Q}_{in})_{actual}$$

2. A similar performance measure, the *heat rate* of the power plant, which is defined to be the inverse of the thermal efficiency, but in mixed units (e.g., Btu/(kW·h)). These two measures are related by

$$\text{heat rate in Btu/(kW}\cdot\text{h)} = \frac{3412 \text{ Btu/(kW}\cdot\text{h)}}{(\eta_T)_{actual}}$$

where the decimal form (*not* percent) of $(\eta_T)_{actual}$ is used.

3. The actual steam flow rate divided by the actual plant electrical output power, $\dot{m}_{steam}/|\dot{W}|_{elect}$, in mixed units of (lbm steam)/(kW·h).

4. The ratio of the actual thermal efficiency of the power plant to the isentropic Rankine cycle thermal efficiency, $(\eta_T)_{actual}/(\eta_T)_{isentropic}$. This ratio is often expressed as a percentage and is commonly called by the misleading term, *engine efficiency*. More accurately, it is an overall heat engine *thermal efficiency ratio*. Typical values of this ratio are shown in Figure 8.16.

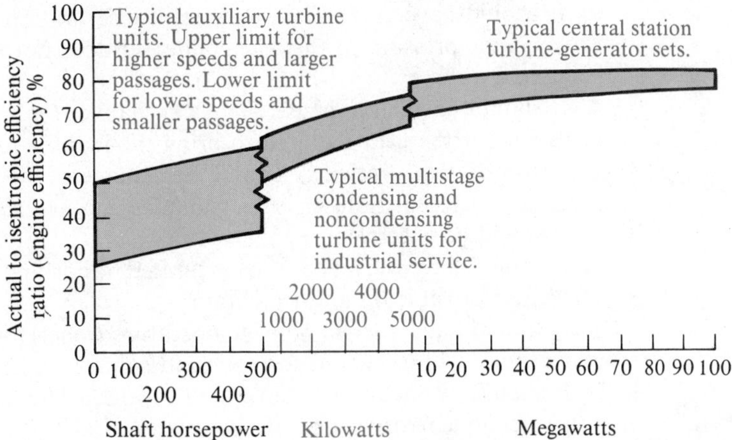

Figure 8.16 Representative power plant actual to isentropic efficiency ratios for some selected steam turbine units. From *Steam, Its Generation and Use*. New York: Babcock & Wilcox, 1963 (with permission). *Source*: Reprinted from *Steam, Its Generation and Use*, 37th ed. (New Orleans: Babcock and Wilcox, 1963), chapter 10, Figure 16 (representative engine efficiencies for some selected steam turbine units), by permission of Babcock and Wilcox, a McDermott company.

By the 1930s it had been realized that water was not necessarily the best working fluid for a vapor cycle heat engine. Since the deviations between the Carnot cycle and the isentropic Rankine cycle are due to the characteristics of the working fluid, then, clearly, the *ideal* working fluid for a heat engine should make the Rankine cycle as close to the Carnot cycle as possible. More specifically, the ideal working fluid should have the following characteristics (see Figure. 8.17):

1. It should have a critical temperature well above the metallurgical limit of the boiler and turbine so that efficient isothermal high-temperature heat transfer can occur in the boiler.
2. It should have a relatively low saturation vapor pressure at high temperatures so that high mechanical stresses are not produced in the boiler or turbine.

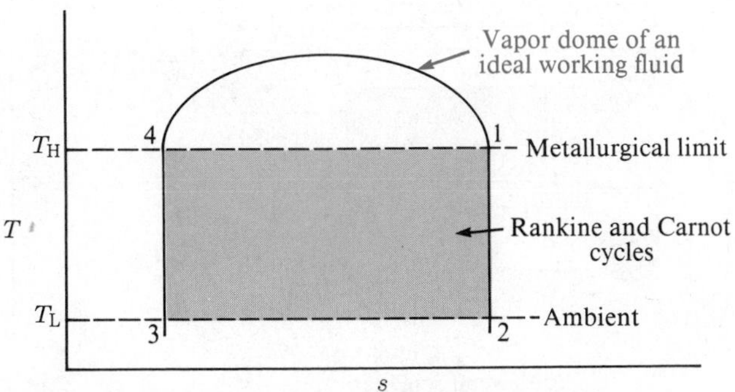

Figure 8.17 The Rankine cycle with the ideal working fluid becomes a Carnot cycle.

3. It should have an ambient temperature saturation pressure slightly above atmospheric pressure so that the condenser does not have to be operated at a vacuum.
4. It should have large phase change enthalpies (h_{fg}) and low liquid specific heats so that the heat required to bring the liquid condensate up to the vaporization temperature is a small percentage of the vaporization heat (this reduces boiler heat transfer irreversibilities and assures that regeneration devices will be effective).
5. It should have the slope of its saturated vapor and liquid lines as nearly vertical as possible on a T-s diagram.
6. It should have a triple-point temperature well below the ambient temperature to prevent the formation of solids (i.e., freezing) within the system.
7. It should be chemically stable (i.e., not dissociate at high temperatures), nontoxic, noncorrosive, and inexpensive.

No known fluid meets all seven of these conditions quite as well as water. But other fluids meet some of these conditions significantly better than water. For example, the critical state of mercury is at 1649 °F and 2646 psia, which meets item 1 much better than water, whose critical state is 705 °F and 3204 psia. However, the saturation pressure of mercury at 100 °F is a very high vacuum (thus violating item 3). At 1000 °F the saturation pressure of mercury is about 180 psia, which makes it attractive for use in a dual working fluid, or *binary cycle* system as shown in Figure 8.18. Here the mercury condenser also serves as the steam generator, and the combined binary cycle thermal efficiency is much higher (percentages in the mid 50s for isentropic systems) than either one operating alone (percentages in the mid 30s for isentropic systems).

Between the 1930s and 1960s several mercury–water binary cycle power plants were put into commercial operation. But, despite their superior thermal efficiencies, the problems of high initial cost, mercury toxicity, and numerous operating and maintenance problems prevented such plants from being commercially successful. However, the use of two or more different working fluids within the same

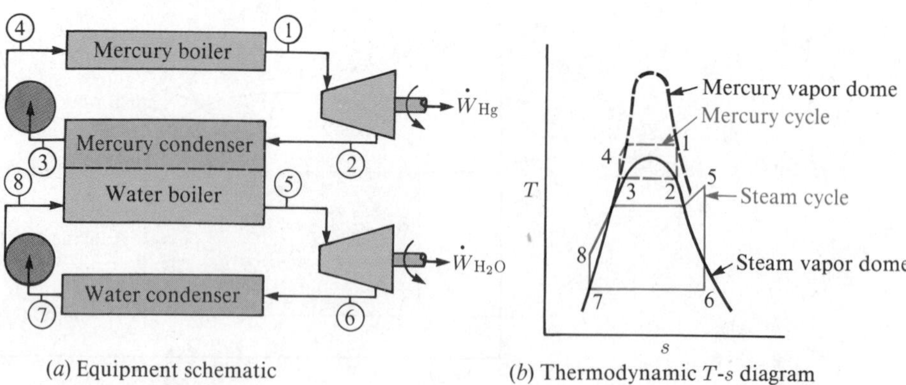

(*a*) Equipment schematic (*b*) Thermodynamic T-s diagram

Figure 8.18 A mercury–water binary power plant.

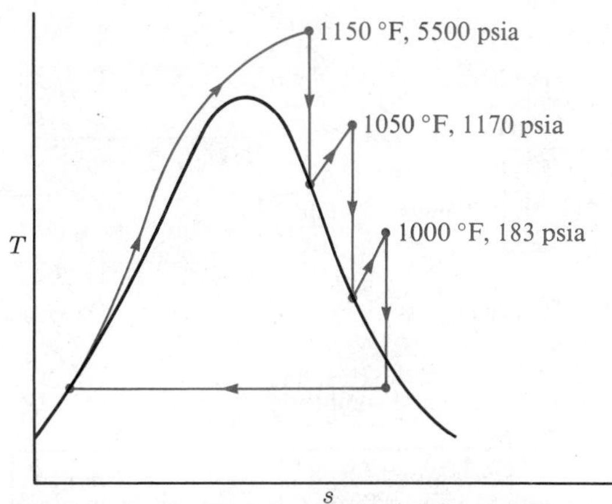

Figure 8.19 A supercritical Rankine cycle with two stages of reheat put into operation in 1957.

power plant still holds promise for significantly improving overall thermal performance in the future.

The 1950s saw the introduction of supercritical pressure power plants with boiler pressures as high as 5500 psia at 1150 °F. Figure 8.19 illustrates a supercritical Rankine cycle with two stages of reheat. However, the high operating and maintenance costs of supercritical plants often offset the cost benefits due to their increased thermal efficiencies.

The introduction of nuclear power in the 1960s added a new facet to heat source technology. Nuclear safety restrictions required the use of a double-loop heat transfer system to keep the radioactive reactor cooling fluid from entering the turbine, and this effectively limited the maximum nuclear power plant secondary loop temperature and pressure to around 1000 °F and 800 psia. This had the effect of limiting nuclear plant thermal efficiencies to percentages in the low 30s, while the thermal efficiencies of conventional fossil fueled plants reached percentages in the low 40s.

Gas Power Cycles

Heat engines whose working fluid is a gas, rather than a vapor, undergo gas power thermodynamic cycles. Like steam power, gas prime movers fall into two broad mechanical design categories, reciprocating and turbine. In addition, unlike steam power prime movers, they fall into two heat source categories, external combustion (EC) and internal combustion (IC). In external combustion engines the working fluid does not enter into the combustion process. Combustion, if it occurs at all,[29] occurs outside the engine with the resulting heat being transferred into the working fluid at some point. All steam engines, therefore, are external combustion prime movers. Since the working fluid of an internal combustion engine always enters

29. A nuclear reactor is an example of a heat source that does not involve chemical combustion.

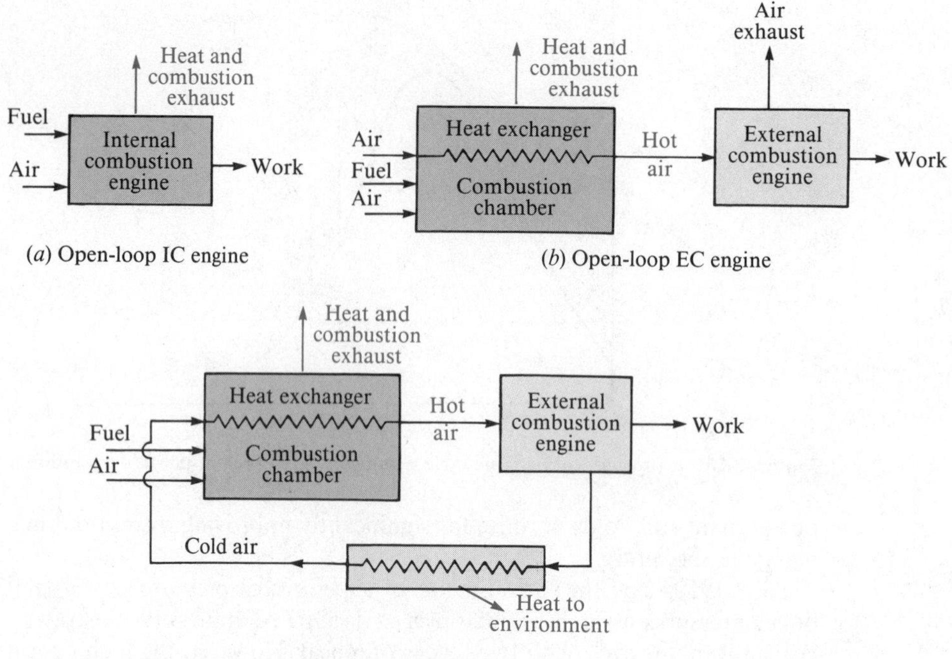

Figure 8.20 Internal and external combustion engine thermodynamic loop classifications.

into the heat generating combustion process, thus depleting the fuel and oxygen supply of the working fluid, the combustion products must be removed and fresh fuel and oxygen added during each thermodynamic cycle. Consequently, all internal combustion engines operate on an open loop process, whereas external combustion engines can operate on either an open loop or a closed loop process (see Figure 8.20).

Gas power cycle prime movers (engines) developed slightly later than their steam engine counterparts. They evolved largely as an alternative to steam power technology, and by 1900 they were already very competitive with small to medium power steam engines. By the mid twentieth century they had replaced all steam power within the transportation industry and the small to medium electrical generating industry, leaving only large electrical power plants as the major commercial users of steam.

Air Standard Power Cycles

Most modern gas power cycles involve the use of open-loop internal or external combustion engines. The working fluid has highly variable physical and chemical properties throughout these engines, and this makes their thermodynamic cycle very difficult to analyze. Since the most abundant chemical constituent of the working fluid of air-breathing engines is nitrogen, which is largely chemically inert within the engine, it is possible to devise an effective *closed-loop* engine model in which air alone is considered to be the working fluid. Such an approximation to real engine thermodynamics is called the *air standard cycle*, or ASC for short. The

ASC allows a simple but highly idealized closed-loop thermodynamic analysis to be carried out on an otherwise very complex open-loop system. The assumptions embodied in an ASC analysis of an IC or EC engine are as follows:

1. The engine operates on a closed-loop thermodynamic cycle and the working fluid is a fixed mass of atmospheric air.
2. This air behaves as an ideal gas throughout the cycle.
3. The combustion process within the engine is replaced by a simple heat addition process from an external heat source.
4. The intake and exhaust processes of the engine are replaced by an external heat rejection process to the environment.
5. All processes within the thermodynamic cycle are assumed to be reversible.

Note that item 5 implies that all processes within a cycle that do not have any associated heat transfer are also isentropic processes (i.e., they are reversible *and* adiabatic). Since the numerical results of an analysis using the ASC will depend upon how the ideal gas specific heat issue is handled, an ASC analysis is further characterized as either a *cold air standard cycle* if the specific heats of air are assumed to be constant and are evaluated at room temperature, or a *hot air standard cycle* if the specific heats of air are assumed to be temperature dependent.[30]

An IC or EC engine operating on an ASC can be represented schematically as shown in Figure 8.21. Since the actual operating thermal efficiency of an IC engine is often compared to its ideal ASC thermal efficiency to evaluate the impact of real world irreversibilities on the engine's performance, the ASC analysis then serves the same type of idealized benchmark comparison function as did the isentropic Rankine cycle analysis of vapor power cycles.

If the working fluid in the Carnot cycle shown in Figure 8.22 is air (functioning as an ideal gas), then we would have a Carnot ASC. Since (by definition) a Carnot cycle is thermodynamically reversible, then, using the notation of Figure 8.22, $s_1 = s_2$ and $s_3 = s_4$.

Isentropic ideal gas compression and expansion processes with constant specific heats were discussed in Chapter 5, and the *p-v-T* relation for these processes is given by Eq. 5.38 as

$$s_1 = s_2$$

$$\frac{T_{2s}}{T_1} = \left(\frac{p_{2s}}{p_1}\right)^{(k-1)/k} = \left(\frac{v_{2s}}{v_1}\right)^{1-k}$$

$$s_3 = s_4$$

$$\frac{T_3}{T_{4s}} = \left(\frac{p_3}{p_{4s}}\right)^{(k-1)/k} = \left(\frac{v_3}{v_{4s}}\right)^{1-k}$$

30. When a more complex analysis is done in which the actual fuel–air mixture and exhaust gases are used, it is usually called a *real mixture standard cycle*.

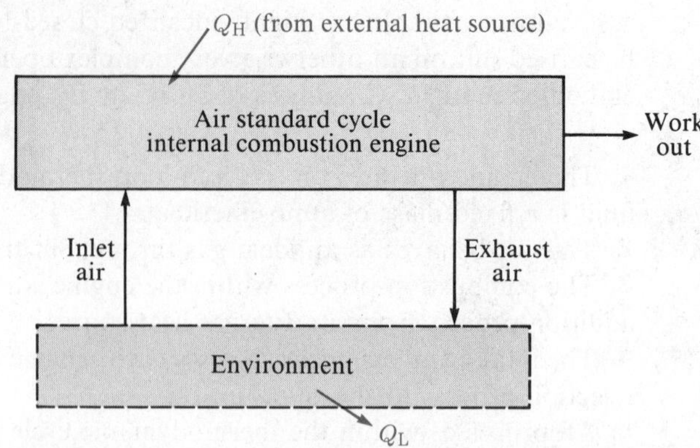

Figure 8.21 Schematic of an IC or EC engine operating on a closed-loop air standard cycle (ASC).

where

$$T_1 = T_{4s} = T_H \quad \text{and} \quad T_{2s} = T_3 = T_L$$

and we further define

a) $v_{2s}/v_1 = v_3/v_{4s}$ = isentropic compression ratio, CR

and

b) $p_1/p_{2s} = p_{4s}/p_3$ = isentropic pressure ratio, PR

The equation for the thermal efficiency of the Carnot cold ASC can now be written as

$$(\eta_T)_{\substack{\text{Carnot}\\ \text{cold ASC}}} = 1 - T_L/T_H = 1 - \text{PR}^{(1-k)/k} = 1 - \text{CR}^{1-k} \qquad \textbf{(8.18)}$$

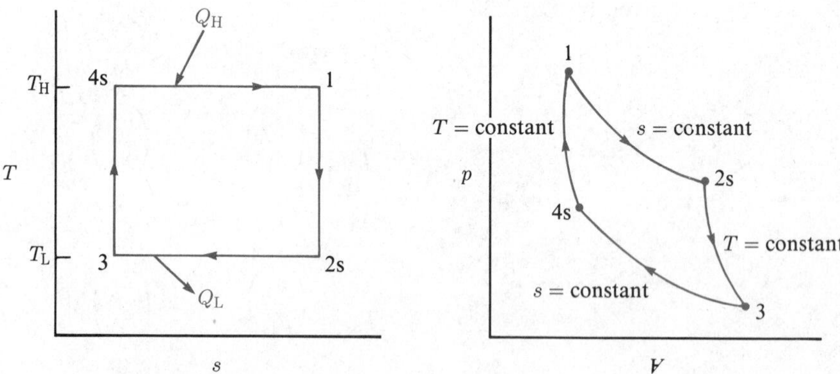

Figure 8.22 The Carnot air standard cycle.

which shows that it can be written directly in terms of either the temperature ratio, pressure ratio, or compression (volume) ratio.

Most vapor power cycles fall at least partially under the vapor dome and can therefore be modeled with a single practical thermodynamic cycle, the Rankine cycle. Unfortunately, outside the vapor dome no one thermodynamic cycle models all possible practical gas power cycles. In the next sections we will discuss a few commercially valuable gas power cycles and evaluate their ASC thermal efficiencies. While these cycles do not cover all possible cycles, they are the ones that have had significant economic success over the years. We will discuss them in the chronological order in which they were developed.

The Stirling Cycle

Many early steam boilers exploded because of weak materials, faulty design, and poor construction. The resulting loss in human life and property inspired many people to attempt to develop engines that did not need a high-pressure boiler. In 1816 the Scottish clergyman Robert Stirling (1790–1878) patented a remarkable closed-loop external combustion engine in which a fixed mass of air passed through a thermodynamic cycle composed of two isothermal processes and two isochoric (constant volume) processes. Figure 8.23 shows the *T*-*s* and *p*-*V* diagrams for this cycle, along with an equipment schematic.

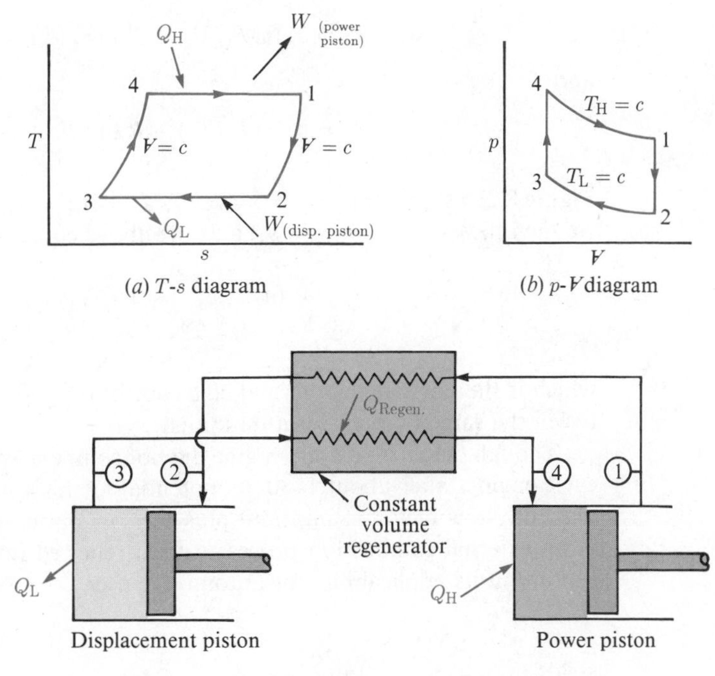

Figure 8.23 The Stirling cycle (1816).

Stirling's engine was remarkable, not only in its mechanical and thermodynamic complexity, but also because he originated a thermal regeneration process in which the heat released during the isochoric expansion process from state 1 to state 2 is stored within the system (in the regenerator) and then reintroduced into the working fluid (air) during the isochoric compression process from state 3 to state 4. This was the first use of thermal regeneration in a power cycle, and predates its use in steam engines by many years.[31] The complexity of construction and high costs limited production of Stirling's engine to small units (0.5 to 10 hp). They were generally known as *hot air* engines, and found extensive use on small farms between 1820 and 1920 for pumping water and other light duties.

The thermal efficiency of the Stirling cycle is given by

$$(\eta_T)_{\text{Stirling}} = \frac{|\dot{W}_{\text{out}}|_{\text{net}}}{\dot{Q}_H} = \frac{\dot{Q}_H - |\dot{Q}_L|}{\dot{Q}_H} = 1 - \frac{|\dot{Q}_L|}{\dot{Q}_H}$$

where (see Figure 8.23*a*) for a reversible ASC engine we can write

$$\dot{Q}_H = \dot{m}T_H(s_1 - s_4) \quad \text{and} \quad |\dot{Q}_L| = \dot{m}T_L(s_2 - s_3)$$

These entropy changes can be evaluated for the cold ASC by using Eq. 5.36 of Chapter 5 as

$$s_1 - s_4 = c_v \ln(T_1/T_4) + R\ln(v_1/v_4) = R\ln(v_1/v_4)$$

and

$$s_2 - s_3 = c_v \ln(T_2/T_3) + R\ln(v_2/v_3) = R\ln(v_2/v_3)$$

Figure 8.23*b* shows that $T_2 = T_3 = T_L$, $T_1 = T_4 = T_H$, and $v_2/v_3 = v_1/v_4$, so that we then have $s_1 - s_4 = s_2 - s_3$, and the above equations give

$$(\eta_T)_{\substack{\text{Stirling}\\ \text{cold ASC}}} = 1 - T_L/T_H \qquad \textbf{(8.19)}$$

which is the same as the thermal efficiency of the Carnot cold ASC operating between the same two temperature limits.

Though the Stirling cycle engine did not compete well with alternate gas power cycle engines after about 1880, its potential for high thermal efficiency (and consequently low fuel consumption) plus the low noise and low air pollution traits of an external combustion process caused renewed interest in the late twentieth century in its applicability for automotive use.

---

31. Note that this is a completely different type of "regeneration" than used with the Rankine vapor cycle.

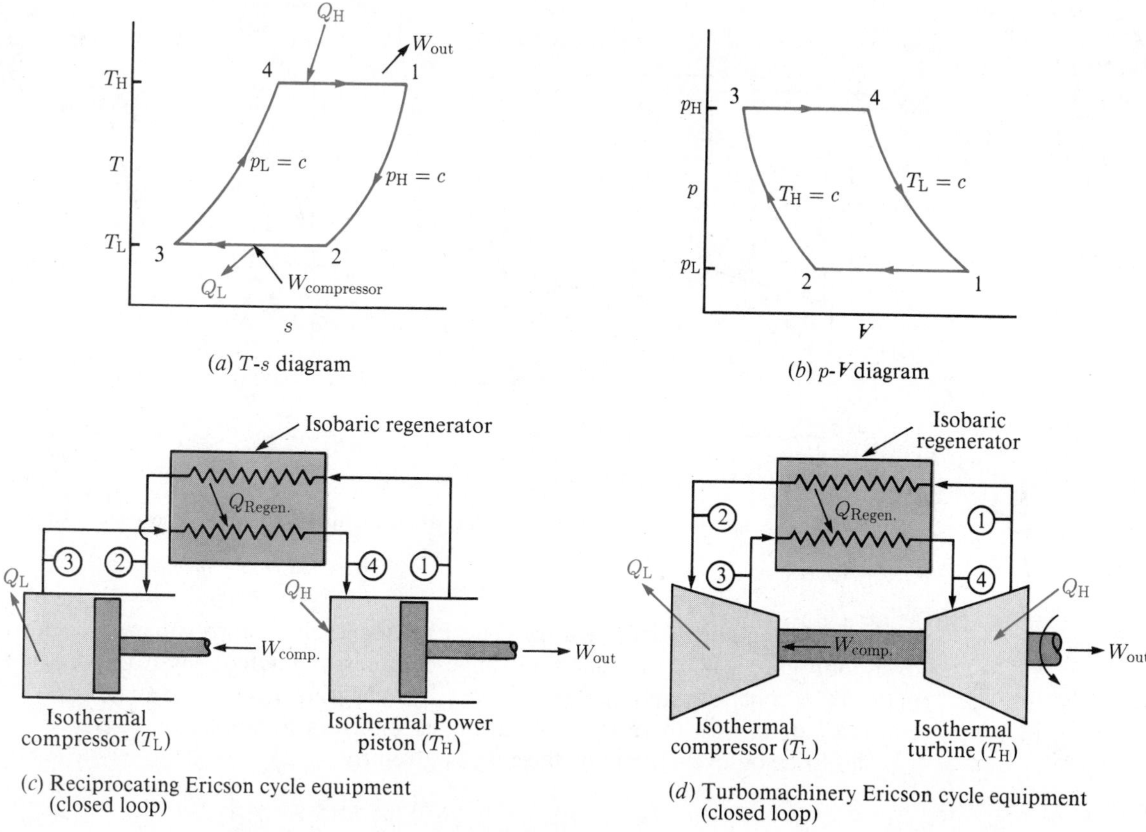

Figure 8.24 The Ericsson cycle (1833).

The Ericsson Cycle

In 1833 the Swedish born engineer John Ericsson (1803–1889) developed a different type of hot air reciprocating external combustion engine that could operate on either an open- or a closed-loop cycle. Ericsson's engine also used a thermal regenerator, but it differed from Stirling's in that the constant volume regeneration process was replaced by a constant pressure regeneration process. Thus the Ericsson cycle consists of two isothermal processes and two isobaric (constant pressure) processes, as shown in Figure 8.24.

In 1839 Ericsson moved to America and continued to develop his engine. His large engines (up to 300 hp, with pistons 14 ft in diameter) were very inefficient and could not compete economically with existing steam engine technology. However, his small engines were reasonably successful and several thousand were sold by 1860. By 1880 the popularity of his engine had dropped off and it was considered to be obsolete technology until modern gas turbine power plants came into

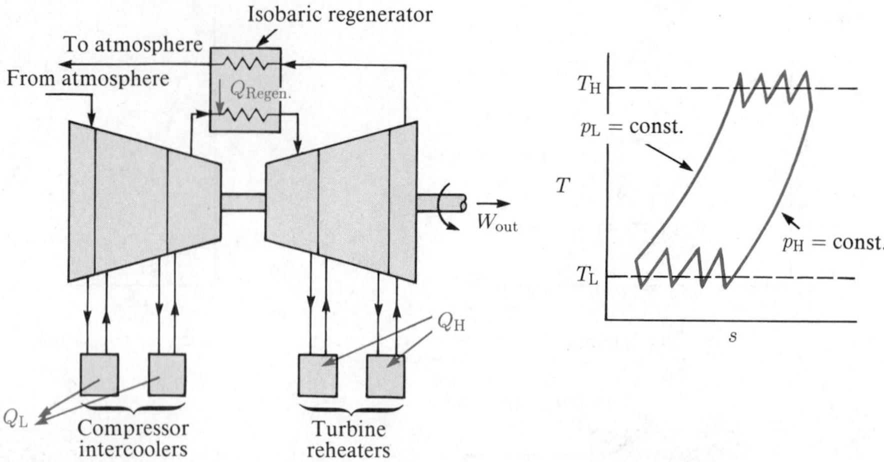

Figure 8.25 An open-loop gas turbine power plant as an approximation to the Ericsson cycle.

being in the mid twentieth century. The Ericsson cycle is approximated by an open-loop gas turbine that has multistage compressor intercooling (to approximate T_L = constant) and multistage turbine reheating (to approximate T_H = constant) along with thermal regeneration, as shown in Figure 8.25.

The Ericsson cycle thermal efficiency is given by

$$(\eta_T)_{\text{Ericsson}} = \frac{|\dot{W}_{\text{out}}|_{\text{net}}}{\dot{Q}_H} = \frac{\dot{Q}_H - |\dot{Q}_L|}{\dot{Q}_H} = 1 - \frac{|\dot{Q}_L|}{\dot{Q}_H}$$

where (see Figure 8.24*a*), for a reversible ASC engine we can write

$$\dot{Q}_H = \dot{m}T_H(s_1 - s_4) \quad \text{and} \quad |\dot{Q}_L| = \dot{m}T_L(s_2 - s_3)$$

Equation 5.37 of Chapter 5 gives these entropy changes for the cold ASC as

$$s_1 - s_4 = c_p \ln(T_1/T_4) - R\ln(p_1/p_4) = -R\ln(p_1/p_4)$$

and

$$s_2 - s_3 = c_p \ln(T_2/T_3) - R\ln(p_2/p_3) = -R\ln(p_2/p_3)$$

Figure 8.24*b* shows that $T_2 = T_3 = T_L$, $T_1 = T_4 = T_H$, and $p_1/p_4 = p_2/p_3$, so that the previous equations yields $s_1 - s_4 = s_2 - s_3$, and the thermal efficiency becomes

$$(\eta_T)_{\substack{\text{Ericsson}\\ \text{cold ASC}}} = 1 - T_L/T_H \tag{8.20}$$

Thus, like the Stirling cold ASC, the Ericsson cold ASC has the same thermal efficiency as the Carnot cold ASC operating between the same two temperature limits.[32]

The Lenoir Cycle

Both the Stirling and the Ericsson cycles are external combustion with thermal regeneration. Initially, an appropriately sized furnace was used as their heat source. This made these engines rather large and awkward, and despite the fact that they could theoretically achieve high (reversible) thermal efficiencies, the mechanical and thermal irreversibilities of the early engines were very large and consequently they had rather low actual operating thermal efficiencies. In 1860 the French engineer Jean Joseph Etienne Lenoir (1822–1900) made the first commercially successful internal combustion engine. He converted a reciprocating steam engine to admit a mixture of air and methane during the first half of the piston's outward (suction) stroke, at which point it was ignited with an electric spark and the resulting combustion pressure acted on the piston for the remainder of the outward (expansion) stroke. The following inward stroke of the piston was used to expel the exhaust gases, and then the cycle began over again. This cycle is (ideally) composed of only three effective processes: constant volume (combustion), constant entropy (power), and constant pressure (exhaust), as shown in Figure 8.26.

The fuel–air mixture was ignited by an electric spark inside the cylinder. The spark was generated by a battery and an induction coil, which was basically the same technique used with all spark ignition engines through the middle of the twentieth century.

The Lenoir engine ran smoothly, but because the air–fuel mixture was not compressed before ignition the engine had a very low actual thermal efficiency (less than 4%).[33] Consequently, Lenoir engines became popular only in small sizes (0.5 to 3 hp) because their fuel comsumption was very high.

The thermal efficiency of the Lenoir cycle is given by

$$(\eta_T)_{\text{Lenoir}} = \frac{|\dot{W}_{\text{out}}|_{\text{net}}}{\dot{Q}_H} = \frac{\dot{Q}_H - |\dot{Q}_L|}{\dot{Q}_H} = 1 - \frac{|\dot{Q}_L|}{\dot{Q}_H}$$

where, from Figure 8.26*a*, for a cold ASC with an isentropic expansion from 1 to 2s we have

$$\begin{aligned} |\dot{Q}_L| = |{}_{2s}\dot{Q}_3| &= \dot{m}(u_{2s} - u_3) + \dot{m}p(v_{2s} - v_3) \\ &= \dot{m}(h_{2s} - h_3) = \dot{m}c_p(T_{2s} - T_3) \end{aligned}$$

---

32. The Stirling and Ericsson cycle engines of the nineteenth century were large and costly, and their actual operating thermal efficiencies were quite poor. They were ultimately replaced by a newer and more efficient engine technology introduced in the second half of the nineteenth century, the internal combustion Otto and Diesel cycles discussed later in this chapter. However, the high thermal efficiency potential of the Stirling and Ericsson cycles produces periodically renewed interest in utilizing these cycles within the framework of modern technology.

33. These engines were often called *atmospheric* gas engines for the same reason.

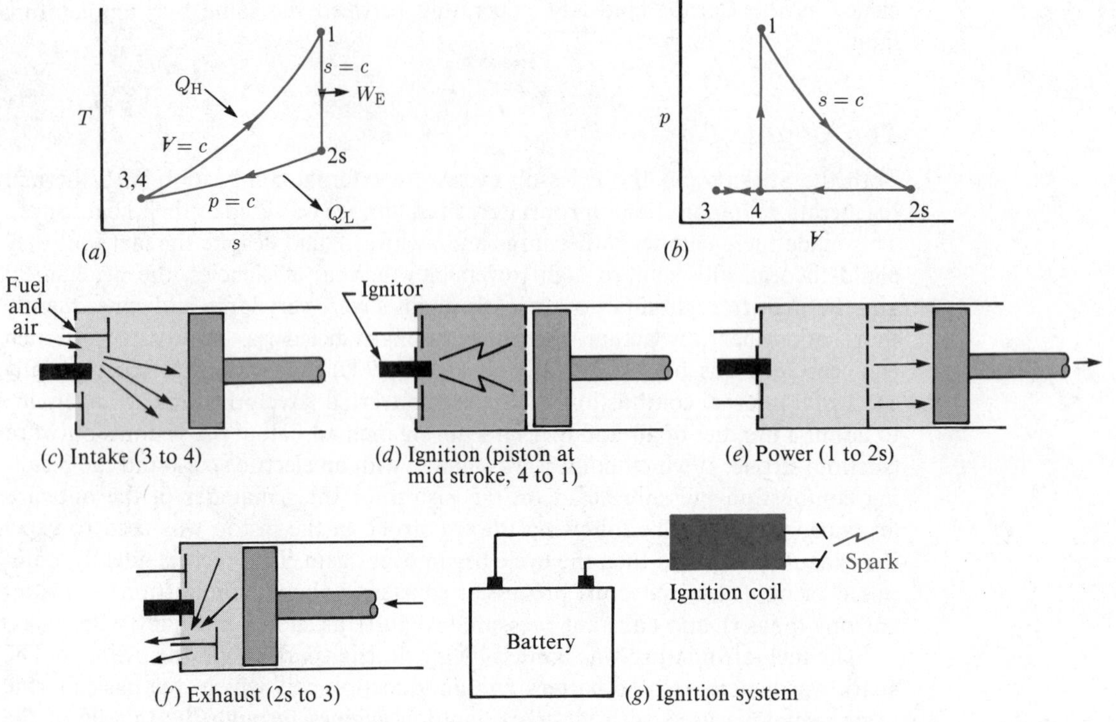

Figure 8.26 The Lenoir cycle (1860).

and

$$\dot{Q}_H = {}_4\dot{Q}_1 = \dot{m}c_v(T_1 - T_4)$$

Because the intake air comes from an isothermal source (the atmosphere), $T_3 = T_4$. However, the exhaust gas is confined to a fixed mass, so the condition $p_{2s} = p_3$ requires that $T_{2s}/T_3 = v_{2s}/v_3$, where v_{2s}/v_3 is the isentropic compression ratio, CR. Then the thermal efficiency becomes

$$\begin{aligned}(\eta_T)_{\substack{\text{Lenoir}\\ \text{cold ASC}}} &= 1 - \frac{c_p(T_{2s} - T_3)}{c_v(T_1 - T_4)} = 1 - kT_3\left(\frac{T_{2s}/T_3 - 1}{T_1 - T_4}\right) \\ &= 1 - kT_3(v_{2s}/v_3 - 1)/(T_1 - T_4) \\ &= 1 - kT_3(\text{CR} - 1)/(T_1 - T_4) \qquad \textbf{(8.21)}\end{aligned}$$

The relatively poor efficiency of this cycle can be illustrated by choosing some representative values for the variables in Eq. 8.21. For example, let $\text{CR} = v_{2s}/v_3 = 4.0$, $T_3 = T_4 = 70\ °\text{F} = 530\ \text{R}$, $T_1 = 2500\ °\text{F} = 2960\ \text{R}$ (a rather mild combustion temperature), and $k = 1.4$. Then Eq. 8.21 gives

$$(\eta_T)_{\substack{\text{Lenoir}\\ \text{cold ASC}}} = 1 - (1.4)(530)(4.0 - 1)/(2960 - 530) = 0.084 = 8.4\%$$

and since this is the efficiency of a reversible engine (the ASC assumes all the processes are reversible), then the thermal efficiency of an actual Lenoir cycle engine would be considerably less.

Even though the Lenoir cycle was inefficient, its relatively simple construction, its good reliability, and the fact that methane was readily available and inexpensive in many urban areas (where it was already being used extensively for illumination) made the engine quite successful from about 1860 to 1890. After the turn of the century the Lenoir engine lost popularity and became obsolete. However, the Lenoir cycle appeared briefly again in the German V-1 rocket engines ("buzz bombs") used during World War II.

The Brayton Cycle

The main reason that the Lenoir cycle had such a poor thermal efficiency was that the fuel–air mixture was not compressed before it was ignited. Many people recognized this fact, but it was not until 1873 that a more efficient internal combustion engine utilizing preignition compression was developed. George B. Brayton (1830–1892), an American engineer, adopted the dual reciprocating piston technique of Stirling and Ericsson but used one piston only as a compressor and the second piston only to deliver power. A combustion chamber was inserted between the two pistons to provide a constant pressure heat addition process. Thus, the Brayton ASC consists (ideally) of two isentropic processes (compression and power) and two isobaric processes (combustion and exhaust), as shown in Figure 8.27.[34]

The thermal efficiency of the Brayton cycle is given by

$$(\eta_T)_{\text{Brayton}} = \frac{|\dot{W}_{\text{out}}|_{\text{net}}}{\dot{Q}_{\text{H}}} = \frac{|\dot{W}_{\text{pm}}| - |\dot{W}_{\text{c}}|}{\dot{Q}_{\text{H}}}$$

For the cold ASC, both the compressor and the prime mover (either reciprocating piston–cylinder or turbine) are considered to be isentropic, and we can write

$$|\dot{W}_{\text{pm}}| = \dot{m}(h_1 - h_{2s}) = \dot{m}c_p(T_1 - T_{2s})$$

and

$$|\dot{W}_{\text{c}}| = \dot{m}(h_{4s} - h_3) = \dot{m}c_p(T_{4s} - T_3)$$

and since the combustion chamber is isobaric

$$\dot{Q}_{\text{H}} = \dot{m}(h_1 - h_{4s}) = \dot{m}c_p(T_1 - T_{4s})$$

---

34. The original Brayton cycle was conceived as a closed-loop external combustion hot air engine like those of Stirling and Ericsson. However, it was found to run more reliably when it was converted into an open-loop internal combustion engine as shown in Figure 8.27. Much later it was discovered to be an adequate model for gas turbine engines.

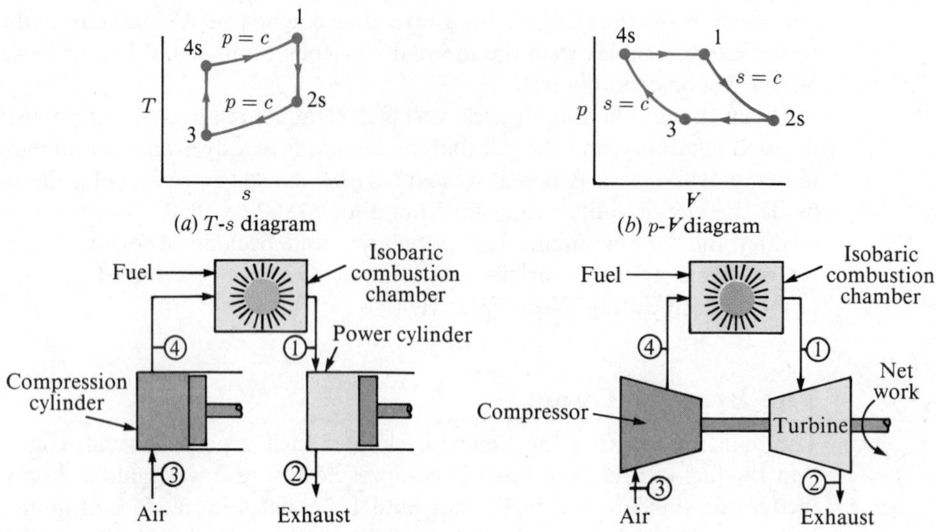

Figure 8.27 The open-loop Brayton cycle (1873).

Then,

$$(\eta_T)_{\substack{\text{Brayton}\\ \text{cold ASC}}} = \frac{(T_1 - T_{2s}) - (T_{4s} - T_3)}{T_1 - T_{4s}} = \frac{(T_1 - T_{4s}) - (T_{2s} - T_3)}{T_1 - T_{4s}}$$

$$= 1 - \frac{T_{2s} - T_3}{T_1 - T_{4s}} \tag{8.22}$$

Now, from the ideal gas isentropic formula used earlier, Eq. 5.38, we see from Figure 8.27*b* that

$$T_1/T_{2s} = (p_1/p_{2s})^{(k-1)/k} = (p_{4s}/p_3)^{(k-1)/k} = T_{4s}/T_3$$

so that $T_{2s}/T_3 = T_1/T_{4s}$, and Eq. 8.22 becomes

$$(\eta_T)_{\substack{\text{Brayton}\\ \text{cold ASC}}} = 1 - \frac{(T_{2s}/T_3 - 1)T_3}{(T_1/T_{4s} - 1)T_{4s}} = 1 - T_3/T_{4s}$$

Equation 5.38 also allows us to write

$$T_3/T_{4s} = (p_{4s}/p_3)^{(1-k)/k} = (v_3/v_{4s})^{1-k}$$

so that

$$(\eta_T)_{\substack{\text{Brayton}\\\text{cold ASC}}} = 1 - T_3/T_{4s} = 1 - PR^{(1-k)/k} = 1 - CR^{1-k} \quad \textbf{(8.23)}$$

where PR is the isentropic pressure ratio p_{4s}/p_3, and CR is the isentropic compression ratio v_3/v_{4s}. Thus, the thermal efficiency of the Brayton cold ASC can be written as a function of the isentropic pressure or compression ratio and the specific heat ratio of the working fluid.

Since $T_3 = T_L$ but $T_{4s} < T_1 = T_H$, then the Brayton cold ASC thermal efficiency will be *less* than that of the Carnot cold ASC working between the same temperature limits (T_1 and T_3). However, for fixed values of the temperature limits T_1 and T_3, there will be an optimum value for the compressor outlet temperature T_{4s} that will maximize the net output work. This can be determined as follows for an isentropic turbine and compressor:

$$|\dot{W}_{out}|_{\substack{\text{net}\\\text{isentropic}}} = |\dot{W}_{pm}| - |\dot{W}_c| = \dot{m}c_p(T_1 - T_{2s} - T_{4s} + T_3)$$

Now, holding T_1 and T_3 fixed, and replacing T_2 with its isentropic equivalent, $T_{2s} = T_1T_3/T_{4s}$, we get

$$|\dot{W}_{out}|_{\substack{\text{net}\\\text{isentropic}}} = \dot{m}c_p(T_1 - T_1T_3/T_{4s} - T_{4s} + T_3)$$

The optimum value of T_{4s} that will cause the net isentropic output work to be a maximum can be found by differentiating $|\dot{W}_{out}|_{\substack{\text{net}\\\text{isentropic}}}$ with respect to T_{4s} and setting the result equal to zero, or

$$\frac{d|\dot{W}_{out}|_{\text{net isentropic}}}{dT_{4s}} = \dot{m}c_p(0 + T_1T_3/T_{4s}^2 - 1 + 0) = 0$$

Then, solving for $T_{4s} = (T_{4s})_{opt}$ gives

$$(T_{4s})_{opt} = \sqrt{T_1T_3} \quad \textbf{(8.24)}$$

The corresponding optimum pressure and compression ratios are

$$PR_{opt} = [(T_{4s})_{opt}/T_3]^{k/(k-1)} = (T_1/T_3)^{k/[2(k-1)]} \quad \textbf{(8.25)}$$

and

$$CR_{opt} = [(T_{4s})_{opt}/T_3]^{1/(k-1)} = (T_1/T_3)^{1/[2(k-1)]} \quad \textbf{(8.26)}$$

while the thermal efficiency at the maximum net isentropic work output is

$$(\eta_T)_{\substack{\text{max work}\\\text{Brayton}\\\text{cold ASC}}} = 1 - T_3/(T_{4s})_{opt} = 1 - (T_3/T_1)^{1/2} = 1 - (T_L/T_H)^{1/2} \quad \textbf{(8.27)}$$

When the isentropic efficiencies of the compressor and prime mover are taken into account, the Brayton cycle thermal efficiency becomes

$$(\eta_T)_{\text{Brayton}} = \frac{|\dot{W}_{\text{pm}}(\eta_s)_{\text{pm}}| - |\dot{W}_c/(\eta_s)_c|}{\dot{Q}_H}$$

$$= \frac{(T_1 - T_{2s})(\eta_s)_{\text{pm}} - (T_{4s} - T_3)/(\eta_s)_c}{T_1 - T_4}$$

where $T_4 = T_3 + (T_{4s} - T_3)/(\eta_s)_c$. It is clear that this efficiency has a positive value only if

$$(\eta_s)_{\text{pm}}(\eta_s)_c \geq (T_{4s} - T_3)/(T_1 - T_{2s}) = T_{4s}/T_1$$

or

$$(\eta_s)_{\text{pm}}(\eta_s)_c \geq (T_3/T_1)\text{PR}^{(k-1)/k} = (T_L/T_H)\text{PR}^{(k-1)/k}$$

$$= (T_3/T_1)\text{CR}^{k-1} = (T_L/T_H)\text{CR}^{k-1} \quad \textbf{(8.28)}$$

The reciprocating piston–cylinder Brayton cycle engine, while more efficient than the Lenoir cycle engine, was at the same time mechanically more complex and costly. Its relatively low compressor pressure ratio limited its efficiency and its ability to compete effectively with existing reciprocating steam engine economics. These factors stifled the development of the reciprocating Brayton cycle engine, and the cycle might have quickly become obsolete if it had not been for a new prime mover technology that was being developed for steam, the turbine. By replacing steam with gas a new type of gas-powered prime mover, the gas turbine, was produced.

Because gas and steam turbines have many characteristics in common, several gas turbine engines were under development at the same time steam turbines were being developed. One characteristic that they do not have in common, however, is that gas turbine power plants require gas compressors, while vapor turbine power plants condense the working fluid to the liquid phase before compressing it with pumps. Early liquid pumps were fairly efficient, but early gas compressors were very inefficient due to a lack of understanding of the dynamics of high-speed compressible flow. This single fact proved to be a major stumbling block in the development of gas turbine engine technology.

This problem is illustrated by Eq. 8.28. For a gas turbine to have a net work output, its thermal efficiency obviously had to be a positive number. This meant that both the turbine (the prime mover) and the compressor had to have high enough isentropic efficiencies for Eq. 8.28 to be obeyed. One of the early major problems in compressible fluid mechanics was to understand how to compress a gas efficiently in a rotary compressor. Turbine prime movers, on the other hand, had already undergone considerable development within the steam power industry and were already 70 to 90% isentropically efficient.

A gas compressor is not simply a turbine running backward, and since compressible flow theory had not yet been completely developed, gas compressor development was carried out largely by trial and error methods. By 1900 most compressors had isentropic efficiencies of less than 50%, so that the product $(\eta_s)_{pm}(\eta_s)_c$ in Eq. 8.28 was of the order of 0.4. Since typical early gas turbines operated with very small compressor pressure ratios, say PR = 1.5, and relatively small combustion chamber temperatures, say 700 °F = 1150 R, then, for an ambient inlet temperature of 70 °F = 530 R, Eq. 8.28 requires that $(\eta_s)_{pm}(\eta_s)_c \geq (530/1160)(1.5)^{0.286} = 0.513$. But this was impossible for early units because, while they may have had good turbine isentropic efficiencies of around 90%, they also had very poor compressor isentropic efficiencies of around 50% or less. Thus, many early prototype gas turbine test engines failed to operate under their own power.

The first Brayton cycle gas turbine unit to produce a net power output (11 hp) was built in 1903. It had a very low actual thermal efficiency (about 3%) and could not compete economically with the other existing prime movers of its time. Compressor efficiency problems continued to plague gas turbine technology, and many new prototype engines were designed and built as late as the 1930s that still could not produce a net power output. Since the thrust produced by an aircraft engine is not considered to be part of the engine's work output (thrust is force, not work), aircraft engines do not necessarily need high thermal efficiencies to be effective. It was in this industry that the gas turbine engine first became successful.

The major function of an aircraft jet engine is to produce a high-velocity exhaust jet whose momentum (thrust) is large enough to propel the aircraft. The engine's thrust T is given by

$$T = \dot{m}(V_{\text{exhaust}} - V_{\text{inlet}})/g_c \tag{8.29}$$

where both the inlet and exhaust velocities are measured in a coordinate system fixed to the engine, and the mass flow rate is $\dot{m} = \dot{m}_{\text{fuel}} + \dot{m}_{\text{air}} = \dot{m}_{\text{exhaust}}$. A jet engine needs to produce only enough net output power to drive the aircraft's accessories (fuel pump, hydraulics, generator, etc.) and consequently it need not have a very high thermal efficiency (the exhaust kinetic energy is considered to be lost energy in a thermal efficiency analysis). This was an ideal application for the inherently inefficient gas turbine engine of the 1930s. The pressures of World War II caused intense research and development in aircraft gas turbine *turbojet* engine development. The first successful turbojet aircraft was the German Heinkel-178, that flew for the first time on August 24, 1939. The engine weighed 800 lbf (364 kg) and produced a thrust of 1100 lbf (4890 N) at 13,000 rpm. As a result of intense wartime technological development, axial flow compressors with pressure ratios of 3.0 and isentropic efficiencies of 75–80% were available by the end of World War II.

Modern aircraft gas turbine engines have compressor pressure ratios as high as 25, and ceramic coated super alloys have allowed turbine inlet temperatures to approach 3000 R. Their turbine isentropic efficiencies are typically in the range of 85 to 95%, and their compressor isentropic efficiencies usually fall in the range

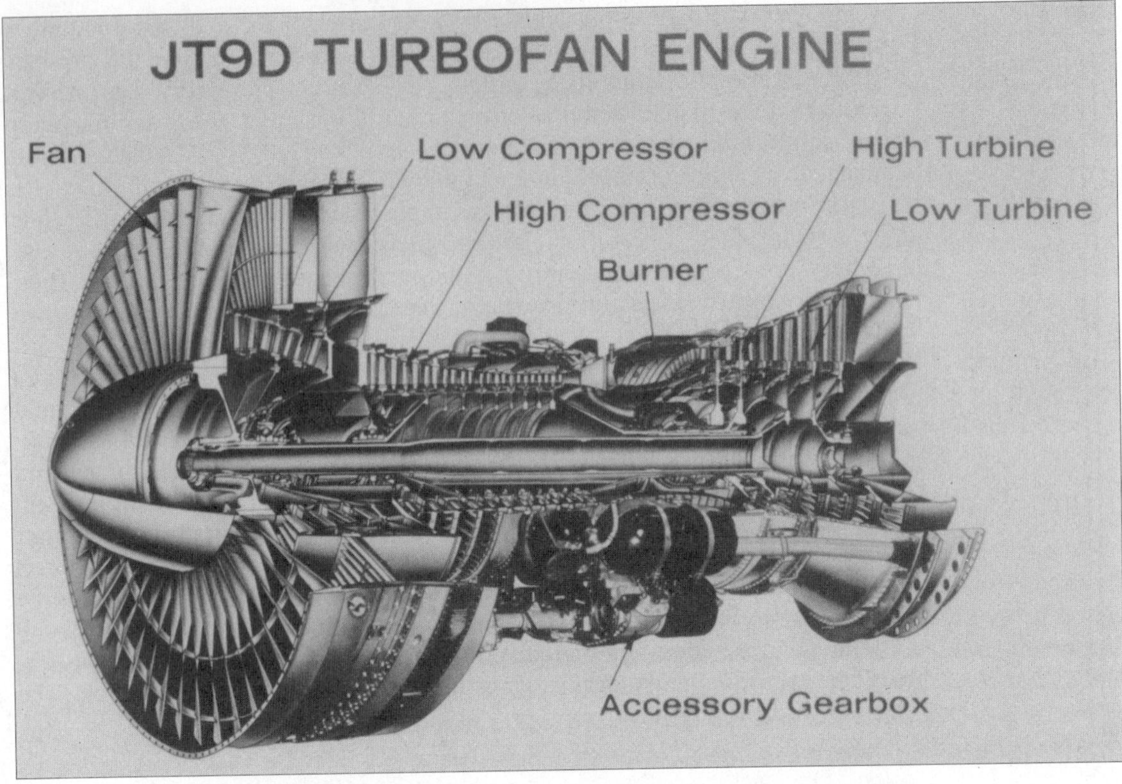

Figure 8.28 Typical gas turbine aircraft engine construction. Courtesy of Pratt and Whitney, East Hartford, CT. *Source*: Courtesy of United Technologies, Pratt & Whitney Aircraft.

of 80 to 90%. Figure 8.28 illustrates the construction of a modern turbojet engine.[35]

When regeneration, interstage compressor cooling, and interstage turbine reheat are added to the Brayton cycle, it approximates the more efficient Ericsson cycle, as shown in Figure 8.25. The major focus of modern gas turbine development centers around increasing the turbine inlet temperature through the development of new high-strength, high-temperature materials. Modern gas turbine heat engines are used mainly in small to medium size stationary power generating stations, and as prime movers throughout the transportation industry.[36]

35. During the 1960s, a turbojet design called the *turbofan*, or *fan-jet* engine was developed wherein some of the inlet air bypassed the combustion chamber and was mixed with the combustion products at the turbine inlet. This cooled the turbine inlet gases slightly and helped to complete the combustion process. Earlier, in 1945, a turbojet engine called the *turboprop* was developed wherein a gas turbine was used to drive a propeller as well as to provide exhaust thrust. The first commercial jet airliners used turboprops in the 1950s, but this type of turbojet engine is used only on short-range aircraft today.

36. In the early 1960s Chrysler Corporation attempted to introduce a gas turbine powered automobile to the mass market without success.

Example 8.6

Under static ground testing at sea level conditions the Pratt and Whitney JT3D-3B Turbofan engine has actual internal temperatures and pressures as shown below.

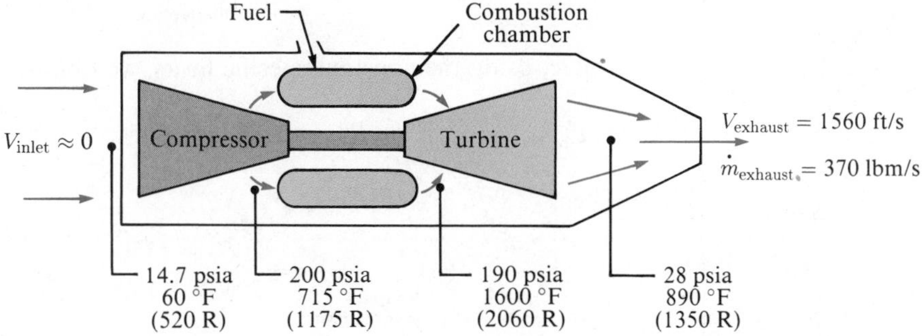

Determine

1. the engine's static thrust,
2. the compressor and turbine isentropic efficiencies for
   a) the Brayton cold air standard cycle, and
   b) the Brayton hot air standard cycle using the gas tables for air, Appendix C.16*a*, and
3. the ASC and actual thermal efficiencies for
   a) the Brayton cold air standard cycle, and
   b) the Brayton hot air standard cycle using the gas tables for air, Appendix C.16*a*.

Solution

1. The engine's static thrust is given directly by Eq. 8.29 as

$$T = \dot{m}(V_{\text{exhaust}} - V_{\text{inlet}})/g_c$$
$$= (370 \text{ lbm/s})(1560 \text{ ft/s} - 0)/[32.2 \text{ lbm}\cdot\text{ft/(lbf}\cdot\text{s}^2)]$$
$$= 17{,}925 \text{ lbf}$$

2a. The compressor's isentropic efficiency is given by

$$(\eta_s)_c = \frac{(\dot{W}_c)_{\text{isentropic}}}{(\dot{W}_c)_{\text{actual}}} = \frac{T_{4s} - T_3}{T_4 - T_3}$$

and, using $k = 1.4$ = constant for the cold ASC, we have

$$T_{4s} = T_3(p_{4s}/p_3)^{(k-1)/k} = (520)(200/14.7)^{(1.4-1)/1.4} = 1096.3 \text{ R} = 636.3 \text{ °F}$$

so that the compressor's isentropic efficiency using constant specific heats is

$$\underset{\text{(constant specific heats)}}{(\eta_s)_c} = \frac{1096.3 - 520}{1175 - 520} = 0.880 = 88.0\%$$

Similarly, the turbine's (prime mover) isentropic efficiency is given by

$$(\eta_s)_{pm} = \frac{|\dot{W}_{pm}|_{actual}}{|\dot{W}_{pm}|_{isentropic}} = \frac{T_1 - T_2}{T_1 - T_{2s}}$$

where, using the constant specific heats, we obtain

$$T_{2s} = T_1(p_{2s}/p_1)^{(k-1)/k} = (2060)(28/190)^{(1.4-1)/1.4} = 1192.0 \text{ R} = 732\ °\text{F}$$

Then,

$$\underset{\substack{\text{(constant}\\ \text{specific heats)}}}{(\eta_s)_{pm}} = \frac{2060 - 1350}{2060 - 1192} = 0.818 = 81.8\%$$

3a. The Brayton cold ASC thermal efficiency is given by

$$\underset{\text{cold ASC}}{(\eta_T)_{\text{Brayton}}} = \frac{T_1 - T_{2s} - (T_{4s} - T_3)}{T_1 - T_{4s}}$$

$$= \frac{2060 - 1192 - (1096.3 - 520)}{2060 - 1096.3} = 0.303 = 30.3\%$$

but the actual thermal efficiency of the engine based on constant specific heats and the data provided in the schematic is

$$\underset{\substack{\text{(actual, constant}\\ \text{specific heats)}}}{(\eta_T)_{\text{Brayton}}} = \frac{T_1 - T_2 - (T_4 - T_3)}{T_1 - T_4}$$

$$= \frac{2060 - 1350 - (1175 - 520)}{2060 - 1175} = 0.062 = 6.2\%$$

2b. We can easily take into account the temperature-dependent specific heats by using Appendix C.16*a*. For the compressor,

$$p_{r4} = p_{r3}(p_{4s}/p_3) = (1.2147)(200/14.7) = 16.527$$

and by interpolation in Appendix C.16*a* we find that

$$T_{4s} = 1084.4 \text{ R} = 624.4\ °\text{F}$$

Then,

$$\underset{\substack{\text{(variable}\\ \text{specific heats)}}}{(\eta_s)_c} = \frac{T_{4s} - T_3}{T_4 - T_3} = \frac{1084.4 - 520}{1175 - 520} = 0.862 = 86.2\%$$

Similarly, for the turbine,

$$p_{r2} = p_{r1}(p_{2s}/p_1) = (196.16)(28/190) = 28.91$$

and by interpolation in Appendix C.16*a* we find that

$$T_{2s} = 1261.2 \text{ R} = 801.2 \text{ °F}$$

Then,

$$(\eta_s)_{\substack{\text{pm}\\ \text{(variable}\\ \text{specific heats)}}} = \frac{T_1 - T_2}{T_1 - T_{2s}} = \frac{2060 - 1350}{2060 - 1261.2} = 0.888 = 88.8\%$$

3b. Finally, the Brayton hot ASC can be easily determined from

$$(\eta_T)_{\substack{\text{Brayton}\\ \text{hot ASC}}} = \frac{h_1 - h_{2s} - (h_{4s} - h_3)}{h_1 - h_{4s}}$$

where, from Appendix C.16*a*,

$$h_3 = 124.27 \text{ Btu/lbm (at 520 R)}$$

$$h_{4s} = 262.07 \text{ Btu/lbm (by interpolation at 1084.4 R)}$$

$$h_1 = 521.39 \text{ Btu/lbm (at 2060 R)}$$

$$h_{2s} = 306.97 \text{ Btu/lbm (by interpolation at 1261.2 R)}$$

Then,

$$(\eta_T)_{\substack{\text{Brayton}\\ \text{hot ASC}}} = \frac{521.39 - 306.97 - (262.07 - 124.27)}{521.39 - 262.07} = 0.295 = 29.5\%$$

and the engine's actual thermal efficiency based on temperature dependent specific heats is

$$(\eta_T)_{\substack{\text{Brayton}\\ \text{(actual, variable}\\ \text{specific heats)}}} = \frac{h_1 - h_2 - (h_4 - h_3)}{h_1 - h_4}$$

where

$$h_4 = 282.94 \text{ Btu/lbm (at 1175 R)}$$

and

$$h_2 = 329.89 \text{ Btu/lbm (at 1350 R)}$$

then,

$$(\eta_T)_{\substack{\text{Brayton}\\ \text{(actual, variable}\\ \text{specific heats)}}} = \frac{521.39 - 329.89 - (284.94 - 124.27)}{521.39 - 284.94} = 0.130 = 13.0\%$$

Note that whereas the Brayton hot ASC cycle thermal efficiency of Example 8.6 is relatively high (about 30%), the actual thermal efficiency of an aircraft turbojet engine is normally quite low. This is not because of poor engine design, but because most of the combustion energy is put into the kinetic energy of the exhaust gas rather than into the mechanical shaft work output. In aircraft engine design the thrust to weight ratio of the engine is a key parameter, and the engine's thermal efficiency is secondary.

The Otto Cycle

The Stirling and Ericsson external combustion gas power cycles were originally developed to combat the dangerous high-pressure boilers of the early steam engines. The Lenoir internal combustion engine was simpler, smaller, and used a more convenient fuel than either of these engines, but it had a very poor thermal efficiency. Brayton managed to increase the thermal efficiency of the internal combustion engine by providing a compression process before combustion by using the two piston Stirling and Ericsson technique with a separate combustion chamber. But the ultimate goal of commercial internal combustion engine development was to combine all the basic processes of intake, compression, combustion, expansion (power), and exhaust within a single piston–cylinder apparatus. This was finally achieved in 1876 by the German engineer Nikolaus August Otto (1832–1891).

After several years of experimentation, Otto finally built a successful internal combustion engine that allowed all the basic processes to occur within a single piston–cylinder arrangement.[37] The thermodynamic cycle of Otto's engine required four piston strokes and two crankshaft revolutions to complete, but it ran smoothly, was relatively quiet, and was very reliable and efficient. Otto's engine was an immediate success, and by 1886 more than 30,000 had been sold. They became the first serious competitor of the steam engine in the small and medium-size engine market.

Initially, Otto's engine used illuminating gas (methane) as its fuel, but by 1885 many were already being converted into liquid hydrocarbon (gasoline) burning engines. The development of the ingenious float-feed carburetor for vaporizing liquid fuel in 1892 by the German Wilhelm Maybach (1847–1929) heralded the dawn of the automobile era.[38]

In 1878 the Scotch engineer, Dugald Clerk (1854–1932) developed a two-stroke version of the Otto cycle, producing one crankshaft revolution per thermodynamic cycle (it was like the Lenoir engine, but with preignition compression).[39] Although Clerk's engine was inherently less fuel efficient than Otto's four-stroke

---

37. Unknown to Otto, the four-stroke cycle IC engine had already been patented in the 1860s by the French engineer Alphonse Eugene Beau de Rochas (1815–1893). However, Rochas did not actually build and test the engine that he had patented. Since Otto was the first to actually construct and operate the engine, the cycle is named after him rather than Rochas.

38. The German engineer Karl Friedrich Benz (1844–1929) is generally credited with building the first practical automobile using a low-speed Otto cycle engine running on liquid hydrocarbon fuel in 1885. He used engine exhaust heat to partially vaporize the fuel before it was fed into the engine.

39. In 1891 Clerk went on to develop the concept of IC engine supercharging. This increased the thermal efficiency of the engine by further compressing the induction charge before ignition.

cycle engine, it gave a more uniform power output (which is only important for single- or dual-cylinder engines) and had almost double the power to weight ratio of the Otto engine. The two-stroke Otto cycle (it never became known as the Clerk cycle) engine became successful as a small lightweight engine for boats, lawn mowers, saws, and so forth.

The basic elements of the ASC model of the Otto cycle are shown in Figure 8.29. It is composed of two isochoric processes and two isentropic processes.

The thermal efficiency of the Otto cycle is given by

$$(\eta_T)_{\text{Otto}} = \frac{|\dot{W}_{\text{out}}|_{\text{net}}}{\dot{Q}_H} = \frac{\dot{Q}_H - |\dot{Q}_L|}{\dot{Q}_H} = 1 - \frac{|\dot{Q}_L|}{\dot{Q}_H}$$

where, from Figure 8.29, for the cold ASC,

$$|\dot{Q}_L| = \dot{m}(u_{2s} - u_3) = \dot{m}c_v(T_{2s} - T_3)$$

and

$$\dot{Q}_H = \dot{m}(u_1 - u_{4s}) = \dot{m}c_v(T_1 - T_{4s})$$

then,

$$(\eta_T)_{\substack{\text{Otto}\\ \text{cold ASC}}} = 1 - \frac{T_{2s} - T_3}{T_1 - T_{4s}} = 1 - \left(\frac{T_3}{T_{4s}}\right)\left(\frac{T_{2s}/T_3 - 1}{T_1/T_{4s} - 1}\right)$$

Now, process 1 to 2s and process 3 to 4s are isentropic, so

$$\begin{aligned} T_1/T_{2s} = T_{4s}/T_3 &= (v_1/v_{2s})^{1-k} = (v_{4s}/v_3)^{1-k} \\ &= (p_1/p_{2s})^{(k-1)/k} = (p_{4s}/p_3)^{(k-1)/k} \end{aligned}$$

then $T_1/T_{4s} = T_{2s}/T_3$, and

$$(\eta_T)_{\substack{\text{Otto}\\ \text{cold ASC}}} = 1 - T_3/T_{4s} = 1 - \text{PR}^{(1-k)/k} = 1 - \text{CR}^{1-k} \tag{8.30}$$

where $\text{CR} = v_3/v_{4s}$ is the isentropic compression ratio and $\text{PR} = p_{4s}/p_3$ is the isentropic pressure ratio.

Since $T_3 = T_L$ but $T_{4s} < T_1 = T_H$, the Otto cold ASC thermal efficiency is less than that of a Carnot cold ASC operating between the same temperature limits (T_1 and T_3). Because the Otto cycle requires a constant volume combustion process, it can be carried out effectively only within the confines of a piston–cylinder or other fixed volume apparatus by a nearly instantaneous rapid combustion process.

The actual pressure–volume diagram from an engine operating on a gas or a vapor power cycle is called an *indicator diagram*[40], and the enclosed area is equal

40. The term *indicator diagram* dates from about 1790 when James Watt developed an apparatus to continuously record (i.e., *indicate*) the variations in pressure within a steam engine cylinder. It is used today to denote any p-V diagram that is constructed from actual pressure–volume data.

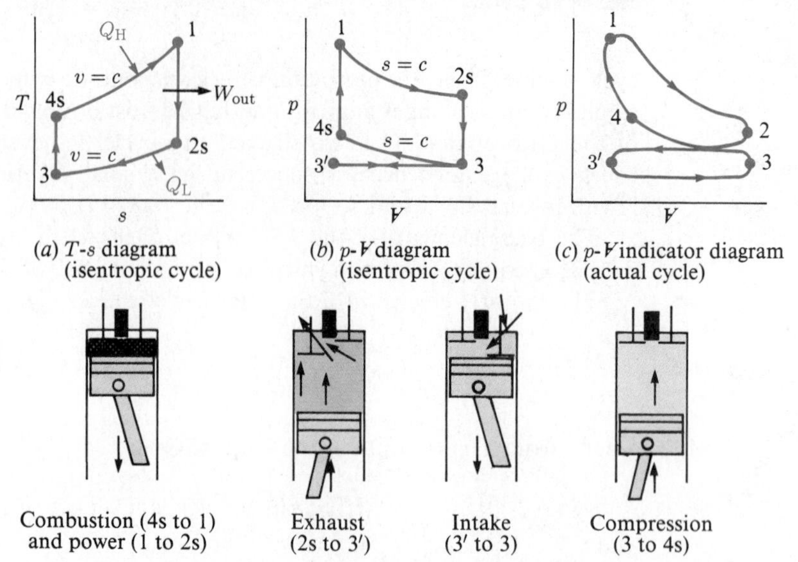

(*a*) *T-s* diagram (isentropic cycle)

(*b*) *p-V* diagram (isentropic cycle)

(*c*) *p-V* indicator diagram (actual cycle)

(*d*) The operation of a four-stroke isentropic Otto cycle

(*e*) A 47 in^3, 19 hp Kohler Series II four cycle, twin cylinder Otto cycle engine.

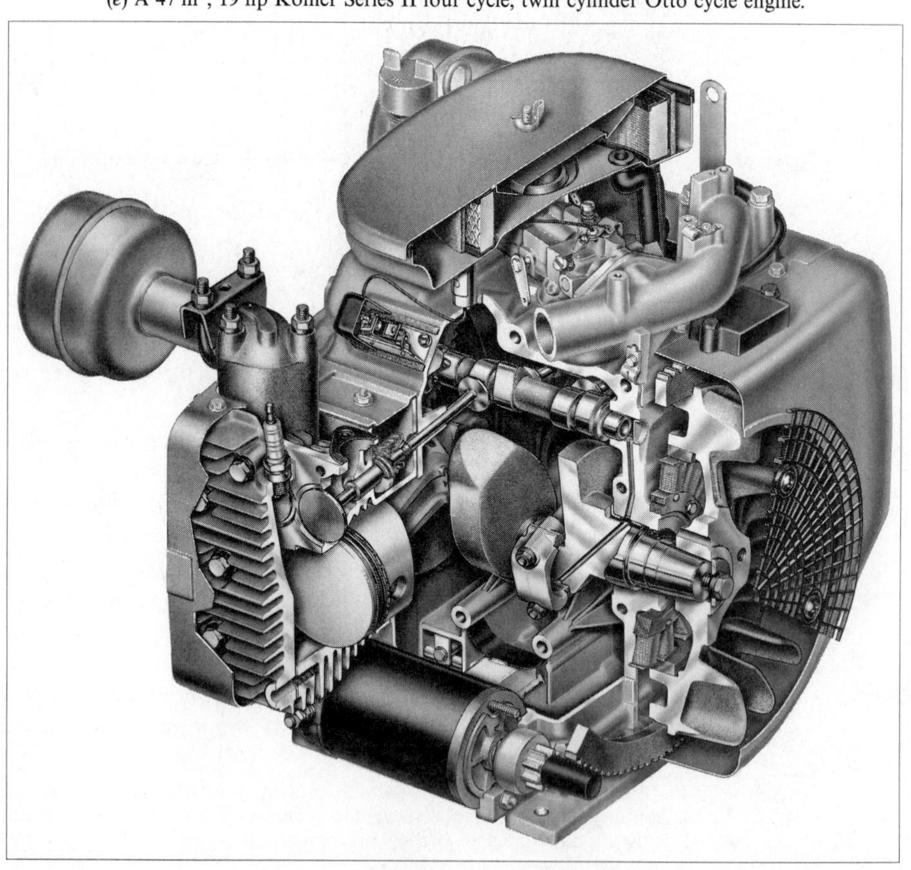

Figure 8.29 The Otto air standard cycle (1876). Photo courtesy of Kohler Co.—Engine Division, Kohler WI.

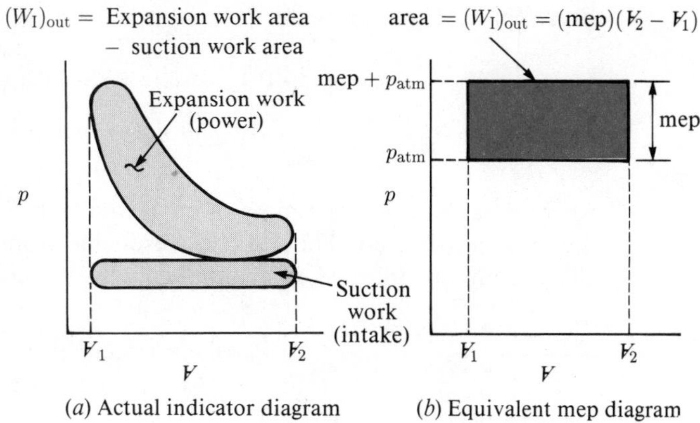

Figure 8.30 Mean effective pressure (mep) and indicator diagram relation.

to the net reversible work produced inside the engine. The *mean effective pressure* (mep) of a reciprocating engine is the *average net pressure* acting on the piston during its displacement. The *indicated* (or reversible) work output $|W_I|_{out}$ of the piston is the net positive area enclosed by the indicator diagram, as shown in Figure 8.30, and is equal to the product of the mep and the piston displacement, $V_2 - V_1$, or

$$|W_I|_{out} = \text{mep}\,(V_2 - V_1) \tag{8.31}$$

The *indicated* power output $|\dot{W}_I|_{out}$ is the net (reversible) power developed *inside* all the combustion chambers of an engine containing *n* cylinders, and is

$$|\dot{W}_I|_{out} = \text{mep}\,(n)(V_2 - V_1)(N/C) \tag{8.32}$$

where N is the rotational speed of the engine and C is the number of crankshaft revolutions per power stroke ($C = 1$ for a two-stroke cycle and $C = 2$ for a four-stroke cycle). The *actual* power output of the engine as measured by a dynamometer is called the *brake* power $|\dot{W}_B|_{out}$, and the difference between the indicated and brake power is known as the *friction* power (i.e., the power dissipated in the internal friction of the engine) $\dot{W}_F$, or

$$|\dot{W}_I|_{out} = |\dot{W}_B|_{out} + \dot{W}_F$$

and therefore the engine's mechanical efficiency η_m is simply (see Table 8.2)

$$\eta_m = \frac{\dot{W}_{actual}}{\dot{W}_{reversible}} = \frac{|\dot{W}_B|_{out}}{|\dot{W}_I|_{out}} = 1 - \frac{\dot{W}_F}{|\dot{W}_I|_{out}} \tag{8.33}$$

From Eq. 8.31 we can write

$$\text{mep} = |W_I|_{out}/(V_2 - V_1) = (|W_I|_{out}/m_a)/(v_2 - v_1)$$
$$= (|\dot{W}_I|_{out}/\dot{m}_a)/(v_2 - v_1)$$

where m_a and $\dot{m}_a$ are the mass of air in the cylinder and the cylinder's air mass flow rate, respectively. The ASC (i.e., reversible or indicated, see Table 8.2) thermal efficiency of *any* internal or external combustion engine can now be written as

$$(\eta_T)_{ASC} = \frac{|\dot{W}_{out}|_{reversible}}{\dot{Q}_{in}} = \frac{|\dot{W}_I|_{out}}{\dot{Q}_{fuel}} = \frac{|\dot{W}_I|_{out}/\dot{m}_a}{\dot{Q}_{fuel}/\dot{m}_a}$$

where $\dot{Q}_{in} = \dot{Q}_{fuel}$ is the heating value of the fuel. Combining these equations gives

$$\text{mep} = \frac{(\eta_T)_{ASC}(\dot{Q}_{fuel}/\dot{m}_a)}{v_2 - v_1} = \frac{(\eta_T)_{ASC}(\dot{Q}_{fuel}/\dot{m}_{fuel})}{(A/F)(v_2 - v_1)}$$

where $A/F = \dot{m}_a/\dot{m}_{fuel}$ is the air–fuel ratio of the engine. Now,

$$v_2 - v_1 = v_1(v_2/v_1 - 1) = RT_1(\text{CR} - 1)/p_1$$

so Eq. 8.32 becomes

$$|\dot{W}_I|_{out} = \frac{(\eta_T)_{ASC}(\dot{Q}/\dot{m})_{fuel}(DNp_1/C)}{(A/F)(RT_1)(\text{CR} - 1)} \tag{8.34}$$

where $D = n(V_2 - V_1)$ is the total piston displacement of the engine. Equation 8.34 allows one to determine the horsepower output of an ideal frictionless internal combustion engine, and when actual dynamometer test data are available Eq. 8.33 allows one to determine the engine's mechanical efficiency.

Example 8.7

A six-cylinder four-stroke Otto cycle internal combustion engine has a total displacement of 260 in^3 and a compression ratio of 9 to 1. It is fueled with gasoline having a specific heating value of 20,000 Btu/lbm and is carbureted with an air–fuel ratio of 16 to 1. During a dynamometer test the intake pressure and temperature were found to be 8 psia and 60 °F while the engine was producing 85 brake horsepower at 4000 rpm. For the Otto cold ASC with $k = 1.4$, determine

a) the cold ASC thermal efficiency of the engine,
b) the maximum pressure and temperature of the cycle,
c) the indicated power output of the engine,
d) the mechanical efficiency of the engine, and
e) the actual thermal efficiency of the engine.

Solution

a) From Eq. 8.30, and using $k = 1.4$ for the cold ASC,

$$(\eta_T)_{\substack{\text{Otto}\\ \text{cold ASC}}} = 1 - \text{CR}^{1-k} = 1 - 9^{-0.4} = 0.585 = 58.5\%$$

b) From Figure 8.29*a*,

$$\dot{Q}_H = \dot{Q}_{\text{fuel}} = (\dot{m}c_v)_a(T_1 - T_{4s}) = \dot{m}_{\text{fuel}}(A/F)(c_v)_a(T_1 - T_{4s})$$

and

$$T_1 = T_{\max} = \frac{(\dot{Q}/\dot{m})_{\text{fuel}}}{(A/F)(c_v)_a} + T_{4s}$$

Since process 3 to 4s is isentropic, Eq. 5.38 gives

$$T_{4s} = T_3\text{CR}^{k-1} = (60 + 460)(9)^{0.4} = 1252.3 \text{ R}$$

Then,

$$T_{\max} = \frac{20{,}000 \text{ Btu/lbm}}{(16)[0.172 \text{ Btu/(lbm}\cdot\text{R)}]} + 1252.3 \text{ R} = 8520 \text{ R}$$

Since process 4s to 1 is isochoric, the ideal gas equation of state gives

$$p_{\max} = p_1 = p_{4s}(T_1/T_{4s})$$

and since the process 3 to 4s is isentropic, then

$$T_{4s}/T_3 = (p_{4s}/p_3)^{(k-1)/k}$$

or

$$p_{4s} = p_3(T_{4s}/T_3)^{k/(k-1)} = (8 \text{ psia})\left(\frac{1252.3 \text{ R}}{520 \text{ R}}\right)^{1.4/0.4} = 173.4 \text{ psia}$$

then,

$$p_{\max} = (173.4 \text{ psia})[(8520 \text{ R})/(1252.3 \text{ R})] = 1180 \text{ psia}$$

c) Equation 8.34 gives the indicated power as

$$|\dot{W}_I|_{\text{out}} = \frac{(0.585)(20{,}000 \text{ Btu/lbm})(260 \text{ in}^3\text{/rev})(4000 \text{ rev/min})(1180 \text{ lbf/in}^2)/2}{(16)[0.0685 \text{ Btu/(lbm}\cdot\text{R)}](8520 \text{ R})(9 - 1)(12 \text{ in/ft})(60 \text{ s/min})}$$

$$= (133{,}400 \text{ ft}\cdot\text{lbf/s})\left(\frac{1 \text{ hp}}{550 \text{ ft}\cdot\text{lbf/s}}\right) = 242.7 \text{ hp}$$

d) Equation 8.33 gives the mechanical efficiency of the engine as

$$\eta_m = \frac{|\dot{W}_B|_{out}}{|\dot{W}_I|_{out}} = \frac{85 \text{ hp}}{242.7 \text{ hp}} = 0.350 = 35.0\%$$

e) Finally, the actual thermal efficiency of the engine can be determined from

$$(\eta_T)_{\substack{\text{Otto}\\ \text{actual}}} = \frac{|\dot{W}_B|_{out}}{\dot{Q}_{fuel}} = \frac{(\eta_m)|\dot{W}_I|_{out}}{\dot{Q}_{fuel}} = (\eta_m)(\eta_T)_{\substack{\text{Otto}\\ \text{cold ASC}}}$$

$$= (0.350)(0.585) = 0.205 = 20.5\%$$

The previous example illustrates that the Otto cold ASC analysis generally predicts thermal efficiencies that are far in excess of the actual thermal efficiencies. Typical Otto cycle IC engines have actual operating thermal efficiencies in the range of 15–25%. The large difference between the cold ASC (which contains at least one isentropic process) thermal efficiency and the actual thermal efficiency is due to the influence of the second law of thermodynamics through the large number of thermal and mechanical irreversibilities inherent in this type of reciprocating piston–cylinder engine. To improve its actual thermal efficiency, the combustion heat losses and the number of moving parts in the engine must be reduced.

The Diesel Cycle

Rudolf Christian Karl Diesel (1858–1913) was a well-educated linguist and social theorist, but most of all he was a remarkable engineer. He was born in Paris, but he received his technical education in Munich under Karl von Linde (1842–1934), a renowned pioneer in mechanical refrigeration.

Though the actual thermal efficiency of Otto's engine was many times better than that of Lenoir's, it was still barely competitive with the ever improving Rankine cycle steam engine. Diesel felt that he could eliminate the electrical ignition system of the Otto cycle engine if he could compress the air to the point where its temperature would be high enough to cause the fuel to ignite spontaneously. This would raise the maximum temperature of the cycle and consequently improve its thermal efficiency. He also felt that a higher combustion temperature would allow cheaper, heavier hydrocarbon fuels (such as kerosene, a common lamp oil in the late nineteenth century) to be used. On August 10, 1893, Diesel's first compression ignition engine ran under its own power for the first time, and by 1898 Diesel had become a millionaire simply by selling franchises for the industrial use of his engine.[41]

Diesel had originally intended to create an isothermal combustion process in the cylinder so as to eliminate the heat transfer irreversibilities and thus approach

41. Diesel's 1893 test engine compressed air to 80 atm, a pressure never before achieved by a machine. He was nearly killed when the engine subsequently exploded.

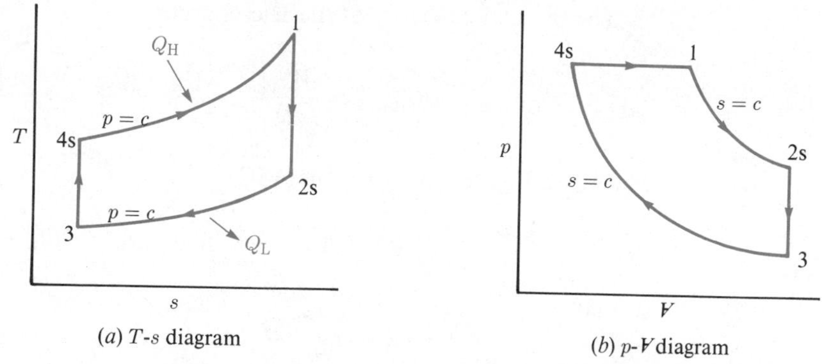

(a) T-s diagram

(b) p-V diagram

(c) A 855 in^3, 300 hp Cummins BC III six cylinder Diesel cycle engine.

Figure 8.31 The Diesel air standard cycle (1893). Photo courtesy of Cummins Engine Company, Columbus, Indiana.

the Carnot cycle thermal efficiency. He was not able to do this; instead the ASC model of his cycle consists of two isentropic processes (compression and power), one isobaric process (combustion) and one isochoric process (exhaust), as shown in Figure 8.31.

The thermal efficiency of the Diesel cycle is

$$(\eta_T)_{\text{Diesel}} = \frac{|\dot{W}_{\text{out}}|_{\text{net}}}{\dot{Q}_H} = \frac{\dot{Q}_H - |\dot{Q}_L|}{\dot{Q}_H} = 1 - \frac{|\dot{Q}_L|}{\dot{Q}_H}$$

where (see Figure 8.31*a*), for the ASC,

$$|\dot{Q}_L| = \dot{m}(u_{2s} - u_3) \quad \text{and} \quad \dot{Q}_H = \dot{m}(h_1 - h_{4s})$$

so that

$$\underset{\text{ASC}}{(\eta_T)_{\text{Diesel}}} = 1 - \frac{u_{2s} - u_3}{h_1 - h_{4s}}$$

and for the cold ASC this becomes

$$\underset{\text{cold ASC}}{(\eta_T)_{\text{Diesel}}} = 1 - \frac{c_v(T_{2s} - T_3)}{c_p(T_1 - T_{4s})} = 1 - \frac{T_3(T_{2s}/T_3 - 1)}{kT_{4s}(T_1/T_{4s} - 1)} \tag{8.35}$$

For the isentropic processes from 1 to 2s and from 3 to 4s we have

$$T_{2s}/T_1 = (v_{2s}/v_1)^{1-k}$$

and

$$T_3/T_{4s} = (v_3/v_{4s})^{1-k} = \text{CR}^{1-k}$$

and for the isobaric process from 4s to 1 we have

$$T_1/T_{4s} = v_1/v_{4s} = \text{CO}$$

where CO is called the *cut off* ratio of the engine.[42] For the isochoric process from 2s to 3 it can easily be shown that $T_{2s}/T_3 = \text{CO}^k$, and then

$$\underset{\text{cold ASC}}{(\eta_T)_{\text{Diesel}}} = 1 - \frac{\text{CR}^{1-k}(\text{CO}^k - 1)}{k(\text{CO} - 1)} \tag{8.36}$$

42. The phrase *cut off* is another archaic steam engine jargon term that has been absorbed into modern IC engine terminology. It was introduced in the 1780s by James Watt when he realized that if the steam entering the cylinder was "cut off" (i.e., shut off) when the piston had completed only a portion of its stroke and the natural expansion of the steam was allowed to complete the stroke, then the engine's thermal efficiency increased significantly. Today this phrase is used to indicate where the combustion process "cuts off" (i.e., stops) in a compression ignition internal combustion engine. It is determined by the geometry of the combustion chamber and the fuel charge. Also, cut off is a popular synonym for shut off in the southern United States. It was probably introduced into this region by the British soldiers stranded there after the American Revolutionary War. Curiously, as a slang phrase it has never spread through the rest of the United States.

Example 8.8 A four-cyclinder, four-stroke cycle Diesel engine with a 20 to 1 compression ratio and a total displacement of 4.5 L burns kerosene with a heating value of 40,000 kJ/kg and has an air to fuel ratio of 30 to 1. During a dynamometer test the intake pressure and temperature were 100 kPa and 20 °C when the engine was running at 2500 rpm and producing 25 hp.

For the Diesel cold ASC with $k = 1.4$, determine

a) the engine's cutoff ratio,
b) the cold ASC thermal efficiency of the engine,
c) the indicated power output of the engine,
d) the mechanical efficiency of the engine, and
e) the actual thermal efficiency of the engine.

Solution

a) The cutoff ratio is defined as

$$\mathrm{CO} = v_1/v_{4s}$$

but since process 4s to 1 is isobaric, then $v_1/v_{4s} = T_1/T_{4s}$, and so

$$\mathrm{CO} = T_1/T_{4s}$$

where, for the isentropic process 3 to 4s,

$$T_{4s} = T_3 \mathrm{CR}^{k-1} = (20 + 273\ \mathrm{K})(20)^{1.4-1} = 971\ \mathrm{K}$$

Now the isobaric process 4s to 1 is the combustion process, so

$$\dot{Q}_{\mathrm{H}} = \dot{Q}_{\mathrm{fuel}} = (\dot{m}c_p)_{\mathrm{a}}(T_1 - T_{4s}) = \dot{m}_{\mathrm{fuel}}(A/F)(c_p)_{\mathrm{a}}(T_1 - T_{4s})$$

Then

$$T_1 = T_{\max} = \frac{(\dot{Q}/\dot{m})_{\mathrm{fuel}}}{(A/F)(c_p)_{\mathrm{a}}} + T_{4s}$$

$$= \frac{40{,}000\ \mathrm{kJ/kg}}{(30)[1.004\ \mathrm{kJ/(kg \cdot K)}]} + 971\ \mathrm{K} = 2299\ \mathrm{K}$$

and then,

$$\mathrm{CO} = (2299\ \mathrm{K})/(971\ \mathrm{K}) = 2.37$$

b) Equation 8.36 gives the thermal efficiency as

$$(\eta_{\mathrm{T}})_{\substack{\mathrm{Diesel} \\ \mathrm{cold\ ASC}}} = 1 - \frac{(20)^{-0.4}[(2.37)^{1.4} - 1]}{1.4(2.37 - 1)} = 0.631 = 63.1\%$$

c) Equation 8.34 gives the indicated power output, where

$p_1 = p_{4s}$

and

$$p_{4s} = p_{max} = p_3(T_{4s}/T_3)^{k/(k-1)} = (100 \text{ kPa})\left(\frac{971 \text{ K}}{293 \text{ K}}\right)^{1.4/0.4} = 6626 \text{ kPa}$$

Then,

$$|\dot{W}_I|_{out} = \frac{(0.631)(40{,}000 \text{ kJ/kg})(0.0045 \text{ m}^3/\text{rev})(2500 \text{ rev/min})(6626 \text{ kN/m}^2)}{2(30)[0.286 \text{ kJ/(kg}\cdot\text{K)}](2299 \text{ K})(20 - 1)(60 \text{ s/min})}$$
$$= 41.8 \text{ kJ/s} = (41.8 \text{ kW})(1.3405 \text{ hp/kW}) = 56 \text{ hp}$$

d) Then, from Eq. 8.33,

$$\eta_m = \frac{25 \text{ hp}}{56 \text{ hp}} = 0.446 = 44.6\%$$

e) Finally, the actual thermal efficiency of the engine can be determined from

$$(\eta_T)_{\substack{\text{Diesel}\\\text{actual}}} = \frac{|\dot{W}_B|_{out}}{\dot{Q}_{fuel}} = \frac{(\eta_m)|\dot{W}_I|_{out}}{\dot{Q}_{fuel}}$$
$$= (\eta_m)(\eta_T)_{\substack{\text{Diesel}\\\text{cold ASC}}} = (0.446)(0.631) = 0.281 = 28.1\%$$

As the previous example illustrates, Diesel cycle engines are somewhat more efficient than Otto cycle engines. Typical Otto cycle engine actual thermal efficiencies are in the range from 15 to 25%, whereas for Diesel cycle engines they normally fall in the range from 25 to 35%.

Because combustion takes place intermittently in IC engines and therefore the cylinder is alternately heated by combustion and cooled by the intake stroke (plus the fact that most of these engines have water jacket cooling), they have the same heat transfer irreversibilities as the early eighteenth century Newcomen steam engines. It was a similar cyclic cylinder heating and cooling process in the Newcomen steam engine that led James Watt to develop the external steam condenser that improved the engine's thermal efficiency fourfold.

Modern Prime Mover Developments

Solving for the power from an energy rate balance (ERB) on a steady state, steady flow, single-inlet, single-outlet prime mover (neglecting any changes in kinetic or potential energy) yields

$$|\dot{W}|_{out} = \dot{m}(h_{in} - h_{out}) - |\dot{Q}|_{loss}$$

Since the primary objective of any prime mover is to produce power ($|\dot{W}|_{out} > 0$), then any heat loss ($|\dot{Q}|_{loss} > 0$) will clearly reduce both the power output and the thermal efficiency of the prime mover. Consequently, most external combustion prime movers are heavily insulated to minimize their heat loss and maximize their thermal efficiency. When there is no heat loss or gain by a prime mover, it can properly be called an adiabatic prime mover.

Current internal combustion engines are not only uninsulated, they are intentionally cooled. This is done to prevent the buildup of excessively high internal temperatures that in turn would cause material failure due to loss of strength. Consequently, about 80% of the chemical energy originally contained in the fuel leaves an IC engine as thermal energy in the coolant and in the exhaust gases.

The development of high-temperature, high-strength ceramic or *super alloy* engine components is a step in the direction of creating a truly adiabatic IC engine. In addition to reducing engine heat loss, these new components allow higher internal operating temperatures to be achieved, and this in turn increases the

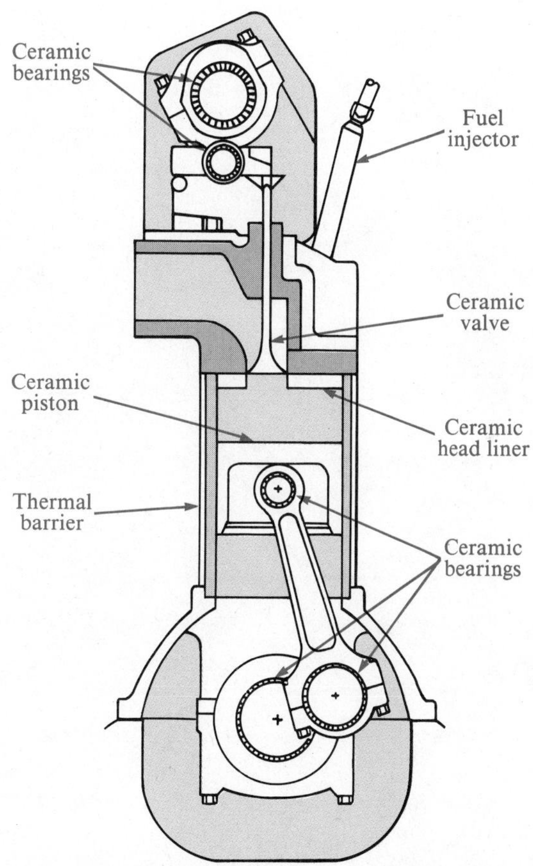

Figure 8.32 Typical ceramic components of a modern IC engine.

maximum theoretical thermal efficiency of the engine. For example, doubling the operating temperature from 2000 °F (1093 °C) to 4000 °F (2204 °C) increases the Carnot isentropic efficiency by about 10%. Figure 8.32 illustrates some of the current uses of ceramics in reciprocating IC engines. Similar advances are being made in gas turbine engine technology.

Other thermal efficiency increasing technology such as turbocompounding[43] can be used to extract some of the thermal energy from the engine's exhaust gases. However, it must be remembered that all cyclic heat engines (including all IC engines when their cycle is closed by the environment) must have a heat loss rate to the environment that is dictated by the second law of thermodynamics of

$$|\dot{Q}|_{\text{loss}} \geq (T_{\text{environment}}/T_{\text{engine max}})|\dot{Q}|_{\text{fuel}}$$

43. Turbocompounding is the use of a small turbine driven by the exhaust flow of an engine to precompress the inlet air (turbocharging) or to perform other work-related functions.

Chapter Eight Section II Vapor and Gas Refrigeration Cycles

The basic concepts of refrigeration, air conditioning, and heat pumps were introduced in Chapter 5. This technology is usually modeled as a backward-running heat engine. When a heat engine runs backward (or in reverse) it receives a net input of work W that causes an amount of heat Q_L to be removed from a low-temperature region and an amount of heat Q_H to be added to a high-temperature region. A backward-running heat engine is a refrigeration machine, but its exact technical name depends on exactly how it is being used. For example, if foodstuff occupies the low-temperature region then the device is indeed called a *refrigerator*, but if people occupy the low-temperature region then it is called an *air conditioner*.[44] On the other hand, if people occupy the high-temperature region and utilize Q_H for space heating purposes, then the device is called a *heat pump*. Though the details of their design and operation differ slightly, refrigerators, air conditioners, and heat pumps can all be modeled as backward-running heat engines. These distinctions are shown in Figure 8.33.

In Chapter 5 we discovered that refrigerators, air conditioners, and heat pumps usually have actual thermal efficiencies in excess of 100%. This is due simply to the mathematical way in which their thermal efficiencies are defined (the desired energy output divided by the required energy input), and does not imply the violation of any physical law. However, claims of thermal efficiency in excess of 100% cause obvious credibility problems in the public domain, and so the term *efficiency* is not often used with this technology. Instead, we simply rename the thermal efficiency the *coefficient of performance* (COP), which is expressed as a pure number, usually between 1 and 10, rather than as a percentage. Equations 5.17 and

44. In addition to lowering room or building air temperature, air conditioners also usually filter the air and alter its humidity (see Chapter 7).

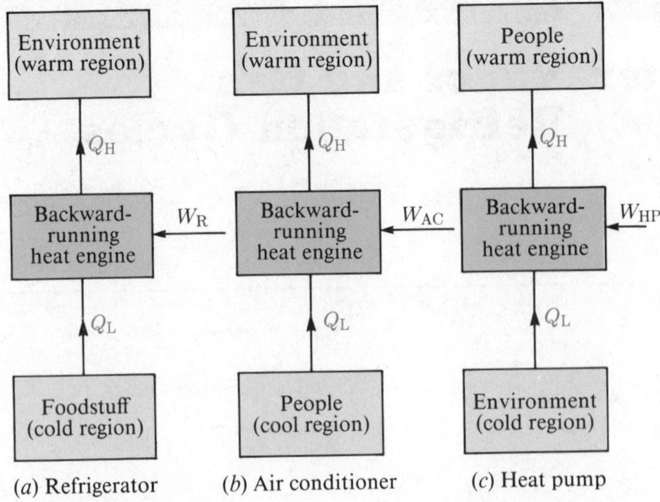

Figure 8.33 Characteristics of refrigerators, air conditioners, and heat pumps.

5.19 give these definitions as

$$(\eta_T)_{\substack{\text{Heat}\\ \text{Pump}}} = \text{COP}_{\text{HP}} = \frac{|Q_H|}{W_{HP}} = \frac{|\dot{Q}_H|}{\dot{W}_{HP}} = \frac{|Q_H|}{|Q_H| - Q_L} = \frac{|\dot{Q}_H|}{|\dot{Q}_H| - \dot{Q}_L} \tag{5.17}$$

and

$$(\eta_T)_{\substack{\text{Refrigerator or}\\ \text{Air Conditioner}}} = \text{COP}_{\text{R/AC}} = \frac{Q_L}{W_{R/AC}} = \frac{\dot{Q}_L}{\dot{W}_{R/AC}} = \frac{Q_L}{|Q_H| - Q_L} = \frac{\dot{Q}_L}{|\dot{Q}_H| - \dot{Q}_L} \tag{5.19}$$

and it is easily shown that

$$\text{COP}_{\text{HP}} = \text{COP}_{\text{R/AC}} + 1 \tag{8.37}$$

From Figure 8.33 and Eq. 8.37 it is evident that Eqs. 5.17 and 5.19 can also be written as

$$\text{COP}_{\text{HP}} = \frac{|\dot{Q}_H|}{(\dot{W}_{\text{in}})_{\text{net}}} \tag{8.38}$$

and

$$\text{COP}_{\text{R/AC}} = \frac{\dot{Q}_L}{(\dot{W}_{\text{in}})_{\text{net}}} = \text{COP}_{\text{HP}} - 1 \tag{8.39}$$

Note that Eq. 8.38 is simply the inverse of the general forward-running heat engine thermal efficiency equation defined at the beginning of this chapter as Eq. 5.5, i.e.,

$$\text{COP}_{\text{HP}} \equiv \frac{1}{(\eta_T)_{\substack{\text{forward-running}\\ \text{heat engine}}}} \tag{8.40}$$

and Eq. 8.39 then gives

$$\text{COP}_{\text{R/AC}} \equiv \frac{1}{(\eta_{\text{T}})_{\substack{\text{forward-running}\\ \text{heat engine}}}} - 1 \tag{8.41}$$

Thus, the COP for any of the heat engines discussed in Section I of this chapter operating on a reversed thermodynamic cycle as a heat pump, refrigerator, or air conditioner can be easily obtained through the use of Eqs. 8.40 and 8.41.

For example, Eqs. 8.18–8.20 show that both the Stirling and the Ericsson cold ASC thermal efficiencies are identical to that of the Carnot cold ASC, or

$$(\eta_{\text{T}})_{\substack{\text{Carnot}\\ \text{cold ASC}}} = (\eta_{\text{T}})_{\substack{\text{Stirling}\\ \text{cold ASC}}} = (\eta_{\text{T}})_{\substack{\text{Ericsson}\\ \text{cold ASC}}} = \frac{T_{\text{H}} - T_{\text{L}}}{T_{\text{L}}}$$

Then Eqs. 8.40 and 8.41 can be used directly to give the COP of these cycles running backwards as a heat pump, refrigerator or air conditioner as

$$\text{COP}_{\substack{\text{HP}\\ \text{reversed}\\ \text{Stirling,}\\ \text{Ericsson or Carnot ASC}}} = \frac{T_{\text{H}}}{T_{\text{H}} - T_{\text{L}}} \tag{8.42}$$

$$\text{COP}_{\substack{\text{R/AC}\\ \text{reversed}\\ \text{Stirling,}\\ \text{Ericsson or Carnot ASC}}} = \frac{T_{\text{L}}}{T_{\text{H}} - T_{\text{L}}} \tag{8.43}$$

Also, it is easy to show that Eq. 8.37 remains valid for these systems.

There are four basic techniques used in refrigeration technology: **1)** evaporative cooling, **2)** gas expansion, **3)** absorption cooling, and **4)** thermoelectric cooling. Only the first three are discussed in this chapter. Thermoelectric effects were mentioned in Section I of Chapter 4, but are not discussed in detail in this text.

The Evolution of Refrigeration Technology

Refrigeration technology did not have the same revolutionary impact on society as did the steam engine. It was basically a spin-off technology from existing steam and gas power cycle prime movers that were simply made to operate thermodynamically backward. But, whereas the working fluid of the steam engine (water) was nearly ideal for vapor power cycles, it was totally unsuitable for the refrigeration cycles of commercial interest. The major problem faced by the early developers of refrigeration technology was not the design of the machinery per se, but finding a suitable nontoxic, inexpensive working fluid with satisfactory low-temperature thermodynamic characteristics.

The first commercial refrigerator using a closed-cycle vaporization process was developed in 1834 by the American Jacob Perkins (1766–1849). His working fluid

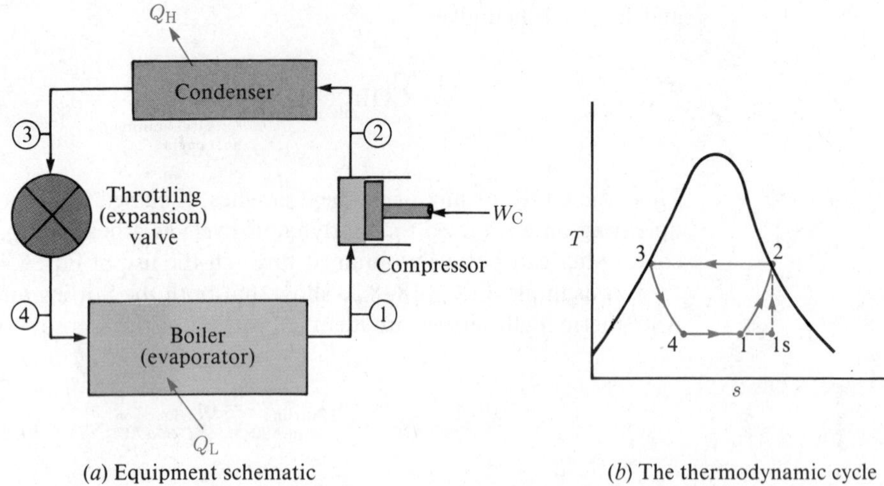

(*a*) Equipment schematic

(*b*) The thermodynamic cycle

Figure 8.34 Jacob Perkins' closed-loop vapor refrigeration cycle (1834).

was ethyl ether (or, more accurately, diethyl ether $C_2H_5OC_2H_5$) that boiled at a low enough pressure such that its resulting saturation temperature was low enough to freeze water on the outside of the boiler.[45] Then the ether vapor was compressed in a piston–cylinder apparatus and condensed into a liquid at a much higher saturation pressure and temperature. Finally, the liquid ether was then throttled through a valve back into the low-pressure boiler. This system is illustrated in Figure 8.34. Since this process occurs beneath the vapor dome of the working fluid (ether) it is clearly a reversed Rankine cycle device.

Though Perkins was an American, his refrigerator was marketed in England and was not an economic success. A similar machine was marketed in the United States in 1856 by Alexander Catlin Twinning (1801–1884), again with little financial success. In 1873 the first commercially successful vapor cycle refrigeration device was developed by the German engineer Karl von Linde (1842–1934). By the end of the nineteenth century ammonia had become the refrigeration working fluid of choice, but it had a number of serious disadvantages. It was very toxic and its extremely pungent odor made even tiny leaks objectionable. This led to the use of carbon dioxide as a refrigeration working fluid, but it required very high pressures to liquefy and consequently carbon dioxide refrigeration equipment was quite massive.

The lack of a suitable refrigerant kept this technology out of the home market (which continued to refrigerate food by using large chunks of ice in an "ice box") and restricted its use to large food processing and preservation industries (e.g.,

45. During the nineteenth and early twentieth centuries it was common practice for physicians to use liquid ether as a local anesthetic by spraying it onto parts of the body where it would freeze the tissue as it evaporated and consequently numb the local sensations. This is the source of the term *freezing* as a synonym for a local anesthetic.

brewing and meat packing). In the late 1920s the American chemist and engineer, Thomas Midgley, Jr. (1889–1944), discovered that certain fluorine compounds were remarkably nontoxic and odorless while simultaneously having the proper thermodynamic properties of a good refrigerant. In the 1930s the E. I. duPont de Nemours Company became commercially involved in the refrigeration industry by manufacturing and selling Midgley's discovery as a refrigerant. DuPont marketed their product under the commercial trade name *Freon.*

Midgley's refrigerants were halogenated hydrocarbons in which halogen atoms (mainly chlorine and fluorine) were substituted for hydrogen atoms in simple hydrocarbon molecules. Midgley replaced the four hydrogen atoms in methane (CH_4) with two chlorine and two fluorine atoms to produce dichloro-difluoromethane (or dichlorodifluoromethane, CCl_2F_2). Other common methane-based refrigerants are monochlorodifluoromethane ($CHClF_2$) and trichloromonofluoromethane (CCl_3F). The complex chemical names of these compounds are logical and technically correct, but they are difficult for the nonchemist to pronounce and remember. Consequently a confusing variety of commercial trade names such as Freon, Genetron, Isotron, Frigen, and so forth came into popular use during the 1940s. Shortly thereafter the American Society of Refrigerating Engineers (ASRE)[46] decided to adopt a standard method of refrigerant designation that was based only upon the use of numbers. Halogen-substitution refrigerants are based upon simple hydrocarbons such as methane (CH_4) and ethane (C_2H_6). For the methane-based refrigerants a two-digit number sequence is used, with the first digit being equal to the number of hydrogen atoms present *plus one*, and the second digit being equal to the number of fluorine atoms present. Thus, Midgley's CCl_2F_2 became *Refrigerant-12* (abbreviated R-12), or *Freon-12* if manufactured by DuPont, because it has zero hydrogen atoms and two fluorine atoms. Similarly, $CHClF_2$ became Refrigerant-22 (or R-22), CCl_3F became Refrigerant-11 (or R-11), and so forth. Other hydrocarbon-based refrigerants are given a three-digit number with the first digit being the series number assigned to the hydrocarbon base and the second and third digits being determined in the same way as for the methane-based refrigerants. Ethane refrigerants were assigned the 100 number series and the ethane-based hexachloroethane (C_2Cl_6) became Refrigerant-110 (or R-110), and so forth. Propane-based refrigerants were assigned the 200 number series and butane based refrigerants were assigned the 600 number series. Inorganic (i.e., nonhydrocarbon-based) refrigerants were assigned the 700 number series with the last two digits being the molecular mass of the refrigerant. For example, ammonia (NH_3) is Refrigerant-717, water (H_2O) is Refrigerant-718, and so forth. Table 8.3 lists the ASHRAE number, chemical formula, and boiling point of some common refrigerants.

A common unit of commercial refrigeration or air conditioning is the *ton.* A ton of refrigeration or air conditioning is the amount of heat that must be removed from one ton (2000 lbf) of water in one day (24 h) to freeze it at 32 °F and 14.7

---

46. The ASRE merged with the American Society of Heating and Air-Conditioning Engineers (ASHAE) to form the American Society of Heating, Refrigerating and Air-Conditioning Engineers (ASHRAE) in 1959.

Table 8.3 The American Society of Heating, Refrigerating and Air Conditioning Engineers (ASHRAE) refrigerant numbering system for some common refrigerants

Refrigerant number	Chemical formula	Boiling point at atmospheric pressure °F	°C
R-10	CCl_4	170.2	76.8
R-11	CCl_3F	74.9	23.8
R-12	CCl_2F_2	−21.6	−29.8
R-21	$CHCl_2F$	48.1	8.9
R-22	$CHClF_2$	−41.4	−40.8
R-30	CH_2Cl_2	105.2	40.7
R-40	CH_3Cl	−10.8	−23.8
R-50	CH_4 (methane)	−259.0	−161.7
R-110	C_2Cl_6	365.0	185.0
R-111	C_2Cl_5F	279.0	137.2
R-112	$C_2Cl_4F_2$	199.0	92.8
R-170	C_2H_6 (ethane)	−127.8	−88.8
R-290	C_3H_8 (propane)	−43.7	−42.1
R-600	C_4H_{10} (butane)	33.1	0.6
R-717	NH_3 (ammonia)	−28.0	−33.3
R-718	H_2O (water)	212.0	100.0

Source: Reprinted by permission from the ASHRAE Handbook—1985 Fundamentals.

psia. It is also the amount of heat absorbed by the melting of one ton of ice in 24 h at 32 °F, 14.7 psia. Using more conventional units,

$$\begin{aligned}\text{1 ton of refrigeration or air conditioning} &= 200 \text{ Btu/min} = 12{,}000 \text{ Btu/h}\\ &= 210 \text{ kJ/min} = 12{,}600 \text{ kJ/h}\end{aligned}$$

The Reversed Rankine Cycle

All vapor cycle refrigeration systems operate on a reversed Rankine cycle, as shown in Figure 8.34*b*. In these systems the boiler is normally called the *evaporator* and the prime mover is replaced by a *compressor*. Also, it would seem reasonable to replace the boiler feed pump of the forward-running Rankine cycle with some form of prime mover in the reversed Rankine cycle whose work output could be used to offset the work input to the compressor. Unfortunately, this is not economically feasible in most small- to medium-scale refrigeration systems, as the following example illustrates.

Example 8.9 A refrigeration system is to be designed using R-22 to maintain frozen food at −15 °C while operating in an environment at 20 °C. Determine the COP for this refrigerator using

a) a reversed Carnot cycle operating between these temperature limits,
b) a reversed isentropic Rankine cycle with an isentropic expansion turbine installed between the high-pressure condenser and the low-pressure evaporator, and
c) a reversed isentropic Rankine cycle with an aergonic, adiabatic, throttling expansion valve installed between the high-pressure condenser and the low-pressure evaporator.

Solution

a) Here, $T_H = 20 + 273 = 293$ K, and $T_L = -15 + 273 = 258$ K. Then Eq. 8.43 gives

$$\text{COP}_{\substack{\text{Carnot}\\\text{refrigerator}}} = \frac{T_L}{T_H - T_L} = \frac{258}{293 - 258} = 7.37$$

b) The system here is as shown below.

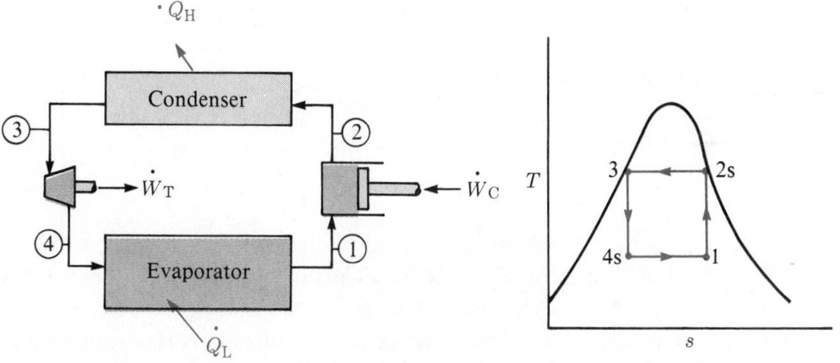

From Appendix C.9*b*, the thermodynamic data at the monitoring stations shown in the schematic are

Station 1

$T_1 = -15\ °\text{C}$
$s_1 = s_{2s} = 0.89973\ \text{kJ/(kg·K)}$

$x_1 = 0.9395$
$h_1 = 231.0\ \text{kJ/kg}$
$p_1 = 295.7\ \text{kPa}$

Station 2s

$T_{2s} = 20\ °\text{C}$
$x_{2s} = 1.0$

$h_{2s} = 256.5\ \text{kJ/kg}$
$s_{2s} = 0.89973\ \text{kJ/(kg·K)}$
$p_{2s} = 909.9\ \text{kPa}$

Station 3

$T_3 = 20\ °\text{C}$
$x_3 = 0.0$

$h_3 = 68.67\ \text{kJ/kg}$
$s_3 = 0.25899\ \text{kJ/(kg·K)}$
$p_3 = P_2 = 909.9\ \text{kPa}$

Station 4s

$T_{4s} = T_1 = -15\ °\text{C}$
$s_{4s} = s_3 = 0.25899\ \text{kJ/(kg·K)}$

$x_{4s} = 0.1765$
$h_{4s} = 65.6\ \text{kJ/kg}$

where we have calculated

$$x_1 = \frac{s_1 - s_{f1}}{s_{fg1}} = \frac{s_{2s} - s_{f1}}{s_{fg1}} = \frac{0.89973 - 0.11075}{0.83977} = 0.9395$$

$$h_1 = h_{f1} + x_1(h_{fg1}) = 27.33 + (0.9395)(216.79) = 231.0 \text{ kJ/kg}$$

$$x_{4s} = \frac{s_3 - s_{f4}}{s_{fg4}} = \frac{0.25899 - 0.11075}{0.83977} = 0.1765$$

and

$$h_{4s} = h_{f4} + x_{4s}(h_{fg4}) = 27.33 + (0.1765)(216.79) = 65.6 \text{ kJ/kg}$$

Then,

$$\text{COP}_{\substack{\text{reversed}\\ \text{isentropic}\\ \text{Rankine cycle}\\ \text{(with expansion}\\ \text{turbine)}}} = \frac{\dot{Q}_L}{\dot{W}_c - \dot{W}_t} = \frac{h_1 - h_{4s}}{(h_{2s} - h_1) - (h_3 - h_{4s})}$$

$$= \frac{231.0 - 65.6}{(256.5 - 231.0) - (68.67 - 65.6)} = 7.37$$

which is identical to the Carnot efficiency of part a as it should be because the Rankine and Carnot cycles are identical in this case (see the *T-s* diagram above).

c) When the isentropic turbine is replaced by an adiabatic, aergonic throttling valve, process 3 to 4 becomes isenthalpic rather than isentropic, as shown in the following schematic.

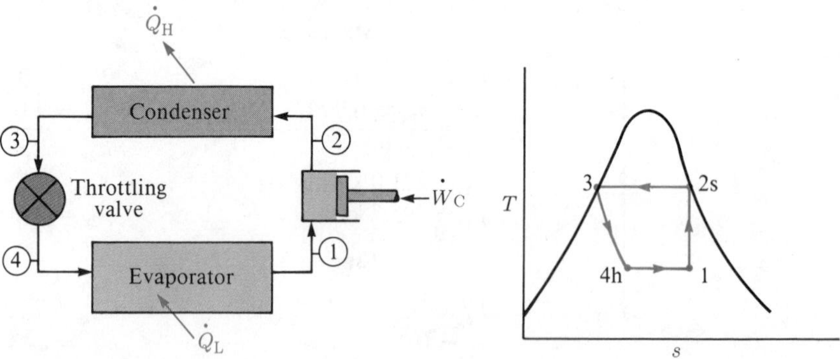

The thermodynamic data for stations 1, 2s, and 3 remain unchanged from part b, but the isenthalpic throttling valve changes the data of station 4s to 4h as follows.

Station 4h

$$T_{4h} = T_1 = -15\ ^\circ\text{C}$$
$$h_{4h} = h_3 = 68.67\ \text{kJ/kg}$$
$$x_{4h} = 0.1910$$
$$s_{4h} = 0.27081\ \text{kJ/(kg}\cdot\text{K)}$$

where we have calculated

$$x_{4h} = \frac{h_{4h} - h_{f4}}{h_{fg4}} = \frac{68.67 - 27.34}{216.79} = 0.1906$$

and

$$s_{4h} = s_{f4} + x_{4h}(s_{fg4}) = 0.11075 + (0.1906)(0.83977) = 0.27081\ \text{kJ/(kg}\cdot\text{K)}$$

Finally,

$$\text{COP}_{\substack{\text{reversed}\\ \text{isentropic}\\ \text{Rankine cycle}\\ \text{(with throttling valve)}}} = \frac{\dot{Q}_L}{\dot{W}_c} = \frac{h_1 - h_{4h}}{h_{2s} - h_1} = \frac{231.0 - 68.67}{256.5 - 231.0} = 6.37$$

The decrease in COP from 7.37 to 6.37 (13.6%) in the previous example is not normally sufficient to justify the increased expense of manufacturing, installing, and maintaining a turbine or other prime mover between the condenser and the evaporator in small and medium-size systems. Also, the working fluid in this part of the cycle contains a mixture of liquid and vapor, and it is difficult to find any prime mover that will operate efficiently and reliably with this type of two-phase fluid. Throttling expansion valves, on the other hand, are very inexpensive and reliable under these conditions.

By introducing the isentropic efficiency of the compressor $(\eta_s)_c$ the general formula for the actual thermal efficiency (COP) of a reversed Rankine cycle can be written as

$$\text{COP}_{\substack{\text{reversed}\\ \text{Rankine cycle}\\ \text{R/AC}}} = \frac{\dot{Q}_L}{\dot{W}_c} = \frac{h_1 - h_{4h}}{(h_{2s} - h_1)/(\eta_s)_c} \tag{8.44}$$

and

$$\text{COP}_{\substack{\text{reversed}\\ \text{Rankine cycle}\\ \text{HP}}} = \frac{|\dot{Q}_H|}{\dot{W}_c} = \frac{h_2 - h_3}{(h_{2s} - h_1)/(\eta_s)_c} \tag{8.45}$$

Because throttling processes are ideally isenthalpic, a pressure–enthalpy diagram is often used to describe vapor refrigeration cycles, as shown in Figure 8.35. Process 1 to 2s in this figure involves the compression of a liquid–vapor mixture. This is technically more difficult than compressing either a pure vapor or a pure liquid. A method of eliminating this problem is to superheat the vapor, as shown in Figure 8.35*b*.

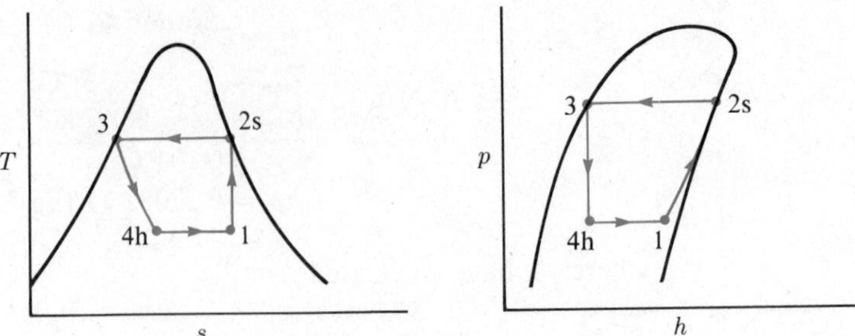

(*a*) Reversed isentropic Rankine cycle with isenthalpic throttling

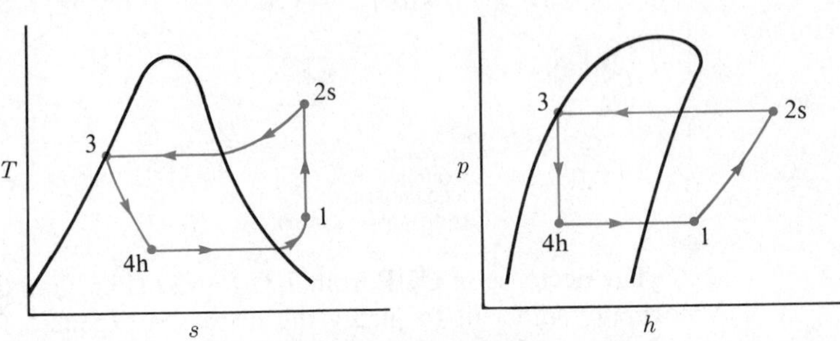

(*b*) Same as (*a*) except with superheat

Figure 8.35 *T-s* and *p-h* diagrams for reversed isentropic Rankine cycles.

Example 8.10 Repeat part c of Example 8.9 by requiring that the evaporator outlet be a saturated vapor at −15 °C, and introduce a compressor isentropic efficiency of 75%.

Solution Now the compressor outlet will be a superheated vapor as shown below.

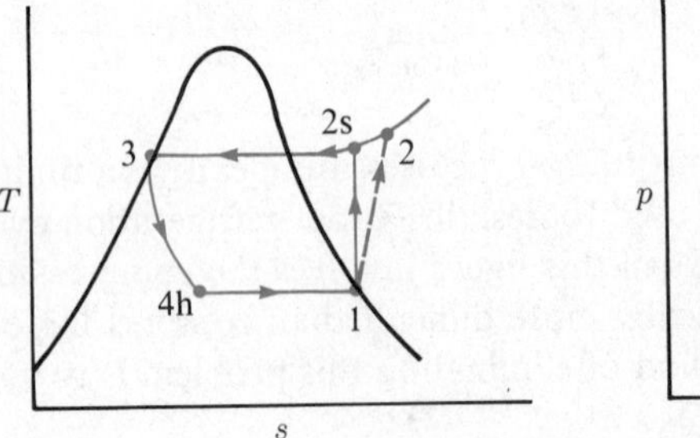

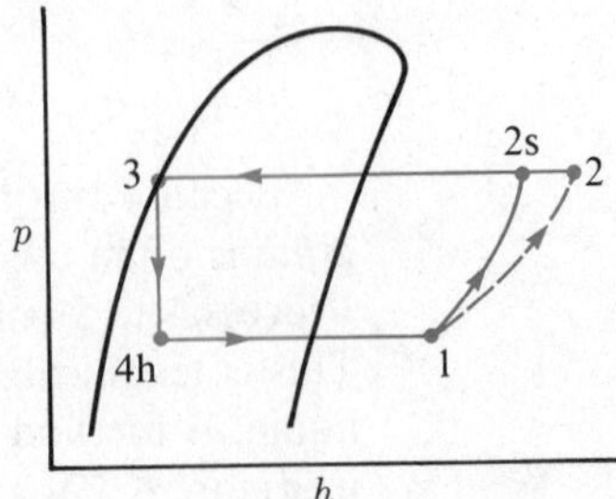

The thermodynamic data for the four monitoring stations are (see Example 8.9 for details)

Station 1	Station 2s
$T_1 = -15\ ^\circ\text{C}$	$p_{2s} = p_2 = 909.9$ kPa
$x_1 = 1.0$	$s_{2s} = s_1 = 0.95052$ kJ/(kg·K)
$h_1 = 244.13$ kJ/kg	$h_{2s} = 271.92$ kJ/kg } from interpolation in
$s_1 = 0.95052$ kJ/(kg·K)	$T_{2s} = 39.3\ ^\circ\text{C}$ } Appendix C.10*b*

Station 3	Station 4s
$T_3 = 20\ ^\circ\text{C}$	$T_{4s} = T_1 = -15\ ^\circ\text{C}$
$x_3 = 0.0$	$h_{4h} = h_3 = 68.67$ kJ/kg
$h_3 = 68.67$ kJ/kg	$x_{4h} = 0.1910$
$s_3 = 0.25899$ kJ/(kg·K)	$s_{4h} = 0.27088$ kJ/(kg·K)

Then, from Eq. 8.44,

$$\text{COP}_{\substack{\text{reversed}\\ \text{Rankine cycle}\\ \text{R/AC}}} = \frac{\dot{Q}_L}{\dot{W}_c} = \frac{h_1 - h_{4h}}{(h_{2s} - h_1)/(\eta_s)_c}$$

$$= \frac{244.13 - 68.67}{(271.92 - 244.13)/0.75} = 4.74$$

Even if the compressor had an isentropic efficiency of 100%, the COP in this example would only be 4.74/0.75 = 6.32, which is still slightly less than the 6.37 of part c in Example 8.9. Thus, adding superheat to the cycle usually does not increase the COP because both $\dot{W}_c/\dot{m}$ and $\dot{Q}_L/\dot{m}$ are increased. However, the required mass flow rate $\dot{m}$ will be significantly reduced by the addition of superheat. Also, because condensers and evaporators are not 100% effective as heat exchangers, the temperature difference between the working fluid in these devices and their local environment is typically about 15 °F (8.3 °C).

The use of the ton unit of cooling defined at the beginning of this section is illustrated in the following example.

Example 8.11 Determine the refrigerant mass flow rate and the compressor power input for Example 8.10 if the system is to produce 20 tons of refrigeration.

Solution Here, $\dot{Q}_L = 20$ tons $= 20(210$ kJ/min$) = 4200$ kJ/min, and an energy rate balance on the evaporator gives

$$\dot{m} = \frac{\dot{Q}_L}{h_1 - h_{4h}} = \frac{4200 \text{ kJ/min}}{(244.13 - 68.67) \text{ kJ/kg}} = 23.9 \text{ kg/min}$$

Then,

$$\dot{W}_c = \frac{\dot{Q}_L}{\text{COP}} = \frac{4200 \text{ kJ/min}}{4.74} = 886.1 \text{ kJ/min} = 14.8 \text{ kW} = 19.8 \text{ hp}$$

Air Standard Refrigeration Cycles

The working fluid in gas refrigeration cycles is less complex than in gas power cycles. For example, refrigeration cycles do not involve internal combustion processes that change the working fluid during the cycle, but they can be either open or closed loop cycles. Therefore, there is much less need for a working fluid simplifying model like the air standard cycle (ASC). Nonetheless we will use its simplifying characteristics in analyzing gas refrigeration cycles in which air is the working fluid. In particular, all gas refrigeration cycles will be assumed to be closed loop cycles when an ASC analysis is used. In addition, the following assumptions apply to gas refrigeration ASC analysis:

1. The working fluid is a fixed mass of air that obeys the ideal gas equation of state.
2. All inlet or exhaust processes in open-loop systems are replaced by heat transfer processes to or from the environment.
3. All processes within the cycle are reversible.
4. The air has constant specific heats.[47]

ASC refrigeration analysis will yield reasonably accurate results for most cycles using air as the working fluid. One notable exception is in the area of throttling or Joule-Thomson cooling in which the amount of cooling depends exclusively upon real gas behavior. This will be illustrated later in this chapter.

The Reversed Brayton Cycle

In 1844 the American physician, John Gorrie (1803–1855), designed and built an air-cooling apparatus in Florida to provide air conditioning for his yellow fever patients. His machine had a piston–cylinder apparatus that compressed air that was cooled back to ambient temperature by circulating water. The cooled compressed air was then expanded in a second piston–cylinder apparatus that caused the air to drop to a sufficiently low temperature to produce ice and satisfy other cooling needs. The expanded air was then drawn back into the compressor and the cycle began again. The two piston–cylinder devices were connected together so that the expansion work was used to offset the compression work. This was clearly a reversed closed-loop Brayton cycle, as shown by comparing Figures 8.17 and 8.36.

The COP of an actual reversed Brayton cycle is given by

$$\text{COP}_{\substack{\text{reversed}\\\text{Brayton cycle}\\\text{HP}}} = \frac{|\dot{Q}_\text{H}|}{(\dot{W}_\text{in})_\text{net}} = \frac{T_2 - T_3}{(T_{2s} - T_1)/(\eta_s)_c - (T_3 - T_{4s})(\eta_s)_e} \tag{8.46}$$

47. Since the temperature variations within a gas refrigeration cycle are not nearly as large as those within a gas power cycle that contains a combustion process, there is no practical need to distinguish between a hot refrigeration ASC in which temperature dependent specific heats are used and a cold refrigeration ASC in which constant specific heats are used.

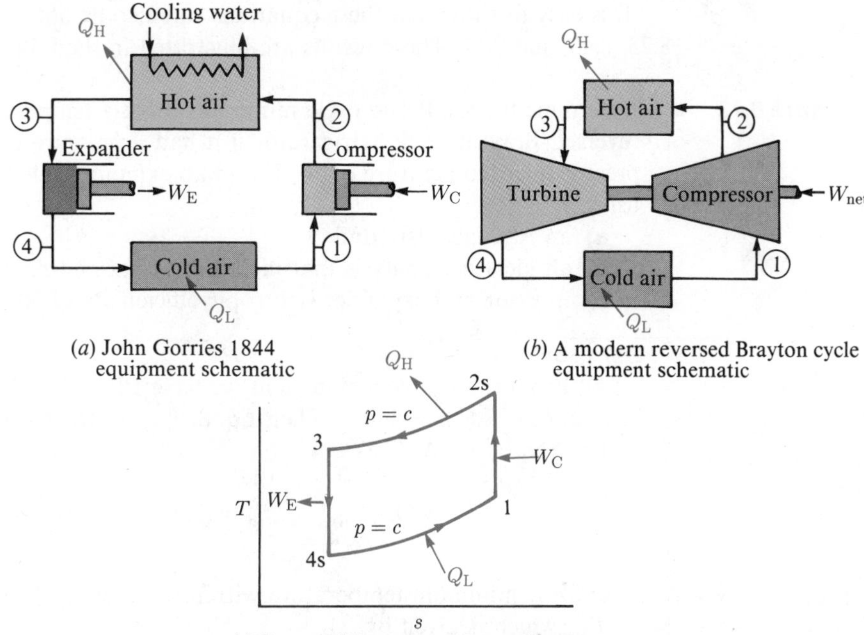

(*a*) John Gorries 1844 equipment schematic

(*b*) A modern reversed Brayton cycle equipment schematic

(*c*) Reversed Brayton ASC *T-s* diagram

Figure 8.36 The reversed Brayton cycle cooling system using air as a working fluid.

and

$$\text{COP}_{\substack{\text{reversed}\\\text{Brayton cycle}\\\text{R/AC}}} = \frac{\dot{Q}_L}{(\dot{W}_{in})_{net}} = \frac{T_1 - T_4}{(T_{2s} - T_1)/(\eta_s)_c - (T_3 - T_{4s})(\eta_s)_e} \tag{8.47}$$

where $T_2 = T_1 + (T_{2s} - T_1)/(\eta_s)_c$ and $T_4 = T_3 - (T_3 - T_{4s})(\eta_s)_e$. Since the processes 1 to 2s and 3 to 4s are isentropic, and the processes 2s to 3 and 4s to 1 are isobaric, then

$$T_{2s} = T_1(p_{2s}/p_1)^{(k-1)/k} = T_1\text{PR}^{(k-1)/k}$$

and

$$T_3 = T_{4s}(p_3/p_{4s})^{(k-1)/k} = T_{4s}\text{PR}^{(k-1)/k}$$

where PR is the isentropic pressure ratio. Hence, $T_{2s}/T_3 = T_1/T_{4s}$, and it can be shown that for an ASC (i.e., $(\eta_s)_c = (\eta_s)_e = 1.0$) Eqs. 8.46 and 8.47 reduce to

$$\text{COP}_{\substack{\text{reversed}\\\text{Brayton ASC}\\\text{HP}}} = \frac{T_3}{T_3 - T_{4s}} = (1 - \text{PR}^{(1-k)/k})^{-1} \tag{8.48}$$

and

$$\text{COP}_{\substack{\text{reversed}\\\text{Brayton ASC}\\\text{R/AC}}} = \frac{T_{4s}}{T_3 - T_{4s}} = (\text{PR}^{(k-1)/k} - 1)^{-1} \tag{8.49}$$

It is easy to show that these equations can also be obtained directly from Eqs. 8.23, 8.40, and 8.41. These results are illustrated in the following example.

Example 8.12 Determine the COP and cycle minimum cooling temperature of Gorrie's 1844 reversed Brayton cycle refrigerator if it had a pressure ratio of 3 to 1, a compressor inlet temperature of 70 °F and an expander inlet temperature of 80 °F using

a) an ASC analysis, and

b) an ideal gas analysis that includes typical mid nineteenth century compressor and expander isentropic efficiencies of 50% each.

Solution

a) From the problem statement we have PR = 3.0, $T_1 = 70\ °\text{F} = 530$ R, and $T_3 = 80\ °\text{F} = 540$ R. Then Eq. 8.49 gives the COP for a reversed Brayton R/AC ASC as

$$\text{COP}_{\substack{\text{reversed Brayton}\\ \text{ASC R/AC}}} = (3.0^{0.4/1.4} - 1)^{-1} = 2.71$$

and the minimum temperature within the cycle is the cooling temperature T_{4s}, which is given by

$$T_{4s} = T_3/\text{PR}^{(k-1)/k} = (540\ \text{R})/3.0^{0.4/1.4}$$
$$= 394.5\ \text{R} = -65.5\ °\text{F}$$

b) In a more realistic analysis we still assume ideal gas behavior, but now we introduce isentropic compressor and expander efficiencies of $(\eta_s)_c = (\eta_s)_e = 0.5$, and use Eq. 8.47, where the coldest temperature in the cycle is now only

$$T_4 = T_3 - (T_3 - T_{4s})(\eta_s)_e$$
$$= 540 - (540 - 394.5)(0.5) = 467.3\ \text{R} = 7.3\ °\text{F}$$

and

$$T_{2s} = T_1 T_3/T_{4s} = \frac{(530\ \text{R})(540\ \text{R})}{394.5\ \text{R}} = 725.5\ \text{R}$$

Then, Eq. 8.47 gives

$$\text{COP}_{\substack{\text{reversed}\\ \text{Brayton cycle}\\ \text{R/AC}}} = \frac{530 - 467.3}{[(725.5 - 530)/0.5] - (540 - 394.5)(0.5)} = 0.135$$

The results of part b of this example are much more realistic than those of part a due to the large thermodynamic irreversibilities (friction, heat loss, etc.) present in early mechanical equipment.

Like modern Brayton power cycles, modern reversed Brayton refrigeration cycles can be constructed with regeneration capability. Unlike power cycles, however, regeneration in refrigeration cycles does not improve the cycles thermal efficiency; instead it *reduces* the COP. However, regeneration does have the advantage of decreasing the minimum cooling temperature T_{4s}. Thus, the purpose of regeneration in refrigeration cycles is simply to be able to reach lower cooling temperatures. The use of a modern reversed Brayton refrigeration cycle is illustrated in the following example.

Example 8.13 Four lbm/s of air at 530 R enter the compressor of a reversed Brayton ASC refrigeration unit. The isentropic pressure ratio of the compressor is 3 to 1 and the inlet temperature of the expander is 600 R. Determine:

a) the expander power,
b) the compressor power,
c) the coefficient of performance of the unit, and
d) the refrigeration capacity of the unit in tons.

Solution State 1 is the compressor inlet, state 2 is the compressor outlet, state 3 is the expander inlet, and state 4 is the expander outlet. For an ASC all the processes are reversible, so the η_s of the expander and the compressor are both 1.0.

a) An energy rate balance on the expander gives

$$\dot{W}_{\text{expander}} = \dot{m}(h_{4s} - h_3) = \dot{m}c_p(T_{4s} - T_3)$$

where $T_{4s} = T_3(p_{4s}/p_3)^{(k-1)/k} = 600(1/3)^{0.4/1.4} = 438.4$ R. Then

$$\dot{W}_{\text{expander}} = (4\text{ lbm/s})[0.24\text{ Btu/(lbm}\cdot\text{R)}](438.4 - 600\text{ R}) = -155.1\text{ Btu/s}$$

b) An energy rate balance on the compressor gives

$$\dot{W}_{\text{compressor}} = \dot{m}(h_{2s} - h_1) = \dot{m}c_p(T_{2s} - T_1)$$

where $T_{2s} = T_1(p_{2s}/p_1)^{(k-1)/k} = 530(3)^{0.4/1.4} = 725.4$ R. Then

$$\dot{W}_{\text{compressor}} = 4(0.24)(725.4 - 530) = 187.6\text{ Btu/s}$$

c) Equation 8.49 gives the COP of this unit as

$$\text{COP} = (\text{PR}^{(k-1)/k} - 1)^{-1} = (3^{0.4/1.4} - 1)^{-1} = 2.71$$

d) Finally, the refrigeration capacity of this unit is

$$\begin{aligned}\dot{Q}_L &= \text{refrigeration capacity} = \text{COP}_{\text{R/AC}}(\dot{W}_{\text{in}})_{\text{net}} = 2.71(187.6 - 155.1)\\ &= (88.1\text{ Btu/s})(60\text{ s/min}) = (5286\text{ Btu/min})(1\text{ ton}/200\text{ Btu/min})\\ &= 26.4\text{ tons of refrigeration.}\end{aligned}$$

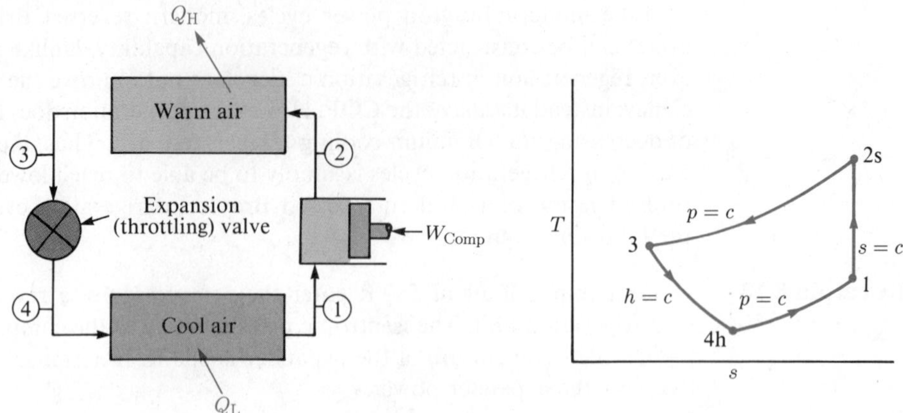

Figure 8.37 A Joule-Thomson refrigeration system.

Expansion (Joule-Thomson) and Absorption Refrigeration

The cooling that results from the expansion or throttling of a gas from a high to a low pressure is called Joule-Thomson cooling. A refrigeration ASC analysis predicts that no cooling will occur in this type of throttling because an ideal gas throttling process is both isenthalpic and isothermal. However, *real* gases and vapors do undergo a temperature change during isenthalpic processes as dictated by their Joule-Thomson coefficient. This coefficient was discussed in Chapter 4, and was defined in Eq. 4.123 as

$$\mu_J = \left(\frac{\partial T}{\partial p}\right)_h \tag{4.123}$$

so that, approximately,

$$(\Delta T)_h = \mu_J(\Delta p)_h \tag{8.50}$$

The value of μ_J can be either positive or negative, and it is usually larger at lower temperatures.[48] For example, the Joule-Thomson coefficient for air at 70 °F and several hundred psi is only about 0.03 °F/psi (see Figure 4.10). Thus, throttling air from 100 psig down to atmospheric pressure would produce a temperature drop in the air of only about 3 °F. Such a system is shown in Figure 8.37.

The refrigeration or air conditioning COP of a Joule-Thomson expansion throttling device is given by

$$\mathrm{COP}_{\substack{\text{J-T}\\ \text{R/AC}}} = \frac{\dot{Q}_L}{\dot{W}_c} = \frac{T_1 - T_{4h}}{(T_{2s} - T_1)/(\eta_s)_c}$$

48. If μ_J is negative, then you will have Joule-Thomson heating of the gas upon throttling (see Table 4.12).

and if $T_1 = T_3$, $p_2 = p_3$, and $p_4 = p_1$, then this reduces to

$$\text{COP}_{\substack{\text{J-T}\\ \text{R/AC}}} = \frac{\mu_J(p_2 - p_1)}{T_1[(p_2/p_1)^{(k-1)/k} - 1]/(\eta_s)_c} \tag{8.51}$$

The vortex tube discussed in Chapter 5 is a variation of this technique. It does not appear to depend upon the Joule-Thomson effect, and it can produce cold temperatures in only part of the outlet flow. The remainder of the outlet flow is quite warm (see Figure 5.18).

Example 8.14

Determine the outlet temperature and COP of a Joule-Thomson expansion throttling device using air when the inlet temperature and pressure are 70 °F and 300 psia and the outlet pressure is 14.7 psia. Assume the Joule-Thomson coefficient for air in this range is 0.03 °F/psi, and that the isentropic efficiency of the air compressor is 90%.

Solution From Eq. 8.50 we have,

$$T_2 - T_1 = \mu_J(p_2 - p_1) = 0.03(14.7 - 300) = -8.6\ ^\circ\text{F}$$

Then, $T_2 = 70 - 8.6 = 61.4$ °F, and Eq. 8.51 gives the COP as

$$\text{COP}_{\substack{\text{J-T}\\ \text{R/AC}}} = \frac{0.03(14.7 - 300)}{(70 + 460)\left[\left(\dfrac{14.7}{300}\right)^{0.4/1.4} - 1\right]\Big/0.9} = 0.025$$

Therefore, the thermal efficiency of this type of Joule-Thomson expansion throttling refrigeration or air conditioner is only 2.5%.[49]

Though the Joule-Thomson refrigerator is not very effective by itself, it is often used in conjunction with other refrigeration systems. Figure 8.38 shows it being used with a reversed Brayton cycle to liquefy the working fluid. This was the basic technique used by Karl von Linde (1842–1934) to produce liquid air on a large commercial scale in 1895.

Other reversed gas cycles such as the Stirling cycle have been used effectively in refrigeration systems. Also, a technique has been developed in which no compressors or expanders are necessary. It is called *absorption* refrigeration and is based upon dissolving the refrigerant vapor in a *carrier* liquid and then pumping this liquid to a high pressure. The pressurized liquid is then fed into a generator where the refrigerant vapor is boiled off, now at a much higher pressure, and the carrier liquid is then returned to the absorber to continue the process. The high-pressure refrigerant vapor then continues through the refrigeration cycle in the

49. Note that the thermal efficiency of a heat pump is always greater than 100% (i.e., its COP > 1.0), but the thermal efficiency of a refrigerator or air conditioner can be less than 100%.

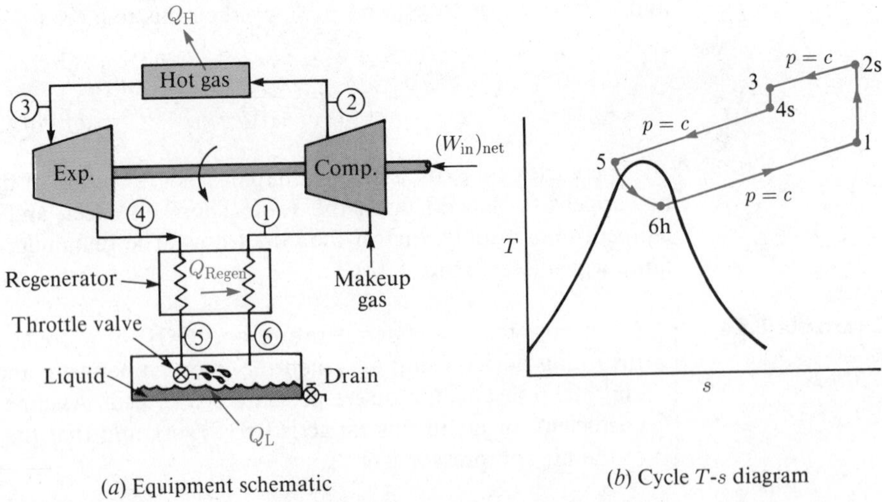

(*a*) Equipment schematic

(*b*) Cycle *T*-*s* diagram

Figure 8.38 The basic Linde process for liquefying air (1895).

normal reversed Rankine manner. Such a system is shown schematically in Figure 8.39. This technique has the advantage that less expensive technology is required to efficiently pump a liquid than is required to efficiently compress a vapor. However, internal irreversibilities keep the actual COPs of absorption systems to around 1.0. Common absorption refrigeration fluid systems are ammonia (refrigerant)–water (carrier), water (refrigerant)–lithium bromide (carrier), and water (refrigerant)–lithium chloride (carrier). The ammonia–water system was widely used in domestic refrigerators until about 1950. Lithium salt systems are common in commercial air conditioning systems today.[50]

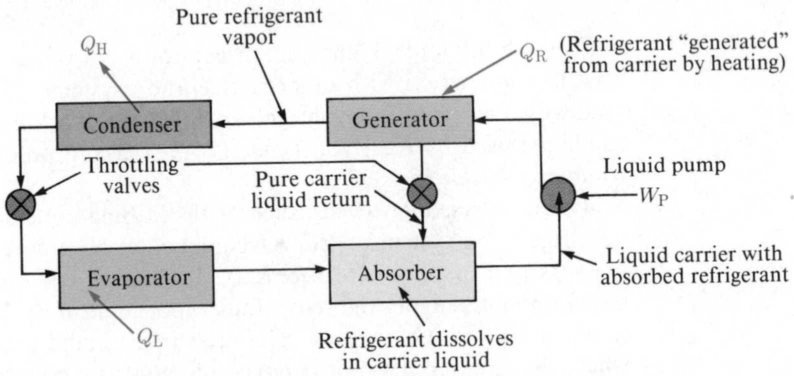

Figure 8.39 A basic absorption refrigeration system.

50. Since water is the refrigerant in these systems they cannot go below 32 °F (0 °C) and consequently are mainly used in air conditioning applications.

Second Law Analysis of Power and Refrigeration Cycles

The difference between the isentropic thermal efficiency and the actual thermal efficiency of a system is due to the effects of the second law of thermodynamics. The second law can be used to determine viscous irreversibilities leading to pressure losses in pipes, valves, and fittings; to determine heat transfer irreversibilities due to incomplete insulation and large temperature gradients; and to determine mechanical and chemical irreversibilities in pumps, compressors, and prime movers due to friction and chemical reactions. However, piping and ancillary viscous losses (irreversibilities) are normally determined through the empirical *friction factor* material introduced in Chapter 5 (and found in most fluid mechanics textbooks), and mechanical and thermal losses in machinery are globally lumped into its empirically determined (by measurement on an actual machine) isentropic efficiency η_s. The application of the second law to complex systems is so difficult today that it usually cannot be used effectively in the engineering design stage of product development. Its influence can only be measured during prototype testing. This will, no doubt, change as technology and engineering analysis advance in the future.

The thermal efficiency η_T is essentially a *first law efficiency* in that it is concerned with the effectiveness of the energy conversion process in terms of the ratio of a desired output to a required input. On the other hand, the isentropic efficiency η_s can be viewed as a *second law efficiency* in that it compares the actual performance of a real irreversible system with its idealized reversible counterpart. Consequently, the primary role of the second law of thermodynamics in the analysis of power and refrigeration cycles today is through the (largely empirical) determination and use of the isentropic efficiency. Many of the pragmatic aspects of courses in heat transfer, fluid mechanics, electrical circuit theory, and machine design today are the result of the consequences of the second law of thermodynamics.

Summary

Power and refrigeration cycles are the heart and soul of applied thermodynamics. Their commercialization has brought humanity from a meager medieval cottage industry to an advanced technological society with a much higher standard of living. The empirical development of power and refrigeration technology beginning in the seventeenth century provided the basis and motivation for the theoretical understanding of thermodynamics as an intellectual pursuit in the mid nineteenth century.

The field of applied thermodynamics is so broad that it is difficult to present it adequately in just one chapter. In this chapter we have attempted to find a new course for its presentation by carefully charting the chronology of its development. You will find that this chapter is unique when compared to those of other thermodynamic textbooks. My goal was to provide you, the reader, with a historical perspectiive on this important technology, to provide some historical benchmarks with which to judge the significance of its impact on society, and to broaden your understanding of your chosen profession. It is my belief that the history of the human race is primarily a history of its technological development,

Table 8.4 Summary of power and refrigeration cycle thermodynamic processes

Cycle name	Constant property processes of the cycle
Carnot (1820)	2 isentropes, 2 isotherms (2s, 2T)
Rankine (1859)	2 isentropes, 2 isobars (2s, 2p), mostly under the vapor dome
Stirling (1816)	2 isotherms, 2 isochors (2T, 2v)
Fricsson (1833)	2 isotherms, 2 isobars (2T, 2p)
Lenoir (1860)	1 isentrope, 1 isochor, 1 isobar (1s, 1v, 1p)
Brayton (1873)	2 isentropes, 2 isobars (2s, 2p)
Otto (1876)	2 isentropes, 2 isochors (2s, 2v)
Diesel (1893)	2 isentropes, 1 isochor, 1 isobar (2s, 1v, 1p)

with the social faux pas of the ruling aristocracy being much less significant than the concurrent advances in mathematics, metallurgy, mechanics, and so forth.

Table 8.4 summarizes the basic elements of the power and refrigeration cycles studied in this chapter.

Selected References

Faires, V. M., and Simmand, C. M. *Thermodynamics*, 6th ed. New York: MacMillan, 1978.

Haberman, W. L., and John, J. E. *Engineering Thermodynamics.* Boston: Allyn & Bacon, 1980.

Holman, J. P. *Thermodynamics*, 3d ed. New York: McGraw-Hill, 1980.

Karlekar, B. V. *Thermodynamics for Engineers.* Englewood Cliffs, NJ: Prentice-Hall, 1983.

Sanford, J. F. *Heat Engines.* Garden City, NY: Doubleday, 1962.

Thurston, R. H. *A History of the Growth of the Steam-Engine*, Centennial ed. Ithaca, NY: Cornell Univ. Press, 1939.

Van Wylen, G. J., and Sonntag, R. E. *Fundamentals of Classical Thermodynamics*, 3d ed. New York: Wiley, 1986.

Wark, K. *Thermodynamics*, 5th ed. New York: McGraw-Hill, 1988.

Wood, B. D. *Applications of Thermodynamics*, 2d ed. Reading, MA: Addison-Wesley, 1982.

Additional References on Early Steam Power

Barnard, W. E., Ellenwood, F. O., and Hirshfeld, C. F. *Elements of Heat-Power Engineering.*, Part 1, *Thermodynamics and Prime Movers*, 3d ed. New York: Wiley, 1926.

Church, E. F. *Steam Turbines*, 3d ed. New York: McGraw-Hill, 1950.

Doolittle, J. S., and Zerban, A. H. *Engineering Thermodynamics*, 2d ed. Scranton, PA: International Textbook, 1954.

Faires, V. M. *Applied Thermodynamics.* New York: MacMillan, 1938.

Gaffert, G. A. *Steam Power Stations*, 4th ed. New York: McGraw-Hill, 1952.

Peabody, C. H. *Thermodynamics of the Steam Engine.* New York: Wiley, 1904.

Vincent, E. T. *The Theory and Design of Gas Turbines and Jet Engines.* New York: McGraw-Hill, 1950.

Chapter Eight Problems

Problems for Section I

1. The duty of a 1718 Newcomen engine was found to be 4.3 million. Determine its thermal efficiency (%).

2. In 1767 John Smeaton measured the performance of a particularly efficient Newcomen engine that had a 42-in (1.07-m) diameter piston and found that it produced 16.7 net horsepower (12.5 kW) with a duty of 7.44 million. Determine **a)** the thermal efficiency of the engine and **b)** the boiler heat input rate.

3. In 1767 John Smeaton measured the performance of a Newcomen engine with a 60-in (1.52-m) diameter piston and found that it produced 40.8 net horsepower (30.4 kW) with a duty of 5.88 million. Determine **a)** the thermal efficiency of this engine and **b)** its boiler heat input rate.

4. In 1767 John Smeaton measured the performance of a Newcomen engine with a 75-in (1.91-m) diameter piston and found that it produced 37.6 net horsepower (28.0 kW) with a duty of 4.59 million. Determine **a)** the thermal efficiency of this engine and **b)** the boiler heat input rate.

5. In 1772 John Smeaton used the results of his tests on various existing Newcomen cycle engines to design and build his own atmospheric steam engine. It had a 52-in (1.32-m) diameter piston with a 7-ft (2.13-m) stroke and operated at 12.5 strokes per minute with a mean effective pressure of 7.5 lbf/in^2 (51.7 kPa). It produced a remarkably high duty of 9.45 million. Determine the **a)** thermal efficiency, **b)** the horsepower output, and **c)** the boiler heat input rate of this engine. Ignore the boiler feed pump power requirement.

6. In 1790 John Curr of Sheffield, England, made an atmospheric steam engine with a 61 in (1.55 m) diameter piston and an 8.5 ft (2.59 m) stroke. The engine operated with a mean effective piston pressure of 7.0 lbf/in^2 (48.3 kPa) and ran at 12 strokes per minute. It produced a duty of 9.38 million. Determine **a)** the thermal efficiency, **b)** the horsepower output, and **c)** the boiler heat input rate of this engine. Ignore the boiler feed pump power requirement.

7. An engine operating on a Carnot cycle extracts 10 kJ of heat per cycle from a thermal reservoir at 1000 °C and rejects a smaller amount of heat to a low-temperature thermal reservoir at 10 °C. Determine the net work produced per cycle of operation.

8. It is desired to obtain 1 kW of power from a heat engine operating on a Carnot cycle. 3 kW of heat is supplied to the engine from a thermal reservoir at 600 K. What is the required temperature of the low temperature reservoir, and how much heat must be rejected to it?

9. For the thermal reservoir temperatures shown below, determine **a)** the Carnot cycle heat engine thermal efficiency, and **b)** which is the more effective method of increasing this efficiency, increasing T_H by an amount ΔT or lowering T_L by an amount ΔT, and why.

No.	T_H (°F)	T_L (°F)
1	4000	500
2	4000	100
3	2000	500
4	2000	100

10. Steam enters the turbine of a power plant at 200 psia, 500 °F. How much will the Carnot cycle thermal efficiency increase if the condenser pressure is lowered from 14.7 to 1.0 psia?

11. Steam enters the piston cylinder of a Newcomen cycle steam engine at 14.7 psia, 212 °F and condenses at 6.0 psia. Plot the thermal efficiency of the reversible cycle vs the averaged cylinder wall temperature over the range 170 °F $\leq (T_b)_{avg} \leq$ 212 °F. Neglect the effect of the boiler feed pump.

12. Determine the maximum possible thermal efficiency of an atmospheric steam engine with a boiler temperature of 212 °F and a condensation temperature of 70 °F if it operates on

a) a Carnot cycle,
b) a Newcomen cycle assuming an average cylinder wall temperature of 141 °F, and
c) a Rankine cycle.

13. Steam with a quality of 1.0 enters the turbine of a Rankine cycle power plant at 400 psia and exits at 1 psia. Neglecting pumping power, determine the Rankine cycle isentropic thermal efficiency.

14. Determine the decrease in Carnot and isentropic Rankine cycle thermal efficiencies if the condenser is removed from the engine discussed in text Example 8.3 and the steam is allowed to exhaust directly into the atmosphere at 14.7 psia. Assume the cycles are still closed loop.

15. Show that the Carnot and isentropic Rankine cycle thermal efficiencies for an engine whose boiler produces dry saturated steam at 100 psia and whose condenser operates at 1.0 psia are 28.7 and 26.1%, respectively. Draw the appropriate *T-s* and *p-v* diagrams for these cycles.

16. Rework Problem 15 for an engine without a condenser, with the steam exhausting directly into the atmosphere at 14.7 psia. Determine the Carnot and isentropic Rankine cycle thermal efficiencies and their percent decrease due to the removal of the condenser. Assume the cycles are still closed loop.

17. Steam enters the turbine of a Rankine cycle power plant at 200 psia and 500 °F. How much will the isentropic Rankine cycle thermal efficiency increase if the condenser pressure is lowered from 14.7 psia to 1.0 psia? Neglect the pump work.

18. A small portable nuclear-powered Rankine cycle steam power plant has a turbine inlet state of 200 psia, 600 °F, and a condenser temperature of 80 °F. The steam mass flow rate is 0.5 lbm/s. Assuming that the condenser exit state is a saturated liquid, that the pump and turbine isentropic efficiencies are 55 and 75%, respectively, and that there are no pressure losses across the boiler or condenser, determine

a) the actual power required to drive the pump,
b) the actual power output of the plant, and
c) the actual thermal efficiency of the plant.

19. A Rankine cycle power plant is to be used as a stationary power source for a polar research station. The working fluid is Refrigerant-12 at a flow rate of 8.0 lbm/s, and the turbine inlet state is saturated vapor at 200 °F. The condenser is air cooled and has an internal temperature of 0 °F. Assuming a turbine and pump isentropic efficiency of 85% and that the refrigerant leaves the condenser as a saturated liquid, determine the overall thermodynamic efficiency and the net power output of the system.

20. A solar-powered Rankine cycle power plant uses 1500 m^2 of solar collectors. Refrigerant-12 is used as the working fluid at a flow rate of 1.0 kg/s, and is transformed from a saturated liquid to a saturated vapor in the solar collectors (which function as the boiler) at a constant temperature of 40 °C. The condenser for the system operates at 20 °C, and the pump and prime mover isentropic efficiencies are 65 and 75%, respectively. Determine the prime mover power output and system thermal efficiency when the incident solar flux is 8.0 W/m^2.

21. Saltwater oceans have subsurface stratification layers called *thermoclines* across which large temperature differences can exist. A 1.0-MW Rankine cycle power plant using ammonia as the working fluid is being designed to operate on a thermocline temperature difference. The ammonia exits the boiler as a saturated vapor at 28 °C, and exits the condenser as a saturated liquid at 10 °C. For an isentropic system, determine

a) the thermal efficiency of the power plant,

b) the pump to turbine power ratio, and

c) the required mass flow rate of ammonia.

22. The condensation that can occur in the low-pressure end of a steam turbine is undesirable because it can cause corrosion and blade erosion thus reducing the turbine's isentropic efficiency. This can be avoided by superheating the steam before it enters the turbine. What degree of superheat would be required if the steam entered an isentropic turbine at 300 psia and exited as a saturated vapor at 1.0 psia?

23. Steam enters the turbine of a Rankine cycle power plant at 12 MPa and 400 °C. How much will the isentropic thermal efficiency increase if the condenser pressure is lowered from 0.1 to 0.001 MPa?

24. Steam enters the turbine of a Rankine cycle power plant at 200 psia and 500 °F. How much will the isentropic thermal efficiency increase if the condenser pressure is lowered from 14.7 to 1.0 psia?

25. Steam leaves the boiler of a Rankine cycle power plant at 3000 psia and 1000 °F. It is isenthalpically throttled to 600 psia before it enters the turbine. It then exits the turbine at 1.0 psia. Determine

a) the maximum thermal efficiency of this plant, and

b) its maximum thermal efficiency if the boiler were operated at 600 psia and 1000 °F and no throttling occurred at the entrance to the turbine.

26. Steam exits a boiler and enters a turbine at 200 psia, 600 °F with a mass flow rate of 30,000 lbm/h. It exits the turbine at 1.0 psia and is condensed. The condensate then reenters the boiler as a saturated liquid at 90 °F. The turbine drives an electrical generator that delivers 3000 kW of power. Determine

a) the Rankine cycle thermal efficiency of the entire system, and

b) the isentropic efficiency of the combined turbine–generator unit.

27. An isentropic Rankine cycle using steam is shown below. For the given data determine.

a) the quality of the turbine exhaust steam,

b) the cycle thermal efficiency, and

c) the mass flow rate required to produce 10,000 Btu/s net output power.

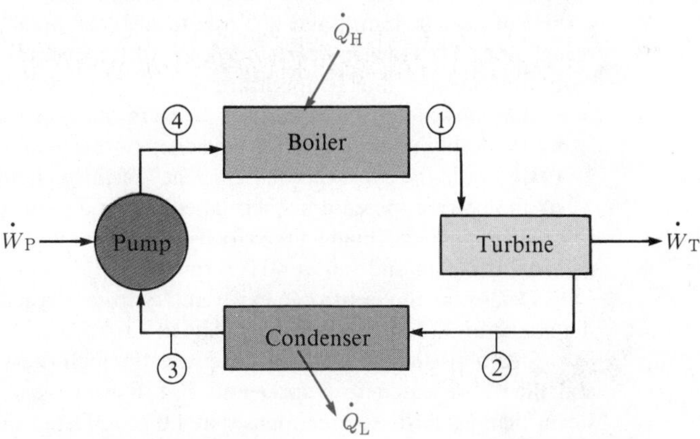

(Continued on the next page.)

Station 1	Station 2	Station 3	Station 4
$p_1 = 1000$ psia	$p_2 = 3.0$ psia	$p_3 = 3.0$ psia	$p_4 = 1000$ psia
$T_1 = 1000$ °F	$s_2 = s_1$	$x_3 = 0.0$	$s_4 = s_3$

The process path from station 1 to 2 is an isentropic expansion, and that from station 3 to 4 is an isentropic compression.

28. For a constant steam boiler temperature of 400 °C, a constant turbine exhaust moisture content of 5.0%, and a constant condenser pressure of 3.0 kPa, plot the Rankine cycle thermal efficiency vs. boiler pressure over the boiler pressure range from 1.0 to 20.0 MPa. Ignore the work required by the boiler feed pump.

29. Steam is supplied to a turbine at a rate of 1,000,000 kg/h at 500 °C and 10.0 MPa, and it exhausts to a condenser at 2.0 kPa. A single open-loop regenerator is used to heat the boiler feedwater with steam extracted from the turbine at 6.0 MPa. The condensate exits the regenerator at 6.0 MPa as a saturated liquid. Determine

a) the mass flow rate of steam extracted from the turbine,

b) the systems isentropic Rankine cycle thermal efficiency,

c) the isentropic Rankine cycle thermal efficiency of the same system without a regenerator, and

d) the percent increase in thermal efficiency due to the regenerator.

30. Steam enters a turbine with an isentropic efficiency of 83% at 300 psia, 800° F, and exhausts to a condenser at 0.25 psia. The boiler feedwater is heated in a single open-loop regenerator with steam extracted from the turbine at 100 psia. Saturated liquid leaves the regenerator at the pressure of the extraction steam. Neglecting all pump work, determine

a) the percent mass flow of steam extracted from the turbine,

b) the turbine power output per unit mass flow of steam,

c) the system thermal efficiency,

d) the turbine power output per unit mass flow of steam when the regenerator is not in use,

e) the system thermal efficiency when the regenerator is not in use, and

f) the percent increase in system thermal efficiency produced by the regenerator.

31. Repeat items a, b and c of Problem 30 for steam extraction pressures of 75, 50, 25, and 10 psia, and plot these results vs. the extraction pressure.

32. A turbine having an isentropic efficiency of 86% receives steam at 4,000,000 lbm/h, 300 psia, 1000 °F, and exhausts it to a condenser at 1.0 psia. Steam is extracted from the turbine at 788,000 lbm/h and 200 psia to heat the boiler feedwater in a single closed-loop regenerator. The extract steam then exits the regenerator as a saturated liquid. Determine

a) the pressure and temperature of the extract steam as it leaves the regenerator and explain how it can be at a lower pressure than the inlet steam,

b) the Rankine cycle thermal efficiency of this system,

c) the Rankine cycle thermal efficiency of this system without regeneration, and

d) the percent increase in thermal efficiency due to the regenerator.

33. Determine the blade tip velocity of DeLaval's first steam turbine. It had a rotor diameter of 3.0 in and ran at 40,000 rpm.

34. Determine the isentropic exit velocity from a reaction turbine nozzle if steam enters the nozzle at 30 MPa, 500 °C and exits at 1.0 MPa.

35. Steam at 600 psia and 800 °F enters the high-pressure stage of an isentropic turbine and then is reheated to 60 psia and 700 °F before entering the low-pressure stage. The steam then exhausts to a condenser at 1.0 psia. Determine

a) the isentropic Rankine cycle thermal efficiency,

b) the isentropic Rankine cycle thermal efficiency that would occur if the steam were not reheated, and

c) the percent increase in thermal efficiency due to the reheating operation.

36. Steam enters the high-pressure turbine of a Rankine cycle power plant at 1200 psia and 700 °C, and exits as a saturated vapor. It is then reheated to 600 °F before it enters the low pressure turbine, which exhausts to a condenser at 1.0 psia. The isentropic efficiencies of the high- and low-pressure turbines and the boiler feed pump are 88, 79, and 65%, respectively. Determine the thermal efficiency and the net power per unit mass flow rate of steam for this plant.

37. Consider a steam turbine with a constant inlet temperature of 500 °C connected to a constant pressure condenser at 1.0 kPa. When the steam expands to a saturated vapor in the turbine it is removed and reheated in the boiler to 500 °C and then returned to the turbine to continue to expand until it reaches the condenser pressure. The turbine isentropic efficiency is constant at 80%. Ignoring the boiler feed pump work, plot

a) the Rankine cycle thermal efficiency, and

b) the percent moisture in the turbine exhaust vs. the boiler pressure over a boiler pressure range of 1.0 to 20.0 MPa. Computerized steam tables are recommended for this problem.

38. The first steam turbine used in an American electrical power plant was a Westinghouse reaction turbine of the Parson's type installed at the Hartford CT Electric Light Company in 1902. The turbine inlet state was 180 psig and 350 °F, the generator produced 2.0 MW, and the plant had a heat rate of 35,000 Btu/(kW·h). Determine its thermal efficiency.

39. In 1903 a General Electric Curtis impulse steam turbine was installed at the Fisk Street Station of the Commonwealth Electric Company in Chicago, Illinois, and was at that time the most powerful steam turbine in the world.[51] The turbine inlet state was 175 psig with 150 °F of superheat, and the condenser pressure was 1.5 in of mercury. When the generator produced 5000 kW, the steam flow rate was 22.5 lbm/(kW·h). For this unit determine

a) the isentropic power output of the turbine,

b) the isentropic efficiency of the turbine–generator unit, and

c) the isentropic Rankine cycle thermal efficiency of the power plant assuming saturated liquid exits the condenser and neglecting pump work.

40. In 1939 the Port Washington, Wisconsin, power plant of the Milwaukee Electric Railway and Light Company[52] had an unusually high heat rate of 10,803 Btu/(kW·h). Determine its thermal efficiency.

41. Refrigerant-12 is used as the working fluid in a 1.0 MW Rankine bottoming cycle for a steam power plant. The bottoming cycle turbine inlet state is saturated vapor at 210 °F, and the condenser outlet is saturated liquid at 70 °F. The turbine and pump isentropic efficiencies are 85 and 70%, respectively. Determine

a) the thermal efficiency of the bottoming cycle,

b) the ratio of the pump to turbine power, and

c) the required mass flow rate of refrigerant.

42. It is common to model hot ASC performance with the same formula used in cold ASC analysis except that a specific heat ratio (k) typical of high-temperature gas is used. Determine the Carnot ASC thermal efficiency of an engine with an 8 to 1 compression

---

51. On May 28, 1975, this turbine–generator unit was designated as the seventh National Historic Mechanical Engineering Landmark by the American Society of Mechanical engineers.

52. In 1980 this power plant was designated as the 48th National Historic Mechanical Engineering Landmark by the American Society of Mechanical Engineers.

ratio using

a) a cold ASC analysis with $k = 1.4$, and

b) a hot ASC analysis with $k = 1.3$.

c) Determine the percent decrease in the Carnot thermal efficiency between the cold and hot ASC analysis.

43. Air enters an engine at 40° F and is compressed isentropically in a 9 to 1 compression ratio. Determine the Carnot ASC thermal efficiency of this engine using

a) a cold ASC analysis with $k = 1.4$, and

b) a hot ASC analysis using the gas tables (Appendix C.16*a*).

c) Determine the percent decrease in the Carnot thermal efficiency between the cold and hot ASC analysis.

44. Air enters an engine at atmospheric pressure and 17 °C, and is isentropically compressed to 871.4 kPa. Determine the Carnot ASC thermal efficiency of the engine using

a) a cold ASC analysis with $k = 1.4$, and

b) a hot ASC analysis using the gas tables (Appendix C.16*b*).

c) Determine the percent decrease in the Carnot thermal efficiency between the cold and hot ASC analysis.

45. Determine the mechanical efficiency of a Stirling cycle engine operating with a 1300 °F heater and a 100 °F cooler. The engine produces a net 10.0-hp output with a heat input of 80,000 Btu/h.

46. In 1964 an experimental Stirling engine was installed in a modified Chevrolet Corvair at the General Motors Research Laboratory. Alumina (aluminum oxide) heated to 1200 °F served as the heat source for the engine while the atmosphere at 100 °F served as the heat sink (because of the use of alumina in the engine, the car was dubbed the "Calvair" by GM researchers). Assuming a mechanical efficiency of 67%, determine the actual thermal efficiency of the engine based on a cold ASC analysis.

47. A Stirling cycle engine uses 0.08 lbm of air as the working fluid. Heat is added to this air isothermally at 1500 °F, and is rejected isothermally at 200 °F. The initial volume of the air before the heat addition ($\mathcal{V}_4$ in Figure 8.23) is 0.75 ft^3 and the final volume after the heat addition ($\mathcal{V}_1$ in Figure 8.23) is 1.00 ft^3. For the cold ASC, determine

a) the air pressure at the beginning and end of the expansion stroke (p_4 and p_1 in Figure 8.23),

b) the air pressure at the beginning and end of the compression stroke (p_2 and p_3 in Figure 8.23),

c) the cold ASC thermal efficiency of the engine, and

d) the net reversible work produced inside the engine per cycle of operation.

48. In 1853 John Ericsson constructed a huge 300-hp hot air engine that ran on the Ericsson cycle. It had pistons 14 ft (4.3 m) in diameter and it consumed 2.0 lbm of coal per indicated horsepower hour. Assuming a heating value for coal of 13,000 Btu/lbm and that the engine was reversible, determine the thermal efficiency of this engine.

49. The air standard Ericsson cycle (see Figure 8.24) is made up of an isothermal compressor ($T_2 = T_3 = T_L$), an isothermal prime mover ($T_1 = T_4 = T_H$) and an isobaric regenerator ($p_1 = p_2$ and $p_3 = p_4$). Show that the compressor and prime mover must have identical pressure ratios, i.e., $p_2/p_3 = p_1/p_4$, and then show that this also requires that $v_3/v_2 = v_4/v_1$.

50. An Ericsson cycle operates with a minimum pressure and volume of 1.0 MPa, 0.02 m^3, and a maximum pressure and volume of 5.0 MPa, 0.04 m^3. For a reversible cycle, determine

a) the heat added,

b) the heat rejected,

c) the work done, and
d) the thermal efficiency of the cycle.

51. An inventor claims to have developed a Lenoir engine with an isentropic compression ratio of 8 to 1 that produces a combustion temperature of 1500 °C when the intake temperature is 20 °C. Assuming $k = 1.4$ and that the engine operates on a cold ASC, show whether or not the inventor's claim is possible.

52. A World War II Lenoir cycle "buzz bomb" has an air intake at 10 °C, a combustion temperature of 1000 °C, and a compression ratio of 2.3. Determine its cold ASC thermal efficiency.

53. Plot the cold ASC thermal efficiency of a Lenoir engine having an air intake at 15 °C and a combustion temperature of 2000 °C vs. the isentropic compression ratio over the range $1.01 \leq CR \leq 5.50$.

54. A Brayton cold ASC has a turbine isentropic efficiency of 92% and a compressor isentropic pressure ratio of 8.37. The compressor and turbine inlet temperatures are 500 and 2200 R, respectively. Determine the value of the compressor isentropic efficiency that will cause the overall thermodynamic thermal efficiency of this system to be exactly zero.

55. A Brayton cold ASC has a turbine that is 80% isentropically efficient and a compressor with an isentropic pressure ratio of 7.0. The compressor inlet temperature is 530 R and the turbine inlet temperature is 2640 R. Determine the compressor isentropic efficiency which would cause the entire cycle efficiency to become exactly zero. Assume $k = 1.4$.

56. Show that the product of the compressor and turbine isentropic efficiencies must be greater than $(T_L/T_H)^{1/2}$ if a Brayton cycle gas turbine unit is to operate at its maximum power output.

57. A test on an open-loop Brayton cycle gas turbine produced the following results:

net power output = 180.5 hp
air mass flow rate = 20,000 1bm/h
inlet air temperature = 80 °F
inlet air pressure = 14.5 psia
compressor exit pressure = 195 psia
compressor isentropic efficiency = 85%
combustion chamber heat addition = 4,000,000 Btu/h

Using a cold ASC analysis and assuming $k = 1.4$, determine
a) the cycle thermal efficiency, and
b) the isentropic efficiency of the turbine.

58. On July 29, 1949, the first gas turbine installed in the United States for generating electric power went into service at the Belle Isle station of the Oklahoma Gas and Electric Company.[53] It had a 15-stage compressor with an isentropic pressure ratio of 6 to 1, a two-stage turbine with overall entrance and exit temperatures of 1400 and 780 °F, respectively, and the turbine–generator unit was rated at 3500 kW. Assuming a Brayton cold ASC, determine
a) the isentropic efficiency of the turbine, and
b) the thermal efficiency of the entire turbine–compressor unit.

59. The regenerator in a Brayton cycle is simply a heat exchanger designed to transfer heat from hot exhaust gas to cool inlet gas. In an "ideal" regenerator the exit temperature of the inlet (heated) gas would be equal to the entrance temperature of the exhaust (cooled) gas. Since this is not normally the case in practice, a *regenerator (or heat exchanger) efficiency*

---

53. On November 8, 1984, the Belle Isle gas turbine was designated as the 73rd National Historic Mechanical Engineering Landmark by the American Society of Mechanical Engineers.

can be defined as

$$\eta_{\text{regeneration}} = \frac{(h_{\text{out}} - h_{\text{in}})_{\text{heated}}}{(h_{\text{in}})_{\text{cooled}} - (h_{\text{in}})_{\text{heated}}}$$

and for constant specific heats this reduces to

$$\eta_{\text{regeneration}} = \frac{(T_{\text{out}} - T_{\text{in}})_{\text{heated}}}{(T_{\text{in}})_{\text{cooled}} - (T_{\text{in}})_{\text{heated}}}$$

Note that regeneration is practical only when the engine exhaust temperature is greater than the compressor exhaust temperature. Therefore, as the compression and expansion ratios of the compressor and prime mover increase, the effectivenss of regeneration decreases. Determine an expression for the limiting isentropic pressure ratio (PR) in terms of T_1, T_3, and k for which regeneration is no longer useful in the Brayton ASC with regeneration shown below. Evaluate this expression to find the limiting pressure ratio when $T_1 = 1500$ °C, $T_3 = 10$ °C, and $k = 1.4$.

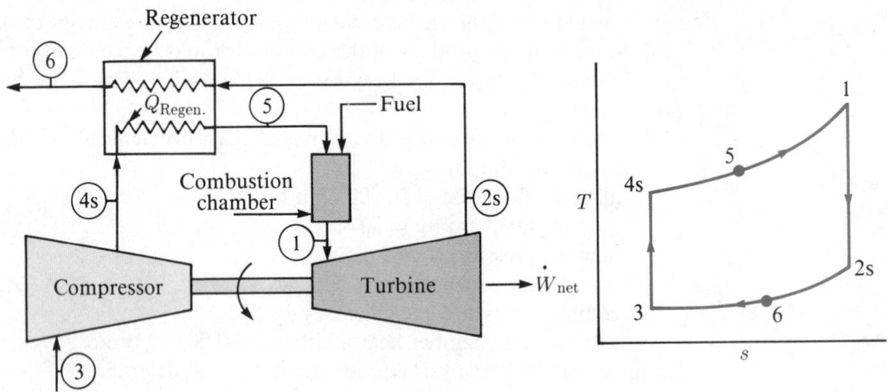

60. An aircraft gas turbine engine operating on a Brayton cycle has a cold ASC thermal efficiency of 25% when the intake air is at 20 °C and the combustion chamber outlet temperature is at 1200 °C. Assuming $k = 1.4$, determine

a) the isentropic pressure ratio of the engine,
b) the isentropic compression ratio of the engine,
c) the isentropic outlet temperature of the engine's compressor,
d) the optimum isentropic pressure ratio for maximum isentropic power output from the engine,
e) the optimum isentropic compression ratio for maximum isentropic power output from the engine, and
f) the engine's thermal efficiency when operated at the maximum isentropic power output.

61. An internal combustion engine operating on the Otto cycle has a pressure and temperature of 13 psia and 70 °F at the beginning of the compression stroke (state 3 in Figure 8.29), and a pressure at the end of the compression stroke of 200 psia. For the cold ASC with $k = 1.4$, determine

a) the compression ratio, CR,
b) the temperature at the end of the compression stroke, and
c) the thermal efficiency of the cycle.

62. An eight-cylinder, four-stroke Otto cycle racing engine has a 4.0-in bore and a 4.0-in stroke with a compression ratio of 10 to 1. Find the mean effective pressure in the cylinders when the engine is running at 5000 rpm and burning fuel at a rate of $\dot{Q}_H = 10{,}000$ Btu/s. Assume $k = 1.4$.

63. Determine the actual brake horsepower produced by a four-stroke Otto cycle internal combustion engine operating with a 7.5 to 1 compression ratio and a mechanical efficiency of 30% when the combustion of the fuel is producing 225,000 Btu/h inside the engine. Assume $k = 1.4$.

64. Air enters an Otto cycle internal combustion engine at 90 kPa and 15 °C. The engine has a compression ratio of 8 to 1. During the compression process 3000 kJ per kg of air is added to the air. Assuming a reversible engine, determine
a) the pressure and temperature at the end of each process of the cycle,
b) the engine's cold ASC thermal efficiency, and
c) the mean effective pressure of the engine.

65. Determine the output horsepower of a small two-stroke Otto cycle internal combustion engine that has the following characteristics
displacement = 5.0 cubic inches
speed = 2000 rpm
compression ratio = 8 to 1
air-fuel ratio = 15 to 1
mechanical efficiency = 30%
fuel heating value = 18,000 Btu/lbm
ambient conditions = 14.7 psia and 70 °F

66. A dynamometer test of a six-cylinder Otto four-stroke cycle engine with a 231-cubic-inch displacement gave the following results at 4000 rpm:
indicated power output = 250 hp
actual (or brake) power output = 75 hp
heating value of the fuel being used = 20,000 Btu/lbm
fuel consumption rate = 54 lbm/h

Determine
a) the mechanical efficiency η_m of the engine,
b) the ASC thermal efficiency of the engine
c) the isentropic compression ratio (CR) of the engine assuming an Otto cold ASC, and
d) the mean effective pressure (mep) inside the combustion chamber.

67. A Diesel cycle internal combustion engine has a compression ratio of 18 to 1 and a cutoff ratio of 2.2. Determine the cold ASC thermal efficiency of this engine. Assume $k = 1.4$.

68. Show that as the cutoff ratio of the Diesel cycle approaches 1.0, the Diesel cold ASC thermal efficiency becomes equal to that of the Otto cycle with the same compression ratio.

69. Determine the value of the cutoff ratio that will cause the Diesel cold ASC thermal efficiency to become zero for an engine with a 20 to 1 compression ratio. Assume $k = 1.4$.

70. A Diesel cycle internal combustion engine has a compression ratio of 15 to 1. At the beginning of the compression process the pressure is 14.7 psia and the temperature is 520 R. The maximum temperature of the cycle is 4868 R. Determine the cold ASC thermal efficiency. Assume $k = 1.4$.

71. A two-cylinder, two-stroke Diesel cycle internal combustion engine with a 16.2 to 1 compression ratio and a total displacement of 1.5 L burns kerosene having a heating value of 40,000 kJ/kg when using an air–fuel ratio of 25 to 1. The intake temperature and pressure are 100 kPa and 15 °C. When the engine is running at 1200 rpm and producing 6.0 kW of power determine (assuming $k = 1.4$) the engine's

a) cutoff ratio, **b)** cold ASC thermal efficiency,
c) indicated power output, **d)** mechanical efficiency, and
e) actual thermal efficiency.

72. The Atkinson cycle is similar to the Otto cycle except that the constant volume exhaust/intake stroke at the end of the Otto cycle power stroke has been replaced by a constant pressure process in the Atkinson cycle, as shown below.

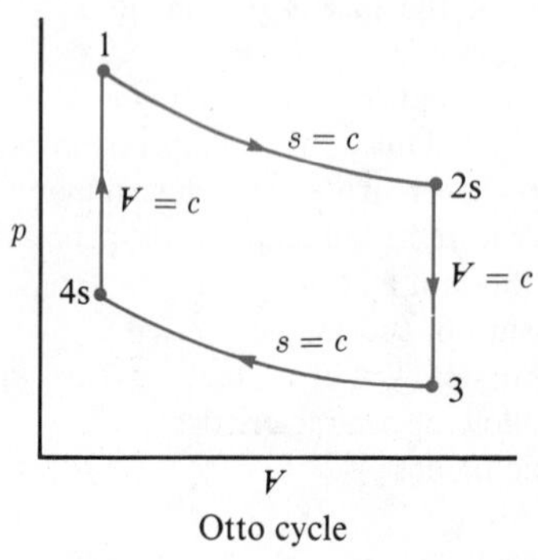

Otto cycle

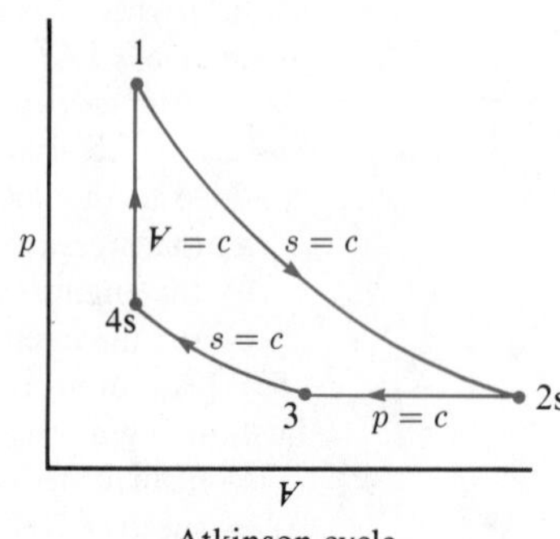

Atkinson cycle

Where Q_H occurs during process 4s to 1, and Q_L occurs during process 2s to 3 in each case.

a) Sketch the T-s diagram for the Atkinson cycle numbering and labeling all the process path lines as in the p-V diagram above.

b) Determine the Atkinson cold ASC thermal efficiency for $k = 1.4$, $T_1 = 8000$ R, $T_3 = 520$ R, and CR $= v_3/v_{4s} = 8.0$.

Design Problems for Section I

The following are open ended design problems. The objective is to carry out a preliminary thermal design as indicated. A detailed design with working drawings is not expected unless otherwise specified. These problems do not have specific answers, so each student's design will be unique.

73. Design a small single-cylinder, piston-type steam engine and boiler that can be used to power a toy vehicle such as a train or a tractor. Choose a convenient fuel such as alcohol, and design the boiler so that it will be able to supply enough steam to your engine. Make sure the boiler has a pressure relief valve, and pay close attention to other safety considerations.

74. Develop a preliminary design for a closed-loop Rankine cycle steam power plant to be used in a compact automobile. The prime mover may be either reciprocating piston or turbine, and must produce a net output of 40.0 hp with a thermal efficiency in excess of 35%.

a) Specify inlet and outlet states for the boiler, prime mover, condenser, and boiler feed pump.

b) Choose typical values for the isentropic efficiencies of the prime mover and boiler feed pump, and calculate the overall thermal efficiency of the power plant.

c) Specify the fuel to be used in the boiler.

d) Estimate the overall power plant weight, including fuel storage.

e) Specify conditions needed to meet part-load operation and prime mover speed control during vehicle acceleration and deceleration.

f) Specify all additional equipment needed to connect the prime mover output shaft to the vehicle drive wheels.

75. Design a small single-cylinder Stirling or Ericsson cycle external combustion engine that can be used to demonstrate the operation of this type of engine in the classroom. Choose a convenient fuel such as alcohol. Provide detailed working drawings and a thermodynamic analysis.

76. Design a Brayton cycle power system to propel a small drone aircraft that will be used for military target practice. The fueled drone must weigh less than 500 kg, and, since these aircraft are not reusable, they must be produced at minimum cost. Determine or specify the air mass flow rate, pressure ratio, compressor and turbine isentropic efficiencies, turbine inlet temperature, thrust, thrust to weight ratio, exhaust temperature, and hot ASC thermal efficiency. A computer program will help you carry out parametric studies of the variables involved.

77. Design a personal exercise machine that uses the otherwise dissipated human exercise energy in some productive way. For example, the exercise energy could be converted into mechanical, chemical, or electrical energy that could then be used in some domestic device (for example, to power a computer, TV set, kitchen appliance, etc.). Another solution would be to design a system that would feed the exercise energy directly into the local electrical power grid for credit against the users electrical bill (like wind power devices today). If one hundred million people exercised for 15 min every day of the year at a power level of 100 W each, how many barrels of crude oil (at 5,800,000 Btu's per barrel) and how many tons of coal (at 26,000,000 Btu's per ton) could be saved annually?

Computer Problems for Section I

The following computer programming assignments were designed to be carried out on any personal computer using BASIC as the programming language. They are meant to be exercises in input/output screen formatting and manipulation of some of the basic formulae of this chapter. They may be used as part of a weekly homework assignment.

78. Write a computer program that will provide data to plot (either manually or with a computer) the thermal efficiency of the isentropic Rankine cycle with regeneration vs. the regeneration mass fraction $y = \dot{m}_5/\dot{m}_1$ for the system given in text Example 8.4b. Maintain the regenerator pressure constant at 80 psia and note that as y ranges from 0 to $y_{max} =$ 0.2, h_6 varies from h_4 to h_f(80 psia). So long as the regenerator pressure is maintained at 80 psia, values of y larger than 0.2 will cause the water entering the boiler feed pump to contain vapor (which will ruin the pumps performance). Plot your results of η_T vs. y and determine the value of y that maximizes the thermal efficiency of this system.

79. Repeat Problem 78 except now allow the regenerator pressure to vary from 1.0 to 80 psia as y varies from 0 to 0.2 and maintain the regenerator outlet state as a saturated liquid (the regenerator outlet state in Problem 78 was a compressed liquid when y was less than 0.2). This can be accomplished by putting a pressure reducer on the turbine–regenerator pipe (station 5) to make sure that the turbine bleed steam always enters the regenerator at the correct pressure.

80. Write a computer program to calculate the Otto ASC thermal efficiency as the compression ratio ranges from 1.0 to 12.0 for the following values of k: 1.40, 1.35, 1.30, 1.25, and 1.20 (note that values of k less than 1.4 give an approximate hot ASC result). Plot these results (either manually or with a computer) with the thermal efficiency on the vertical axis and the compression ratio on the horizontal axis using k as a parameter for the family of curves. Utilize at least 25 points per curve.

81. Write a computer program to calculate the Diesel cold ASC thermal efficiency as the compression ratio (CR) ranges from 12.0 to 30.0 for the following cutoff ratios: 1.5, 2.0, 2.5, 3.0, and 3.5. Plot these results (either manually or with a computer) with the thermal efficiency on the vertical axis and the compression ratio on the horizontal axis using the cutoff ratio as a parameter for the family of curves. Utilize at least 25 points per curve.

82. Write a computer program that will determine the value of the cutoff ratio that will cause the Diesel ASC thermal efficiency to become zero as the compression ratio ranges from 12.0 to 30.0 for the following values of k: 1.40, 1.35, 1.30, 1.25, and 1.20. Plot these results (either manually or with a computer) with the cutoff ratio on the vertical axis and the compression ratio on the horizontal axis using k as a parameter for the family of curves.

Problems for Section II

83. Using the definition of thermal efficiency, show that the coefficient of performance (COP) of a heat pump is always greater than 1.0.

84. It is proposed to operate a heat pump on a reversed Carnot cycle to remove 1500 W of thermal energy from a freezer at -10 °C and to discharge heat to the environment at 20 °C. Determine

a) the COP of the system,
b) the heat transfer rate to the environment, and
c) the required input power.

85. Determine the proper chemical formula and name for the following refrigerants:

a) R-10, **b)** R-110,
c) R-210, and **d)** R-744.

86. Determine the chemical formula and R-number of the following refrigerants:

a) pentachloroethane, **b)** trichloroethane, and
c) octafluoropropane.

87. Determine the proper chemical name and R-number of the following refrigerants:

a) $CCLF_3$, **b)** CHF_3, and **c)** CH_2ClF.

88. In 1937 Willis Haviland Carrier (1876–1950) developed an air conditioning system to cool the air in the Magma Copper Mine in Superior Arizona.[54] It reduced the air temperature at the 3600-ft level from 133 to 71 °F after 4 months of operation. Each air conditioning unit had a capacity of 140 tons of cooling and was driven by a 200-hp electric motor. Determine the coefficient of performance.

89. A reversed Rankine cycle refrigeration system using R-12 has an evaporator temperature of -20 °C and a condenser temperature of 20 °C. The refrigerant leaves the compressor as a saturated vapor and leaves the condenser as a saturated liquid. Determine

a) the isentropic COP of this system,
b) the COP of a Carnot refrigerator operating between the same temperature limits, and
c) the tons of isentropic refrigeration per unit mass flow rate of refrigerant.

90. A reversed Rankine cycle refrigerator uses R-12 as the working fluid. The evaporator temperature is -20 °C, the condenser temperature is 40 °C, and the flow rate of R-12 is 0.1 kg/s. If the refrigerant exits the compressor as a saturated vapor, determine

---

54. In 1976 this air conditioning system was designated as the 13th National Historic Mechanical Engineering Landmark by the American Society of Mechanical Engineers.

a) the isentropic coefficient of performance,
b) the equivalent reversed Carnot cycle coefficient of performance, and
c) the amount of refrigeration (in tons) that this system can provide.

91. A reversed Rankine cycle heat pump using R-12 is used to provide 20,000 Btu/h of heat to a house. The evaporator temperature is 10 °F and the condenser temperature is 70 °F. The refrigerant leaves the compressor as a saturated vapor, and leaves the condenser as a saturated liquid. The isentropic efficiency of the compressor is 80%. Determine
a) the mass flow rate of the refrigerant,
b) the power input to the compressor, and
c) the coefficient of performance of this system.

92. A reversed Rankine cycle refrigerator using R-12 as the working fluid has an evaporator temperature of −30 °C and a condenser temperature of 50 °C. The refrigerant enters the compressor at 7.5 kg/min as a saturated vapor. The isentropic efficiency of the compressor is 82.5%. Determine
a) the COP for the system,
b) the COP for a reversed Carnot cycle with the same temperature limits, and
c) the refrigeration (in tons) that this system can provide.

93. A reversed Rankine cycle heat pump is proposed that uses low-pressure water as the working fluid. The evaporator is to be buried in the ground below the frost line and consequently will remain at 50 °F year around. The condenser is to be inside a house and will operate at a constant 80 °F. The water enters the condenser as a saturated vapor at 12.6 lbm/min. Assume the isentropic efficiency of the compressor is 100%. Determine
a) the coefficient of performance of this system, and
b) the amount of heat (in Btu/h) transferred into the house.

94. A reversed Brayton cycle with an isentropic pressure ratio of 1.75 is to be used to refrigerate a food locker. The refrigerant is air. The compressor and expander inlet temperatures are 0 and 10 °C, respectively. Determine
a) the ASC COP of this system,
b) the Carnot COP for a refrigerator operating between the same temperature limits, and
c) the compressor and expander outlet temperatures.

95. In calculating the reversed Carnot ASC COP for comparison with that of a reversed Brayton ASC, the temperature limits are always taken as T_L = the compressor inlet temperature, and T_H = the expander inlet temperature.
a) Why is this done, and
b) what would happen if the *cycle* limit temperatures were used instead (i.e., taking T_L = the expander outlet temperature, and T_H = the compressor outlet temperature)?

96. A reversed Brayton ASC refrigerator operates with air between 0 °F (the compressor inlet temperature) and 80 °F (the expander inlet temperature) with an isentropic pressure ratio of 2.85. Determine the ASC coefficient of performance of this system assuming
a) constant specific heats, and
b) temperature dependent specific heats (use Appendix C.16*a*).

97. Consider the possibility of converting an automobile turbocharger with radiator intercooling at 100 °F into a reversed Brayton ASC air conditioning system. For inlet conditions of 14.7 psia at 70 °F, and a compressor pressure ratio of 2.0, determine
a) the ASC COP of this system as an air conditioner, and
b) the coldest possible air conditioning temperature attainable with this system.

98. Show that Eqs. 8.46 and 8.47 for the reversed Brayton cycle obey Eq. 8.37.

99. 1.75 kg/s of air at 300 K enters the compressor of a reversed Brayton cycle heat pump. The isentropic pressure ratio of the compressor is 3.0 to 1, and the inlet temperature of the expander is 335 K. The isentropic efficiencies of the compressor and expander are 91 and

85%, respectively. Determine

a) the actual power output from the expander,

b) the actual power input to the compressor, and

c) the COP of the unit.

100. Show that the coefficient of performance of a reversed Brayton ASC heat pump can be written as

$$\text{COP}_{\substack{\text{reversed}\\\text{Brayton ASC}\\\text{HP}}} = \frac{\text{CR}^{k-1}}{\text{CR}^{k-1} - 1}$$

where CR is the isentropic compression ratio of the system.

101. Using the notation of Figure 8.36, and beginning with the relation

$$\text{COP}_{\text{reversed Carnot ASC R/AC}} = T_L/(T_H - T_L) = T_1/(T_3 - T_1)$$

show that the minimum possible isentropic pressure ratio of a reversed Brayton ASC refrigerator is

$$\text{PR}_{\text{min}} = (T_3/T_1)^{k/(k-1)}$$

102. Determine the cooling temperature and the COP of an isenthalpic expansion cooler that expands air from 1500 psia, 70 °F to 14.7 psia. The isentropic efficiency of the compressor is 85%. The mean Joule-Thomson coefficient for this process is 0.02 °F/psi.

103. When air expands from 20 °C, 100 atm to 1.0 atm the mean Joule-Thomson coefficient is 0.15 °C/atm. Determine the outlet temperature and the coefficient of performance of an expansion air conditioning system operating under these conditions when the compressor isentropic efficiency is 80%.

104. A Joule-Thomson expansion refrigeration system is being considered for use in a meat storage facility. The working fluid is to be carbon dioxide that is to be expanded from 20 atm at 20 °C to 1.0 atm. The system is to have a compressor with an isentropic efficiency of 75%. Determine the cooling temperature and the COP for this system.

Design problems for Section II

The following are open ended design problems. The objective is to carry out a preliminary thermal design as indicated. A detailed design with working drawings is not expected unless otherwise specified. These problems do not have specific answers, so each student's design will be unique.

105. Design a small reversed Rankine cycle refrigeration system that can serve as experimental apparatus for a junior or senior level mechanical engineering laboratory course. The system must be instrumented with the proper pressure, temperature, and mass flow transducers so that its COP can be accurately determined. The system should have at least one variable parameter (such as refrigerant mass flow rate) to provide a range of performance to study. You may wish to start by modifying the components of an existing domestic refrigerator. Either construct the apparatus yourself, or else provide sufficiently accurate and detailed drawings and instructions such that it can be made by an engineering technician.

106. Carry out the preliminary thermal design of a reversed Rankine cycle heat pump that uses a solar collector as the heat source. Use Refrigerant-12 as the working fluid, and assume an average solar flux of 496 Btu per square foot per day in December (the worst case) with a yearly average solar flux of 1260 Btu per square foot per day. The heat pump must provide 400,000 Btu per day to a house during December, and average 200,000 Btu per day during the year. Be sure to determine the following items in your analysis:

a) the required collector surface area for worst case and average conditions (is either too large for an average roof?),
b) the resulting system COP, and
c) the required mass flow rate of R-12.

Note: Assume a solar flux (sunshine) period of 8 to 10 h per day.

107. Design a domestic heating system that uses a heat pump to extract heat from the earth to heat a house. The evaporator is to be made of long lengths of plastic pipe buried below the frost line in the earth at a constant temperature of 50 °F. The heat pump system must provide 200,000 Btu/h to the house at 70 °F. Specify the refrigerant, the length, diameter, and type of plastic to be used for the evaporator piping, the mass flow rate of the refrigerant, the compressor efficiency, and determine the pumping losses (i.e., the pressure drop) in the evaporator. Estimate or compute an appropriate temperature differential between the outside and the inside of the condenser and the evaporator.

108. Design a small laboratory-scale reversed Brayton cycle air conditioning system that can serve as experimental apparatus for a junior or senior level mechanical engineering laboratory course. The system must be instrumented with the proper pressure, temperature, and mass flow transducers so that its COP can be accurately determined. The system should have at least one variable parameter to provide a range of performance to study. You may wish to start by modifying an automotive turbocharger to provide the turbine and compressor stages. Either construct the apparatus yourself, or provide sufficiently accurate and detailed drawings and instructions such that it can be made by an engineering technician.

109. Design an inexpensive reversed Brayton cycle air conditioning system for an automobile using air as the working fluid. Convert one of the engine's cylinders into an air compressor or add a separate compressor driven off the fan belt. Determine the amount of cooling required (in tons) when the outside air temperature is 100 °F and the inside temperature is maintained at 70 °F. Size and locate the components on the automobile. Estimate the units COP, its input power requirement and manufacturing cost. The final unit must add no more than five percent to the retail cost of the automobile.

Computer Problems for Section II

The following computer programming assignments were designed to be carried out on any personal computer using BASIC as the programming language. They are meant to be exercises in input/output screen formatting and manipulation of some of the basic formulae of this chapter. They may be used as part of a weekly homework assignment.

110. Write a computer program that will provide data to plot (either manually or with a computer) the coefficient of performance of a reversed Rankine cycle heat pump, refrigerator or air conditioner vs. the throttling valve outlet quality x_{4h}. Prompt the user for all the relevant input information including the compressor's isentropic efficiency.

111. Write an interactive computer program that will determine either the system's coefficient of performance or its cooling capacity in tons (allow the user to chose which) of a reversed Rankine cycle air conditioner, refrigerator or heat pump (again allow the user to chose which). Prompt the user for all necessary information (in proper units), and produce a screen diagram of the system with all the variables and the unknown shown.

112. Write an interactive reversed Brayton ASC computer program that utilizes a constant specific heat ideal gas equations of state as the source of the enthalpy values. Allow the user to select either a refrigeration, air conditioning, or heat pump application. Have the user input the appropriate gas constants (or chose the gas from a screen menu), the source and sink temperatures, the mass flow rate of the gas, and the isentropic pressure ratio, PR. Output the coefficient of performance, the source and sink heat transfer rates, and the net power input. Use this program to plot the COP vs. the PR for a reversed Brayton cycle refrigerator operating between −10 and 20 °C. Allow the PR to range from 1.0 to 10.0.

113. Expand Problem 112 by replacing the ideal gas properties with a gas menu that contains a computerized version of the isentropic gas tables (see, for example, Problem 85 at the end of Chapter 6) as the source of the enthalpy values.

114. Write an interactive computer program that will determine the coefficient of performance of a reversed Stirling ASC refrigerator or heat pump (allow the user to choose which). Prompt the user for all necessary input information (in the proper units).

115. Write an interactive computer program that will determine the coefficient of performance of a Joule-Thomson refrigeration system using air or carbon dioxide (allow the user to chose which). Curve fit the information given in Figure 4.10 as the source of the proper Joule-Thomson coefficient. Prompt the user for the appropriate temperatures and pressures, and the isentropic compressor efficiency.

Chapter Nine Chemical Thermodynamics

This chapter deals with an area of application of the laws of thermodynamics upon which entire textbooks have been written. Chemists call this topic *physical chemistry*, and it forms the basis of much of applied chemistry. It is important to engineers because it provides a fundamental understanding of combustion and other chemically based energy conversion processes.

A practical chemical technology can be traced to prehistoric times. Primitive metallurgy, medicine, and food preparation are typical examples. They were purely empirical "recipe"-driven processes without any form of chemical theory to explain their results. Before the sixth century B.C. it was generally believed that all things were composed of a single primitive element. The Greek philosophers Heracleitus (540–480 B.C) and Empedocles (490–430 B.C.) began a new era when they proposed that instead of a single element, all matter was made up of four elements, air, earth, fire, and water, and that the continual mixing of these elements formed all the objects of the real world.

The Greek philosopher Pythagoras (580–500 B.C.) is generally credited with recognizing the functional significance of numbers in quantifying the processes of the real world.[1] Empedocles adopted Pythagoras' numerology technique in an attempt to quantify the chemistry of his four elements. For example, according to Empedocles, animal bone consisted of two parts water, two parts earth, and four parts fire. Because he believed that all of his four elements were most thoroughly mixed in blood, he concluded that people think mainly with their blood!

From about the second century A.D. until nearly the nineteenth century the world embraced what is considered today to be a scientific and chemical curios-

1. Pythagoras established an academy of learning in Crotona, Italy, in about 532 B.C. The academy prospered long after his death until its destruction in about 390 B.C. It is believed that his disciples (known as Pythagoreans) working at the academy during this time developed many of the mathematical discoveries now attributed to him (e.g., the Pythagorean theorem for right triangles).

ity, *alchemy*. Alchemy was a combination of the occult, astrology, and primitive chemistry. Even its name, derived from Arabic and introduced in the twelfth century, is obscure because the root *chem* seems to have no relevant etymological meaning.

The basic function of alchemy was *transmutation*, which was concerned with transmuting age to youth, sickness to health, death to immortality. More notorious was its preoccupation with the physical transmutation of base metals into gold (i.e., transmuting poverty to wealth). Its central elements were mercury (*quicksilver*, the liquid metal), sulfur (the stone that burns), and ammonium chloride (*sal ammoniac*, a source of hydrochloric acid). Successful alchemists tended to be charlatans whose work was shrouded in mystery. From the medieval period forward the central focus of alchemy was the making of gold (religion had successfully taken over the immortality issue), and many prominent scientists, including Isaac Newton (1642–1717), experimented with it seriously.[2] The false science of alchemy, which appealed primarily to the human weakness of greed, went without serious intellectual challenge for nearly two thousand years.

In the Seventeenth century Johann Jochim Becher (1635–1682)[3] proposed that all substances were made up of the classical alchemical elements of mercury, sulfur, and corrosive salts,[4] plus a new fourth weightless element which was *produced* by combustion. In 1697 the German physician Georg Ernst Stahl (1660–1734) named this supposed fourth element *phlogiston*, and used it to develop a coherent theory of combustion, respiration, and corrosion. His phlogiston theory quickly won universal scientific approval and was the only scientifically accepted theory of matter for nearly one hundred years afterward.

In 1774 the English clergyman and scientist Joseph Priestley (1733–1804) described some of his experimental results in removing phlogiston from air (the "dephlogistication" of air) to the French chemist Antione Laurent Lavoisier (1743–1794) who immediately recognized their importance and subsequently carried out similar experiments himself. Lavoisier soon realized that the dephlogiston that Priestly thought he had been working with was actually a unique chemical, and in 1777 he named it *oxygen* (from the Greek for *acid forming*). By the early nineteenth century Lavoisier's oxidation theory and completely replaced Stahl's phlogiston theory and the era of modern chemistry had begun.[5] Lavoisier had done for

2. Newton is thought to have contracted mercury poisoning in about 1690 as a result of his alchemy experiments.

3. Becher was an established alchemist, and at one time he was engaged in attempting to transmute Danube river sand into gold.

4. Sal ammoniac, the chloride of ammonia, NH_4Cl, was the most popular alchemical corrosive salt because when heated to 350 °C it decomposes into ammonia and hydrochloric acid. It is commonly used as a soldering flux today.

5. In 1793 Priestly was driven from England because of his public support of the French revolution and settled in America. Because Lavoisier maintained a career in the French government as well as science (he was on the original 1790 weights and measures committee that led to the development of the metric system we now use) he was caught up in the French revolution and was accused of political crimes (such as stopping the circulation of air in Paris by a city wall erected at his suggestion in 1787). He was convicted and guillotined on the same day in 1794.

chemistry what a century earlier Newton had done for mechanics; he had put the subject on a firm analytical foundation.

Originally, reactions in which oxygen was consumed were called *oxidations*, those in which oxygen initially bound to other chemical elements was lost to the reaction products were called *reductions*, and oxidation–reduction reactions soon became known as *redox* reactions. Today we define a redox process much more broadly as any reaction that causes a change in chemical *oxidation numbers*. The oxidation number of an atom is the number of electrons it has that can be involved in forming bonds with other atoms. It has the same magnitude as the atom's valence, but it may have either a positive or negative sign. An increase in the oxidation number corresponds to an oxidation process, and a decrease to a reduction process. With this definition, redox reactions are no longer limited just to those involving oxygen. A redox reaction can involve the transfer of oxygen atoms, hydrogen atoms, or electrons. Examples are

a) $C + O_2 \rightarrow CO_2$
b) $H_2 + Cl_2 \rightarrow 2(HCl)$
c) Zn(metal) + Cu^{2+} (aqueous copper ion) $\rightarrow$ Zn^{2+} (aqueous zinc ion) + Cu(metal)

In the first reaction carbon is oxidized by oxygen (or, equivalently, the oxygen is reduced by the carbon), in the second the hydrogen is oxidized by the chlorine, and in the third the zinc metal is oxidized by the copper ion.

Oxidation–reduction reactions important to modern engineering include the combustion of fuels for heat engines, electrochemical direct energy conversion devices (e.g., batteries and fuel cells), and biological processing of food. Some of these topics will be taken up in this chapter.

Stoichiometric Equations

While Empedocles spread his belief that all matter was made up of the four elements, air, earth, fire, and water, a contemporary Greek philosopher Leucippus and his student Democritus (460–370 B.C.), put forth an alternative theory that all matter was made up of an infinite number of small invisible objects called *atoms* (from the Greek *atoma* meaning *invisibles*). More than twenty centuries were to pass before the theories of the Greek atomists were finally placed on a firm experimental foundation by the English chemist and physicist John Dalton (1766–1844). By 1808 Dalton had devised a system of chemical symbols and had determined the relative masses of some of his elemental atoms. He had also formulated the theory that chemical combinations of different chemical elements occur in simple numerical ratios by mass, which then led him to the development of a way of writing a chemical formula that mathematically represented (or modeled) chemical reactions. For example, if elements A and B combine in a two to one ratio by mass to form C, Dalton wrote this as

$$2 \text{ atoms of A} + 1 \text{ atom of B} = 1 \text{ atom of C} \quad \textbf{(9.1)}$$

In modern notation this would simply be

$$\underbrace{2A + B}_{\text{reactants}} \rightarrow \underbrace{C}_{\text{products}}$$

where the equality has been replaced by an arrow which indicates the direction of the reaction. The items on the left side of this equation are called the *reactants*, and those on the right side are called the *products* of the reaction.

A description of the net combining properties of atoms and compounds that occur in a chemical reaction is known today as the *stoichiometry* of the reaction.[6] Dalton's chemical equation notation provides a shorthand mathematical version of such a description, and the numerical values that precede the chemical symbols in these equations are called the *stoichiometric coefficients* of the reaction. These coefficients represent the number of atoms or molecules involved in the reaction and, since mass is conserved in ordinary chemical reactions, then the number of atoms of each chemical element must be the same in both the reactants and the products. Therefore, a chemical equation can be *balanced* (i.e., mass balanced) by requiring stoichiometric coefficients that produce the same number of atoms of each chemical species on both sides of the reaction equation. For example, the reaction that occurs in burning hydrogen to completion in a pure oxygen atmosphere can be written in modern notation as

$$a(H_2) + b(O_2) \rightarrow c(H_2O)$$

where a, b, and c are the stoichiometric coefficients for the reaction. An individual atomic species balance now gives

Atomic hydrogen (H) balance

$$2a = 2c$$

Atomic oxygen (O) balance

$$2b = c$$

thus producing two equations in the three unknowns, a, b, and c. Since such reactions are usually of interest per unit mass of fuel supplied, we can arbitrarily set $a = 1$, and then the atomic hydrogen and oxygen balances gives $c = 1$ and $b = \frac{1}{2} = 0.5$. Therefore, our final balanced equation would read

$$H_2 + 0.5(O_2) \rightarrow H_2O \quad \textbf{(9.2)}$$

6. The term *stoichiometry* comes from the Greek words *stoicheion* (component) and *metron* (measure). It was introduced in 1792 by the German chemist Jeremias Benjamin Richter when he suggested that substances react chemically according to relations that resemble mathematical formulae.

After an extensive period of experimentation, the Italian chemist Count Amado Avogadro (1776–1856) proposed in 1811 that equal volumes of different gases at the same temperature and pressure contained equal numbers of molecules.[7]

With this proposition he was able to show that hydrogen, oxygen, nitrogen, etc., exist as diatomic molecules in nature. Modern experiments have determined that the actual number of molecules in any substance whose mass in kilograms is equal to its (relative) molecular mass M is 6.023×10^{26}. Therefore, the mass of one molecule of this substance would be $M/(6.023 \times 10^{26})$ kilograms.

The acceptance of Avogadro's law soon led to the development of the *mole* (sometimes abbreviated *mol*, both being a contraction of the German word *molekul*) as a convenient chemical mass unit. Originally, a mole was the mass in grams equal to the (relative) molecular mass M of a substance (i.e., gram mole, or gmole).[8] However, since the mole unit is used in so many different units systems today it now must carry a prefix showing the mass unit of the units system being used (e.g., gmole, kgmole or lbmole). Since equal moles of different substances contain the same number of molecules, then the stoichiometric coefficients, which initially represented only individual molecules, can also be used to represent the number of moles of each element present. Therefore Eq. 9.1 can be written in the equivalent form

$$2 \text{ kgmole of A} + 1 \text{ kgmole of B} = 1 \text{ kgmole of C}$$

or

$$2 \text{ lbmole of A} + 1 \text{ lbmole of B} = 1 \text{ lbmole of C}$$

and Eq. 9.2 can be interpreted as a reaction between 1 kgmole of H_2 and $\frac{1}{2}$ kgmole of O_2 yielding 1 kgmole of H_2O, etc. (note that 1 kgmole $\neq$ 1 lbmole $\neq$ 1 gmole).

Combustion generally occurs in air, not pure oxygen. The composition of air used to determine its thermodynamic properties is 78.09% nitrogen, 20.95% oxygen, 0.93% argon, and 0.03% carbon dioxide and trace elements (on a molar or volume basis). For convenience we will round this off to 79% N_2 and 21% O_2. In doing this we are essentially dividing air into two components: pure oxygen and a mixture of noncombustibles (N_2, Ar, CO_2). The noncombustible group is called *atmospheric nitrogen* and has a mole fraction composition of

$$x_{N_2} = \frac{78.09}{78.09 + 0.93 + 0.03} = \frac{78.09}{79.05} = 0.9879 = 98.79\%$$

$$x_{Ar} = \frac{0.93}{79.05} = 0.0118 = 1.18\%$$

7. This is known as Avogadro's law today. Although Avogadro introduced it in 1811 it was not generally accepted by the scientific community until after 1858. Incidentally, it was Andre Marie Ampere (1775–1836) who popularized the term *molecule* for an assembly of atoms in about 1814.

8. Alternatively we can say that a gram mole of a substance is the amount of that substance that contains exactly the same number of molecules as there are atoms in 12 grams of carbon-12 (carbon-12 is the reference standard for molecular mass).

and

$$x_{CO_2} = \frac{0.03}{79.05} = 0.00038 = 0.038\%$$

Then, from Eq. 7.12, the equivalent molecular mass of this mixture is

$$(M)_{\substack{\text{atmospheric}\\\text{nitrogen}}} = \sum x_i M_i = (0.9879)(28.016) + (0.0118)(39.944) + (0.00038)(44.01)$$

$$= 28.16 \text{ kg/kgmole} = 28.16 \text{ lbm/lbmole}$$

From this point on we will refer to the atmospheric nitrogen mixture as simply nitrogen, and we will assume that air has a molar composition of 21% oxygen and 79% nitrogen where the molecular mass of oxygen is still 32.00, but the molecular mass of nitrogen is now 28.16 instead of 28.016. The equivalent molecular mass of air is still 28.97 since the argon and carbon dioxide are now merely grouped with the nitrogen.

For this air composition each mole of oxygen will be accompanied by 79/21 = 3.76 moles of nitrogen. Thus, if the hydrogen combustion reaction described by Eq. 9.2 were carried out in air instead of pure oxygen it would be written as

$$H_2 + 0.5[O_2 + 3.76(N_2)] \rightarrow H_2O + 1.88(N_2) \tag{9.3}$$

In this equation the nitrogen was assumed to be inert and therefore passed through the reaction unchanged.

The amount of air or oxygen used in a combustion process can be described as

1. the percent theoretical air or oxygen required to carry out the reaction,
2. the percent excess or deficit air or oxygen actually used in the reaction, and
3. the air–fuel (A/F) or fuel–air (F/A) ratio used in the reaction measured on either a mass or a mole basis.

One hundred percent *theoretical air* is the minimum amount of air that supplies enough oxygen to carry out complete combustion. The percent *excess air* is simply the percent theoretical air minus 100, and the percent *deficit air* is 100 minus the percent theoretical air. The air–fuel (A/F) ratio is the mass of air used per unit mass of fuel consumed and it can be expressed either in mass or mole units. The fuel–air (F/A) ratio is simply the inverse of the air–fuel ratio.

With these definitions it is easy to see that the hydrogen combustion described in Eq. 9.3 uses 100% theoretical air and that no excess or deficit air is involved. The air–fuel ratio for this reaction is

$$A/F = \frac{(0.5)(1 + 3.76)}{1} = 2.38 \text{ moles of air/mole } H_2$$

or

$$A/F = (2.38)(28.97)/(2.016) = 34.2 \text{ lbm air/lbm } H_2 = 34.2 \text{ kg air/kg } H_2$$

Then the fuel–air ratio is simply

$$F/A = (A/F)^{-1} = 0.42 \text{ moles } H_2\text{/mole air} = 0.029 \text{ lbm } H_2\text{/lbm air}$$
$$= 0.029 \text{ kg } H_2\text{/kg air}$$

If this reaction were carried out with 150% theoretical air (i.e., 50% excess air), it would have the form

$$H_2 + 1.5(0.5)[O_2 + 3.76(N_2)] \rightarrow H_2O + 0.25(O_2) + 2.82(N_2)$$

with an air–fuel ratio of

$$A/F = \frac{1.5(0.5)(1 + 3.76)}{1} = 3.57 \text{ moles air/mole } H_2$$

Similarly, if it had been carried out at 75% theoretical air (i.e., 25% deficit air) it would be

$$H_2 + 0.75(0.5)[O_2 + 3.76(N_2)] \rightarrow 0.75(H_2O) + 0.25(H_2) + 1.41(N_2)$$

with an air–fuel ratio of

$$A/F = \frac{0.75(0.5)(1 + 3.76)}{1} = 1.785 \text{ moles air/mole } H_2$$

and so forth.

Organic Fuels

The term *organic* has been used in chemistry since the late eighteenth century and originally referred only to materials occurring in or derived from living organisms. Today this term is used to represent *all* compounds of carbon, whether derived from living organisms or not. Other elements frequently found in organic compounds are hydrogen, oxygen, nitrogen, sulfur, and phosphorous. Since the number of organic compounds is very large they are subdivided into groups having similar properties. Hydrocarbons, alcohols, carbohydrates, proteins, and fats are typical organic compound subdivision classifications.

Many common organic fuels are made up of only carbon and hydrogen atoms and are consequently called *hydrocarbons*. The hydrocarbon class of organic molecules can be further subdivided into the groups shown in Figure 9.1.

In the early part of the nineteenth century chemists were puzzled by the fact that it was possible to construct two seemingly different compounds that had dissimilar physical properties yet identical chemical formula. For example, ethanol

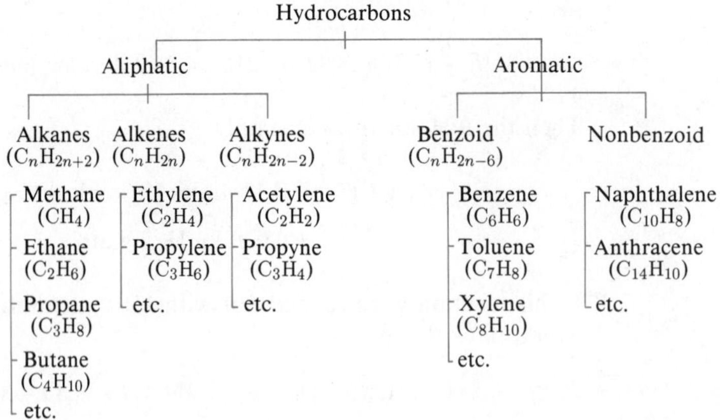

Figure 9.1 Classification of hydrocarbons.

and dimethyl ether both have the same chemical formula, C_2H_6O, yet ethanol boils at 79 °C while dimethyl ether boils at -24 °C. Materials that have the same chemical formula but dissimilar physical properties are called *isomers*. The isomer puzzle was solved by the German chemist Friedrich August Kekulé (1829–1896) in a dream while dozing on the top deck of a horse drawn bus in London. In his dream he realized that the atoms of a molecule could be arranged in different geometric structures, and in 1858 he introduced the schematic notation still used today in which bonds between atoms are represented by lines drawn between their corresponding chemical symbols (e.g., H_2 as H—H). He was then able to show that isomers were simply the result of different bonding patterns. For example, butane (C_4H_{10}) has the isomers *n*-butane, that boils at -0.5 °C and isobutane, that boils at -12 °C. (The *n* prefix is always used to denote the *normal*, or chain-like structure whereas the iso prefix is used to denote the branched structure). These two isomer bonding patterns are shown below:

```
     H   H   H   H              H   H   H
     |   |   |   |              |   |   |
 H — C — C — C — C — H      H — C — C — C — H
     |   |   |   |              |   |   |
     H   H   H   H              H   |   H
                                    |
                                H — C — H
                                    |
                                    H
```

n-Butane (normal butane) (C_4H_{10})   **Isobutane (C_4H_{10})**

Another nineteenth century hydrocarbon curiosity was the existence of the two classes, *aliphatic* (fatty) and *aromatic* (fragrant) compounds. Aromatic hydrocarbons always had at least six carbon atoms and had a smaller proportion of hydrogen atoms than did the aliphatic hydrocarbons. In 1865 Kekulé again found the solution in a dream. He envisioned a six-carbon chain closing upon itself to form a ring, like a snake biting its own tail, and he concluded that the aromatic compounds contain such rings whereas the aliphatic compounds contain only straight chains.

Within the aliphatic group, the *alkanes* are characterized by having carbon atoms with single bonds between them, while the *alkenes* have carbon atoms with double bonds between them and *alkynes* have carbon atoms with triple bonds between them. If all the bonds within an organic compound are *single*, then the compound is said to be *saturated*, but if multiple bonds exist between any two carbon atoms in the compound it is said to be *unsaturated*. Thus, the alkanes are all saturated hydrocarbons, while all the remaining hydrocarbons are unsaturated.

```
  H H            H     H
  | |             \   /
H-C-C-H            C=C            H-C≡C-H
  | |             /   \
  H H            H     H
```

Ethane (C_2H_6)	**Ethylene (C_2H_4)**	**Acetylene (C_2H_2)**
(alkane, saturated)	**(alkene, unsaturated)**	**(alkyne, unsaturated)**

Using the atomic mass balance technique discussed at the beginning of this chapter it is easily shown that the stoichiometric reaction equation for the combustion of a typical hydrocarbon of the form C_nH_m using 100% theoretical air is

$$C_nH_m + (n + m/4)[O_2 + 3.76(N_2)] \rightarrow n(CO_2) + (m/2)(H_2O) + 3.76(n + m/4)(N_2) \qquad \textbf{(9.4a)}$$

Also, its combustion with excess air using $100(x)$ percent theoretical air (i.e., $100(x - 1)$ percent excess air), where $x \geq 1.0$, is

$$C_nH_m + x(n + m/4)[O_2 + 3.76(N_2)] \rightarrow n(CO_2) + (m/2)(H_2O) + (x - 1)(n + m/4)(O_2) + x(3.76)(n + m/4)(N_2) \qquad \textbf{(9.4b)}$$

And its combustion in deficit air using $100(y)$ percent theoretical air (i.e., $100(1 - y)$ percent deficit air), where $(2n + m)(4n + m) \leq y \leq 1.0$, is

$$C_nH_m + y(n + m/4)[O_2 + 3.76(N_2)] \rightarrow [n(2y - 1) - m(1 - y)/2](CO_2) + (2n + m/2)(1 - y)(CO) + (m/2)(H_2O) + y(3.76)(n + m/4)(N_2) \qquad \textbf{(9.4c)}$$

In Eq. 9.4*c* it has been assumed that the hydrogen is much more reactive than the carbon so that it will take up all the oxygen it needs to be converted into water. This leaves only the carbon subject to incomplete combustion.

Example 9.1 Determine the stoichiometric reaction equation for methane (CH_4) burned in
a) 100% theoretical air,
b) 150% excess air, and
c) 20% deficit air.

Solution We could solve this problem by using $m = 1$ and $n = 4$ is Eqs. 9.4*a–c*. However, since methane is a simple compound it will be more enlightening to carry out the individual atomic balances to obtain the correct reaction equations.

a) The general combustion equation for 1 mole of methane in 100% theoretical air is

$$CH_4 + a[O_2 + 3.76(N_2)] \rightarrow b(CO_2) + c(H_2O) + d(N_2)$$

The element balances are

Carbon (C) balance: $1 = b$
Hydrogen (H_2) balance: $2 = c$
Oxygen (O_2) balance: $a = b + c/2 = 1 + 2/2 = 2$
Nitrogen (N_2) balance: $a(3.76) = d = 2(3.76) = 7.52$

The resulting stoichiometric equation for 100% theoretical air is then

$$CH_4 + 2[O_2 + 3.76(N_2)] \rightarrow CO_2 + 2(H_2O) + 7.52(N_2)$$

b) 150% excess air corresponds to 250% theoretical air. The reaction equation now has O_2 in the products and consequently has the form

$$CH_4 + 2.5(2)[O_2 + 3.76(N_2)] \rightarrow a(CO_2) + b(H_2O) + c(O_2) + d(N_2)$$

and again element balances can be used to find that $a = 1$, $b = 2$, $c = 3$, and $d = 2.5(2)(3.76) = 18.8$, so that for 150% excess air we have

$$CH_4 + 5[O_2 + 3.76(N_2)] \rightarrow CO_2 + 2(H_2O) + 3(O_2) + 18.8(N_2)$$

c) 20% deficit air corresponds to 80% theoretical air. Again assuming all the hydrogen reacts to water, the reaction now has CO in the products and has the form

$$CH_4 + 0.8(2)[O_2 + 3.76(N_2)] \rightarrow a(CO_2) + b(CO) + c(H_2O) + d(N_2)$$

and again the element balances can be used to yield the coefficients $a = 0.2$, $b = 0.8$, $c = 2.0$, and $d = 6.016$. Note that these results correspond to the same coefficients one would obtain by using Eq. 9.4*c*. The final reaction equation for 20% deficit air is

$$CH_4 + 1.6[O_2 + 3.76(N_2)] \rightarrow 0.2(CO_2) + 0.8(CO) + 2(H_2O) + 6.016(N_2)$$

Hydrocarbon fuels refined from petroleum normally contain a mixture of many different organic components. Gasoline, for example, is a mixture of over thirty different compounds. It is, however, convenient to model these fuels as a single *average* hydrocarbon compound of the form C_nH_m, as discussed in the following section.

Fuel Modeling

It is fairly easy to obtain accurate composition analysis of combustion products with modern gas chromatography or mass spectroscopy techniques. With an accurate combustion analysis of a fuel that is in reality a complex mixture of hydrocarbons, an *equivalent* or *average* hydrocarbon model of the form C_nH_m can be determined from a chemical element balance. For example, if the combustion products contained only CO_2, CO, O_2, H_2O and N_2, then Eqs. 9.4*a*–*c* could be used to determine the composition parameters n and m if the stoichiometric coefficients of the products were measured. Since the fuel model formula C_nH_m represents an average of all the different hydrocarbon compounds present in the fuel mixture, n and m usually do not turn out to be integers and the resulting model does not represent any real hydrocarbon (except possibly when n and m are rounded to integers).

The Orsat analysis technique is a particularly quick, simple, and inexpensive method of obtaining an approximate combustion analysis. It is often used to determine furnace or boiler exhaust gas (called *flue gas*) composition as a means of monitoring the efficiency of the combustion process. An Orsat analyzer uses a chemical absorption technique to determine the volume fractions (which are also equivalent to the mole fractions) of CO_2, CO, and O_2 in the exhaust gas (see Figure 9.2). Since it cannot measure the H_2O content, the exhaust gas sample is

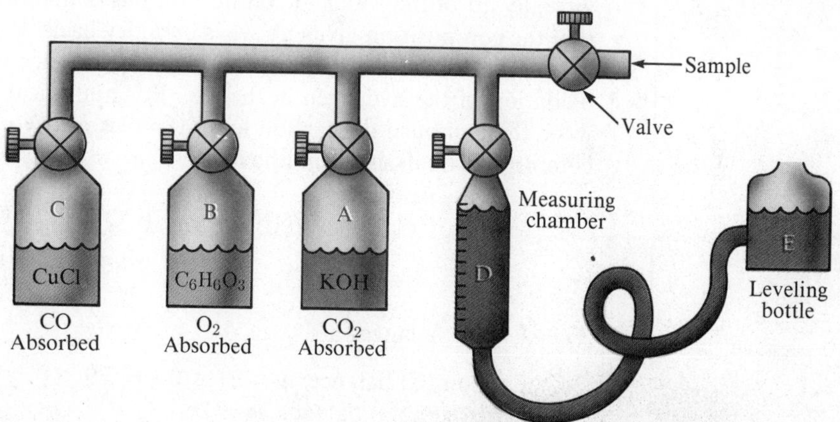

Figure 9.2 A typical Orsat analyzer. Vessel A contains a potassium hydroxide (KOH) solution that absorbs CO_2. Vessel B contains a pyrogallic acid (1, 2, 3-trihydroxybenzene, $C_6H_6O_3$) solution that absorbs O_2. Vessel C contains a cuprous chloride (CuCl) solution that absorbs CO. The remaining gas is assumed to be N_2. Vessel D is the measuring chamber, and vessel E is the leveling bottle.

always cooled to room temperature, or below the dew point of any water vapor present, so that most of the water in the combustion products will condense out. Therefore, the Orsat technique is said to produce a *dry products* analysis. Also, the Orsat technique cannot detect unburned hydrocarbons (typically CH_4) and free hydrogen (H_2) in the exhaust gas. These are usually small and can normally be neglected. However, studies have shown that the mole fractions of methane and hydrogen in the combustion products of a hydrocarbon can be approximated as $x_{CH_4} \approx 0.0022$ and $x_{H_2} \approx 0.5(x_{CO})$, and these relations can be used with an Orsat analysis if necessary.

Example 9.2

The exhaust gas of a gasoline fueled automobile engine was cooled to 20 °C and then subjected to an Orsat analysis. The results (on a volume or mole basis) were

$$\begin{aligned} CO_2 &= 7.1\% \\ CO &= 0.8\% \\ O_2 &= 9.9\% \\ N_2 &= 82.2\% \\ \hline \text{Total} &= 100\% \end{aligned}$$

Determine

a) the hydrocarbon model (C_nH_m) of the fuel,
b) the composition of the fuel on a molar and a mass basis,
c) the air–fuel ratio on a molar and a mass basis, and
d) the % theoretical air used in the combustion process.

Solution

a) Since the Orsat analysis was carried out at 20 °C we will assume that virtually all of the water of combustion has condensed out, and therefore that the composition given above is on a dry basis. However, the water term must be left in the chemical reaction equation since it results from the oxidation of the hydrogen in the fuel. For numerical convenience we will write the combustion reaction for 100 moles of dry product using the combustion analysis given above as

$$C_nH_m + a[O_2 + 3.76(N_2)] \rightarrow 7.1(CO_2) + 0.8(CO) + 9.9(O_2) + b(H_2O) + 82.2(N_2)$$

The element balances are

Carbon (C) balance: $n = 7.1 + 0.8 = 7.9$
Hydrogen (H) balance: $m = 2b$
Nitrogen (N_2) balance: $3.76a = 82.2$, or $a = 82.2/3.76 = 21.9$
Oxygen (O_2) balance: $a = 21.9 = 7.1 + 0.8/2 + 9.9 + b/2$, or $b = 9.0$.

Then, from the hydrogen balance above, $m = 2b = 18.0$. Consequently, the fuel model is $C_{7.9}H_{18.0}$, which is approximately octane, C_8H_{18}. The final reaction equation is then

$$C_{7.9}H_{18.0} + 21.9[O_2 + 3.76(N_2)] \rightarrow 7.1(CO_2) + 0.8(CO) + 9.9(O_2) + 9.0(H_2O) + 82.2(N_2)$$

b) On a molar basis, 1 mole of fuel contains 7.9 moles of C and 18.0 moles of H, and on a molar percentage basis this becomes [7.9/(7.9 + 18.0)](100) = 31% C and [18.0/(7.9 + 18.0)](100) = 69% H. The molecular mass of the fuel in this model is

$$M_{\text{fuel}} = 7.9(12) + 18.0(1) = 112.8 \text{ kg/kgmole} = 112.8 \text{ lbm/lbmole}$$

and so the fuel's composition on a mass basis is

$$(7.9 \text{ kgmole C/kgmole fuel})(12.0 \text{ kg C/kgmole C})/(112.8 \text{ kg fuel/kgmole fuel}) = 0.84 \text{ kg C/kg fuel} = 0.84 \text{ lbm C/lbm fuel}$$

and

$$(9.0)(2.0)/112.8 = 0.16 \text{ kg H/kg fuel} = 0.16 \text{ lbm H/lbm fuel}$$

Thus, the fuel can be said to consist of 31% carbon and 69% hydrogen on a molar basis, or 84% carbon and 16% hydrogen on a mass basis.
c) Referring to the final combustion equation determined in part a, the air–fuel ratio on a molar basis is

$$A/F = \frac{21.9(1 + 3.76) \text{ moles of air}}{1 \text{ mole of fuel}} = 104.2 \text{ moles air/mole fuel}$$

and on a mass basis it is

$$A/F = (104.2 \text{ kgmole air/kgmole fuel})\left(\frac{28.97 \text{ kg air/kgmole air}}{112.8 \text{ kg fuel/kgmole fuel}}\right) = 26.8 \text{ kg air/kg fuel} = 26.8 \text{ lbm air/lbm fuel}$$

d) To determine the percent theoretical air used we must first determine the minimum air required for complete combustion. This reaction has the form

$$C_{7.9}H_{18.0} + a[O_2 + 3.76(N_2)] \rightarrow b(CO_2) + c(H_2O) + d(N_2)$$

The element balances are

Carbon (C) balance: $7.9 = b$
Hydrogen (H) balance: $18.0 = 2c$, or $c = 9.0$
Oxygen (O_2) balance: $a = b + c/2 = 7.9 + 9.0/2 = 12.4$
Nitrogen (N_2) balance: $3.76a = d = 3.76(12.4) = 46.6$

Then the theoretical air–fuel ratio (for 100% theoretical air) is

$$(A/F)_{theo} = \frac{12.4(1 + 3.76)}{1} = 59.0 \text{ moles air/mole fuel}$$

and finally, the percent theoretical air used in the actual combustion process is

$$\begin{aligned}\% \text{ theoretical air} &= [(A/F)_{act}/(A/F)_{theo}] \times 100 \\ &= [104.2/59.0](100) = 176.6\%\end{aligned}$$

or 76.6% excess air.

In the previous example we assumed that nearly all the water produced by the combustion process had condensed out by the time the combustion products had been cooled to 20 °C. For this to be a valid assumption, the dew point of the combustion products must be at 20 °C or higher. The determination of the dew point temperature for this reaction is illustrated in the next example.

Example 9.3 Determine the dew point temperature of the combustion products given in Example 9.2 if the total pressure of the mixture is 14.7 psia.

Solution From Eq. 7.25 of Chapter 7, the volume fractions, mole fractions, and partial pressure ratios are all equal for a mixture of ideal gases. Exhaust products at atmospheric pressure are sufficiently ideal to allow us to determine the water vapor partial pressure at its condensation temperature (i.e., dew point) from this relation. The total number of moles of product, from part a of Example 9.2, is 109 moles. Then using Eq. 7.25 wherein p_m is the total pressure of the mixture gives

$$\pi_i = p_{H_2O}/p_m = \psi_{H_2O} = x_{H_2O} = \frac{9.0}{109.0} = 0.08257$$

so

$$p_{H_2O} = 0.08257(14.7) = 1.214 \text{ psia}$$

The saturation temperature of water vapor at this pressure is defined to be the dew point temperature. By interpolation in Appendix C.1*a* we find that

$$T_{sat}(1.214 \text{ psia}) = T_{DP} = 108.1 \text{ °F} = 42.3 \text{ °C}$$

Thus, the exhaust products must be cooled to 108.1 °F (42.3 °C) or below to condense the water of combustion and have an essentially dry exhaust gas.

If moisture enters the combustion process as humidity in the inlet air, this moisture is carried through the reaction as an inert element and adds to the combustion water in the products.[9] This has the net effect of raising the dew point temperature. This is illustrated in the next example.

Example 9.4 During the automobile engine fuel combustion test discussed in Example 9.2 the dry bulb and wet bulb temperatures of the inlet air were measured to be 90 and 76 °F, respectively. Determine the amount of water carried into the engine in the form of inlet humidity, and the new dew point temperature of the exhaust products. Assume the exhaust is at a total pressure of 14.7 psia.

Solution From the psychrometric chart, Figure D.6*a* of the appendix, we find that for $T_{DB} = 90\ °F$ and $T_{WB} = 76\ °F$, that the relative humidity $\phi = 50\%$, and the humidity ratio, $\omega = 0.0150$ lbm H_2O/lbm dry air. On a molar basis the humidity ratio is

$$\omega = (0.0150 \text{ lbm H}_2\text{O/lbm dry air})\left(\frac{28.97 \text{ lbm dry air/lbmole dry air}}{18.016 \text{ lbm H}_2\text{O/lbmole H}_2\text{O}}\right)$$

$$= 0.02412 \text{ lbmole H}_2\text{O/lbmole dry air}$$

From the balanced reaction equation of part a of Example 9.2 we found that the amount of dry air used per mole of fuel was 21.9 (1 + 3.76) = 104.2 moles, and this now carries with it 0.02412(104.2) = 2.5 moles of water. Assuming this water passes through the reaction unchanged, the total amount of water now in the exhaust will be 9.0 + 2.5 = 11.5 moles per mole of fuel. Consequently, the total moles of product will be 111.5, and the mole fraction of water vapor in the exhaust is now

$$x_{H_2O} = 11.5/111.5 = 0.1031$$

and Eq. 7.25 gives the partial pressure of the water vapor in the exhaust as

$$p_{H_2O} = 0.1031(14.7) = 1.516 \text{ psia}$$

Again interpolating in Appendix C.1*a* we find

$$T_{sat}(1.516 \text{ psia}) = T_{DP} = 115.7\ °\text{F} = 46.5\ °\text{C}$$

9. Water will condense in an automobile's exhaust system and drip out the tailpipe until the entire exhaust system has been heated above the dew point temperature by the exhaust gases. This water promotes corrosion and will cause the exhaust system to rust out sooner if the vehicle is used for short trips as compared to trips that are long enough (a half hour or more) to dry out the exhaust system.

By comparing the results of Examples 10.3 and 10.4 we see that combustion air with 50% relative humidity has a dew point temperature 7.6 °F (4.2 °C) higher than that of dry combustion air.

The Standard Reference State

Because we deal with a wide variety of elements and compounds in combustion reactions it is necessary to define a common thermodynamic reference state for all these substances. Recall that in developing the steam tables we chose the triple point of water as the reference state and arbitrarily set the specific internal energy of liquid water equal to *zero* at that point. Therefore, the values of u and h in the steam tables are not the *actual* specific internal energies and enthalpies of steam, they are only *relative* values. This was sufficient since most of our formulae use $u_2 - u_1$ or $h_2 - h_1$ for changes occurring within a system, and the effect of the reference state cancels out in the subtraction process. In the case of the gas tables we took 0 K and 1 atm as the thermodynamic reference state and arbitrarily set the specific internal energy equal to *zero* at this state. However, in the case of combustion processes a more pragmatic thermodynamic reference state of 25 °C and 0.1 MPa (appproximately 1 atm) has been chosen. This is called the *standard reference state* (SRS) for combustion reactions. However, since most of the calorrimeters that are used to study combustion processes are steady state, steady flow, open systems, it is more convenient to set the specific *enthalpy* rather than the specific internal energy of the reactants equal to *zero* at this state.[10]

Thermodynamic properties that are evaluated at the standard reference state are denoted by a superscript °. For example

$$T^\circ = 25\ ^\circ\text{C} = 298\ \text{K} = 77\ ^\circ\text{F} = 537\ \text{R}$$

and

$$p^\circ = 0.1\ \text{MPa} = 14.504\ \text{psia} \approx 1\ \text{atm}$$

The Heat of Formation

When a reaction gives off or liberates heat the reaction is said to be *exothermic*, and when it absorbs heat it is said to be *endothermic*. Our sign convention for heat transport of energy requires that $Q_{\text{exothermic}} < 0$ whereas $Q_{\text{endothermic}} > 0$. The *heat of formation* of a compound is the heat liberated or absorbed in the reaction wherein the compound is formed from its elements when the products (i.e., the compound) of this reaction are cooled to the initial temperature of the reactants. For example, if the elements and the resulting compound are both at the standard

10. Consequently, the specific internal energy of the reactants at the SRS are always negative and are computed from $u^\circ = -p^\circ v^\circ$, where $p^\circ = 0.1$ MPa and v° is the corresponding specific volume of the element in question.

reference state, then we can write

$$\text{elements (at } T^\circ) \rightarrow \text{compound (at } T^\circ) + (\bar{q}_f^\circ)_{\text{compound}}$$

where $(\bar{q}_f^\circ)_{\text{compound}}$ is the molar heat of formation of the compound at the standard reference state.

In 1840 the Swiss chemist Germain Henri Hess (1802–1850) discovered that the total amount of heat liberated or absorbed during a chemical reaction is independent of the thermodynamic path followed by the reaction.[11] This is known as Hess' law, or the law of constant heat sums. It allows us to determine heats of formation for compounds that cannot be synthesized directly from their elements. For example, the complete combustion of a hydrocarbon compound of the form C_nH_m in pure oxygen wherein the reactants and the products are both maintained at the standard reference state can be written as

$$C_nH_m + a(O_2) \rightarrow n(CO_2) + (m/2)(H_2O) + \text{HHV}_{C_nH_m}$$

where HHV is the higher heating value of the hydrocarbon (see Table 9.2). We also have the following carbon dioxide and water formation reactions:

$$C + O_2 \rightarrow CO_2 - 393.5 \text{ MJ/kgmole } CO_2$$

and

$$H_2 + (1/2)(O_2) \rightarrow H_2O - 285.8 \text{ MJ/kgmole } H_2O$$

Now Hess' law states that the heats liberated or absorbed in these reactions are independent of the reaction path, so we can rearrange them as

$$CO_2 \rightarrow C + O_2 + 393.5 \text{ MJ/kgmole } CO_2$$

and

$$H_2O \rightarrow H_2 + (1/2)(O_2) + 285.8 \text{ MJ/kgmole } H_2O$$

Then the combustion equation for the compound C_nH_m can be written as

$$\begin{aligned} C_nH_m + a(O_2) &\rightarrow n(C + O_2 + 393.5) + (m/2)(H_2 + (1/2)O_2 + 285.8) + \text{HHV}_{C_nH_m} \\ &\rightarrow n(C) + (m/2)(H_2) + (n + m/4)(O_2) \\ &\quad + [n(393.5) + (m/2)(285.8) + \text{HHV}_{C_nH_m}] \end{aligned}$$

11. Using caloric theory, Hess tried to extend Dalton's interpretation of chemical reactions by attempting to find examples of the combination of caloric with chemical elements in simple mass ratios. He discovered that for a given reaction the total amount of caloric (heat) involved was always the same, independent of the number of intermediate steps contained within the reaction. Today we know that this is really only true for aergonic, steady state, steady flow, open systems and for isobaric closed systems where the heat of reaction equals the change in total enthalpy (because enthalpy is a point function and is therefore independent of the actual chemical path taken by the reaction).

Now, an oxygen balance on the original compound combustion equation gives $a = n + m/4$, so the O_2 terms in the previous equation cancel, and again using Hess' law to rearrange this equation we get

$$n(\mathrm{C}) + (m/2)(\mathrm{H_2}) \rightarrow \mathrm{C}_n\mathrm{H}_m - [n(393.5) + (m/2)(285.8) + \mathrm{HHV}_{\mathrm{C}_n\mathrm{H}_m}]$$
$$\rightarrow \mathrm{C}_n\mathrm{H}_m + (\bar{q}^\circ_\mathrm{f})_{\mathrm{C}_n\mathrm{H}_m} \qquad \textbf{(9.5)}$$

where the HHV must be in MJ/kgmole of compound. Consequently, the heat of formation of the compound C_nH_m at the standard reference state is $(\bar{q}^\circ_\mathrm{f})_{\mathrm{C}_n\mathrm{H}_m} = -[n(393.5) + (m/2)(285.8) + \mathrm{HHV}_{\mathrm{C}_n\mathrm{H}_m}]$ in MJ/kgmole. For example, we do not know how to form methane (CH_4) from a direct reaction of carbon (graphite) and hydrogen gas. Therefore, the heat of formation of methane cannot be directly measured. However, Eq. 9.5 and Table 9.2 allow us to determine the heat of formation of methane at the standard reference state as

$$\mathrm{C(s)} + 2(\mathrm{H_2(g)}) \rightarrow \mathrm{CH_4(g)} - [393.5 + 2(285.8) + (-890.4)]$$
$$\rightarrow \mathrm{CH_4(g)} - 74.7 \text{ MJ/kgmole } \mathrm{CH_4}$$

where the symbols in parentheses denote the physical state of the substances as a gas (g), liquid (ℓ), or solid (s), and the negative sign on the HHV of methane indicates that its combustion is exothermic (i.e., heat liberating). Thus, the heat of formation of methane from its elements at the standard reference state is $(\bar{q}^\circ_\mathrm{f})_{\mathrm{CH_4}} = -74.7$ MJ per kgmole of methane formed. Notice that in this example we did not take into account the heat of formation of H_2 from atomic hydrogen H, or O_2 from atomic oxygen O. This is because we define the elements used in the formation of a compound to be the reactants of the formation reaction in their *stable molecular forms* at the initial pressure and temperature of the reaction. In the case of methane, its elements are solid carbon (graphite), C, and diatomic hydrogen gas, H_2.

Consider a chemical reaction occurring in the steady state, steady flow, aergonic, open system shown in Figure 9.3. The energy rate balance (ERB) applied

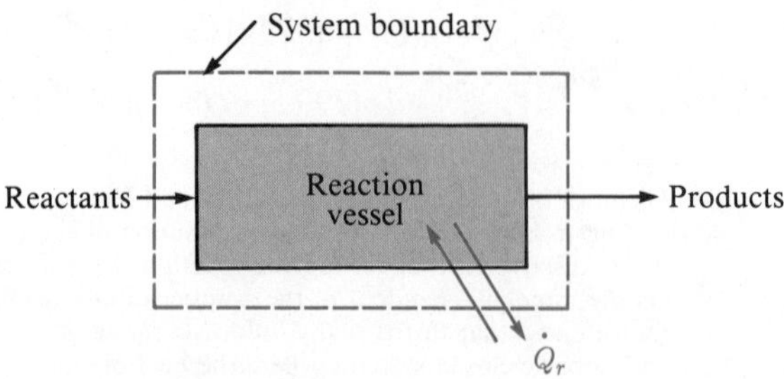

Figure 9.3 A steady state, steady flow, aergonic reaction vessel.

to this system yields

$$\dot{Q}_r = \sum_P (\dot{m}h) - \sum_R (\dot{m}h) = \sum_P (\dot{n}\bar{h}) - \sum_R (\dot{n}\bar{h}) = \dot{H}_P - \dot{H}_R$$

where $\dot{Q}_r$ is the exothermic or endothermic heat transfer rate of the reaction, and $\dot{H}_P$ and $\dot{H}_R$ are the total enthalpy rates of the products and reactants, respectively.

If this reaction is to be used to determine the standard reference state heat of formation of a compound, then the temperature and pressure of the reactants and the products must be maintained by sufficient heat transfer at 25 °C and 0.1 MPa. In this case the specific enthalpies of all the reactant elements will be zero (by definition), so $\dot{H}_R = \dot{H}^\circ_R = \dot{H}_{\text{elements}} = \dot{H}^\circ_{\text{elements}} = 0$, and the previous equation reduces to

$$\dot{Q}^\circ_r = \dot{Q}^\circ_f = \dot{H}^\circ_P = \dot{H}^\circ_{\text{compound}}$$

where $\dot{Q}^\circ_f$ is the standard reference state *heat rate of formation* of the compound. Thus, in this case, the heat rate of formation, the heat transfer rate of the reaction, and the total enthalpy rate of the products are all equal. We now define the *molar specific enthalpy of formation*, $\bar{h}^\circ_f$, of a compound at the standard reference state as[12]

$$(\bar{h}^\circ_f)_{\text{compound}} = (\dot{H}^\circ/\dot{n})_{\text{compound}} = (\dot{Q}^\circ_f/\dot{n})_{\text{compound}} = (\bar{q}^\circ_f)_{\text{compound}} \quad \textbf{(9.6)}$$

where $\dot{n}$ and $\bar{q}^\circ_f$ are the molar flow rate and the molar heat of formation of the compound, respectively. For example, the heat transfer required for the formation of 1 kg mole of liquid water at 25 °C and 0.1 MPa from the isothermal and isobaric combustion of 1 kg mole of gaseous hydrogen and 0.5 kg mole of gaseous oxygen, both at 25 °C and 0.1 MPa, is −285.838 MJ. Therefore, from Eq. 9.6, the specific molar enthalpy of formation of $H_2O(\ell)$ is

$$(\bar{q}^\circ_f)_{H_2O(\ell)} = (\bar{h}^\circ_f)_{H_2O(\ell)} = -285.838 \text{ MJ/kgmole } H_2O$$

Because of our sign convention that heat energy entering the system is positive while that leaving the system is negative, the heats and enthalpies of formation of *exothermic* reactions are always *negative* while those of *endothermic* reactions are always *positive*. Table 9.1 gives the specific molar enthalpies (heats) of formation for some common compounds. Heats of formation can also be estimated from the atomic bond energies of the compound. See the fifth reference at the end of this chapter for detailed information on this technique.

12. The current standard reference state was chosen on the recommendation of the IUPAC Division of Physical Chemistry, Commission of Symbols, Terminology and Units in 1979. Older texts have combustion property tables referenced to 298 K and 1 atm pressure (0.101325 MPa). The pressure difference between these reference states is very small and does not affect the enthalpy of formation ($\bar{h}^\circ_f$ (298 K, 0.1 MPa) = $\bar{h}^\circ_f$ (298 K, 1 atm), but does affect the entropy slightly ($\bar{s}$(298 K, 0.1 MPa) = $\bar{s}$(298 K, 1 atm) + 0.1094 kJ/(kgmole·K)). Other corrections due to this change in reference state can be found in the eighth reference at the end of this chapter.

Table 9.1 Molar specific enthalpy of formation at 25 °C (77 °F) and 0.1 MPa

Substance	M	$\bar{h}_f^\circ$ MJ/kgmole	$\bar{h}_f^\circ$ Btu/1bmole
Carbon monoxide, $CO(g)$	28.011	−110.529	−47,522
Carbon dioxide, $CO_2(g)$	44.011	−393.522	−169,195
Water, $H_2O(g)$	18.016	−241.827	−103,973
Water, $H_2O(\ell)$	18.016	−285.838	−122,896
Methane, $CH_4(g)$	16.043	−74.873	−32,192
Acetylene, $C_2H_2(g)$	26.038	+226.731	+97,483
Ethylene, $C_2H_4(g)$	28.054	+52.283	+22,479
Ethane, $C_2H_6(g)$	30.070	−84.667	−36,403
Propane, $C_3H_8(g)$	44.097	−103.847	−44,649
Butane, $C_4H_{10}(g)$	58.124	−126.148	−54,237
Octane, $C_8H_{18}(g)$	114.23	−208.447	−89,622
Octane, $C_8H_{18}(\ell)$	114.23	−249.952	−107,467

Where (g) indicates the gas or vapor state and (ℓ) indicates the liquid state

Source: Gordon J. Van Wylen and Richard E. Sonntag, *Fundamentals of Classical Thermodynamics, SI Version*, 2d ed. (New York: Wiley, 1976), p. 496 (Table 12.3).

The Heat of Reaction

In the previous section we saw that the heat of formation of a compound was the same as the heat of reaction when that compound was formed from its elements at the standard reference state. An oxidation reaction of a *fuel* is normally called a *combustion*, and therefore the heat of reaction of the oxidation of a fuel in air or pure oxygen is also known as the *heat of combustion* or the *heating value* of the fuel.

A *bomb calorimeter* is a closed rigid vessel which can be used to determine the heat of reaction of a liquid or solid fuel sample (see Figure 9.4). When the final temperature in the bomb has been reduced to its initial standard state temperature of 25°C by the water bath, the resulting energy balance on the bomb is

$$Q_r = m(u_P - u_R) = n(\bar{u}_P - \bar{u}_R) = U_P - U_R = U_{RP} \quad \textbf{(9.7)}$$

Then, from the definition of enthalpy, we can write

$$H_P - H_R = H_{RP} = U_{RP} + (p\Psi)_{RP}$$

and since the reactants are likely to be solids or liquids with a small volume and a low pressure, we can ignore them and write

$$H_{RP} = U_{RP} + (p\Psi)_P = Q_r + (n\mathcal{R}T)_P \quad \textbf{(9.8)}$$

which provides a convenient relation between the constant volume heat of reaction measured by the bomb calorimeter and the total enthalpy change of the reaction occurring inside the bomb calorimeter.

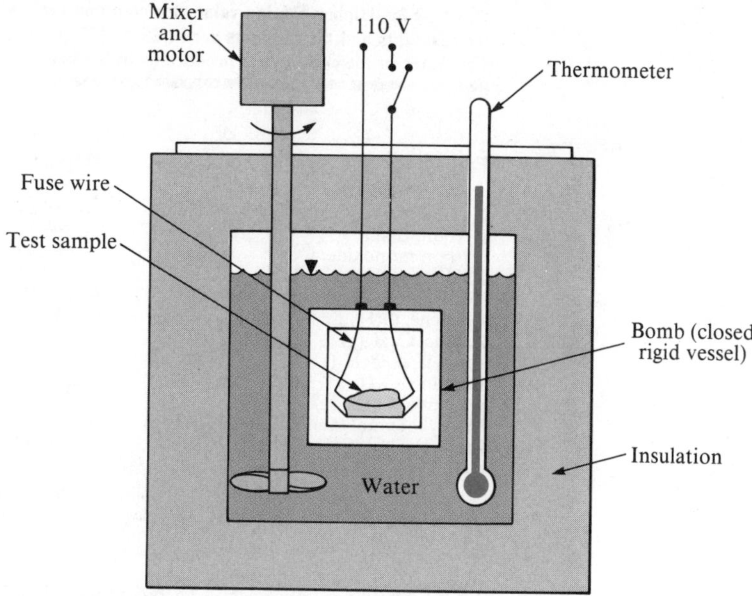

Figure 9.4 An adiabatic bomb calorimeter.

The heat of reaction of gases, liquids, and some solids is more often measured in a steady state, steady flow, aergonic calorimeter, similar to that shown in Figure 9.3. An energy rate balance on this type of calorimeter gives the heat transfer rate of the reaction as

$$\dot{Q}_r = \dot{H}_P - \dot{H}_R = \dot{H}_{RP}$$

and dividing through by the fuel molar flow rate $\dot{n}_{\text{fuel}}$ gives the molar heat of reaction $\bar{q}_r$ as

$$\bar{q}_r = \dot{Q}_r/\dot{n}_{\text{fuel}} = \bar{h}_P - \bar{h}_R = \bar{h}_{RP} \quad \textbf{(9.9)}$$

In this equation we have defined the quantities

$$\bar{h}_R = \dot{H}_R/\dot{n}_{\text{fuel}} = \sum_R (\dot{n}_i/\dot{n}_{\text{fuel}})\bar{h}_i = \sum_R (n_i/n_{\text{fuel}})\bar{h}_i \quad \textbf{(9.10)}$$

and

$$\bar{h}_P = \dot{H}_P/\dot{n}_{\text{fuel}} = \sum_P (\dot{n}_i/\dot{n}_{\text{fuel}})\bar{h}_i = \sum_P (n_i/n_{\text{fuel}})\bar{h}_i \quad \textbf{(9.11)}$$

as the total reactant and product enthalpies per unit mole of fuel consumed. Also, as noted above, $\bar{q}_r$ is the heat of reaction, the heat of combustion, or the heating value of the fuel per unit mole of fuel consumed.

The combustion of hydrocarbon fuels with oxygen will produce water in the combustion products. When this water has condensed into its liquid phase its heat of vaporization is given up to the combustion products and the resulting heat of

Table 9.2 Higher heating values for common fuels wherein both the reactants and the products are at 25 °C (77 °F) and 0.1 MPa. The water in the combustion products is in the liquid phase.

Fuel	HHV MJ/kgmole	HHV Btu/lbmole
Hydrogen, H_2(g)	−285.84	−122,970
Carbon, C(s)	−393.52	−169,290
Carbon monoxide, CO(g)	−282.99	−121,750
Methane, CH_4(g)	−890.36	−383,040
Acetylene, C_2H_2(g)	−1299.60	−559,120
Ethylene, C_2H_4(g)	−1410.97	−607,010
Ethane, C_2H_6(g)	−1559.90	−671,080
Propylene, C_3H_6(g)	−2058.50	−885,580
Propane, C_3H_8(g)	−2220.00	−955,070
n-Butane, C_4H_{10}(g)	−2877.10	−1,237,800
Methyl alcohol (methanol), CH_3OH(g)	−764.54	−328,700
Ethyl alcohol, C_2H_5OH(g)	−1409.30	−606,280

Source: Reprinted by permission of the publisher from J. P. Holman, *Thermodynamics*, 3d ed. (New York: McGraw-Hill, 1980), p. 466 (Table 11-1).

reaction of the combustion process is called the *higher heating value* (HHV) of the fuel. On the other hand, if the temperature of the combustion products is above the dew point temperature, then the water will remain in its vapor phase and the resulting heat of reaction will be somewhat less and consequently is called the *lower heating value* (LHV) of the fuel.

If the reactants *and* the products are both at the standard reference state (25 °C, 0.1 MPa), then Eqs. 9.9 through 9.11 give the *standard reference state heat of reaction* $\bar{q}_r^\circ$, as

$$\bar{q}_r^\circ = \bar{h}_{RP}^\circ = \sum_P (n_i/n_{\text{fuel}})(\bar{h}_f^\circ)_i - \sum_R (n_i/n_{\text{fuel}})(\bar{h}_f^\circ)_i \tag{9.12}$$

This equation can be used to determine the standard reference state HHV heats of combustion tabulated in Table 9.2, as illustrated in the following example.

Example 9.5

Determine the higher and lower heating values of methane. Note that for the determination of the HHV and LHV the combustion reaction must occur with 100% theoretical air, and that both the reactants and the products must be at the standard reference state of 25 °C and 0.1 MPa. For the HHV calculation the water in the combustion products must be in the liquid phase, and for the LHV calculation it must be in the vapor phase.

Solution For 100% theoretical air, the combustion equation for methane is

$$CH_4 + 2[O_2 + 3.76(N_2)] \rightarrow CO_2 + 2(H_2O) + 7.52(N_2)$$

Since both the reactants and the products are at the standard reference state, we can use Eq. 9.12 to find the heat of combustion, which will be either the

HHV or the LHV depending upon how the water term is handled. Then

$$\bar{h}_R^\circ = \sum_R (n_i/n_{\text{fuel}})(\bar{h}_f^\circ)_i = (\bar{h}_f^\circ)_{CH_4} + 2(\bar{h}_f^\circ)_{O_2} + 7.52(\bar{h}_f^\circ)_{N_2}$$

and from Table 9.1 we find that

$$(\bar{h}_f^\circ)_{CH_4} = -74.873 \text{ MJ/kgmole } CH_4$$

Since O_2 and N_2 are the elements of the compound CH_4, in their standard states $(\bar{h}_f^\circ)_{O_2} = (\bar{h}_f^\circ)_{N_2} = 0$. Then $\bar{h}_R^\circ = -74.873$ MJ/kgmole CH_4. Similarly

$$\bar{h}_P^\circ = \sum_P (n_i/n_{\text{fuel}})(\bar{h}_f^\circ)_i = (\bar{h}_f^\circ)_{CO_2} + 2(\bar{h}_f^\circ)_{H_2O(\ell)} + 7.52(\bar{h}_f^\circ)_{N_2}$$

Again $(\bar{h}_f^\circ)_{N_2} = 0$, and from Table 9.1 we find that

$$(\bar{h}_f^\circ)_{CO_2} = -393.522 \text{ MJ/kgmole } CO_2$$

$$(\bar{h}_f^\circ)_{H_2O(g)} = -241.827 \text{ MJ/kgmole } H_2O \text{ vapor}$$

$$(\bar{h}_f^\circ)_{H_2O(\ell)} = -285.838 \text{ MJ/kgmole } H_2O \text{ liquid}$$

Then,

$$(\bar{h}_P^\circ)_{LHV} = -393.522 + 2(-241.827) + 0 = -877.176 \text{ MJ/kgmole } CH_4$$

and

$$(\bar{h}_P^\circ)_{HHV} = -393.522 + 2(-285.838) + 0 = -965.198 \text{ MJ/kgmole } CH_4$$

Finally,

$$\begin{aligned} \text{LHV} = (\bar{q}_r^\circ)_{LHV} = (\bar{h}_P^\circ)_{LHV} - \bar{h}_R^\circ &= -877.176 - (-74.873) \\ &= -802.303 \text{ MJ/kgmole } CH_4 \end{aligned}$$

and

$$\begin{aligned} \text{HHV} = (\bar{q}_r^\circ)_{HHV} = (\bar{h}_P^\circ)_{HHV} - \bar{h}_R^\circ &= -965.198 - (-74.873) \\ &= -890.325 \text{ MJ/kgmole } CH_4 \end{aligned}$$

Note that this HHV is essentially the same as that listed in Table 9.2 for methane.

When the reactants and/or products are *not* at the standard reference state, then their enthalpies are determined from Hess' law by adding to the standard reference state enthalpies, the change in enthalpy between the actual temperature and pressure and the standard reference state temperature and pressure. Normally we can ignore the effect of pressure on enthalpy, so that the molar enthalpy of any compound at temperature T and pressure p is $h_{T,p}$, given by

$$\bar{h}_{T,p} = \bar{h}_f^\circ + (\bar{h}_T - \bar{h}_{T^\circ}) \tag{9.13}$$

If the material can be considered to be an ideal gas with constant specific heats over the temperature range from the standard reference state temperature T° to the actual temperature T, then we can write

$$\bar{h}_{T,p} = \bar{h}_f^\circ + \bar{c}_p(T - T^\circ) \tag{9.14}$$

Otherwise, $\bar{h}_T - \bar{h}_{T^\circ}$ must be be determined from a more accurate source such as the gas tables (Appendix C.16*c*). Combining Eqs. 9.9, 9.10, 9.11, and 9.13 gives the general formula for the heat of reaction (or combustion) of a substance *not* at the standard reference state as

$$\bar{q}_r = \sum_P (n_i/n_{\text{fuel}})(\bar{h}_f^\circ + \bar{h}_T - \bar{h}_{T^\circ})_i - \sum_R (n_i/n_{\text{fuel}})(\bar{h}_f^\circ + \bar{h}_T - \bar{h}_{T^\circ})_i \tag{9.15}$$

The use of Eq. 9.15 is illustrated in the following example.

Example 9.6

Compute the heat of reaction of methane when the reactants are at the standard reference state but the products are at 500 °C. Assume that the product gases can be treated as ideal gases with constant specific heats, and that the combustion water is in its vapor state.

Solution Here, $\bar{q}_r = \bar{h}_P - \bar{h}_R^\circ$ where, from Example 9.5, $\bar{h}_R^\circ = -74.873$ MJ/kgmole CH_4. Assuming all the components of the products behave as ideal gases with constant specific heats, we can use Eq. 9.14 in Eq. 9.11 to find

$$\begin{aligned}\bar{h}_P &= \sum_P (n_i/n_{\text{fuel}})[\bar{h}_f^\circ + \bar{c}_p(T - T^\circ)]_i \\ &= (\bar{h}_f^\circ)_{CO_2} + 2(\bar{h}_f^\circ)_{H_2O(g)} + 7.52(\bar{h}_f^\circ)_{N_2} \\ &\quad + [(\bar{c}_p)_{CO_2} + 2(\bar{c}_p)_{H_2O(g)} + 7.52(\bar{c}_p)_{N_2}](T - T^\circ) \\ &= -393.522 + 2(-241.827) + 0 + [0.03719 + 2(0.03364) \\ &\quad + 7.52(0.02908)](500 - 25) = -723.679 \text{ MJ/kgmole } CH_4\end{aligned}$$

Where the molar specific heats were obtained from Appendix C.13*b* (note that they were converted from kJ/kgmole to MJ/kgmole for use here). Then,

$$\bar{q}_r = -723.679 - (-74.873) = -648.806 \text{ MJ/kgmole } CH_4$$

In this example note that even though the nitrogen did not enter into the chemistry of the reaction, it did enter into the thermodynamics of the reaction because a significant portion of the heat of combustion went into heating the nitrogen from 25 to 500 °C. Thus, it is easy to see why the use of too much excess air can reduce the net heat production of a combustion reaction and consequently cause significant energy losses to the environment via hot exhaust gases.

The Adiabatic Flame Temperature

The maximum possible combustion temperature will occur when a combustion takes place inside an adiabatic (i.e., insulated) system. This temperature is called the *adiabatic combustion temperature*, or the *adiabatic flame temperature*. In practice, though, the combustion temperature can never reach this temperature because

1. no system can be made truly adiabatic,
2. the combustion reaction is always somewhat incomplete, and
3. the combustion products will ionize at high temperatures and thus lower the reaction temperature.

Nonetheless, the adiabatic flame temperature does provide a useful upper bound on combustion temperatures and can be used to estimate the thermal effects of combustion on material physical properties and on exhaust gas states.

For an adiabatic system, $\bar{q}_r = 0$, and Eq. 9.9 reduces to $\bar{h}_{RP} = 0$, or $\bar{h}_R = \bar{h}_P$, and then

$$\sum_R (n_i/n_{\text{fuel}})(\bar{h}_f^\circ + \bar{h}_T - \bar{h}_{T^\circ})_i = \sum_P (n_i/n_{\text{fuel}})(\bar{h}_f^\circ + \bar{h}_{T_A} - \bar{h}_{T^\circ})_i$$

where T_A is the adiabatic flame temperature and T is the temperature of the reactants. If the reactants are all at the standard reference state and if the products can all be treated as ideal gases with constant specific heats over the temperature range from T° to T_A, then the previous equation reduces to

$$\sum_R (n_i/n_{\text{fuel}})(\bar{h}_f^\circ)_i = \sum_P (n_i/n_{\text{fuel}})[\bar{h}_f^\circ + \bar{c}_p(T_A - T^\circ)]_i$$

Now let's suppose that all of the reactants except the fuel are elements: then their $\bar{h}_f^\circ$ values are all zero. This equation can then be solved for T_A as

$$T_A\Big|_{\substack{\text{open}\\\text{system}}} = \frac{(\bar{h}_f^\circ)_{\text{fuel}} - \sum_P (n_i/n_{\text{fuel}})(\bar{h}_f^\circ)_i}{\sum_P (n_i/n_{\text{fuel}})(\bar{c}_{pi})_{\text{avg}}} + T^\circ \tag{9.16}$$

Equation 9.16 represents the only method for calculating the adiabatic flame temperature directly. It requires ideal gas behavior, which is usually reasonable, and it requires constant specific heats over the range $T^\circ = 25$ °C to T_A, which is not so reasonable unless average values are used (as noted in the equation). Average molar specific heats for typical combustion products in the range 25 to 3000 °C are given in Table 9.3. This range covers most adiabatic flame temperatures.

In the case of an adiabatic, aergonic, closed system bomb calorimeter, Eq. 9.7 tells us that $\bar{u}_P = \bar{u}_R$, and if the products can again be treated as ideal gases with constant (or average) specific heats it is easy to show that the adiabatic flame

Table 9.3 Molar specific heats averaged over the temperature range from 25 to 3000 °C (77 to 5400 °F)

	$(\bar{c}_p)_{avg}$		$(\bar{c}_v)_{avg}$	
Substance	kJ/(kgmole·K)	Btu/(lbmole·R)	kJ/(kgmole·K)	Btu/(lbmole·R)
Carbon Dioxide (CO_2)	58.18	13.90	49.87	11.91
Water Vapor ($H_2O(g)$)	42.50	10.15	34.19	8.17
Oxygen (O_2)	32.99	7.88	24.68	5.89
Nitrogen (N_2)	31.18	7.45	22.87	5.46

temperature in this system is given by

$$T_A\Big|_{\substack{\text{closed}\\ \text{system}}} = \frac{(\bar{u}_f^\circ)_{\text{fuel}} - \sum_R (n_i/n_{\text{fuel}})\mathscr{R}T^\circ - \sum_P (n_i/n_{\text{fuel}})(\bar{h}_f^\circ - \mathscr{R}T^\circ)_i}{\sum_P (n_i/n_{\text{fuel}})(\bar{c}_{vi})_{\text{avg}}} + T^\circ \quad \textbf{(9.17)}$$

where we have again assumed that the reactants contain only the fuel and its combustion elements. Also, we have used the definition of enthalpy to find

$$\bar{u}_f^\circ = \bar{h}_f^\circ - (p\bar{v})^\circ = \bar{h}_f^\circ - \mathscr{R}T^\circ$$

for the ideal gas products and the nonfuel reactants, where T° is the standard reference state absolute temperature (298 K or 537 R). Also, for most liquids and solids at the standard reference state we can use the approximation $(\bar{u}_f^\circ)_{\text{fuel}} \approx (\bar{h}_f^\circ)_{\text{fuel}}$.

Example 9.7

Determine the adiabatic flame temperature of liquid octane, $C_8H_{18}(\ell)$, burning with

a) 100% theoretical air, and
b) 200% theoretical air

when the reactants are in the standard reference state and the combustion products are assumed to be ideal gases.

Solution

a) The combustion equation for octane burning with 100% theoretical air is

$$C_8H_{18} + 12.5[O_2 + 3.76(N_2)] \rightarrow 8(CO_2) + 9(H_2O) + 47(N_2)$$

Since the products can be considered to be ideal gases, we can use Eq. 9.16 and the average specific heat values given in Table 9.3. From Table 9.1, we find,

$$(\bar{h}_f^\circ)_{\text{fuel}} = (\bar{h}_f^\circ)_{C_8H_{18}(\ell)} = -249.952 \text{ MJ/kgmole}$$

$$(\bar{h}_f^\circ)_{CO_2} = -393.522 \text{ MJ/kgmole}$$

$$(\bar{h}_f^\circ)_{H_2O(g)} = -241.827 \text{ MJ/kgmole}$$

and

$$(\bar{h}_f^\circ)_{N_2} = 0 \text{ because it is an element}$$

Then,

$$\sum_P (n_i/n_{\text{fuel}})(\bar{h}_f^\circ)_i = 8(\bar{h}_f^\circ)_{CO_2} + 9(\bar{h}_f^\circ)_{H_2O} + 47(\bar{h}_f^\circ)_{N_2}$$

$$= 8(-393.522) + 9(-241.827) + 47(0)$$

$$= -5324.62 \text{ MJ/kgmole } C_8H_{18}$$

Also,

$$\sum_P (n_i/n_{\text{fuel}})(\bar{c}_{pi})_{\text{avg}} = 8[(\bar{c}_p)_{CO_2}]_{\text{avg}} + 9[(\bar{c}_p)_{H_2O}]_{\text{avg}} + 47[(\bar{c}_p)_{N_2}]_{\text{avg}}$$

$$= 8(0.05818) + 9(0.04250) + 47(0.03118)$$

$$= 2.3134 \text{ MJ/(kgmole·K) } C_8H_{18}$$

Then Eq. 9.16 gives

$$T_A = \frac{-249.952 - (-5324.619)}{2.3134} + 25 = 2218.6\ °C = 4025.5\ °F$$

b) The reaction equation when 200% theoretical air is used is

$$C_8H_{18} + 2(12.5)[O_2 + 3.76(N_2)] \rightarrow 8(CO_2) + 9(H_2O) + 12.5(O_2) + 94(N_2)$$

The numerator in Eq. 9.16 is the same here as it was in part a since we have only added more elements to the reaction equation. The denominator represents the energy required to raise the temperature of all the product gases to T_A and is consequently different here. In this case,

$$\sum_P (n_i/n_{\text{fuel}})(\bar{c}_{pi})_{\text{avg}} = 8[(\bar{c}_p)_{CO_2}]_{\text{avg}} + 9[(\bar{c}_p)_{H_2O}]_{\text{avg}}$$

$$+ 12.5[(\bar{c}_p)_{O_2}]_{\text{avg}} + 94[(\bar{c}_p)_{N_2}]_{\text{avg}}$$

$$= 8(0.05818) + 9(0.04250)$$

$$+ 12.5(0.03299) + 94(0.03118)$$

$$= 4.1912 \text{ MJ/(kgmole·K) } C_8H_{18}$$

Then Eq. 9.16 gives

$$T_A = \frac{-249.952 - (-5324.619)}{4.1912} + 25 = 1235.8\ °C = 2256.4\ °F$$

Thus, the addition of 100% excess air, a practice sometimes necessary to get complete combustion in high-velocity combustion processes, has the effect of reducing the adiabatic combustion temperature by nearly a factor of two.

An alternate and somewhat more accurate approach to finding the adiabatic flame temperature is to use the gas tables (Appendix C.16*c*) to determine the thermodynamic properties of CO_2, H_2O, O_2, N_2, and so forth. However, since T_A and the other thermodynamic properties at this state are unknown, T_A must be determined by a trial and error method as follows:

1. $\bar{h}_R$ is calculated from Eq. 9.10 utilizing Eqs. 9.13 or 9.14 if necessary.
2. A trial value for T_A is then assumed.
3. $\bar{h}_P$ is the calculated from the $(\bar{h}_f^\circ)_P$ values and the values of $(h_{T_A} - h_{T^\circ})_P$ in Appendix C.16*c*.
4. If the value of $\bar{h}_P$ calculated in step 3 above equals that of $\bar{h}_R$ calculated in step 1, then the correct value of T_A was assumed in step 2. Otherwise a new T_A value is chosen and the process is repeated until $\bar{h}_P \approx \bar{h}_R$.

This manual iteration scheme is rather tedious and inaccuracies will be introduced by the linear interpolations in Appendix C.16*c* that will be required to obtain a solution. These inaccuracies can be eliminated by programming accurate molar enthalpy formulae for the products into a microcomputer. The computer can then be programmed to calculate the heat of combustion and iterate to find the adiabatic flame temperature in a small fraction of the time required to carry out these calculations manually. Appendix C.14 gives accurate correlations for the variation in $\bar{c}_p$ with temperature for various substances. Using this information we can determine accurate values for

$$\bar{h}_T - \bar{h}_{T^\circ} = \int_{T^\circ}^{T} \bar{c}_p \, dT$$

For example, Appendix C.14*b* gives $\bar{c}_p$ in kJ/(kgmole·K) for nitrogen as

$$\bar{c}_p = 39.060 - 512.79(\theta^{-1.5}) + 1072.7(\theta^{-2}) - 820.40(\theta^{-3})$$

for $300 \le T \le 3500$ K with a maximum error of only 0.43%, where $\theta = T(K)/100$. Then $dT = 100(d\theta)$, and $\bar{h}_T - \bar{h}_{T^\circ}$ (in kJ/(kgmole·K)) can be calculated for nitrogen from

$$\begin{aligned}\bar{h}_T - \bar{h}_{T^\circ} &= 100 \int_{\theta^\circ}^{\theta} \bar{c}_p \, d\theta \\ &= 3906(\theta - \theta^\circ) + 102{,}558[(\theta)^{-1/2} - (\theta^\circ)^{-1/2}] \\ &\quad - 107{,}270[(\theta)^{-1} - (\theta^\circ)^{-1}] + 41{,}020[(\theta)^{-2} - (\theta^\circ)^{-2}]\end{aligned}$$

where $\theta^\circ = T^\circ/100 = 298/100 = 2.98$, and $\theta = T/100$. Combining this equation with that for O_2, CO_2, and H_2O provides a very good computer-based thermodynamic analysis of combustion reactions.

The BASIC language computer program shown in Figure 9.5 was written for an IBM compatible personal computer. It calculates the heat of combustion of

```
10 REM: ********************** LIQUID OCTANE LHV PROGRAM **********************
20 CLS:PRINT:PRINT:PRINT
30 PRINT "THIS PROGRAM CALCULATES THE LOWER HEAT OF COMBUSTION (LHV) OF LIQUID
        OCTANE WHEN THE REACTANTS ARE AT THE SRS, 25 C AND 0.1 MPA."
40 PRINT:PRINT:INPUT "ENTER THE PERCENT THEORETICAL AIR:";PCTA
50 IF PCTA > = 100 THEN 80
60 PRINT "THE THEORETICAL AIR MUST BE 100% OR GREATER. PLEASE RE-ENTER."
70 PRINT:PRINT:GOTO 40
80 TA = PCTA/100
90 HLOCTF = -249.952
100 HCO2F = -393.522
110 HH2OF = -241.827
120 PRINT:PRINT:INPUT "ENTER THE TEMPERATURE OF THE PRODUCTS IN DEGREES C:";TP
130 REM: CONSTANTS NEEDED IN THE CALCULATIONS BELOW.
140 T1 = 2.98
150 T2 = (TP + 273)/100
160 C1 = T2 - T1
170 C2 = T2^1.25 - T1^1.25
180 C3 = T2^1.5 - T1^1.5
190 C4 = T2^2 - T1^2
200 C5 = T2^2.5 - T1^2.5
210 C6 = T2^3 - T1^3
220 C7 = 1/T2^.5 - 1/T1^.5
230 C8 = 1/T2 - 1/T1
240 C9 = 1/T2^2 - 1/T1^2
250 REM: NOW BEGIN THE ENTHALPY CALCULATIONS (IN KJ/KGMOLE).
260 HN2 = 3906*C1 + 102558*C7 - 107270*C8 + 41020*C9
270 HO2 = 3743.2*C1 + .8*C5 + 35714*C7 - 23688*C8
280 HCO2 = -373.57*C1 + 2035.3*C3 - 205.17*C4 + .8*C6
290 HH20 = 14305*C1 - 14683*C2 + 5516.7*C3 - 184.95*C4
300 REM: NOW BEGIN THE HEAT OF REACTION CALCULATIONS (IN MJ/KGMOLE).
310 H1 = HCO2F + HCO2/1000
320 H2 = HH2OF + HH20/1000
330 H3 = HO2/1000
340 H4 = HN2/1000
350 QR = 8*H1 + 9*H2 + 12.5*(TA - 1)*H3 + 47*TA*H4 - HLOCTF
360 PRINT:PRINT "THE LHV OF LIQUID OCTANE WITH";PCTA;"% THEORETICAL AIR IS";
    QR;"MJ/KGMOLE"
370 PRINT "WHEN THE COMBUSTION TEMPERATURE IS";TP; "DEGREES C."
380 IF QR < 0 THEN GOTO 410
390 PRINT:PRINT "A POSITIVE HEAT OF COMBUSTION MEANS THAT THE PRODUCTS ARE AT
               A TEMPERATURE HIGHER THAN THE ADIABATIC FLAME TEMPERAURE."
400 REM: THE STANDARD RE-RUN OPTION.
410 PRINT:PRINT "DO YOU WISH TO RE-RUN WITH A DIFFERENT TEMPERATURE (Y/N)";
420 INPUT A$
430 IF A$ = "N" OR A$ = "n" THEN GOTO 460
440 IF A$ < > "Y" AND A$ < > "y" THEN GOTO 410
450 CLS:PRINT:PRINT:PRINT:GOTO 120
460 PRINT:PRINT:PRINT "THIS PROGRAM HAS ENDED. THANK YOU.":  END
```

Figure 9.5 A BASIC language computer program for calculating the lower heat of combustion of liquid octane at user selected theoretical air level and combustion products temperature.

liquid octane $C_8H_{18}(\ell)$ as was done in Example 9.7, except it uses the accurate molar specific heat formula discussed above to find the enthalpies of the products. It accepts any theoretical air value greater than or equal to 100%, and any combustion products temperature. Since it assumes the water in the combustion products is in the vapor state, it calculates the lower heating value (LHV) only. This program can be used interactively from the keyboard to converge to the adiabatic flame temperature by repeatedly choosing a combustion products temperature that ultimately causes the heat of combustion to become zero. This only takes a few seconds of keyboard work, and the result for 100% theoretical air is $T_A = 2122.8$ °C, while that for 200% theoretical air is 1233.3 °C. Note that using the temperature averaged specific heats in Example 9.7 gave values within 5% of these values.

The program shown in Figure 9.5 can be easily expanded to treat any hydrocarbon of the form C_nH_m with either excess or deficit air by using Eqs. 9.4*b* and 9.4*c* in place of the octane reaction. Also, it can be easily modified to provide either the LHV or the HHV at the users request. These and other modifications are left up to the imagination of the reader.

The Maximum Explosion Pressure

The maximum possible internal pressure produced by combustion in a closed rigid system is the pressure that occurs at the adiabatic flame temperature. It is the pressure that occurs when the system is insulated or when the combustion reaction occurs too fast for significant heat transfer to occur (as in explosions). This maximum pressure can be estimated from the ideal gas equation of state as

$$p_{\max} = n_p \mathscr{R} T_A / V \qquad \textbf{(9.18)}$$

where n_p is the total number of moles of product present in the volume V, and T_A is the adiabatic flame temperature of the reaction. Even though the adiabatic flame temperature is never reached in practice, this value of $p_{\max}$ is useful as an upper bound in explosion safety calculations.

Example 9.8

We wish to measure the heat of combustion of liquid octane by burning it in a rigid, sealed, adiabatic bomb calorimeter whose internal volume is 0.05 ft^3. We want to use 10 g of fuel and to fill the bomb with enough pure oxygen to have 50% excess oxygen for the combustion reaction. Determine the maximum possible explosion pressure inside the bomb when the fuel is ignited.

Solution The molecular mass of octane (C_8H_{18}) is 114 kg/kgmole, so 10 g (0.01 kg) of it contains

$$(0.01 \text{ kg})/(114 \text{ kg/kgmole}) = 8.77 \times 10^{-5} \text{ kgmole}$$

The reaction equation for 50% excess pure oxygen is,

$$C_8H_{18} + 1.5(12.5)(O_2) \rightarrow 8(CO_2) + 9(H_2O) + 6.25(O_2)$$

and 8.77×10^{-5} kgmole of octane will yield

$$(8.77 \times 10^{-5})(8 + 9 + 6.25) = 0.0020 \text{ kgmole of product}$$

or

$$(0.0020 \text{ kgmole})(2.2046 \text{ lbmole/kgmole}) = 0.0044 \text{ lbmole of product}$$

We can estimate the adiabatic flame temperature for this closed system reaction from Eq. 9.17 using the temperature-averaged molar constant volume specific heats found in Table 9.3. Since the fuel is in liquid form at a low pressure here, we will use the approximation $(\bar{u}_f^\circ)_{fuel} \approx (\bar{h}_f^\circ)_{fuel}$. Since $\mathscr{R}T^\circ = (0.0083143)(298) = 2.478$ MJ/kgmole is a constant, the numerator of Eq. 9.17 becomes

$$-249.952 - 1.5(12.5)(2.478) - 8(-393.522 - 2.478)$$
$$- 9(-241.827 - 2.478) - 6.25(0 - 2.478) = 5085.82 \text{ MJ}$$

and the denominator is

$$8(0.04987) + 9(0.03419) + 6.25(0.02468) = 0.8609 \text{ MJ/K}$$

Then Eq. 9.17 gives

$$(T_A)_{\substack{\text{bomb}\\\text{calorimeter}}} = \frac{5085.82}{0.8609} + 25 = 5933\ °\text{C} = 6206 \text{ K} = 11{,}170 \text{ R}$$

and Eq. 9.18 gives

$$p_{max} = \frac{(0.0044 \text{ lbmole})[1545.35 \text{ ft}\cdot\text{lbf}/(\text{lbmole}\cdot\text{R})](11{,}170 \text{ R})}{(0.05 \text{ ft}^3)(144 \text{ in}^2/\text{ft}^2)}$$
$$= 10{,}550 \text{ psi}$$

More accurate calculations that include the energy–absorbing effects of chemical dissociation of the products at high temperatures show that the maximum adiabatic flame temperature of octane with pure oxygen is only about 3100 K (5580 R). Therefore, the maximum explosion temperature calculated above is high by a factor of about two, and the actual maximum pressure inside the bomb calorimeter will be closer to 5400 psi. Gas pressures at this level can be very dangerous (especially at high temperatures) and the calorimeter must be designed to withstand them.

Entropy Production in Chemical Reactions

The entropy rate balance applied to a steady state, steady flow *open system* combustion or reaction chamber with isothermal boundaries at temperature T_b gives the total entropy production rate for the reaction as

$$(\dot{S}_P)_r = \sum_{out} \dot{m}s - \sum_{in} \dot{m}s - \dot{Q}_r/T_b$$
$$= \sum_{out} \dot{n}\bar{s} - \sum_{in} \dot{n}\bar{s} - \dot{Q}_r/T_b$$

where $\dot{Q}_r$ is the heat transport rate of the reaction. In most instances the products will exit the system mixed together in a single flowstream, but the reactants can enter the system **a)** either premixed in a single flowstream, or **b)** in separate individual flowstreams. If the reactants enter through separate flowstreams, each carrying a pure substance, then the entropy production rate of the mixing process that must occur inside the system before the reaction can occur will be included in the previous equation. It will then have the form

$$(\dot{S}_P)_r = \dot{n}_P\bar{s}_P - \sum_R \dot{n}_i\bar{s}_i - \dot{Q}_r/T_b$$

On the other hand, if the reactants enter the system already mixed together in a single flowstream, then the above equation becomes

$$(\dot{S}_P)_r = \dot{n}_P\bar{s}_P - \dot{n}_R\bar{s}_R - \dot{Q}_r/T_b$$

where the mixture molar specific entropies are given by Eq. 7.9*d* as

$$\bar{s}_P = \sum_P x_i\hat{\bar{s}}_i \quad \text{and} \quad \bar{s}_R = \sum_R x_i\hat{\bar{s}}_i$$

where x_i are the mole fractions of substance i, and the $\hat{\bar{s}}$ are the partial molar specific entropies defined in Chapter 7. If both the reactants and the products can be considered to be mixtures of ideal gases that obey the Gibbs-Dalton ideal gas mixture law discussed in Chapter 7, then $\bar{s}_i = \hat{\bar{s}}_i$, the molar specific entropy of gas i. If one or more of the reactants or products is a liquid or a solid, or if the mixture does not obey the Gibbs-Dalton ideal gas mixture law, then a much more complex analysis must be carried out.

Assuming both the reactants and the products to be premixed ideal gases, then the total entropy production rate of the reaction is

$$(\dot{S}_P)_r = \dot{n}_P \sum_P x_i\bar{s}_i - \dot{n}_R \sum_R x_i\bar{s}_i - \dot{Q}_r/T_b$$
$$= \sum_P \dot{n}_i\bar{s}_i - \sum_R \dot{n}_i\bar{s}_i - \dot{Q}_r/T_b$$

and dividing through by the fuel molar flow rate $\dot{n}_{\text{fuel}}$ gives

$$(\dot{S}_P)_r/\dot{n}_{\text{fuel}} = (S_P)_r/n_{\text{fuel}} = (\bar{s}_P)_r \\ = \sum_P (n_i/n_{\text{fuel}})\bar{s}_i - \sum_R (n_i/n_{\text{fuel}})\bar{s}_i - \bar{q}_r/T_b \tag{9.19}$$

where $(\bar{s}_P)_r$ is the specific entropy production per unit mole of fuel consumed.

In the case of a *closed system* with an isothermal boundary, the entropy balance equation gives the total entropy production of the reaction as (see Eq. 5.76)

$$(S_P)_r = (S_2 - S_1)_r - {}_1(Q_r)_2/T_b \\ = n_P\bar{s}_P - n_R\bar{s}_R - Q_r/T_b$$

where the reactants and products are assumed to be mixed at the beginning and end of the reaction respectively. Again assuming the reactants and the products to be ideal gases, and dividing through by the number of moles of fuel present in the reactants, gives

$$(S_P)_r/n_{\text{fuel}} = (\bar{s}_P)_r = \sum_P (n_i/n_{\text{fuel}})\bar{s}_i - \sum_R (n_i/n_{\text{fuel}})s_i - q_r/T_b$$

which is identical to Eq. 9.19. This is as it should be since the specific entropy production per unit mole of fuel consumed should only depend upon the reaction itself and not upon the analysis frame (i.e., open or closed) used to determine it.

As in the case of enthalpy discussed earlier, we will need a common zero point reference state from which to measure the entropies of all of the components in the reaction. Enthalpy and internal energy have no physically well-defined absolute zero values. Even at absolute zero temperature it can be shown that the enthalpy and internal energy are not generally zero. Entropy, on the other hand, does have an absolute zero point dictated by a state of absolutely perfect molecular order. This is the postulate called the *third law of thermodynamics*.

Unlike the first two laws of thermodynamics the third law is not a statement about conservation or production. It was developed from quantum statistical mechanics theories in 1906 by Walther Hermann Nernst (1864–1941), for which he won the 1920 Nobel Prize in Chemistry. Basically it states that the entropy of a perfect crystalline substance vanishes at absolute zero temperature, and is independent of the pressure at that point. That is

$$\lim_{T\to 0} (S)_{\substack{\text{perfect}\\ \text{crystal}}} = \left(\frac{\partial S}{\partial p}\right)\Bigg|_{T=0} = 0$$

Therefore, if we choose absolute zero temperature and any convenient pressure as a reference state for an entropy scale we will have produced an *absolute entropy scale* (i.e., one with an absolute zero point). Normally a pressure of 0.1 MPa (about

1 atm) is chosen for the reference state pressure. Consequently, we will construct an absolute entropy scale from the point $S(0.1\text{ MPa}, 0\text{ K})_{abs} = 0$.

The primary value of the third law of thermodynamics as far as we are concerned is that it gives us a reference state from which we can construct an absolute entropy scale. This means that we now have three thermodynamic properties with well-defined absolute zero value states: pressure, temperature, and entropy. We assume that all the substances we will be dealing with have ordered crystalline rather than amorphous solid phases at absolute zero temperature. Therefore, we can compute the absolute molar specific entropy of an *incompressible* substance at any pressure and temperature from Eq. 5.32 of Chapter 5 as

$$[\bar{s}(p, T)_{abs}]_{\substack{\text{incompressible}\\ \text{substance}}} = \int_0^T \bar{c}(dT/T) \tag{9.20}$$

where $\bar{c}$ is the molar specific heat and T is in absolute temperature units (K or R). Similarly, the absolute molar specific entropy in SI units of an *ideal gas* at any pressure and temperature can be determined from Eq. 5.35 of Chapter 5 as

$$[\bar{s}(p, T)_{abs}]_{\text{ideal gas}} = \int_0^T \bar{c}_p(dT/T) - \mathscr{R}\ln(p/0.1\text{ MPa}) \tag{9.21}$$

where T is in K and p is in MPa.[13]

Since all of the enthalpy values used thus far in this chapter are based on a standard reference state of $T^\circ = 25\ ^\circ\text{C}$ and $p^\circ = 0.1$ MPa, it would be convenient to be able to shift our absolute entropy scale to this reference state. To do this, we define $\bar{s}^\circ$ to be the absolute molar specific entropy at the standard reference state and use Eq. 5.35 with $p = p^\circ =$ a constant to obtain

$$\bar{s}^\circ = \bar{s}(p^\circ, T^\circ)_{abs} = \int_0^{T^\circ} \bar{c}_p(dT/T)$$

Values for the $\bar{s}^\circ$ of various compounds can be found in Table 9.4. The absolute molar specific entropy at any other state at pressure p and temperature T is given by

$$\bar{s}(p, T)_{abs} = \bar{s}^\circ + \Delta\bar{s}(p^\circ \to p, T^\circ \to T)$$

where $\Delta\bar{s}$ represents the change in molar specific entropy between the state at (p°, T°) and that at (p, T). For an *incompressible* substance this becomes

$$[\bar{s}(p, T)_{abs}]_{\substack{\text{incompressible}\\ \text{substance}}} = \bar{s}^\circ + \int_{T^\circ}^T \bar{c}(dT/T) \tag{9.22}$$

13. Note that both $\bar{c}$ and $\bar{c}_p \to 0$ as $T \to 0$ and consequently Eqs. 9.20 and 9.21 cannot be integrated by assuming constant specific heats in the temperature range from 0 to T.

Table 9.4 **Molar specific absolute entropy and molar specific Gibbs' function of formation at 25 °C and 0.1 MPa**

	$\bar{s}^{\circ}$		$\bar{g}_f^{\circ}$	
Substance	**kJ/(kgmole·K)**	**Btu/(lbmole·R)**	**MJ/kgmole**	**Btu/lbmole**
Carbon monoxide, CO	197.653	47.219	−137.150	−59,003
Carbon dioxide, CO_2	213.795	52.098	−394.374	−169,664
Water, H_2O(g)	188.833	45.132	−228.583	−98,333
Water, H_2O(l)	70.049	16.742	−237.178	−102,036
Methane, CH_4	186.256	44.516	−50.751	−21,834
Acetylene, C_2H_2	200.958	48.030	+209.234	+90,015
Ethylene, C_2H_4	219.548	52.473	+68.207	+29,343
Ethane, C_2H_6	229.602	54.876	−32.777	−14,101
Propane, C_3H_8	270.019	64.361	−23.316	−10,031
Butane, C_4H_{10}	310.227	74.146	−16.914	−7,276
Octane, C_8H_{18}(g)	466.835	111.576	+16.859	+7,253
Octane, C_8H_{18}(l)	360.896	86.256	+6.940	+2,986
Carbon, C(s)	5.740	1.372	0	0
Oxygen, O_2	205.138	49.029	0	0
Hydrogen, H_2	130.684	31.234	0	0
Nitrogen, N_2	191.610	45.796	0	0

Source: Gordon J. Van Wylen and Richard E. Sonntag, *Fundamentals of Classical Thermodynamics, SI Version*, 2d ed. (New York: Wiley, 1976), p. 496 (Table 12.3). Copyright © 1976 John Wiley & Sons. Reprinted by permission of John Wiley & Sons. C, O_2, H_2, and N_2 are from the *Journal of Physical and Chemical Reference Data*, 11, Suppl. 2 (1982). Used with permission.

and for an *ideal gas* it becomes

$$[\bar{s}(p, T)_{\text{abs}}]_{\substack{\text{ideal}\\ \text{gas}}} = \bar{s}^{\circ} + \int_{T^{\circ}}^{T} \bar{c}_p(dT/T) - \mathscr{R}\ln(p/p^{\circ}) \tag{9.23}$$

If these substances have constant (or averaged) specific heats in the range of T° to T, then these equations can be integrated to give

$$[\bar{s}(p, T)_{\text{abs}}]_{\substack{\text{incompressible}\\ \text{substance}}} = \bar{s}^{\circ} + \bar{c}\ln(T/T^{\circ}) \tag{9.24}$$

and

$$[\bar{s}(p, T)_{\text{abs}}]_{\substack{\text{ideal}\\ \text{gas}}} = \bar{s}^{\circ} + \bar{c}_p\ln(T/T^{\circ}) - \mathscr{R}\ln(p/p^{\circ}) \tag{9.25}$$

In the case of mixtures of ideal gases that obey the Gibbs-Dalton ideal gas mixture law, the absolute molar specific entropy of chemical species i, $\bar{s}_i$, needed for the entropy balance of Eqs. 9.19 is given by

$$\bar{s}_i = \bar{s}_i^{\circ} + \int_{T^{\circ}}^{T} \bar{c}_{pi}(dT/T) - \mathscr{R}\ln(p_i/p^{\circ}) \tag{9.26a}$$

and when $\bar{c}_{pi}$ is constant (or averaged) over T° to T then

$$\bar{s}_i = \bar{s}_i^{\circ} + \bar{c}_{pi}\ln(T/T^{\circ}) - \mathscr{R}\ln(p_i/p^{\circ}) \tag{9.26b}$$

where p_i is the partial pressure of chemical species i in the mixture.

Accurate integrated values can be found for $\bar{s}_i$ through the use of Appendix C.16*c*. Note that in this appendix we have used the condensed notation

$$\bar{\phi}_i = \bar{s}_i^\circ + \int \bar{c}_{pi}(dT/T) \tag{9.27}$$

so that Eq. 9.26*a* reduces for use with Appendix C.16*c* to

$$\bar{s}_i = \bar{\phi}_i - \mathscr{R} \ln(p_i/p^\circ) \tag{9.26c}$$

Alternatively, a computer program similar to that shown in Figure 9.5 could be easily written to calculate accurate integrated values for $\bar{s}_i$.

The partial pressure p_i of component i in the mixture is determined from the mixture composition via Eq. 7.25 as

$$p_i = x_i p_m = w_i(M_m/M_i)p_m$$

where x_i is the mole fraction, w_i is the mass (or weight) fraction, M_i is the molecular mass of chemical species i in the mixture, M_m is the equivalent molecular mass of the mixture, and p_m is the total pressure of the mixture.

Example 9.9

Calculate the entropy produced per mole of fuel when methane is burned with 100% theoretical air. The reactants are premixed at 25 °C at a mixture total pressure of 0.1 MPa, and the products are at 200 °C at a total pressure of 0.1 MPa. The molar heating value of methane under these conditions with the water of combustion in the vapor phase is −134.158 MJ per kgmole of methane. Assume constant specific heat ideal gas behavior for all the combustion components.

Solution Equation 9.19 gives the required entropy production as

$$(\bar{s}_P)_r = \sum_P (n_i/n_{fuel})\bar{s}_i - \sum_R (n_i/n_{fuel})\bar{s}_i - \bar{q}_r/T_b$$

where we are given $\bar{q}_r = -134.158$ MJ/kgmole and we will assume that $T_b = 200 + 273 = 473$ K. The reaction equation for 100% theoretical air is

$$CH_4 + 2[O_2 + 3.76(N_2)] \rightarrow CO_2 + 2(H_2O) + 7.52(N_2)$$

The partial pressures of the reactants can then be found from Eq. 7.25 as

$$p_{CH_4} = (n_{CH_4}/n_R)p_m = [1/(1 + 2 + 7.52)](0.1) = 9.51 \text{ kPa}$$

$$p_{O_2} = (2/10.52)(0.1) = 19.01 \text{ kPa}$$

$$p_{N_2} = (7.52/10.52)(0.1) = 71.48 \text{ kPa}$$

and the partial pressures of the products are

$$p_{CO_2} = (n_{CO_2}/n_P)p_m = (1/10.52)(0.1) = 9.51 \text{ kPa}$$

$$p_{H_2O} = (2/10.52)(0.1) = 19.01 \text{ kPa}$$

$$p_{N_2} = (7.52/10.52)(0.1) = 71.48 \text{ kPa}$$

Now,

$$\sum_R (n_i/n_{fuel})\bar{s}_i = \bar{s}_{CH_4} + 2(\bar{s}_{O_2}) + 7.54(\bar{s}_{N_2})$$

where, from Eq. 9.26*b* with $T = 298$ K, and using Table 9.4,

$$\begin{aligned}\bar{s}_{CH_4} &= \bar{s}^\circ_{CH_4} - \mathscr{R}\ln[p_{CH_4}(\text{MPa})/0.1 \text{ MPa}]\\ &= 186.256 - 8.3143(\ln 0.0951)\\ &= 205.818 \text{ kJ/(kgmole}\cdot\text{K)}\end{aligned}$$

$$\begin{aligned}\bar{s}_{O_2} &= 205.138 - 8.3143(\ln 0.1901)\\ &= 218.941 \text{ kg/(kgmole}\cdot\text{K)}\end{aligned}$$

$$\begin{aligned}\bar{s}_{N_2} &= 191.610 - 8.3143(\ln 0.7148)\\ &= 194.402 \text{ kJ/(kgmole}\cdot\text{K)}\end{aligned}$$

Then,

$$\begin{aligned}\sum_R (n_i/n_{fuel})\bar{s}_i &= 205.818 + 2(218.941) + 7.52(194.402)\\ &= 2105.603 \text{ kJ/(kgmole}\cdot\text{K)}\end{aligned}$$

Also, for the products,

$$\sum_P (n_i/n_{fuel})\bar{s}_i = \bar{s}_{O_2} + 2(\bar{s}_{H_2O}) + 7.52(\bar{s}_{N_2})$$

where, again from Eq. 9.26*b* with $T = 473$ K, and using Table 9.4,

$$\begin{aligned}\bar{s}_{CO_2} &= \bar{s}^\circ_{CO_2} + (\bar{c}_p)_{CO_2}\left(\ln\frac{473}{298}\right) - \mathscr{R}\{\ln[p_{CO_2}(\text{MPa})/0.1 \text{ MPa}]\}\\ &= 213.795 + 37.19\left(\ln\frac{473}{298}\right) - 8.3143(\ln 0.0951)\\ &= 250.539 \text{ kJ/(kgmole}\cdot\text{K)}\end{aligned}$$

$$\begin{aligned}\bar{s}_{H_2O} &= 188.833 + 33.64\left(\ln\frac{473}{298}\right) - 8.3143(\ln 0.1901)\\ &= 218.178 \text{ kJ/(kgmole}\cdot\text{K)}\end{aligned}$$

and

$$\bar{s}_{N_2} = 191.610 + 29.08\left(\ln\frac{473}{298}\right) - 8.3143(\ln 0.7148)$$

$$= 207.837 \text{ kJ/(kgmole}\cdot\text{K)}$$

Then,

$$\sum_P (n_i/n_{\text{fuel}})\bar{s}_i = 250.539 + 2(218.178) + 7.52(207.837)$$

$$= 2249.829 \text{ kJ/(kgmole}\cdot\text{K)}$$

Finally, the desired result is

$$(\bar{s}_P)_r = 2249.829 - 2105.603 - (-134{,}158/473)$$

$$= 427.86 \text{ kJ/(kgmole}\cdot\text{K)}$$

Only about one-third of the value of $(\bar{s}_P)_r$ here is due to the reaction itself; the remaining two-thirds comes from the associated heat transfer. Note that $(\bar{s}_P)_r > 0$ as required by the second law of thermodynamics.

The Entropy and Gibbs Function of Formation

Since the specific molar Gibbs function, $\bar{g} = \bar{h} - T\bar{s}$, depends upon *both* $\bar{h}$ and $\bar{s}$ it does not have an absolute zero reference state. But, since $\bar{s}$ does have an absolute zero reference state, we cannot arbitrarily set the molar specific entropies of the elements of the reaction equal to zero at the standard reference state as was done earlier with their $\bar{h}_f^\circ$ values. Therefore, we define the *molar specific entropy of formation* $\bar{s}_f^\circ$, of a compound as

$$(\bar{s}_f^\circ)_{\text{compound}} = \bar{s}^\circ_{\text{compound}} - \sum_{\text{elements}} (n_i/n_{\text{compound}})\bar{s}_i^\circ \tag{9.28}$$

Then the *molar specific Gibbs function of formation* of a compound, $\bar{g}_f^\circ$, is given by

$$(\bar{g}_f^\circ)_{\text{compound}} = (\bar{h}_f^\circ)_{\text{compound}} - T^\circ(\bar{s}_f^\circ)_{\text{compound}} \tag{9.29}$$

where T° is either 298 K or 537 R depending on whether SI or English units are being used. For example, the molar specific Gibbs function of formation of methane gas CH_4(g) from the hypothetical reaction

$$C(s) + 2(H_2(g)) \rightarrow CH_4(g)$$

can be determined by combining Eqs. 9.28 and 9.29, and using values from Tables 9.1 and 9.4 as

$$(\bar{g}_f^\circ)_{CH_4} = (\bar{h}_f^\circ)_{CH_4} - T^\circ(\bar{s}_f^\circ)_{CH_4} = (\bar{h}_f^\circ)_{CH_4} - T^\circ[\bar{s}^\circ_{CH_4} - \bar{s}^\circ_C - 2\bar{s}^\circ_{H_2}]$$
$$= -74.873 - 298[0.1863 - 0.0057 - 2(0.1307)] = -50.795 \text{ MJ/kgmole}$$

Table 9.4 lists values of $\bar{s}^\circ$ and $\bar{g}_f^\circ$ for the same substances found in Table 9.1. Note that because the elements of the reaction are not considered to be compounds themselves (even though they may be diatomic molecules) they cannot have an entropy of formation. Therefore, for all of these elements we can set $\bar{h}_f^\circ = \bar{s}_f^\circ = \bar{g}_f^\circ = 0$.

Chemical Equilibrium and Dissociation

In 1877 the Dutch chemist Jacobus Hendricus van't Hoff (1852–1911) developed the basic principles of chemical equilibrium from the fundamental laws of thermodynamics. For this, among other things, he won the first Nobel Prize for Chemistry in 1901.

Irreversible reaction equations are written as $n_A A + n_B B \rightarrow n_C C + n_D D$ with the implication that A and B are completely and irreversibly consumed in the reaction as C and D are produced. In an irreversible reaction equation the stoichiometric coefficients represent the actual number of moles of each element present in the reaction vessel. In an equilibrium reaction equation, on the other hand, while the stoichiometric coefficients still represent the number of moles that enter into the equilibrium reaction, they do not necessarily represent the number of moles *present* in the reaction vessel. Therefore, the mole fraction concentrations present cannot be determined from the equilibrium reaction equation alone. Consequently, we will continue to use the symbol n_i to represent the total number of moles of species i present in the reaction vessel, but we must now introduce the symbol $\nu_i \le n_i$ to represent the number of moles of species i that actually enter into the equilibrium reaction.

For example, at high temperature the reaction of A and B to form C and D may partially reverse and reform A and B from C and D, and at equilibrium both the forward and the reverse reactions take place simultaneously resulting in a reversible "equilibrium" composition containing all four substances. To denote a reversible chemical equilibrium reaction that implies the coexistence of all four substances A, B, C, and D we use a *double arrow* between the reactants and the products and we use ν_i for the stoichiometric coefficients of the reaction as follows

$$\nu_A A + \nu_B B \leftrightarrows \nu_C C + \nu_D D$$

Van't Hoff argued that chemical equilibrium occurs only when a reversible system is in a state of constant uniform pressure and temperature. For a closed system whose only work mode is p-V, the combined first and second laws in differential form (neglecting any changes in kinetic or potential energy) are

$$\bar{d}Q + \bar{d}W = dU = T\,dS - Td(S_P) - p\,d\maltese$$

or

$$T\,dS = dU + p\,d\maltese + Td(S_P) = dH - \maltese\,\mathrm{dp} + Td(S_P) \quad \textbf{(9.30)}$$

where we have used the definition of total enthalpy $H = U + p\maltese$, and $d(S_P)$ is the differential entropy production rate which is required to be greater than or equal to zero by the second law of thermodynamics. In Chapter 6 we introduced the Gibbs function G as (see Eq. 6.14) $G = H - TS$, and upon differentiation it becomes

$$dG = dH - T\,dS - S\,dT$$

Rearranging gives

$$T\,dS = dH - dG - S\,dT$$

and combining this result with Eq. 9.30 gives

$$dG = \maltese\,dp - S\,dT - Td(S_P) \quad \textbf{(9.31)}$$

For chemical equilibrium we require that T, p, and S_P all be constants; then $dG = 0$, and consequently $G =$ constant. Otherwise, for nonequilibrium chemical reactions that take place at constant temperature and pressure, the second law of thermodynamics requires that

$$dG = -Td(S_P) < 0$$

or

$$G_2 - G_1 = -\int Td(S_P) < 0$$

Consequently, we have the following three results for the Gibbs' function of a chemical reaction that occurs at constant temperature and pressure:

a) $dG < 0$ (or $G_2 - G_1 < 0$) implies that the chemical reaction has the *potential to occur* (but this does not imply that it *will* spontaneously occur),

b) $dG = 0$ (or $G_2 = G_1 =$ constant) implies that chemical equilibrium exists and *no further reactions can occur* beyond the equilibrium reactions, and

c) $dG > 0$ (or $G_2 - G_1 > 0$) implies that the reaction *cannot occur* at all because to do so would violate the second law of thermodynamics.

For a system that has undergone a chemical reaction at constant temperature and pressure, item b) above requires that a final state of chemical equilibrium occurs only when $G_{P'} = G_{R'} =$ constant, where P' and R' denote the products and the reactants in the *equilibrium* reaction. Then

$$G_{R'} = \sum_{R'} \nu_i \bar{g}_i = \sum_{P'} \nu_i \bar{g}_i = G_{P'} \quad \textbf{(9.32)}$$

Equation 9.31 can be written on a per unit mole basis for chemical species i with partial pressure p_i and negligible entropy production as

$$d\bar{g}_i = \bar{v}_i\,dp_i - \bar{s}_i\,dT$$

When the system has a constant temperature T and a constant total pressure p_m, and when the substances involved can be treated as ideal gases, then this equation reduces to

$$d\bar{g}_i = \bar{v}_i\,dp_i = \mathscr{R}T(dp_i/p_i)$$

which can be easily integrated from the standard reference state pressure p° to any other state at partial pressure p_i and temperature T as

$$\bar{g}_i(p, T) = \bar{g}_i^\bullet(p^\circ, T) + \mathscr{R}T\ln(p_i/p^\circ) \tag{9.33}$$

where p° is the standard reference state pressure of 0.1 MPa, and $\bar{g}_i^\bullet$ is known as the molar specific Gibbs function at (unfortunately) a *new* reference state of 0.1 MPa and temperature T. The new reference temperature is normally chosen to be the mixture temperature T_m, rather than the traditional standard reference state temperature of 25 °C.[14] Although the introduction of an additional reference state at this point whose temperature is not given a fixed value (like 25 °C) tends to complicate the logic somewhat, it does simplify the notation and the resulting calculations. Using the definition of the Gibbs function and some simple algebraic manipulation we can arrive at a working formula for calculating accurate values of $\bar{g}_i(p, T)$ by using property values listed in Appendix C.16*c* and in Table 9.4. The required algebraic manipulations are

$$\begin{aligned}\bar{g}_i^\bullet &= (\bar{g}_f^\circ)_i + [\bar{g}_i^\bullet - (\bar{g}_f^\circ)_i]\\ &= (\bar{g}_f^\circ)_i + [(\bar{h}_T - T\bar{s}_T)_i - (\bar{h}_{T^\circ} - T^\circ\bar{s}_{T^\circ}^\circ)_i]\\ &= (\bar{g}_f^\circ)_i + (\bar{h}_T - \bar{h}_{T^\circ})_i - T(\bar{s}_T)_i + T^\circ(\bar{s}_{T^\circ}^\circ)_i\end{aligned} \tag{9.34}$$

where T° is the standard reference state temperature of 298 K or 537 R. The superscript $\circ$ on a quantity implies that it is at the standard reference state, whereas the superscript $\bullet$ implies that it is at the new reference state of $T = T_m$ and 0.1 Mpa. Values for $(\bar{g}_f^\circ)_i$ and $(\bar{s}_{T^\circ}^\circ)_i$ can be found in Table 9.4, and values for $(\bar{h}_T - \bar{h}_{T^\circ})_i$ and

14. This makes the *fourth* reference state for thermodynamic properties discussed in this chapter. They are

1. the *arbitrarily chosen reference state* (e.g., the triple point as in the steam tables),
2. the *standard reference state* at 0.1 MPa and 25 °C,
3. the *absolute value reference state* at 0.1 MPa and 0 K, and
4. the *mixture temperature reference state* at 0.1 MPa and T_m.

Confusing isn't it?

$(\bar{s}_T)_i$ (and also $(\bar{s}^\circ_{T^\circ})_i$) can be found in Appendix C.16*c* for various common substances.

Substituting Eq. 9.33 into Eq. 9.32 gives

$$\sum_{R'} \nu_i \bar{g}_i^\bullet - \sum_{P'} \nu_i \bar{g}_i^\bullet = \mathscr{R}T\left[\sum_{P'} \nu_i \ln(p_i/p^\circ) - \sum_{R'} \nu_i \ln(p_i/p^\circ)\right]$$
$$= \mathscr{R}T\left\{\ln\left[\prod_{P'} (p_i/p^\circ)^{\nu_i}\right] - \ln\left[\prod_{R'} (p_i/p^\circ)^{\nu_i}\right]\right\}$$
$$= \mathscr{R}T \ln\left[\frac{\prod_{P'} (p_i/p^\circ)^{\nu_i}}{\prod_{R'} (p_i/p^\circ)^{\nu_i}}\right] = \mathscr{R}T \ln\,[K_e]$$

where K_e is the equilibrium constant for the reaction, defined as[15]

$$K_e = \frac{\prod_{P'} (p_i/p^\circ)^{\nu_i}}{\prod_{R'} (p_i/p^\circ)^{\nu_i}} = \frac{(p_C/p^\circ)^{\nu_C}(p_D/p^\circ)^{\nu_D}(\cdots)}{(p_A/p^\circ)^{\nu_A}(p_B/p^\circ)^{\nu_B}(\cdots)} \tag{9.35}$$

and from the previous equation we also have

$$K_e = \exp\left[\left(\sum_{R'} \nu_i \bar{g}_i^\bullet - \sum_{P'} \nu_i \bar{g}_i^\bullet\right)\Big/\mathscr{R}T\right] \tag{9.36}$$

Equation 9.35 indicates that the equilibrium constant is a measure of how much product has been generated by the reaction. Equation 9.35 (or 9.37) is normally used to find the actual concentrations ν_i if the equilibrium constant K_e is known, whereas Eq. 9.36 is normally used to find K_e if the ν_i are known.

If the components of the reaction are ideal gases that obey the Gibbs-Dalton ideal gas mixture law, then the partial pressures can be expressed in terms of the mole fractions x_i and the total mixture pressure p_m as (see Eq. 7.25)

$$p_i = x_i p_m$$

15. In these equations we have used $\prod$ as the repeated multiplication symbol just as we have been using $\sum$ as the repeated summation symbol, that is,

$$\sum_{i=1}^{N} (\alpha_i) = \alpha_1 + \alpha_2 + \alpha_3 + \cdots + \alpha_N,$$

and

$$\prod_{i=1}^{N} (\alpha_i) = (\alpha_1)(\alpha_2)(\alpha_3)(\cdots)(\alpha_N)$$

Then Eq. 9.35 reduces to

$$K_e = \frac{\prod_{P'} (x_i)^{\nu_i}}{\prod_{R'} (x_i)^{\nu_i}} \left(\frac{p_m}{p^\circ}\right)^{\left(\sum_{P'} \nu_i - \sum_{R'} \nu_i\right)} \tag{9.37}$$

Note that the ν_i and the repeated multiplication ranges (P' and R') in Eqs. 9.35 and 9.37 come from the *equilibrium* reaction equation, but the p_i and x_i in these equations come from *only the products* of the *irreversible* reaction equation. For example, consider an equilibrium reaction equation for a simple dissociation of the form

$$\nu_A A \leftrightarrows \nu_B B + \nu_C C$$

which is also subject to an overall irreversible reaction equation in which $y\%$ of the A present dissociates into B and C as

$$A \rightarrow (1 - y)A + y[A_{\text{dissociated}}]$$

Then the overall irreversible reaction equation can be written as

$$A \rightarrow (1 - y)A + y[(\nu_B/\nu_A)B + (\nu_C/\nu_A)C]$$

and the equilibrium constant for this reaction is given by Eq. 9.37 as

$$K_e = \frac{(x_B)^{\nu_B}(x_C)^{\nu_C}}{(x_A)^{\nu_A}} \left(\frac{p_m}{p^\circ}\right)^{(\nu_B + \nu_C - \nu_A)} \tag{9.38}$$

where x_A, x_B, and x_c are determined from the products of the overall irreversible reaction equation as

$$x_A = \frac{1 - y}{1 - y + y(\nu_B/\nu_A + \nu_C/\nu_A)}$$

$$x_B = \frac{y(\nu_B/\nu_A)}{1 - y + y(\nu_B/\nu_A + \nu_C/\nu_A)}$$

and

$$x_C = \frac{y(\nu_C/\nu_A)}{1 - y + y(\nu_B/\nu_A + \nu_C/\nu_A)}$$

Appendix C.17 lists values of K_e for a variety of simple dissociation reactions of this form at various temperatures.

Example 9.10 Calculate the equilibrium constant for the reversible equilibrium water vapor dissociation reaction equation $H_2O \rightleftarrows H_2 + \frac{1}{2}O_2$ at 0.1 MPa and at the following temperatures: **a)** 298 K and **b)** 2000 K.

Solution Here we do not have an irreversible reaction equation to contend with, so we can find K_e directly from Eq. 9.36. Then

$$\mathscr{R}T\ln(K_e) = \sum_{R'} \nu_i \bar{g}_i^{\bullet} - \sum_{P'} \nu_i \bar{g}_i^{\bullet}$$
$$= \bar{g}^{\bullet}_{H_2O} - \bar{g}^{\bullet}_{H_2} - \tfrac{1}{2}\bar{g}^{\bullet}_{O_2}$$

where the $\bar{g}_i^{\bullet}$ are determined from Eq. 9.34.

a) At $T = T^{\circ} = 298$ K, Eq. 9.34 reduces to $\bar{g}_i^{\bullet} = (\bar{g}_f^{\circ})_i$, then

$$\mathscr{R}T\ln(K_e) = (\bar{g}_f^{\circ})_{H_2O} - (\bar{g}_f^{\circ})_{H_2} - \tfrac{1}{2}(\bar{g}_f^{\circ})_{O_2}$$

and since H_2 and O_2 are elements, their molar specific Gibbs function of formation is zero. Then, from Table 9.4 we have for water vapor (g)

$$\ln K_e = [(\bar{g}_f^{\circ})_{H_2O}]/\mathscr{R}T = \frac{-228.583}{0.0083143(298)} = -92.258$$

and then

$$K_e = \exp(-92.258) = 8.57 \times 10^{-41}$$

b) At 2000 K = 3600 R, Eq. 9.34 with Table 9.4 and Appendix C.16*c* gives[16]

$$\bar{g}^{\bullet}_{H_2O} = (\bar{g}_f^{\circ})_{H_2O} + (\bar{h}_{2000} - \bar{h}_{298})_{H_2O} - 2000(\bar{s}_{2000})_{H_2O} + 298(\bar{s}^{\circ}_{298})_{H_2O}$$
$$= -228{,}583 + (35{,}540.1 - 4258.3)(2.3258) - 2000(63.221)(4.1865)$$
$$+ 298(188.833) = -628{,}905 \text{ kJ/kgmole}$$

$$\bar{g}^{\bullet}_{H_2} = 0 + (26{,}398.5 - 3640.3)(2.3258)$$
$$- 2000(44.978)(4.1865) + 298(130.684) = -284{,}726 \text{ kJ/kgmole}$$

and

$$\bar{g}^{\bullet}_{O_2} = 0 + (29{,}173.9 - 3725.1)(2.3258)$$
$$- 2000(64.168)(4.1865) + 298(205.138) = -416{,}959 \text{ kJ/kgmole}$$

16. The multipliers 2.3258 and 4.1865 in these equations are necessary to convert the Btu/lbmole and Btu/(lbmole · R) values in Appendix C.16*c* into kJ/kgmole and kJ/(kgmole · K), respectively.

Then,

$$\mathscr{R}T \ln K_e = -628{,}904 - (-284{,}726) - (1/2)(-416{,}959)$$
$$= -135{,}698 \text{ kJ/kgmole}$$

so

$$\ln K_e = \frac{-135{,}698}{8.3143(2000)} = -8.161$$

and then

$$K_e = \exp(-8.161) = 0.000286$$

The magnitude of K_e is a good indicator of the degree to which a reaction will go to completion. Generally, if K_e is less than about 0.01 (or $\ln K_e < -4.6$) then the reaction will not occur to any significant degree. However, if K_e is greater than about 100 (or $\ln K_e > 4.6$) then the reaction will essentially go to completion. This is illustrated in the following example.

Example 9.11

The overall irreversible carbon dioxide dissociation reaction equation wherein $y\%$ of the CO_2 dissociates into CO and O_2 is

$$CO_2 \rightarrow (1 - y)(CO_2) + y(CO_2)_{\text{dissociated}}$$

subject to the reversible equilibrium dissociation reaction

$$CO_2 \rightleftarrows CO + \tfrac{1}{2}O_2$$

Then the overall irreversible dissociation reaction equation is

$$CO_2 \rightarrow (1 - y)(CO_2) + y(CO) + (y/2)(O_2)$$

For this reaction, determine

a) the variation in the degree of dissociation (y) with temperature at a total pressure of 0.1 MPa, and

b) the influence of total pressure on the degree of dissociation (y) at 3000 K.

Solution The total number of moles of product in the overall irreversible reaction equation is $(1 - y) + y + y/2 = (2 + y)/2$. Then the mole fractions of the products are

$$x_{CO_2} = 2(1 - y)/(2 + y)$$

$$x_{CO} = 2y/(2 + y)$$

$$x_{O_2} = y/(2 + y)$$

The reversible equilibrium dissociation reaction equation gives the stoichiometric coefficients, ν_i, as $\nu_{CO_2} = 1.0$, $\nu_{CO} = 1.0$, and $\nu_{O_2} = \frac{1}{2}$. Then Eq. 9.38 gives the equilibrium constant as

$$K_e = \left[\frac{(x_{CO})(x_{O_2})^{1/2}}{(x_{CO_2})}\right]\left(\frac{p_m}{p^\circ}\right)^{(1+1/2-1)}$$

$$= \left[\frac{\left(\dfrac{2y}{2+y}\right)\left(\dfrac{y}{2+y}\right)^{1/2}}{\dfrac{2(1-y)}{2+y}}\right]\left(\frac{p_m}{p^\circ}\right)^{1/2}$$

$$= \left[\left(\frac{y}{1-y}\right)\left(\frac{y}{2+y}\right)^{1/2}\right]\left(\frac{p_m}{p^\circ}\right)^{1/2}$$

a) To determine the required results for part a of this problem we set $p_m = p^\circ = 0.1$ MPa, and then K_e can be found in Appendix C.17 for various temperatures. Our task is now to pick several reaction temperatures, look up their corresponding K_e values, and then solve the previous equation for y. This equation is cubic in y and has no easy algebraic solution, so we are left with the problem of solving for y either by using a tedious manual solution or by developing a more efficient computer technique.

In Chapter 6 we introduced the Newton-Raphson technique for finding the roots of a polynomial equation by using a microcomputer. We can use this same technique here to find the values of y. The polynomial we need to solve can be written as

$$f(y) = y^3 - K_e^2(p^\circ/p_m)(1-y)^2(2+y) = 0$$

and then

$$f'(y) = 3y^2 - K_e^2(p^\circ/p_m)[-2(1-y)(2+y) + (1-y)^2]$$

The Newton-Rahpson estimate of the desired root y_0 calculated from a close guess y is

$$y_0 = y - f(y)/f'(y)$$

Then, $f(y_0)$ should be (approximately) equal to zero. However, $f(y_0)$ will probably not be close enough to zero based on just one arbitrary guess for y, so we must iterate by taking our calculated value y_0 as the next guess for y and continue until $f(y_0)$ is as close to zero as we desire. The following BASIC language computer program was written on an IBM compatible personal computer using this technique.

```
10 REM:******************* CARBON DIOXIDE DISSOCIATION ******************
20 CLS:PRINT:PRINT:PRINT
30 PRINT"   THIS PROGRAM CALCULATES THE EQUILIBRIUM CONCENTRATION FOR THE
   DISSOCIATION OF CARBON DIOXIDE AT HIGH TEMPERATURES."
40 PRINT:PRINT:PRINT
50 INPUT "ENTER THE BASE 10 LOG OF THE EQUILIBRIUM CONSTANT, LOG(KE) = ";L1OKE
60 KE = 10^(L1OKE)
70 PRINT:PRINT:INPUT"ENTER THE TOTAL PRESSURE (IN MPA) = ";P
80 PRINT:PRINT:INPUT"ENTER THE MIXTURE TEMPERATURE (IN K) = ";T
90 PR = 0.1/P
100 REM: BEGIN THE NEWTON-RAPHSON TECHNIQUE.
110 Y = 1
120 A = (KE^2)*PR
130 F = Y^3- A*(2*+ Y)*(
140 DF = 3*(Y^2) + A*(2*(1 - Y)*(2 + Y) - (1 - Y)^2)
150 IF ABS(F) < = .0000001 THEN 180
160 YO = Y - F/DF
170 Y = YO: GOTO 130
180 REM: PRINT THE RESULTS.
190 CLS:PRINT:PRINT:PRINT:PRINT"THE REACTION EQUATION AT P = ";P;" MPA, "
200 PRINT"T = ";T;" K AND LOG(KE) = ";L1OKE;" IS:"
210 B = INT(10000*(1 - Y))/10000
220 C = INT(10000*Y)/10000
230 PRINT"CO2 ->";B;"*CO2 +";C;"*CO +";C/2;"*02"
240 REM: THE STANDARD RE-RUN OPTION.
250 PRINT:PRINT:PRINT:PRINT"ANOTHER RUN (Y/N) ";
260 INPUT Q$
270 IF Q$ = "N" OR Q$ = "n" THEN 300
280 IF Q$ <> "Y" AND Q$ <> "y" THEN 250
290 CLS:GOTO 40
300 PRINT:PRINT:PRINT"THIS PROGRAM HAS ENDED.        THANK YOU. ":END
```

By feeding this program various values of log K_e from Appendix C.17, an accurate dissociation reaction equation will be produced. Some sample results are:

```
THE REACTION EQUATION AT P = 0.1 MPA,
T = 2000 K AND LOG(KE) = -2.863 IS:
CO2 -> 0.9845*CO2 + 0.0154*CO + 0.0077*02

THE REACTION EQUATION AT P = 0.1 MPA,
T = 3000 K AND LOG(KE) = -0.469 IS:
CO2 -> 0.5564*CO2 + 0.4435*CO + 0.2217*02

THE REACTION EQUATION AT P = 1.0 MPA,
T = 3000 K AND LOG(KE) = -0.469 IS:
CO2 -> 0.7547*CO2 + 0.2452*CO + 0.1226*02
```

These results can then be plotted either by hand or with the use of additional computer software. The final plot showing the variation in the degree of dissociation (y) versus reaction equilibrium temperature is shown below.

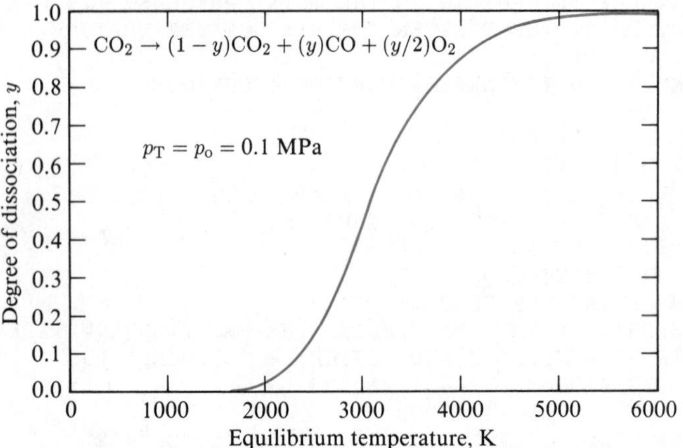

b) With the program listed above it is a simple matter to generate reaction equations for various total pressures at $T = 3000$ K. The curve below shows the results of this effort, and provides a graphical representation of the effect of total pressure on the degree of dissociation (y) at 3000 K.

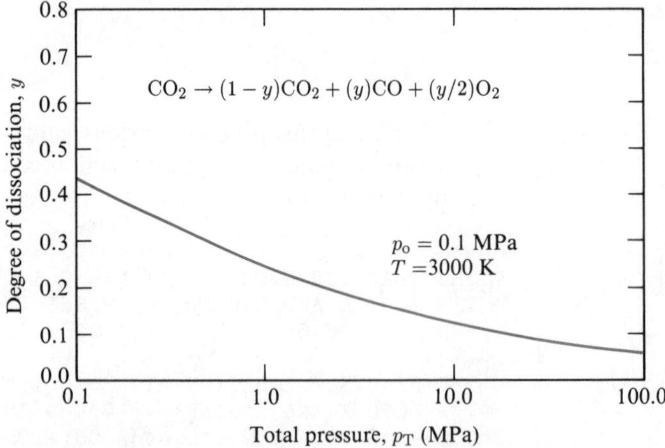

An equivalent and perhaps more straightforward way of approaching a dissociation equilibrium reaction is illustrated in the next example.

Example 9.12

Determine the amount of H_2 produced as a function of temperature in the thermal dissociation of water vapor at the SRS pressure (i.e., $p_m = p^\circ$).

Solution The overall irreversible dissociation reaction equation for water vapor is

$$H_2O \rightarrow (1-y)H_2O + y(\nu_{H_2})H_2 + y(\nu_{O_2})O_2$$

subject to the following reversible equilibrium dissociation reaction equation

$$H_2O \rightleftarrows H_2 + \tfrac{1}{2}O_2$$

Thus, $\nu_{H_2} = 1.0$ and $\nu_{O_2} = \frac{1}{2}$, and the overall reaction equation becomes

$$H_2O \rightarrow (1-y)H_2O + yH_2 + (y/2)O_2$$

Thus, $\nu_{H_2O} = 1$, $\nu_{H_2} = 1$, and $\nu_{O_2} = \frac{1}{2}$, and then Eq. 9.38 gives

$$K_e = \frac{x_{H_2} x_{O_2}^{1/2}}{x_{H_2O}} \left(\frac{p_m}{p^\circ}\right)^{(1+1/2-1)}$$

where

$$x_{H_2O} = \frac{2(1-y)}{2+y} \qquad x_{H_2} = \frac{2y}{2+y} \qquad \text{and} \qquad x_{O_2} = \frac{y}{2+y}$$

so that

$$K_e = \frac{y}{1-y}\left(\frac{2}{2+y}\right)^{1/2}(1)^{1/2} = \frac{y}{1-y}\left(\frac{y}{2+y}\right)^{1/2}$$

Arbitrarily choosing values for y and solving for K_e from the previous equation, then looking up the corresponding temperature in Appendix C.17 will give the desired relation between the amount of H_2 present (y) and the system temperature (T). The following table illustrates some typical values:

y	$\log K_e$	T (K)
0.001	−4.650	1710
0.010	−3.147	2020
0.100	−1.615	2850
0.500	−0.349	3950

The Van't Hoff Equation

Both the equilibrium constant K_e and the molar Gibbs function $\bar{g}_i^\bullet$ depend upon the mixture temperature T. To investigate the temperature dependence of K_e we differentiate Eq. 9.36 with respect to temperature to obtain

$$\frac{dK_e}{dT} = -\frac{1}{\mathscr{R}T^2}\left[\left(\sum_{R'} \nu_i \bar{g}_i^\bullet - \sum_{P'} \nu_i \bar{g}_i^\bullet\right) + T\frac{d}{dT}\left(\sum_{R'} \nu_i \bar{g}_i^\bullet - \sum_{P'} \nu_i \bar{g}_i^\bullet\right)\right] K_e$$

From Eq. 6.15 we have the relation $dg = v\,dp - s\,dT$, so that for a constant pressure process we can write

$$\frac{d\bar{g}_i^{\bullet}}{dT} = -\bar{s}_i^{\bullet}$$

Introducing this result along with the definition of the molar specific Gibbs function, $\bar{g} = \bar{h} - T\bar{s}$, into the equation for dK_e/dT and rearranging gives

$$\frac{1}{K_e}\left(\frac{dK_e}{dT}\right) = \frac{d(\ln K_e)}{dT} = \frac{1}{\mathscr{R}T^2}\left(\sum_{R'} \nu_i \bar{h}_i^{\bullet} - \sum_{P'} \nu_i \bar{h}_i^{\bullet}\right) = \frac{\dot{Q}_r}{\mathscr{R}T^2} \tag{9.39}$$

where $\dot{Q}_r$ is the heat transfer rate of the reaction (see Eq. 9.5). This equation is known as the Van't Hoff equation. It shows that for a heat-producing (i.e., exothermic) reaction the value of K_e decreases when the reaction temperature increases, and increases when the reaction temperature decreases. While for a heat absorbing (i.e., endothermic) reaction the value of K_e increases when the temperature of the reaction increases, and decreases when the reaction temperature decreases. Since the equilibrium constant is a relative measure of the amount of product present, by changing the reaction temperature we can change the amount of product formed. For example, consider the equilibrium equation for the formation of ammonia from hydrogen and nitrogen gas, $N_2 + 3(H_2) \rightleftarrows 2(NH_3) - 91.25$ kJ. We can increase the amount of ammonia produced by increasing the K_e of the reaction. Since this is an exothermic reaction, this can be done by lowering the reaction temperature.

Fuel Cells

A fuel cell is an electrochemical device that converts the chemical energy of a fuel *directly* into electrical energy by an oxidation reaction in which energy is liberated as electrical work rather than as heat. Therefore, a fuel cell is not a heat engine and consequently is not subject to the severe efficiency limitation of the Carnot cycle. Fuel cell energy conversion efficiencies can approach 100% under the proper conditions.

Though fuel cells offer an exciting high-efficiency alternative to the traditional heat engine-driven electrical generating technology, they are not a new concept. The first fuel cells were developed from the early nineteenth century work of the English chemist Humphry Davy (1778–1829), and continued to evolve technically until they were displaced by the simpler but lower efficiency heat engine-driven electro-mechanical generators at the end of the nineteenth century. Their superior energy conversion efficiency periodically causes renewed interest in their technological development.

Consider a general steady state, steady flow, open system. Neglecting any changes in kinetic or potential energy, the energy rate balance on this system gives its work transport rate of energy (i.e., power) as

$$\dot{W} = \sum_{\text{out}} \dot{m}_i h_i - \sum_{\text{in}} \dot{m}_i h_i - \dot{Q} = \sum_{\text{out}} \dot{n}_i \bar{h}_i - \sum_{\text{in}} \dot{n}_i \bar{h}_i - \dot{Q}$$

and if the system has isothermal boundaries at temperature T_b, then the entropy rate balance gives its heat transport rate as

$$\dot{Q} = T_b\left(\sum_{\text{out}} \dot{m}_i s_i - \sum_{\text{in}} \dot{m}_i s_i - \dot{S}_P\right) = T_b\left(\sum_{\text{out}} \dot{n}_i \bar{s}_i - \sum_{\text{in}} \dot{n}_i \bar{s}_i - \dot{S}_P\right)$$

Combining these two equations and using the definition of the molar specific Gibbs function, $\bar{g} = \bar{h} - T\bar{s}$, gives

$$\begin{aligned} \dot{W} &= \sum_{\text{out}} \dot{m}_i(h - T_b s)_i - \sum_{\text{in}} \dot{m}_i(h - T_b s)_i + T_b\dot{S}_P \\ &= \sum_{\text{out}} \dot{n}(\bar{h} - T_b\bar{s})_i - \sum_{\text{in}} \dot{n}_i(\bar{h} - T_b\bar{s})_i + T_b\dot{S}_P \\ &= \sum_{\text{out}} \dot{n}_i\bar{g}_i - \sum_{\text{in}} \dot{n}_i\bar{g}_i + T_b\dot{S}_P \end{aligned} \tag{9.40}$$

where the second law of thermodynamics requires that $\dot{S}_P \geq 0$.

We can now calculate the "reaction efficiency," η_r, with the following general formula[17]

$$\eta_r = \frac{\text{desired result}}{\text{cost}} = \frac{\dot{W}}{\sum_{\text{out}} \dot{m}_i h_i - \sum_{\text{in}} \dot{m}_i h_i} = \frac{\dot{W}}{\sum_{\text{out}} \dot{n}_i \bar{h}_i - \sum_{\text{in}} \dot{n}_i \bar{h}_i}$$

or

$$\eta_r = \frac{\sum_{\text{out}} \dot{m}_i g_i - \sum_{\text{in}} \dot{m}_i g_i + T_b\dot{S}_P}{\sum_{\text{out}} \dot{m}_i h_i - \sum_{\text{in}} \dot{m}_i h_i} = \frac{\sum_{\text{out}} \dot{n}_i \bar{g}_i - \sum_{\text{in}} \dot{n}_i \bar{g}_i + T_b\dot{S}_P}{\sum_{\text{out}} \dot{n}_i \bar{h}_i - \sum_{\text{in}} \dot{n}_i \bar{h}_i} \tag{9.41}$$

The maximum power $\dot{W}_{\max}$ and maximum reaction efficiency $(\eta_r)_{\max}$ occur when the device is completely reversible, or $\dot{S}_P = 0$. Then

$$(\eta_r)_{\max} = \frac{\sum_{\text{out}} \dot{m}_i g_i - \sum_{\text{in}} \dot{m}_i g_i}{\sum_{\text{out}} \dot{m}_i h_i - \sum_{\text{in}} \dot{m}_i h_i} = \frac{\sum_{\text{out}} \dot{n}_i \bar{g}_i - \sum_{\text{in}} \dot{n}_i \bar{g}_i}{\sum_{\text{out}} \dot{n}_i \bar{h}_i - \sum_{\text{in}} \dot{n}_i \bar{h}_i} \tag{9.42}$$

Utilizing Eq. 9.33, the molar form of Eqs. 9.40, 9.41, and 9.42 are

$$\dot{W} = \sum_P \dot{n}_i \bar{g}_i^\circ - \sum_R \dot{n}_i \bar{g}_i^\circ + T_b\dot{S}_P + \mathscr{R}T \ln\left[\prod_P (p_i/p^\circ)^{n_i} \Big/ \prod_R (p_i/p^\circ)^{n_i}\right] \tag{9.43}$$

$$\eta_r = \frac{\sum_P \dot{n}_i \bar{g}_i^\circ - \sum_R \dot{n}_i \bar{g}_i^\circ + T_b\dot{S}_P + \mathscr{R}T \ln\left[\prod_P (p_i/p^\circ)^{n_i} \Big/ \prod_R (p_i/P^\circ)^{n_i}\right]}{\sum_P \dot{n}_i \bar{h}_i - \sum_R \dot{n}_i \bar{h}_i} \tag{9.44}$$

17. Recall that work *out* of a system is negative with our sign convention.

and

$$(\eta_r)_{max} = \frac{\sum_P (n_i/n_{fuel})\bar{g}_i^\bullet - \sum_R (n_i/n_{fuel})\bar{g}_i^\bullet + \mathscr{R}T \ln\left[\prod_P (p_i/p^\circ)^{(n_i/n_{fuel})} \Big/ \prod_R (p_i/p^\circ)^{(n_i/n_{fuel})}\right]}{\sum_P (n_i/n_{fuel})\bar{h}_i - \sum_R (n_i/n_{fuel})\bar{h}_i} \tag{9.45}$$

If the reactants or products are *unmixed*, and the pressure of each species (or component) in the reaction is 0.1 MPa, then $p_i = p^\circ$ and $\prod_P (p_i/p^\circ)^{n_i} = \prod_R (p_i/p^\circ)^{n_i} = 1.0$ in the above three equations. Otherwise, if the reactants are *premixed*, or the product gases are *mixed* (as they normally are) at a total pressure p_m, then the partial pressure of each component gas must be determined. Further, if all the gases present are ideal gases that obey the Gibbs-Dalton ideal gas mixture law, then the partial pressures can be expressed in terms of the mole fractions as: $p_i/p^\circ = (x_i p_m)/p^\circ$, where x_i is the mole fraction of gas i and $p^\circ = 0.1$ MPa. Then, $\ln[\prod(p_i/p^\circ)^{n_i}] = \ln[\prod(x_i p_m/p^\circ)^{n_i}]$ in Eqs. 9.43, 9.44, and 9.45.

In the case of a fuel cell, the output power appears as an electrical current I flowing through a potential (voltage) difference ϕ, and using Ohm's law we can calculate the actual power output of the cell as

$$\dot{W} = -\phi I = -I^2 R_e$$

where ϕ is the cell voltage, I is its current flow, and R_e is the external resistance (recall that work *output* must be negative with our sign convention). Combining this equation with Eq. 9.40 gives the entropy production rate of the fuel cell as

$$(\dot{S}_P)_{\substack{fuel\\cell}} = \left(\sum_R \dot{n}_i \bar{g}_i - \sum_P \dot{n}_i \bar{g} - \phi I\right) \Big/ T_b \geq 0 \tag{9.46}$$

Also, it can be shown that the electrical current I produced by a fuel cell is given by

$$I = (\dot{n}_{fuel}) jF$$

where I is in amperes when $\dot{n}_{fuel}$ is in kgmole/s. In this equation j is the total valence of the fuel ions[18] in kgmole of electrons per kgmole of fuel, and F is Faraday's constant, defined as

$$F = (6.023 \times 10^{26} \text{ electrons/kgmole electrons})(1.602 \times 10^{-19} \text{ coulombs/electron})$$

$$= 96{,}487 \text{ kilocoulombs/kgmole electrons}$$

18. That is, the number of electrons that are involved in the cell reaction per kgmole of fuel consumed. For example, for any hydrocarbon fuel, C_nH_m, then $j = n(4) + m(1) = 4n + m$ kgmole of electrons per kgmole of C_nH_m.

but since 1 coulomb = 1 joule/volt = 1 J/V, this can be written as

$$F = 96{,}487 \text{ kJ/(V·kgmole electrons)}$$

Then we can define the maximum, or reversible, power output of a fuel cell as

$$\dot{W}_{rev} = \dot{W}_{max} = -\phi_o I = -\phi_o(\dot{n}_{fuel})jF \quad \textbf{(9.47)}$$

where ϕ_o is the open circuit voltage. Then the maximum reaction efficiency of the fuel cell becomes

$$(\eta_r)_{max} = \frac{(-\phi_o jF)}{\sum_P (n_i/n_{fuel})\bar{h}_i - \sum_R (n_i/n_{fuel})\bar{h}_i} \quad \textbf{(9.48)}$$

Example 9.13 Determine the maximum theoretical reaction efficiency, open circuit voltage, and maximum theoretical work output per mole of hydrogen consumed for the hydrogen–oxygen fuel cell operating at 25 °C and 0.1 MPa shown below.

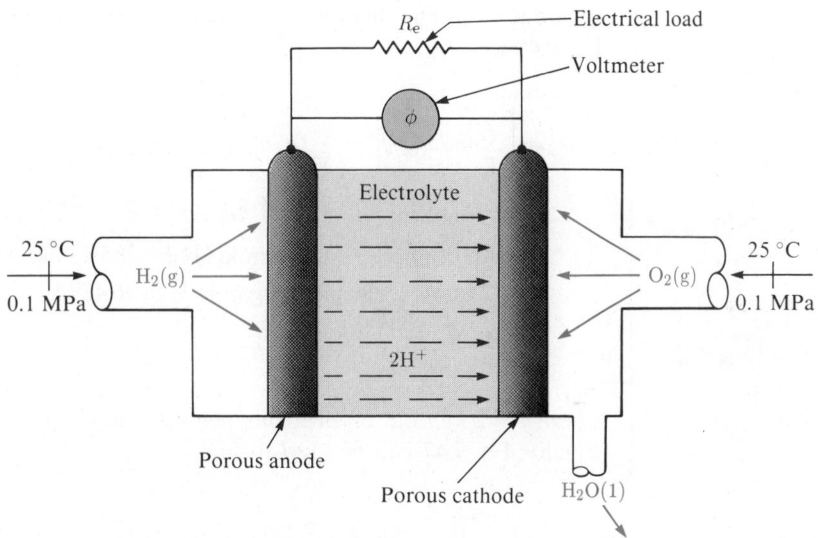

The anode reaction is $H_2(g) \rightarrow 2(H^+) + 2(e^-)$, the Cathode reaction is $0.5(O_2(g)) + 2(H^+) + 2(e^-) \rightarrow H_2O(\ell)$ and the overall reaction is $H_2(g) + 0.5(O_2(g)) \rightarrow H_2O(\ell)$. Also, $(p_i/p^\circ)_{H_2} = (p_i/p^\circ)_{O_2} = 1.0$

Solution Equation 9.45 can be used to calculate the maximum energy conversion reaction efficiency as

$$(\eta_r)_{max} = \frac{\bar{g}^\bullet_{H_2O(\ell)} - \bar{g}^\bullet_{H_2(g)} - (0.5)(\bar{g}^\bullet_{O_2(g)}) + \mathcal{R}T \ln 1.0}{\bar{h}_{H_2O(\ell)} - \bar{h}_{H_2(g)} - (0.5)(\bar{h}_{O_2(g)})}$$

where the $\bar{g}_i^{\bullet}$ are determined from Eq. 9.34, and the $\bar{h}_i$ are determined from Eq. 9.13. Since the pressure and temperature given in this problem statement are the standard reference state values, Eqs. 9.13 and 9.34 reduce to $\bar{h}_i = (\bar{h}_f^\circ)_i$ and $\bar{g}_i^{\bullet} = (\bar{g}_f^\circ)_i$. Then the maximum theoretical reaction efficiency equation becomes

$$(\eta_r)_{max} = \frac{(\bar{g}_f^\circ)_{H_2O(\ell)} - (\bar{g}_f^\circ)_{H_2(g)} - (0.5)(\bar{g}_f^\circ)_{O_2(g)} + \mathscr{R}T \ln 1.0}{(\bar{h}_f^\circ)_{H_2O(\ell)} - (\bar{h}_f^\circ)_{H_2(g)} - (0.5)(\bar{h}_f^\circ)_{O_2(g)}}$$

and since the enthalpies and Gibbs functions of formation of the elements H_2 and O_2 are always zero, the maximum reaction efficiency becomes (using Tables 9.1 and 9.4)

$$(\eta_r)_{max} = \frac{(\bar{g}_f^\circ)_{H_2O(\ell)}}{(\bar{h}_f^\circ)_{H_2O(\ell)}} = \frac{-237.178 \text{ MJ/kgmole}}{-285.838 \text{ MJ/kgmole}} = 0.8298$$

or about 83%. The theoretical open circuit voltage can now be determined from Eq. 9.48 as

$$\begin{aligned}\phi_o &= \left[\sum_R (n_i/n_{fuel})\bar{h}_i - \sum_P (n_i/n_{fuel})\bar{h}_i\right][(\eta_r)_{max}]/jF \\ &= [-(n_{H_2O}/n_{H_2})(\bar{h}_f^\circ)_{H_2O(\ell)}][(\eta_r)_{max}]/jF \\ &= \frac{[-(1 \text{ kgmole } H_2O/\text{kgmole } H_2)(-285{,}838 \text{ kJ/kgmole } H_2O)](0.8298)}{(2 \text{ kgmole electrons/kgmole } H_2)[96{,}487 \text{ kJ/(V}\cdot\text{kgmole electrons)}]} \\ &= 1.23 \text{ V}\end{aligned}$$

where $j = 2$ kgmole of electrons per kgmole of H_2 (i.e., the valence of $2H^+$). Finally, Eq. 9.47 can be used to find

$$\begin{aligned}\dot{W}_{max}/\dot{n}_{fuel} = W_{max}/n_{fuel} &= -\phi_o jF \\ &= -(1.23 \text{ V})(2 \text{ kgmole electrons/kgmole } H_2) \\ &\quad \times [96{,}487 \text{ kJ/(V}\cdot\text{kgmole electrons)}] \\ &= -237{,}358 \text{ kJ/kgmole } H_2\end{aligned}$$

Table 9.5 lists the maximum theoretical reaction efficiencies and open circuit voltages for a variety of fuel cell materials at the standard reference state. Those reactions showing efficiencies greater than 100% must absorb heat from the surrounding to maintain steady state operation.

Table 9.5 Fuel cell maximum reaction efficiency and open circuit voltage for various fuels at 25 °C and 0.1 MPa

Fuel reaction	ϕ_o (V)	$(\eta_r)_{max}$ (%)
$H_2 + 0.5(O_2) \rightarrow H_2O(\ell)$	1.23	83.0
$CO + 0.5(O_2) \rightarrow CO_2$	1.33	90.9
$C(s) + O_2 \rightarrow CO_2$	1.02	100.2
$C_3H_8 + 5(O_2) \rightarrow 3(CO_2) + 4(H_2O(g))$	1.08	101.5
$C_8H_{18}(g) + 12.5(O_2) \rightarrow 8(CO_2) + 9(H_2O(\ell))$	1.10	96.3

(Unlabeled elements and compounds are in a gaseous (g) physical state.)

Summary

In this chapter we have dealt with the fundamental elements of chemical thermodynamics. Chemistry has its roots in thousands of years of alchemy; however, its accurate mathematical notation is relatively recent. The nineteenth century stoichiometric mass balance and the basic concepts of stereochemistry provide a framework on which an accurate combustion analysis of organic fuels can be built. Concepts such as percent theoretical air, fuel modeling, heat of formation, and the standard reference state plus the first law of thermodynamics applied to a chemical reaction lead to a useful understanding of the heat of combustion of a chemical compound. The adiabatic flame temperature and maximum explosion pressure calculations provide conservative upper bounds for real combustion processes. The introduction of the third law of thermodynamics provided the basis upon which to build an absolute entropy scale that can be used to determine chemical reaction irreversibilities via the entropy balance. Also, the Gibbs' function from the combined first and second laws was found to be a controlling factor in chemical reactions, chemical equilibrium, and dissociation reactions. Finally, the fuel cell analysis provided a means of investigating the maximum possible work that can be produced directly from a chemical reaction.

The often complex formulae of chemical thermodynamics provide an excellent topic for personal computer software development. In this chapter simple BASIC language programs are presented for calculating heats of combustion and dissociation equilibrium conditions. The reader is encouraged to utilize and modify this material, and to take full advantage of the computer's ability to remove the tedium of calculation and to expand the scope of the analysis.

Selected References

Angrist, S. W. *Direct Energy Conversion.* Boston: Allyn & Bacon, 1965.

Balzhiser, R. E., Samuels, M. R., and Eliassen, J. D. *Chemical Engineering Thermodynamics.* Englewood Cliffs, NJ: Prentice-Hall, 1972.

Burghardt, M. D. *Engineering Thermodynamics with Applications,* 2d ed. New York: Harper & Row, 1982.

Holman, J. P. *Thermodynamics,* 3d ed. New York: McGraw-Hill, 1980.

Janz, G. J. *Thermodynamic Properties of Organic Compounds*, rev. ed. New York: Academic, 1967.

Raznjevic, K. *Handbook of Thermodynamic Tables and Charts.* New York: Hemisphere, 1976.

Van Wylen, G. J., and Sonntag, R. E. *Fundamentals of Classical Thermodynamics*; 3d ed. New York: Wiley, 1986.

Wagman, D. D., Evans, W. H., Parker, V. B., Schumm, R H., and Halow, I., Bailey, S. M., Churney, K. L., and Nuttall, R. The NBS tables and chemical thermodynamic properties. *Journal of Physical and Chemical Reference Data*, 11, Suppl. 2 (1982).

Wark, K. *Thermodynamics*, 5th ed. New York: McGraw-Hill, 1988.

Chapter Nine Problems

1. Determine the mass in kg of one molecule of water.

2. Determine the mass in lbm of one molecule of methane.

3. The density of benzene (C_6H_6) is 879 kg/m^3. Determine the volume of

a) 1 kgmole of benzene, and

b) 1 molecule of benzene.

4. Determine the percentage by mass of carbon in C_8H_{18}.

5. Determine the percentage by mass of aluminum in Al_2O_3.

6. Determine the percentage by mass of oxygen atoms in a molecule of casein of milk, $C_{708}H_{1130}O_{224}N_{180}S_4P_4$.

7. Determine the percentage by mass of carbon, hydrogen, and oxygen in methyl alcohol, $CH_3(OH)$.

8. The spectral analysis of a chemical compound gave the following composition on a mass basis: 29.1% Na, 40.5% S, 30.4% O. Determine the chemical formula of this substance (i.e., find x, y, and z in $Na_xS_yO_z$).

9. How many lbm are in 1 lbmole of

a) $C_{12}H_{22}O_{11}$ (sucrose, a typical carbohydrate),

b) $C_{57}H_{110}O_6$ (stearin, a typical fat), and

c) $C_{3032}H_{4816}O_{872}N_{780}S_8Fe_4$ (human hemoglobin, a typical protein)?

10. Convert the following to mass units (kg or lbm):

a) 1 kgmole of CO_2 **b)** 0.002 lbmole of Fe_2O_3

c) 6 gmoles of SO_2 **d)** 0.7 kgmole of CH_4

11. Convert the following to molar units (kgmole or lbmole):

a) 14 lbm of CO **b)** 0.37 kg of H_2O

c) 123 g of C_2H_2 **d)** 5 kg of C_8H_{18}

12. When 2 kgmoles of $KClO_3$ are heated, 2 kgmoles of KCl and 3 kgmoles of O_2 are produced. If 50 kg of $KClO_3$ are heated, how many kg of KCl and O_2 will be produced?

13. Determine the reaction equation and molal analysis of the combustion products for the combustion of carbon disulfide, CS_2, with

a) 100% theoretical air,

b) 150% theoretical air, and

c) an air–fuel ratio of 47.6 moles of air per mole of fuel to produce CO_2, SO_2, and excess air products.

14. Determine the reaction equation and molal analysis of the combustion products of ammonia, NH_3, on the surface of a heated platinum wire in the presence of

a) 0% excess oxygen,

b) 125% theoretical oxygen, and
c) 25% deficit oxygen
to form NO, H_2O, and excess air products.

15. Determine the reaction equation and volumetric analysis of the combustion products for the combustion of methyl alcohol, $CH_3(OH)$, with
a) 100% theoretical oxygen,
b) 150% theoretical oxygen, and
c) 50% theoretical oxygen.

16. Determine the reaction equation and volumetric analysis of the combustion products for the combustion of natural rubber, $[C_3H_8]_{2000}$ or $(C_{6000}H_{16,000})$, with
a) 100% theoretical oxygen,
b) 400% excess oxygen, and
c) 90% deficit oxygen.

17. Determine the reaction equation and molal air–fuel ratio for the combustion of ethyl alcohol, C_2H_5 (OH), with
a) 100% theoretical air,
b) 100% excess air, and
c) 50% deficit air.

18. Determine the reaction equation and molal air–fuel ratio for the combustion of dimethyl ketone (acetone), $CO(CH_3)_2$, with
a) 0% excess air,
b) 100% excess air, and
c) 30% theoretical air.

19. Determine the reaction equation and molar fuel–air ratio for the combustion of wood cellulose, $C_6H_{10}O_5$, with
a) 100% theoretical air,
b) 250% excess air, and
c) 25% deficit air.

20. Determine the reaction equation, molal analysis of the combustion products and mass air–fuel ratio for the combustion of kerosene, $C_{10}H_{22}$, with 187% excess air.

21. Determine the reaction equation, volumetric analysis of the combustion products, and molal fuel–air ratios for the combustion of tetraethyl lead, $Pb(C_2H_5)_4$, the common antiknock gasoline additive, with
a) 100% theoretical air,
b) 10% excess air, and
c) an air–fuel ratio of 20 lbm of air per lbm of fuel to form PbO, CO_2, H_2O and excess air products.

22. Develop a reaction equation for the combustion of polyethylene, $[CH_2CH_2]_n$, in 100% theoretical air.

23. A simple alcohol can be obtained from a hydrocarbon by replacing one of the hydrogen atoms by a hydroxyl group (OH). Develop a reaction equation for the combustion of a generalized alcohol of this type, $C_nH_{2n+1}(OH)$, in 100% theoretical air and test it out with
a) methyl alcohol (also known as methanol or wood alcohol), $CH_3(OH)$,
b) ethyl alcohol (also known as ethanol or grain alcohol), $C_2H_5(OH)$, and
c) isopropyl alcohol, $C_3H_7(OH)$.

24. Propane, C_3H_8, is burning with 130% theoretical air in a camp stove. Determine
a) the reaction equation,
b) the molar air–fuel ratio of the combustion,
c) the volumetric analysis of the combustion products, and

d) the dew point temperature of the combustion products if the total pressure of the combustion products is 14.7 psia.

25. The combustion of an unknown amount of benzene (x moles of C_6H_6) in pure oxygen in a chemical reactor produced the following dry exhaust gas analysis: 44.71% CO_2 and 55.29% O_2. Determine

a) the actual molar and mass fuel–oxygen ratios,

b) the percent theoretical oxygen used, and

c) the molar percentage of water vapor in the exhaust gas before it was dried for the above analysis.

26. The combustion of an unknown amount of ethylene (x moles of C_2H_4) in pure oxygen in a laboratory experiment produced the following dry exhaust gas analysis on a molar basis: 84.75% CO_2 and 15.25% O_2. Determine

a) the actual molar and mass oxygen–fuel ratios,

b) the percent excess oxygen used, and

c) the molar percentage of water vapor in the exhaust gas before it was dried for the above analysis.

27. The combustion of an unknown amount of acetylene (x moles of C_2H_2) with pure oxygen in an oxyacetylene torch produced the following dry exhaust gas analysis: 39.14% CO_2 and 60.86% O_2. Determine

a) the actual molar and mass fuel–oxygen ratios,

b) the percent excess oxygen used, and

c) the molar percentage of each combustion product before the exhaust gas was dried for the above analysis.

28. An unknown amount of butane (x moles of C_4H_{10}) is burned with pure oxygen in a bomb calorimeter. The dry gas molal analysis of the products is 48.72% CO_2 and 51.28% O_2. Determine

a) the actual molar and mass oxygen–fuel ratios,

b) the percent excess oxygen used, and

c) the molar percentage of each combustion product before the exhaust gas was dried for the above analysis.

29. The combustion of an unknown amount of methane (x moles of CH_4)in a furnace resulted in the following dry exhaust gas molar analysis: 9.52% CO_2, 4.00% O_2, and 86.47% N_2. Determine

a) the actual molar and mass air–fuel ratios,

b) the percent excess air used, and

c) the molar percentage of water vapor in the exhaust gas before it was dried for the above analysis.

30. The combustion of an unknown amount of propane (x moles of C_3H_8) in an industrial oven produced the following dry exhaust gas analysis on a volume basis: 5.52% CO_2, 12.59% O_2, and 81.89% N_2. Determine

a) the actual molar and mass air–fuel ratios,

b) the percent theoretical air used, and

c) the volume percentage of water vapor in the exhaust gas before it was dried for the above analysis.

31. An unknown amount of ethane (x moles of C_2H_6) is burned in a combustion chamber with air. The dry gas molal analysis of the exhaust products is 6.64% CO_2, 10.46% O_2, and 82.90% N_2. Determine

a) the actual molar and mass fuel–air ratios,

b) the percent excess air used, and

c) the molar percentage of each combustion product before the exhaust gas was dried for the above analysis.

32. The combustion of an unknown amount of propylene (x moles of C_3H_6) with air in a prototype space heater produced the following dry exhaust gas molar analysis: 4.27% CO_2, 15.05% O_2, and 80.68% N_2. Determine

a) the actual molar and mass air–fuel ratios,
b) the percent theoretical air used, and
c) the molar percentage of each combustion product before the exhaust gas was dried for the above analysis.

33. The following dry exhaust volumetric analysis resulted from the combustion of an unknown amount of octane (x moles of C_8H_{18}) in a spark ignition internal combustion engine: 8.8% CO_2, 8.2% CO, 4.1% H_2, 1.0% NO, 0.2% CH_4, and 77.7% N_2. Determine

a) the actual molar and mass air–fuel ratios,
b) the percent theoretical air used, and
c) the molar percentage of water vapor in the exhaust gas before it was dried for the above analysis.

34. The following dry exhaust gas molar analysis resulted from the combustion of an unknown amount of kerosene (x moles of $C_{10}H_{22}$) in a compression ignition internal combustion engine: 6.3% CO_2, 9.4% CO, 4.7% C, 4.7% H_2, 1.5% NO, 0.2% CH_4, and 73.2% N_2. Determine

a) the actual molar and mass air–fuel ratios,
b) the percent deficit air used, and
c) the volumetric percentage of water vapor in the exhaust gas before it was dried for the above analysis.

35. An unknown hydrocarbon material was burned in a calorimeter with air. An Orsat analysis indicated that the (dry) exhaust gas was made up of only 17.5% CO_2 and 82.5% N_2, with no CO or O_2 being present. Determine

a) the fuel model (C_nH_m),
b) the composition of the fuel on a mass basis,
c) the percent theoretical air used, and
d) the dew point temperature if the combustion products are at 0.1013 MPa.

36. An unknown hydrocarbon material was burned in air for chemical analysis. An Orsat test indicated that the (dry) exhaust gas did not contain any CO or O_2, but consisted of only 14.9% CO_2 and 85.1% N_2. Determine

a) the fuel model (C_nH_m),
b) the composition of the fuel on a percent mass basis,
c) the molar and mass air–fuel ratios used in the combustion process, and
d) the dew point temperature if the combustion products are at 0.1013 MPa.

37. An Orsat analysis of the (dry) products of combustion of a gas emanating from the bowels of a creature of immense hypocrisy produced the following composition: 1.0% CO_2, 19.2% O_2, and 79.8% N_2. Determine

a) the chemical formula (C_nH_m) and name of the gas,
b) the composition of the fuel on a percent molar basis,
c) the percent excess air used in the combustion process, and
d) the dew point temperature of the products at atmospheric pressure.

38. An Orsat analysis of the (dry) products of combustion of an unknown hydrocarbon indicated that it consisted of only 26.1% CO and 73.9% N_2, with no CO_2 or O_2 present. Determine

a) the fuel model (C_nH_m),

b) the composition of the fuel on a percent mass basis,
c) the percent theoretical air used, and
d) the dew point temperature of the combustion products at atmospheric pressure.

39. The combustion of a new fuel that is a mixture of a liquid hydrocarbon and hydrogen gas is to be modeled as a single hydrocarbon. An Orsat analysis of the dry exhaust products of this new fuel is: 6.0% CO, 6.0% O_2, and 88.0% N_2 (no CO_2 was present). Determine
a) the fuel model (C_nH_m) of this mixture,
b) the percentages by mass of carbon and hydrogen present in the mixture,
c) the mass air–fuel ratio used in the combustion process, and
d) the dew point temperature of the exhaust products at 0.152 MPa.

40. An unknown hydrocarbon fuel produced an Orsat dry exhaust gas analysis of 8.3% CO_2, 0% CO, 9.1% O_2, and 82.6% N_2. Determine
a) the fuel model (C_nH_m),
b) the composition of the fuel on a percent mass basis,
c) the percent theoretical air used, and
d) the dew point temperature of the exhaust gas when it is at 0.1015 MPa.

41. 11.7% CO_2, 1.1% CO, 0% O_2, and 87.2% N_2 were the Orsat analysis results of the dry exhaust gas produced by the cataclysmic combustion of an unknown hydrocarbon substance in air. Determine
a) the fuel model (C_nH_m) of the hydrocarbon,
b) the mass percentages of carbon and hydrogen in the fuel,
c) the percent deficit air used, and
d) the molar percentage of water vapor in the exhaust before it was dried.

42. The Orsat analysis of the (dry) products of combustion of an unknown hydrocarbon is 9.1% CO_2, 8.9% CO, and 82.0% N_2 (no O_2 was present). Determine
a) the fuel model (C_nH_m),
b) the mass percentages of C and H present in the fuel,
c) the molar air–fuel ratio and percent theoretical air used in the combustion, and
d) the dew point temperature at 0.106 MPa.

43. The Orsat analysis of the (dry) exhaust gas from the combustion of an unknown hydrocarbon is 1.1% CO_2, 1.1% CO, 18.8% O_2, and 79.0% N_2. Determine
a) the fuel model (C_nH_m),
b) the percent mass composition of the fuel,
c) the fuel–air ratio used, and
d) the dew point temperature at 0.644 MPa.

44. The combustion of a mysterious unknown hydrocarbon fuel in the dimensional stabilization module of the temporal drive unit produced the following Orsat (dry) exhaust gas analysis: 4.5% CO_2, 1.9% CO, 14.1% O_2, and 79.5% N_2. Determine
a) the fuel model (C_nH_m) and its probable name,
b) the percent mass composition of the fuel,
c) the percent theoretical air used in the combustion, and
d) the dew point temperature of the exhaust products at 1.0 MPa.

45. A Wingbarton hydrocarbon bomb exploded in the dry air near an Orsat analyzer. A slightly injured but quick-witted technician quickly carried out a dry gas analysis in the shattered remains of the laboratory to produce the following results: 2.8% CO_2, 0.5% CO, 16.2% O_2, and 80.5% N_2. Determine
a) the fuel model (C_nH_m) and probable name of the mysterious hydrocarbon explosive used in the Wingbarton bomb,
b) the mass percentage composition of the carbon and hydrogen in the bomb,
c) the percentage of excess air available in the laboratory when the bomb exploded, and

d) the dew point temperature in the lab after the bomb exploded (assume atmospheric pressure).

46. An international espionage agent used a computerized pocket-sized Orsat apparatus to grab and analyze a dry sample of the exhaust gases from the new air-breathing, hydrocarbon-burning, Blood-Sucker guided missile. The Orsat readout was 6.2% CO_2, 2.1% CO, 9.9% O_2, and 81.8% N_2. Determine

a) the fuel model C_nH_m and probable name of the Blood-Sucker's fuel,
b) the percentages of carbon and hydrogen by mass in the fuel, and
c) the mass fuel–air ratio used by the missile.

47. An ancient internal combustion Mugwump bilge-pump engine burns a mixture of obscure hydrocarbon fuels that can be modeled as a single fuel. An Orsat analysis of the dry exhaust gas from this engine gives the following results: 5.9% CO_2, 5.5% CO, 7.5% O_2, and 81.1% N_2. Determine

a) the single fuel hydrocarbon model (C_nH_m),
b) the carbon and hydrogen composition by mass of this fuel, and
c) the percent theoretical air used in the engine.

48. An Orsat analysis of the combustion of a strange unearthly hydrocarbon gas produces a (dry) result of 5.0% each for CO_2, CO, and O_2, with N_2 making up the remainder. Determine

a) the hydrocarbon fuel model C_nH_m for this strange and somewhat putrid gas,
b) the mass composition of this gas, and
c) the percent excess air used in the combustion.

49. The coagulated remains of a fiendish mutant humanoid creature that evolved on an oxygen-free planet are oxidized and dried in air by a laser beam and then processed through a nuclear-powered Orsat analyzer that reports the following composition using a computerized synthetic voice: "Thee oxseegin, carbon deoxside and carbon monoxside concentrations are each seven percent. Thee remaining gas is nitrogen. This is very unusual." As chief engineer of the Star Ship Entropy, determine

a) the synthetic formula (C_nH_m) of the mutant's body tissue,
b) the carbon and hydrogen percentages by mass in the tissue, and
c) the percent excess air available in the atmosphere where the tissue was oxidized.

50. An icky unknown hydrocarbon fuel of the form $(CH_2)_n$ was burned with an unknown amount of excess air x in the following gosh awful reaction:

$$(CH_2)_n + 1.5n(1 + x)[O_2 + 3.76(N_2)] \rightarrow n(CO_2) + n(H_2O) + 1.5x(O_2) + 5.64n(1 + x)(N_2)$$

An exhaust gas analysis of the products of this combustion yielded the following percentage composition on a volume basis:

Component	Molecular mass	%
N_2	28	77.4
O_2	32	13.6
H_2O	18	4.5
CO_2	44	4.5
		100.0

Using the above data, determine

a) the temperature to which the exhaust must be cooled to cause the water vapor to condense if the exhaust is at a total pressure of 22.223 psia,
b) the amount of excess air x used in the combustion process,

c) the fuel composition n if 1 lbmole of fuel produced 44.45 lbmoles of product (n is an integer), and

d) the air–fuel ratio on a mass basis.

In Problems 51 through 55 use Eqs. 9.5, 9.6, and the higher heating value data given in Table 9.2 to compute the molar specific enthalpy of formation at the standard reference state, $(\bar{h}_f^\circ)_{compound}$, of each compound from its elements. Compare your results with the values given in Table 9.1.

51. Acetylene: $2(C(s)) + H_2(g) \rightarrow C_2H_2(g) + (\bar{q}_f^\circ)_{C_2H_2(g)}, (\bar{h}_f^\circ)_{C_2H_2(g)} = ?$

52. Ethylene: $2(C(s)) + 2(H_2(g)) \rightarrow C_2H_4(g) + (\bar{q}_f^\circ)_{C_2H_4(g)}, (\bar{h}_f^\circ)_{C_2H_4(g)} = ?$

53. Propane: $3(C(s)) + 3(H_2(g)) \rightarrow C_3H_6(g) + (\bar{q}_f^\circ)_{C_3H_6(g)}, (\bar{h}_f^\circ)_{C_3H_6(g)} = ?$

54. Ethane: $2(C(s)) + 3(H_2(g)) \rightarrow C_2H_6(g) + (\bar{q}_f^\circ)_{C_2H_6(g)}, (\bar{h}_f^\circ)_{C_2H_6(g)} = ?$

55. Butane: $4(C(s)) + 5(H_2(g)) \rightarrow C_4H_{10}(g) + (\bar{q}_f^\circ)_{C_4H_{10}(g)}, (\bar{h}_f^\circ)_{C_4H_{10}(g)} = ?$

56. Repeat text Example 9.5 using 150% theoretical air.

57. Repeat text Example 9.5 using 90% theoretical air. Assume the hydrogen is much more reactive than the carbon and is all converted into water.

58. Repeat text Example 9.6 using 150% theoretical air in the combustion process.

59. The higher heating value of glucose, $C_6H_{12}O_6(s)$, is −2817.5 MJ/kgmole. Determine the standard reference state molar specific enthalpy of formation of glucose using the reaction

$$C_6H_{12}O_6(s) + 6(O_2(g)) \rightarrow 6(CO_2(g)) + 6(H_2O(\ell))$$

60. Determine the heat of combustion of propane gas with 100% theoretical air when the reactants are at the standard reference state, but the products are at 2000 R. Use the gas tables, Appendix C.16*c*.

61. Using the gas tables, Appendix C.16*c*, determine the heat of combustion of liquid octane with 200% theoretical air when the reactants are at 537 R and the products are at 4000 R. Explain the significance of your answer.

62. Liquid ethyl alcohol at 77 °F is burned in 100% theoretical air. Determine the heat produced per kgmole of fuel when the products are at 540 °F. The molar specific enthalpy of formation of this fuel is −277.69 MJ/kgmole.

63. Methane gas at −60 °C is burned during a severe winter with 200% theoretical air at the same temperatuure. The products of combustion are at 300 °C. Assuming constant specific heats, find the heat released per kgmole of fuel.

64. Kerosene (decane, $C_{10}H_{22}$) with a density of 49.3 lbm/ft^3 has a HHV of 20,484 Btu/lbm and costs 0.50 dollars per gallon. Calculate the cost of 1.0 therm (10^5 Btu) obtained by burning kerosene.

65. The *explosive energy* of a high explosive is defined to be the lower heating value (LHV) of the detonation reaction. The heat of formation of nitroglycerin, $C_3H_5(NO_3)_3$, is −354 MJ/kgmole, and its molecular mass is 227 kg/kgmole.

a) Find the values of *a*, *b*, *c*, and *d* in the following reaction describing the detonation of nitroglycerin:

$$C_3H_5(NO_3)_3 \rightarrow a(CO_2) + b(H_2O) + c(O_2) + d(N_2)$$

b) Determine the explosive energy of nitroglycerin in MJ/kg.

66. In Problem 65 the explosive energy of a high explosive was defined to be the lower heating value (LHV) of the detonation reaction. The heat of formation of trinitrotoluene (TNT), $C_7H_5(NO_2)_3$, is −54.4 MJ/kgmole, and its molecular mass is 227 kg/kgmole.

a) Find the values of *a*, *b*, *c*, and *d* in the following simplified reaction describing the detonation of TNT:

$$C_7H_5(NO_2)_3 \rightarrow a(CO) + b(CH_4) + c(H_2O) + d(N_2)$$

b) Determine the explosive energy of TNT in MJ/kg.

67. Determine the adiabatic flame temperature of methane burned in 400% theoretical air in a steady flow process.

68. Determine the adiabatic flame temperature of acetylene burned in a steady flow process with

a) 100% theoretical air, **b)** 200% theoretical air, and
c) 400% theoretical air.

69. Determine the adiabatic flame temperature of propane burned in a steady flow process with

a) 0% excess air, **b)** 100% excess air, and
c) 300% excess air.

70. Determine the adiabatic flame temperature of benzene burned in a steady flow process with

a) 0% excess air, **b)** 100% excess air, and
c) 300% excess air.

71. Determine the adiabatic flame temperature and maximum explosion pressure as 0.001 kgmole of butane is burned in 100% theoretical air in a 0.1 m^3 adiabatic bomb calorimeter.

72. Determine the molar specific entropy production $(\bar{s}_P)_r$ for the reaction $C + O_2 \rightarrow CO_2$ when both the products and the reactants are at the standard reference state. Assume an isothermal boundary at 298 K.

73. Determine the molar specific entropy production $(\bar{s}_P)_r$ for the combustion of methane in pure oxygen, $CH_4 + 2(O_2) \rightarrow CO_2 + 2(H_2O)$ when both the products and the reactants are at the standard reference state. Assume an isothermal boundary at 298 K.

74. Determine the molar specific entropy production $(\bar{s}_P)_r$ as ethylene is burned in an adiabatic combustion chamber with 100% theoretical air. The reactants are at the standard reference state, but the products are at 5.0 MPa. The adiabatic flame temperature is 2291.6 °C. Assume constant specific heats (Appendix C.13*b*).

75. Using the gas tables (Appendix C.16*c*), determine the molar specific entropy production $(\bar{s}_P)_r$ for the combustion of propane with 100% theoretical air. The reactants are at the standard reference state. The products are at 2000 R and 4.0 MPa, and the heat transfer from the combustion chamber is 571,126 Btu/(lbmole·R). Assume the combustion chamber has isothermal walls at 2000 R.

76. Determine the molar specific entropy of formation $\bar{s}_f^\circ$ for

a) CO, **b)** CO_2, and **c)** H_2O.

77. Determine the molar specific entropy of formation $\bar{s}_f^\circ$ for

a) methane, **b)** acetylene, and **c)** propane.

78. Determine the molar specific entropy of formation $\bar{s}_f^\circ$ of liquid octane and explain why it is negative.

79. Determine the specific molar Gibbs function of formation $\bar{g}_f^\circ$ at 25 °C and 0.1 MPa for the reaction $C + O_2 \rightarrow CO_2$, and compare your result with the value given in Table 9.4.

80. Use Eq. 9.36 and Appendix C.17 to find the molar specific Gibbs function of formation at 25 °C and 0.1 MPa of atomic hydrogen gas from the equilibrium reaction $H_2 \rightleftarrows 2H$.

81. The equilibrium constant for the reaction $0.5(N_2) + 0.5(O_2) \rightleftarrows NO$ is 0.0455 at 4500 R and atmospheric pressure. Assume that air at room temperature and atmospheric pressure contains 21% oxygen and 79% nitrogen on a molar basis.

A. As the dissociation occurs, the total number of moles in the reaction
a) increases, **b)** decreases, **c)** remains constant.

B. The equilibrium constant formula (K_e) for the dissociation equation is
a) $\dfrac{p_{NO}}{p_{N_2}p_{O_2}}$ **b)** $\dfrac{p_{N_2}p_{O_2}}{p_{NO}}$ **c)** $\dfrac{p_{NO}}{\sqrt{p_{N_2}p_{O_2}}}$ **d)** $\dfrac{(p_{NO})^2}{p_{N_2}p_{O_2}}$

C. Air at 4500 R and atmospheric pressure will contain what percentage of NO on a molar basis?
a) 0.617, **b)** 1.617,
c) 4.55, **d)** more than 4.55,
e) less than 0.617.

82. Determine the equilibrium constant (K_e) for the reaction $CH_4 + H_2O \rightleftarrows CO + 3(H_2)$ at 25 °C and 0.1 MPa.

83. Algebraically solve the cubic equation given in Example 9.11 for the degree of dissociation (y) and use Appendix C.17 to verify the three example computer results given there for
a) $p_m = 0.1$ MPa, $T = 2000$ K,
b) $p_m = 0.1$ MPa, $T = 3000$ K, and
c) $p_m = 1.0$ MPa, $T = 3000$ K.

84. Carbon is burned with 100% excess oxygen to form an equilibrium mixture of CO_2, CO, and O_2 at 3000 K and 1.0 MPa pressure. Determine the equilibrium composition when only the CO_2 dissociates as $CO_2 \rightleftarrows CO + 0.5(O_2)$. Assume ideal gas behavior.

85. The equilibrium constant for the water–carbon monoxide reaction $CO + H_2O \rightleftarrows CO_2 + H_2$ at 0.1 MPa and 1000 K is 1.442. Determine the equilibrium mole fraction of each gas present under these conditions. Assume ideal gas behavior.

86. Determine the maximum reversible electrical work output of the fuel cell shown below, where g is the specific Gibbs free energy.

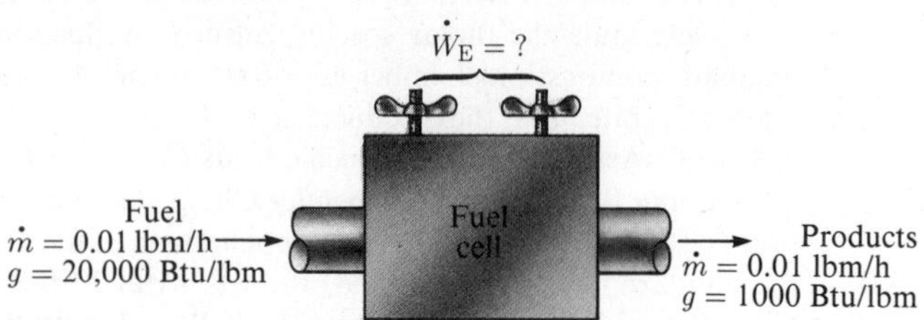

87. Determine the maximum theoretical efficiency, open circuit voltage, and maximum theoretical work output per mole of carbon consumed in a carbon–oxygen fuel cell operating with the reaction $C(s) + O_2 \rightarrow CO_2$ when each component in the reaction is at 25 °C and 0.1 MPa.

88. Repeat text Example 9.13 for a fuel cell that operates on hydrogen and 100% theoretical air (instead of pure oxygen), each at 25 °C and 0.1 MPa.

89. Determine the maximum efficiency and open circuit voltage for the methane–oxygen fuel cell, $CH_4 + 2(O_2) \rightarrow CO_2 + 2(H_2O(\ell))$, when each component in the reaction is at 25 °C and 0.1 MPa.

90. Repeat Problem 89 for the case where the reactants are premixed to a total pressure of 0.1 MPa at 25 °C.

91. Determine the maximum efficiency and open circuit voltage for the propane–oxygen fuel cell, $C_3H_8 + 5(O_2) \rightarrow 3(CO_2) + 4(H_2O(\ell))$ when each component in the reaction is at 25 °C and 0.1 MPa.

92. Repeat Problem 91 for a propane–air fuel cell in which the propane is premixed with 200% theoretical air at a total pressure of 0.1 MPa and 25 °C. Assume the combustion products are also mixed and are at a total pressure of 0.1 MPa at 25 °C.

93. An inventor claims to have perfected a hydrogen-oxygen fuel cell, $H_2 + 0.5(O_2) \rightarrow H_2O(\ell)$, that will produce 300 MJ per kgmole of hydrogen consumed at 25 °C and 0.1 MPa. Is this possible? If not, what is the maximum possible power output? Assume each component in the reaction is at 25 °C and 0.1 MPa.

94. Determine the open circuit internal entropy production rate per unit molar flow rate of CO in the carbon monoxide-oxygen fuel cell, $CO + 0.5(O_2) \rightarrow CO_2$, when each component in the reaction is at 25 °C and 0.1 MPa.

95. An inventor claims to have invented a fuel cell that contains a catalyst for the ammonia reaction $N_2 + 3H_2 \rightarrow 2NH_3$ at the standard reference state. The molar enthalpy of formation of ammonia $= -19{,}750$ Btu/lbmole and the Gibbs function of formation of ammonia $= -7140$ Btu/lbmole. Determine

a) the maximum theoretical reaction efficiency, and

b) the maximum theoretical electrical work output of this fuel cell per lbmole of N_2 consumed.

Design Problems

The following are open ended design problems. The objective is to carry out a preliminary thermal design as indicated. A detailed design with working drawings is not expected unless otherwise specified. These problems do not have specific answers, so each student's design will be unique.

96. Design a burner for a furnace that will produce 2×10^6 Btu/h at 1500 °F. Choose the fuel, flow rates, air–fuel ratio, burner material, burner geometry, flow controls, etc.

97. Design a bomb calorimeter to be used to measure the heat of combustion of municipal solid waste. Because of the heterogeneous nature of the waste, the test sample size must be at least 1 lbm. Make the calorimeter either adiabatic or isothermal. Assume all noncombustibles (e.g., metal, glass, etc.) have been removed from the waste before it is tested.

98. Design a system to produce 0.1 kg/h of hydrogen gas from the catalytic reaction of methane and steam, $CH_4 + H_2O(g) \rightleftarrows 3(H_2) + CO$, at 1500 R and 14.7 psia. Assume the system has an equilibrium composition of $CH_4 + H_2O(g) \rightleftarrows a(CH_4) + b(H_2O(g)) + c(H_2) + d(CO)$.

99. Design a combustion chamber for a rocket that will oxidize liquid hydrazine, $N_2H_4(\ell)$, with liquid hydrogen peroxide, $H_2O_2(\ell)$, at 1.0 MPa and 2000 K as follows: $N_2H_4(\ell) + 2(H_2O_2(\ell)) \rightarrow 4(H_2O(g)) + N_2$ and will supply the rocket nozzle with 1000 kg/s of exhaust gas. Data: $(\bar{h}_f^\circ)_{N_2H_4(\ell)} = 50.417$ MJ/kgmole, and $(\bar{h}_f^\circ)_{H_2O_2(\ell)} = -187.583$ MJ/kgmole.

100. Design a bench top laboratory-scale facility to produce methanol from the reaction $CO + 2(H_2) \rightleftarrows CH_3(OH)$. Determine all flow rates, heat transfers, reaction vessel optimum temperature and pressure, reaction vessel material, and geometry.

Computer Problems

The following open ended computer problems are designed to be done on a personal computer using BASIC language programming.

101. Modify the program listed in Figure 9.5 to compute the LHV of *gaseous* octane, and then use it to find the adiabatic flame temperature for

a) 100%, and **b)** 200% theoretical air.

102. Write an interactive computer program to balance the combustion reaction of any simple alcohol of the type $C_nH_{2n+1}(OH)$ with excess or deficit air or oxygen.

103. Write an interactive computer program with temperature dependent specific heats for any (or instructor assigned) hydrocarbon fuel listed in Table 9.1 to do one or more of the following.

a) Compute the heat of reaction of the fuel when the reaction temperature and percent excess air or oxygen are input by the user.

b) Add a subroutine option to calculate the adiabatic flame temperature of the fuel for any excess air or oxygen value.

c) Advanced programmers may wish to develop a menu-driven program then will cover all the hydrocarbon fuels listed in Table 9.1.

104. Write an interactive computer program that will output the entropy production rate for any (or a series of) reaction(s) of your (or your instructor's) choice. Input from the keyboard in response to properly formatted screen prompts the stoichiometric coefficients, the heat of reaction, the reaction temperature and pressure, and the isothermal heat transfer boundary temperature. Use the program to determine

a) the maximum pressure for a given isothermal boundary temperature at which the reaction can occur, and

b) the maximum isothermal boundary temperature possible for any given reaction pressure and temperature.

105. Write an interactive computer program that will output the equilibrium constant K_e when the stoichiometric coefficients are input in response to properly formatted screen prompts from the keyboard. Assume all the components obey the Gibbs-Dalton ideal gas mixture law.

106. Write an interactive computer program that will replace Appendix C.17 for the dissociation of H_2O, CO_2 and NO. You will have to find the relevant information on H, O, and N in other texts if you wish to also include the dissociation of H_2, O_2, and N_2.

107. Write an interactive computer program that will output the molar specific enthalpy ($\bar{h}_i$), entropy ($\bar{s}_i$), and Gibbs function ($\bar{g}_i$) for any substance of your (or your instructor's) choice at any user input pressure and temperature.

108. Write an interactive computer program that will output the power and reaction efficiency of any reaction you (or your instructor) desire. Apply this program to a fuel cell analysis and plot the reaction efficiency η_r vs.

a) the percent excess oxidizer present,

b) the reaction temperature,

c) the reaction pressure,

d) the entropy production rate, and

e) the fuel cell heat transfer rate $\dot{Q}$.

Assume isothermal boundaries and input T_b from the keyboard along with all other necessary information.

Chapter Ten Compressible Fluid Flow

It may seem rather strange to encounter a chapter on classical fluid mechanics in a thermodynamics textbook, but there is a good reason why it should be here. At the beginning of the nineteenth century when the industrial revolution was in full swing and the technology of the high-pressure steam engine was in the process of being developed, it became clear that under certain circumstances some very peculiar things were happening inside the engine. At that time engineers were attempting to determine how to increase the power output of a given engine while at the same time improving its operating efficiency. The relation between power output and operating conditions can best be viewed through the application of the energy rate balance.

The energy rate balance applied to a simple adiabatic power-producing engine gives (neglecting any changes in flowstream kinetic and potential energy)

$$\dot{W} = \dot{m}(h_{\text{out}} - h_{\text{in}})$$

This equation clearly indicates that an effective way to increase the power output $\dot{W}$ is simply to increase the mass flow rate $\dot{m}$ through the engine. This can be done either by increasing the inlet pressure or by decreasing the exhaust pressure. As the inlet pressure was increased engineers found that the power output did in fact increase, and when the exhaust pressure was decreased the power also increased, but only up to a certain point. Beyond a certain operating point a phenomenon occurred such that no matter how much the exhaust pressure was decreased the mass flow rate and consequently the engine's power did not increase further. They called this phenomenon *choked* flow, and it was not fully understood until the study of *compressible* fluid mechanics was completely developed in the early twentieth century. Thus, compressible fluid mechanics is of vital importance to the study of applied thermodynamics because it helps us to understand the effect that fluid compressibility has on the thermodynamic performance of systems containing high-speed compressible working fluids.

A compressible flow is any flow in which the fluid density (or specific volume) is not constant in time and/or space. Though all real substances are compressible to some extent, in normal engineering practice only gases and vapors are significantly compressible. Liquids and solids are normally considered to be incompressible, except at extremely high pressures of the order of 10^5 psia (0.7 GPa) or more. Because a great deal of modern engineering deals with thermodynamics processes involving gases and vapors, it is important to understand the unique flow characteristics of these substances.

In the previous chapters we discussed the conservation of mass and energy laws and made extensive use of the one-dimensional mass, energy, and entropy balance equations for open and closed systems. In this chapter we introduce the conservation of linear momentum law and the corresponding closed and open system one-dimensional momentum balance equations and apply them to systems containing compressible substances. This law, along with the conservation of mass and the two laws of thermodynamics, will complete the set of fundamental physical laws and corresponding balance equations necessary for proper engineering design and analysis.

In Chapters 4 and 5 we studied the energy and entropy characteristics of nozzles and diffusers. In this chapter we discover that the conservation of linear momentum adds new facets to this subject for compressible flows. We investigate the nature of supersonic flows, choked flows, and shock waves. We also generalize the balance concept through the Reynolds Transport theorem so that all our balance equations may be easily expanded to multidimensional analytical tools.

Stagnation Properties

The *stagnation state* of a moving fluid is the state it would achieve if it underwent an adiabatic, aergonic deceleration to zero velocity. The energy rate balance (ERB) for an adiabatic, aergonic, steady state, steady flow, single-inlet, single-outlet open system with negligible change in flowstream potential energy reduces to

$$h_{\text{in}} + V_{\text{in}}^2/(2g_c) = h_{\text{out}} + V_{\text{out}}^2/(2g_c)$$

If we let the subscript "o" refer to the stagnation (or zero velocity) state, then $V_o = 0$, and the above equation can be used to define the stagnation specific enthalpy h_o as

$$h_o = h + V^2/(2g_c) \tag{10.1}$$

For an ideal gas or a low pressure vapor with constant specific heats this equation can be written as

$$V^2/(2g_c) = h_o - h = c_p(T_o - T)$$

or

$$T_o/T = 1 + V^2/(2g_c c_p T) \tag{10.2}$$

where T_o is the *stagnation temperature* (the temperature at zero velocity).

Isentropic Stagnation Properties

If, in addition, we decelerate the flow reversibly (i.e., without friction or other losses) and aergonically, then the entire process becomes isentropic and Eq. 5.38 of Chapter 5 can be combined with Eq. 10.2 to provide equations for the *isentropic stagnation pressure* p_{os} and the *isentropic stagnation density* ρ_{os} based on the (isentropic) stagnation temperature $T_o = T_{os}$ as

$$\frac{T_{os}}{T} = \left(\frac{p_{os}}{p}\right)^{(k-1)/k} = \left(\frac{v_{os}}{v}\right)^{1-k} = \left(\frac{\rho_{os}}{\rho}\right)^{k-1} \tag{5.38}$$

Then Eq. 10.2 becomes

$$p_{os}/p = [1 + V^2/(2g_c c_p T)]^{k/(k-1)} \tag{10.3}$$

and

$$\rho_{os}/\rho = [1 + V^2(2g_c c_p T)]^{1/(k-1)} \tag{10.4}$$

where the "os" subscript has been added to indicate the *isentropic stagnation state* condition. These states are shown schematically in Figure 10.1.

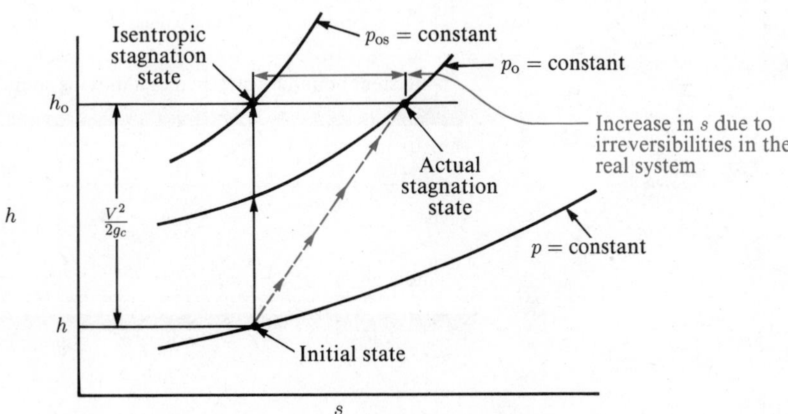

Figure 10.1 Schematic of an isentropic and a real deceleration to the stagnation state on a Mollier diagram.

Table 10.1 Compressible flow Mach number regimes (ϵ is a small fluctuation)

Flow regime	Name
$\mathbf{M} < 1$	Subsonic
$\mathbf{M} = 1$	Sonic
$1 - \epsilon \leq \mathbf{M} \leq 1 + \epsilon$	Transonic
$\mathbf{M} > 1$	Supersonic
$\mathbf{M} \geq 5$	Hypersonic

The Mach Number

The Mach number **M** was introduced in 1929 and named in honor of Ernst Mach (1838–1916), an Austrian physicist and philosopher who studied high-speed compressible flow in the 1870s. It is the dimensionless ratio of the local fluid velocity V to the velocity of sound at the same point c, or

$$\mathbf{M} = V/c \tag{10.5}$$

Table 10.1 lists the jargon terms that have been developed to describe the different flow regimes. Transonic flow is a flow in which the Mach number fluctuates around 1.0 by a small amount ($\pm\epsilon$).

We can deduce a relation for the dependence of the isentropic sonic velocity c on local thermodynamic properties from a mass and energy balance analysis of a moving acoustical wave. Figure 10.2 shows an open system attached to an isentropic sound wave moving at velocity c through a stationary fluid in a duct that has a constant cross sectional area A. Our coordinate system is attached to the moving wave, so the fluid appears to be approaching the wave with velocity c. For an adiabatic, aergonic, reversible, steady state, steady flow, single-inlet, single-outlet, open system the mass rate balance (MRB) reduces to

$$\dot{m}_{\text{in}} = \dot{m}_{\text{out}}$$

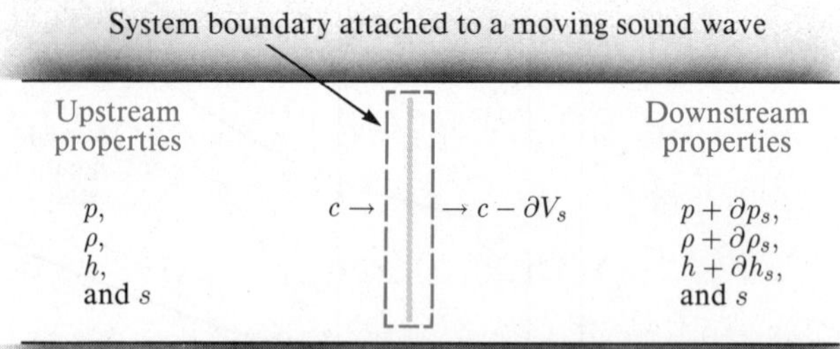

Figure 10.2 Schematic of an isentropic sound wave moving through a stationary fluid in a horizontal duct of constant cross-sectional area A. The coordinate system is fixed to the moving wave so that the surrounding fluid appears to be moving. The "s" subscript is used to indicate isentropic changes in the properties.

or

$$\begin{aligned}\rho A c &= (\rho + \partial\rho_s)(A)(c - \partial V_s)\\ &= A(\rho c - \rho\,\partial V_s + c\,\partial\rho_s - \partial\rho_s\,\partial V_s)\end{aligned}$$

Where the subscript "s" indicates that entropy is held constant during the differentiation process. Neglecting second-order differential terms (i.e., setting $\partial\rho_s\,\partial V_s = 0$), this equation can be rearranged to give

$$\left(\frac{\partial V}{\partial \rho}\right)_s = c/\rho \tag{10.6}$$

Similarly, the energy rate balance for this system becomes

$$h + c^2/2g_c = (h + \partial h_s) + (c - \partial V_s)^2/(2g_c)$$

Again neglecting second-order differential terms, this can be expanded and rearranged to give

$$\left(\frac{\partial h}{\partial V}\right)_s = c/g_c \tag{10.7}$$

Finally, the Gibbs Eq. 6.31 for an isentropic process yields

$$T\,\partial s_s = \partial h_s - v\,\partial p_s = 0$$

or

$$\left(\frac{\partial h}{\partial p}\right)_s = v = \frac{1}{\rho} \tag{10.8}$$

Multiplying Eq. 10.6 by Eq. 10.7 and then dividing by Eq. 10.8 gives a relation for the sonic velocity c in terms of the measurable properties p and ρ:

$$\left(\frac{\partial V}{\partial \rho}\right)_s\left(\frac{\partial h}{\partial V}\right)_s\left(\frac{\partial p}{\partial h}\right)_s = \left(\frac{\partial p}{\partial \rho}\right)_s = \rho(c/g_c)(c/\rho) = c^2/g_c$$

or

$$c = \sqrt{g_c\left(\frac{\partial p}{\partial \rho}\right)_s} \tag{10.9}$$

Equation 10.9 is a valid equation for the isentropic sonic velocity in any compressible substance. In particular, in the case of an ideal gas, Eq. 5.39 relates pressure and density for an isentropic process by

$$pv^k = p\rho^{-k} = \text{constant} \tag{5.39}$$

Therefore,

$$\left(\frac{\partial h}{\partial \rho}\right)_s = kp/\rho = kRT$$

where we have used the ideal gas law, $p = \rho RT$. Then, from Eq. 10.9,

$$c_{\substack{\text{ideal}\\\text{gas}}} = \sqrt{kg_c RT} \quad \textbf{(10.10)}$$

and from Eq. 10.5,

$$\mathbf{M}_{\substack{\text{ideal}\\\text{gas}}} = \frac{V}{\sqrt{kg_c RT}} \quad \textbf{(10.11)}$$

Since for ideal gases $c_p - c_v = R$ and $k = c_p/c_v$, we can write $c_p = R + c_v = kR/(k-1)$. Also, from Eq. 10.10, we find that $R = c^2/(kg_c T)$. Then the equations for the isentropic stagnation temperature, pressure, and density (Eqs. 10.2, 10.3, and 10.4) for an ideal gas become

$$\frac{T_{os}}{T} = 1 + V^2/(2g_c c_p T) = 1 + \frac{k-1}{2}\mathbf{M}^2 \quad \textbf{(10.12)}$$

$$\frac{p_{os}}{p} = \left(1 + \frac{k-1}{2}\mathbf{M}^2\right)^{k/(k-1)} \quad \textbf{(10.13)}$$

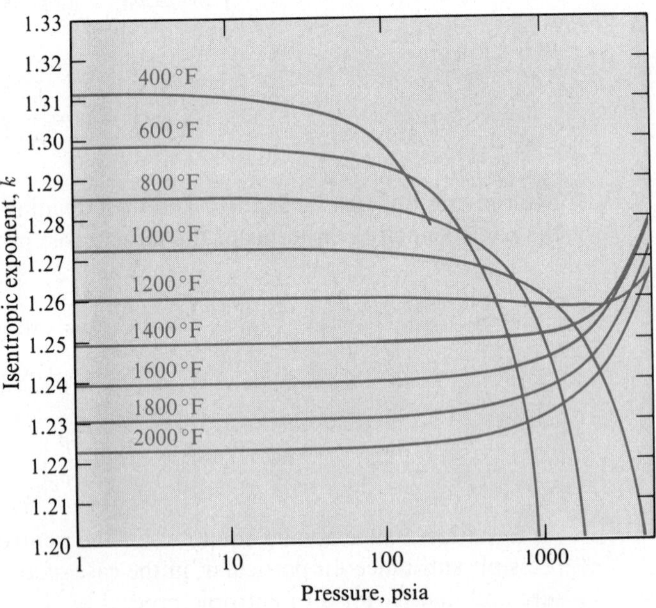

Figure 10.3 The variation in the isentropic exponent of water vapor, where $k = -(v/p)(\partial p/\partial v)_T(c_p/c_v)$.

Table 10.2 Typical values of the specific heat ratio k

Gas	$k = c_p/c_v$
Monatomic	
Argon, helium, neon, xenon, etc.	1.67
Diatomic	
Air	1.40
Nitrogen	1.40
Oxygen	1.39
Carbon monoxide	1.40
Hydrogen	1.40
Triatomic	
Carbon dioxide	1.29
Sulfur dioxide	1.25

and

$$\frac{\rho_{os}}{\rho} = \left(1 + \frac{k-1}{2}\mathbf{M}^2\right)^{1/(k-1)} \tag{10.14}$$

Appendix C.18 contains tabulated values of T/T_{os}, p/p_{os}, and ρ/ρ_{os} for air ($k = 1.4$) for various values of $\mathbf{M}$. These tabulations were made by using Eqs. 10.12, 10.13, and 10.14, and may be used in place of these equations when convenient.

Figure 10.3 shows the variation in the isentropic exponent for water vapor, which (see Problem 16 at the end of Chapter 6) can be written as $k = -(v/p)(\partial p/\partial v)_T(c_p/c_v)$. Table 10.2 summarizes values of the specific heat ratio k for some common engineering substances.

Example 10.1 Find the velocity, isentropic stagnation temperature, and isentropic stagnation pressure on an aircraft flying at Mach 0.85 at an altitude where the temperature is $-20\,°\text{C}$ and the pressure is 0.5 atm. Assume air is an ideal gas with a constant specific heat ratio of $k = 1.4$ and a gas constant of $R = 286\ \text{J/(kg}\cdot\text{K)}$.

Solution From Eq. 10.11 we can calculate the aircraft's velocity as

$$V = \mathbf{M}\sqrt{kg_cRT}$$
$$= (0.85)\{(1.4)(1)[286\ \text{m}^2/(\text{s}^2\cdot\text{K})](273 - 20\ \text{K})\}^{1/2} = 271\ \text{m/s}$$

The isentropic stagnation pressure and temperature can be determined from Eqs. 10.12 and 10.13 as

$$T_{os} = T\left(1 + \frac{k-1}{k}\mathbf{M}^2\right)$$
$$= (273 - 20\ \text{K})\left[1 + \frac{1.4-1}{2}(0.85)^2\right] = 290\ \text{K} = 17\,°\text{C}$$

and

$$p_{os} = p\left[1 + \frac{k-1}{2}\mathbf{M}^2\right]^{k/(k-1)}$$

$$= (0.5\text{ atm})\left[1 + \frac{1.4-1}{2}(0.85)^2\right]^{1.4/(1.4-1)} = 0.802\text{ atm} = 81.2\text{ kPa}$$

This example shows that even at moderate subsonic velocities there can be a considerable temperature and pressure rise at the stagnation points of moving objects.

Converging–Diverging Flows

We now wish to investigate the effect of variations in the flow cross-sectional area on the Mach number of the flow. If we differentiate the mass rate balance equation, $\dot{m} = \rho A v = \text{constant}$, for an isentropic flow we obtain

$$\rho A\, \partial V_s + \rho V\, \partial A_s + AV\, \partial \rho_s = 0$$

or

$$\partial V_s/V + \partial A_s/A + \partial \rho_s/\rho = 0$$

or

$$\partial A_s/A = -\partial V_s/V - \partial \rho_s/\rho \tag{10.15}$$

Now differentiate Eq. 10.1 for a constant isentropic stagnation enthalpy to get

$$\partial h_{os} = \partial h_s + V\, \partial V_s/g_c = 0$$

or

$$\partial h_s = -V\, \partial V_s/g_c$$

Now combine this with Gibbs Eq. 6.31 for an isentropic process to get

$$T\, \partial s_s = \partial h_s - v\, \partial p_s = 0$$

or

$$\partial h_s = v\, \partial p_s = \partial p_s/\rho = -V\, \partial V_s/g_c$$

then

$$\partial V_s/V = -g_c\, \partial p_s/\rho V^2 \tag{10.16}$$

Substituting Eq. 10.16 into 10.15 and using Eqs. 10.5 and 10.9 gives the desired result

$$\partial A_s/A = -\partial V_s/V - \partial \rho_s/\rho = \left[g_c/V^2 - \left(\frac{\partial \rho}{\partial p}\right)_s\right](\partial p_s/\rho)$$

$$= [g_c/V^2 - g_c/c^2](\partial p_s/\rho) = (1 - \mathbf{M}^2)(g_c/V^2)(\partial p_s/\rho)$$

or

$$\left(\frac{\partial A}{\partial p}\right)_s = (1 - \mathbf{M}^2)\left(\frac{Ag_c}{\rho V^2}\right) \quad \textbf{(10.17)}$$

Clearly, if $\mathbf{M} < 1$ then $(\partial A/\partial p)_s > 0$, and if $\mathbf{M} > 1$ then $(\partial A/\partial p)_s < 0$. A nozzle is a device whose function is to convert pressure into kinetic energy, so $\partial p_s < 0$ in the direction of flow. Consequently, a subsonic ($\mathbf{M} < 1$) nozzle must have $\partial A_s < 0$ for $(\partial A/\partial p)_s > 0$. Therefore, the cross-sectional area of a subsonic nozzle must *decrease* in the direction of flow. Similarly, if a nozzle contains supersonic flow ($\mathbf{M} > 1$) and by definition has $\partial p_s < 0$, then $\partial A_s > 0$ and its cross-sectional area must *increase* in the direction of flow. This is shown in Figure 10.4*a*.

Diffusers, on the other hand, are devices whose function is to convert kinetic energy into pressure, and therefore have $\partial p_s > 0$ in the direction of flow. Then $\partial A_s > 0$ for a subsonic diffuser and its cross-sectional area must *increase* in the direction of flow, while $\partial A_s < 0$ for a supersonic diffuser and its cross-sectional area must therefore *decrease* in the direction of flow. This geometry–Mach number dependence is shown in Figure 10.4*b*.

When $\mathbf{M} = 1.0$ in Eq. 10.17 then $(\partial A/\partial p)_s = 0$. This corresponds to a point of minimum cross-sectional area. This point is called the *throat* of the device, and is characterized by the fact that it can never have a Mach number greater than one, i.e.,

$$\mathbf{M}_{\text{throat}} \leq 1.0$$

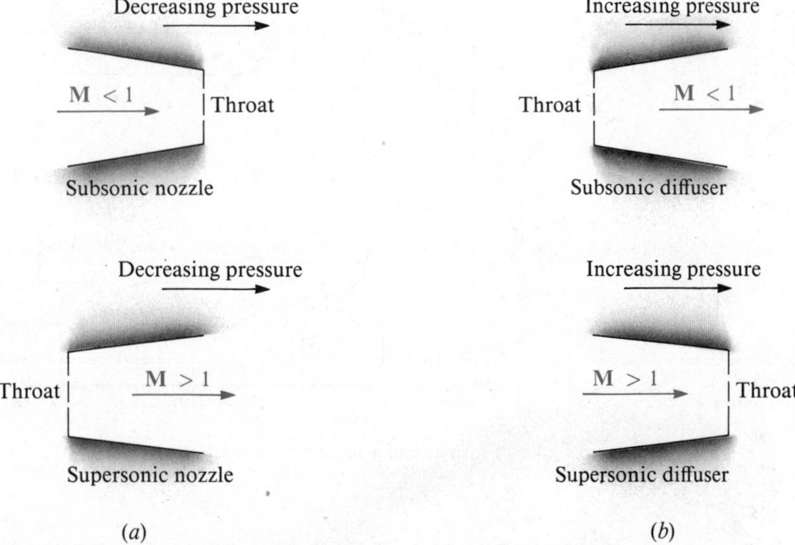

Figure 10.4 Cross-sectional area–Mach number dependence for (*a*) nozzles, $\Delta p < 0$, and (*b*) diffusers, $\Delta p > 0$.

When the Mach number at the throat is equal to one, we say that the throat is at its *critical* condition and denote its properties in this state with a superscript asterisk. Then $\mathbf{M}^*_{\text{throat}}$ is *always* equal to 1.0, and from Eqs. 10.12, 10.13, and 10.14 the critical condition properties at the throat are[1]

$$T^* = T_{\text{os}} \frac{2}{k+1} \tag{10.18}$$

$$p^* = p_{\text{os}} \left(\frac{2}{k+1}\right)^{k(k-1)} \tag{10.19}$$

and

$$\rho^* = \rho_{\text{os}} \left(\frac{2}{k+1}\right)^{1/(k-1)} \tag{10.20}$$

When a subsonic nozzle and a supersonic nozzle are joined at their throats they form a converging–diverging nozzle that can be used to generate supersonic velocities. Also, connecting a supersonic diffuser to a subsonic diffuser forms a converging–diverging diffuser that can be used to decelerate a supersonic flow and recover its kinetic energy by converting it into pressure. These two converging–diverging geometries are often combined in the design of a supersonic wind tunnel as shown in Figure 10.5. Note that the diverging part of the nozzle cannot become supersonic until the throat becomes critical at a Mach number of 1.0. This is called *choked flow* and is discussed in the next section.

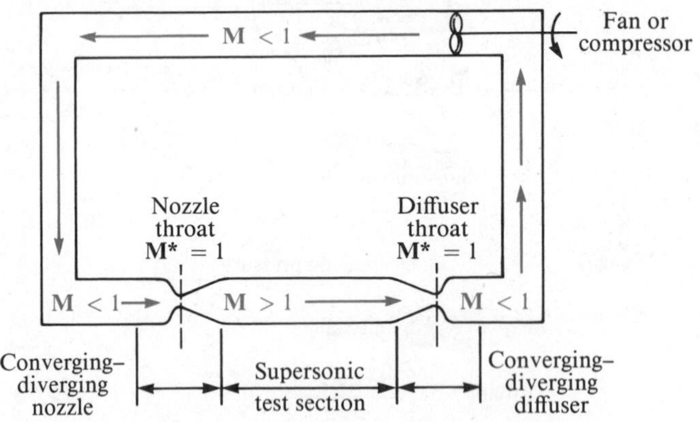

Figure 10.5 Schematic of a supersonic wind tunnel design.

1. These are not the same as the thermodynamic *critical state* properties. The use of the word "critical" here refers to a different type of phenomenon.

Example 10.2 A converging–diverging nozzle is attached via a valve to a pipe holding compressed air at 1.0 MPa and 20 °C. The valve is opened and the air passes through the nozzle and into the atmosphere. Assuming isentropic flow throughout, determine

a) the exit Mach number,
b) the exit temperature,
c) the exit velocity,
d) the pressure at the throat of the nozzle, and
e) the temperature at the throat of the nozzle.

Solution Assume air is a constant specific heat ideal gas with $k = 1.4$.

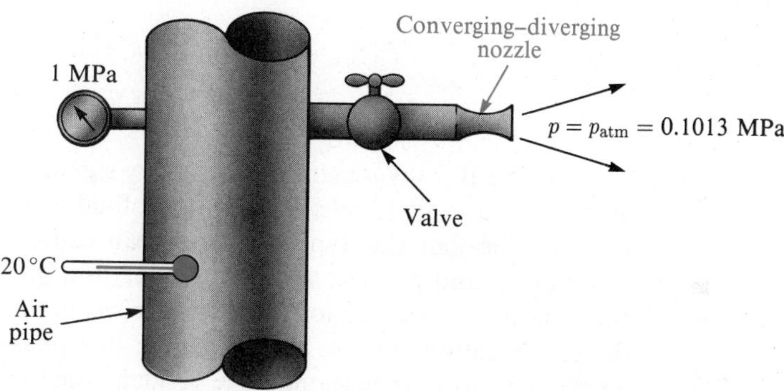

a) Since the fluid is air either we can use Appendix C.18 with

$$p/p_{os} = (0.1013 \text{ MPa})/(1.0 \text{ MPa}) = 0.1013$$

or we can use Eqs. 10.12 and 10.13. Instead of interpolating in Appendix C.18, it is easier to solve Eq. 10.13 directly for **M**:

$$\mathbf{M} = \left\{\frac{2}{k-1}\left[(p_{os}/p)^{(k-1)/k} - 1\right]\right\}^{1/2}$$

$$= \left\{\frac{2}{0.4}\left[\left(\frac{1.0}{0.1013}\right)^{0.4/1.4} - 1\right]\right\}^{1/2} = 2.15$$

Note that this agrees with what we would have interpolated from Appendix C.18.

b) Here Eq. 10.12 can be used to give

$$T = \frac{T_{os}}{1 + \dfrac{k-1}{2}\mathbf{M}^2} = \frac{273 + 20 \text{ K}}{1 + \dfrac{0.4}{2}(2.15)^2} = 152 \text{ K} = -121 \text{ °C}$$

c) Equation 10.11 can now be used to find the exit velocity as

$$V = \mathbf{M}\sqrt{kg_c RT} = (2.15)\{(1.4)(1)[286\ \text{m}^2/(\text{s}^2\cdot\text{K})](152\ \text{K})\}^{1/2} = 530\ \text{m/s}$$

d) Since the exit velocity is supersonic, the throat must be sonic and therefore Eq. 10.19 can be used to determine the throat pressure as

$$p_{\text{throat}} = p^* = p_{os}[2/(k+1)]^{k/(k-1)}$$
$$= (1.0\ \text{MPa})\left(\frac{2}{2.4}\right)^{1.4/0.4} = 0.528\ \text{MPa}$$

e) Similarly, Eq. 10.18 can be used to calculate the throat temperature as

$$T_{\text{throat}} = T^* = T_{os}[2/(k+1)]$$
$$= (273 + 20\ \text{K})(2/2.4) = 244\ \text{K} = -29\ °\text{C}$$

Example 10.2 demonstrates that a very significant temperature drop can occur inside a supersonic nozzle. If the flowing fluid is a vapor near its saturation state it is possible that this type of cooling can cause the state to drop through the vapor dome and produce a two-phase mixture inside the nozzle. This is a rather common occurrence for low-temperature steam flow through a nozzle. However, the condensation process that produces this phase change generally requires a longer time to complete than the resident time of the high-speed vapor in the converging part of the nozzle. When this occurs the vapor exits the nozzle's throat in a nonequilibrium state at a much lower temperature than the proper equilibrium saturation temperature at the exit pressure. This nonequilibrium state is called *supersaturated* and is very unstable. After a sufficient time has passed, the fluid will undergo a rapid condensation downstream from the throat due to a nucleation and growth process of the second phase. This process is irreversible and causes the temperature of the two-phase mixture to rise to the proper equilibrium saturation value (see Figure 10.6). The irreversible condensation process from a' to b shown in Figure 10.6 is sometimes called a *condensation shock.*

Choked Flow

The mass flow rate per unit area in an isentropic nozzle can be determined for an ideal gas from Eqs. 10.11, 10.12, and 10.13 and the ideal gas formula, $\rho = p/RT$, as

$$\dot{m}/A = \rho V = (p/RT)(\mathbf{M}c)$$
$$= p\mathbf{M}(\sqrt{kg_c RT})(T_{os}/T_{os})^{1/2}(p_{os}/p_{os})/RT$$
$$= p_{os}\mathbf{M}(kg_c/RT_{os})^{1/2}(T_{os}/T)^{1/2}(p/p_{os})$$
$$= p_{os}\mathbf{M}\left(\frac{kg_c}{RT_{os}}\right)^{1/2}\left(1 + \frac{k-1}{2}M^2\right)^{(k+1)/2(1-k)} \qquad \textbf{(10.21)}$$

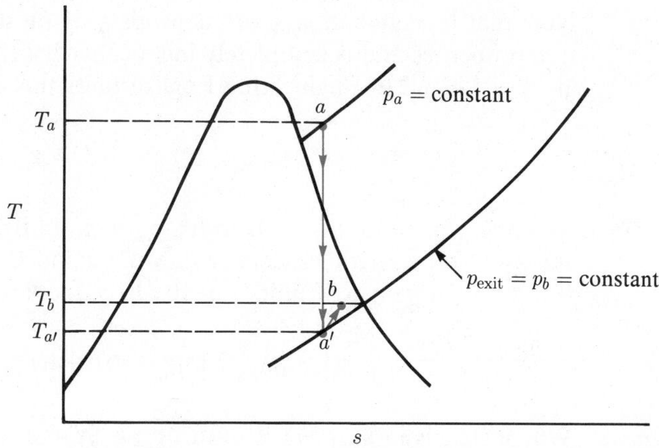

Figure 10.6 Isentropic expansion of a vapor near its saturation at state a through a nozzle to a nonequilibrium supersaturated state at a'. This is followed by an irreversible nucleation and condensation process to equilibrium state b.

Figure 10.7 is a schematic of the variation in $\dot{m}/A$ with the ratio of the back pressure p_B to the upstream stagnation pressure p_{os}. When $\mathbf{M}_{throat} = \mathbf{M}^* = 1.0$, the nozzle is passing the maximum possible flow $\dot{m}_{max}$.

Since we always have $\mathbf{M}_{throat} \leq 1.0$, then clearly the maximum nozzle mass flow rate will occur when the throat velocity is sonic. Then $\dot{m} = \dot{m}_{max}$, $\mathbf{M}_{throat} = \mathbf{M}^* = 1.0$, $A_{throat} = A^*$, and Eq. 10.21 becomes

$$\dot{m}_{max}/A^* = p_{os}\left(\frac{kg_c}{RT_{os}}\right)^{1/2}\left(\frac{k+1}{2}\right)^{(k+1)/2(1-k)} \qquad \textbf{(10.22a)}$$

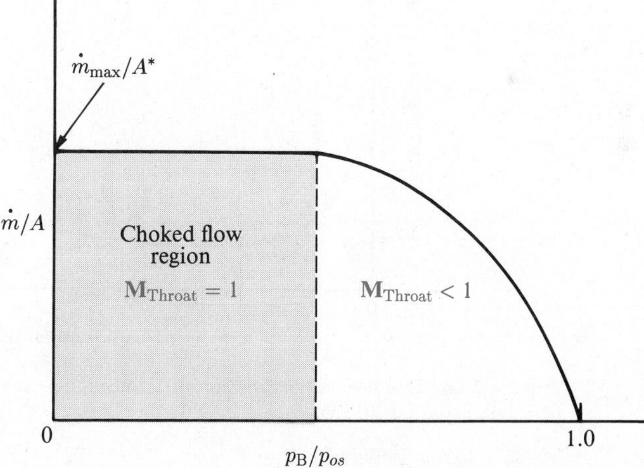

Figure 10.7 The relative variation in dimensionless isentropic converging nozzle air mass flow rate with increasing backpressure to upstream stagnation pressure ratio. Since the Mach number in a converging nozzle cannot exceed 1.0, the maximum flow rate through the nozzle occurs when the Mach number at the throat is 1.0.

Note that the value of $\dot{m}_{max}/A^*$ depends only on the upstream isentropic stagnation properties and is completely independent of the downstream conditions. For air, $k = 1.4$ and in Engineering English units this equation reduces to[2]

$$(\dot{m}_{max}/A^*)_{air} = 0.532(p_{os}/\sqrt{T_{os}}) \tag{10.22b}$$

where $\dot{m}_{max}$ is in lbm/s, A^* is in ft^2, p_{os} is in lbf/ft^2, and T_{os} is in R. This is called Fliegner's (or sometimes Zeuner's) formula and was experimentally discovered in the 1870s. In metric SI units Eq. 10.22*a* reduces to[3]

$$(\dot{m}_{max}/A^*)_{air} = 0.0404(p_{os}/\sqrt{T_{os}}) \tag{10.22c}$$

Where $\dot{m}_{max}$ is in kg/s, A^* is in m^2, p_{os} is in N/m^2, and T_{os} is in K.

When $\mathbf{M}_{throat} = 1.0$, the nozzle is passing its maximum flow rate and no changes made *downstream* of the throat (such as lowering the exit pressure) will cause the flow to increase. Consequently, the nozzle is said to be choked when the velocity of the fluid at its throat reaches sonic velocity.

Dividing Eq. 10.22*a* by 10.21 gives the nozzle to throat cross-sectional area ratio for a supersonic nozzle at its maximum flow rate as

$$A/A^* = \frac{1}{\mathbf{M}}\left[\frac{2}{k+1}\left(1 + \frac{k-1}{2}\mathbf{M}^2\right)\right]^{(k+1)/2(k-1)} \tag{10.23a}$$

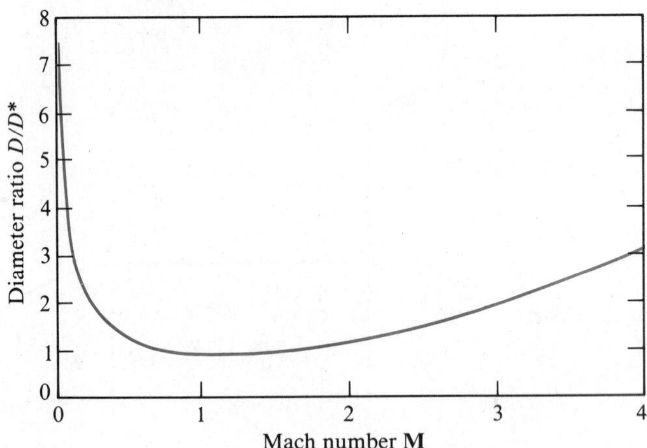

Figure 10.8 Diameter ratio variation in a converging–diverging isentropic nozzle for air ($k = 1.4$), From Eq. 10.23*b*.

---

2. Note that the dimensional constant in this equation is 0.532 lbm$\cdot\sqrt{\text{R}}$/(lbf$\cdot$s).
3. Note that the dimensional constant in this equation is 0.0404 kg$\cdot\sqrt{\text{K}}$/(N$\cdot$s), or 0.0404 s$\cdot\sqrt{\text{K}}$/m.

and for air ($k = 1.4$), this becomes

$$A/A^* = \frac{1}{\mathbf{M}}\left(\frac{1 + 0.2\mathbf{M}^2}{1.2}\right)^3 \qquad \textbf{(10.23\textit{b})}$$

For a circular cross section, $A/A^* = (D/D^*)^2$. Figure 10.8 shows how this diameter ratio varies with Mach number for air according to Eq. 10.23*b*.

If a converging–diverging nozzle does not have the exact shape dictated by Eqs. 10.23 it may still produce supersonic flow; however, the flow will not be isentropic.

Example 10.3

To deflate an automobile tire the valve core must be removed from the tire's valve stem. When the core is removed, the valve stem then approximates an isentropic converging nozzle with an internal diameter of 0.09375 in. If the tire is initially at 50 psia (35.3 psig) and 70 °F,

a) is the flow in the open valve stem initially choked?

b) If so, at what tire pressure will it unchoke?

c) How long will it take to unchoke if the tire is assumed to have a constant volume of 1.0 ft³ and a constant internal temperature (T_{os}) of 70 °F?

Solution The system is shown below.

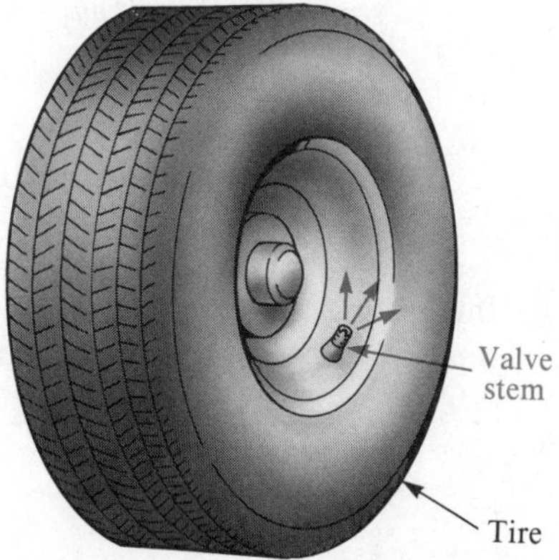

a) From Eq. 10.19 for air ($k = 1.4$), the flow will be choked if

$$p_{exit}/p_{os} < p^*/p_{os} = \left(\frac{2}{k+1}\right)^{k/(k-1)} = \left(\frac{2}{2.4}\right)^{1.4/0.4} = 0.528$$

Here, $p_{exit}/p_{os} = 14.7/50 = 0.294 < 0.528$; therefore, initially the flow will be choked.

b) The flow will remain choked until the tire deflates to a pressure of

$$p_{os} = p_{exit}/0.528 = 14.7/0.528 = 27.8 \text{ psia} = 13.1 \text{ psig}$$

c) During the deflation process with a choked flow, $\dot{m} = \dot{m}_{max}$, and then Eq. 10.22*b* gives

$$\dot{m}_{max} = -\left(\frac{dm_T}{dt}\right) = 0.532(A^* p_{os}/\sqrt{T_{os}})$$

where

$$A^* = \pi D_{exit}^2/4 = \frac{\pi(0.09375 \text{ in})^2}{4(144 \text{ in}^2/\text{ft}^2)} = 4.79 \times 10^{-5} \text{ ft}^2$$

Also, $T_{os} = 70\ °\text{F} = 530 \text{ R} = \text{constant}$, and $p_{os} = m_T R T_{os}/\mathcal{V}_T$ where m_T and $\mathcal{V}_T$ are the mass of air in the tire and volume of the tire, respectively. Then

$$\begin{aligned} dm_T/dt &= -0.532[A^* m_T R T_{os}/(\mathcal{V}_T \sqrt{T_{os}})] \\ &= -0.532[A^* R \sqrt{T_{os}}/\mathcal{V}_T] m_T \\ &= -[0.532 \text{ lbm} \cdot \sqrt{\text{R}}/(\text{lbf} \cdot \text{s})](4.79 \times 10^{-5} \text{ ft}^2)[53.34 \text{ ft} \cdot \text{lbf}/(\text{lbm} \cdot \text{R})] \\ &\quad \times [(460 + 70 \text{ R})^{1/2}/(1.0 \text{ ft}^3)] m_T \\ &= -(0.0313 \text{ s}^{-1}) m_T \end{aligned}$$

or

$$\frac{dm_T}{m_T} = -(0.0313)\, dt$$

Integrating this result from the initial mass in the tire m_{Ti} to the mass in the tire $m_{T\tau}$ when the valve stem unchokes at time τ gives

$$\ln(m_{T\tau}/m_{Ti}) = -(0.0313)\tau$$

or

$$\tau = 31.95[\ln(m_{Ti}/m_{T\tau})] \text{ seconds}$$

Now $m_{Ti}/m_{T\tau} = [p_{os}\mathcal{V}_T/(RT_{os})]_i/[p_{os}\mathcal{V}_T/(RT_{os})]_\tau = p_{osi}/p_{os\tau}$ so $\tau = 31.95 \ln(p_{osi}/p_{os\tau}) = 31.95 \ln(50/27.8) = 18.8$ seconds.

The Reynolds Transport Theorem

In Chapter 2 we defined a closed system as any system in which mass does not cross the system boundary, but energy (heat and work) may cross the boundary. An open system was then defined to be any system in which both mass and energy may cross the system boundary. In classical mechanics closed and open systems are called *Lagrangian* and *Eulerian* systems, respectively, and their use in problem solving is referred to as *Lagrangian analysis* and *Eulerian analysis.*

The Lagrangian analysis technique is named after the French mathematician Joseph Louis Lagrange (1736–1813), and basically involves trying to solve the equations of energy and motion for a fixed mass (or closed) system. The Eulerian analysis technique is named after the Swiss mathematician Leonhard Euler (1707–1783), and involves attempting to solve the equations of energy and motion for a nonconstant spatial volume (or open system). For a given situation usually one or the other of these techniques is easier to use, but regardless of their ease of application they both must give the same results. Therefore, we must be able to mathematically transform our governing equations back and forth between these two analysis frames. The *Reynolds transport theorem* is a method of carrying out this transformation.

In Chapter 2 we defined a simple balance equation for any extensive property X as

$$X_G = X_T + X_P \tag{2.11}$$

and on a rate basis as

$$\dot{X}_G = \dot{X}_T + \dot{X}_P \tag{2.12}$$

where $\dot{X} = dX/dt$ is the rate of change of X within the system (either closed or open) that we are analyzing. X_G is the net gain in X by the system, X_T is the net amount of X transported into the system, and X_P is the net amount of X produced inside the system boundaries by some internal process. We noted in Chapter 2 that if X was conserved then $X_P = \dot{X}_P = 0$.

This balance equation is conceptually accurate. The only problem that arises in its use is that the form of the derivative for the net gain rate of X by the system depends on whether the system is open or closed. We have never had to consider this in the past because these two derivative forms happen to be identical for the simple one-dimensional analysis discussed in this book. However, many times (especially in the study of fluid mechanics) a one-dimensional analysis is not sufficient to solve the problem, and we have to expand to a multidimensional approach that is often supported by a computer-based numerical technique. Because of the basic power of the Reynolds transport theorem in being able to transform differentiation operations back and forth between multidimensional closed and open systems, because our general rate balance equations have such differentials, and because we deal with both closed and open systems in thermodynamics, the Reynolds transport theorem is being introduced at this point in its full three-dimensional form. We will use it *only* to transform the left side of Eq. 2.12, the system rate of gain term. The remaining transport and production rate terms will be handled differently.

The Reynolds transport theorem is named after the British engineer and physicist, Osborne Reynolds (1842–1912). Its derivation is quite complex and will not be presented here, but the interested reader may wish to consult the fluid mechanics texts listed at the end of this chapter for more information. Because there is a

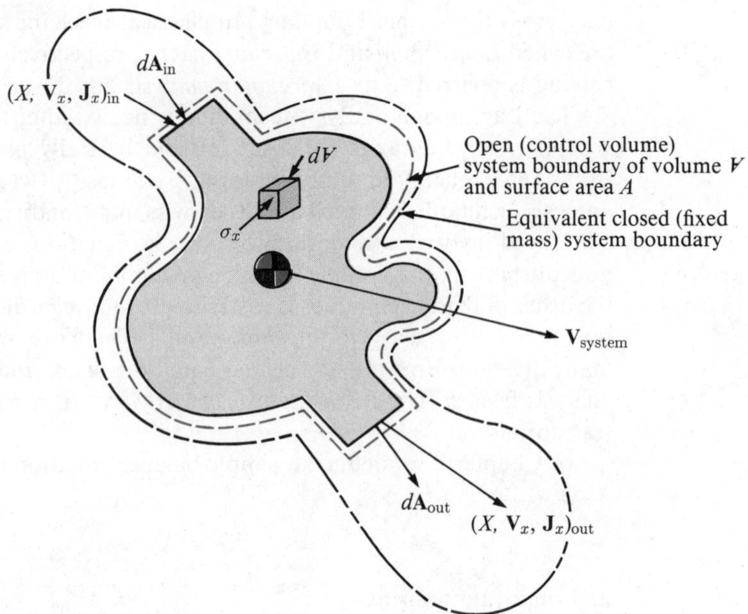

Figure 10.9 Schematic illustrating the vector quantities of Eqs. 10.24, 10.25, and 10.26, and the difference between the open and equivalent closed systems.

difference between the differentiation operation for a closed system and that for an open system we must create a new notation that acknowledges this difference.[4] Therefore, let

$$\dot{X}_G = \frac{DX}{Dt} = \text{the rate of gain of } X \text{ by a closed (Lagrangian) system}$$

where we have used the operator symbol D/Dt to denote a fixed mass or closed system time derivative. The same time derivative measured in an open system is given by the Reynolds transport theorem as

$$\underbrace{\frac{DX}{Dt}}_{\substack{\text{Closed system}\\ \text{(Lagrangian) rate}}} = \underbrace{\int_{\forall} \frac{\partial(\rho x)}{\partial t}\, d\forall + \int_A \rho x(\mathbf{V} \cdot d\mathbf{A})}_{\substack{\text{Open system}\\ \text{(Eulerian) rate}}} \tag{10.24}$$

where $x = X/m$ is the intensive (specific) version of X, and $\mathbf{V}$ is the velocity vector of x as it crosses the surface area element $d\mathbf{A}$ as shown in Figure 10.9. The trans-

4. In fluid mechanics texts this derivative is often given a special name such as the *material derivative* or the *substantial derivative.*

port and production rate terms on the right side of Eq. 2.12 can be generalized for a *closed system* to be of the form

$$\dot{X}_T = -\int_A \mathbf{J}_x \cdot d\mathbf{A} \tag{10.25}$$

and

$$\dot{X}_P = \int_{\mathcal{V}} \sigma_x \, d\mathcal{V} \tag{10.26}$$

where $\mathbf{J}_x$ is the flux (flow per unit area per unit time) of x through the area element $d\mathbf{A}$, and σ_x is the local production rate per unit volume of x inside the volume element $d\mathcal{V}$. Note that the closed and open systems described by the Reynolds transport theorem do not have the same system boundary and in fact are not the same physical system. A closed system that is to be considered equivalent to a given open system must be much larger than the open system. It must be large enough to include *all* the mass that will cross the boundary of the open system during the analysis period, and it is therefore always much larger than the open system it emulates. Consequently, equivalent closed systems are generally quite awkward and difficult to define, and it was this characteristic that ultimately provided the motivation for developing the open system (or Eulerian) analysis technique.

Combining Eqs. 10.24, 10.25, and 10.26 into the general rate balance Eq. 2.12 and rearranging it slightly gives the generalized *open system* rate balance equation:

$$\int_V \frac{\partial(\rho x)}{\partial t} \, d\mathcal{V} = -\int_A \mathbf{J}_x \cdot d\mathbf{A} - \int_A \rho x(\mathbf{V} \cdot d\mathbf{A}) + \int_{\mathcal{V}} \sigma_x \, d\mathcal{V} \tag{10.27}$$

In a one-dimensional analysis, ρ, x, $\mathbf{J}_x$, and $\mathbf{V}$ do not vary across their flowstreams and consequently they do not depend upon the cross-sectional area $\mathbf{A}$. In the following equations we denote the *magnitude* of a vector quantity by using the same quantity symbol in italic rather than boldface type. For example, the magnitudes of $\mathbf{V}$, $\mathbf{J}_x$, and $d\mathbf{A}$ are V, J_x, and dA, respectively. Then, in a one-dimensional flow, the following simplifications occur

$$\begin{aligned} \int_A \mathbf{J} \cdot d\mathbf{A} &= -\left(J_x \int_A dA\right)_{\text{in}} + \left(J_x \int_A dA\right)_{\text{out}} \\ &= -\sum_{\text{in}} J_x A + \sum_{\text{out}} J_x A \end{aligned} \tag{10.28}$$

and

$$\begin{aligned} \int_A \rho x(\mathbf{V} \cdot d\mathbf{A}) &= -\left(\rho x V \int_A dA\right)_{\text{in}} + \left(\rho x V \int_A dA\right)_{\text{out}} \\ &= -\sum_{\text{in}} \rho V A x + \sum_{\text{out}} \rho V A x \\ &= -\sum_{\text{in}} \dot{m} x + \sum_{\text{out}} \dot{m} x \end{aligned} \tag{10.29}$$

In Eqs. 10.28 and 10.29 we have used the fact that the inflow area vector always points in a direction opposite to the inflow velocity and flux, while the outflow area vector always points in the same direction as the outflow velocity and flux vectors (see Figure 10.9) so that

$$(\mathbf{J}_x \cdot d\mathbf{A})_{\text{in}} = -(J_x\, dA)_{\text{in}}$$

and

$$(\mathbf{V} \cdot d\mathbf{A})_{\text{in}} = -(V\, dA)_{\text{in}}$$

whereas

$$(\mathbf{J}_x \cdot d\mathbf{A})_{\text{out}} = +(J_x\, dA)_{\text{out}}$$

and

$$(\mathbf{V} \cdot d\mathbf{A})_{\text{out}} = +(V\, dA)_{\text{out}}$$

For our one-dimensional analysis we now require that the system volume $\forall$ not be a function of time; then we can write

$$\int_V \frac{\partial(\rho x)}{\partial t}\, d\forall = \frac{d}{dt}\int_\forall \rho x\, d\forall$$

and from the definitions of ρ and x inside the differential volume $d\forall$ we get

$$\rho x\, d\forall = (dm/d\forall)(dX/dm)\, d\forall = dX$$

so that

$$\frac{d}{dt}\int_\forall \rho x\, d\forall = \frac{d}{dt}\int_\forall dX = \left(\frac{dX}{dt}\right)_{\text{sys}} \tag{10.30}$$

where X_{sys} is the value of dX integrated over the system volume $\forall$. Substituting Eqs. 10.28, 10.29, and 10.30 into Eq. 10.27 gives the complete one-dimensional open system rate balance equation:

$$\underbrace{(dX/dt)_{\text{sys}}}_{\substack{\text{Net rate}\\ \text{of change}\\ \text{of } X \text{ inside}\\ \text{the open}\\ \text{system}}} = \underbrace{\Big(\sum_{\text{in}} J_x A - \sum_{\text{out}} J_x A\Big)}_{\substack{\text{Net ``conduction''}\\ \text{(i.e., non-mass}\\ \text{flow) transport}\\ \text{rate of X into}\\ \text{the open system}}} + \underbrace{\Big(\sum_{\text{in}} \dot{m}x - \sum_{\text{out}} \dot{m}x\Big)}_{\substack{\text{Net mass flow}\\ \text{transport rate}\\ \text{of } X \text{ into the}\\ \text{open system}}} + \underbrace{\int_\forall \sigma_x\, d\forall}_{\substack{\text{Net production}\\ \text{rate of } X \text{ inside}\\ \text{the boundary of}\\ \text{the open system}}} \tag{10.31}$$

If X is a conserved property like mass, energy or momentum, then $\sigma_x = 0$ and the last term on the right side of Eq. 10.31 vanishes. If X is not conserved, like entropy, then a formula must be found for the variation of σ_x inside $\forall$ so that the integration of σ_x over $\forall$ can be carried out as indicated (this is what was done for the entropy production terms discussed in Chapter 5).

Example 10.4

Show that Eq. 10.31 reduces to the standard one-dimensional

a) mass rate balance, Eq. 4.94,

b) energy rate balance, Eqs. 4.90 and 4.91, and

c) entropy rate balance, Eq. 5.78.

Solution

a) For mass, $X = m$, and $x = X/m = m/m = 1$. Mass is conserved so $\sigma_x = \sigma_1 = 0$, and since there are no conduction (i.e., non-mass flow) mechanisms that will move mass across a system boundary, then $J_x = J_1 = 0$. Then Eq. 10.31 reduces to

$$(dm/dt)_{\text{sys}} = \sum_{\text{in}} \dot{m} - \sum_{\text{out}} \dot{m}$$

which is identical to the one-dimensional mass rate balance introduced in Eq. 4.94 of Chapter 4.

b) For energy, $X = E$, and $x = E/m = e$. Energy is conserved, so $\sigma_x = \sigma_e = 0$, and the non-mass flow energy fluxes were identified in Chapter 4 as *heat* and *work*, so $J_e = \dot{q} + \dot{w}$. Then Eq. 10.31 reduces to

$$(dE/dt)_{\text{sys}} = \dot{Q} + \dot{W} + \sum_{\text{in}} \dot{m}e - \sum_{\text{out}} \dot{m}e$$

where

$$\dot{Q} = \sum_{\text{in}} \dot{q}A - \sum_{\text{out}} \dot{q}A \quad \text{and} \quad \dot{W} = \sum_{\text{in}} \dot{W}A - \sum_{\text{out}} \dot{W}A$$

are the *net* heat and work transport rates of energy, and $e = u + V^2/(2g_c) + mgZ/g_c$ is the flowstream specific energy. These results are identical to those for the one-dimensional energy rate balance originally presented in Chapter 4 in Eqs. 4.90 and 4.91.

c) For entropy, $X = S$, and $x = S/m = s$. Entropy is not conserved, so $\sigma_s \neq 0$. The non-mass flow entropy flux was identified in Chapter 5 as $J_s = \dot{q}/T_b$. Then, for an isothermal (i.e., one-dimensional) boundary, Eq. 10.31 reduces to

$$(dS/dt)_{\text{sys}} = \frac{\dot{Q}}{T_b} + \sum_{\text{in}} \dot{m}s - \sum_{\text{out}} \dot{m}s + \dot{S}_P$$

where

$$\dot{Q}/T_b = \sum_{\text{in}} \dot{q}/T_b - \sum_{\text{out}} \dot{q}/T_b$$

is the net non-mass flow entropy transport rate, and

$$\dot{S}_P = \int_{\mathcal{V}} \sigma_s \, d\mathcal{V}$$

is the entropy production rate. These results are identical to those developed in Chapter 5 for the one-dimensional entropy rate balance originally presented in Eq. 5.78.

The Linear Momentum Rate Balance

The linear momentum rate balance (LMRB) for a one-dimensional open system can be easily developed from Eq. 10.31 by letting $X = m\mathbf{V}$, and then $x = m\mathbf{V}/m = \mathbf{V}$. Since momentum is conserved, $\sigma_x = \sigma_\mathbf{V} = 0$. External forces are the source of the non-mass flow momentum transport rate across the system boundary, so the one-dimensional momentum flux, $J_x = J_\mathbf{V}$, is the external force per unit area, or

$$J_\mathbf{V} = (\mathbf{F}_{\text{ext}}/A)g_c$$

Then, Eq. 10.31 gives the LMRB as[5]

$$\frac{d}{dt}(m\mathbf{V})_{\substack{\text{open}\\ \text{system}}} = \sum_{\text{net}} \mathbf{F}_{\text{ext}} g_c + \sum_{\text{in}} \dot{m}\mathbf{V} - \sum_{\text{out}} \dot{m}\mathbf{V} \tag{10.32}$$

where $\sum_{\text{net}} \mathbf{F}_{\text{ext}} g_c$ is the net sum of all the external forces acting on the system. Note that for a closed system, $\dot{m} = 0$ and $m_{\text{closed system}} = \text{constant}$. Then Eq. 10.32 reduces to Newton's second law for a fixed mass closed system

$$\frac{d}{dt}(m\mathbf{V})_{\substack{\text{closed}\\ \text{system}}} = m\left(\frac{d\mathbf{V}}{dt}\right)_{\substack{\text{closed}\\ \text{system}}} = m\mathbf{a}_{\substack{\text{closed}\\ \text{system}}} = \sum_{\text{net}} \mathbf{F}_{\text{ext}} g_c$$

Also, the external forces are normally divided into two categories: **1)** *surface* forces, such as pressure and contact forces, and **2)** *body* forces, such as gravity and magnetic forces. That is,

$$\sum \mathbf{F}_{\text{ext}} = \sum \mathbf{F}_{\text{surface}} + \sum \mathbf{F}_{\text{body}}$$

For a steady state, steady flow, single-inlet, single-outlet open system, Eq. 10.32 further reduces to

LMRB (SS, SF, SI/SO)

$$\sum \mathbf{F}_{\text{ext}} = \dot{m}(\mathbf{V}_{\text{out}} - \mathbf{V}_{\text{in}})/g_c \tag{10.33}$$

5. The vector nature of momentum necessarily causes Eq. 10.32 to be three dimensional. The one-dimensional restriction on this equation only implies that $\mathbf{V}$ and $\mathbf{F}_{\text{ext}}$ are *area-averaged* quantities over the surface of the system. There may, however, be components of $\mathbf{V}$ and $\mathbf{F}_{\text{ext}}$ in each of the three coordinate directions.

Example 10.5 An air jet is used to levitate a 0.005-kg sheet of paper as shown below. The diameter of the jet at the nozzle exit is 0.003 m and it is at atmospheric pressure at 20 °C. Determine the velocity of the jet.

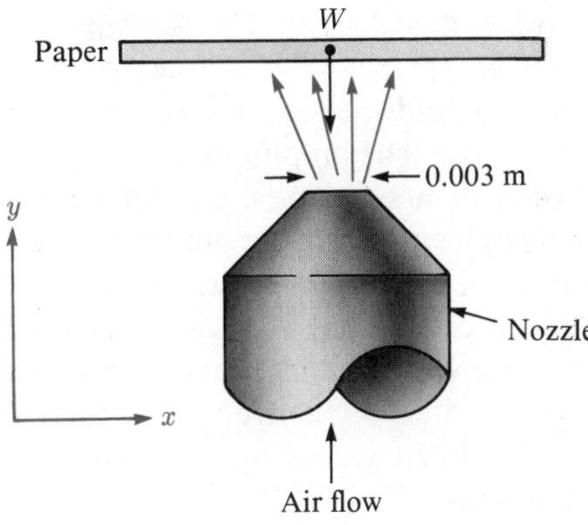

Solution Assume the flow is steady state and steady flow. Then the y component of Eq. 10.33 is

$$F_y = -W = \dot{m}(V_{out} - V_{in})_y/g_c$$

where W is the weight of the paper, given by

$$W = mg/g_c = (0.005\text{ kg})(9.8\text{ m/s}^2)/(1) = 0.049\text{ N}$$

and

$$(V_{out})_y = 0$$

Also, $\dot{m} = \rho AV = \rho\pi D^2V/4$, where

$$\rho = p/RT = [101.3 \times 10^3\text{ kg/(m}\cdot\text{s}^2)]/\{[286\text{ m}^2/(\text{s}^2\cdot\text{K})](293\text{ K})\} = 1.21\text{ kg/m}^3$$

Then,

$$W = \dot{m}(V_{in})_y/g_c = \rho AV_{in}^2/g_c = \rho\pi D^2V_{in}^2/4g_c$$

so

$$V_{in} = \left(\frac{4g_cW}{\rho\pi D^2}\right)^{1/2}$$

$$= \left[\frac{4(1)(0.049\text{ kg}\cdot\text{m/s}^2)}{(1.21\text{ kg/m}^3)(\pi)(0.003\text{ m})^2}\right]^{1/2} = 75.7\text{ m/s}$$

Shock Waves

Shock waves can occur only in compressible substances and are often thought of as strong acoustical (sound) waves. However, they differ from sound waves in two important ways: **1)** they travel much faster than normal sound waves, and **2)** there is a large and nearly discontinuous change in pressure, temperature, and density across a shock wave. The thickness of a shock wave over which these changes occur is typically of the order of 10^{-7} m (4×10^{-6} in) and consequently large property gradients occur across the shock wave that make it very dissipative and irreversible. The amplitude of a large shock wave such as that created by an explosion or a supersonic aircraft decreases nearly with the inverse square of the distance from the source until it weakens sufficiently to become an ordinary sound wave. The *sonic boom* heard at the surface of the earth from a high-altitude supersonic aircraft is the weak acoustical remnants of its shock wave.

Since strong shock waves are highly irreversible they cannot be treated even approximately as isentropic processes. Ordinary sound waves, on the other hand, are very much weaker by comparison and can sometimes be modeled by isentropic processes.

When a shock wave occurs perpendicular (i.e., normal) to the velocity it is called a *normal* shock, and it can be analyzed with the one-dimensional balance equations. A shock wave that is inclined to the direction of flow is called an *oblique* shock, and requires a two- or three-dimensional analysis. We will limit our analysis to normal shock waves in this chapter.

Normal shock waves form as a result of a piling up of pressure waves into a strong compression wave front. A similar phenomenon occurs as gravity waves in the ocean approach a beach. The front of each wave steepens as it approaches the beach, but unlike shock waves it eventually topples over forming a breaker. Shock waves do not topple over, they continue to grow in strength as their velocity increases.

The easiest way to generate normal shock waves for laboratory study is to use a supersonic converging–diverging nozzle. Equation 10.13 gives the pressure profile along the nozzle in terms of the isentropic stagnation pressure p_{os} and the local Mach number $\mathbf{M}$ as

$$p/p_{os} = \left(1 + \frac{k-1}{2}\mathbf{M}^2\right)^{k/(1-k)}$$

This equation is shown schematically along the nozzle in Figure 10.10. When the back pressure p_B is greater than the throat critical pressure p^* given in Eq. 10.19 the Mach number at the throat will be less than 1 and the flow will remain subsonic throughout the entire nozzle with nozzle exit pressure p_{exit} equal to the back pressure, p_B. When p_B is less than p^* the Mach number at the throat will be equal to 1 and the flow will become supersonic in the diverging section of the nozzle. If p_B/p_{os} is between the points *b* and *c* on Figure 10.10, then a normal shock will occur within the diverging section at the point where the flow can isentropically recover to $p_{exit} = p_B$. If we let p_E be the pressure at the exit of the supersonic nozzle when the flow expands isentropically throughout the nozzle (see Figure 10.10), then

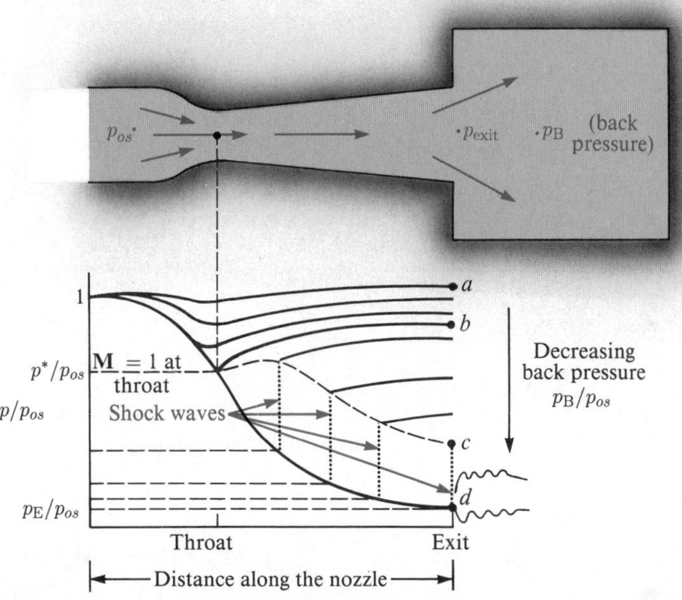

Figure 10.10 The pressure distribution in a converging–diverging nozzle when the upstream stagnation pressure is held constant and the downstream back pressure is decreased. Shock waves occur in the diverging section when the flow is supersonic but the back pressure is not low enough to allow complete expansion to the end of the nozzle.

when p_B/p_{os} is between the points c and d on Figure 10.10 a normal shock will occur at the exit plane of the nozzle and $p_{exit} = p_E < p_B$. Finally, when p_B/p_{os} is below point d on Figure 10.10 then shock waves occur downstream from the nozzle and $p_{exit} = p_E > p_B$.

If we apply the mass, energy, entropy, and linear momentum balances to the normal shock wave system shown in Figure 10.11 we can relate the upstream (x) and downstream (y) properties across the shock. Assuming a steady state, steady

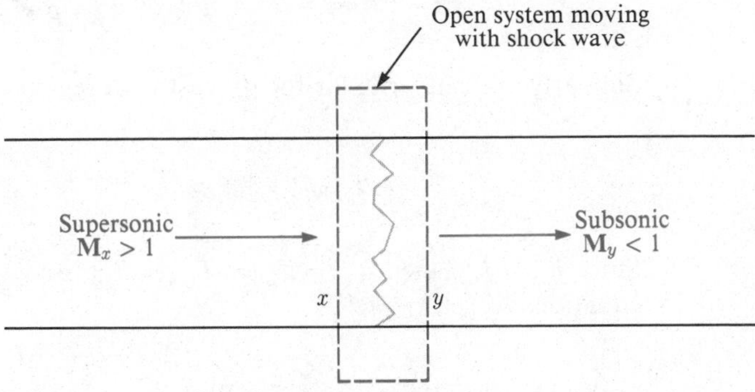

Figure 10.11 A normal shock wave moving at supersonic velocity in a constant area adiabatic duct. The coordinate system here is fixed to the shock wave.

flow, single-inlet, single-outlet, adiabatic and aergonic system, the mass, energy, and linear momentum rate balances give

MRB (SS, SF, SI, SO)

$$\dot{m}_x = \rho_x A_x V_x = \dot{m}_y = \rho_y A_y V_y$$

but since $A_x = A_y = A$ in Figure 10.11, then

$$\rho_x V_x = \rho_y V_y$$

Now, $\rho = p/RT$, so

$$\rho_x V_x = \frac{p_x V_x}{RT_x} = \frac{kg_c p_x V_x}{kg_c RT_x} = p_x M_x \left(\frac{kg_c}{RT_x}\right)^{1/2}$$

and

$$\rho_y V_y = p_y \mathbf{M}_y \left(\frac{kg_c}{RT_y}\right)^{1/2} = \rho_x V_x$$

or

$$p_x \mathbf{M}_x / \sqrt{T_x} = p_y \mathbf{M}_y / \sqrt{T_y} \tag{10.34}$$

ERB (SS, SF, SI, SO, A, A)

$$h_{ox} = h_x + V_x^2/(2g_c) = h_y + V_y^2/(2g_c) = h_{oy}$$

and for an ideal gas with constant specific heats,

$$h_{ox} - h_x = c_p(T_{ox} - T_x) = V_x^2/(2g_c)$$

Since $c_p = kR/(k-1)$ for constant specific heat ideal gases, then

$$T_{ox}/T_x = T_{osx}/T_x = 1 + \frac{k-1}{2}\left(\frac{V_x^2}{kg_c RT_x}\right) = 1 + \frac{k-1}{2}\mathbf{M}_x^2$$

Similarly, we can write for the downstream region that

$$T_{oy}/T_y = T_{osy}/T_y = 1 + \frac{k-1}{2}\mathbf{M}_y^2$$

Since $h_{ox} = h_{oy}$, then $T_{ox} = T_{oy} = T_{osx} = T_{osy}$ and we can divide the above two equations to get

$$T_x/T_y = \frac{1 + \frac{k-1}{2}\mathbf{M}_y^2}{1 + \frac{k-1}{2}\mathbf{M}_x^2} \tag{10.35}$$

LMRB (SS, SF, SI, SO)

$$F_x - F_y = (p_x - p_y)A = \dot{m}(V_y - V_x)/g_c$$

or

$$\begin{aligned} p_x - p_y &= (\dot{m}/A)(V_y - V_x)/g_c \\ &= (\rho_y V_y^2 - \rho_x V_x^2)/g_c \end{aligned}$$

Now $\rho = p/RT$, so

$$\begin{aligned} p_x - p_y &= kp_y V_y^2/(kg_c RT_y) - kp_x V_x^2/(kg_c RT_x) \\ &= k(p_y \mathbf{M}_y^2 - p_x \mathbf{M}_x^2) \end{aligned}$$

or

$$p_x/p_y = \frac{1 + k\mathbf{M}_y^2}{1 + k\mathbf{M}_x^2} \tag{10.36}$$

Substituting Eqs. 10.35 and 10.36 into Eq. 10.34 yields an equation for $\mathbf{M}_x$, $\mathbf{M}_y$, and k which can be solved to give

$$\mathbf{M}_y^2 = \frac{(k-1)\mathbf{M}_x^2 + 2}{2k\mathbf{M}_x^2 + 1 - k} \tag{10.37}$$

Because Eq. 10.34 is symmetrical in x and y, then the x, y subscripts in Eq. 10.37 can be interchanged to produce an equation for $\mathbf{M}_x$ in terms of $\mathbf{M}_y$ and k.

Equations 10.35, 10.36, and 10.37 have been tabulated for air ($k = 1.4$) in Appendix C.19. The reader is encouraged to use this table when its direct entry is convenient. However, rather than interpolating for nondirect entry values, the equations given above can be used to make accurate direct calculations since they were used to generate the table.

Finally, an entropy rate balance on the shock wave gives

SRB (SS, SF, SI/SO, A)

$$\dot{S}_P = \dot{m}(s_y - s_x) \geq 0$$

So,

$$\begin{aligned} \dot{S}_P/\dot{m} = s_y - s_x &= c_p \ln(T_y/T_x) - R \ln(p_y/p_x) \\ &= R \ln[(p_x/p_y)(T_y/T_x)^{k/(k-1)}] \geq 0 \end{aligned} \tag{10.38}$$

Therefore,

$$p_x/p_y \geq (T_x/T_y)^{k/(k-1)}$$

and by substituting Eqs. 10.35 and 10.36 into this relation it can be shown that $\mathbf{M}_x \geq \mathbf{M}_y$. Consequently the second law of thermodynamics stipulates that shock

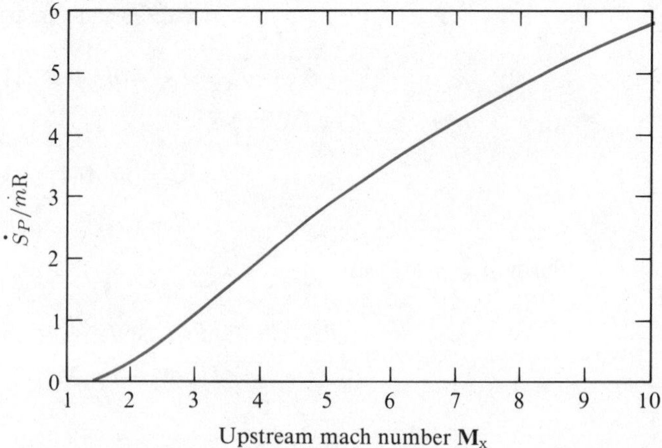

Figure 10.12 A plot of Eq. 10.38 for air ($k = 1.4$) utilizing Eqs. 10.35, 10.36 and 10.37. Note that the second law of thermodynamics requires that $\dot{S}_P/\dot{m}R \geq 0$ for all processes.

waves can only occur in supersonic flows, from $\mathbf{M}_x \geq 1$ to $\mathbf{M}_y \leq 1$, and can never occur in subsonic flows. Equation 10.38 is shown in Figure 10.12 for air ($k = 1.4$).

Example 10.6

A spacecraft directional control thrustor is a converging–diverging nozzle that uses high-pressure and high-temperature air. The air enters with isentropic stagnation properties of 7.0 MPa and 2000 °C. The throat diameter is 0.02 m and the diameter of the exit of the diverging section is 0.10 m. Determine

a) the mass flow rate required for supersonic flow in the diverging section,

b) the Mach number, pressure, and temperature at the exit of the diverging section with this mass flow rate, and

c) the outside back pressure required to produce a standing normal shock wave at the exit of the diverging section.

Solution

a) To have supersonic flow in the diverging section of a converging–diverging nozzle the throat must have a Mach number of unity (i.e., be choked). Therefore, the mass flow rate will be the maximum value for air in SI units given by Eq. 10.22*c*, or

$$\dot{m} = \dot{m}_{\text{max}} = 0.0404(p_{\text{os}}A^*/\sqrt{T_{\text{os}}})$$

where $A^* = \pi(D^*)^2/4 = \pi(0.02\text{ m})^2/4 = 3.142 \times 10^{-4}\text{ m}^2$. Then,

$$\dot{m} = \frac{[0.0404\text{ kg}\cdot\sqrt{\text{K}}/(\text{N}\cdot\text{s})](7 \times 10^6\text{ N/m}^2)(3.142 \times 10^{-4}\text{ m}^2)}{\sqrt{273 + 2000\text{ K}}} = 1.864\text{ kg/s}$$

b) Here, $A_{exit}/A^* = (D_{exit}/D^*)^2 = (0.1/0.02)^2 = 25.0$. Then Eq. 10.23 can be inverted to find $\mathbf{M}_{exit}$, and then p_{exit} and T_{exit} can then be found from Eqs. 10.13 and 10.12, respectively. Unless these equations are programmed into a computer this can be a tedious set of calculations. Appendix C.18 was created to eliminate this tedium by tabulating these equations. The above area ratio is a direct entry into this appendix, so we will use it, and read

$$\mathbf{M}_{exit} = 5.0,$$

$$p_{exit}/p_{os} = 1.89 \times 10^{-3}, \text{ and}$$

$$T_{exit}/T_{os} = 0.16667.$$

Then, $p_{exit} = (1.89 \times 10^{-3})(7 \times 10^6 \text{ N/m}^2) = 13.23 \text{ kN/m}^2$ and

$$T_{exit} = (0.16667)(273 + 2000 \text{ K}) = 378.8 \text{ K}$$

The velocity of sound at the exit is

$$c_{exit} = \sqrt{kg_c R T_{exit}} = \sqrt{(1.4)(1)[286 \text{ m}^2/(\text{s}^2 \cdot \text{K})](378.8 \text{ K})} = 389.5 \text{ m/s}$$

then, $V_{exit} = c_{exit}\mathbf{M}_{exit} = (389.5 \text{ m/s})(5.0) = 1947 \text{ m/s}$.

c) An exit plane shock wave is illustrated by region c to d in Figure 10.10. The required back pressure p_B here is equal to the downstream isentropic stagnation pressure p_{osy} necessary to cause a normal shock to occur in the exit plane. Then $\mathbf{M}_x = 5.0$, $p_x = 13.23 \text{ kN/m}^2$, and $T_x = 378.8$ K. The downstream Mach number $\mathbf{M}_y$ can be found from Eq. 10.37, and then p_y can be found from Eq. 10.36. Finally, Eq. 10.13 can be used to find p_{osy}. However, Appendix C.19 is a tabular version of these equations, and at $\mathbf{M}_x = 5.0$ we again have a direct entry. From this appendix we find that

$$\mathbf{M}_y = 0.415 \qquad p_{osy}/p_{ox} = 0.06172$$

$$p_y/p_x = 29.000 \qquad p_{osy}/p_x = 32.654$$

$$T_y/T_x = 5.800$$

Therefore, the required back pressure p_B is

$$p_B = p_{osy} = (0.06172)p_{ox} = (0.06172)(7 \times 10^3 \text{ kN/m}^2) = 432 \text{ kN/m}^2$$

or, alternatively,

$$p_B = p_{osy} = (32.654)p_x = (32.654)(13.23 \text{ kN/m}^2) = 432 \text{ kN/m}^2$$

Example 10.7 Air enters a converging–diverging nozzle with isentropic stagnation properties of 3.0 atm and 20 °C, and exhausts into the atmosphere. The exit to throat area ratio for the nozzle is 2.00. Determine the pressure, temperature and velocity at the exit.

Solution We are given the upstream isentropic stagnation state of 3.0 atm, 20 °C and a back pressure of 1.0 atm. In order to find the conditions in the exit plane we must first determine whether or not a shock wave occurs inside the diverging section of the nozzle. This will occur if $p_E < p_B < p^*$ where, from Eq. 10.19,

$$p^* = p_{os}\left(\frac{2}{k+1}\right)^{k/(k-1)} = (3.0 \text{ atm})(0.5283) = 1.585 \text{ atm}$$

and from Eq. 10.13,

$$p_E = p_{os}\{1 + [(k-1)/2]\mathbf{M}_E^2\}^{k/(1-k)}$$

Since we are given $A_{exit}/A^* = A_E/A^* = 2.00$ we can find $\mathbf{M}_E$ by inverting Eq. 10.23b. However, in this case it is again much easier to use Appendix C.18 for this area ratio and read (approximately), $\mathbf{M}_E = 2.20$ and $p_E/p_{os} = 0.09352$. Then, $p_E = 0.09352$ (3.0 atm) $= 0.281$ atm. Thus $p_E < p_B < p^*$ here and a normal shock must occur somewhere in the diverging section of the nozzle.

Since we now know that a shock wave occurs, we also need to know whether or not it occurs in the exit plane of the nozzle. We could find $\mathbf{M}_x$ from the upstream and downstream isentropic stagnation pressures from the relation,

$$p_{osy}/p_{osx} = (p_{osy}/p_y)(p_y/p_x)(p_x/p_{osx})$$

by using Eqs. 10.13, 10.36 and 10.37. This results in the equation

$$\frac{p_{osy}}{p_{osx}} = \frac{\left[\dfrac{k+1}{2}\mathbf{M}_x^2 \Big/ \left(1 + \dfrac{k-1}{2}\mathbf{M}_x^2\right)\right]^{k/(k-1)}}{\left(\dfrac{2k}{k+1}\mathbf{M}_x^2 - \dfrac{k-1}{k+1}\right)^{1/(k-1)}} = \frac{1.0}{3.0} = 0.3333$$

However, it is quite tedious to solve this equation for $\mathbf{M}_x$ without using a computer, and since we have a direct entry in Appendix C.19 at this value of p_{osy}/p_{osx}, we will use this appendix in our solution. From Appendix C.19 at $p_{osy}/p_{osx} = 0.3333$ we read $\mathbf{M}_x \approx 2.98$ and $\mathbf{M}_y \approx 0.476$. From Appendix C.18 at $\mathbf{M} = \mathbf{M}_x = 2.98$ we find that $A/A^* \approx 4.16$. But our nozzle only has an $A_e/A^* = 2.00$, so the shock wave must be in the exit plane, and therefore $p_{exit} = p_E = 0.281$ atm, $\mathbf{M}_{exit} = \mathbf{M}_E = 2.20$, and $T_{exit} = 0.5082(293) = 148.9$ K. The pressure readjustment from p_{exit} to p_B occurs outside the exit (see region c to d in Figure

10.10). Finally, the exit velocity is given by,

$$V_{\text{exit}} = \mathbf{M}_{\text{exit}} c_{\text{exit}} = \mathbf{M}_{\text{exit}} \sqrt{k g_c R T_{\text{exit}}}$$
$$= (2.2)\sqrt{(1.4)(1)[286\ \text{m}^2/(\text{s}^2\cdot\text{K})](148.9\ \text{K})} = 537.2\ \text{m/s}$$

Nozzle and Diffuser Efficiencies

Inefficiencies in nozzles and diffusers result from irreversibilities that occur within their boundaries. Shock waves and fluid friction (viscosity) in the wall boundary layer are the most common types of irreversibilities that occur. If a nozzle or diffuser is not designed with exactly the correct wall contour, oblique shocks, boundary layer separation, and turbulence will destroy the nozzle's performance.

Because nozzle and diffuser performance depends upon their internal irreversibilities, we can base their efficiency equation on the second law of thermodynamics by taking the *isentropic* nozzle and diffuser to be 100% efficient. Then, since the function of a nozzle is to convert pressure (or thermal energy in the case of an ideal gas) into kinetic energy, we can define its efficiency η_N to be (see Figure 10.13)

$$\eta_N = \frac{\text{actual exit kinetic energy}}{\text{isentropic exit kinetic energy at the actual exit pressure}}$$
$$= \frac{(V_{\text{exit}}^2/2g_c)_{\text{actual}}}{(V_{\text{exit}}^2/2g_c)_{\text{isentropic}}} = \frac{(V_{\text{exit}}^2/2g_c)_{\text{actual}}}{(h_{\text{inlet}} - h_{\text{exit}})_s} = \frac{(V_{\text{exit}}^2/2g_c)_{\text{actual}}}{c_p(T_{\text{inlet}} - T_{\text{exit}})_s}$$
$$= \frac{\dfrac{k-1}{2}(V_{\text{exit}}/c_{\text{inlet}})^2}{1 - (p_{\text{exit}}/p_{\text{inlet}})^{(k-1)/k}} \tag{10.39}$$

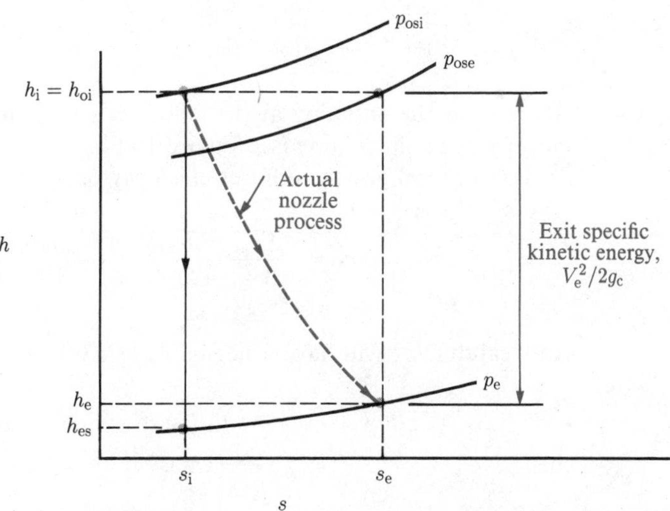

Figure 10.13 The thermodynamic process path of a nozzle plotted on *h-s* coordinates.

If the inlet velocity is very slow then the entrance can be taken to be the isentropic stagnation state, or $p_{\text{inlet}} = p_{\text{os}}$ and $c_{\text{inlet}} = c_{\text{os}} = \sqrt{kg_cRT_{\text{os}}}$. The p_{exit} and V_{exit} terms in Eq. 10.39 are the *actual* exit pressure and exit velocity values that must be determined from measurements on the actual nozzle. Typical efficiencies for well-designed nozzles vary from 0.90 to 0.99 at high flow rates.

We can also define a *nozzle velocity coefficient* C_v for the nozzle in a similar way:

$$C_v = \frac{\text{actual exit velocity}}{\text{isentropic exit velocity at the actual exit pressure}} = \sqrt{\eta_{\text{N}}} \tag{10.40}$$

Also, it is common to define a *nozzle discharge coefficient* C_{d} as

$$C_{\text{d}} = \frac{\text{actual mass flow rate}}{\text{isentropic mass flow rate}} = \frac{\dot{m}_{\text{actual}}}{\dot{m}_{\text{isentropic}}} = \frac{(\rho AV)_{\text{actual}}}{(\rho AV)_{\text{isentropic}}} \tag{10.41}$$

Typical nozzle discharge coefficients run from 0.60 for sharp edged nozzles (i.e., orifices) at low flow rates to 0.99 for properly designed nozzles at high flow rates.

The function of a diffuser, on the other hand, is to convert kinetic energy into pressure. Therefore we define its efficiency η_{D} as

$$\eta_{\text{D}} = \frac{\text{isentropic enthalpy increase at the actual exit stagnation pressure}}{\text{inlet kinetic energy}} = \frac{h_{\text{es}} - h_{\text{inlet}}}{V_{\text{inlet}}^2/(2g_c)} = \frac{h_{\text{es}} - h_{\text{inlet}}}{h_{\text{oi}} - h_{\text{inlet}}}$$

where h_{es} is the enthalpy at the actual exit stagnation pressure but at the same entropy as the inlet state (see Figure 10.14).

For an ideal gas the diffuser efficiency becomes

$$\eta_{\text{D}} = \frac{c_p(T_{\text{es}} - T_{\text{inlet}})}{V_{\text{inlet}}^2/(2g_c)} = \frac{T_{\text{inlet}}(T_{\text{es}}/T_{\text{inlet}} - 1)}{V_{\text{inlet}}^2/(2g_c c_p)}$$

An ideal diffuser will have a negligible exit velocity, then $p_{\text{es}} = p_{\text{ose}}$ and

$$T_{\text{es}}/T_{\text{inlet}} = (p_{\text{es}}/p_{\text{inlet}})^{(k-1)/k} = (p_{\text{ose}}/p_{\text{inlet}})^{(k-1)/k}$$

then

$$\eta_{\text{D}} = \frac{(p_{\text{ose}}/p_{\text{inlet}})^{(k-1)/k} - 1}{(k-1)\mathbf{M}_{\text{inlet}}^2/2}$$

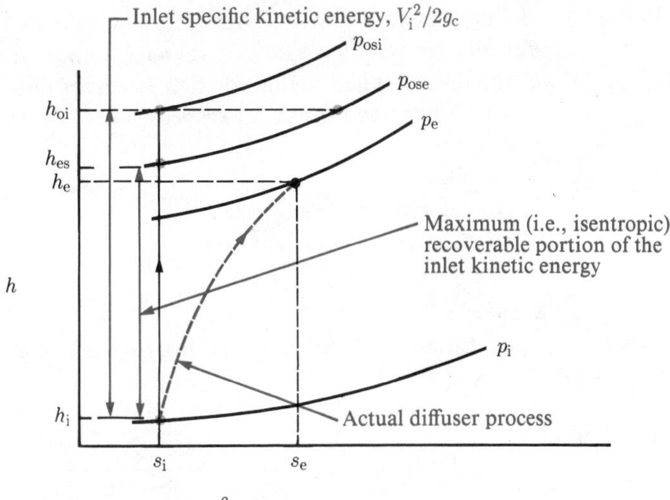

Figure 10.14 Thermodynamic process path of a diffuser plotted on *h-s* coordinates.

Now, from Eq. 10.13

$$p_{\text{inlet}} = p_{\text{osi}}\left(1 + \frac{k-1}{2}\mathbf{M}_{\text{inlet}}^2\right)^{-k/(k-1)}$$

so that the diffuser efficiency can be written in terms of the inlet Mach number and the isentropic stagnation pressure ratio as

$$\eta_{\text{D}} = \frac{\left(1 + \frac{k-1}{2}\mathbf{M}_{\text{inlet}}^2\right)(p_{\text{ose}}/p_{\text{osi}})^{(k-1)/k} - 1}{(k-1)\mathbf{M}_{\text{inlet}}^2/2} \tag{10.42}$$

Therefore, for a constant isentropic stagnation pressure ratio, the diffuser efficiency *decreases* as the inlet Mach number *increases*, asymptotically approaching the value $(p_{\text{ose}}/p_{\text{osi}})^{(k-1)/k}$ as the inlet Mach number goes to infinity.

A more direct measure of a diffusers ability to convert kinetic energy into pressure is the *diffuser pressure recovery coefficient* C_{p} defined as

$$C_{\text{p}} = \frac{\text{actual diffuser pressure rise}}{\text{isentropic diffuser pressure rise}}$$

$$= \frac{(p_{\text{exit}})_{\text{actual}} - p_{\text{inlet}}}{p_{\text{osi}} - p_{\text{inlet}}} \tag{10.43}$$

Because of flow separation from the diffuser wall, C_{p} values are typically around 0.6.

Example 10.8 Helium enters a newly designed test nozzle at 456.2 kN/m^2 and 283.7 K with a negligible velocity. The exit velocity, temperature and pressure are measured at the instant when the nozzle first becomes choked and found to be 474.8 m/s, 370.4 kN/m^2, and 260.1 K, respectively. For these conditions, determine the nozzle's

a) efficiency,
b) velocity coefficient, and
c) discharge coefficient.

Solution

a) Equation 10.39 gives the nozzle's efficiency η_N as

$$\eta_N = \frac{\frac{k-1}{2}(V_{exit}/c_{inlet})^2}{1-(p_{exit}/p_{inlet})^{(k-1)/k}}$$

For helium, $k = 1.67$ and $R = 2.077$ kJ/kg·K, and since the flow enters the nozzle with a negligible inlet velocity, we can take $T_{inlet} \approx T_{osi}$ and $p_{inlet} \approx p_{osi}$. Then

$$c_{inlet} \approx c_{osi} = \sqrt{(1.67)(1)[2077\ \mathrm{m^2/(s^2 \cdot K)}](283.7\ \mathrm{K})} = 992\ \mathrm{m/s}$$

and

$$\eta_N = \frac{\frac{0.67}{2}(474.8/992)^2}{1-(370.4/456.2)^{0.67/1.67}} = 0.957$$

b) Equation 10.40 quickly gives the nozzle's velocity coefficient C_v as

$$C_v = \sqrt{\eta_N} = \sqrt{0.957} = 0.978$$

c) The nozzle's discharge coefficient C_d is determined from Eq. 10.41 as

$$C_d = \frac{(\rho A V)_{actual}}{(\rho A V)_{isentropic}} = \frac{(\rho_e V_e)_{actual}}{(\rho_e V_e)_{isentropic}}$$

Now,

$$(\rho_{exit})_{actual} = p_{exit}/RT_{exit} = \frac{370.4\ \mathrm{kN/m^2}}{[2.077\ \mathrm{kN \cdot m/(kg \cdot K)}](260.1\ \mathrm{K})} = 0.686\ \mathrm{kg/m^3}$$

Since the flow is choked, $\mathbf{M}_{exit} = 1.0$, and the isentropic exit temperature and density can be determined from Eqs. 10.18 and 10.20 as

$$(T_{exit})_s = T^* = T_{os}[2/(k+1)] = (283.7)[2/2.67] = 212.5\ \mathrm{K}$$

and

$$(\rho_{\text{exit}})_s = \rho_{\text{os}}[2/(k+1)]^{1/(k-1)} = (p_{\text{os}}/RT_{\text{os}})[2/(k+1)]^{1/(k-1)}$$
$$= \frac{(456.2\ \text{kN/m}^2)(2/2.67)^{1/0.67}}{(2.077\ \text{kN}\cdot\text{m/(kg}\cdot\text{K))}(283.7\ \text{K})} = 0.503\ \text{kg/m}^3$$

and

$$(V_{\text{exit}})_s = c_{\text{exit}}|_s = \sqrt{kg_c R(T_c)|_s}$$
$$= \sqrt{(1.67)(1)(2077\ \text{m}^2/(\text{s}^2\cdot\text{K}))(212.5\ \text{K})} = 858.5\ \text{m/s}$$

Then,

$$C_d = \frac{(0.686\ \text{kg/m}^3)(474.8\ \text{m/s})}{(0.503\ \text{kg/m}^3)(858.5\ \text{m/s})} = 0.754$$

Summary

In this chapter we have investigated the basic phenomena that occur in high-speed compressible flows of gases and vapors. New concepts such as the stagnation state, Mach number, choked flow, and shock waves were introduced to fully explain the basic characteristics of these flows. We focused our attention on converging–diverging nozzle and diffuser flow geometries because of their industrial value and their ability to generate supersonic flows and shock waves. Finally, we considered the overall performance of nozzles and diffusers in terms of their actual operating efficiencies.

We also introduced the Reynolds transport theorem in this chapter. This allowed us to generalize our open system balance concept and subsequently to easily develop a linear momentum rate balance for open systems.

Selected References

Anderson, J. D. *Modern Compressible Flow.* New York: McGraw-Hill, 1982.

Holman, J. P. *Thermodynamics*, 3d ed. New York: McGraw-Hill, 1980.

Janna, W. S. *Introduction to Fluid Mechanics.* Monterey, CA.: Brooks/Cole, 1983.

Reynolds, W. C., and Perkins, H. C. *Engineering Thermodynamics*, 2d ed. New York: McGraw-Hill, 1977.

Roberson, J. A., and Crowe, C. T. *Engineering Fluid Mechanics*, 2d ed. Boston: Houghton Mifflin, 1980.

Shapiro, A. H. *The Dynamics and Thermodynamics of Compressible Fluid Flow.* New York: Ronald, 1958.

Van Wylen, G. J., and Sonntag, R. E. *Fundamentals of Classical Thermodynamics*, 3d ed. New York: Wiley, 1986.

Chapter Ten Problems

1. Explain the difference between T_o and T_{os}.
2. Explain why we use both symbols T_o and T_{os}, but use only p_{os} and do not refer to p_o at all.

3. The absolute maximum exit velocity from any type of nozzle can be obtained by multiplying Eq. 10.2 by T and then setting $T = 0$ R. Then

$$(V_{\text{exit}})_{\max} = \sqrt{2g_c c_p T_o} = \sqrt{2g_c c_p T_{os}}$$

Determine the absolute maximum exit velocity for the nozzle in Example 10.2, and determine the percentage of this value achieved by the actual exit velocity.

4. Saturated water vapor at 150 °C enters an isentropic converging nozzle with a negligible velocity and exits at 0.3 MPa. Determine the exit quality, temperature, and velocity. Do not assume ideal gas behavior.

5. Air flows in a circular tube with a velocity of 275 ft/s at a temperature of 103 °F and a pressure of 175 psig. Determine its stagnation pressure and temperature.

6. Calculate the isentropic stagnation temperature and pressure on your hand as you hold it outside the window of an automobile traveling at 55 mph on a day when the static temperature and pressure are 70 °F and 14.7 psia.

7. Steam at 600 °F and 200 psia is traveling at 1500 ft/s. Determine the isentropic stagnation temperature and pressure of the steam by

a) assuming steam to be an ideal gas, and

b) using the steam tables (or Mollier diagram or computer program).

8. A steam jet with a static pressure and temperature of 10 MPa and 400 °C has a velocity of 750 m/s. Determine the isentropic stagnation pressure and temperature of the jet. Do not assume ideal gas behavior.

9. Using Eq. 10.9 show that the speed of sound is infinite in an incompressible substance.

10. If the speed of sound in saturated liquid water at 90 °C is 1530 m/s, determine the *isentropic compressibility* α of the water, where

$$\alpha = -\frac{1}{v}\left(\frac{\partial v}{\partial p}\right)_s$$

11. Determine the Mach number of a meteor traveling at 5000 m/s through still air at 0 °C.

12. Determine the Mach number of a bullet traveling at 3000 ft/s through still air at 70 °F.

13. The rotor of an axial flow air compressor has a diameter of 2.3 ft. What is the maximum rpm of the rotor such that its blade tips do not exceed the local sonic velocity when the air in the compressor is at 150 °F?

14. Determine the stagnation temperature and Mach number of carbon dioxide gas flowing in a 0.01 m diameter circular tube at a rate of 0.1 kg/s. The temperature and pressure are 30 °C and 0.5 MPa.

15. The isentropic stagnation–static property formula given in Eqs. 10.12–10.14 and 10.18–10.20 are valid only for ideal gases. In Chapter 6 the conditions under which steam behaves as an ideal gas were discussed (steam gas). Suppose steam at 4.0 MPa, 400 °C is to be expanded through a converging nozzle under choked flow conditions. Use Eq. 10.18 to calculate T^* and then use the steam tables (or Molier diagram or computer program) with this value of T^* and $s^* = s_{os}$ to find p^* and $\rho^* = 1/v^*$. Then compare these values with the ones calculated from Eqs. 10.19 and 10.20.

16. A nozzle is to be designed to accelerate the flow of air from a Mach number of 0.1 to 1.0. Determine the inlet to exit area ratio of the nozzle assuming isentropic flow.

17. A diffuser is to be designed to reduce the Mach number of air from 0.9 to 0.1. Assuming isentropic flow, determine the exit to inlet area ratio of the diffuser.

18. Argon escapes into the atmosphere at 0.101325 MPa from a 1.0-m^3 storage tank initially at 5.0 MPa and 25 °C through a converging–diverging nozzle with a throat area of 0.001 m^2.

a) Is the flow through the nozzle initially choked?
b) If so, at what tank pressure will it unchoke?
c) How long will it take to unchoke if the tank is maintained at 25 °C?

19. Air at 100 psia and 70 °F enters a converging nozzle with a negligible velocity and is expanded isentropically until the exit temperature is 32 °F. Determine the exit Mach number and pressure.

20. Air at 150 kPa, 100 °C enters a converging nozzle with a negligible velocity and is expanded isentropically until the exit pressure reaches 101 kPa. Determine the exit Mach number and temperature.

21. 1.86 kg/s of air flows through a converging–diverging supersonic wind tunnel whose reservoir isentropic stagnation conditions are 18 atm at 300 K, and whose exit Mach number is 4.8. If the reservoir isentropic stagnation pressure is raised to 20 atm at the same temperature, find the new mass flow rate and exit Mach number if the exit pressure remains constant.

22. Air enters a converging–diverging isentropic nozzle at 10 MPa and 500 K with a negligible velocity, and is accelerated to a Mach number of 4.5. Determine the static temperature, pressure, and density at
a) the throat, and
b) the exit.
c) Find the exit to throat area ratio.

23. Low-velocity helium enters a converging–diverging isentropic nozzle at 250 psia and 120 °F. It is accelerated to a Mach number of 2.0 at the exit. Determine the static temperature, pressure, and density at
a) the throat, and
b) the exit.
c) Find the exit to throat area ratio.

24. A converging–diverging nozzle is attached to a compressed air reservoir at 1.0 MPa and 27 °C. There are two positions in the nozzle where $A/A^* = 2.0$, one is in the converging section and the other is in the diverging section. Determine the Mach number, pressure, temperature, density, and velocity at each section.

25. Air at 0.5 MPa and 21 °C enters an isentropic converging–diverging nozzle with a negligible velocity. The exit to throat area ratio of the nozzle is 1.34. If the throat velocity is sonic, determine the exit static pressure, temperature, and Mach number if **a)** the exit is subsonic, and **b)** the exit is supersonic.

26. A supersonic converging–diverging nozzle is to be designed to be attached to a standard machine shop air supply having isentropic stagnation conditions of 100 psia and 70 °F. The throat of the nozzle is to have a diameter of 0.25 in, and the nozzle will exhaust into the atmosphere at 14.7 psia. For an isentropic nozzle, determine
a) the exit Mach number,
b) the exit temperature,
c) the mass flow rate of air through the nozzle, and
d) the exit diameter of the diverging section.

27. Air enters a supersonic isentropic diffuser with a Mach number of 3.0, a temperature of 0 °C, and a pressure of 0.01 MPa. Assuming the air exits with negligible velocity, determine the exit temperature, pressure, and mass flow rate per unit inlet area.

28. Propane at 100 kPa, 40 °C is expanded isentropically through a converging–diverging nozzle that has an exit to throat diameter ratio of 2.0. The propane enters with a negligible velocity but reaches sonic velocity at the throat. Determine the exit temperature, pressure, and Mach number if **a)** the exit pressure is high enough so that the exit velocity is subsonic, and **b)** the exit pressure is low enough so that the exit velocity is supersonic.

29. An isentropic converging–diverging nozzle that will reach a Mach number of 4.0 at the exit when the exit pressure is atmospheric (14.7 psia) and the inlet isentropic stagnation temperature is 70 °F is to be built using air as the working fluid. Determine the required inlet isentropic stagnation pressure, the exit static temperature, and the exit to throat area ratio.

30. Acetylene at 50 psia, 65 °F is accelerated through a converging–diverging nozzle isentropically until it reaches an exit pressure of 14.7 psia. Assuming the flow enters the nozzle with a negligibly small velocity, determine the exit Mach number, temperature, and exit to throat area ratio.

31. Carbon dioxide gas at 13.8 MPa, 20 °C is expanded isentropically through a converging–diverging nozzle until its exit temperature reaches −100 °C. Assuming the flow enters with a negligible inlet velocity, determine the exit Mach number, pressure, and exit to throat area ratio.

32. 800-psia, 600 °F steam expands through an *uninsulated* nozzle to a saturated vapor at 600 psia at a rate of 100 lbm/h. The surface temperature of the nozzle is measured and found to be 450 °F. The entropy production rate of the nozzle is equal to 10% of the magnitude of the heat transport of entropy for the nozzle. The potential energies and the inlet velocity can be neglected, but the exit velocity cannot be neglected. Determine

a) the nozzle's heat transfer rate,
b) the nozzle's entropy production rate,
c) the nozzle's exit velocity, and
d) the exit area of the nozzle.

33. Determine the maximum possible mass flow rate of air through a nozzle with a 0.001-m-diameter throat and inlet stagnation conditions of 5.0 MPa and 30 °C.

34. Determine the maximum flow rate of helium that will pass through a nozzle with a 0.01-m-diameter throat from an upstream stagnation state of 35 MPa at 27 °C.

35. Determine the minimum throat diameter required for a nozzle to pass 0.25 lbm/s of air from a stagnation state of 100 psia at 70 °F.

36. Atmospheric air (14.7 psia, 70 °F) leaks into an initially evacuated 2.0-ft^3 tank through a tiny hole whose area is 10^{-6} ft^2. Determine the time required for the pressure in the tank to rise to 0.5283 times the atmospheric pressure if the air inside the tank is maintained at 70 °F.

37. A tiny leak in a 1.0-m^3 vacuum chamber causes the internal pressure to rise from 1.0 to 10 Pa in 3.77 h when the vacuum pump is not operating. Air leaks into the chamber from the atmosphere at 101.3 kPa, 20 °C, and the air inside the chamber is maintained at 20 °C by heat transfer with the walls. Determine the diameter of the leak hole.

38. An initially evacuated 1.5-ft^3 tank is to be isothermally filled with air to 50 psia and 70 °F. It is to be filled from a very large constant pressure source at 100 psia and 70 °F. The tank is connected to the source by a single 0.125-in-inside-diameter tube. How long will it take to fill the tank?

39. An initially evacuated 0.5-m^3 tank is to be isothermally filled with air to 1.0 MPa and 20 °C. It is to be filled from a very large constant pressure source at 2.5 MPa and 20 °F. The tank is connected to the source by a single 0.001-m-inside-diameter tube. How long will it take to fill the tank?

40. Use the Reynolds transport equation (Eq. 10.31) to develop a formula for a one-dimensional angular momentum rate balance (AMRB), and show that for steady flow with a single inlet and a single outlet the AMRB reduces to

$$\sum \mathbf{T}_{\text{ext}} = \dot{m}[(\mathbf{V} \times \mathbf{r})_{\text{out}} - (\mathbf{V} \times \mathbf{r})_{\text{in}}]/g_c$$

where $\mathbf{T}_{\text{ext}} = \mathbf{F}_{\text{ext}} \times \mathbf{r}$ is the torque vector due to external forces, $\mathbf{V}$ is the average velocity vector, and **r** is the radius vector. *Hint*: Start with $X = m(\mathbf{V} \times \mathbf{r})$ and utilize the conservation of angular momentum principle.

41. Use the linear momentum rate balance (LMRB) to show that the thrust force F of a rocket engine nozzle is given by

$$F = \dot{m}(V_{\text{exit}}/g_c) + (p_{\text{exit}} - p_a)A_{\text{exit}}$$

and show that the absolute maximum thrust produced as $\mathbf{M}_{\text{exit}} \to \infty$ is given by

$$F_{\max} = 2c_p(\rho_{\text{exit}}A_{\text{exit}}T_{os}) + (p_{\text{exit}} - p_a)A_{\text{exit}}$$

(*Hint*: See Problem 3 at the beginning of this problem set.)

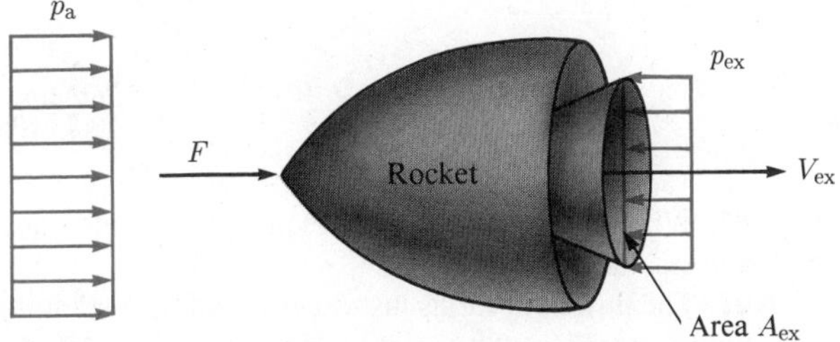

42. The thrust F produced by the supersonic flow in the converging–diverging nozzle of a rocket engine is

$$F = \dot{m}(V_{\text{exit}}/g_c) + (p_{\text{exit}} - p_a)A_{\text{exit}}$$

where p_{exit} and A_{exit} are the pressure and area at the nozzle exit and p_a is the local atmospheric pressure.

a) Suppose the stagnation *temperature* were increased by 100% while maintaining the stagnation and exit pressures and nozzle geometry constant. What would be the percent increase in thrust?

b) Suppose the stagnation *pressure* were increased by 100% while maintaining the stagnation and exit temperatures and nozzle geometry constant. What would be the percent increase in thrust?

(*Hint*: Assume the nozzle is choked in each case, and use air as the exhaust gas.)

43. 0.8 lbm/s of air passes through an insulated converging nozzle that has an inlet to exit area ratio of 1.59 to 1. The nozzle is choked, and the stagnation temperature is 80 °F. The exit pressure is 14.7 psia. Determine the force required to hold the nozzle in place.

44. Determine the horizontal and vertical forces on the stationary turbine blade shown below when it is exposed to a 0.3 kg/s jet of air at 100 m/s.

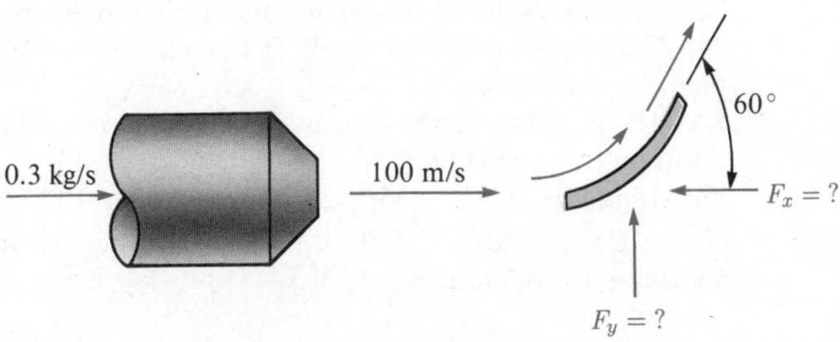

45. Determine the horizontal and vertical restraining forces on the air flow divider shown below.

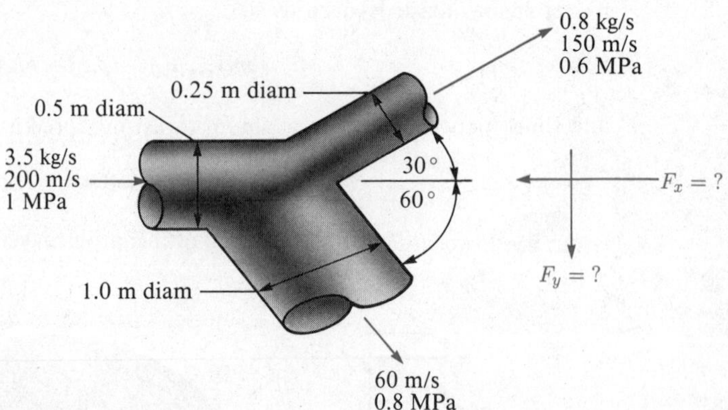

46. What two conditions are required of an ideal gas in order to have $T_{osy} = T_{osx}$ across a normal shock wave?

47. The flow conditions just downstream of a standing normal shock wave in air in a wind tunnel are $\mathbf{M}_y = 0.5$, $p_y = 0.1$ MPa, and $T_y = 450$ K. Determine the flow conditions just upstream of the shock (i.e., $\mathbf{M}_x$, p_x, and T_x).

48. A nuclear blast generates a normal shock wave that travels through still air with a Mach number of 5.0. The pressure and temperature in front of the shock (i.e., downstream) are 0.101 MPa and 20 °C. Determine the air velocity relative to a stationary observer (i.e., the wind velocity), the pressure, and the temperature immediately after the shock wave has passed.

49. The upstream and downstream temperatures were measured across a normal shock wave in air and found to be 306.3 and 717.6 K, respectively. Determine the upstream and downstream Mach numbers and the pressure ratio across the shock wave.

50. The upstream and downstream static pressures were measured across a normal shock wave in air and found to be 0.5 and 3.0 MPa, respectively. Determine the upstream and downstream Mach numbers and the temperature ratio across the shock wave.

51. The upstream and downstream isentropic stagnation pressures were measured across a normal shock wave in air and found to be 124.6801 kPa and 0.101325 MPa, respectively. Determine the upstream and downstream Mach numbers and static pressure and temperature ratios across the shock wave.

52. A converging–diverging nozzle has an exit to throat area ratio of 2.0. The inlet isentropic stagnation air pressure is 2.0 atm and the exit static pressure is 1.0 atm. This flow will be supersonic in a portion of the nozzle, terminating in a normal shock inside the nozzle. Determine the local area ratio A/A^* at which the shock occurs.

53. Air with a velocity of 450 m/s and a static pressure and temperature of 1.0 MPa and 200 K undergoes a normal shock. Determine the velocity and static pressure and temperature after the shock.

54. Use the conservation of mass condition across a shock wave ($\dot{m}_x = \dot{m}_y$) to show that $p_x\mathbf{M}_x(T_x)^{-0.5} = p_y\mathbf{M}_y(T_y)^{-0.5}$.

55. Using Eqs. 10.34, 10.35, and 10.36, derive Eq. 10.37. (*Hint*: Use Eqs. 10.35 and 10.36 to eliminate p_x/p_y and $\sqrt{T_y/T_x}$ in Eq. 10.34. Then square both sides of the resulting equation and solve for $\mathbf{M}_y^2$ in terms of $\mathbf{M}_x^2$.)

56. Using Eqs. 10.13, 10.36, and 10.37, show that

$$\frac{P_{osy}}{P_{osx}} = \left[\frac{(k+1)\mathbf{M}_x^2/2}{1+(k-1)\mathbf{M}_x^2/2}\right]^{k/(k-1)} \times \left[\frac{2k\mathbf{M}_x^2}{k+1} - \frac{k-1}{k+1}\right]^{1/(1-k)}$$

57. It may be shown algebraically that across a normal shock,

$$\frac{V_x}{c^*}\left(\frac{V_y}{c^*}\right) = 1.0$$

where $c^* = \sqrt{kg_cRT^*}$ is the sonic velocity at the throat. Consequently, it has become customary to use the rather awkward notation $\mathbf{M}^* = V/c^*$ so that this relation can be written as $\mathbf{M}_x^*\mathbf{M}_y^* = 1.0$. Appendix C.18 includes an $\mathbf{M}^*$ column for this purpose. Verify this relation for the normal shock data given in Example 10.6 by

a) calculating V_x, V_y, c^* and $V_xV_y/(c^*)^2$, and

b) using Appendix C.18 to calculate $\mathbf{M}_x^*\mathbf{M}_y^*$.

58. It can be shown for a normal shock wave,

$$\frac{\rho_y}{\rho_x} = \frac{V_x}{V_y} = \frac{(k+1)\mathbf{M}_x^2}{(k-1)\mathbf{M}_x^2 + 2}$$

Using this relation determine the maximum density ratio $(\rho_y/\rho_x)_{max}$ that can occur across a normal shock wave in air.

59. Use Eqs. 10.36 and 10.37 to develop the relation

$$\frac{p_y}{p_x} = 1 + \frac{2k}{k+1}(\mathbf{M}_x^2 - 1)$$

60. The *strength* of a normal shock wave is defined as $(p_y - p_x)/p_x$. Using the results of Problem 55, show that this can be written as

$$\frac{p_y - p_x}{p_x} = \left(\frac{2k}{k+1}\right)(\mathbf{M}_x^2 - 1)$$

61. Use Eqs. 10.35 and 10.37 to develop the relation

$$\frac{T_y}{T_x} = \frac{[(k-1)\mathbf{M}_x^2 + 2][2k\mathbf{M}_x^2 - (k-1)]}{[(k+1)\mathbf{M}_x]^2}$$

62. In a supersonic wind tunnel utilizing air similar to that shown in Figure 10.5, the converging–diverging nozzle section has an inlet isentropic stagnation pressure of 3.2 atm. The test section has a Mach number of 2.7, and the converging–diverging diffuser section has an exit pressure of 1.0 atm. Determine the efficiency of the converging–diverging diffuser section.

63. Measurements on a prototype nozzle using air produced inlet and exit temperatures of 70 and 60 °F, respectively while the exit velocity was 325 ft/s. Determine the nozzle's efficiency and velocity coefficient.

64. An air diffuser has inlet and exit isentropic stagnation pressures of 3.5 and 3.1 MPa, respectively. The inlet velocity is 300 m/s and the inlet static temperature is 27 °C. Determine the diffuser efficiency, pressure recovery coefficient, and exit static temperature if the air leaves the diffuser with a negligible velocity.

65. 8.0 kg/s of air flows through a diffuser with an inlet diameter of 0.035 m and a static pressure and temperature of 0.50 MPa and 22 °C. The air exits through a diameter of 0.9 m at static conditions of 0.54 MPa and 25 °C. Determine the diffusers efficiency and pressure recovery coefficient.

66. A diffuser decelerates 15 kg/s of carbon dioxide from 200 m/s at 20 °C and 0.8 MPa to 1.0 m/s at 30 °C and 1.0 MPa. Determine the diffuser efficiency, pressure recovery coefficient, and the inlet and exit areas.

67. Experimental measurements on a new methane fuel nozzle for a furnace produced an exit velocity, pressure, and temperature for methane of 335 m/s, 0.1 MPa, and 0 °C. The upstream stagnation pressure and temperature were 0.15 MPa and 22 °C. Determine

a) the nozzle efficiency,
b) the nozzle's velocity coefficient, and
c) the nozzle's discharge coefficient.

68. A diffuser having an efficiency of 92% is to be used to reduce the velocity of an air stream initially at 450 ft/s, 65 °F, and 50 psia down to a Mach number of 0.1. Calculate

a) the exit to inlet area ratio (A_{exit}/A_{inlet}) required, and
b) the pressure recovery factor for the diffuser.

69. A sonic converging nozzle with a negligible inlet velocity and inlet and throat areas of 2.0 and 0.5 in^2, respectively, has a velocity coefficient of 0.82 when the upstream stagnation pressure and temperature are 100 psia and 70 °F. Determine the thrust produced by the nozzle in atmospheric air.

Design Problems

The following are open ended design problems. The objective is to carry out a preliminary thermal design as indicated. A detailed design with working drawings is not expected unless otherwise specified. These problems do not have specific answers, so each student's design will be unique.

70. Design a converging–diverging nozzle system that can be used to demonstrate supersonic flow in the classroom. Choose a convenient gas, inlet conditions, and exit Mach number. Determine the necessary area ratios, pressures, and temperatures throughout the system.

71. Design an attitude control nozzle for a spacecraft that will produce 50 N of thrust (see Problem 42) using compressed helium gas stored at 50 MPa and 0 °C. Assume the nozzle discharges into a total vacuum. Specify the nozzle inlet, throat, and exit areas as well as the exit Mach number.

72. Design a system that has no moving mechanical parts to cool machine shop compressed air at 0.5 MPa, 25 °C to 0 °C at 0.101 MPa. The outlet velocity must be at least 10 m/s. If possible, fabricate and test your design.

73. Design a small demonstration wind tunnel to be driven from a standard compressed air supply line at 100 psia and 70 °F. Assume that the maximum volumetric air flow rate available from this supply is 10 ft^3/min at 14.7 psia and 70 °F. The wind tunnel test section must be at least 1.0 in in diameter and must reach a Mach number of at least 2.25. The air may be exhausted to the atmosphere, but it first must be decelerated to subsonic velocity to minimize noise generation. If possible, fabricate and test your design.

74. Design a converging–diverging nozzle for a spacecraft thruster that will have an exit Mach number of 5.0 when using compressed helium at 50 MPa, and 0 °C. Assume the nozzle exhausts into a total vacuum. Plot the nozzle diameter vs. length along the nozzle keeping the angle of the diverging wall to less than 10° with the horizontal to prevent flow separation. Show the positions along the nozzle where $\mathbf{M} = 1.0, 2.0, 3.0, 4.0$, and 5.0. Determine the mass flow rate through your nozzle.

75. Design a system that will produce a constant mass flow rate of 0.01 lbm/s of oxygen from one or more 3.0 ft^3 high-pressure storage bottles initially at 2000 psia and 400 R. The oxygen must be delivered at 50 ft/s at 60 °F and 175 psia. The system must operate continuously for 6 months and must have a fail safe backup.

Computer Problems

The following open ended computer problems are designed to be done on a personal computer using BASIC language programming.

76. Write an interactive computer program that will return values for T^*/T_{os}, p^*/p_{os}, and ρ^*/ρ_{os} when k is input in response to a screen prompt.

77. Write an interactive computer program that will return values for p/p_{os}, T/T_{os}, ρ/ρ_{os}, and A/A^* when k and $\mathbf{M}$ are input from the keyboard in response to a screen prompt.

78. Write an interactive computer program that will return values for $\mathbf{M}_y$, p_y/p_x, T_y/T_x, ρ_y/ρ_x, $\dot{S}_P/\dot{m}$, and p_{osy}/p_{osx} when k and $\mathbf{M}_x$ are input from the keyboard in response to a screen prompt.

79. Using Eqs. 10.35, 10.36, 10.37, and 10.38, plot

$$\dot{S}_P/(\dot{m}R) \text{ vs. } \mathbf{M}_x \text{ for } 1 \le \mathbf{M}_x \le 50 \text{ for}$$

a) air,
b) carbon dioxide,
c) methane, and
d) water vapor (use $k = 1.33$ here).

80. *Fanno line*: An analysis of the adiabatic aergonic flow of a *viscous* ideal gas with constant specific heats traveling through a constant area duct can be carried out by combining the continuity equation, the energy rate balance (Eq. 10.1) and the entropy rate balance (using Eq. 5.36) to obtain the following relation:

$$\frac{\dot{S}_P}{(\dot{m}c_v)} = \frac{s_{out} - s_{in}}{c_v} = \ln\left[\frac{T_{out}}{T_{in}}\left(\frac{T_{os} - T_{out}}{T_{os} - T_{in}}\right)^{(k-1)/2}\right] \ge 0$$

A plot of this function is called the Fanno line for the flow. Plot T_{out} vs. $\dot{S}_P/(\dot{m}c_v)$ for air using $0 \le T_{out} \le T_{in}$. Take $T_{os} = 300$ K and $T_{in} = 290$ K. Note that $\dot{S}_P/(\dot{m}c_v)$ is double valued in T_{out}, and that its maximum value occurs at $\mathbf{M} = 1.0$. Determine the two values of T_{out} for which $\dot{S}_P = 0$ when $T_{os} = 300$ K and $T_{in} = 290$ K.

81. *Rayleigh line*: An analysis of the frictionless aergonic flow of an ideal gas with constant specific heats traveling through a constant area duct with heat transfer at the walls can be carried out by combining the continuity equation and the linear momentum rate balance equation to yield the following set of equations:

$$\frac{p_{\text{out}}}{p_{\text{in}}} = \frac{1 + k\mathbf{M}_{\text{in}}^2}{1 + k\mathbf{M}_{\text{out}}^2}$$

$$\frac{T_{\text{out}}}{T_{\text{in}}} = \left(\frac{\mathbf{M}_{\text{out}}}{\mathbf{M}_{\text{in}}}\right)^2 \times \frac{1 + k\mathbf{M}_{\text{in}}^2}{1 + k\mathbf{M}_{\text{out}}^2}$$

$$\frac{(T_{\text{os}})_{\text{out}}}{(T_{\text{os}})_{\text{in}}} = \left(\frac{\mathbf{M}_{\text{out}}}{\mathbf{M}_{\text{in}}} \frac{1 + k\mathbf{M}_{\text{in}}}{1 + k\mathbf{M}_{\text{out}}}\right)^2 \times \frac{1 + \frac{k-1}{2}\mathbf{M}_{\text{out}}^2}{1 + \frac{k-1}{2}\mathbf{M}_{\text{in}}^2}$$

and Eq. 5.37 gives $s_{\text{out}} = s_{\text{in}} + c_p \ln(T_{\text{out}}/T_{\text{in}}) - R \ln(p_{\text{out}}/p_{\text{in}})$. For air, with $(T_{\text{os}})_{\text{in}} =$ 100 °C, $p_{\text{in}} = 0.5$ MPa, $\mathbf{M}_{\text{in}} = 0.5$, and $s_{\text{in}} = 2.2775$ kJ/(kg·K), generate the following plots for $0 \le \mathbf{M}_{\text{out}} \le 10$:

a) T_{out} vs. s_{out} (this plot is called the Rayleigh line),

b) $\dot{Q}/\dot{m} = c_p[(T_{\text{os}})_{\text{out}} - (T_{\text{os}})_{\text{in}}]$ vs. $\mathbf{M}_{\text{out}}$ (this is the heat transfer per unit mass to or from the air), and

c) $\dot{S}_P/(\dot{m}c_p) = (s_{\text{out}} - s_{\text{in}})/c_p - \dfrac{\dot{Q}/\dot{m}}{c_p T_{\text{w}}}$ vs. $\mathbf{M}_{\text{out}}$,

where $T_{\text{w}} = \frac{1}{2}(T_{\text{in}} + T_{\text{out}})$ is the mean wall temperature. Note that s_{out} is a maximum when $\mathbf{M}_{\text{out}} = 1.0$.

Chapter Eleven Thermodynamics of Biological Systems

Over the years thermodynamics has remained essentially an engineering discipline with only infrequent applications elsewhere. In chemistry departments there are courses entitled "Physical Chemistry" that are courses specializing in thermodynamics applied to chemical systems of the type treated in Chapter 9 of this book. Only relatively recently has the newly developing field of bioengineering begun to apply the macroscopic mass, energy, and entropy balance concepts of classical thermodynamics to living biological systems. In this chapter the results of applying the basic laws of thermodynamics to biological systems are reviewed. The conclusions reached will help you to understand better how your body functions, and will give you some insight into the operation of the complex molecular phenomena necessary to sustain life on this or any other planet.

Evolution and Life

Initially it was felt that life was not governed by the laws of the physical world. The development of a relatively simple biological seed or sperm–egg union into an incredibly complex biological entity seemed to go against the classical equilibrium predictions of the second law of thermodynamics. However, it has now been recognized that while living systems may be viewed as being approximately steady state systems, they are in fact never in thermodynamic equilibrium. Even though the entropy production itself must always be positive, the total entropy of any system can either increase or decrease, depending upon the magnitude and direction of the entropy transport terms. In Chapter 5 we saw that the entropy transport across a system boundary is linked to the energy transport across that same boundary, and this condition must obviously hold for living systems. Thus, the thermodynamics of biological systems is an example of the thermodynamics of nonequilibrium open systems treated in Chapter 5.

It has been only in the past few years that science has begun to realize that the evolution of life is completely compatible with the laws of physics. A key to this understanding has been the entropic explanation of self-organizing systems and the connection between self-organization and energy flow. Self-organization can exist in both living and nonliving systems, but living systems are self-organizing *and* self-replicating. The origin of life is apparently not an unusual phenomenon. Fairly complex living microscopic creatures existed on earth within a few hundred million years of its formation.

There is, in fact, no clear-cut definition as to just what the term *life* really means. Perhaps the best definition available today is a biochemical one that defines living organisms as follows:

> Living systems sustain their low-entropy molecular complexity by a metabolic energy transport from a high-energy source to a low-energy sink via complex catalytic macromolecules called enzymes. They contain low-entropy hereditary information coded into very large macromolecules that is transmitted to offspring upon reproduction.

Hereditary information is carried by macromolecules known as *genes*, which are usually made up of nucleic acids. Different genes are responsible for the development of different aspects of the final organism.

The many different living systems on earth have numerous items in common. For example, they all use the same class of molecules for energy storage, the nucleotide phosphates. Also, of the billions of chemically possible organic compounds, only about 1500 are actually used by living systems. And these 1500 compounds are all made with less than 50 simpler molecular building blocks utilizing no more than 24 of the available elements. Hydrogen atoms make up 63% of all the atoms in the human body. Oxygen accounts for 25.5%, carbon 9.5%, nitrogen 1.4%, and the 20 remaining elements essential for mammalian life account for only about 0.6%. Only 3 of the 24 elements known to be essential to life on this planet have atomic numbers greater than 34, and these 3 are needed in only trace amounts. Thus, since living systems are made up of the simplest atomic elements, they can be expected to develop early on any planet that has the proper environmental conditions.

Living systems are organized around a *cell* structure of some kind. A cell is like a small factory whose main function is to carry out its metabolic process, and the cell boundaries appear to exist to provide the high enzyme concentration necessary for efficient metabolism.[1] The smallest free-living cell known today is the pleuropneumonia-like organism that has a mass of only about 5×10^{-19} kg and has a diameter of only about 10^{-7} m (about $\frac{1}{5}$ of the wavelength of visible light). This cell contains about 100 enzymes, and can be seen only with a high-

1. *Metabolism* is the name given to the processes of breakdown and synthesis of macromolecules within the cell.

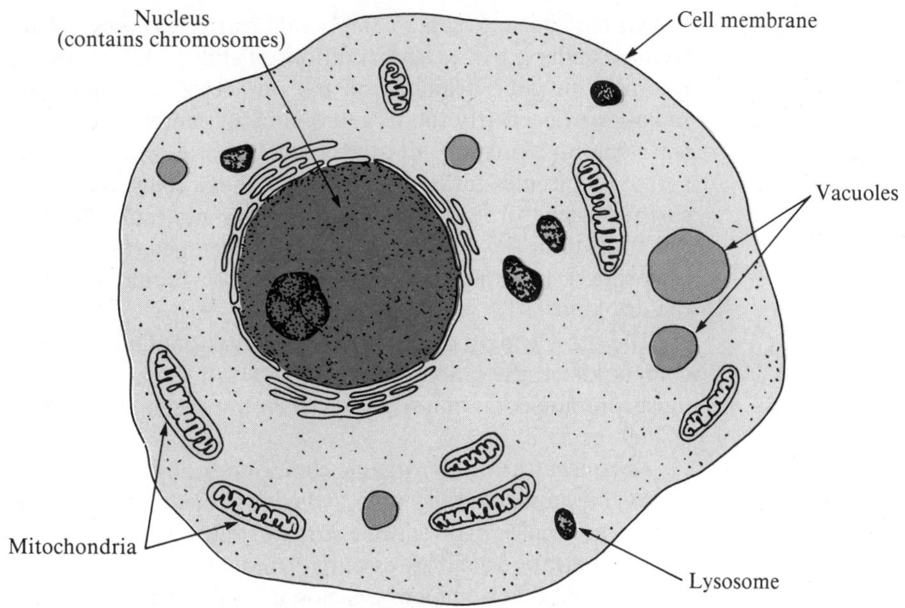

Figure 11.1 Schematic of a typical living cell.

power electron microscope. The human body contains about 10^{14} cells with an average diameter of 10^{-5} m. Each cell typically consists of a central nucleus, with the remaining material being the cytoplasm (see Figure 11.1). The chemical activity inside the cell is very high, with each enzyme entering into the synthesis of about 100 molecules per second.

The oldest remnants of life on earth are cellular microfossils that are over 3.5 billion years old. Since the age of the earth is only about 4.5 billion years, the thermal and chemical requirements for the evolution of living systems must have developed remarkably fast. All known living systems on earth are water based and therefore cannot exist far outside the temperature range from 0 to 100 °C. It is amazing that the surface of the earth had regions in this temperature range for at least 80% of its existence.[2]

The Thermodynamics of Biological Cells

It is unlikely that a single energy source was directly responsible for the synthesis of all the organic molecules on the newly formed earth. In recent decades laboratory experiments with the elements of carbon, hydrogen, oxygen, and nitrogen have

---

2. Radioactive decay inside the earth is believed to have provided the heat necessary to prevent the earth from cooling down below this surface temperature range. Before radioactivity was discovered, Lord Kelvin (William Thomson) calculated the heat loss to space and found that the earth could have cooled from molten rock to the present temperature within only a few million years.

shown that basic organic compounds can be synthesized by a variety of energy sources under early earth conditions. Table 11.1 lists an estimate of the energy rate per unit area available on the surface of the primitive earth. Though solar radiation was clearly the largest source of energy, the energy contained in long-wavelength (150 to 200 nm) ultraviolet light is so strong that it decomposes absorbing molecules rather than building them. However, the water of the primitive earth's oceans protected complex organic molecules from disruptive ultraviolet radiation until the earth's ozone layer developed. It was not until this protective atmospheric layer had developed that life forms could leave the oceans and populate the dry land.

The most widely used source of energy for the synthesis of primitive organic compounds in the laboratory is an electrical discharge in a mixture of gases. The most common compounds produced by this technique are amino acids, with yields as high as 5%.

As concentrations of organic compounds built up in the primitive oceans, biological life processes began to synthesize and replicate molecules. Enzymes and genetic molecules evolved, but reaction rates were limited by the comparatively low concentrations of these essential building blocks. Specialized molecular barriers then evolved that completely enclosed small volumes of fluid containing complex molecular machinery. These barriers are called *membranes* and the resulting enclosure is called a *cell*. The purpose of biological membranes is to maintain concentration differences that would be advantageous to the molecular operation of the cell. To do this the membrane must be able to transport certain ions *against* the concentration gradient (this is called *active* transport). This requires that the membrane operate as an energy converter with some of the internal energy of the

Table 11.1 **Estimates of energy rates available for the formation of simple organic compounds averaged over the surface area of primitive earth**

Source	Energy rates per unit area [kJ/(m^2·yr)]
Electric discharge (lightning, etc.)	170
Solar radiation in the 0–150-nm range	71
Thermal quenching of hot gases from	
(a) Shock waves from meteors and lightning	46
(b) Volcanoes	5.4
Highly ionizing radiation from	
(a) Radioactivity from 1.0 km Deep in the earth	33
(b) Solar wind	8.4
(c) Cosmic rays	0.1

Source: Material drawn from J. Oró, Stanley L. Miller, and Harold C. Urey, "Energy Conversion in the Context of the Origin of Life." in *Living Systems as Energy Converters*, ed. R. Buvet, M. J. Allen, and J.-P. Massué (New York: North-Holland Publishing, 1977), p. 9. Reprinted by permission of Elsevier Science Publishers (Biomedical Division), Amsterdam, and the authors.

Table 11.2 Approximate ion concentration inside and outside human cells

Ion	Concentration in Osmoles per cm³ of water: Outside the cell	Inside the cell
Na^+	144	14
K^+	4.1	140
Ca^{2+}	2.5	0
Mg^{2+}	1.5	31
Cl^-	107	4
HCO_3^-	27.7	10
SO_4^{2-}	0.5	1
HPO_4^{2-}, $H_2PO_4^-$	2	11

Where one Osmole is the number of gram moles of the substance that do not diffuse or dissociate in solution. Also, $pH_{outside} = 7.4$ and $pH_{inside} = 7.0$, where the concentration of hydrogen ions (H^+) in gmoles/liter is 10^{-pH}.

cell being used to maintain the various concentration gradients across the membrane. Table 11.2 lists some ion concentrations inside and outside common human cells.

Because cell membranes are molecular machines, their exact structure is not yet completely understood. The most universally accepted model of a membrane is the biomolecular lipid leaflet structure shown schematically in Figure 11.2. In this model the membrane structure consists of two parallel rows of phospholipid molecules oriented with their hydrophobic chains pointing inward and their hydrophilic (polar) ends pointing outward. The inner and outer surfaces of the membrane are covered with various protein layers, and the membrane thickness is typically 7 to 10 nanometers (10^{-9} m). It is also felt that the membrane must contain a uniform distribution of holes, or *pores*, about 0.8 nm in diameter through which water and certain hydrated ions can pass. Approximately 0.06% of the membrane

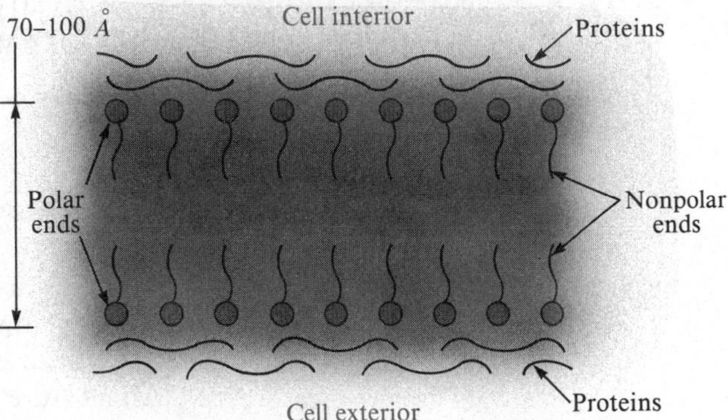

Figure 11.2 Schematic of membrane construction.

area is made up of these pores. The concentration of the materials inside the cell is determined exclusively by concentration differences across the membrane.

Membranes of living cells maintain an electrical potential difference between the inside and outside of the cell. With very small electrodes, a reasonably constant current can be continuously drawn from a cell. A cell can produce electricity in this way only if it has a molecular mechanism for maintaining an unequal ion charge difference across its membrane. It has been proposed that the membrane contains some sort of molecular level *ion pump* that pumps ion species in only one direction (into or out of the cell).

How much work is required to pump a charged ion from the solution outside the cell into the solution inside the cell? The answer to this question can be developed by considering the transport process to be carried out in two steps. First consider moving an ion from infinity through a vacuum, through the membrane and into the cell. Assume in this first step that the cell membrane has no dipole layer (i.e., no net charge on its surface) and that the inside of the cell is electrically neutral. Now, as the charged ion moves from infinity to the membrane, it encounters no resistance, so its transport work is zero. As it moves through the cell membrane, it begins to feel electrostatic ion–solvent and ion–ion interactions. We will lump all these interactions together and call them *chemical* effects, and therefore the work done against these interactions in moving the charged ion into the cell is called chemical work. The chemical work done in moving a mole of ions of chemical species i from infinity into an uncharged cell through a dipole layer free membrane is equal to the molar *chemical potential* $\bar{\mu}_i$ of ion species i. The second step in this process is to allow the membrane to have a dipole layer and to allow the cell to have a net internal charge. We call the work required to move the ion into this system of net charges the *electrical* work, and thus the total work required to move the ion from infinity through a dipole layered membrane into a charged cell is the sum of the chemical work plus the electrical work. This total work is called the *electrochemical* work of the cell.

Define ϕ_{ic} as the electrical potential (in volts) required to transport a unit charge of species i into the cell. Then the electrical work required to transport one ion of species i with valence z_i kgmole of electrons per kgmole of species i (and thus a charge $z_i e$) is $z_i e\phi_{ic}$, where e is the charge on one electron. The electrical work required to transport one mole of species i into the cell is $N_o z_i e\phi_{ic} = z_i F\phi_{ic}$, where N_o is Avogadro's number and $F = N_o e$ = Faraday's constant = 96,487 kilocoulombs/kgmole of electrons. Let $(\bar{w}_{EC})_{ic}$ be the electrochemical work required to transport one mole of species i with valence z_i *into* a cell. Then we can write

$$(\bar{w}_{EC})_{ic} = (W_{EC})_{ic}/n_i = \bar{\mu}_{ic} + z_i F\phi_{ic} \qquad \textbf{(11.1)}$$

Unfortunately, neither $\bar{\mu}_{ic}$ or ϕ_{ic} is directly measurable. They were introduced as conceptual quantities for the purpose of separating chemical effects from electrical effects; however, only their combined effect can be observed in the laboratory.

Then what can we measure? We can measure the electrical potential difference (i.e., voltage) between the inside and outside of the cell. Now, as soon as we introduce an electrode into the cell we set up a current path, so that the measured potential $\Delta\phi_m$ is not the same as the zero current (no electrode) equilibrium potential $\Delta\phi_e$. Again, $\Delta\phi_e$ cannot be measured but we can get around that as follows. From Eq. 11.1 we find that the electrochemical work required to move a mole of ions of species i with valence z_i from infinity into the solution *outside* the cell is

$$(\bar{w}_{EC})_{io} = (W_{EC})_{io}/n_i = \bar{\mu}_{io} + z_i F \phi_{io} \tag{11.2}$$

and that the electrochemical work required to move that same mole from infinity *into* the cell is

$$(\bar{w}_{EC})_{ic} = \bar{\mu}_{ic} + z_i F \phi_{ic} \tag{11.3}$$

then from Eqs. 11.2 and 11.3 we find that the zero current equilibrium electrical potential difference between the inside and outside of the cell due to the presence of species i is

$$(\Delta\phi_e)_i = \phi_{ic} - \phi_{io} = \frac{1}{z_i F}[(\bar{w}_{EC})_{ic} - (\bar{w}_{EC})_{io} - (\bar{\mu}_{ic} - \bar{\mu}_{io})] \tag{11.4}$$

The molar chemical potential of species i can be written for isothermal dilute solutions as

$$\bar{\mu}_i = \bar{\mu}_i^{\circ} + \mathscr{R}T \ln c_i \tag{11.5}$$

where $\bar{\mu}_i^{\circ}$ is the molar chemical potential when $c_i = 1.0$, $\mathscr{R}$ is the universal gas constant, T is the absolute temperature, and c_i is the molar concentration of i. Using Eq. 11.5 we can write Eq. 11.4 as

$$(\Delta\phi_e)_i = \frac{1}{z_i F}[(\bar{w}_{EC})_{ic} - (\bar{w}_{EC})_{io} - (\bar{\mu}_{ic}^{\circ} - \bar{\mu}_{io}^{\circ})] + \frac{\mathscr{R}T}{z_i F}\ln\frac{c_{io}}{c_{ic}} \tag{11.6}$$

To simplify the algebra we will call the first term on the right side of Eq. 11.6 $(\Delta\phi_e^{\circ})_i$, which is the value of $(\Delta\phi_e)_i$ when $c_{ic} = c_{io}$. Then Eq. 11.6 becomes

$$(\Delta\phi_e)_i = (\Delta\phi_e^{\circ})_i + \frac{\mathscr{R}T}{z_i F}\ln\frac{c_{io}}{c_{ic}} \tag{11.7}$$

However, we still cannot measure either $(\Delta\phi_e)_i$ or $(\Delta\phi_e^{\circ})_i$. At this point we arbitrarily assign the electrical potential outside the cell the value zero, and then we define the *membrane potential* E_i due to species i as

$$E_i = (\Delta\phi_e)_i - (\Delta\phi_e^{\circ})_i \tag{11.8}$$

which is given by Eq. 11.7 as

$$E_i = \frac{\mathscr{R}T}{z_i F}\ln\frac{c_{io}}{c_{ic}} \tag{11.9}$$

At 37 °C, Eq. 11.9 becomes (recall that 1 coulomb = 1 joule/volt)

$$E_i(37\,^\circ\text{C}) = \frac{[8314.3\ \text{J/(kgmole}\cdot\text{K)}](273 + 37\ \text{K})}{z_i(96{,}487\ \text{kilocoulombs/kgmole})} \ln \frac{c_{io}}{c_{ic}}$$

$$= \frac{26.7\ \text{millivolts}\cdot(\text{kgmole electrons/kgmole } i)}{z_i} \ln \frac{c_{io}}{c_{ic}} \tag{11.10}$$

where z_i is the valence[3] of species i in kgmole of electrons per kgmole of species i.

Using the concentrations given in Table 11.2, Eq. 11.10 gives

$$E_{\text{Na}^+} = +62.2\ \text{mV}$$

$$E_{\text{K}^+} = -94.3\ \text{mV}$$

$$E_{\text{Cl}^-} = -87.8\ \text{mV}$$

The actual measured potentials are generally in the range of −70 to −90 mV, and represent the cumulative effect of all the ion species present. However, Na^+, K^+, and Cl^- are the primary high-transport ions in most mammal membranes and their cell potentials, listed above, average out to about the measured value.

Applying the open system energy rate balance equation to a living cell gives

$$\dot{Q} + \dot{W} + \sum_{\text{in}} \dot{m}e - \sum_{\text{out}} \dot{m}e = \left(\frac{dU}{dt}\right)_{\text{cell}} \tag{11.11}$$

Here, $\dot{Q}$ is the irreversible metabolic heat transfer resulting from the life processes within the cell, $\sum_{\text{in}} \dot{m}e$ is the food energy intake, $\sum_{\text{out}} \dot{m}e$ is the waste product output, and $\dot{W}$ is the total work done on or by the cell. The food taken into the cell can be generalized as glucose and molecular oxygen, and the waste products can be generalized as carbon dioxide and water. The total work done on or by the cell is the electrochemical work done in maintaining the chemical differences across the cell membrane, $(\bar{w}_{\text{EC}})_i = (\bar{w}_{\text{EC}})_{ic} - (\bar{w}_{\text{EC}})_{io}$, and occasional p-$\mathcal{V}$ work done in enlarging the cell plus γ-A surface tension work done in generating new membrane surface area.[4] Then,

$$\dot{W} = \sum \dot{m}_i \left(\frac{\bar{w}_{\text{EC}}}{M}\right)_i + \sum \dot{m}_i \left(\frac{\bar{\mu}}{M}\right)_i + \gamma \dot{A} + p\dot{\mathcal{V}} \tag{11.12}$$

where we have written all terms on a mass rather than a molar basis (using $\dot{n}_i = \dot{m}_i/M_i$, where M_i is the molecular mass of species i) and where the intensive proper-

3. Note, z_i can be either positive or negative in this equation.

4. Some cells also have mobility, in which case a *locomotion work* must be added to Eq. 11.12. The energetics of locomotion are considered later in this chapter.

ties have been assumed to be constant in time. Thus, the time rate of change of the cell's total internal energy is

$$\left(\frac{dU}{dt}\right)_{\text{cell}} = \dot{Q} + \sum \dot{m}_i\left(\frac{\overline{w}_{\text{EC}}}{M}\right)_i + \sum \dot{m}_i\left(\frac{\overline{\mu}}{M}\right)_i + \gamma\dot{A} + p\dot{V} + \sum_{\text{in}} \dot{m}e - \sum_{\text{out}} \dot{m}e \quad \textbf{(11.13)}$$

Most of the various cellular processes that require energy use adenosine triphosphate (ATP) as the energy source. This compound has about 33 MJ/kgmole of energy stored in each of two phosphate bonds. When these bonds are split by enzyme action to form adenosine diphosphate (ADP), their energy is then made available for other uses. The cell contains many enzymes that can catalyze the splitting of the ATP bonds and utilize the liberated energy.

Energy storage reactions within the cell, on the other hand, are limited to two basic types: photosynthetic (in plant cells) wherein incoming light is used as the energy source, and metabolism (in animal cells) wherein the food brought into the cell (generally glucose and molecular oxygen) are utilized to reconstitute ATP from ADP with the production of carbon dioxide and water waste products which must be expelled from the cell. Figure 11.3 shows how these two energy transport mechanisms are linked together in the life cycle, and Figure 11.4 illustrates the ATP–ADP cycle.

An open system entropy rate balance applied to a living cell gives

$$\frac{\dot{Q}}{T_{\text{b}}} + \sum_{\text{in}} \dot{m}s - \sum_{\text{out}} \dot{m}s + \dot{S}_{\text{P}} = \left(\frac{dS}{dt}\right)_{\text{cell}} \quad \textbf{(11.14)}$$

where T_{b} is the temperature of the cell boundary (assumed isothermal here). Because the metabolic heat must leave the cell for it to survive, we know that $\dot{Q} < 0$. Also, $\dot{S}_{\text{P}} > 0$ due to the irreversibilities of the life process within the cell. Since

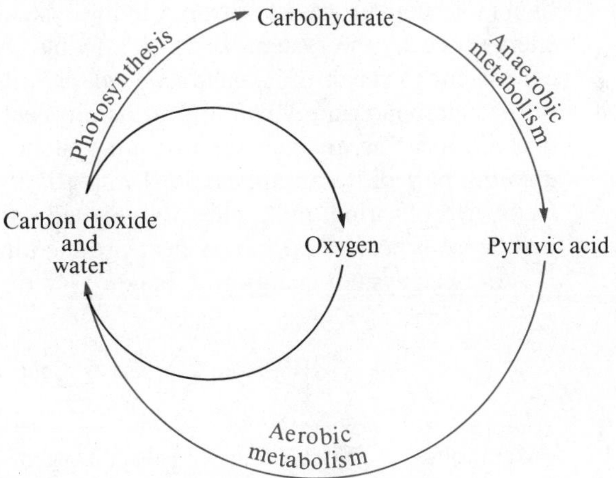

Figure 11.3 Energy transport mechanisms in living systems.

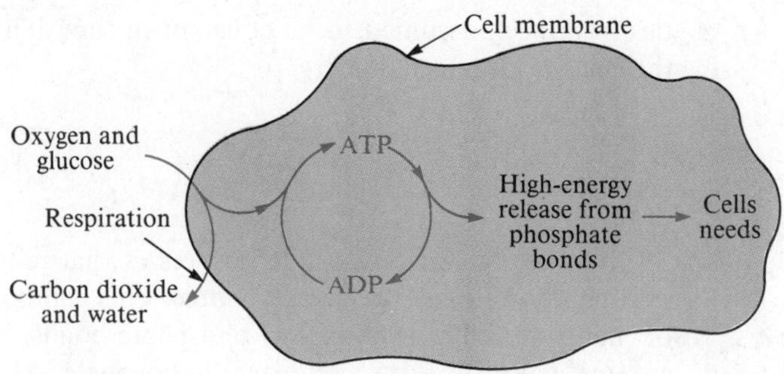

Figure 11.4 The ATP–ADP cycle.

food products are brought into the cell and waste products expelled, then $\sum_{out} \dot{m}s > \sum_{in} \dot{m}s$ (since these two flowstreams are at the same temperature and the molecular order of the waste material is less than that of the food). For a cell to grow and to continue to maintain its elaborate internal molecular order we must have $(dS/dt)_{cell} < 0$, or

$$\left| \sum_{in} \dot{m}s - \sum_{out} \dot{m}s + \dot{Q}/T_b \right| \geq \dot{S}_P \tag{11.15}$$

which is perfectly reasonable so long as the cell remains alive (i.e., $\dot{Q} < 0$ and $\sum_{in} \dot{m}s < \sum_{out} \dot{m}s$).

The Energy Conversion Efficiency of Biological Systems

Metabolism is the name given to all anabolic (constructive) and catabolic (destructive) molecular processes within a living system, and it is a direct measure of the energy used by the system. Because a living system is an open system, it is more convenient to speak of its *metabolic rate*, i.e., its energy usage per unit time. Part of the metabolic energy can appear as physical work done by the system, part of it can appear as an increase in total system internal energy (as in the case of growth), part of it can appear in the creation of high-energy items such as eggs, seeds, live offspring, milk, etc., and virtually all of the irreversibilities associated with these processes appear as heat production within the system.

An open system energy rate balance for the life form shown in Figure 11.5 is

$$\underbrace{\dot{Q}}_{\substack{\text{Metabolic}\\\text{heat transfer}\\(<0)}} + \underbrace{\dot{W}}_{\substack{\text{Work done}\\\text{on or by}\\\text{the system}}} + \underbrace{\sum_{in} \dot{m}e - \sum_{out} \dot{m}e}_{\substack{\text{Food, oxygen}\\\text{and}\\\text{waste material}}} = \underbrace{\frac{dU}{dt} + \frac{d}{dt}\left(\frac{mV^2}{2g_c}\right) + \frac{d}{dt}\left(\frac{mgZ}{g_c}\right)}_{\text{System changes}} \tag{11.16}$$

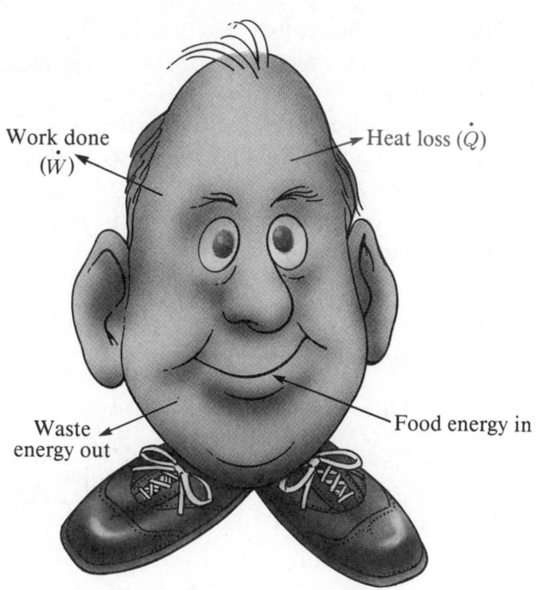

Figure 11.5 Energy flows in living systems.

Life processes all have some degree of irreversibility. Therefore, $\dot{Q}$ will normally be negative since the internal irreversibilities will generally produce internal heat generation which must be removed from the system if the system is not to overheat.

Classically, the concept of work in thermodynamic analysis has been somewhat ambiguous. As discussed in Chapter 4, during the development of thermodynamics it was convenient to separate the changes in kinetic and potential energies from the work term. These energy terms are written separately and usually grouped with the system's total internal energy change as shown in Eq. 11.16. Thus, the work term in the thermodynamic energy balance encompasses all the work transport of energy into or out of a system *except* the work associated with changes in the system's kinetic and potential energy. This can be quite confusing when analyzing biological systems since one of their major work modes in a social or cultural context is that of mobility, i.e., running and climbing, which are the kinetic and potential energy terms we are discussing. Also, whereas a classical thermodynamic system can either do work or have work done on it, in general a biological system only does work (i.e., the work term is always negative).

As with nonliving work-producing systems, we can define an energy conversion efficiency as

$$\text{energy conversion efficiency} = \eta_E = \frac{\text{desired energy result}}{\text{required energy input}} \tag{11.17}$$

The term *energy* used in this equation must include relevant kinetic and potential energy changes. For example, the energy conversion efficiency of a human climbing a hill could be calculated by choosing the change in potential energy of the person as the desired energy output while at the same time ignoring other types of energy output simultaneously performed (such as aerodynamic drag against the atmosphere). This is acceptable, providing the meaning of the efficiency is clearly defined in each case.

The required energy input part of Eq. 11.17 is more difficult to evaluate. Since for warm blooded animals the net $\dot{Q}$ is always out of the system, it cannot be considered as a source of energy input. Also, one cannot generally input useful energy into a biological system via changes in the system's kinetic or potential energies. Thus, what remains is

$$\text{required energy input} = -\frac{dU}{dt} \tag{11.18}$$

Then we may write Eq. 11.17 as

$$\eta_E = \frac{-\dot{W} + \frac{d}{dt}\left(\frac{mV^2}{2g_c}\right) + \frac{d}{dt}\left(\frac{mgZ}{g_c}\right)}{-dU/dt} = 1 + \frac{\dot{Q}}{-dU/dt} \tag{11.19}$$

and since both $\dot{Q}$ and dU/dt are always negative, it is clear that Eq. 11.19 gives an energy conversion efficiency that is always less than 100%.

On the other hand, in the case of most plants and some animals there is either direct energy conversion of incoming solar radiation or a metabolic reduction resulting from direct body warming from incoming solar radiation. Since radiation is one of the classical heat transfer mechanisms, solar radiation belongs to the $\dot{Q}$ term. In this case part of the system's $\dot{Q}$ is actually incoming and used within the system and must be considered as part of the total energy input.

The energy conversion efficiency of plant photosynthesis can be defined as

$$(\eta_E)_{\text{photosynthesis}} = \frac{\text{energy converted to organic molecules by photosynthesis (per unit area)}}{\text{solar energy input to earth (per unit area)}} \tag{11.20}$$

It is quite low, typically ranging between 0.01 and 1.0%. Part of the reason for this low efficiency is that not all the solar energy incident upon a unit area of the earth is intercepted by a plant. As the plants become smaller and more uniformly cover the earth, this efficiency rises somewhat. For example, in the case of algae (a microscopic one-celled plant), the photosynthetic energy conversion efficiency at a small densely packed test site can be as high as 10%.

The energy conversion efficiency of animals can be defined as

$$(\eta_E)_{\text{animal}} = \frac{\text{rate of food energy stored in the body as complex organic molecules}}{\text{rate of energy taken into the body as food}} \tag{11.21}$$

Although the energy conversion efficiency of food by animals is quite high (as we will see later), the overall energy conversion efficiency defined by Eq. 11.21 turns out to be quite low. This is due to the fact that Eq. 11.21 does not take into account the metabolic energy required to maintain the animal's body temperature nor the energy required by these animals to forage or hunt for food. Plant-eating animals (herbivores) can graze with little effort and consequently have energy conversion efficiencies that are typically in the range of 15 to 20%. Meat-eating animals (carnivores), on the other hand, must hunt for food and often travel great distances between meals. Consequently, they have energy conversion efficiencies of only about 5%.

The overall efficiency from sunlight to plant to herbivore to carnivore is therefore only about $(0.01)(0.2)(0.05) \times 100 = 0.01\%$. Thus, for every 10,000 J of solar energy incident on the surface of the earth, only 1 J ends up as organic energy in the body of a carnivore. In more recognizable terms, it would take the total output of one day's growth of a 1.5-acre cornfield to feed the beef cattle necessary to provide enough meat to meet the energy needs of one human for one day.

Our conceptual understanding of the physiological work is often quite different from our earlier (Chapter 4) definition of thermodynamic work. For example, when an animal walks along a horizontal surface it does *no* net thermodynamic work. There is no net change in kinetic or potential energy, and there is no appreciable sliding friction between the animal's feet and the ground. Only when the animal moves against an external force (such as hydrodynamic drag or inertia forces) is any classical thermodynamic work done. Walking does involve what we culturally call work, but in thermodynamic jargon the energy associated with constant velocity motion along a horizontal plane (in the absence of hydrodynamic drag) merely involves a net conversion of internal energy into heat. Thus, the thermodynamic efficiency of this type of motion in animals (or machines) is zero. If, instead, an animal walks on a horizontal treadmill, then it does do thermodynamic work. This work appears as friction or electricity, depending in the treadmill design. Part of the friction in this case is external to the animal and is measurable as work in the classical thermodynamic sense. The remaining part of the energy expenditure is internal losses within the animal and appears as metabolic heat. Note, however, that the thermodynamic work efficiency of walking on a treadmill returns to zero if the entire treadmill apparatus is included in the system with the animal.

A key element in understanding the thermodynamics of biological systems is comprehending the role of the heat transfer term in the energy rate balance equation of these systems. Since this equation by itself is useful only if you have just one unknown term, and since it is not usually satisfactory to simply ignore or set equal to zero those terms for which we do not have values, and further since $(dU/dt)_{\text{system}}$ is perhaps the most difficult term of all to measure accurately, then it becomes absolutely necessary that a means be found to give accurate measurements of $\dot{Q}$.

Metabolism

The metabolic energy in the resting state is called the *basal metabolic rate* (BMR). The BMR is essentially the energy required to keep the molecular machinery of life operating at a zero activity level. Similar measurements at a higher activity level produce *intermediary metabolic rate* results. The basal metabolic rate for

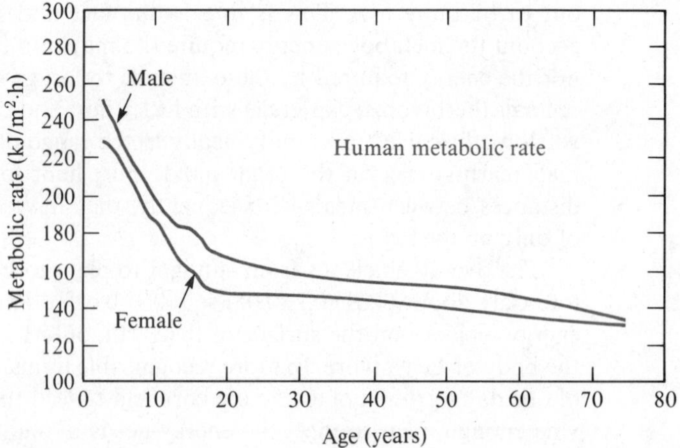

Figure 11.6 Average BMR for humans vs. age.

humans depends on age, sex, height, general health conditions, etc. Figure 11.6 shows the variation in the average BMR per unit body surface area for human males and females as a function of age. It is not uncommon to have BMR variations around these normal (or average) values of $\pm 15\%$ for any one individual. Table 11.3 shows the breakdown in energy consumption comprising the BMR in the adult human body. The large energy consumption of the brain is surprising; the brain of a five-year-old child may account for up to 50% of its BMR.

Measuring an animal's metabolic heat transfer directly is called *direct calorimetry*. This technique is very difficult to carry out because the animal's conductive, convective, and radiation heat transport rates must all be measured directly. This is commonly done by putting the animal in a closed box that has water circulating through all six of its sides. If the outside of the box is well insulated, then an energy balance shows that all of the metabolic heat produced by the animal will end up in the circulating water. However, virtually all metabolic measurements done today use a method called *indirect calorimetry*, wherein the CO_2 production

Table 11.3 **Breakdown of the contributions to the basal metabolic rate of the various organs of the adult human body**

Organ	Mass (kg)	% of body mass	% of BMR
Liver	1.5	2.14	27
Brain	1.4	2.00	20
Heart	0.3	0.43	10
Kidneys	0.3	0.43	8
Muscles	30.0	42.8	26
Remaining body tissue	36.5	52.2	9
Total	70.0	100.0	100.0

Source: Reprinted by permission of the publisher and the author from Sheldon Margen, "Energy Metabolism," in *Hypodynamics and Hypogravics*, ed. Michael McCally (New York: Academic Press, 1968), p. 119 (Table 1).

and the O_2 consumption are measured instead. Generally, indirect calorimetric techniques are found to be as accurate as the direct techniques and are usually considerably easier and less expensive to use.

The ratio of the number of moles of CO_2 produced to the number of moles of O_2 consumed during an indirect calorimetry test is called the *respiratory quotient* (RQ) whose value depends upon the type of food being metabolized. For example, in the metabolism of one mole of a typical carbohydrate, glucose,

$$C_6H_{12}O_6 + 6(O_2) \rightarrow 6(CO_2) + 6(H_2O) \quad \textbf{(11.22)}$$

we see that 6 moles of O_2 and 6 moles of CO_2 are involved. Thus the RQ of carbohydrate is 1.0. On the other hand, the RQ of protein is 0.8 and that of fat is 0.7. An animal generally consumes a mixture of these substances, so how do we know which value to use as the energy equivalent per liter of O_2 consumed? Tests show that under basal conditions, the RQ is approximately 0.82 (which is very nearly the average value for the RQs of carbohydrate, protein and fat), and it can be shown that this gives a mixture composition of these three substances that corresponds to an energy equivalent of 20.2 MJ/m^3 of O_2, or 20.2 kJ/L of O_2. Thus, if we measure the number of liters of O_2 consumed per unit time by an animal in the resting state and multiply this value by 20.2 kJ/L O_2, we obtain the resting energy consumption rate (or basal metabolic rate) of the animal. In the case of a fasting (starving) animal which is living on the consumption of its own body fat and protein, the energy equivalent per liter of O_2 consumed is 21.3 kJ/L O_2.

A comparison of the basal metabolic rates for a large number of warm-blooded animals from mice to elephants and birds produced the following empirical correlation

$$\text{BMR} = 293(m^{0.75}) \quad \textbf{(11.23)}$$

where BMR is the animal's basal metabolic rate in kJ/day, and m is the animal's body mass in kg. Thus the basal metabolic rate per unit mass of the animal is

$$\text{BMR}/m = 293(m^{-0.25}) \quad \textbf{(11.24)}$$

and it clearly increases with decreasing body mass. For example, for an adult 80 kg human, Eq. 11.24 gives BMR/m = 97.97 kJ/(kg·day), but for an 0.008-kg mouse, Eq. 11.24 gives BMR/m = 979.7 kJ/(kg·day). This huge difference occurs mainly because the smaller the animal is, the larger its surface area to volume ratio becomes. Since convective heat transfer is proportional to surface area, and the internal heat generation is proportional to animal volume, then as the area to volume ratio increases the internal heat generation rate must also increase or else the animal will be unable to maintain its body temperature. To produce this higher heat generation rate small animals must feed very often or else they will quickly starve to death. Thus there is a lower limit to the size of warm-blooded animals. The shrew and hummingbird are the smallest known animals of this kind. The body temperature of insects and cold-blooded animals is roughly the same as the local environmental temperature, and consequently there is no thermodynamic lower limit to their size.

The Thermodynamics of Nutrition and Exercise

The molecular form of the food we eat can be broken down into the following three categories:

1. *Carbohydrates.* Carbohydrates always contain hydrogen and oxygen atoms in a 2 to 1 ratio, as in water, and they can have very large macromolecules built up from the glucose ($C_6H_{12}O_6$) monomer with molecular masses as high as 2×10^6 (as in the case of plant starch and glycogen).
2. *Proteins.* Proteins are very large molecules containing carbon, hydrogen, oxygen, and often nitrogen. For example, a single molecule of human hemoglobin ($C_{3032}H_{4816}O_{872}N_{780}S_8Fe_4$) contains a total of 9512 atoms and has a molecular mass of 66,552 kg/kgmole.
3. *Fats (glycerol and fatty acids).* Fatty acids are much smaller molecules with typically 16 or 18 carbon atoms per molecule plus attached hydrogen atoms and a carboxyl group (—COOH) at one end. An example of a *saturated* (with hydrogen atoms) fatty acid is

$$\begin{array}{ccccccccc} & & H & & H & & H & & H \\ & & | & & | & & | & & | \\ H & - & C & - & C & - & C & - & C - COOH \\ & & | & & | & & | & & | \\ & & H & & H & & H & & H \end{array}$$

An example of the same acid *unsaturated* is

$$\begin{array}{ccccccccc} & & H & & H & & H & & H \\ & & | & & | & & | & & | \\ H & - & C & - & C & = & C & = & C - COOH \\ & & | & & & & & & \\ & & H & & & & & & \end{array}$$

The energy value of different foods is normally determined by direct calorimetry in a device called a *bomb calorimeter* (see Figure 11.7). In this device a sample of known mass is ignited in a pressurized atmosphere of excess pure oxygen. The liberated heat of combustion is transferred to water surrounding the combustion chamber and it can easily be calculated from an energy balance on the calorimeter. The end product of this type of combustion is always CO_2 and H_2O (and nitrogen products when the sample contains bound nitrogen). Since this is exactly the same end state that occurs in the body as a result of enzyme decomposition of food molecules, the same amount of energy must be released in each case. Thus, bomb calorimeter energy measurements represent the total energy available in the sample that can be converted into heat or another form of energy.

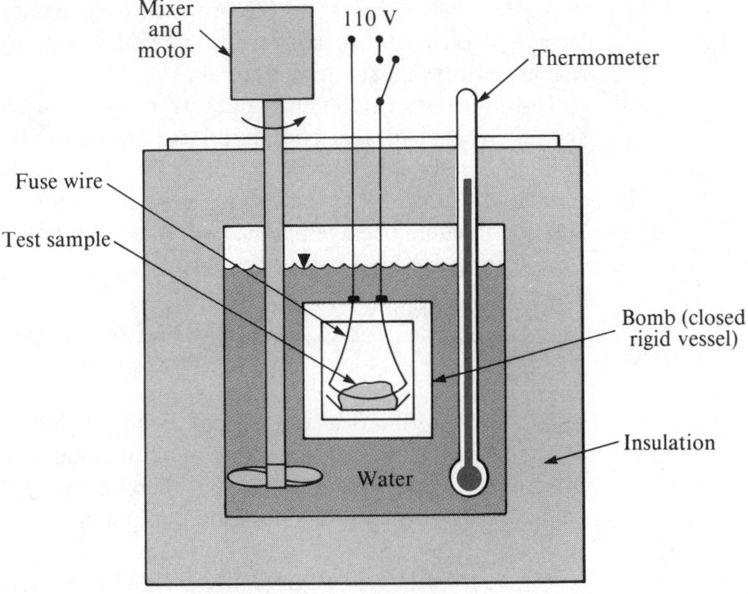

Figure 11.7 A schematic of a typical bomb calorimeter.

Bomb calorimeter studies on dry (water-free) foods give the following averaged results for the specific energies of the basic food components:

$$\left.\begin{array}{ll}\text{Carbohydrate:} & 18.0 \text{ MJ/kg} \\ \text{Protein:} & 22.2 \text{ MJ/kg} \\ \text{Fat:} & 39.8 \text{ MJ/kg}\end{array}\right\} \text{Total energy content (water free)}$$

When these same substances are metabolized in the human body they produce the following specific energy releases:

$$\left.\begin{array}{ll}\text{Carbohydrate:} & 17.2 \text{ MJ/kg} \\ \text{Protein:} & 17.2 \text{ MJ/kg} \\ \text{Fat:} & 38.9 \text{ MJ/kg}\end{array}\right\} \text{Metabolizable energy content (water free)}$$

Using these two sets of values we can compute the food energy conversion efficiency of the human body as

$$\eta_{\text{carbohydrate}} = \frac{17.2}{18.0} \times 100 = 95.5\%$$

$$\eta_{\text{protein}} = \frac{17.2}{22.2} \times 100 = 77.5\%$$

$$\eta_{\text{fat}} = \frac{38.9}{39.8} \times 100 = 97.7\%$$

Thus, 22.5% of the energy in the protein we eat passes through the body unused. The low protein energy conversion efficiency supports the theory that humans were not always meat-eating animals.

The above energy content values were for dry or water-free foods. Most foods, especially carbohydrates, contain a large amount of functional water (the mass of the human body, for example, is about 72% water). The energy content of natural or *wet* food is lower that that of dry food due to the dilution effect of the energetically inert water. The average natural state metabolizable specific energy content of the three basic food components is

$$\left.\begin{array}{ll}\text{Carbohydrate:} & 4.2\ \text{MJ/kg}\\ \text{Protein:} & 8.4\ \text{MJ/kg}\\ \text{Fat:} & 33.1\ \text{MJ/kg}\end{array}\right\}\ \begin{array}{l}\text{Metabolizable energy content of}\\ \text{natural state foods}\end{array}$$

Note the extraordinarily large specific energy content of natural state fat.

The average meal consumed by an adult American consists of about 45% carbohydrate, 15% protein, and 40% fat. Therefore, the specific energy content of this average meal with natural state food components is

$$0.45(4.2) + 0.15(8.4) + 0.40(33.1) = 16.4\ \text{MJ/kg meal}$$

Thus, a person whose body requires 10.5 MJ per day should eat "average" meals whose total mass per day is

$$\frac{10.5}{16.4} = 0.64\ \text{kg food/day} = 1.4\ \text{lbm food/day}$$

Overweight conditions place a greatly increased load on the heart and other organs. For example, each kilogram of body tissue contains 0.885 km of tiny blood vessels. If an individual is 10 kg (22 lbm) overweight the heart must pump blood through an extra 8.85 km (5.5 miles) of small blood vessels.

People living in an affluent society generally know little about starvation. Most feel that it is a quick way of dying, and that if they miss a day's food they are on death's doorstep. By bomb calorimetric measurements we know that 1 kg of human body fat contains about 33.1 MJ of metabolizable energy. Thus, if one uses 8.4 MJ of energy per day in normal activities while fasting (not eating at all), then one will consume 0.25 kg (0.56 lbm) of body fat per day. If you have 10 kg (22 lbm) of excess body fat, you can theoretically fast for 10/0.25 = 40 days just living on that body fat alone. This also gives you some idea why weight loss by dieting is such a slow process. Fasting for long periods is not a medically sound method of weight loss since the body soon begins to consume its own protein, and this can seriously affect the functioning of the body's organ systems (especially the heart). No one should ever willingly attempt a total fasting diet without consulting a qualified physician.

Whereas most adult humans can survive long periods of fasting, they cannot withstand long periods without water intake. Since the body continually loses water through the skin and lungs, it must be replaced or the body soon becomes dehydrated and death quickly follows. Healthy adults have been known to fast for over 100 days, but no human can survive for more than 10 to 20 days without water.

Tables 11.4 and 11.5 present the metabolizable energy content values for various common foods and the average energy expenditure requirements for various human exercises. Common nutritional tables today have food energy content and exercise energy expenditure levels listed in *Calories*. The capitalization of the word Calorie indicates what nutritionists call a *large calorie*, i.e., a *kilocalorie*: 1 Calorie = 1000 calories = 1 kilocalorie. This is confusing notation since only the capital C

Table 11.4 Approximate energy content of some common foods

	Metabolizable energy content		
Food	**Calories**	**MJ**	**Btu**
Fast foods (average values)			
Hamburger	275	1.15	1090
Cheeseburger	325	1.36	1490
Quarter pound hamburger	450	1.88	1790
With cheese	550	2.30	2180
With cheese and bacon	650	2.72	2580
Fish sandwich	450	1.88	1790
With cheese	500	2.09	1980
Hot dog	300	1.26	1190
With chili or cheese	350	1.47	1390
Regular fries	250	1.05	992
Regular onion rings	350	1.47	1390
Baked potato	250	1.05	992
With sour cream and chives	450	1.88	1790
With chili and cheese	500	2.09	1980
With broccoli and cheese	500	2.09	1980
With bacon and cheese	550	2.30	2180
With cheese	550	2.30	2180
Pizza (per slice, 8 slices per 13-in pizza)			
With cheese	350	1.47	1390
With cheese and pepperoni	500	2.09	1980
Salads (1 cup each)			
Lettuce with French dressing	150	0.63	595
Potato with mayonnaise	375	1.57	1490
Chicken and mayonnaise	550	2.30	2180
Egg and mayonnaise	400	1.67	1590
Tuna fish and mayonnaise	500	2.09	1980
Drinks			
Shakes (all flavors, 10 fluid ounces)	350	1.47	1390
Milk (skim, per pint)	180	0.75	714
Cola (all flavors, 10 fluid ounces)	130	0.54	516
Diet cola	0	0.0	0
Beer (per fluid ounce)	8	0.033	30
Whiskey (per fluid ounce)	38	0.16	150
Desserts			
Ice cream (per pint, 10% fat)	600	2.51	2380
Pie (per slice, 8 slices per 9-in pie)	300	1.26	1190
Chocolate candy (milk, per ounce)	150	0.63	595
Marshmallows (1 large)	25	0.10	99

Source: From *The Fast-Food Guide* by Michael Jacobsen and Sarah Fritschner.

Table 11.5 **Approximate adult human energy expenditure in exercise**

Exercise	Energy required during exercise		
	Calories/h	MJ/h	Btu/h
Fast running	910	3.8	3610
Cross-country skiing	910	3.8	3610
Fast swimming	860	3.6	3410
Wrestling	810	3.4	3210
Boxing	690	2.9	2740
Hard cycling	600	2.5	2380
Jogging	600	2.5	2380
Football	600	2.5	2380
Fast dancing	600	2.5	2380
Basketball	550	2.3	2180
Handball	550	2.3	2180
Sawing wood	500	2.1	1980
Shoveling	500	2.1	1980
Tennis	480	2.0	1900
Climbing stairs (normal gait)	410	1.7	1630
Baseball	360	1.5	1430
Volleyball	360	1.5	1430
Fast walking	310	1.3	1230
Sexual intercourse	270	1.1	1070
Golf	240	1.0	952
Hoeing	190	0.8	754
Driving a car	140	0.6	556
Card playing	96	0.4	381
Watching TV	72	0.3	286
Basal metabolism	72	0.3	286

tells you that it is not the normal calorie energy unit, a subtle point often overlooked by the publishers of nutrition tables. When a nutrition table states that your caloric intake should be 2500 Calories per day, it really means 2500 kilocalories per day. Since 1 kilocalorie = 4.186 kilojoules, then 2500 Calories/da = 2500 kcal/da = 10,465 kJ/da = 10.465 MJ/da.

Thus, if you wanted to exercise off the energy content of one 1.5-oz milk chocolate candy bar you would have to cycle hard, jog, play football, or fast dance continuously for (1.5 oz)(150 Calories/oz)/(600 Calories/h) = 0.375 h (see Tables 11.4 and 11.5).

Example 11.1

Suppose you want to exercise off the energy added to your body as a result of eating one pint of ice cream by lifting weights. The external work done by the body will equal the change in potential energy of the weights as they are lifted (there is no significant energy recovery within the body, however, when the weights are lowered again). Suppose you are lifting 490 N (110 lbm) a vertical distance of 1.0 m, and you can make one lift in one second. Approximately how many lifts are required and how long will it take to work off the energy content of the ice cream?

Solution Each lift requires that an amount of energy be put into the weights of

$$(mgZ/g_c)_{\text{weights}} = (490\text{ N})(1.0\text{ m})/(1) = 490\text{ N}\cdot\text{m} = 490\text{ J}$$

If we take the human body as the thermodynamic system and apply the energy rate balance and ignore all mass flow energy movements into or out of the system during the exercise period (thus we are ignoring perspiration energy losses and all O_2 and CO_2 exchanges), then we can write

$$\dot{Q} + \dot{W} = \left[\frac{dU}{dt} + \frac{d}{dt}\left(\frac{mV^2}{2g_c}\right) + \frac{d}{dt}\left(\frac{mgZ}{g_c}\right)\right]_{\text{body}}$$

Since the kinetic and potential energies of the human body do not change significantly during the exercise, we can set

$$\left[\frac{d}{dt}\left(\frac{mV^2}{2g_c}\right) + \frac{d}{dt}\left(\frac{mgZ}{g_c}\right)\right]_{\text{body}} = 0$$

and the energy rate balance becomes

$$\dot{Q} + \dot{W} = \left(\frac{dU}{dt}\right)_{\text{body}} = \dot{U}_{\text{body}}$$

Now, the external work rate that must be done by the system is

$$\dot{W} = \frac{(mgZ/g_c)_{\text{weights}}}{\Delta t} = -490 \text{ J/s}$$

where we have set $\Delta t = 1.0$ s (the time required to raise the weights). It has been shown experimentally that the energy conversion efficiency of animal muscular contraction defined by Eq. 11.17 is about 25%, or

$$(\eta_T)_{\text{muscle}} = \frac{\dot{W}}{\dot{U}_{\text{body}}} = 0.25$$

Then the rate of total internal energy expenditure within the body is

$$\dot{U}_{\text{body}} = \frac{\dot{W}}{(\eta_T)_{\text{muscle}}} = \frac{-490 \text{ J/s}}{0.25} = -1960 \text{ J/s}$$

Therefore $\dot{Q} = \dot{U} - \dot{W} = -1960 - (-490) = -1470$ J/s. Consequently the time, τ, required to produce a change in the total internal energy of the system that equals the energy content of one pint of ice cream (see Table 11.4) is

$$\tau = \left(\frac{\Delta U}{\dot{U}}\right)_{\text{body}} = \frac{-(1 \text{ pint})(2.51 \text{ MJ/pint})}{-1.96 \times 10^{-3} \text{ MJ/s}} = 1280 \text{ s} = 21.3 \text{ min}$$

Thus, the 490-N weight in this example must be lifted continuously at a rate of one lift per second until a total of 1280 lifts have been made. This is clearly a great deal of physical labor just to overcome the enjoyment of a pint of ice cream. Note that only 25% of the energy in the ice cream gets converted into external work while 75% of its energy is utilized elsewhere within the body to keep the circulatory, respiratory, etc., subsystems operating, and is ultimately converted into heat inside the body due to the internal irreversibilities of these processes.

Physiologically, it is very hard to lose weight by exercising alone. Most of the weight loss that appears after exercising is really water loss due to perspiration. Perspiration is a convection–evaporation heat transfer mechanism that removes the heat generated within the body due to the biological irreversibilities of exercise. Its function is to help maintain a constant body temperature. This type of water loss is quickly replaced in the meals following the exercise and should never be considered as part of a permanent weight loss.

The Limits to Biological Size

For purposes of simplification, consider living systems to have a characteristic length L such that their surface and cross-sectional areas are proportional to L^2 and their volumes are proportional to L^3. The most obvious effect of size on animal evolution is the ability of an animal's skeleton to support its body weight. The ability of a leg bone to withstand direct compression loading is proportional to its yield modulus and to the cross-sectional area of the bone. Hence, the strength of a leg varies with L^2. However, the body weight of the animal is proportional to its volume, which varies with L^3. The ratio of body weight to leg loading then increases with the animal's size, L. Clearly there exists an upper limit (dictated by the elastic properties of bone) to an animal's size where its legs can no longer support its weight. The giant dinosaurs of 100 million years ago apparently evolved up to this critical size. Some aquatic dinosaurs were too large to leave the water because without the buoyant supporting force of the water their skeletons could not support their body weight.

Even more crucial to mobile land animals are the bending stresses developed in their bones during walking and running. Small animals can run with very nimble and flexible legs while heavy animals like elephants must walk stiff legged to minimize leg bone bending stresses.

The internal heat generated by biochemical irreversibilities in animals is proportional to the amount of tissue present and consequently it varies with L^3. The rate of heat loss by an animal depends upon the convective and radiative heat transfer mechanisms which in turn depend directly upon the animal's surface area and consequently vary with L^2. Therefore, the ratio of heat generation to heat loss is proportional to $L^3/L^2 = L$, and if an animal's size were to increase indefinitely, a point would eventually be reached where the animal would overheat and die. Thus, there are at least two mechanisms that provide an upper limit to the size of animals, the strength of their supporting tissue and their ability to maintain a moderate body temperature.

The rate at which oxygen and food reaches the body's cells depends upon the volume of blood in the circulatory system and the pumping capacity of the heart. The volume of blood delivered to the heart is proportional to the cross-sectional area of the aorta, and consequently varies with L^2, whereas the volume of the heart itself is proportional to L^3. Therefore, the ratio of blood flow rate to heart volume varies with $L^2/L^3 = L^{-1}$, and consequently the pulse rate will also vary with L^{-1}. For mammals, the pusle rate has been correlated with body mass according to

$$\text{pulse rate (in beats per minute)} = 241(m^{-0.25}) \tag{11.25}$$

where the body mass m is in kilograms.

The same argument can be made for the respiratory system. The ratio of the gas transport rate through the lung wall to the lung volume also varies with L^{-1}, and thus the breathing rate is also proportional to L^{-1}. Experimentally we find that the ratio of pulse rate to breathing rate is constant at about 4.5 in all mammals regardless of their size.[5] The breathing rate for mammals has been correlated with body mass as

$$\text{breathing rate (in breaths per minute)} = 54(m^{-0.25}) \tag{11.26}$$

where the body mass is in kilograms.

Because plants lack mobility, their size criteria are generally simpler than those for animals. The main strength concerns in plants center around the buckling of their central trunk and excessive deflections of their cantilevered limbs. Consider a circular cylinder of height h and diameter d. Then, for slender cylinders ($h/d > 25$) the critical height for a cylinder buckling under its own weight can be shown to be

$$h_{\text{critical}} = 0.85\left(\frac{E}{\gamma}\right)^{1/3} d^{2/3} \tag{11.27}$$

where E is the elastic modulus of the trunk and γ is its weight density. It can also be shown that the tallest self-supporting homogeneous tapering conical column with base diameter d is about twice as tall as the critical height given by Eq. 11.27. For live wood the ratio of $(E/\gamma)^{1/3}$ is approximately 120 $m^{1/3}$ for all trees. Thus, the critical height of trees varies approximately with their base diameter to the 2/3 power according to

$$h_{\text{critical}} = 68(d^{2/3}) \tag{11.28}$$

where h_{critical} and d are in meters.

5. This ratio is about 9.0 for all birds (regardless of their size) because birds have a continuous flow of air in only one direction through their lungs as compared to the two-way in–out breathing of mammals. The unidirectional air flow in birds is also countercurrent (in the opposite direction to) the blood flow in the lungs, thus improving the efficiency of gas exchange.

Example 11.2 Determine the critical buckling height of a small tree whose base diameter is 0.005m.

Solution From Eq. 11.28 we have

$$h_{\text{critical}} = 68(d^{2/3}) = 68(0.005^{2/3}) = 1.99 \text{ m}$$

Tree limbs are sized to withstand the bending forces due to their own weight. If a branch is considered to be a cantilever beam attached at an angle α to the trunk, then there exists a critical length ℓ_{crit} that allows the tip of the branch to extend horizontally. Longer branches will droop below the horizontal and shorter branches will point upward at an angle approximately the same as its attachment angle α. It can be shown that the equation for ℓ_{crit} is identical in form to Eq. 11.27 except with a different multiplying constant (in this case the diameter d is the limb diameter at the point of attachment). Thus, the shape and size of trees and other plants is proportional to the 2/3 power of the base diameter of the limbs and trunk.

It can be shown that muscular power for animal locomotion is also proportional to the square of the characteristic body dimension. Therefore, the work (i.e., power × time) done by a muscle is proportional to $L^2 \times (L/V)$, or L^3,where V is the locomotion velocity. The kinetic energy of motion at constant velocity is also proportional to L^3 because the animal's mass is proportional to its volume. Since both the work done by the muscle and the system kinetic energy it produces are proportional to L^3 (if we ignore any aerodynamic drag and acceleration effects), we see that there can be no significant size effect in the horizontal locomotion of animals. That is, *all* animals should be able to run at about the same maximum velocity on a horizontal surface.[6]

Consider now an animal running uphill at constant velocity. The rate of energy expenditure in increasing its potential energy (again, ignoring aerodynamic and other effects) is proportional to $L^3 \times (dZ/dt)$. Since its muscular power is always proportional to L^2, an energy rate balance on the animal tells us that its ascent velocity dZ/dt must therefore be proportional to L^{-1}. That is, the speed of an animal running uphill should be inversely proportional to its size. A hill that a rabbit can easily run up may reduce a dog to a trot and a hunter to a walk.

A similar argument can be made for large flying animals. It can be shown with an energy rate balance that the rate of energy expenditure required for hovering or forward flight is proportional to $L^{3.5}$. Since the flight muscles can only supply power proportional to L^2 (again ignoring aerodynamic drag and inertia), the ratio of required power to available power is proportional to $L^{1.5}$. Thus, an upper limit to the size of flying animals is quickly reached. In the case of birds, their aerodynamic designs sets this upper limit at about 16 kg (35 lbm).

6. This conclusion is borne out from observations of animals from rabbits to horses. However, smaller animals can accelerate and decelerate (i.e., maneuver) faster than larger animals.

The Locomotion Transport Number

Air, water, and land comprise the three common transport media available on earth. Accordingly, we assign the following locomotion mechanisms to these media: air—flying, water—swimming, and land—running.[7] An effective way to study the energy consumption of locomotion is through the dimensionless locomotion transport number T, defined as

$$T = \frac{P}{wV} \tag{11.29}$$

where P is the animal 's total rate of energy (power) expenditure during locomotion (often determined by measuring the rate of O_2 consumption during locomotion), w is the animal's weight (not mass), and V is its locomotion velocity. At zero velocity, $P = P_o$ (the BMR) and T becomes infinite. The most efficient transport velocity is the velocity for which T is a minimum. If we ignore aerodynamic drag and assume that P is independent of V, then $T \to 0$ as $V \to \infty$. The faster the animal moves, the more efficient is its locomotion. This, clearly, is unrealistic since aerodynamic drag becomes important at even moderate speeds, and inertia also becomes important because the animal increases its velocity by flexing its locomotion muscles (legs, wings, etc.) faster. Therefore P cannot be independent of V.

We can represent P as

$$P = P_o + P_D + P_m \tag{11.30}$$

where P_D is the power absorbed by aerodynamic drag and P_m is the rate of muscle energy absorption. From fluid mechanics we know that the power required to overcome viscous drag is given by

$$P_D = \tfrac{1}{2}\rho A C_D V^3 \tag{11.31}$$

where ρ is the fluid density, A is the frontal projected area of the animal, and C_D is its drag coefficient. We can therefore determine the most efficient transport velocity by minimizing T as follows:

$$\frac{\partial T}{\partial V} = 0 = -\frac{P_o + P_m}{wV^2} + \frac{\rho A C_D V}{w} + \frac{1}{wV}\left(\frac{\partial P_m}{\partial V}\right) \tag{11.32}$$

where we have assumed the weight to be constant during the locomotion. Equation 11.32 can be rewritten as

$$\rho A C_D V^3 + V\left(\frac{\partial P_m}{\partial V}\right) - (P_o + P_m) = 0 \tag{11.33}$$

7. The common usage of the verb "run" implies that the animal has legs. However, we use this term to cover all forms of land locomotion including the crawling of legless animals such as snakes.

which could be solved for the most efficient locomotion velocity if we knew how P_m depended upon V. If we assume that P_m increases linearly with V, then we can write

$$P_m = KV \tag{11.34}$$

where K is a constant. Then Eq. 11.33 becomes

$$\rho A C_D V^3 - P_o = 0 \tag{11.35}$$

and then

$$V\big|_{\text{Most Eff}} = \left(\frac{P_o}{\rho A C_D}\right)^{1/3} \tag{11.36}$$

Figure 11.8 shows T vs. V for a 70-kg human. The minimum value of T occurs at about $V = 1.75$ m/s, which corresponds to a fast walk. Locomotion velocities faster or slower than this value require more energy consumption per distance traveled, and are hence less efficient locomotion speeds.

Mechanical locomotion devices have the potential of altering the T vs. V curve by moving its minimum to a higher velocity. Of course, the weight of the locomotion device must be added to the animal's weight such that w in Eq. 11.29 is

$$w = w_{\text{animal}} + w_{\text{device}} \tag{11.37}$$

and therefore the weight of the locomotion device alone tends to decrease the value of V at minimum T. Bicyclists are willing to carry along the extra weight of their machines because, at their most efficient velocity, their minimum value of

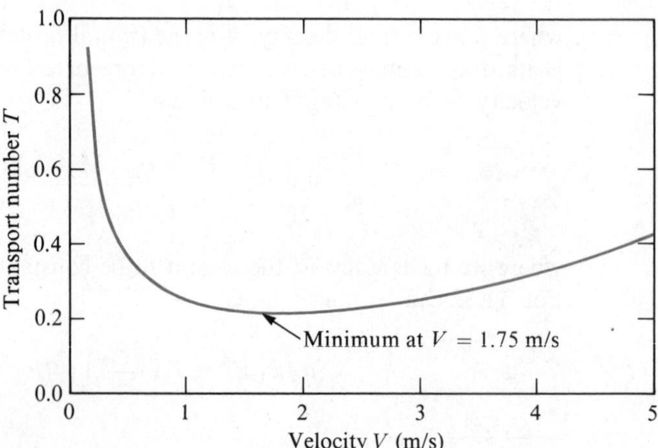

Figure 11.8 The locomotion transport number vs. velocity calculated from Eq. 11.29 for a 70-kg human.

T is about 0.064, which is about 25% of their minimum value of T in normal leg locomotion without the bicycle. In fact, the bicyclist has the lowest value of T ever measured for any animal or machine–animal combination.

Example 11.3 Determine the locomotion transport number of a 60-kg person traveling at 15 miles per hour on a 15-kg bicycle while expending 400 W of power pedaling.

Solution Using Eq. 11.29 with $P = 400$ W, $w = (60 + 15)(9.8) = 735$ N, and $V = 15$ mph $= (15)(1.609) = 24.135$ km/h gives

$$T = \frac{(400\ \text{N}\cdot\text{m/s})(3600\ \text{s/h})}{(735\ \text{N})(24{,}135\ \text{m/h})} = 0.081$$

Figure 11.9 presents data on the dimensionless locomotion transport number T vs. body mass for a large variety of birds, fish, land animals, and machines. The value of the locomotion transport number for an animal of a given mass clearly depends directly upon the percentage of its body mass that is dedicated to locomotion muscles. This percentage is greatest in fish, next largest in birds, and smallest in two- and four-legged runners. Note that fish have the lowest T values and are therefore the most efficient mobile animals. Figure 11.9 also has points for various machines, and the machines that are the most efficient at transport are trains and ships.

The locomotion efficiency for a given animal becomes much lower when it is forced to travel in a different medium. A human consumes 30 times more energy in swimming than does a fish of equivalent mass. Penguins are highly adapted to swimming, but on land they waddle around with a locomotion transport number twice as high as any land animal of equivalent mass.

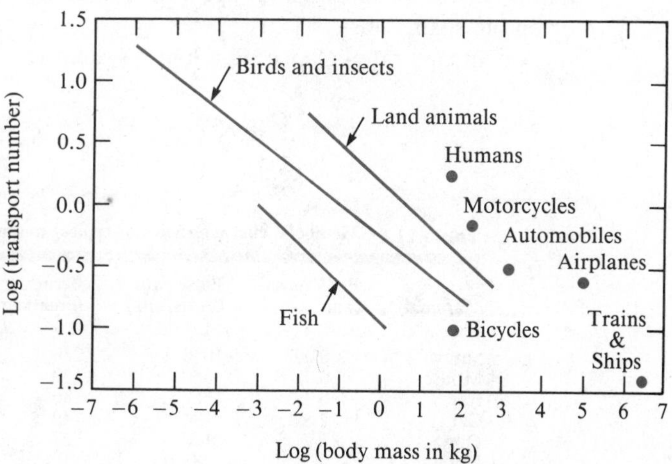

Figure 11.9 The average locomotion transport number vs. mass for a variety of animals and machines. Adapted from the last reference listed at the end of this chapter.

The Thermodynamics of Aging and Death

There are several important theories of biological aging, but perhaps the most popular is that of molecular error propagation. This theory states that molecular reproduction by enzymes is not perfect. The entropy production of molecular synthesis over a significant period of time cannot be insignificant with regard to the information content (or structure) of the molecule being synthesized. Thus, both evolution *and* aging depend upon how the living system responds to error accumulation at the molecular level. Ultimately, the errors will build up such that the system can no longer function properly and a catastrophic event leading to death occurs. Equation 11.16 is the energy rate balance applied to the living system of Figure 11.5. It accounts for all the energy flows into and out of the system and the state of the energy within the system at any time. It does not reveal anything about the aging process or life span of the system. However, the life span of mammals in captivity has been accurately correlated with body mass as

$$\text{life span (in years)} = 11.8(m^{0.2}) \tag{11.38}$$

where the body mass m is in kilograms. Table 11.6 lists the pulse rates, breath rates, and life spans of various mammals calculated using Eqs. 11.25, 11.26, and 11.38. Except for human life span, the results of these calculations are reasonably accurate.

Even though we know that the metabolic heat generation rate $\dot{Q}$ decreases with increasing age (e.g., see Figure 11.6), this effect must be offset by increasing size (i.e., growth), eating less or exercising less as age increases. Experiments in which test animals were fed a very low (starvation level) daily diet showed that they generally had a lower metabolic rate and lived longer than did their counterparts who were fed a normal or excessive diet. These particular results, however, occurred only when the starvation diet was begun before the animal reached sexual maturity. If it was begun later in life, it had no significant effect on metabolic rate or on life span.

An entropy rate balance on a living system is

$$\frac{\dot{Q}}{T_b} + \sum_{\text{in}} \dot{m}s - \sum_{\text{out}} \dot{m}s + \dot{S}_P = \frac{dS}{dt} \tag{11.39}$$

Table 11.6 **Metabolic characteristics of typical mammals**

Mammal	Body mass (kg)	Pulse rate (beats/min)	Breathing rate (breaths/min)	Life span (years)
Shrew	0.003	1030	230	3.7
Mouse	0.03	580	130	5.9
Rat	0.2	360	80	8.6
Cat	2.8	190	42	14
Dog	15.9	120	27	21
Human	70	83	19	28 (not accurate)
Horse	700	47	10	44
Elephant	4000	30	6.7	62

The first term is the entropy transport due to the metabolic heat transfer, and since $\dot{Q} < 0$, it is negative. The combination of the second and third terms is the net entropy transport into the system via the mass flow of food, respiration, and wastes. Since the entropy of the incoming food is lower than the entropy of the outgoing wastes (they are both at the same temperature, but the molecular order of the food is more complex than that of the wastes) and the input and output mass flow rates averaged over a long period of time are essentially the same, then these two terms taken together will also be negative. The last term on the left side of Eq. 11.39 is the rate of entropy production, which by the second law of thermodynamics must always be positive. The term on the right side is the time rate of change of the entropy of the entire biological system, and can be either positive or negative depending upon the net sign of the left side. Thus, we find that for any living system,

$$\dot{S}_P > 0$$

$$\frac{\dot{Q}}{T_b} < 0$$

and

$$\sum_{\text{in}} \dot{m}s - \sum_{\text{out}} \dot{m}s < 0$$

But these conditions alone are not sufficient to define a living system. The one characteristic that seems to make a living system unique is its peculiar affinity for self-organization, and this characteristic corresponds to a continual decrease in the system's entropy over its life span. As the system "lives" it grows and ages and generally becomes more complex at the molecular level. Note that this does not happen with the aging of machines, whose entropy generally increases monotonically with age. Consequently, we can postulate that living systems are defined by the following unique characteristic:

> Living systems are uniquely characterized by energy and entropy flows such that the relation
>
> $$\left(\frac{dS}{dt}\right)_{\text{living system}} = \left(m\frac{ds}{dt} + s\frac{dm}{dt}\right)_{\text{living system}} < 0 \qquad \textbf{(11.40)}$$
>
> holds over their life spans.

Thus, we postulate that for all living systems

$$\left|\frac{\dot{Q}}{T_b} + \sum_{\text{in}} \dot{m}s - \sum_{\text{out}} \dot{m}s\right| > \dot{S}_P \qquad \textbf{(11.41)}$$

and that death occurs when this inequality is violated. What does Eq. 11.41 tell us about the system as it ages? Based on our experiences with the machinery of the industrial age, we intuitively feel that old age corresponds to degeneration. In humans, the skin becomes wrinkled, teeth and hair are permanently lost, hearing and sight diminish, joints stiffen—it seems as though people "wear out" as they become older. Actually, what are normally described as degenerative signs of aging are really the result of continued growth, i.e., continued systemic molecular organization. Skin becomes wrinkled because the collagen molecules of the skin cross-link to form a more rigid (less elastic) and complex structure. The same thing happens in the lens of the eye, where the macromolecular cross-linking makes the lens so rigid that the eye muscles can no longer change its shape to make it focus properly. Molecular cross-linking also causes loss of hearing sensitivity, and cross-linking within the lubricating fluid of the joints causes this fluid to thicken, which makes the joints arthritic and painful to move. We also see cross-linking and thickening in other biofluids such as blood. It appears that growth in molecular complexity continues long after physical maturity is reached and is the cause of many of the common symptoms of aging. If a biological system were to continue to grow (but not add mass), then its ultimate state would be one of complete rigidity with a very low entropy but with little mobility potential and very low predator survivability. Thus, a living system becomes more delicate as it ages beyond physical maturity and consequently is more prone to death resulting from failure of one of its major subsystems such as the circulatory or the respiratory system. Cancer is curious in that it represents a reversion to cellular growth and appears to function as a mechanism for preventing the entropy of a living system from becoming too low.

According to the inequality of Eq. 11.41, the life span of a living system could be extended by decreasing the system (or body) temperature. Thus, even though $\dot{Q}$ is decreasing with age, the ratio $\dot{Q}/T_b$ could be made as large as desired by selectively lowering the body temperature. Figure 11.10 presents survival curves for common house flies raised from birth in environments of different (but constant) temperatures. The longest life spans occur at the lowest environmental temperature (16 °C). These insects have also been shown to exhibit increased life-spans when

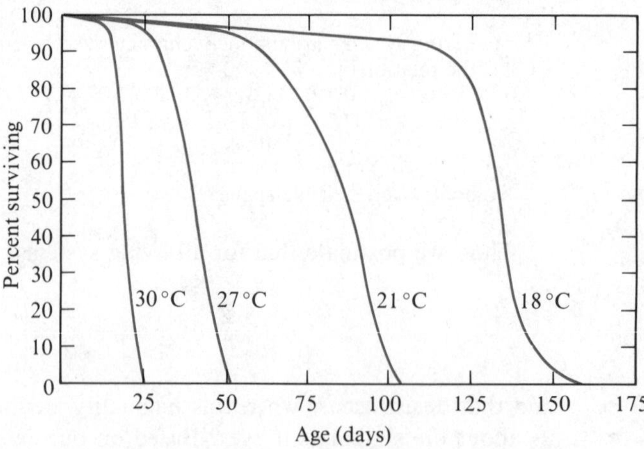

Figure 11.10 Survival curves for houseflies raised at different constant environmental temperatures.

they were raised for part of their lives at one temperature and then spent the remainder of their lives at a lower temperature. Similarly, their life spans have been shortened by raising the environmental temperature slightly.

Using survival curves such as those of Figure 11.10 researchers have developed survival equations similar to those used in describing the kinetics of first order chemical reactions,

$$\frac{dN}{dt} = -k_d N \tag{11.42}$$

where N is the number of survivors at time t, and k_d is a death rate constant. The constant k_d is often found to be independent of t, but dependent upon the environmental absolute temperature T. A plot of ln k_d vs. ln T yields a straight line from which the following equation can be obtained

$$k_d = \alpha T\left[\exp\left(\frac{\bar{s}_d}{\mathscr{R}} - \frac{\bar{h}_d}{\mathscr{R}T}\right)\right] \tag{11.43}$$

where α is a constant, T is the absolute temperature, and $\bar{s}_d$ and $\bar{h}_d$ are the specific molar activation entropy and enthalpy of death. It has been shown from data on the death of unicellular organisms and the irreversible thermal denaturization of proteins that $\bar{s}_d$ and $\bar{h}_d$ are related by

$$\bar{s}_d = \frac{\bar{h}_d}{T_c} + \beta \tag{11.44}$$

where $T_c = 330$ K and is called the *compensation* temperature, and β is a constant equal to -276 kJ/(kgmole·K). Equation 11.44 is often called a *compensation law* because changes in $\bar{s}_d$ are partially compensated for by changes in $\bar{h}_d$, resulting in a relatively constant value of k_d. The compensation is exact at $T = T_c$ as can be seen by substituting Eq. 11.44 into Eq. 11.43. For the common housefly, the data reduction gives $\bar{h}_d \approx 800$ MJ/kgmole. Since k_d is the death rate constant, the smaller it is, the smaller the death rate becomes and the longer the life span becomes.

Combining Eqs. 11.43 and 11.44 gives

$$k_d = \alpha T\left\{\exp\left[\frac{\bar{h}_d}{\mathscr{R}}\left(\frac{T - T_c}{T \times T_c}\right) + \frac{\beta}{\mathscr{R}}\right]\right\} \tag{11.45}$$

Now, because $\bar{h}_d$ is such a large value and because $T < T_c$ for most living systems, then a small decrease in T can produce a significant decrease in k_d. Using $\mathscr{R} = 8.3143$ kJ/(kgmole·K), $\bar{h}_d = 800{,}000$ kJ/kgmole, $\beta = -276$ kJ/(kgmole·K), and $T_c = 330$ K, then Eq. 11.45 becomes

$$\frac{K_d}{\alpha} = T\left\{\exp\left[9.62 \times 10^4\left(\frac{T - 330}{330 \times T}\right) - 33.2\right]\right\} \tag{11.46}$$

When $T = 310$ K (37 °C) Eq. 11.46 gives $k_d/\alpha = 8 \times 10^{-21}$ K. But when T is lowered to 308 K (35 °C) then k_d/α drops by almost a factor of 8 to 1.1×10^{-21} K. If T is dropped all the way down to 293 K (20 °C), then $k_d/\alpha = 1.1 \times 10^{-28}$ K, a drop of a factor of 10^7! Thus, the death rate constant is very sensitive to the body temperature. It has been estimated that if the core temperature of humans were lowered from its present value of 37 °C to 31 °C, then the average age at death would increase from about 75 to around 200 years.

Example 11.4 The death rate constant for mice at 7 °C is 0.035 months^{-1}. Determine the coefficient α in Eq. 11.46 for mice.

Solution At $T = 7$ °C = 300 K, we find from Eq. 11.46 that

$$k_d/\alpha = 300\{\exp[9.62 \times 10^4(300 - 330)/[(330)(300)] - 33.2]\} = 2.5 \times 10^{-25}\ \text{K}$$

then,

$$\alpha = 0.035\ \text{months}^{-1}/(2.5 \times 10^{-25}\ \text{K}) = 1.4 \times 10^{23}\ \text{months}^{-1}\cdot\text{K}^{-1}$$

One of the most interesting unsolved problems in evolutionary biology is that of biological aging and development. What determines the beginning and the end of growth? Why do some cells develop into one kind of organ and other cells into a completely different organ? Also, there is a remarkable similarity between the following biological groups.

- The grouping of elements to form active biochemical entities (such as amino acids).
- The grouping of these entities to form macromolecules.
- The grouping of macromolecules to form cells.
- The grouping of cells to form living creatures (plants and animals).
- The grouping of these living creatures into productive units (families, industries, etc.).
- The grouping of these families into cultures (or societies).
- The grouping of these cultures into nations.

Thus, there seems to be a common phenomenological driving force that is not only responsible for the organization of molecular structure but is also responsible for the organization of the cultural bonds of nations and beyond. The entropy balance and the second law of thermodynamics may well be the key to understanding the fundamentals of both biomolecular and biosocial phenomena.

Summary

Classical thermodynamics can be used to develop a fundamental understanding of the operation of biological systems. The conservation laws of mass, momentum, and energy are all obeyed by biological systems. The second law of thermodynamics seems to be critical in the understanding of the self-organization, growth, and aging of these systems. It has been argued that evolution via nature selection would be impossible without death; therefore, a death mechanism must be programmed into every living creature. On the other hand, from a thermodynamic point of view such an argument is not necessary. All one needs to do is to recognize that no real process is completely reversible and that the entropy production for any real process is a positive finite value. Thus, the internal irreversibilities would eventually accumulate to the point of system failure, or death.

The field of biological thermodynamics covers not only individual living plants and animals, but also (in ways that we do not yet fully understand) interacting groups of plants and animals, societies, corporations, and nations. Just as a living animal is made up of billions of living cells, each with its own unique function and characteristics, a society is made up of many unique living animals, each having its unique function within the society. Thus, the first and second laws of thermodynamics have the potential to also be the basic laws of social organization, and they may contain the key to the birth, growth, maturity, and decline of social structures.

Selected References

Brokris, J. M., and Reddy, A. K. N. *Modern Electrochemistry*, Vols. 1 and 2, New York: Plenum, 1971.

Buvet, R., Allen, M. J., and Massue, J. P. *Living Systems as Energy Converters.* Amsterdam: North-Holland, 1977.

Cooney, D. O. *Biomedical Engineering Principles.* New York: Dekker, 1976.

Finch, C. E., and Hayflick, L. *Handbook of the Biology of Aging.* New York: Van Nostrand-Reinhold, 1977.

Hershey, D. *Lifespan.* Springfield, IL: Thomas, 1974.

Katchalsky, A., and Curran, P. F. *Nonequilibrium Thermodynamics in Biophysics.* Cambridge MA: Harvard Univ. Press, 1965.

Kemeny, G., and Rosenberg, B. Compensation law in thermodynamics and thermal death. *Nature* 243, 400–401 (1973).

Kleiber, M. *The Fire of Life.* Huntington, NY: Krieger, 1975.

Lehninger, A. L. *Bioenergetics.* New York: Benjamin, 1965.

Prect, H., Christophersen, J., Hensel, H., and Larcher, W. *Temperature and Life.* New York: Springer-Verlag, 1973.

Robinson, R. A., and Stokes, R. H. *Electrolyte Solutions*, 2d ed. London: Butterworths, 1970.

Schmidt-Nielsen, K. *Scaling, Why Is Animal Size So Important*? New York: Cambridge Univ. Press, 1984.

Segrave, R. C. *Biomedical Applications of Heat and Mass Transfer.* Ames, IA: The Iowa State University Press, 1971.

Simpson, G. G., Pittendrigh, C. S., and Triffany, L. H. *Life, an Introduction to Biology.* New York: Harcourt, Brace, & World, 1957.

Smith, J. M. *Mathematical Ideas in Biology.* Cambridge, MA: Cambridge Univ. Press, 1968.

Strehler, B. L. *Time, Cells, and Aging*, 2d ed. New York: Academic, 1977.

Tucker, V. A. The energetic cost of moving about. *American Scientist* 63, 413–419 (1975).

Chapter Eleven Problems

1. Use Eq. 11.10 to determine the membrane potentials of all the ions listed in Table 11.2.

2. An alien scientist from a galaxy in the star system Luepke has been able to *directly* measure the electrical potential required to transport a unit charge of divalent carbon ions from outside a human cell into the cell and found it to be 4.1 μV. The alien also measured the value of the chemical potential of the carbon ion and found it to be 0.52 J/kgmole. Using these measurements, determine the amount of electrochemical work required to transport 1 kgmole of carbon ions across the cell membrane.

3. A muscle contraction is brought about by the release of calcium ions from storage vacuoles where its concentration is 0.7 mg/mL into the cell's cytoplasm where its concentration is 0.1 mg/mL.

a) What is the electrical potential between the vacuole and the cytoplasm?

b) If 1.0 mg of calcium ions is released in a contraction, how much adenosine triphosphate (ATP) must be hydrolyzed from adenosine diphosphate (ADP) according to the reaction

$$\text{ATP} + \text{water} \rightarrow \text{ADP} + \text{P} + 29.3\ \text{MJ/kgmole}$$

to restore the muscle to its initial state?

4. Assume that an individual adult in our society requires an energy intake of 10 MJ/day. Let this energy come exclusively from eating beef that was produced with a 10% energy conversion efficiency. Let the beef be fed by corn produced with another 10% energy conversion efficiency, and let the corn be produced from sunlight with a 1% energy conversion efficiency. Further, let the corn be grown in a region where the solar energy flux is 20 MJ/(m^2·day).

a) Compute the number of acres (1 acre = 4047 m^2) of land necessary to grow the corn required to feed the beef which is ultimately consumed by one adult person.

b) If some 16×10^9 acres are available for cultivation on earth today, estimate the total earth population that can be supported by this food chain.

c) If the current world population is 4.0×10^9 people and the population growth rate is given by $p = p_o \exp 0.03t$, where p is the population at time t, p_o is the initial population, and t is time measured in years from the present, determine the number of years into the future when the population calculated in part b will be reached.

5. Stewart has a BMR of 160 kJ/da and climbs to the 13th floor of his office building in 4 min while consuming only 0.010 kg of carbohydrate having an energy content of 17.2 MJ/kg. The distance between the floors is 7.6 m. What is Stewart's energy conversion efficiency if he does not loose any weight during the climb. *Note*: Stewart must supply energy to achieve his kinetic energy motion, but this energy is not recovered when he stops.

6. Find the energy conversion efficiency of a 2000-lbf thoroughbred race horse with a 120-lbf jockey and tack running 1.25 miles on a flat track in 144 s. The horse accelerates to a constant speed at the starting gate and maintains this speed throughout the race. During the race the horse expends energy at the rate of 33,000 Btu/h. Ignore any aerodynamic effects.

7. Greg, a professional weightlifter, has the capacity to convert his internal energy into output work at a rate of 2700 J/s. If the distance from his chest to his extended arms is 0.75 m, how much weight can he bench press in 2.0 s? What is the horsepower output of his arms under these conditions? Assume his arm muscles have an energy conversion efficiency of 25%.

8. During an experiment it was found that an 80-kg adult male lost 0.26 kg of body fat having an energy content of 33.1 MJ/kg by lifting one 50-kg mass from the floor to a 1.5-m-high shelf every 5 s continuously for 4.0 h. Ignoring respiratory and perspiration losses, determine the energy conversion efficiency of the muscular contractions.

9. The per capita electrical power consumption in the United States is about 200 kW·h/da. Suppose this power were generated by having mice run in wheels that turn electrical generators. These mice are to be feed Swiss cheese that has a metabolizable energy content of 15.5 MJ/kg and costs $4.00 per kilogram. If the mice have an energy conversion efficiency of 25%, how much will it cost to buy the cheese needed to feed the mice who will then supply the per capita energy needs?

10. Determine the horsepower corresponding to 1 MJ/h. If in an average 24-h day your energy output is 8.4 MJ, determine your average daily horsepower output.

11. In 6.0 h the heat from a guinea pig melted 0.2 kg of ice in an adiabatic calorimeter. Assuming that the heat of fusion of ice is 334.9 kJ/kg, determine the average metabolic heat production rate of the animal while it was in the calorimeter.

12. If a person's body has a specific heat equal to that of water and produces 6.28 kJ per minute per kilogram of body mass, what would be the rate of increase in body temperature in °C per minute if the person were suddenly made adiabatic?

13. Rumor has it that Frankenstein's monster was brought to life by charging it with 1000 W of power for 2 h, after which it operated with an efficiency of only 25%.

a) If the monster consumed its stored energy at a rate of 1.3 MJ/h, how long before it needed to be recharged again?

b) If the monster had a mass of 100 kg, what would its mean metabolic rate be in MJ/da if it were a normal mammal?

14. The heat of formation of glucose ($C_6H_{12}O_6$) is −996.4 MJ/kgmole. Using the material presented in Chapter 9, determine

a) the amount of heat liberated (i.e., the heat of reaction) at the standard reference state as one mole of glucose is metabolized according to the reaction

$$C_6H_{12}O_6 + 6(O_2) \rightarrow 6(H_2O(\ell)) + 6(CO_2) + \text{heat}$$

b) How long will it take to completely metabolize 1 kg of pure glucose at a basal metabolic rate of 0.3 MJ/h?

15. Human blood contains 1 g of glucose ($C_6H_{12}O_6$) per liter, and the average person contains 5.2 L of blood. In metabolizing glucose, 17.1 MJ/kg of energy is released, of which 50% is lost as heat and 50% is used to form adenosine triphosphate (ATP).

a) How much energy potentially could be stored in the ATP of the blood of an average person?

b) If the metabolic heat of the glucose is removed from the body by the evaporation of perspiration, how much perspiration will be evaporated per gram of glucose metabolized? Assume the heat of vaporization of perspiration (H_2O) is 40.6 MJ/kgmole.

16. During a weekend of fun and frolic, Homer, a humanities student, consumed 8.5 kg of beer with a metabolizable energy content of 1.1 MJ/kg. Homer then went to bed with the intent of sleeping off his entire caloric intake of beer. Assuming he falls asleep at 2:00 a.m. Wednesday morning, when should he wake up?

17. In an experiment the contribution of Joe's brain to his total BMR was found to be 0.05 MJ/h.

a) What is Joe's total mass?

b) How long would it take Joe to metabolize the energy content of one candy bar containing 0.75 MJ while resting?

18. A serious problem that arises in performing surgery on cats and small dogs is the additional heat loss produced as a result of an open body cavity. For these small animals this type of surgery effectively doubles the normal heat loss rate. If the anesthetic used depresses the BMR of a 5-kg dog by 50%, estimate the resulting reduction in the animal's body temperature from its normal body temperature of 102 °F (39.2 °C) during 2 h of

a) minor surgery not requiring the body cavity to be opened, and

b) major surgery requiring an open body cavity procedure.

Assume the body of the dog has a specific heat of 4.17 kJ/(kg·K).

19. What is Superman's top flying speed if he gets all his energy by eating as many 1.0-MJ chocolate candy bars as he wishes? Neglect his potential energy, aerodynamic drag, and all other losses.

20. If you consume 25 Calories per day more food energy than you use, how many years will it take you to gain 10 kg of fat if there are 33.1 MJ per kg of body fat?

21. During a basal metabolic test Steve consumed 460 L of O_2.

a) What is Steve's body mass?

b) What will be the change in his BMR oxygen intake if he looses 15 kg of body mass?

22. Broiled lobster contains 3.6 MJ/kg of metabolizable food energy. If Sharla has 45 min of hard cycling planned later in the day, how much lobster can she eat so that she will be sure not to gain weight?

23. On February 9, 1989 Suzanne Malaxos, 27, from Perth Australia won the 12th annual Empire State Building Run-up in New York city by climbing the 102 story building in 12 minutes and 24 seconds. If her body mass was 50 kg, and each story was 4 m high, determine the amount of body fat she consumed in the race. Assume a muscle energy conversion efficiency of 25% and a body fat energy content of 33.1 MJ/kg.

24. You are at a tailgate party before a baseball game and have just eaten three hot dogs with chili. The mass of the container and the remaining contents of your quarter barrel of beer is 30.3 kg. How many times would you have to lift this barrel 0.5 m in 2.0 s to work off the energy content of the hot dogs? How many hours would it take to do this?

25. Gasoline has a heating value of 20,000 Btu/lbm. How many 10-oz colas must Ted drink to produce enough power by turning a crank to light a 100-W light bulb for the same number of hours that an internal combustion engine running on one pound of gasoline with an overall efficiency of 25% could light the same bulb?

26. Mark decides to build a cabin cruiser. After many hours of sawing wood it was determined that the sawing had required a total of 63 MJ of energy from Mark, and that 15% of this energy came from protein (at 17.2 MJ/kg), 60% came from fat (at 33.1 MJ/kg), and 25% came from carbohydrates (at 17.2 MJ/kg). Determine the mass of protein, fat, and carbohydrate consumed in the process.

27. In 1983 a 60-kg mountain climber made a vertical climb of 2000 m in 5.9 h. From a chemical analysis of the urine samples collected during the climb, it was found that 0.02 kg of water-free protein was catabolized. Assuming a 25% muscle energy conversion efficiency, find

a) the percentage of the total energy need for the climb that came from protein and the percentage that came from fat, and

b) the mass of natural (wet) fat catabolized (i.e., consumed) during the climb.

28. If you consume two hamburgers, one regular fries, and one 10-oz cola, how many hours on this meal alone can you

a) cross country ski, **b)** play tennis, and **c)** watch television?

29. Brian was somewhat overweight and calculated that his excess body fat contained 18.0 miles of extra small blood vessels. Brian's weight was stable, but he consumed 10.5 MJ/da of metabolizable food energy. To reduce his weight he decided to eat one less cheeseburger per day plus jog for one hour per day.

a) How much extra fat did Brian have at the beginning of his diet?
b) How many days will it take for Brian to eliminate this fat?

30. Steve is jogging at a constant speed of 5 mph and encounters a hill that requires an average energy expenditure rate of 3.1 MJ/h. If the hill is 0.4 miles long, determine the mass of natural state foods that Steve must consume to replenish the energy spent climbing the hill if he consumes
a) only carbohydate with an energy content of 4.2 MJ/kg,
b) only protein with an energy content of 8.4 MJ/kg, and
c) only fat with an energy content of 33.1 MJ/kg.

31. In a laboratory experiment two engineering students were asked to determine the caloric value of a commercial brand of diet cocoa. They were provided with a bomb calorimeter which had to be calibrated by measuring the heat liberated by a substance with a known heat of combustion. They elect to use benzoic acid, which has a known heat of combustion of 6.318 kcal/g. The test consists of igniting a tablet of the test material inside the bomb and then measuring the temperature rise of the surrounding water. The energy equivalent (EQ) of a bomb calorimeter is defined to be the product of the mass of the system multiplied by its specific heat. Then the relation between the heat liberated by a test sample and the measured temperature change of the water is $Q = EQ(T_{final} - T_{initial})$.
a) If the change in temperature of the water was 2.905 °C when a 1.1523-g tablet of benzoic acid was tested, determine the energy equivalent of the calorimeter.
b) Then a 1.0825-g tablet of diet cocoa was tested and produced a temperature change of 1.699 °C. Using the results of part a, determine the caloric energy content of the cocoa in kilocalories per gram.

32. Rob, a young engineer, notices that over a long period of time he has added 20 lbm (9.07 kg) of excess body fat, and decides to loose this extra weight by dieting alone. Rob's activities are such that his caloric intake and energy output are identical. He normally eats *two* of the following meals per day, seven days per week: one cheeseburger, one regular fries, and one 10-oz cola. Also, he consumes 2.0 MJ per day of snack food while working. How long will it take him to loose the extra 20 lbm of body fat by
a) eliminating the daily snack food only,
b) eliminating the daily snack food plus eating only one of the above meals per day, and
c) going on a total starvation diet with no food whatsoever being consumed.

33. Christine, an aspiring lawyer, notices that over the past year she has added 10 lbm (4.54 kg) of excess body fat, and she decides to work off this extra weight by jogging each evening after work without changing her eating habits. She works 8 h per day (including weekends) with an energy expenditure rate of 0.6 MJ/h. The time spent not working or jogging is spent sleeping or watching television at 0.3 MJ/h. Christine eats *two* of the following meals per day, seven days per week: one baked potato with cheese, one lettuce salad with French dressing, and one pint of skim milk, plus she consumes 1.0 MJ per day of munchies while working. How many hours must she jog *each night* for 3 weeks to loose the extra 10 pounds?

34. Do you eat like a bird? How much birdseed would a 70-kg person have to eat in a day to consume proportionally as much birdseed as does a 0.012-kg sedentary canary per day? Birdseed contains 60% carbohydrate, 12% protein, 6% fat, and 22% water.

35. Jim is a college wrestler weighing 145 lbf and he decides to wrestle in the 132-lbf-weight class for the upcoming season. He plans to start his weight loss program early so that he can be down to the desired weight by the first practice of the season. To accomplish this he will restrict his food intake to 1000 Calories per day and begin an exercise program consisting of jogging for 20 min a day plus 10 min of other daily exercises that are equivalent to climbing 20 flights of stairs at 12 ft per flight. When he is not exercising his average energy expenditure rate is 500 Btu/h for the remainder of the 24-h day.

a) What is Jim's total energy expenditure during his 30-min workout?

b) Assuming his excess weight is all body fat, how many days before his first wrestling practice must he start the program?

36. The amount of body fat on an average male is 19% of his total mass. Tim has a body mass of 80 kg and it is determined that 24% of his total mass is body fat. He decides to swim 0.5 h each day until his body fat has been reduced to the average. If his daily caloric intake and energy output are equal before he begins swimming and he does not change his caloric input, how many days must he swim to reach his goal?

37. In January 1975 Mary Anne Sorensen's airplane crashed on a mountain in the Yukon wilderness. Ms. Sorensen weighed 150 pounds at the time of the crash and 110 pounds when she was rescued 50 days later. Assuming that death will occur when 50% of her body weight is lost, estimate Ms. Sorensen's survival time assuming

a) a constant weight loss rate, and

b) an exponential weight loss–time relation of the form $w = w_0 \exp - \alpha t$ where α is a constant and w_0 is her weight at the time of the crash.

38. Tamara Arendt was was in the same plane crash as Mary Anne Sorensen (see the previous problem). Tamara was trained in mountaineering and wants to hike down the mountain to safety. However, it will take her 27 days of climbing at 15 h per day with 9 h of rest per day to reach her destination. Her food supply consists of 11 MJ of candy bars, 16.2 MJ of peanuts, and 8.3 MJ of soda. The only body tissue she is able to consume during the climb is body fat, which is 20% of her initial body weight. When her body fat has been consumed she will die of exhaustion. If she weighs 59 kg at the time of the crash, is she better off waiting to be rescued with Mary Anne, or climbing down the mountain?

39. In 1638 Galileo estimated that a tree over 300 ft tall would collapse under its own weight. Using the modern theory, determine the diameter of the base of such a tree.

40. What is the maximum height of a California Redwood tree whose base diameter is 10 ft if its weight density is 40 lbf/ft^3 and its elastic modulus is 1.3×10^6 psi?

41. Since the uncertainty in the exponent in Eqs. 11.25 and 11.26 is ± 0.08, show that the total number of heart beats and breaths that occur over a life span is approximately the same for all of the mammals listed in Table 11.6.

42. In a laboratory test a student's resting pulse rate and lung volume were measured and found to be 60 beats per minute and 8.35×10^{-5} m^3, respectively. What was the student's body mass?

43. Compute the locomotion transport number of a 4000-lbf automobile using 60 hp to move the automobile at a speed of 55 mph.

44. Compute the locomotion transport number of a pedal-powered aircraft whose total mass (including the operator) is 126 kg. The aircraft flies at 15 mph when the operator is supplying 1.5 hp to the pedals.

45. It has been proposed to design a human-powered vehicle (HPV) whose total mass including the 70-kg operator is only 95 kg. The vehicle would be capable of traveling at 64 km/h (40 mph) while the operator supplies power equal to that of a person running at 5 m/s. Determine the locomotion transport number of this vehicle.

46. While Paul was driving his classic 220-hp, 3000-lbf Mustang convertible to his thermodynamics final exam, he was stopped by a state patrolman for traveling 95 mph in a 55 mph speed zone. Paul's excuse to the police officer was that he was performing a locomotion transport number homework experiment for his thermo class. Having heard this excuse countless times before the officer asked Paul for the value of his experimental LTN, promising to release him if his answer was correct. Paul replied, "0.289, sir." The officer then consulted the state patrolman's guide to locomotion transport numbers for the correct value. Did Paul get arrested?

47. Tom is a 75-kg bicyclist who recently averaged 42 km/h during a 240-kilometer race with an 8.4-kg racing bike. If he consumed 4100 L of oxygen and had a muscle energy conversion efficiency of 25%, determine

a) his rate of conversion of oxygen in liters/minute, and

b) his locomotion transport number.

48. Sharla, weighing 140 lbf, absorbs 0.5 hp in her muscles while pedaling a 7-lbf bicycle at 25 mph into a 5-mph head wind in air at 70 °F. Her frontal cross section is 4 ft by 2 ft, and her drag coefficient is 0.5.

a) Compute her locomotion transport number, and

b) determine her most efficient velocity on the bicycle.

49. Jim has a frontal cross section of 2 m high by 0.5 m wide and can run at 4 m/s and swim at 1 m/s. His drag coefficients in air and water are 1.3 and 1.1, respectively. What speeds should Jim run and swim at to be most efficient? Assume Jim's BMR is 0.3 MJ/h.

50. Determine which of the following will expend the most energy over a 20-mile course:

a) a 126-kg pedal-powered aircraft flying at a speed of 15 mph with a locomotion transport number of 0.134, or

b) a fast walking 75-kg person walking at a speed of 2.5 mph?

c) Determine the energy expenditure *rates* of the person powering the aircraft and the person walking and comment on the feasibility of maintaining these rates over the 20-mile course.

51. If King Kong was ten times bigger than a normal human being

a) find his locomotion transport number while riding a bicycle (assume his bicycle locomotion transport number is 25% of the minimum value shown on Figure 11.8).

b) What was his most efficient walking velocity (assume the same drag coefficient as for a human).

52. Convert the k_d/α information associated with Eq. 11.46 from metric units into Engineering English units.

53. If a cold-blooded animal has an activation entropy of death of 3087.64 kJ/(kgmole·K) at 25 °C, what will be the change in k_d/α for the animal if it moves to an environment at 20 °C?

54. If the specific molar activation enthalpy of death is 800 MJ/kgmole, the compensation temperature is 330 K, and the constant $\beta = -276$ kJ/(kgmole·K), determine the specific molar activation entropy of death.

Design Problems

The following are open ended design problems. The objective is to carry out a preliminary thermal design as indicated. A detailed design with working drawings is not expected unless otherwise specified. These problems do not have specific answers, so each student's design will be unique.

55. Design an inexpensive apparatus that will measure the energy conversion efficiency of an in vivo human arm or leg muscle. Measure the oxygen consumption rate of the test subject to determine the energy input rate. Include proper transducer instrumentation for the necessary input data, and specify adequate output electronics. Provide assembly and detail drawings sufficient to allow a technician to fabricate, assemble, and test your design.

56. One of the problems with the commercially available bomb calorimeters is that they can test only small samples on the order of a few grams. Design a bomb calorimeter large enough to burn a sample as large as one pound. Pay special attention to safety considerations in your design. Do not attempt to construct or test your design.

57. Design a system that will measure the rate of metabolic heat production of a small warm-blooded animal. You may use either a direct or an indirect calorimetry technique. Provide engineering drawings and instrumentation specifications.

58. Design a whole-body calorimeter that will measure the instantaneous metabolic heat loss rate from an entire human body. Your system must be large enough or else sufficiently mobile such that measurements can be made while the test subject is doing physical labor without restraint from your system.

59. Design a variable resistance rowing exercise machine that has a direct digital readout of the instantaneous energy expenditure rate of the user. This means you will have to specify or design transducers that will measure the instantaneous work rate (i.e., power) done on the machine. This power can be absorbed by the machine either electrically or mechanically. Provide assembly and detail drawings of your design plus specify all the electronics necessary to process the transducer signals and provide the proper digital output.

60. Design an apparatus that will measure the metabolic heat loss rate and surface temperature of a yeast culture or a small insect at various environmental temperatures. Construct and calibrate this apparatus if possible, and make enough measurements to plot $\dot{Q}/T_b$ for some living system vs. time at various environmental temperatures. Does $\dot{Q}/T_b$ increase or decrease as the environmental temperature decreases?

Computer Problems

The following open ended computer problems were designed to be done on a personal computer using BASIC language programming.

61. Write an interactive computer program that will return the user's basal metabolic rate, oxygen uptake rate, carbon dioxide production rate, pulse rate, and breathing rate when the user inputs his/her mass or weight.

62. Write an interactive computer program that will output the energy conversion efficiency of a person or an animal. The user must be prompted for input data regarding work performed, energy output resulting in increases in potential or kinetic energies, and changes in body total internal energy. You may assume that the specific internal energy of the body is constant for activities that occur over short time periods.

63. Write an interactive computer program that will provide the user with the metabolizable energy content of foods chosen from a menu. Allow the user to specify the desired energy units (Calories, Btu, MJ) of the output.

64. Write an interactive computer program that will return the user's daily caloric food intake needs when the user selects their activities from a screen menu and then inputs the time devoted to each activity.

65. Combine the programs of Problems 63 and 64 to produce an interactive computer program that will return a series of three possible exercise programs that will achieve a weight loss goal input by the user. The user must also input their current caloric consumption and physical activities. (*Note*: This is a computer exercise only. You are not qualified to give medical advice to anyone regarding their eating or exercise habits, so do not allow *anyone* (including yourself) to use your program to develop an actual weight loss schedule. Anyone seeking this advice must consult a qualified physician.)

Chapter Twelve Introduction to Statistical Thermodynamics

In this chapter we explore some of the basic concepts of statistical thermodynamics that lead to useful engineering results. In Chapter 2 we discussed the difference between *microscopic* and *macroscopic* systems and noted that classical thermodynamics is based on a continuum macroscopic system approach. Recognition of the existence of atoms and molecules was not necessary for the development of classical thermodynamics, the results of which are valid for all processes in which the continuum hypothesis holds. Statistical thermodynamics, on the other hand, is based on the use of standard statistical methods in the analysis of molecular behavior, and therefore corresponds to a microscopic system approach.

There are four basic attributes of statistical thermodynamics. First, it can be used to explain certain apparent discontinuities in physical behavior such as superconductivity. Second, it can be used to extend classical thermodynamic results into regions where the continuum hypothesis is no longer valid, as in the case of rarefied gases. Third, it can often provide a molecular interpretation of physical phenomena that are observed at the macroscopic level but originate at the molecular level (such as fluid viscosity). Fourth, and perhaps most importantly, it can function as a tool to provide accurate equations of state that describe the behavior of nonmeasurable thermodynamic properties such as internal energy, enthalpy, and entropy as a function of measurable properties such as pressure, temperature, and density without ever resorting to experimental measurements. These equations of state are very useful when dealing with a substance for which empirically derived thermodynamic tables and charts do not yet exist but where the basic molecular structure of the substance is known.

The development of statistical thermodynamics began in the late nineteenth century shortly after William Thomson (1824–1907) and Rudolf Clausius (1822–1888) unified classical thermodynamics in the 1860s. Starting from basic mechanics principles, James Clerk Maxwell (1831–1879) developed a simple molecular interpretation of ideal gas behavior, called the *kinetic theory* of gases, that led many physicist to conclude that all thermodynamic phenomena could be fully explained from mechanics principles. However, the mechanical approach was never able to predict the classical thermodynamic laws of the conservation of energy and positive entropy production, and consequently thermodynamics has held its own as an independent science.

In the 1870s Ludwig Boltzman (1844–1906) made great progress in the understanding of entropy when he postulated that a mathematical relation existed between entropy and mathematical probability by arguing that equilibrium states are not simply inevitable, but are instead merely highly probable states of molecular order.

Between 1900 and 1930 quantum mechanics blossomed under Max Planck (1858–1947), Albert Einstein (1879–1955), Peter Debye (1884–1966), Niels Bohr (1885–1962), Enrico Fermi (1901–1954), Erwin Schrödinger (1887–1961), and many others. It was only natural that their results be extended into the thermodynamic area whenever possible, and thus evolved the new area of *quantum statistical thermodynamics*, which is still an important research area today.

In this chapter we survey the main engineering results of statistical thermodynamics by treating its two main components, kinetic theory and quantum statistical thermodynamics, as separate topics. The goal will be the development of thermodynamic property relationships and equations of state of engineering value.

The Value of a Statistical Approach

To begin with, we should explain why we are resorting to a statistical approach rather than simply a molecular approach. Suppose you have a large number of particles N in a box. To find out what happens inside the box without using a statistical analysis, we would have to follow the motion of each of the N individual particles. The motion of each particle must satisfy Newton's second law, and because of collisions and long-range forces between particles, each particle could conceivably influence the motion of every other particle in the box. Let $\mathbf{F}_{ij}$ be the force exerted on particle i by particle j. Then the sum of all the forces on particle i due to all the other j particles must equal the mass m_i of particle i times its acceleration $\mathbf{a}_i$, or

$$\sum_{j=1}^{N-1} \mathbf{F}_{ij} = m_i \mathbf{a}_i = m_i\left(\frac{d\mathbf{V}_i}{dt}\right) = m_i\left(\frac{d^2\mathbf{x}_i}{dt^2}\right) \tag{12.1}$$

where the terms $\mathbf{V}_i$ and $\mathbf{x}_i$ are the time-dependent velocity and position vectors of particle i. Since each of the N particles must obey Eq. 12.1, and since particle–particle interactions couple all N Eqs. 12.1 together, they must all be solved simultaneously. Also, since Eq. 12.1 is a vector equation, then there are really $3N$ scalar second-order coupled differential equations to be solved.

For a typical gas at standard temperature and pressure, $N \approx 10^{20}$ molecules/cm^3. Thus, if we were to try to follow the molecules of the gas contained in one cubic centimeter at STP using the methods of classical mechanics we would need to solve about 3×10^{20} scalar second-order coupled differential equations, each containing 10^{20} terms. This is impossible today even with the fastest digital computers. Thus, we must abandon the approach of applying the equations of classical mechanics to each particle in the system. Instead of formulating a theory based on knowing the exact position of each particle in time and space, we will develop a theory based on knowing only the *average* behavior of the particle.

The Kinetic Theory of Gases

The elements of kinetic theory were developed by Maxwell, Boltzmann, Clausius, and others between 1860 and 1880. Though kinetic theory results are currently available for solids, liquids, and gases, we will be concerned only with the behavior of gases. The following eight assumptions underlie the kinetic theory of gases:

1. The gas is composed of N identical molecules moving in random directions.
2. There is always a large number of molecules ($N \gg 1$) in the system.
3. The molecules all behave like rigid elastic spheres.
4. The molecules exert no forces on each other except when they collide (i.e., there are no long-range forces).
5. All molecular collisions are perfectly elastic.
6. The molecules are always distributed uniformly in their container.
7. The molecular velocities range continuously between zero and infinity.[1]
8. The laws of classical mechanics govern the behavior of all molecules in the system.

Each of the N molecules has its own unique velocity V_i. Using this velocity we can define the following concepts for the system of molecules:

$$\text{the } \textit{average molecular velocity } V_{avg} = \frac{1}{N}\sum_{i=1}^{N} V_i \tag{12.2}$$

$$\text{the } \textit{root mean square molecular velocity } V_{rms} = \frac{1}{N}\left(\sum_{i=1}^{N} V_i^2\right)^{1/2} \tag{12.3}$$

and in the limit as $N \to \infty$ we can extend the summations in Eqs. 12.2 and 12.3

1. Clearly, no molecule can have a velocity greater than the speed of light, but allowing the velocities to range to infinity will be of tremendous mathematical value in the development of this theory. Though fundamentally wrong, we will find that this assumption adds little error to the results.

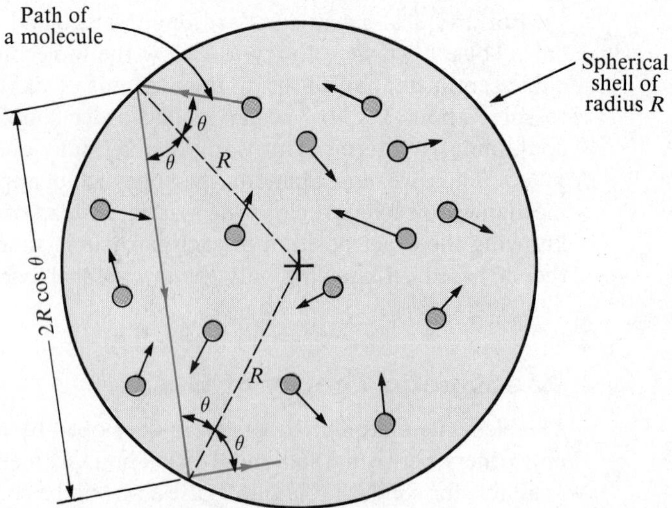

Figure 12.1 Motion of molecules inside a spherical shell of radius R.

into integrals as follows

$$V_{\text{avg}} = \int_0^\infty V \, dN_V \tag{12.4}$$

$$V_{\text{rms}} = \left(\int_0^\infty V^2 \, dN_V\right)^{1/2} \tag{12.5}$$

where dN_V is the number of molecules with velocities between V and $V + dV$. We also define the *translational total internal energy* U_{trans} as the sum of the kinetic energies of all the molecules in the system, or[2]

$$U_{\text{trans}} = \sum_{i=1}^{N} (m_i V_i^2/2) \tag{12.6}$$

Since assumption 1) above requires that all the molecules have identical mass, we can set $m_i = m$ and Eq. 12.6 then becomes

$$U_{\text{trans}} = \frac{m}{2}\left(\sum_{i=1}^{N} V_i^2\right) = \tfrac{1}{2}Nm. \tag{12.7}$$

Consider now a spherical shell of radius R containing $N \gg 1$ molecules. The radial force F_r on the shell due to a single molecular collision is (see Figure 12.1)

$$(F_r)_{\substack{\text{per}\\\text{molecule}}} = ma_r = m\frac{dV_r}{dt} \approx m\frac{\Delta V_r}{\Delta t}$$

---

2. Since the formulae presented in this chapter were developed by physicists using the SI units system wherein $g_c = 1$, we have elected to set $g_c = 1$ in all the relevant equations in order to simplify them somewhat. Thus we will write $mV^2/2$ instead of $mV^2/(2g_c)$ for kinetic energy, and so forth.

where a_r and V_r are the radial components of the acceleration and velocity. Using the geometry shown in Figure 12.1, this equation becomes

$$(F_r)_{\substack{\text{per}\\ \text{molecule}}} \approx m \frac{V_i \cos\theta - (-V_i \cos\theta)}{\Delta t} = \frac{2mV_i \cos\theta}{\Delta t}$$

and the total radial force on the shell due to collisions by all N molecules is

$$(F_r)_{\text{total}} = \sum_{i=1}^{N} (F_r)_{\substack{\text{per}\\ \text{molecule}}} = \sum_{i=1}^{N} \frac{2mV_i \cos\theta}{\Delta t}$$

The internal pressure inside the shell can now be computed from

$$p = \frac{(F_r)_{\text{total}}}{\text{area}} = \frac{1}{4\pi R^2} \sum_{i=1}^{N} \frac{2mV_i \cos\theta}{\Delta t} \tag{12.8}$$

In these equations, Δt is the time increment between successive molecular collisions. This can be calculated by dividing the distance that a molecule travels between successive collisions by its velocity, or

$$\Delta t = \frac{2R\cos\theta}{V_i}$$

Then Eq. 12.8 becomes

$$p = \frac{1}{4\pi R^2} \sum_{i=1}^{N} \frac{2mV_i^2 \cos\theta}{2R\cos\theta} = \frac{m}{4\pi R^3} \sum_{i=1}^{N} V_i^2 \tag{12.9}$$

Since the volume of the spherical shell is $\forall = \frac{4}{3}\pi R^3$, we can then write Eq. 12.9 as

$$p\forall = p\frac{4\pi R^3}{3} = \frac{m}{3} \sum_{i=1}^{N} V_i^2 = \tfrac{1}{3} NmV_{\text{rms}}^2 \tag{12.10}$$

In this equation the product Nm is the total mass of gas in the shell m_T, and therefore Eq. 12.10 can be written as

$$p\forall = \tfrac{1}{3} m_T V_{\text{rms}}^2 \tag{12.11}$$

If we now limit our attention to gases that obey the ideal gas equation of state, then Eq. 12.11 becomes

$$p\forall = \tfrac{1}{3} m_T V_{\text{rms}}^2 = m_T R T \tag{12.12}$$

where R is the specific gas constant given by

$$R = \frac{\mathcal{R}}{M} = \frac{N_o k}{M} = \frac{k}{m} \tag{12.13}$$

where $\mathscr{R}$ = universal gas constant, 8314.3 J/(kgmole·K) or 1545.35 ft·lbf/(1bmole·R)
M = molecular mass (kg/kgmole or lbm/lbmole) of the gas
N_o = Avogadro's number, 6.023×10^{26} molecules/kgmole
k = Boltzmann's constant, 1.380×10^{-23} J/(molecule·K)
$m = M/N_o$, which is the mass of one molecule of the gas

Thus, from Eqs. 12.12 and 12.13 we see that

$$V_{rms} = \sqrt{3RT} = \sqrt{\frac{3kT}{m}} \tag{12.14}$$

and therefore, from Eq. 12.6, the kinetic theory interpretation of the translational total internal energy of an ideal gas is

$$U_{trans} = \tfrac{1}{2}NmV_{rms}^2 = \tfrac{3}{2}NkT \tag{12.15}$$

We see from Eq. 12.15 that U_{trans} depends only on temperature, which is in agreement with our definition of an ideal gas given in Chapter 3.

Intermolecular Collisions

To better understand molecule–molecule collisions, imagine that all the molecules except one are frozen in space. Then a moving molecule will travel through this stationary forest of molecules colliding with them at random. This model can be further simplified if the moving molecule is enlarged to twice its normal diameter while all the stationary molecules are reduced to points of zero diameter (see Figure 12.2). The area swept out by the motion of the enlarged molecule is called its molecular *collision cross section*, and is given by

$$\sigma = \pi(2r)^2 = 4\pi r^2$$

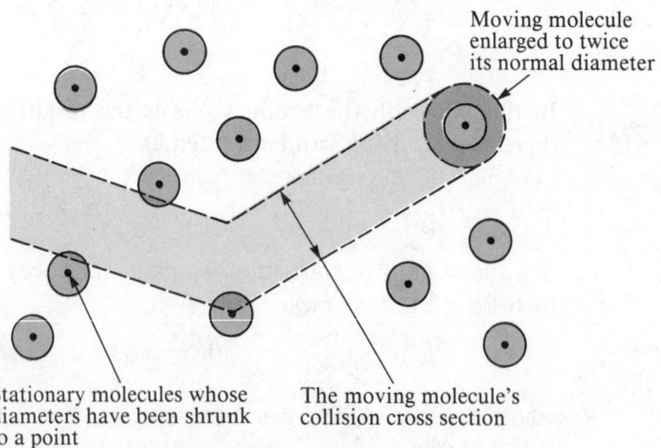

Figure 12.2 A simplified model illustrating the molecular collision cross section.

where r is the effective radius of the kinetic theory spherical molecule. Typical values for the effective radius of simple molecules are given in Table 12.1.

The *collision frequency* $\mathscr{F}$ is the number of collisions per unit time made by the moving molecule, and is determined from

$$\mathscr{F} = \frac{N}{\varPsi}\left(\frac{8}{3\pi}\right)^{1/2}(\sigma)V_{\text{rms}}$$

where

$$N/\varPsi = N_o/\bar{v} = pN_o/\mathscr{R}T = p/kT$$

is the number of molecules per unit volume, σ is the molecular collision moving cross section, and V_{rms} is the root mean square velocity of the average molecule. The molecular *mean free path* λ is defined to be the distance traveled between molecular collisions, and is calculated from

$$\lambda = \frac{1}{(N/\varPsi)\sigma} \tag{12.16}$$

Table 12.1 Typical values of the effective molecular radius

Molecule	Effective radius, $r \times 10^{10}$ m
He	1.37
Ne	1.30
Ar	1.82
H_2	0.74
N_2	1.10
O_2	1.21
Br_2	2.28
Cl_2	1.99
F_2	1.41
I_2	2.67
HBr	1.41
HCl	1.27
HF	0.92
HI	1.60
CO	1.13
NO	1.15
CO_2	2.30
NH_3	2.22
CH_4	2.07

Source: Material drawn from the *JANAF Thermochemical Tables*, 1st ed., Thermal Research Laboratory, Dow Chemical Corporation, Midland Michigan, 1964. Reprinted by permission of the author, Malcom Chase. Also from Francis W. Sears, *An Introduction To Thermodynamics, The Kinetic Theory of Gases, And Statistical Thermodynamics*, 2nd ed., © 1953, Addison-Wesley Publishing Co., Inc., Massachusetts, Table 13-1, p. 266. Reprinted with permission.

Example 12.1 Determine the collision frequency and mean free path for neon at 273 K where $(N/V)_{Ne} = 3 \times 10^{25}$ molecules/m^3. The molecular mass of neon is 20.183 kg/kgmole.

Solution For neon,

$$m = \frac{M}{N_o} = \frac{20.183 \text{ kg/kgmole}}{6.023 \times 10^{26} \text{ molecules/kgmole}} = 3.35 \times 10^{-26} \text{ kg/molecule}$$

Then the root mean square velocity of the neon molecules is

$$V_{rms} = \left(\frac{3kT}{m}\right)^{1/2} = \left[\frac{3[1.38 \times 10^{-23} \text{ J/(molecule}\cdot\text{K)}](273 \text{ K})}{3.35 \times 10^{-26} \text{ kg/molecule}}\right]^{1/2} = 581 \text{ m/s}$$

From Table 12.1 we find that the radius of the neon molecule is 1.3×10^{-10} m, so the collision cross section is

$$\sigma = 4\pi r^2 = 4\pi(1.3 \times 10^{-10} \text{ m})^2 = 2.12 \times 10^{-19} \text{ m}^2$$

and the collision frequency is

$$\begin{aligned} \mathscr{F} &= \frac{N}{V}\left(\frac{8}{3\pi}\right)^{1/2}(\sigma)V_{avg} \\ &= (3 \times 10^{25} \text{ molecules/m}^3)\left(\frac{8}{3\pi}\right)^{1/2}(2.12 \times 10^{-19} \text{ m}^2)(581 \text{ m/s}) \\ &= 3.4 \times 10^9 \text{ collisions/s} \end{aligned}$$

so that the molecular mean free path is

$$\lambda = \frac{1}{(N/V)\sigma} = \frac{1}{(3 \times 10^{25} \text{ molecules/m}^3)(2.12 \times 10^{-19} \text{ m}^2)} = 1.57 \times 10^{-7} \text{ m}$$

Molecular Velocity Distributions

Theories attempting to explain population behavior in living systems often begin with the following simple differential equation for the time rate of change of the population N:

$$\frac{dN}{dt} = \pm\alpha N \tag{12.17}$$

which says that the rate of change of the population N depends directly on the instantaneous value of the population. If α is a constant, Eq. 12.17 can be integrated to give

$$N = N_0 e^{\pm\alpha t} \tag{12.18}$$

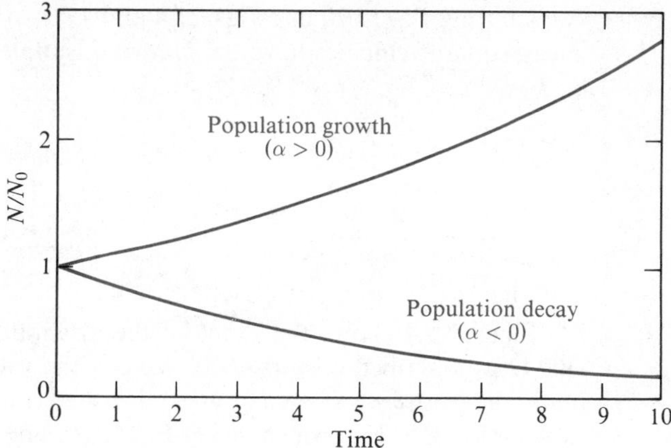

Figure 12.3 Population growth and decay as predicted by Eq. 12.18.

where N_0 is the initial population at time zero. This equation predicts an exponential growth or decay in population depending upon the sign of α (see Figure 12.3). In biological systems Eq. 12.18 is usually inaccurate over long time intervals because α is not constant, but instead depends on a number of variables and is often dependent upon N itself.

The problem of determining the distribution of velocities among the molecules of a gas can be thought of as a population problem, except that we are no longer interested in how the population size N varies with time, but rather how it varies with molecular velocity. Using the general form of Eqs. 12.17 we can postulate a velocity distribution population model as follows

$$\frac{dN_V}{dV} = f(V)N \tag{12.19}$$

where α has been replaced by a more general function $f(V)$, called the *velocity distribution function.* The problem now is to find the mathematical form of $f(V)$. For example, if we assumed a Gaussian velocity distribution we would have

$$f(V) = \frac{1}{\sqrt{2\pi}\,\delta} \exp\left(-\frac{V^2}{2\delta^2}\right)$$

where δ is the standard deviation.

By utilizing the assumptions stated at the beginning of this section, Maxwell was able to show that $f(V)$ is not Gaussian, but instead has the following form:

$$f(V) = \frac{4}{\sqrt{\pi}} \left(\frac{m}{2kT}\right)^{3/2} V^2 \exp\left(-\frac{mV^2}{2kT}\right) \tag{12.20}$$

Substituting Eq. 12.20 into Eqs. 12.4 and 12.5 one finds that the average and root mean square velocities have the following simple formula

$$V_{avg} = \sqrt{\frac{8kT}{\pi m}} \tag{12.21}$$

$$V_{rms} = \sqrt{\frac{3kT}{m}} \tag{12.22}$$

Figure 12.4 shows the shape of the distribution function $f(V)$ for oxygen at 300 K as described by Eq. 12.20. We call the velocity at which $f(V)$ has a maximum the *most probable velocity* V_{mp}. It is determined by setting $df(V)/dV = 0$ and solving for $V = V_{mp}$, which, using Eq. 12.20, gives

$$V_{mp} = \sqrt{\frac{2kT}{m}} \tag{12.23}$$

By comparing Eqs. 12.21, 12.22, and 12.23 it is clear that

$$V_{mp} < V_{avg} < V_{rms}$$

as shown in Figure 12.4.

Let $\int_{V_1}^{V_2} dN_V = N(V_1 \to V_2)$ be the number of molecules with velocities between V_1 and V_2. Then it follows from Eq. 12.19 that

$$\frac{N(V_1 \to V_2)}{N} = \int_{V_1}^{V_2} f(V)\, dV \tag{12.24}$$

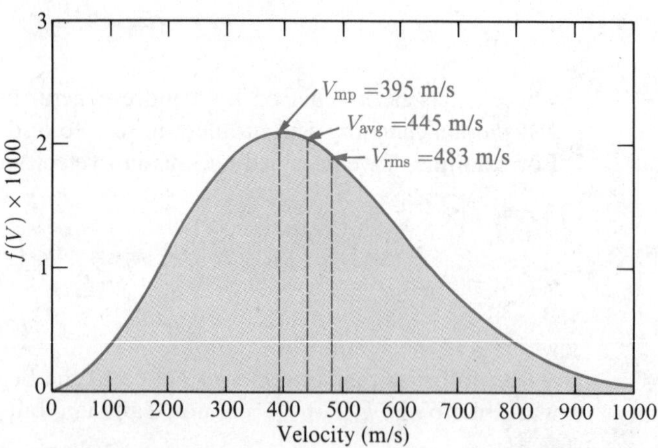

Figure 12.4 The Maxwell velocity distribution function $f(V)$ for oxygen (O_2) at 300 K as defined by Eq. 12.20.

Substituting Eq. 12.20 into Eq. 12.24 and carrying out the integration gives

$$\frac{N(V_1 \to V_2)}{N} = \text{erf}(x_2) - \text{erf}(x_1) - \frac{2}{\sqrt{\pi}}(x_2 e^{-x_2^2} - x_1 e^{-x_1^2}) \tag{12.25}$$

where

$$x_1 = V_1/V_{\text{mp}}$$

$$x_2 = V_2/V_{\text{mp}}$$

and

$$\text{erf}(x) = \text{error function of } x = \frac{2}{\sqrt{\pi}} \int_0^x e^{-x^2}\, dx$$

Representative values for the error function can be found in Table 12.2. Note that erf(0) = 0 and erf(∞) = 1.

Equation 12.25 can be evaluated to find the fraction of molecules whose velocities lie in the range from 0 to V as

$$\frac{N(0 \to V)}{N} = \text{erf}(x) - \frac{2}{\sqrt{\pi}} x e^{-x^2} \tag{12.26}$$

Table 12.2 Values of the error function

x	erf(x)
0.0	0.0
0.1	0.1125
0.2	0.2227
0.3	0.3286
0.4	0.4284
0.5	0.5205
0.6	0.6039
0.7	0.6778
0.8	0.7421
0.9	0.7969
1.0	0.8427
1.2	0.9103
1.4	0.9523
1.6	0.9764
1.8	0.9891
2.0	0.9953
2.2	0.9981
2.4	0.9993
2.6	0.9998
2.8	0.9999
∞	1.0

Note: For all x, $\text{erf}(x) = \frac{2}{\sqrt{\pi}}\left(x - \frac{x^3}{3(1!)} + \frac{x^5}{5(2!)} - \frac{x^7}{7(3!)} + \cdots\right)$,
and $\exp(-x^2) = 1 - x^2/1! + x^4/2! - x^6/3! + x^8/4! - \cdots$

and to find the fraction of molecules whose velocities lie in the range from V to ∞ as

$$\frac{N(V \to \infty)}{N} = 1 - \frac{N(0 \to V)}{N} = 1 - \operatorname{erf}(x) + \frac{2}{\sqrt{\pi}} x e^{-x^2} \qquad \textbf{(12.27)}$$

where $x = V/V_{mp}$ in each case.

Example 12.2 Test assumption 7 at the beginning of this section by computing the fraction of Neon molecules at 273 K whose velocities are faster than V_{mp}, V_{avg}, V_{rms}, and c (the speed of light). Use the molecular data for neon given in Example 12.1.

Solution

a) The fraction having velocities greater than V_{mp} is given by Eq. 12.27 with $x = V_{mp}/V_{mp} = 1.0$ as

$$\frac{N(V_{mp} \to \infty)}{N} = 1 - \operatorname{erf}(1.0) + \frac{2}{\sqrt{\pi}}(1.0)e^{-1.0}$$

or

$$\frac{N(V_{mp} \to \infty)}{N} = 1 - 0.8427 + 0.4151 = 0.5724$$

Thus, 57.24% of the molecules have velocities faster than V_{mp}.

b) Here,

$$V_{avg} = \sqrt{\frac{8kT}{\pi m}} \quad \text{and} \quad V_{mp} = \sqrt{\frac{2kT}{m}}$$

and

$$x = \frac{V_{avg}}{V_{mp}} = \sqrt{\frac{8}{2\pi}} = 1.128$$

Thus, the fraction of molecules having velocities greater than V_{avg} is given by interpolating in Table 12.2 to find

$$\frac{N(V_{avg} \to \infty)}{N} = 1 - \operatorname{erf}(1.128) + \frac{2}{\sqrt{\pi}}(1.128)e^{-1.272}$$

$$= 1 - 0.8893 + 0.3566 = 0.4673$$

Consequently, 46.73% of the molecules have velocities faster than V_{avg}.

c) Here,

$$V_{rms} = \sqrt{\frac{3kT}{m}},$$

so

$$x = V_{rms}/V_{mp} = \sqrt{\tfrac{3}{2}} = 1.225$$

and

$$\frac{N(V_{\text{rms}} \to \infty)}{N} = 1 - \text{erf}(1.225) + \frac{2}{\sqrt{\pi}}(1.225)e^{-1.501}$$

$$= 1 - 0.9168 + 0.3081 = 0.3913$$

or 39.13% of the molecules have velocities greater than V_{rms}.

d) It can be shown (see Problem 10 at the end of this chapter) that when $V/V_{\text{mp}} \gg 1$, the fraction of molecules with velocities in the range from V to ∞ is approximately given by

$$\frac{N(V \to \infty)}{N} \approx \frac{2}{\sqrt{\pi}}\left(x + \frac{1}{2x}\right)e^{-x^2} \qquad \text{(for } x \gg 1 \text{ only)}$$

consider $x = V/V_{\text{mp}} = 10$; then

$$\frac{N(V \to \infty)}{N} \approx \frac{2}{\sqrt{\pi}}(10.05)e^{-100} = 4.22 \times 10^{-43}$$

Thus, only one molecule in about 10^{20} moles of a gas has a velocity ten times greater than V_{mp}. Now, the velocity of light c is 3×10^8 m/s, and for neon at 273 K we have $m = 3.35 \times 10^{-26}$ kg (see Example 12.1), and $V_{\text{mp}} = \sqrt{2kT/m} = 474.3$ m/s. Thus,

$$x = \frac{V}{V_{\text{mp}}} = \frac{c}{V_{\text{mp}}} = \frac{3 \times 10^8 \text{ m/s}}{474.3 \text{ m/s}} = 6.33 \times 10^5$$

so that

$$\frac{N(c \to \infty)}{N} \approx \frac{2}{\sqrt{\pi}}(6.33 \times 10^5)e^{-4.0 \times 10^{11}} \approx 0$$

Thus, even though we allow molecules to move faster than the speed of light in our mathematical model, we find that for all practical purposes this model predicts that virtually no molecules have velocities this fast at ordinary temperatures.

Equipartition of Energy

Equation 12.15 gives the total translational kinetic energy of a system of N *molecules as* $\frac{3}{2}NkT$. The principle of *equipartition of energy* requires that the translational kinetic energy of an unrestricted molecule be equally divided among the three translational degrees of freedom (one for each independent coordinate direction). Therefore, the translational total internal energy in each of the x, y, and z coordinate directions must be one-third of that given in Eq. 12.15, or

$$(U_{\text{trans}})_x = (U_{\text{trans}})_y = (U_{\text{trans}})_z = U_{\text{trans}}/3 = \tfrac{1}{2}NkT$$

We can therefore conclude that the total energy of a system of N molecules with F degrees of freedom per molecule is given by

$$U = \frac{F}{2} NkT = \frac{F}{2} m_T RT \tag{12.28}$$

and that its specific internal energy is $u = U/m_T = FRT/2$. From the definition of constant volume specific heat introduced in Chapter 3 we have

$$c_v = \left(\frac{\partial u}{\partial T}\right)_v = \frac{\partial}{\partial T}\left(\frac{F}{2} RT\right)_v = \frac{FR}{2} \tag{12.29}$$

and since $c_p - c_v = R$ for an ideal gas, then

$$c_p = R + c_v = \left(1 + \frac{F}{2}\right) R \tag{12.30}$$

and finally the specific heat ratio k becomes

$$k = \frac{c_p}{c_v} = \frac{F + 2}{F} \tag{12.31}$$

For a molecule containing b atoms there are $F = 3b$ degrees of freedom. If $b = 1$, then $F = 3$ and the three degrees of freedom are all translational. If $b = 2$, then $F = 6$ and there are three degrees of freedom in translation, two in rotation and one in vibration. If $b > 2$, then $F = 3b$, and there are three degrees of freedom in translation, three in rotation and $3b - 6$ in vibration. In the case of monatomic (single-atom) molecules like He, Ne, Ar, Kr, Xe, etc., there are only 3 degrees of freedom (all translational). Then Eqs. 12.29, 12.30, and 12.31 give

$$\left.\begin{aligned} c_v &= 1.5\ \mathrm{R} \\ c_p &= 2.5\ \mathrm{R} \\ k &= 1.67 \end{aligned}\right\} \text{monatomic gases}$$

For diatomic (two-atom) molecules such as H_2, O_2, CO, NO, etc., we have $b = 2$ and consequently $F = 3(2) = 6$. Then we have

$$\left.\begin{aligned} c_v &= 3\ \mathrm{R} \\ c_p &= 4\ \mathrm{R} \\ k &= 1.35 \end{aligned}\right\} \text{diatomic gases}$$

Similarly for triatomic gases such as CO_2, H_2O, NO_2, SO_2, etc., we have $b = 3$ and $F = 9$. Then,

$$\left.\begin{aligned} c_v &= 4.5\ \mathrm{R} \\ c_p &= 5.5\ \mathrm{R} \\ k &= 1.22 \end{aligned}\right\} \text{triatomic gases}$$

Table 12.3 Measured values of the specific heats of various gases at room temperature

Gas	c_v/R	c_p/R	$k = \frac{c_p}{c_v}$
Monatomic			
He	1.50	2.50	1.67
Ne	1.50	2.50	1.67
Ar	1.51	2.52	1.67
Kr	1.00	1.68	1.68
Xe	1.52	2.51	1.65
Diatomic			
CO	2.51	3.51	1.40
NO	2.51	3.51	1.40
H_2	2.44	3.42	1.40
O_2	2.53	3.53	1.40
N_2	2.50	3.50	1.40
Triatomic			
CO_2	3.48	4.48	1.29
SO_2	3.97	4.97	1.25
H_2O	3.05	4.05	1.33

A comparison of these values with the measured specific heats of some real gases given in Table 12.3 reveals that for simple molecules (e.g., monatomic gases) the kinetic theory works quite well. For complex molecules, however, kinetic theory predictions are much less accurate.

In summary, then, the thermodynamic properties of an ideal gas as predicted by Maxwell's kinetic theory are

$$pV\!\!\!\!- = mRT$$

$$u_2 - u_1 = c_v(T_2 - T_1)$$

$$h_2 - h_1 = c_p(T_2 - T_1)$$

$$s_2 - s_1 = c_p \ln(T_2/T_1) - R \ln(p_2/p_1) = c_v \ln(T_2/T_1) + R \ln(v_2/v_1)$$

$$c_p - c_v = R$$

where

$$c_v = FR/2$$

$$c_p = (1 + F/2)R$$

$$F = 3b$$

$$b = \text{number of atoms in the molecule}$$

Example 12.3 Estimate the heat transfer rate required to heat low-pressure gaseous carbon tetrachloride (CCl_4) from 500 to 1200 K in a steady state, steady flow, single-inlet, single-outlet, aergonic process at a flow rate of 1.0 kg/min.

Solution The system here will be just the gas in the heating zone. Neglecting the flowstream kinetic and potential energies, the energy rate balance for this system reduces to

$$\dot{Q} + \dot{m}(h_{\text{in}} - h_{\text{out}}) = 0$$

so that

$$\dot{Q} = \dot{m}(h_{\text{out}} - h_{\text{in}}) = \dot{m}c_p(T_{\text{out}} - T_{\text{in}})$$

For CCl_4, $b = 5$; consequently, $F = 3b = 15$. Then Eq. 12.30 gives

$$c_p = (1 + 15/2)R = 8.5(R)$$

Now, the molecular mass of carbon tetrachloride is

$$M = 12 + 4(35.5) = 154 \text{ kg/kgmole}$$

and its gas constant is

$$R = \frac{\mathcal{R}}{M} = \frac{8.3143 \text{ kJ/(kgmole} \cdot \text{K)}}{154 \text{ kg/kgmole}} = 0.054 \text{ kJ/(kg} \cdot \text{K)}$$

so

$$c_p = 8.5[0.054 \text{ kJ/(kg} \cdot \text{K)}] = 0.46 \text{ kJ/(kg} \cdot \text{K)}$$

Therefore,

$$\dot{Q} = (1.0 \text{ kg/min})[0.46 \text{ kJ/(kg} \cdot \text{K)}](1200 - 500 \text{ K}) = 322 \text{ kJ/min}$$

Introduction to Mathematical Probability

If there are N mutually exclusive[3] equally likely outcomes of an experiment, M of which results in event A, then we write the *probability of the occurrence* of event A, P_A, as

$$P_A = \frac{M}{N} \tag{12.32}$$

Now, if $P_A = 0$, then event A is *impossible* and if $P_A = 1$, then event A is a *certainty*. Generally, probabilities do not take on these extreme values but instead lie some-

3. *Mutually exclusive* means that no two of the N outcomes can occur simultaneously.

where in the region

$$0 \le P_A \le 1 \tag{12.33}$$

Let $\sim P_A$ be the probability of event A *not* occurring. Then, because it is a certainty that either event A will occur or it will not occur, we can write

$$P_A + \sim P_A = 1 \tag{12.34}$$

Example 12.4

a) Consider the toss of a single evenly weighted die. What are the six possible mutually exclusive results that can occur?
b) Now consider the toss of a pair of evenly weighted die and add their individual results. What is the probability of each of the resulting sums?
c) What is the most probable sum in item b above?

Solution

a) Since the die is an evenly weighted cube, all six sides have the same probability of landing face up, so we have $N = 6$. Consequently the six possible mutually exclusive results are

$$P_1 = P_2 = P_3 = P_4 = P_5 = 1/6$$

Also, we can write

$$\sim P_1 = \sim P_2 = \sim P_3 = \sim P_4 = \sim P_5 = \sim P_6 = 5/6$$

b) The total number of combinations of results is shown in Table A below. From this table it is seen that $N = 6 \times 6 = 36$. Using this table

Table A The total number of combinations of tossing two die

Die 1	Die 2	Die 1	Die 2
1	1	4	1
1	2	4	2
1	3	4	3
1	4	4	4
1	5	4	5
1	6	4	6
2	1	5	1
2	2	5	2
2	3	5	3
2	4	5	4
2	5	5	5
2	6	5	6
3	1	6	1
3	2	6	2
3	3	6	3
3	4	6	4
3	5	6	5
3	6	6	6

Table B An event-frequency table for tossing two die

Sum M of die values	Number of results producing sum M	Ways of obtaining sum M
0	0	
1	0	
2	1	$1+1$
3	2	$1+2, 2+1$
4	3	$2+2, 1+3, 3+1$
5	4	$2+3, 3+2, 1+5, 4+1$
6	5	$3+3, 4+2, 2+5, 5+1, 1+5$
7	6	$6+1, 1+6, 5+2, 2+5, 4+3, 3+4$
8	5	$4+4, 5+3, 3+6, 6+2, 2+6$
9	4	$4+5, 5+4, 3+7, 6+3$
10	3	$6+4, 4+6, 5+6$
11	2	$6+5, 5+6$
12	1	$6+6$

we can construct an event vs. frequency table as shown in Table B above. Thus, we can compute the following probabilities for the sum of the results of the individual die.

$$P_0 = P_1 = 0 \qquad P_5 = P_9 = 4/36 = 1/9$$

$$P_2 = P_{12} = 1/36 \qquad P_6 = P_8 = 5/36$$

$$P_3 = P_{11} = 2/36 = 1/18 \qquad P_7 = 6/36 = 1/6$$

$$P_4 = P_{10} = 3/36 = 1/12$$

c) From Table B it is clear that in the toss of two evenly weighted die, the number 7 is the most probable outcome, appearing on the average of once every 6 tosses. It has a probability given by Eq. 12.32 of

$$P_7 = 1/6 = 0.1667 = 16.67\%$$

This probability concept can be used to further investigate the collision frequency characteristics of the kinetic theory model of ideal gases. Let the number of molecular collisions occurring in an ideal gas during some time interval $\Delta t = t_2 - t_1$ be δN, and let $N(t)$ be the number of molecules of the gas at time t that have not yet had a collision. Then, $\delta = N(t_1) - N(t_2)$. Since we have defined the Δ symbol to be evaluated at time t_2 minus time t_1, then ΔN becomes

$$\Delta N = N(t_2) - N(t_1) = -\delta N$$

We postulate that δN will be proportional to the product of $N(t)$, Δt, and the average molecular velocity V_{avg} as follows:

$$\delta N = -\Delta N \propto -NV_{avg}(\Delta t)$$

This proportionality can be reduced to an equality by the introduction of a proportionality constant P_c, which we call the *collision probability*. Then the number of collisions that occur in time interval Δt becomes

$$\delta N = -P_c N V_{avg} (\Delta t)$$

In the limit as $\Delta t \to 0$ this equation becomes

$$dN = -P_c N V_{avg}\, dt$$

Let $V_{avg}\, dt = dX$ where X is the distance between collisions. Then this equation can be written as

$$\frac{dN}{N} = -P_c\, dX$$

which can be integrated to give

$$N = N(t) = N_0 \exp(-P_c X) \tag{12.35}$$

where $N_0 = N(t = 0)$. In Eq. 12.16 we defined the mean free path λ as the average distance between collisions, which can be determined from X as

$$\lambda = X_{avg} = \frac{1}{N_0} \int_0^\infty X(-dN)$$

where the minus sign has been introduced because $N(t)$ is decreasing with time, and therefore $dN < 0$. From Eq. 12.35 we find that

$$dN = -N_0 P_c \exp(-P_c X)\, dX$$

and thus the mean free path is given by

$$\lambda = \frac{1}{N_0} \int_0^\infty X N_0 P_c \exp(-P_c X)\, dX = \frac{1}{P_c}$$

Consequently, we have the result that the collision probability is exactly equal to the inverse of the mean free path,

$$P_c = \frac{1}{\lambda} = \sigma \frac{N}{V}$$

where σ is the collision cross section discussed earlier. Finally, Eq. 12.35 takes the form

$$N(t) = N_0 \exp(-X/\lambda) \tag{12.36}$$

so that by the time all the molecules in the gas have traveled a distance of only one mean free path ($X = \lambda$), then

$$\frac{N}{N_0} = e^{-1} = 0.368 = 36.8\%$$

of them have not yet had a collision.

Probabilities of related events that are not mutually exclusive have the following interpretation. Assume that event B depends in some way on another event A. Then the *conditional* probability of event B occurring given the fact that event A has already occurred is written $P_{B/A}$. The *compound* probability that both events A and B will occur is written as P_{AB}. The relation between these two probabilities is the basic AND logic probability statement, written as

$$P(\text{A and B}) = P_{AB} = P_A P_{B/A} = P_B P_{A/B} \tag{12.37}$$

If events A and B are totally *independent*, then their probabilities are uncoupled and $P_{A/B} = P_A$ and $P_{B/A} = P_B$. Then

$$P(\text{A and B}) = P_{AB} = P_A P_B$$

Similarly, the basic OR logic probability statement can be written as

$$P(\text{A or B}) = P_A + P_B - P_{AB} \tag{12.38}$$

If events A and B are mutually exclusive (i.e., they cannot occur simultaneously), then $P_{AB} = 0$ and $P(\text{A or B}) = P_A + P_B$.

Example 12.5

In the draw of a single card from a full deck of playing cards what is the probability that it will be an ace or a spade?

Solution

$$P(\text{ace or spade}) = P_{\text{ace}} + P_{\text{spade}} - P_{\text{ace of spades}}$$

Now,

$$P_{\text{ace}} = \tfrac{4}{52} = \tfrac{1}{13}$$

$$P_{\text{spade}} = \tfrac{13}{52} = \tfrac{1}{4}$$

$$P_{\text{ace of spades}} = \tfrac{1}{52}$$

so

$$P(\text{ace or spade}) = \tfrac{1}{13} + \tfrac{1}{4} - \tfrac{1}{52} = \tfrac{16}{52} = 0.3077 = 30.77\%$$

The last mathematical concepts needed in our study of probability are those of permutations and combinations. A specific ordered arrangement of N distinguishable objects is called a *permutation*. The total number of ways of making different ordered arrangements of the N objects taken R at a time without using any object more than once is given by

$$P_R^N = \frac{N!}{(N-R)!} \tag{12.39a}$$

where $N! = N(N-1)(N-2)(N-3)\cdots(3)(2)(1)$ is N *factorial*. Note that we define $0! = 1$. Thus, the total number of permutations of N distinct objects taken N at a time is

$$P_R^N = N!/0! = N!$$

However, if the objects are allowed to be repeated within an arrangement, then the total number of arrangements becomes

$$P_N^N = N^R \tag{12.39b}$$

We define *combinations* as the ways of choosing a sample of R objects from a group of N objects without regard to order within the sample (e.g., the groupings AB and BA are different permutations of A and B but they are the same combination of A and B). The total number of combinations of N unique objects taken R at a time without using any object more than once is given by

$$C_R^N = \frac{P_R^N}{R!} = \frac{N!}{(N-R)!R!} \tag{12.40a}$$

But if the objects are allowed to be repeated within the sample, then the number of combinations becomes

$$C_R^N = \frac{P_R^N}{R!} = \frac{(N+R-1)!}{(N-1)!R!} \tag{12.40b}$$

Suppose that not all objects in the group of N are different from each other. The number of permutations of N objects, R_1 of one kind, R_2 of a second kind, $\ldots$, R_k of a kth kind is given by

$$P_{R_1,R_2,\ldots,R_k}^N = \frac{N!}{R_1!R_2!R_3!\cdots R_k!} \tag{12.41}$$

and since the objects within the k groups are no longer unique, then the total number of combinations and permutations are equal, or

$$C_{R_1,R_2,\ldots,R_k}^N = P_{R_1,R_2,\ldots,R_k}^N$$

Quantum Statistical Thermodynamics

We begin by defining the *microstate* of a group of molecules as the state produced by specifying the instantaneous energy state of each molecule of the group. We define the *macrostate* as the instantaneous average state of the collection of molecules, and the thermodynamic *equilibrium state* as being the most probable macrostate. The mathematical probability of macrostate A is defined as

$$P_{\mathrm{A}} = \frac{W(\mathrm{A})}{\sum_{i} W(i)} \tag{12.42}$$

where $W(\mathrm{A})$ is the number of different ways that macrostate A can occur (i.e., the number of microstates per macrostate A), and $\sum_i W(i)$ is the total number of macrostates possible. Then the condition we call thermodynamic equilibirum is simply the macrostate that has the largest value of P.

A macrostate is an overview of a complex situation whereas a microstate describes the details of how each element of the system functions. As an analogy, consider a national presidential election. The macrostates are the various possible winners of the election, and the microstates are the various different combinations of ways in which the voters may cast their ballots.

Late in the nineteenth century electrical discharge experiments in various gases produced light emission spectra that were very unusual. Instead of being an emission with a continuous color frequency (like *white* light), the emissions consisted of discrete spectral lines located at fixed wavelengths. Figure 12.5 shows the emission spectrum of atomic hydrogen in the visible region of the electromagnetic spectrum. From these emission spectra it was clear that if the emission phenomenon is attributed to photon ejection by electrons as they move from an atom's outer orbit to an inner orbit, then the electrons must occupy discrete orbits and consequently are not simply clustered around the nucleus in a random manner.

In 1913 Niels Bohr hypothesized that the electron orbits of an atom were *quantitized* (i.e., made discrete) according to the value of the electron's angular momentum as

$$m\omega = mVr = n\frac{h}{2\pi}$$

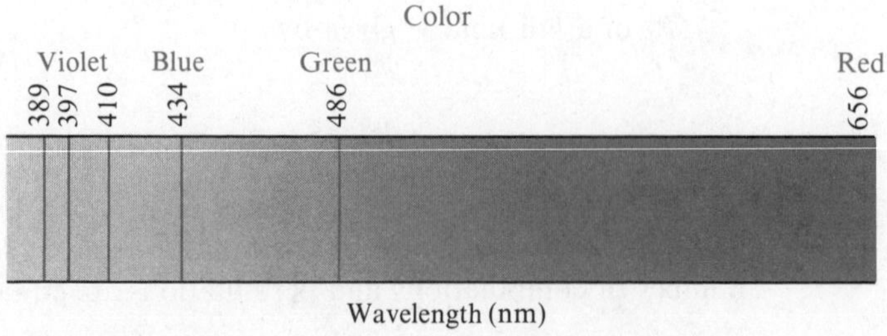

Color

Violet 389 397 410 · Blue 434 · Green 486 · Red 656

Wavelength (nm)

Figure 12.5 The emission spectrum of atomic hydrogen.

where ω is the angular velocity of the electron, V is the electron's orbital velocity, r is the radius of the orbit, h is Planck's constant, and $n = 1, 2, 3, \ldots$ is the (primary) quantum number. Therefore, the radius of an electron's orbit is given by

$$r = \frac{h}{2\pi m V} n$$

As the years passed other quantum numbers had to be introduced to account for such things as the elliptical shape of the orbit (this accounted for the finite width of the emission lines and was called the *azimuthal* quantum number), the splitting of the spectral lines in a strong magnetic field (the *magnetic* quantum number), the magnetic moment associated with the direction of electron spin (the *electron spin* quantum number), and so forth.

The continual modification of the original Bohr model required to make it conform to experimental observations started physicists looking for a new model. In 1924 Louis Victor Pierre Raymond de Broglie (1892–1987) used an analogy between classical mechanics and geometric optics to formulate a dual particle-wave model for matter. He argued that since the energy ϵ of a photon is given by

$$\epsilon = h\nu$$

where h is Planck's constant and ν is the photon's frequency, and since Einstein's mass–energy relation for the photon is

$$\epsilon = mc^2$$

where m is its mass and c is the velocity of light, then the linear momentum p of the photon can be written as

$$p = mc = \frac{h\nu}{c} = \frac{h}{\lambda}$$

where $\lambda = c/\nu$ is the wavelength of the photon. De Broglie then extended the argument to mass particles (like electrons) by postulating that for them

$$p = mV = \frac{h}{\lambda}$$

where λ is the particle's *wavelength.* This postulation was experimentally verified in 1927 when it was demonstrated that electrons could be diffracted in a wave-like manner from a ruled diffraction surface. Thus electrons appeared to have both particle-like and wave-like behavior, and the *duality* principle of matter was established.

Once the wave-like character of matter was recognized it became clear that the kinetic behavior of atomic particles ought to be governed by the same equations that govern the propagation of waves in a continuum. In 1926 Erwin

Schrödinger developed an unsteady wave equation appropriate to matter waves of the form

$$\nabla^2\psi = \frac{2m(\epsilon - \epsilon_p)}{\epsilon^2}\left(\frac{\partial^2\psi}{\partial t^2}\right) \tag{12.43}$$

where ψ is the *wave function* (the wave amplitude), ϵ is the total energy of the particle, ϵ_p is the potential energy of the particle, m is the particle's mass, and ∇^2 is the differential operator defined by

$$\nabla^2(\ ) = \frac{\partial^2}{\partial x^2}(\ ) + \frac{\partial^2}{\partial y^2}(\ ) + \frac{\partial^2}{\partial z^2}(\ )$$

Remarkably, the solutions to (12.43) are inherently quantitized (i.e., solutions only exist for discrete values of ϵ); thus, it has become a fundamental equation in quantum mechanics.

Three Classical Quantum Statistical Models

Consider a system composed of $N = \sum N_i$ particles that are distributed in some manner among ϵ_i different energy levels. Then the total internal energy of the system will be $U = \sum N_i\epsilon_i$. The most probable distribution $(N_i)_{mp}$ of the N particles will be the one that corresponds to the macrostate with the maximum probability P, and the total internal energy of that macrostate will be $U_{mp} = \sum (N_i)_{mp}\epsilon_i$. Once an equation for W is found, then the distribution N_i that maximizes it can easily be found by setting $d(W) = 0$ subject to the constraint that the total energy and total number of particles in the system are constant (i.e., $dN = dU = 0$), and then solving for $N_i = (N_i)_{mp}$.

A particle N_i has a total energy ϵ_i which, in general, is made up of a number of different energy modes. For example, we could partition the total energy of the particle into kinetic energy, rotational energy, vibrational energy, and so forth, and there are many different ways whereby the particle's total energy can be divided among these modes. The total number of arrangements of a particle's different energy modes that will add up to a given energy level ϵ_i is called the *degeneracy* of that energy level and is given the symbol g_i.

The following three classical statistical models have been developed to describe the basic particle-wave nature of certain material particles, and their corresponding W and $(N_i)_{mp}$ equations can be found in Table 12.4.

1. *The Maxwell-Boltzmann model.*[4] Here, all the N_i particles are assumed to be indistinguishable from each other and are distributed among various degenerate energy levels. This model accurately represents the behavior of most simple gases at low pressures.

4. This is called the "corrected" Maxwell-Boltzmann model in most statistical thermodynamics texts.

Table 12.4 Formula for computing the number of microstates in the ith macrostate for various statistical models

Model	Number of microstates per macrostate, W	Most probable distribution $(N_i)_{mp}$
Maxwell-Boltzmann	$\prod_i \frac{g_i^{N_i}}{N_i!}$	$\left(\frac{N}{Z}\right) g_i \exp\left(-\frac{\epsilon_i}{kT}\right)$
Fermi-Dirac	$\prod_i \frac{g_i!}{N_i!(g_i - N_i)!}$	$g_i\left[B \exp\left(\frac{\epsilon_i}{kT}\right) + 1\right]^{-1}$
Bose-Einstein	$\prod_i \frac{(g_i + N_i - 1)!}{N_i!(g_i - 1)!}$	$g_i\left[B \exp\left(\frac{\epsilon_i}{kT}\right) - 1\right]^{-1}$

Here, $Z = \sum g_i \exp(-\epsilon_i/kT)$ = partition function, and $B = \exp(-\bar{\mu}/kT)$ where $\bar{\mu}$ is the molar chemical potential.

2. *The Fermi-Dirac Model.* Here the particles are assumed to be indistinguishable and are distributed among various degenerate energy levels with only one particle per degeneracy (g_i) value. This model accurately represents the behavior of electron and proton gases.

3. *The Bose-Einstein model.* Here the particles are assumed to be indistinguishable and are distributed among various degenerate energy levels with no limit on the number of particles per degeneracy. This model accurately represents the behavior of photon and phonon gases.

The second law of thermodynamics states that S_P or $\dot{S}_P \geq 0$, which implies that at equilibrium, the entropy of a closed system will be a maximum. Also, since thermodynamic equilibrium corresponds to the system being in its most probable macrostate, then it is logical to assume that a functional relation exists between the entropy of the system and the statistical probability of the most probable macrostate. We postulate that this relation has the form:

$$S = f(W_{mp})$$

The problem that we now face is that total entropy S of a system is an additive property whereas W_{mp} is not. In the probability mathematics presented earlier we found that the probability that independent events A and B would both simultaneously occur was $P(\text{A and B}) = P_{AB} = P_A P_B$, and since W_{mp} is related to mathematical probability through Eq. 12.42, we can write

$$W(\text{A and B}) = W_A W_B$$

but

$$S(\text{A and B}) = S_A + S_B$$

Therefore, we must find a function f such that

$$S(\text{A and B}) = f(W_A) + f(W_B) = f[W(\text{A and B})] = f(W_A W_B)$$

The only general function that satisfies this relation is the logarithm, since

$$\ln W_A + \ln W_B = \ln W_A W_B$$

Therefore, we choose to set S proportional to $\ln W_{mp}$. It can be shown that the constant of proportionality in this relation is just Boltzmann's constant k, so we end up with the following entropy–probability relation:

$$S = k \ln W_{mp} \tag{12.44}$$

Thus, we see that entropy is a measure of the molecular order within a system.

Maxwell-Boltzmann Gases

To limit the algebraic complexity of the resulting property formula, we will restrict our attention to the Maxwell-Boltzmann model. It can be shown that for Maxwell-Boltzmann gases with $N \gg 1$

$$u = RT^2\left(\frac{\partial \ln Z}{\partial T}\right) \tag{12.45}$$

and

$$h = u + RT \tag{12.46}$$

where

$$Z = \sum g_i \exp(-\epsilon_i/kT) \tag{12.47}$$

Z is called the *partition function* of the system and g_i is the degeneracy of the ith energy level ϵ_i. At high temperatures the number of quantum states (or degeneracy levels g_i) available at any energy level is much larger than the number of particles N_i in that energy level, or

$$\frac{g_i}{N_i} \gg 1$$

Then the number of microstates per macrostate for the three statistical models shown in Table 12.4 are approximately the same, i.e.,

$$W_{BE} \approx W_{FD} \approx W_{MB} = \prod_i \frac{g_i^{N_i}}{N_i!} \tag{12.48}$$

Also, under this condition, the most probable particle distribution of these three models are approximately the same

$$(N_i)_{\substack{BE\\mp}} \approx (N_i)_{\substack{FD\\mp}} \approx (N_i)_{\substack{MB\\mp}} = \left(\frac{N}{Z}\right) g_i \exp(-\epsilon_i/kT) \tag{12.49}$$

These two results can then be inserted into Eq. 12.44 to produce an equation for entropy as follows. First we calculate ln W_{mp} from Table 12.4 as

$$\ln W_{mp} = \sum_i (N_i \ln g_i - \ln N_i!)_{mp}$$

We then use Stirling's approximation

$$\ln N! \approx N \ln N - N$$

for the factorial term to obtain

$$\ln W_{mp} \approx \sum_i (N_i)_{mp}[\ln(g_i/N_i)_{mp} + 1]$$

Then we use equation 12.49 to evaluate the term

$$(g_i/N_i)_{mp} = \frac{Z}{N} \exp(\epsilon_i/kT)$$

which produces the result

$$\ln W_{mp} \approx \sum_i (N_i)_{mp}[\ln(Z/N) + \epsilon_i/kT + 1]$$

which simplifies to

$$\ln W_{mp} \approx N[\ln(Z/N) + 1] + U/kT$$

The total entropy is then given by Eq. 12.44 as

$$S = Nk[\ln(Z/N) + 1] + U/T \tag{12.50}$$

and since $Nk = N\mathscr{R}/N_o = n\mathscr{R} = (m/\text{M})\mathscr{R} = mR$, the specific entropy can then be written as

$$s = R[\ln(Z/N) + 1] + u/T \tag{12.51}$$

The molecular model we will consider here is that of a relatively simple molecule in which the total molecular energy can be separated into only three modes: translational, rotational, and vibrational. Then, the partition function Z will be made up of translational, rotational, and vibrational molecular energy storage mechanisms, and can be written as

$$Z = (Z_{\text{trans}})(Z_{\text{rot}})(Z_{\text{vib}}) \tag{12.52}$$

Consequently, we will be able to determine the molecular translational, rotational, and vibrational contribution to each of the properties, u, h, and s. Because these partition functions depend upon the geometry of the molecule, we begin their study with the simplest possible structure, a monatomic gas.

Monatomic Maxwell-Boltzmann Gases

For a Maxwell-Boltzmann monatomic gas it can be shown that

$$Z_{\text{trans}} = \mathcal{V}(2\pi mkT/h^2)^{3/2} \tag{12.53}$$

where $\mathcal{V}$ is the total volume of the system, h and k are Planck's constant and Boltzmann's constant, and $Z_{\text{rot}} = Z_{\text{vib}} = 0$. Then Eqs. 12.45, 12.46, and 12.51 give

$$\left.\begin{aligned} u &= \tfrac{3}{2}RT \\ h &= u + RT = \tfrac{5}{2}RT \\ c_v &= \tfrac{3}{2} \\ c_p &= \tfrac{5}{2} \\ s &= R\{\ln[(2\pi m/h^2)^{3/2}(kT)^{5/2}/p] + \tfrac{5}{2}\} \end{aligned}\right\} \text{For monatomic gases only} \qquad \begin{aligned} &(12.54a)\\ &(12.54b)\\ &(12.54c)\\ &(12.54d)\\ &(12.54e)\end{aligned}$$

These formulae for u, h, c_v, and c_p are the same as those obtained from the kinetic theory of gases discussed earlier in the chapter. The equation for entropy, on the other hand, is more complex and therefore one would expect it to be more accurate. We now progress on to the next most complex geometric molecular structure, diatomic gases.

Diatomic Maxwell-Boltzmann Gases

For a diatomic Maxwell-Boltzmann gas it can be shown that the translational partition function is the same as that for a monatomic gas, Eq. 12.53. However, there are now 2 rotational and 1 vibrational degrees of freedom present. In this case the rotational and vibrational partition functions are

$$T_{\text{rot}} = T/\sigma\Theta_r \tag{12.55}$$

and

$$T_{\text{vib}} = [1 - \exp(-\Theta_v/T)]^{-1} \tag{12.56}$$

where σ is the rotational symmetry number (the number of axes about which the molecule can be rotated 180° and be indistinguishable from the original configuration), Θ_r is called the *characteristic rotational temperature*, and Θ_v is called the *characteristic vibrational temperature.* Tables 12.5 and 12.6 give values for Θ_r, Θ_v, and σ for various substances. The various components to the resulting specific property equations then become

$$u_{\text{trans}} = \tfrac{3}{2}RT \tag{12.57a}$$

$$u_{\text{rot}} = RT \tag{12.57b}$$

$$u_{\text{vib}} = (u_o)_{\text{vib}} + R\Theta_v/[\exp(\Theta_v/T) - 1] \tag{12.57c}$$

Table 12.5 **Characteristic vibrational and rotational temperatures of some common diatomic materials**

Material	Θ_v (K)	Θ_r (K)
H_2	6140	85.5
HF	5954	30.3
OH	5360	27.5
HCl	4300	15.3
CH	4100	20.7
N_2	3340	2.86
HBr	3700	12.1
HI	3200	9.0
CO	3120	2.77
NO	2740	2.47
O_2	2260	2.09
Cl_2	810	0.35
Br_2	470	0.12
I_2	309	0.05
Na_2	230	0.22
K_2	140	0.08

Source: From John F. Lee, Francis W. Sears, and Donald L. Turcotte, *Statistical Thermodynamics*, © 1963, Addison-Wesley Publishing Co., Inc., Reading, Massachusetts. Adapted from Table 10–1 on page 204. Reprinted with permission.

Table 12.6 **Rotational symmetry number for some simple materials**

Material	σ
Any diatomic molecule with two different atoms (e.g., HCl, HI, NO, . . .)	1
Any diatomic molecule with two identical atoms (e.g., H_2, O_2, N_2, . . .)	2
Any triatomic molecule with two different atoms forming an isosceles triangle (such as H_2O), or any linear triatomic molecule (e.g., CO_2, NO_2, . . .)	2
Any quatratomic molecule with two different atoms forming an equilateral triangular pyramid (such as NH_3)	3
Any molecule forming a plane rectangle (such as C_2H_4)	4
Any pentatomic molecule with two different atoms forming a regular tetrahedron with the carbon atom at the center of mass (e.g., CCl_4, CH_4, . . .)	12

Thus,

$$u = u_{\text{trans}} + u_{\text{rot}} + u_{\text{vib}}$$
$$= (u_o)_{\text{vib}} + \tfrac{5}{2}RT + R\Theta_v/[\exp(\Theta_v/T) - 1] \tag{12.57d}$$

where

$$(u_o)_{\text{vib}} = R\Theta_v/2 \tag{12.58}$$

is the vibrational energy at absolute zero temperature.[5] Similarily

$$h_{\text{trans}} = \tfrac{5}{2}RT \tag{12.59a}$$

$$h_{\text{rot}} = u_{\text{rot}} = RT \tag{12.59b}$$

$$h_{\text{vib}} = u_{\text{vib}} = (u_o)_{\text{vib}} + R\Theta_v/[\exp(\Theta_v/T) - 1] \tag{12.59c}$$

Thus,

$$h = h_{\text{trans}} + h_{\text{rot}} + h_{\text{vib}}$$
$$= (u_o)_{\text{vib}} + \tfrac{7}{2}RT + R\Theta_v/[\exp(\Theta_v/T) - 1] \tag{12.59d}$$

Then we can find

$$(c_v)_{\text{trans}} = \tfrac{3}{2}R \tag{12.60a}$$

$$(c_v)_{\text{rot}} = R \tag{12.60b}$$

$$(c_v)_{\text{vib}} = R(\Theta_v/T)^2[\exp(\Theta_v/T)]/[\exp(\Theta_v/T) - 1]^2 \tag{12.60c}$$

Thus,

$$c_v = (c_v)_{\text{trans}} + (c_v)_{\text{rot}} + (c_v)_{\text{vib}}$$
$$= \tfrac{5}{2}R + R(\Theta_v/T)^2[\exp(\Theta_v/T)]/[\exp(\Theta_v/T) - 1]^2 \tag{12.60d}$$

and

$$(c_p)_{\text{trans}} = \tfrac{5}{2}R \tag{12.61a}$$

$$(c_p)_{\text{rot}} = (c_v)_{\text{rot}} = R \tag{12.61b}$$

$$(c_p)_{\text{vib}} = (c_v)_{\text{vib}} = R(\Theta_v/T)^2[\exp(\Theta_v/T)]/[\exp(\Theta_v/T) - 1]^2 \tag{12.61c}$$

Thus,

$$c_p = (c_p)_{\text{trans}} + (c_p)_{\text{rot}} + (c_p)_{\text{vib}}$$
$$= \tfrac{7}{2}R + R(\Theta_v/T)^2[\exp(\Theta_v/T)]/[\exp(\Theta_v/T) - 1]^2 \tag{12.61d}$$

5. In this model the concept of absolute zero temperature corresponds to the cessation of all translational and rotational molecular motion, but vibrational motion is still allowed to occur. Thus, the internal energy does not vanish at absolute zero temperature in this model.

Finally,

$$s_{\text{trans}} = R\{\ln[(2\pi m/h^2)^{3/2}(kT)^{5/2}/p] + \tfrac{5}{2}\} \tag{12.62a}$$

$$s_{\text{rot}} = R\{\ln[T/(\sigma\Theta_r)] + 1\} \tag{12.62b}$$

$$s_{\text{vib}} = R\{\ln[1 - \exp(-\Theta_v/T)]^{-1} + (\Theta_v/T)[\exp(\Theta_v/T) - 1]^{-1}\} \tag{12.62c}$$

Thus,

$$\begin{aligned} s &= s_{\text{trans}} + s_{\text{rot}} + s_{\text{vib}} \\ &= R\{\ln[(2\pi m/h^2)^{3/2}(kT)^{5/2}/p] + \tfrac{5}{2}\} + R\{\ln[T/\sigma\Theta_r)] + 1\} \\ &\quad + R\{\ln[1 - \exp(-\Theta_v/T)]^{-1} + (\Theta_v/T)[\exp(\Theta_v/T) - 1]^{-1}\} \end{aligned} \tag{12.62d}$$

These equations produce reasonable accurate results for diatonic gases at moderate to high temperatures, as illustrated by the following example.

Example 12.6

Compute c_v for NO at 2000 K and compare it with the measured results given in Table 12.3.

Solution For a diatomic Maxwell-Boltzmann gas Eq. 12.60*d* gives

$$c_v = \frac{5}{2}R + \frac{R(\Theta_v/T)^2 \exp(\Theta_v/T)}{[\exp(\Theta_v/T) - 1]^2}$$

and from Table 12.5 we find that for NO, $\Theta_v = 2740$ K. Then,

$$\begin{aligned} c_v &= \left[\frac{5}{2} + \frac{\left(\frac{2740}{2000}\right)^2 \exp\frac{2740}{2000}}{\left(\exp\frac{2740}{2000} - 1\right)^2}\right][8.3143\ \text{kJ/(kgmole}\cdot\text{K)}]/(30.01\ \text{kg/kgmole}) \\ &= 0.93\ \text{kJ/kg} \end{aligned}$$

But,

$$\frac{c_v}{R} = \frac{0.93}{8.3143/30.01} = 3.36$$

This value is considerably higher than the value of 2.51 found in Table 12.3 for NO, but in this example the NO was at a temperature of 2000 K whereas the table values are for materials at 293 K. At 293 K the calculation gives

$$\frac{c_v}{R} = \frac{5}{2} + \frac{\left(\frac{2740}{293}\right)^2 \exp\frac{2740}{293}}{\left(\exp\frac{2740}{293} - 1\right)^2} = 2.51$$

as in Table 12.3.

Polyatomic Maxwell-Boltzmann Gases

Polyatomic gases are divided into two catagories of molecular geometry: linear and nonlinear. Linear polyatomic molecules have only two degrees of rotational freedom, as in the case of diatomic molecules. However, they have $3b - 5$ degrees of vibrational freedom, where b is the number of atoms in the molecule. Therefore, the equations used to calculate the translational and rotational contributions to the molecular energy are the same as those used for the diatomic molecule (i.e., parts a and b of Eqs. 12.57, and 12.59–12.62). The equations for the vibrational contribution to the molecular energy of a linear polyatomic Maxwell-Boltzmann gas are

$$u_{\text{vib}} = (u_o)_{\text{vib}} + R \sum_{i=1}^{3b-5} \Theta_{vi}/[\exp(\Theta_{vi}/T) - 1] \tag{12.63a}$$

$$h_{\text{vib}} = u_{\text{vib}} = (u_o)_{\text{vib}} + R \sum_{i=1}^{3b-5} \Theta_{\text{v}i}/[\exp(\Theta_{\text{v}i}/T) - 1] \tag{12.63b}$$

$$(c_v)_{\text{vib}} = R \sum_{i=1}^{3b-5} (\Theta_{\text{v}i}/T)^2[\exp(\Theta_{\text{v}i}/T) - 1]^2 \tag{12.63c}$$

$$(c_p)_{\text{vib}} = (c_v)_{\text{vib}} = R \sum_{i=1}^{3b-5} (\Theta_{\text{v}i}/T)^2[\exp(\Theta_{\text{v}i}/T)]/[\exp(\Theta_{\text{v}i}/T) - 1]^2 \tag{12.63d}$$

and

$$s_{\text{vib}} = R \sum_{i=1}^{3b-5} \{\ln[1 - \exp(-\Theta_{\text{v}i}/T)]^{-1} + (\Theta_{\text{v}i}/T)[\exp(\Theta_{\text{v}i}/T) - 1]^{-1}\} \tag{12.63e}$$

where the vibrational internal energy at absolute zero temperature is now found from

$$(u_o)_{\text{vib}} = \sum_{i=1}^{3b-5} R\Theta_{\text{v}i}/2 \tag{12.64}$$

since there are now $3b - 5$ characteristic vibrational temperatures $\Theta_{\text{v}i}$.

Example 12.7

Carbon dioxide is a linear triatomic molecule that has the following characteristic temperatures

$$\Theta_{\text{r}} = 0.562 \text{ K}$$

$$\Theta_{\text{v}1} = 1932 \text{ K}$$

$$\Theta_{\text{v}2} = \Theta_{\text{v}3} = 960 \text{ K}$$

$$\Theta_{\text{v}4} = 3380 \text{ K}$$

Determine the specific internal energy, specific enthalpy, and specific entropy of CO_2 at a temperature of 1000 K and a pressure of 1 atm.

Solution The mass of the CO_2 molecule is

$$m = M/N_o = 44.01/6.023 \times 10^{26} = 7.31 \times 10^{-26} \text{ kg/molecule}$$

and the gas constant for CO_2 is

$$R = \mathscr{R}/M = 8.3143/44.01 = 0.1889 \text{ kJ/(kg}\cdot\text{K)}$$

Equation 12.64 gives the vibrational specific internal energy at absolute zero temperature as

$$(u_o)_{\text{vib}} = (0.1889)(1932 + 960 + 960 + 3380)/2 = 683.1 \text{ kJ/kg}$$

and Eq. 12.63*a* gives the vibrational component of the specific internal energy as

$$\begin{aligned} u_{\text{vib}} = 683.1 + (0.1889)\{&(1932)[\exp(1.932) - 1]^{-1} \\ &+ 2(960)[\exp(0.960) - 1]^{-1} \\ &+ (3380)[\exp(3.380) - 1]^{-1}\} = 992.4 \text{ kJ/kg} \end{aligned}$$

The translational and rotational components are given by Eqs. 12.57*a* and 12.57*b* as

$$u_{\text{trans}} = \tfrac{3}{2}RT = \tfrac{3}{2}(0.1889)(1000) = 283.4 \text{ kJ/kg}$$

$$u_{\text{rot}} = RT = (0.1889)(1000) = 188.9 \text{ kJ/kg}$$

Then

$$u = u_{\text{trans}} + u_{\text{rot}} + u_{\text{vib}} = 283.4 + 188.9 + 992.4 = 1464.7 \text{ kJ/kg}$$

The specific enthalpy is now given simply by

$$h = u + RT = 1464.7 + (0.1889)(1000) = 1653.6 \text{ kJ/kg}$$

The translational and rotational specific entropy values are calculated from Eqs. 12.62*a* and 12.62*b*. First we calculate

$$\begin{aligned} (2\pi m/h^2)^{3/2}(kT)^{5/2}/p &= [2\pi(7.31 \times 10^{-26})/(6.626 \times 10^{-34})^2]^{3/2} \\ &\quad \times [(1.38 \times 10^{-23})(1000)]^{5/2}/101{,}325 \\ &= 2.36 \times 10^{8} \text{ per molecule} \end{aligned}$$

and then Eq. 12.62*a* gives

$$s_{\text{trans}} = (0.1889)[\ln(2.36 \times 10^{8}) + \tfrac{5}{2}] = 4.1142 \text{ kJ/(kg}\cdot\text{K)}$$

and Eq. 12.62*b* with $\sigma = 2$ from Table 12.6 gives

$$s_{rot} = (0.1889)\{\ln[1000/(2)(0.562)] + 1\} = 1.4715 \text{ kJ/(kg·K)}$$

Equation 12.63*e* is then used to find the vibrational component of the specific entropy as

$$\begin{aligned} s_{vib} = (0.1889)\{&\ln[1 - \exp(-1.932)]^{-1} + (1.932)[\exp(1.932) - 1]^{-1} \\ &+ \ln[1 - \exp(-0.960)]^{-1} + (0.960)[\exp(0.960) - 1]^{-1} \\ &+ \ln[1 - \exp(-0.960)]^{-1} + (0.960)[\exp(0.960) - 1]^{-1} \\ &+ \ln[1 - \exp(-3.380)]^{-1} + (3.380)[\exp(3.380) - 1]^{-1} \\ = 0.5270 &\text{ kJ/(kg·K)} \end{aligned}$$

Then the specific entropy is

$$\begin{aligned} s = s_{trans} + s_{rot} + s_{vib} &= 4.1142 + 1.4715 + 0.5270 \\ &= 6.1127 \text{ kJ/(kg·K)} \end{aligned}$$

The nonlinear polyatomic molecule has three translational degrees of freedom, three rotational degrees of freedom, and $3b - 6$ degrees of vibrational freedom. Thus, it has the same equations for the translational molecular energy as in the linear polyatomic case, but the rotational and vibrational contribution equations are different. In this case

$$u_{rot} = h_{rot} = \tfrac{3}{2}RT \tag{12.65a}$$

$$(c_v)_{rot} = (c_p)_{rot} = \tfrac{3}{2}R \tag{12.65b}$$

$$s_{rot} = R\{\ln[T/(\sigma\Theta_r)] + \tfrac{3}{2}\} \tag{12.65c}$$

and

$$u_{vib} = (u_o)_{vib} + R\sum_{i=1}^{3b-6} \Theta_{vi}/[\exp(\Theta_{vi}/T) - 1] \tag{12.66a}$$

$$h_{vib} = u_{vib} = (u_o)_{vib} + R\sum_{i=1}^{3b-6} \Theta_{vi}/[\exp(\Theta_{vi}/T) - 1] \tag{12.66b}$$

$$(c_v)_{vib} = R\sum_{i=1}^{3b-6} (\Theta_{vi}/T)^2[\exp(\Theta_{vi}/T)]/[\exp(\Theta_{vi}/T) - 1]^2 \tag{12.66c}$$

$$(c_p)_{vib} = (c_v)_{vib} + R\sum_{i=1}^{3b-6} (\Theta_{vi}/T)^2[\exp(\Theta_{vi}/T)]/[\exp(\Theta_{vi}/T) - 1]^2 \tag{12.66d}$$

and

$$s_{\text{vib}} = R \sum_{i=1}^{3b-6} \{\ln[1 - \exp(-\Theta_{vi}/T)]^{-1} + (\Theta_{vi}/T)[\exp(\Theta_{vi}/T) - 1]^{-1}\} \quad \text{(12.66e)}$$

where the vibrational internal energy at absolute temperature is now found from

$$(u_o)_{\text{vib}} = \sum_{i=1}^{3b-6} R\Theta_{vi}/2 \quad \text{(12.67)}$$

since the nonlinear polyatomic molecule has $3b - 6$ characteristic vibrational temperatures Θ_{vi}.

Summary

The subject of statistical thermodynamics is inherently mathematically complex and conceptually difficult. It is often the subject of an entire advanced engineering course, usually at the graduate level. The material presented in this chapter is intended only as an introduction to this subject.

In this chapter we have summarized the essential concepts of statistical thermodynamics and presented it in a simple enough manner to make the results useful. This subject is very effective when experimental data are not available and values of various thermodynamic properties are needed to carry out an engineering analyses. The interested reader is encouraged to fill in the various theoretical gaps in the material presented in this chapter by additional reading in this area. Many excellent texts are available on this subject, some of which are listed below.

Selected References

Fay, J. A. *Molecular Thermodynamics.* Reading MA: Addison-Wesley, 1965.

Jackson, E. A. *Equilibrium Statistical Mechanics.* Englewood Cliffs, NJ: Prentice-Hall, 1968.

Kauzmann, W. *Kinetic Theory of Gases.* New York: Benjamin, 1966.

Kelly, D. C. *Thermodynamics and Statistical Physics.* New York: Academic, 1973.

Kestin, J., and Dorfman, J. R. *A Course in Statistical Thermodynamics.* New York: Academic, 1971.

Lee, J. F., Sears, F. W., and Turcotte, D. L. *Statistical Thermodynamics.* Reading, MA: Addison-Wesley, 1963.

Pierce, F. J. *Microscopic Thermodynamics.* Scranton, PA: International Textbook, 1968.

Resibois, P., and de Leener, M. *Classical Kinetic Theory of Fluids.* New York: Wiley, 1977.

Sonntag, R. E., and Van Wylen, G. J. *Fundamentals of Statistical Thermodynamics.* New York: Wiley, 1966.

Tien, C. L., and Lienhard, J. H. *Statistical Thermodynamics.* New York: Holt, Rinehard & Winston, 1971.

Chapter Twelve Problems

1. Determine the number of diatomic nitrogen (N_2) molecules in 1 cubic inch at 70 °F and a pressure of 10^{-10} mm of mercury absolute (a very high vacuum).

2. Determine the mean free path and the collision frequency of diatomic nitrogen at 1000 k and 10 MPa. The effective radius of the nitrogen molecule is 1.10×10^{-10} m.

3. For 10^{10} bromine (Br_2) molecules confined in a volume of 1.0 m^3 at a pressure of 1 Pascal, assume ideal gas kinetic theory behavior and determine

a) the temperature in the container,

b) the mean free path between collisions, and

c) the collision frequency $\mathscr{F}$.

4. Find the temperature T at which $V_{mp} = c$ (the velocity of light) for the neon atoms discussed in Examples 12.1 and 12.2.

5. Hydrogen (H_2) at 3 MPa and 1000 K is confined in a volume of 1.0 m^3. Determine, V_{avg}, V_{rms}, V_{mp}, and the collision frequency $\mathscr{F}$.

6. Oxygen (O_2) at 300 K and 1 atm pressure is confined in a volume of 10^{-4} m^3. Determine

a) the number of oxygen molecules present,

b) the average molecular velocity,

c) the rms molecular velocity,

d) the most probable molecular velocity,

e) the number of molecules with a velocity in the range of 0 to 10^{-4} m/s, and

f) the number of molecules with velocities greater than 10^6 m/s.

7. Using the following infinite series expansion

$$\exp(-x^2) = 1 - x^2/1! + x^4/2! - x^6/3! + x^8/4! - \cdots$$

show that the equivalent expansion for the error function is

$$\text{erf}(x) = \frac{2}{\sqrt{\pi}}\left(x - \frac{x^3}{3(1!)} + \frac{x^5}{5(2!)} - \frac{x^7}{7(3!)} + \cdots\right)$$

8. Show that Eq. 12.27 can be written as

$$\frac{N(V \to \infty)}{N} = \frac{2}{\sqrt{\pi}}\left(\int_x^\infty e^{-x^2}\,dx + xe^{-x^2}\right)$$

where $x = V/V_{mp}$

9. Show that if $a \gg 1$, then

$$\int_a^\infty e^{-x^2}\,dx \approx \frac{1}{2a}e^{-a^2}$$

(*Hint*: Set $x = a + y$, then $dx = dy$ and the integral over dy will have limits from 0 to ∞).

10. Using the results from Problems 8 and 9 above, show that for $x \gg 1$,

$$\frac{N(V \to \infty)}{N} = \frac{2}{\sqrt{\pi}}\left(x + \frac{1}{2x}\right)e^{-x^2}$$

11. Using the equations of kinetic theory it can be shown that the number of molecules per unit time that leak out of an isothermal pressurized container of volume $\mathcal{V}$ through a small hole of area A is

$$\dot{N}_{leak} = (N/\forall)(A/4)V_{avg}$$

Show that the pressure in the container will then decay according to

$$p = p_0 \exp(-AV_{avg}t/4\forall)$$

where $V_{avg} = (8kT/\pi m)^{1/2}$, and p_0 is the pressure in the container at time $t = 0$.

12. Using the information given in Problem 11 and the equations of kinetic theory, calculate the mass rate of separation of the isotope U^{235} from a gaseous mixture of U^{238} and U^{235} by a molecular sieve. The sieve is a porous pipe 0.03 m in diameter and 2000 m long. The area of each pore is 2.6×10^{-19} m^2, and there are 10^9 pores per meter of pipe length. The internal sieve temperature is 1000 K, and the partial pressure difference of the U^{235} across the sieve is 10 Pa.

13. The probability of failure of a space shuttle primary computer system is 0.0015. This computer system has a secondary back up computer system with the same failure probability. What is the probability of simultaneous failure of both the primary and secondary computer systems?

14. An eight-cyclinder engine has one bad spark plug. If the mechanic removes two spark plugs at random, what is the probability that he will find the defective spark plug on the first try?

15. A single die is tossed. What is the probability that it will come up with a value greater than 4?

16. Two die are tossed. Determine the probability that their sum will be greater than **a)** 2, **b)** 4, **c)** 6, **d)** 8, and **e)** 10.

17. Two cards are to be drawn from a standard deck of 52 cards. Calculate the probability that these two cards will be an ace and a ten, drawn in any order.

18. A coin is flipped twice. Determine the probability that only one head will result.

19. Two coins are flipped simultaneously. Determine the probablity that at least one will be a head.

20. If three coins are simultaneously flipped, what is the probability of getting **a)** at least two heads, and **b)** exactly two heads.

21. Show that $C_R^N \equiv C_{N-R}^N$ for any N and R.

22. An electronic component is available from five different suppliers. How many different ways can two suppliers be chosen from the five available?

23. How many different 10-digit phone numbers can be made from the digits 0 through 9 if the first 3 digits must be 414.

24. How many different 6-digit automobile license plates can be made using only the digits 0 through 9 if the digits may be repeated?

25. How many different 9-digit social security numbers can be made if

a) no digit is allowed to be repeated, and

b) the digits can be repeated.

26. How many different three-letter "words" can be made from the 26 letters of the English alphabet without regard to vowels if the letters can be used more than once per word?

27. A component subassembly consists of 5 separate pieces which can be assembled in any order. A production test is to be designed to determine the minimum time required to assemble the subassembly. If each sequence of assembly is to be tested once, how many tests need to be conducted?

28. A person is shopping for a new car. One dealer offers a choice of 5 body styles, 4 engine types, 10 color combinations, 3 transmissions, and 3 accessory packages. How many different cars are there to choose from?

29. Determine the collision probability of the bromine molecules in Problem 4.

30. A typical galaxy occupies a volume of about 10^{61} m^3 and contains 10^{11} stars, each with an effective radius of 10^9 m. Determine

a) the collision probability of two stars within the galaxy, and

b) the number of stars that have experienced a collision by the time they have traveled a distance of 0.01 mean free paths.

31. Show that for a Maxwell-Boltzmann gas the total enthalpy H is given by

$$H = -N\partial(\ln Z)/\partial\beta + NkT\mathcal{V}[\partial(\ln Z)/\partial\mathcal{V}]$$

where $\beta = 1/kT$, and the pressure is $p = NkT(\partial \ln Z/\partial\mathcal{V})$.

32. Compute the percent error in Stirling's approximation, $\ln N! \approx N \ln N - N$, for the following values of N

a) $N = 5$, **b)** $N = 10$, and **c)** $N = 50$.

33. Use the Maxwell-Boltzmann formulae for diatomic gases and calculate the value of c_p for molecular iodine I_2 at 0 °C.

34. Use the Maxwell-Boltzmann formulae for diatomic gases and calculate the value of c_p/R at 2000 °C for

a) hydrogen, **b)** carbon monoxide, and **c)** oxygen.

Use the characteristic vibrational temperatures found in Table 12.5. Compare your results with the values given in Table 12.3.

35. An experimentally determined relation for the temperature dependence of the constant pressure specific heat of molecular oxygen O_2 over a wide temperature range is

$$c_p = 0.3598 + 47.81/T - 5.406/\sqrt{T}$$

where c_p is in Btu/(lbm·R) and T is in R. Use the Maxwell-Boltzmann equations for a diatomic molecule and attempt to predict the coefficients of the first two terms (i.e., 0.3598 and 47.81) of the equation. (*Hint*: At very high temperatures, $\exp(\Theta_v/T) \approx 1 + \Theta_v/T$). Explain why your results may not be very accurate.

36. Use the Maxwell-Boltzmann formulae for diatomic gases and calculate the value of c_p for water vapor at 400 °F and 1 psia. The characteristic temperatures of H_2O are $\Theta_r =$ 0.337 R, $\Theta_{v1} = 4131$ R, $\Theta_{v2} = 9459$ R, and $\Theta_{v3} = 9720$ R.

37. The experimentally measured value for c_v/R for ammonia NH_3 at 15 °C is 3.42. Use the Maxwell-Boltzmann formulae for nonlinear polyatomic gases to calculate the value of c_v/R for ammonia, and then compute the percent error in your result. The characteristic vibrational temperatures of ammonia are $\Theta_{v1} = 1367$ K, $\Theta_{v2} = \Theta_{v3} = 2341$ K, $\Theta_{v4} = 4801$ K, and $\Theta_{v5} = \Theta_{v6} = 4955$ K.

38. The experimentally measured value for c_v/R for methane CH_4 at 300 K is 3.2553. Use the Maxwell-Boltzmann formulae for nonlinear polyatomic gases to calculate the value of c_v/R for methane, and then compute the percent error in your result. The characteristic vibrational temperatures of methane are $\Theta_{v1} = \Theta_{v2} = \Theta_{v3} = 1879$ K, $\Theta_{v4} = \Theta_{v5} = 2207$ K, $\Theta_{v6} = 4197$ K, and $\Theta_{v7} = \Theta_{v8} = \Theta_{v9} = 4344$ K.

39. Calculate the specific entropy of HF at 0 °C and atmospheric pressure.

40. Calculate the change in specific entropy as HCl gas is heated at a constant pressure of 2 atmosphere from 300 to 3000 K.

41. Determine the heat transfer required to heat 11.3 lbm of HBr gas from 100 to 1000 °F in a closed, rigid, 1.5-ft^3 container.

42. Determine the power produced as 0.3 kg/s of HI passes through a steady state adiabatic turbine from 2000 K, at 50 atm, to 1000 K at 1 atm pressure.

43. Determine the entropy production rate for the turbine in Problem 42.

Design problems

The following are open ended design problems. The objective is to carry out a preliminary thermal design as indicated. A detailed design with working drawings is not expected unless otherwise specified. These problems do not have specific answers, so each student's design will be unique.

44. Design a heater that will raise the temperature of diatomic chlorine gas from 70 to 2500 °F without changing the pressure significantly. Do not assume ideal gas behavior. Use Eqs. 12.57*a*–12.62*d* to calculate the necessary thermodynamic properties of chlorine. Provide an assembly drawing of your design along with all the relevant thermodynamic and design calculations.

45. Design a flowmeter that uses a measurement of one or more of the thermodynamic u, h, or s to calculate the mass flow rate $\dot{m}$. For example, we can construct an open system such that $\dot{m}$ can be calculated from $\dot{Q}$, h_1, and h_2 as $\dot{m} = \dot{Q}/(h_2 - h_1)$. Provide an assembly drawing of your design along with all the relevant thermodynamic and design calculations.

46. Using the equation given in Problem 11, design an instrument that will determine the porosity of a small square flat test sample of material. Be sure to explain how to calculate the porosity from the measurements taken. If possible, set up an experiment and test your technique with samples of known porosity. Provide an assembly drawing of your design along with all the relevant thermodynamic and design calculations.

47. Design a spring-loaded throttling valve that will isothermally throttle 8.3 lbm/s of molecular bromine gas from 1000 psia, 70 °F, to atmospheric pressure using choked flow conditions (see Chapter 10). Provide an assembly drawing of your design along with all the relevant thermodynamic and design calculations.

48. Design a system that will increase the temperature of 0.35 kg of diatomic sodium gas Na_2 from 1500 K at 20 kPa to 3000 K simply by compressing it by some mechanism in a closed system. No auxiliary heaters or coolers may be used. Provide an assembly drawing of your design along with all the relevant thermodynamic and design calculations.

Computer Problems

The following open ended computer problems are designed to be done on a personal computer using BASIC language programming.

49. Using the equations from the kinetic theory of gases, write an interactive computer program that will return values for u, h, and s when p, T, M, and b are input by the user from the keyboard. Allow the user to chose either the English or the SI units system for the input values, and output values in the same units system.

50. Using the data on NO given in Example 12.6, plot curves of c_p and c_v for NO vs. temperature for $0 \leq T \leq 5000$ K. Compute at least 100 points for each curve.

51. Using the equations for the thermodynamic properties of diatomic gases given in the text, write an interactive computer program that will return values for u, h, and s when p and T are input by the user from the keyboard for one or more (instructor's choice) of the gases listed in Table 12.5. Assume $u_o = 0$, and allow the user to chose to work in either the English or the SI units system. Output values in the same units system that was chosen for input values.

52. In an isentropic process using an ideal gas, $T_2 = T_1(p_2/p_1)^{k/(k-1)}$. However, this simple equation is not valid for the diatomic statistical model whose thermodynamic properties are given by Eqs. 12.57*a*–12.62*d*. Use the Newton-Raphson technique on Eq. 12.62*d* for s to solve for the temperature T if values for the specific entropy s and the pressure p are known. Apply these results to carbon monoxide gas (CO) and plot a curve of T_2/T_1 vs. p_2/p_1 for $0 < p_2/p_1 \leq 100$ when $T_1 = 1000$ K and $s = 4.5$ kJ/(kg·K).

53. Using the appropriate equations from the text, plot $k = c_p/c_v$ vs. T for molecular oxygen over the range $0 \leq T \leq 5000$ K.

Postface

Getting to this point in the book has been quite a challenge for both of us. Before we leave this subject altogether, I wish to take one last digression into the life and philosophy of one of the most remarkable geniuses of the Industrial Revolution, Oliver Evans (1755–1819).

Oliver Evans was apprenticed to a wheelwright at the age of 16, and often observed village boys heating a corked rifle barrel containing a small amount of water in a blacksmith's forge until the cork blew out with considerable force. This kindled his interest in steam propulsion and later he pioneered the development of the high pressure expansion steam engine, a considerable improvement on the inventions of Newcomen and Watt, that eventually brought about the development of railroads, steamboats and factories. In 1784 he developed the first automatic production line for grinding grain into flour. Grain was fed into one end of a water-powered mill and finished flour emerged from the other end without any human assistance.

Beginning in 1805 he built and operated a steam powered amphibious vehicle he called the "Orukter Amphibolos" (Greek for amphibious digger) that was designed to dredge commercial waterways. It also had wheels so it could travel land as well as water, making it simultaneously the first steamboat and self-propelled road vehicle in the United States. His steam carriage was far ahead of its time and did not become popular because the roads at that time were much too rough to provide a suitable path for a 15 ton self-propelled vehicle. It took nearly 100 years before the bicycling craze of the late 19th century produced the construction of roads smooth enough for the horseless carriage to be reinvented.

Like so many other innovators, Evans' contributions to society have been largely neglected and he is little known today. Even in this text where I have made some attempt to acknowledge the individual and chronicle the technology, he is mentioned only in this postface.

Understanding people like Evans and the technological contributions they make that change society is an important way of gaining insight into who we are and the times in which we live. History often holds many lessons of universal value, some of which seem destined to be learned over and over again. By understanding the past we can better chart the future, and since technology is always a double edged sword, history can help us judge how best to control its development and use.

Evans collected material for several years for a book he tentatively titled *The Young Steam Engineers Guide*, but poor financial circumstances forced him to publish a condensed version in 1805 appropriately entitled *The Abortion of the Young Steam Engineer's Guide* in which he accurately predicts the need for government funding in order to sustain technological advances. Curiously, Evans' philosophy of human behavior was found written in his own hand on the last page of a copy of this book that he willed to his son upon his death. It is worth repeating here and remembering as you travel through your career.

Oliver Evans' Philosophy

When we see a man, one of the first ideas that strikes our minds is that he can know but little more than ourselves.

When we read of a man in some distant country who has made some useful discovery either in art or science, we give more credit to what we hear than we would if we had seen him.

But when we read of a man who lived centuries ago and who had laid down theories and rules as fundamental in the sciences, we can place implicit faith in them if we do not plainly see an absurdity in them, for we do not know but that he was more than human.

Therefore he that studies and writes on the improvements of the arts and sciences labours to benefit generations yet unborn, for it is not probable that his contemporaries will pay any attention to him, especially those of his relations, friends and intimates; therefore improvements progress so slowly.

Evans' Orukter Amphibolos (1805).

A Appendix A: Physical Constants and Conversion Factors

Physical Constants

Avogadro's number, $N_o = 6.023 \times 10^{26}$ molecules/kgmole
Boltzmann's constant, $k = 1.381 \times 10^{-23}$ J/(molecule·K)
Electron charge, $e = 1.602 \times 10^{-19}$ C
Electron mass, $m_e = 9.110 \times 10^{-31}$ kg
Faraday's constant, F = 96,487 kC/kgmole electrons
= 96,487 kJ/(V·kgmole electrons)
Gravitational acceleration (standard), $g = 32.174\ \text{ft/s}^2 = 9.807\ \text{m/s}^2$
Gravitational constant, $k_G = 6.67 \times 10^{-11}\ \text{m}^3/(\text{kg}\cdot\text{s}^2)$
Newton's second law constant, $g_c = 32.174\ \text{lbm}\cdot\text{ft}/(\text{lbf}\cdot\text{s}^2)$
$= 1.0\ \text{kg}\cdot\text{m}/(\text{N}\cdot\text{s}^2)$
Planck's constant, $\hbar = 6.626 \times 10^{-34}$ J·s/molecule
Stefan-Boltzmann constant, $\sigma = 0.1714 \times 10^{-8}\ \text{Btu}/(\text{h}\cdot\text{ft}^2\cdot\text{R}^4)$
$= 5.670 \times 10^{-8}\ \text{W}/(\text{m}^2\cdot\text{K}^4)$
Universal gas constant, $\mathscr{R}$ = 1545.35 ft·lbf/(lbmole·R)
= 8314.3 J/(kgmole·K)
= 8.3143 kJ/(kgmole·K)
= 1.9858 Btu/(lbmole·R)
= 1.9858 kcal/(kgmole·K)
= 1.9858 cal/(gmole·K)
$= 0.08314\ \text{bar}\cdot\text{m}^3/(\text{kgmole}\cdot\text{K})$
= 82.05 L·atm/(kgmole·K)
Velocity of light in a vacuum, $c = 9.836 \times 10^8\ \text{ft/s} = 2.998 \times 10^8\ \text{m/s}$

Unit Definitions

1 coulomb (C) = 1 A·s
1 dyne = 1 g·cm/s^2
1 erg = 1 dyne·cm
1 farad (F) = 1 C/V
1 henry (H) = 1 Wb/A
1 hertz (Hz) = 1 cycle/s
1 joule (J) = 1 N·m
1 lumen = 1 candela·steradian
1 lux = 1 lumen/m^2
1 newton (N) = 1 kg·m/s^2
1 ohm (Ω) = 1 V/A
1 pascal (Pa) = 1 N/m^2
1 poundal = 1 lbm·ft/s^2
1 siemens (S) = 1 A/V
1 slug = 1 lbf·s^2/ft
1 tesla (T) = 1 Wb/m^2
1 volt (V) = 1 W/A
1 watt (W) = 1 J/s
1 weber (Wb) = 1 V·s

Conversion Factors

Length

1 m = 3.2808 ft = 39.37 in = 10^2 cm = 10^{10} Å
1 cm = 0.0328 ft = 0.394 in = 10^{-2} m = 10^8 Å
1 mm = 10^{-3} m = 10^{-1} cm
1 km = 1000 m = 0.6215 miles = 3281 ft
1 in = 2.540 cm = 0.0254 m
1 ft = 12 in = 0.3048 m
1 mile = 5280 ft = 1609.36 m = 1.609 km

Area

1 m^2 = 10^4 cm^2 = 10.76 ft^2 = 1550 in^2
1 ft^2 = 144 in^2 = 0.0929 m^2 = 929.05 cm^2
1 cm^2 = 10^{-4} m^2 = 1.0764×10^{-3} ft^2 = 0.155 in^2
1 in^2 = 6.944×10^{-3} ft^2 = 6.4516×10^{-4} m^2 = 6.4516 cm^2

Volume

1 m^3 = 35.313 ft^3 = 6.1023×10^4 in^3 = 1000 L = 264.171 gal
1 L = 10^{-3} m^3 = 0.0353 ft^3 = 61.03 in^3 = 0.2642 gal
1 gal = 231 in^3 = 0.13368 ft^3 = 3.785×10^{-3} m^3
1 ft^3 = 1728 in^3 = 28.3168 L = 0.02832 m^3 = 7.4805 gal
1 in^3 = 16.387 cm^3 = 1.6387×10^{-5} m^3 = 4.329×10^{-3} gal

Mass

1 kg = 1000 g = 2.2046 lbm = 0.0685 slug
1 lbm = 453.6 g = 0.4536 kg = 3.108×10^{-2} slug
1 slug = 32.174 lbm = 1.459×10^4 g = 14.594 kg

Force

1 N = 10^5 dyne = 1 kg·m/s^2 = 0.225 lbf
1 lbf = 4.448 N = 32.174 poundals
1 poundal = 0.138 N = 3.108×10^{-2} lbf

Energy

$1 \text{ J} = 1 \text{ N}\cdot\text{m} = 1 \text{ kg}\cdot\text{m}^2/\text{s}^2 = 9.479 \times 10^{-4} \text{ Btu} = 0.2389 \text{ cal}$
$1 \text{ kJ} = 1000 \text{ J} = 0.9479 \text{ Btu} = 238.9 \text{ cal}$
$1 \text{ Btu} = 1055.0 \text{ J} = 1.055 \text{ kJ} = 778.16 \text{ ft}\cdot\text{lbf} = 252 \text{ cal}$
$1 \text{ cal} = 4.186 \text{ J} = 3.968 \times 10^{-3} \text{ Btu}$
$1 \text{ Cal (in food value)} = 1 \text{ kcal} = 1000 \text{ cal} = 4186 \text{ J} = 3.968 \text{ Btu}$
$1 \text{ erg} = 1 \text{ dyne}\cdot\text{cm} = 1 \text{ g}\cdot\text{cm}^2/\text{s}^2 = 10^{-7} \text{ J}$
$1 \text{ eV} = 1.602 \times 10^{-19} \text{ J}$

Power

$1 \text{ W} = 1 \text{ J/s} = 1 \text{ kg}\cdot\text{m}^2/\text{s}^3 = 3.412 \text{ Btu/h} = 1.3405 \times 10^{-3} \text{ hp}$
$1 \text{ kW} = 1000 \text{ W} = 3412 \text{ Btu/h} = 737.3 \text{ ft}\cdot\text{lbf/s} = 1.3405 \text{ hp}$
$1 \text{ Btu/h} = 0.293 \text{ W} = 0.2161 \text{ ft}\cdot\text{lbf/s} = 3.9293 \times 10^{-4} \text{ hp}$
$1 \text{ hp} = 550 \text{ ft}\cdot\text{lbf/s} = 33000 \text{ ft}\cdot\text{lbf/min} = 2545 \text{ Btu/h} = 746 \text{ W}$

Pressure

$1 \text{ Pa} = 1 \text{ N/m}^2 = 1 \text{ kg/(m}\cdot\text{s}^2) = 1.4504 \times 10^{-4} \text{ lbf/in}^2$
$1 \text{ lbf/in}^2 = 6894.76 \text{ Pa} = 0.068 \text{ atm} = 2.036 \text{ in Hg}$
$1 \text{ atm} = 14.696 \text{ lbf/in}^2 = 1.01325 \times 10^5 \text{ Pa} = 101.325 \text{ kPa} = 760 \text{ mm Hg}$
$1 \text{ bar} = 10^5 \text{ Pa} = 0.987 \text{ atm} = 14.504 \text{ lbf/in}^2$
$1 \text{ dyne/cm}^2 = 0.1 \text{ Pa} = 10^{-6} \text{ bar} = 145.04 \times 10^{-7} \text{ lbf/in}^2$
$1 \text{ in Hg} = 3376.8 \text{ Pa} = 0.491 \text{ lbf/in}^2$
$1 \text{ in H}_2\text{O} = 248.8 \text{ Pa} = 0.0361 \text{ lbf/in}^2$

Miscellaneous

Specific Heat Units

$1 \text{ Btu/(lbm}\cdot{}^\circ\text{F}) = 1 \text{ Btu/(lbm}\cdot\text{R})$, i.e., no °F to R conversion is needed here
$1 \text{ kJ/(kg}\cdot\text{K}) = 0.23884 \text{ Btu/(lbm}\cdot\text{R}) = 185.8 \text{ ft}\cdot\text{lbf/(lbm}\cdot\text{R})$
$1 \text{ Btu/(lbm}\cdot\text{R}) = 778.16 \text{ ft}\cdot\text{lbf/(lbm}\cdot\text{R}) = 4.186 \text{ kJ/(kg}\cdot\text{K})$

Energy Density Units

$1 \text{ kJ/kg} = 1000 \text{ m}^2/\text{s}^2 = 0.4299 \text{ Btu/lbm}$
$1 \text{ Btu/lbm} = 2.326 \text{ kJ/kg} = 2326 \text{ m}^2/\text{s}^2$

Energy Flux

$1 \text{ W/m}^2 = 0.317 \text{ Btu/(h}\cdot\text{ft}^2)$
$1 \text{ Btu/(h}\cdot\text{ft}^2) = 3.154 \text{ W/m}^2$

Heat Transfer Coefficient

$1 \text{ W/(m}^2\cdot\text{K}) = 0.1761 \text{ Btu/(h}\cdot\text{ft}^2\cdot\text{R})$
$1 \text{ Btu/(h}\cdot\text{ft}^2\cdot\text{R}) = 5.679 \text{ W/(m}^2\cdot\text{K})$

Thermal Conductivity

$1 \text{ W/(m}\cdot\text{K}) = 0.5778 \text{ Btu/(h}\cdot\text{ft}\cdot\text{R})$
$1 \text{ Btu/(h}\cdot\text{ft}\cdot\text{R}) = 1.731 \text{ W/(m}\cdot\text{K})$

Temperature

$T(°F) = \frac{9}{5}T(°C) + 32 = T(R) - 459.67$
$T(°C) = \frac{5}{9}[T(°F) - 32] = T(K) - 273.15$
$T(R) = \frac{9}{5}T(K) = (1.8)T(K) = T(°F) + 459.67$
$T(K) = \frac{5}{9}T(R) = T(R)/1.8 = T(°C) + 273.15$

Density

1 lbm/ft^3 = 16.0187 kg/m^3
1 kg/m^3 = 0.062427 lbm/ft^3 = 10^{-3} g/cm^3
1 g/cm^3 = 1 kg/L = 62.4 lbm/ft^3 = 10^3 kg/m^3

Viscosity

1 Pa·s = 1 N·s/m^2 = 1 kg/(m·s) = 10 poise
1 poise = 1 dyne·s/cm^2 = 1 g/(cm·s) = 0.1 Pa·s
1 poise = 2.09×10^{-3} lbf·s/ft^2 = 6.72×10^{-2} lbm/(ft·s)
1 centipoise = 0.01 poise = 10^{-3} Pa·s
1 lbf·s/ft^2 = 1 slug/(ft·s) = 47.9 Pa·s = 479 poise
1 stoke = 1 cm^2/s = 10^{-4} m^2/s = 1.076×10^{-3} ft^2/s
1 centistoke = 0.01 stoke = 10^{-6} m^2/s = 1.076×10^{-5} ft^2/s
1 m^2/s = 10^4 stoke = 10^6 centistoke = 10.76 ft^2/s

Electrical Units

1 watt = 1 J/s = 1 V·A = 621 lumens at 5500 Å
1 kilowatt hour = 3413 Btu = 1.341 hp·h
1 volt = 1 J/C = 1 W/A = 1 Ω·A
1 ampere = 1 C/s = 6.24183×10^{18} electrons/s
1 electron volt (eV) = 1.6021×10^{-19} J
1 gilbert = 0.7958 A
1 ostered = 79.58 A/m
1 maxwell = 10^{-8} Wb
1 gauss = 10^{-4} T

1 unit of	Electromagnetic Units (emu)	Electrostatic Units (esu)
current	10 amperes	3.3856×10^{-10} ampere
potential	10^{-8} volt	299.8 volts
capacitance	10^9 farads	1.1126×10^{-12} farad
inductance	10^{-9} henry	8.9876×10^{11} henrys
resistance	10^{-9} ohm	8.9876×10^{11} ohms

B Appendix B: Greek and Latin Origins of Engineering Terms

English is a complex combination of numerous languages, and is thought by some to be the most colorful and expressive language we have. To understand why English is such a complicated language, you need to be aware of several milestones in the history of the English culture. Around 1000 B.C. Celtic speaking armies from central Europe conquered the British Isles, and after several centuries of occupation the language of the prehistoric Britain's was completely replaced by Celtic. Gaelic, Welsh, Irish, and Scotch are modern remnants of Celtic. Britain was again conquered in the first century A.D. by the Roman empire, and for the next several centuries Latin words began to be absorbed into the British Celtic tongue. Also, some Greek words were introduced during this period by Roman Christian missionaries. The Roman occupation ended in the fourth century, before the British Celtic language was completely replaced by Latin. In the fifth century Britain was conquered by the Teutonic Angles, Saxons, and Jutes from Germanic Europe. Their combined language is called Anglo-Saxon, and was the basis of modern English (in fact the word English is really *Anglish*). In the eighth century the Danish invaded parts of Britain and fragments of their language were assimilated into the Celtic-Anglo-Saxon English. In the eleventh century Britain was again conquered, this time by the French. Norman-French then became the official language of the country, but the masses continued to speak English. By 1500, the French had been driven out, and English, now ripe with French words, was reestablished as the official language of the land. It is clear that the English language has had a long and colorful history, and that the assimilation of numerous words from various different languages is one of the things that gives it its versatility and complexity.

New words normally enter a language not as replacements for existing words, but to describe new concepts or ideas. The words most often taken from the occupying forces in Britain were of this type. The new concepts were often, as they are today, from science, technology, or religion. During the Middle Ages Arabian science and technology was quite advanced. Consequently, technical words such as algebra, alcohol, and alkali entered the English language (they can be recognized by the fact that they begin with the Arabic definite article, *al*). The Greek language has had a much smaller impact than Latin on the evolution of English. Greek words have generally entered the English language indirectly, having been absorbed into Latin first, borrowed directly from Greek authors, or through the coining of new scientific or technical terms.

Long ago it became customary for professionals to carry out their business in a dead language from an earlier culture. Thus, the Romans used Greek, and the English used Latin (with a smattering of Greek). Whether this was to keep the masses from understanding professional dialogue or merely to exercise scholarly activity is not known. Even today we go to either Latin or Greek to name a new scientific phenomenon or technology. Xerox, for example, is a trade name that comes from the word xerography, which is Greek for dry (*xero*) copying process (*graphy*).

Many long technical words are compound words formed from the following basic elements: **a)** the root word, **b)** the combining vowel, and **c)** the suffix or prefix. The root word is the core of any technical term. It can be either Latin or Greek, and it is often linked to the prefix or suffix by a combining vowel. For example, *therm* is a root word meaning heat, *o* is a connecting vowel, and *dynamics* is a suffix meaning able to produce power. Thus, the term *thermodynamics* loosely translates as *the process of converting heat into power*.

A prefix is a syllable or syllables placed in front of a root word to alter its meaning. The following is a list of common Greek and Latin technical prefixes.

Prefix	Meaning	Example
a-	without or not	asymmetric
dia-	through	diameter
hemi-	half	hemisphere
hyper-	above	hypersonic
hypo-	under	hypodermic
infra-	below	infrared
is-	equal or constant	isothermal
para-	beside	paramagnetic
peri-	around	perimeter
semi-	half	semicircle
syn-	with or together	synthetic
trans-	across	transport

A suffix is a syllable or syllables that are added to the end of a word to change the meaning of the root word or to form a new word. The following is a list of common Greek and Latin technical suffixes.

Suffix	Meaning	Example
-e	noun-forming, often means *instrument*	metronome
-er	one who	worker
-ic, -al, -ar	pertaining to	electric, electrical
-ist	one who specializes	scientist
-graph	instrument to record	polygraph
-graphy	process of recording	xerography
-gram	record	electrocardiogram
-meter	measuring instrument	psychrometer
-ology	the study of	technology
-ologist	one who studies	technologist

Finally, below is a short list of common technical Greek and Latin root words and their normal connecting vowels.

Root word	Meaning	Example
aer/o	air	aeroplane
bar/o	air weight	barometer
electr/o	electricity	electromagnetic
therm/o	heat	thermodynamics
phon/o	sound or voice	phonograph
lith/o	stone	lithographer
flu/i	flow	fluid, flux
hydr/o	water	hydrodynamic
hygr/o	moist	hygrocyst
psychr/o	cold	psychrometer
cry/o	extreme cold	cryogenic
xer/o	dry	xerography
meteor/o	weather	meteorology

There are also many hybrid technical words such as *automobile*, which is composed of the Greek word *aut* (self), a connecting vowel *o*, and the Latin word *mobilis* (movable).

In English the plural of a word is usually formed by adding *s* to the end of the word. However, in many Greek and Latin technical terms we retain all of their original spelling, including their plural ending. The following list illustrates the proper plural ending for these words.

Singular ending	Plural ending	Example
-um	-a	datum, data
-a	-ae	formula, formulae
-on	-a	phenomenon, phenomena
-ix	-ices	matrix, matrices

The first ending in the above list is particularly important because it occurs in so many common technical terms. Other examples are continuum, continua; medium, media; symposium, symposia; colloquium, colloquia; quantum, quanta; and so forth. Thus, in technical writing we should not refer to a singular *data point*, but rather to a singular *datum point*, or to a set of *data points*.

Occasionally there are different Greek and Latin words that mean the same thing, and this can be confusing when both are used in the literature. This occurs, for example, in the names of numbers. The list below illustrates this problem.

Greek number	Latin number	English meaning	Example
mon/o	uni	one or single	monoplane, unicycle
di	bi	two or double	disulfate, bicycle
tri, tripl/i	tri	three or triple	triplicate, tripod
tetr/a	quadr/a	four or fourfold	tetrahedron, quadrangle
pent/a	quinqu/e	five	pentagon, quinquevalent
hex/a	sex/a	six, sixth	hexadecimal, sexagenarian
hept/a	sept/a	seven, seventh	heptagon, septet
oct/a	oct/a	eight, eighth	octane
enne/a	non/i	nine or ninth	ennead, nonillion
dec/i	dec/i	ten or tenth	decimal
kil/o		one thousand	kilometer
	mill/i	one thousandth	millimeter
poly	mult/i	many	polytropic, multistage
hemi	semi	half	hemisphere, semicircle

Thus, we begin to see the structure of thermodynamic terms such as energy (*en* meaning *in* plus *ergon* meaning *work*), adiabatic (*a* meaning *without* plus *dia* meaning *through* plus *bainein* meaning *to go*), aergonic (*a* meaning *without* plus *ergon* meaning *work*), entropy (*en* meaning *in* plus *trope* meaning *turning*), enthalpy (*en* meaning *in* plus *thalpos* meaning *warmth*), isochoric, isothermal, isenthalpic, polytropic, and so forth. If you understand the etymology of a word, it will cease to be a mysterious sound without connotation or meaning.

Perhaps the most commonly used word in the English language is *OK* (occasionally spelled *okay*). It has neither a Greek nor a Latin nor an ancient Teutonic origin. The letters *OK* are an abbreviation of Martin Van Buren's nickname, Old Kinderhook (the name of his home town). During Van Buren's second bid for the presidency in 1840 his supporters started a series of Old Kinderhook Clubs, which soon became known as OK Clubs. Though Van Buren was not successful in his election attempt, the initials of his nickname will live on forever signifying our personal approval of something.

C Appendix C: Thermodynamic Tables

Appendix C.1a Saturated water, temperature table (English units)†

		Volume, ft³/lbm		Energy, Btu/lbm		Enthalpy, Btu/lbm			Entropy, Btu/(lbm·R)		
T, °F	p, psia	v_f	v_g	u_f	u_g	h_f	h_{fg}	h_g	s_f	s_{fg}	s_g
32.018	0.08866	0.01602	3302.	0.0	1021.2	0.0	1075.4	1075.4	0.0000	2.1871	2.1871
35	0.09992	0.01602	2948.	3.0	1022.2	3.0	1073.7	1076.7	0.0061	2.1705	2.1766
40	0.1217	0.01602	2445.	8.0	1023.8	8.0	1070.9	1078.9	0.0162	2.1432	2.1594
45	0.1475	0.01602	2037.	13.0	1025.5	13.0	1068.1	1081.1	0.0262	2.1163	2.1425
50	0.1780	0.01602	1704.	18.1	1027.2	18.1	1065.2	1083.3	0.0361	2.0900	2.1261
55	0.2140	0.01603	1431.	23.1	1028.8	23.1	1062.4	1085.5	0.0458	2.0643	2.1101
60	0.2563	0.01603	1207.	28.1	1030.4	28.1	1059.6	1087.7	0.0555	2.0390	2.0945
65	0.3057	0.01604	1021.	33.1	1032.1	33.1	1056.8	1089.9	0.0651	2.0142	2.0793
70	0.3632	0.01605	867.6	38.1	1033.7	38.1	1053.9	1092.0	0.0746	1.9898	2.0644
75	0.4300	0.01606	739.7	43.1	1035.4	43.1	1051.1	1094.2	0.0840	1.9659	2.0499
80	0.5073	0.01607	632.7	48.1	1037.0	48.1	1048.3	1096.4	0.0933	1.9425	2.0358
85	0.5964	0.01609	543.1	53.1	1038.6	53.1	1045.5	1098.6	0.1025	1.9195	2.0220
90	0.6989	0.01610	467.6	58.1	1040.2	58.1	1042.6	1100.7	0.1116	1.8969	2.0085
95	0.8162	0.01611	403.9	63.0	1041.9	63.1	1039.8	1102.9	0.1206	1.8747	1.9953
100	0.9503	0.01613	350.0	68.0	1043.5	68.0	1037.0	1105.0	0.1296	1.8528	1.9824
110	1.276	0.01617	265.1	78.0	1046.7	78.0	1031.3	1109.3	0.1473	1.8103	1.9576
120	1.695	0.01621	203.0	88.0	1049.9	88.0	1025.5	1113.5	0.1646	1.7692	1.9338
130	2.225	0.01625	157.2	98.0	1053.0	98.0	1019.7	1117.7	0.1817	1.7294	1.9111
140	2.892	0.01629	122.9	107.9	1056.2	108.0	1013.9	1121.9	0.1985	1.6909	1.8894
150	3.722	0.01634	96.98	117.9	1059.3	117.9	1008.2	1126.1	0.2150	1.6535	1.8685
160	4.745	0.01640	77.23	127.9	1062.3	128.0	1002.1	1130.1	0.2313	1.6173	1.8486
180	7.515	0.01651	50.20	148.0	1068.3	148.0	990.2	1138.2	0.2631	1.5480	1.8111
200	11.53	0.01663	33.63	168.0	1074.2	168.1	977.8	1145.9	0.2941	1.4823	1.7764
212	14.696	0.01672	26.80	180.1	1077.6	180.1	970.4	1150.5	0.3122	1.4447	1.7569
220	17.19	0.01677	23.15	188.2	1079.8	188.2	965.3	1153.5	0.3241	1.4202	1.7443
240	24.97	0.01692	16.33	208.4	1085.3	208.4	952.3	1160.7	0.3534	1.3611	1.7145
260	35.42	0.01708	11.77	228.6	1090.5	228.7	938.9	1167.6	0.3820	1.3046	1.6866
280	49.19	0.01726	8.650	249.0	1095.4	249.2	924.9	1174.1	0.4100	1.2504	1.6604
300	66.98	0.01745	6.472	269.5	1100.0	269.7	910.5	1180.2	0.4373	1.1985	1.6358
320	89.60	0.01765	4.919	290.1	1104.2	290.4	895.4	1185.8	0.4641	1.1484	1.6125
340	117.9	0.01787	3.792	310.9	1108.0	311.3	879.5	1190.8	0.4904	1.0998	1.5902
360	152.9	0.01811	2.961	331.8	1111.4	332.3	862.9	1195.2	0.5163	1.0527	1.5690
380	195.6	0.01836	2.339	352.9	1114.3	353.6	845.4	1199.0	0.5417	1.0068	1.5485
400	247.1	0.01864	1.866	374.3	1116.6	375.1	826.9	1202.0	0.5668	0.9618	1.5286
420	308.5	0.01894	1.502	395.8	1118.3	396.9	807.2	1204.1	0.5916	0.9177	1.5093
440	381.2	0.01926	1.219	417.6	1119.3	419.0	786.3	1205.3	0.6162	0.8740	1.4902
460	466.3	0.01961	0.9961	439.7	1119.6	441.4	764.1	1205.5	0.6405	0.8309	1.4714
480	565.5	0.02000	0.8187	462.2	1118.9	464.3	740.3	1204.6	0.6647	0.7879	1.4526
500	680.0	0.02043	0.6761	485.1	1117.4	487.7	714.8	1202.5	0.6889	0.7448	1.4337
520	811.4	0.02091	0.5605	508.5	1114.8	511.7	687.2	1198.9	0.7132	0.7015	1.4147
540	961.4	0.02145	0.4658	532.6	1111.0	536.4	657.4	1193.8	0.7375	0.6577	1.3952
560	1132.	0.02207	0.3877	557.3	1105.8	562.0	625.0	1187.0	0.7622	0.6129	1.3751
580	1324.	0.02278	0.3225	583.0	1098.9	588.6	589.4	1178.0	0.7873	0.5669	1.3542
600	1541.	0.02363	0.2677	609.9	1090.0	616.6	549.8	1166.4	0.8131	0.5188	1.3319
620	1784.	0.02465	0.2209	638.3	1078.5	646.4	505.0	1151.4	0.8399	0.4678	1.3077
640	2057.	0.02593	0.1805	668.7	1063.2	678.6	453.3	1131.9	0.8683	0.4122	1.2805
660	2362.	0.02767	0.1446	702.0	1042.3	714.3	391.2	1105.5	0.8992	0.3493	1.2485
680	2705.	0.03032	0.1113	741.7	1011.0	756.9	309.8	1066.7	0.9352	0.2718	1.2070
700	3090.	0.03666	0.07444	801.7	947.7	822.7	167.7	990.4	0.9903	0.1447	1.1350
705.445	3203.8	0.05053	0.05053	872.6	872.6	902.5	0.0	902.5	1.0582	0.0000	1.0582

† Saturated liquid entropies have been adjusted to make the Gibbs functions of the liquid and vapor phases exactly equal. For this reason there are some small differences between values presented here and the original tables.

Sources: Reprinted by permission from William C. Reynolds and Henry C. Perkins, *Engineering Thermodynamics*, 2d ed. (New York: McGraw-Hill, 1977), pp. 630–631 (Table B-1a). Recalculated from equations given in Joseph H. Keenan, Frederick G. Keyes, Philip G. Hill, and Joan G. Moore, *Steam Tables* (New York: Wiley, 1969).

Appendix C.1*b* **Saturated water, temperature table (metric units)**[†]

		Volume, m³/kg		Energy, kJ/kg		Enthalpy, kJ/kg			Entropy, kJ/(kg·K)		
T, °C	p, MPa	v_f	v_g	u_f	u_g	h_f	h_{fg}	h_g	s_f	s_{fg}	s_g
0.010	0.0006113	0.001000	206.1	0.0	2375.3	0.0	2501.3	2501.3	0.0000	9.1571	9.1571
2	0.0007056	0.001000	179.9	8.4	2378.1	8.4	2496.6	2505.0	0.0305	9.0738	9.1043
5	0.0008721	0.001000	147.1	21.0	2382.2	21.0	2489.5	2510.5	0.0761	8.9505	9.0266
10	0.001228	0.001000	106.4	42.0	2389.2	42.0	2477.7	2519.7	0.1510	8.7506	8.9016
15	0.001705	0.001001	77.93	63.0	2396.0	63.0	2465.9	2528.9	0.2244	8.5578	8.7822
20	0.002338	0.001002	57.79	83.9	2402.9	83.9	2454.2	2538.1	0.2965	8.3715	8.6680
25	0.003169	0.001003	43.36	104.9	2409.8	104.9	2442.3	2547.2	0.3672	8.1916	8.5588
30	0.004246	0.001004	32.90	125.8	2416.6	125.8	2430.4	2556.2	0.4367	8.0174	8.4541
35	0.005628	0.001006	25.22	146.7	2423.4	146.7	2418.6	2565.3	0.5051	7.8488	8.3539
40	0.007383	0.001008	19.52	167.5	2430.1	167.5	2406.8	2574.3	0.5723	7.6855	8.2578
45	0.009593	0.001010	15.26	188.4	2436.8	188.4	2394.8	2583.2	0.6385	7.5271	8.1656
50	0.01235	0.001012	12.03	209.3	2443.5	209.3	2382.8	2592.1	0.7036	7.3735	8.0771
55	0.01576	0.001015	9.569	230.2	2450.1	230.2	2370.7	2600.9	0.7678	7.2243	7.9921
60	0.01994	0.001017	7.671	251.1	2456.6	251.1	2358.5	2609.6	0.8310	7.0794	7.9104
65	0.02503	0.001020	6.197	272.0	2463.1	272.0	2346.2	2618.2	0.8934	6.9384	7.8318
70	0.03119	0.001023	5.042	292.9	2469.5	293.0	2333.8	2626.8	0.9549	6.8012	7.7561
75	0.03858	0.001026	4.131	313.9	2475.9	313.9	2321.4	2635.3	1.0155	6.6678	7.6833
80	0.04739	0.001029	3.407	334.8	2482.2	334.9	2308.8	2643.7	1.0754	6.5376	7.6130
85	0.05783	0.001032	2.828	355.8	2488.4	355.9	2296.0	2651.9	1.1344	6.4109	7.5453
90	0.07013	0.001036	2.361	376.8	2494.5	376.9	2283.2	2660.1	1.1927	6.2872	7.4799
95	0.08455	0.001040	1.982	397.9	2500.6	397.9	2270.2	2668.1	1.2503	6.1664	7.4167
100	0.1013	0.001044	1.673	418.9	2506.5	419.0	2257.0	2676.0	1.3071	6.0486	7.3557
110	0.1433	0.001052	1.210	461.1	2518.1	461.3	2230.2	2691.5	1.4188	5.8207	7.2395
120	0.1985	0.001060	0.8919	503.5	2529.2	503.7	2202.6	2706.3	1.5280	5.6024	7.1304
130	0.2701	0.001070	0.6685	546.0	2539.9	546.3	2174.2	2720.5	1.6348	5.3929	7.0277
140	0.3613	0.001080	0.5089	588.7	2550.0	589.1	2144.8	2733.9	1.7395	5.1912	6.9307
150	0.4758	0.001090	0.3928	631.7	2559.5	632.2	2114.2	2746.4	1.8422	4.9965	6.8387
160	0.6178	0.001102	0.3071	674.9	2568.4	675.5	2082.6	2758.1	1.9431	4.8079	6.7510
170	0.7916	0.001114	0.2428	718.3	2576.5	719.2	2049.5	2768.7	2.0423	4.6249	6.6672
180	1.002	0.001127	0.1941	762.1	2583.7	763.2	2015.0	2778.2	2.1400	4.4466	6.5866
190	1.254	0.001141	0.1565	806.2	2590.0	807.5	1978.8	2786.4	2.2363	4.2724	6.5087
200	1.554	0.001156	0.1274	850.6	2595.3	852.4	1940.8	2793.2	2.3313	4.1018	6.4331
210	1.906	0.001173	0.1044	895.5	2599.4	897.7	1900.8	2798.5	2.4253	3.9340	6.3593
220	2.318	0.001190	0.08620	940.9	2602.4	943.6	1858.5	2802.1	2.5183	3.7686	6.2869
230	2.795	0.001209	0.07159	986.7	2603.9	990.1	1813.9	2804.0	2.6105	3.6050	6.2155
240	3.344	0.001229	0.05977	1033.2	2604.0	1037.3	1766.5	2803.8	2.7021	3.4425	6.1446
250	3.973	0.001251	0.05013	1080.4	2602.4	1085.3	1716.2	2801.5	2.7933	3.2805	6.0738
260	4.688	0.001276	0.04221	1128.4	2599.0	1134.4	1662.5	2796.9	2.8844	3.1184	6.0028
270	5.498	0.001302	0.03565	1177.3	2593.7	1184.5	1605.2	2789.7	2.9757	2.9553	5.9310
280	6.411	0.001332	0.03017	1227.4	2586.1	1236.0	1543.6	2779.6	3.0674	2.7905	5.8579
290	7.436	0.001366	0.02557	1278.9	2576.0	1289.0	1477.2	2766.2	3.1600	2.6230	5.7830
300	8.580	0.001404	0.02168	1332.0	2563.0	1344.0	1405.0	2749.0	3.2540	2.4513	5.7053
310	9.856	0.001447	0.01835	1387.0	2546.4	1401.3	1326.0	2727.3	3.3500	2.2739	5.6239
320	11.27	0.001499	0.01549	1444.6	2525.5	1461.4	1238.7	2700.1	3.4487	2.0883	5.5370
330	12.84	0.001561	0.01300	1505.2	2499.0	1525.3	1140.6	2665.9	3.5514	1.8911	5.4425
340	14.59	0.001638	0.01080	1570.3	2464.6	1594.2	1027.9	2622.1	3.6601	1.6765	5.3366
350	16.51	0.001740	0.008815	1641.8	2418.5	1670.6	893.4	2564.0	3.7784	1.4338	5.2122
360	18.65	0.001892	0.006947	1725.2	2351.6	1760.5	720.7	2481.2	3.9154	1.1382	5.0536
370	21.03	0.002213	0.004931	1844.0	2229.0	1890.5	442.2	2332.7	4.1114	0.6876	4.7990
374.136	22.088	0.003155	0.003155	2029.6	2029.6	2099.3	0.0	2099.3	4.4305	0.0000	4.4305

[†] Saturated liquid entropies have been adjusted to make the Gibbs functions of the liquid and vapor phases exactly equal. For this reason there are some small differences between values presented here and the original tables.

Appendix C.2a Saturated water, pressure table (English units)†

		Volume, ft³/lbm		Energy, Btu/lbm		Enthalpy, Btu/lbm			Entropy, Btu/(lbm·R)		
p, psia	T, °F	v_f	v_g	u_f	u_g	h_f	h_{fg}	h_g	s_f	s_{fg}	s_g
0.0887	32.018	0.01602	3302.0	0.0	1021.2	0.0	1075.4	1075.4	0.0000	2.1871	2.1871
0.1	35.0	0.01602	2946.0	3.0	1022.2	3.0	1073.7	1076.7	0.0061	2.1705	2.1768
0.12	39.6	0.01602	2477.0	7.7	1023.7	7.7	1071.0	1078.7	0.0155	2.1451	2.1606
0.14	43.6	0.01602	2140.0	11.7	1025.0	11.7	1068.8	1080.5	0.0234	2.1237	2.1471
0.16	47.1	0.01602	1886.0	15.2	1026.2	15.2	1066.8	1082.0	0.0304	2.1050	2.1354
0.18	50.3	0.01602	1686.0	18.3	1027.2	18.3	1065.1	1083.4	0.0366	2.0886	2.1252
0.2	53.1	0.01603	1526.0	21.2	1028.2	21.2	1063.5	1084.7	0.0422	2.0738	2.1160
0.25	59.3	0.01603	1235.0	27.4	1030.2	27.4	1060.0	1087.4	0.0542	2.0425	2.0967
0.3	64.5	0.01604	1040.0	32.5	1031.9	32.5	1057.1	1089.6	0.0641	2.0168	2.0809
0.4	72.8	0.01606	792.0	40.9	1034.7	40.9	1052.4	1093.3	0.0799	1.9762	2.0561
0.6	85.2	0.01609	540.0	53.3	1038.7	53.3	1045.3	1098.6	0.1028	1.9187	2.0215
0.8	94.3	0.01611	411.7	62.4	1041.6	62.4	1040.2	1102.6	0.1195	1.8775	1.9970
1	101.7	0.01614	333.6	69.7	1044.0	69.7	1036.0	1105.7	0.1326	1.8455	1.9781
1.2	107.9	0.01616	280.9	75.9	1046.0	75.9	1032.5	1108.4	0.1435	1.8193	1.9628
1.4	113.2	0.01618	243.0	81.2	1047.7	81.2	1029.5	1110.7	0.1529	1.7969	1.9498
1.6	117.9	0.01620	214.3	85.9	1049.2	85.9	1026.8	1112.7	0.1611	1.7775	1.9386
1.8	122.2	0.01621	191.8	90.2	1050.6	90.2	1024.3	1114.5	0.1684	1.7604	1.9288
2	126.0	0.01623	173.8	94.0	1051.8	94.0	1022.1	1116.1	0.1750	1.7450	1.9200
3	141.4	0.01630	118.7	109.4	1056.6	109.4	1013.1	1122.5	0.2009	1.6854	1.8863
4	152.9	0.01636	90.64	120.9	1060.2	120.9	1006.4	1127.3	0.2198	1.6428	1.8626
6	170.0	0.01645	61.98	138.0	1065.4	138.0	996.2	1134.2	0.2474	1.5820	1.8294
8	182.8	0.01653	47.35	150.8	1069.2	150.8	988.5	1139.3	0.2676	1.5384	1.8060
10	193.2	0.01659	38.42	161.2	1072.2	161.2	982.1	1143.3	0.2836	1.5043	1.7879
12	201.9	0.01665	32.40	170.0	1074.7	170.0	976.7	1146.7	0.2970	1.4762	1.7732
14	209.6	0.01670	28.05	177.6	1076.9	177.7	971.9	1149.6	0.3085	1.4523	1.7608
14.696	212.0	0.01672	26.80	180.1	1077.6	180.1	970.4	1150.5	0.3122	1.4447	1.7569
16	216.3	0.01675	24.75	184.4	1078.8	184.5	967.6	1152.1	0.3186	1.4315	1.7501
18	222.4	0.01679	22.17	190.6	1080.5	190.6	963.8	1154.4	0.3277	1.4129	1.7406
20	228.0	0.01683	20.09	196.2	1082.0	196.2	960.2	1156.4	0.3359	1.3963	1.7322
30	250.3	0.01700	13.75	218.8	1088.0	218.9	945.4	1164.3	0.3683	1.3315	1.6998
40	267.3	0.01715	10.50	236.0	1092.3	236.2	933.8	1170.0	0.3922	1.2847	1.6769
60	292.7	0.01738	7.177	262.0	1098.3	262.2	915.8	1178.0	0.4274	1.2172	1.6446
80	312.1	0.01757	5.474	281.9	1102.6	282.2	901.4	1183.6	0.4535	1.1681	1.6216
100	327.9	0.01774	4.434	298.3	1105.8	298.6	889.2	1187.8	0.4745	1.1291	1.6036
120	341.3	0.01789	3.730	312.3	1108.3	312.7	878.4	1191.1	0.4921	1.0967	1.5888
140	353.1	0.01802	3.221	324.6	1110.3	325.0	868.8	1193.8	0.5074	1.0688	1.5762
160	363.6	0.01815	2.836	335.6	1112.0	336.2	859.8	1196.0	0.5209	1.0443	1.5652
180	373.1	0.01827	2.533	345.7	1113.4	346.3	851.5	1197.8	0.5330	1.0225	1.5555
200	381.9	0.01839	2.289	354.9	1114.6	355.6	843.7	1199.3	0.5441	1.0025	1.5466
300	417.4	0.01890	1.544	393.0	1118.1	394.1	809.8	1203.9	0.5885	0.9232	1.5117
400	444.7	0.01934	1.162	422.8	1119.4	424.2	781.3	1205.5	0.6219	0.8639	1.4858
600	486.3	0.02013	0.7702	469.4	1118.5	471.6	732.5	1204.1	0.6724	0.7742	1.4466
800	518.4	0.02087	0.5691	506.6	1115.0	509.7	689.6	1199.3	0.7112	0.7050	1.4162
1000	544.8	0.02159	0.4459	538.4	1109.9	542.4	650.0	1192.4	0.7434	0.6471	1.3905
1200	567.4	0.02232	0.3623	566.7	1103.5	571.7	612.2	1183.9	0.7714	0.5961	1.3675
1400	587.3	0.02307	0.3016	592.6	1096.0	598.6	575.5	1174.1	0.7966	0.5497	1.3463
1600	605.1	0.02386	0.2552	616.9	1087.4	624.0	538.9	1162.9	0.8198	0.5062	1.3260
2000	636.0	0.02565	0.1881	662.4	1066.6	671.9	464.4	1136.3	0.8624	0.4239	1.2863
2600	674.1	0.02938	0.1210	729.2	1021.8	743.3	336.8	1080.1	0.9237	0.2971	1.2208
3203.8	705.445	0.05053	0.05053	872.6	872.6	902.5	0.0	902.5	1.0582	0.0000	1.0582

† Saturated liquid entropies have been adjusted to make the Gibbs functions of the liquid and vapor phases exactly equal. For this reason there are some small differences between values presented here and the original tables.

Sources: Reprinted by permission from William C. Reynolds and Henry C. Perkins, *Engineering Thermodynamics*, 2d ed. (New York: McGraw-Hill, 1977), pp. 632–633 (Table B-1b). Recalculated from equations given in Joseph H. Keenan, Frederick G. Keyes, Philip G. Hill, and Joan G. Moore, *Steam Tables* (New York: Wiley, 1969).

Appendix C.2b Saturated water, pressure table (metric units)†

		Volume, m^3/kg		Energy, kJ/kg		Enthalpy, kJ/kg			Entropy, kJ/(kg·K)		
p, MPa	T, °C	v_f	v_g	u_f	u_g	h_f	h_{fg}	h_g	s_f	s_{fg}	s_g
0.000611	0.01	0.001000	206.1	0.0	2375.3	0.0	2501.3	2501.3	0.0000	9.1571	9.1571
0.0008	3.8	0.001000	159.7	15.8	2380.5	15.8	2492.5	2508.3	0.0575	9.0007	9.0582
0.001	7.0	0.001000	129.2	29.3	2385.0	29.3	2484.9	2514.2	0.1059	8.8706	8.9765
0.0012	9.7	0.001000	108.7	40.6	2388.7	40.6	2478.5	2519.1	0.1460	8.7639	8.9099
0.0014	12.0	0.001001	93.92	50.3	2391.9	50.3	2473.1	2523.4	0.1802	8.6736	8.8538
0.0016	14.0	0.001001	82.76	58.9	2394.7	58.9	2468.2	2527.1	0.2101	8.5952	8.8053
0.0018	15.8	0.001001	74.03	66.5	2397.2	66.5	2464.0	2530.5	0.2367	8.5259	8.7626
0.002	17.5	0.001001	67.00	73.5	2399.5	73.5	2460.0	2533.5	0.2606	8.4639	8.7245
0.003	24.1	0.001003	45.67	101.0	2408.5	101.0	2444.5	2545.5	0.3544	8.2240	8.5784
0.004	29.0	0.001004	34.80	121.4	2415.2	121.4	2433.0	2554.4	0.4225	8.0529	8.4754
0.006	36.2	0.001006	23.74	151.5	2424.9	151.5	2415.9	2567.4	0.5208	7.8104	8.3312
0.008	41.5	0.001008	18.10	173.9	2432.1	173.9	2403.1	2577.0	0.5924	7.6371	8.2295
0.01	45.8	0.001010	14.67	191.8	2437.9	191.8	2392.8	2584.6	0.6491	7.5019	8.1510
0.012	49.4	0.001012	12.36	206.9	2442.7	206.9	2384.1	2591.0	0.6961	7.3910	8.0871
0.014	52.6	0.001013	10.69	220.0	2446.9	220.0	2376.6	2596.6	0.7365	7.2968	8.0333
0.016	55.3	0.001015	9.433	231.5	2450.5	231.5	2369.9	2601.4	0.7719	7.2149	7.9868
0.018	57.8	0.001016	8.445	241.9	2453.8	241.9	2363.9	2605.8	0.8034	7.1425	7.9459
0.02	60.1	0.001017	7.649	251.4	2456.7	251.4	2358.3	2609.7	0.8319	7.0774	7.9093
0.03	69.1	0.001022	5.229	289.2	2468.4	289.2	2336.1	2625.3	0.9439	6.8256	7.7695
0.04	75.9	0.001026	3.993	317.5	2477.0	317.6	2319.1	2636.7	1.0260	6.6449	7.6709
0.06	85.9	0.001033	2.732	359.8	2489.6	359.8	2293.7	2653.5	1.1455	6.3873	7.5328
0.08	93.5	0.001039	2.087	391.6	2498.8	391.6	2274.1	2665.7	1.2331	6.2023	7.4354
0.1	99.6	0.001043	1.694	417.3	2506.1	417.4	2258.1	2675.5	1.3029	6.0573	7.3602
0.12	104.8	0.001047	1.428	439.2	2512.1	439.3	2244.2	2683.5	1.3611	5.9378	7.2989
0.14	109.3	0.001051	1.237	458.2	2517.3	458.4	2232.0	2690.4	1.4112	5.8360	7.2472
0.16	113.3	0.001054	1.091	475.2	2521.8	475.3	2221.2	2696.5	1.4553	5.7472	7.2025
0.18	116.9	0.001058	0.9775	490.5	2525.9	490.7	2211.1	2701.8	1.4948	5.6683	7.1631
0.2	120.2	0.001061	0.8857	504.5	2529.5	504.7	2201.9	2706.6	1.5305	5.5975	7.1280
0.3	133.5	0.001073	0.6058	561.1	2543.6	561.5	2163.8	2725.3	1.6722	5.3205	6.9927
0.4	143.6	0.001084	0.4625	604.3	2553.6	604.7	2133.8	2738.5	1.7770	5.1197	6.8967
0.6	158.9	0.001101	0.3157	669.9	2567.4	670.6	2086.2	2756.8	1.9316	4.8293	6.7609
0.8	170.4	0.001115	0.2404	720.2	2576.8	721.1	2048.0	2769.1	2.0466	4.6170	6.6636
1	179.9	0.001127	0.1944	761.7	2583.6	762.8	2015.3	2778.1	2.1391	4.4482	6.5873
1.2	188.0	0.001139	0.1633	797.3	2588.8	798.6	1986.2	2784.8	2.2170	4.3072	6.5242
1.4	195.1	0.001149	0.1408	828.7	2592.8	830.3	1959.7	2790.0	2.2847	4.1854	6.4701
1.6	201.4	0.001159	0.1238	856.9	2596.0	858.8	1935.2	2794.0	2.3446	4.0780	6.4226
1.8	207.2	0.001168	0.1104	882.7	2598.4	884.8	1912.3	2797.1	2.3986	3.9816	6.3802
2	212.4	0.001177	0.09963	906.4	2600.3	908.8	1890.7	2799.5	2.4478	3.8939	6.3417
3	233.9	0.001216	0.06668	1004.8	2604.1	1008.4	1795.7	2804.1	2.6462	3.5416	6.1878
4	250.4	0.001252	0.04978	1082.3	2602.3	1087.3	1714.1	2801.4	2.7970	3.2739	6.0709
6	275.6	0.001319	0.03244	1205.4	2589.7	1213.3	1571.0	2784.3	3.0273	2.8627	5.8900
8	295.1	0.001384	0.02352	1305.6	2569.8	1316.6	1441.4	2758.0	3.2075	2.5365	5.7440
9	303.4	0.001418	0.02048	1350.5	2557.8	1363.3	1378.8	2742.1	3.2865	2.3916	5.6781
10	311.1	0.001452	0.01803	1393.0	2544.4	1407.6	1317.1	2724.7	3.3603	2.2546	5.6149
12	324.8	0.001527	0.01426	1472.9	2513.7	1491.3	1193.6	2684.9	3.4970	1.9963	5.4933
14	336.8	0.001611	0.01149	1548.6	2476.8	1571.1	1066.5	2637.6	3.6240	1.7486	5.3726
16	347.4	0.001711	0.009307	1622.7	2431.8	1650.0	930.7	2580.7	3.7468	1.4996	5.2464
18	357.1	0.001840	0.007491	1698.9	2374.4	1732.0	777.2	2509.2	3.8722	1.2332	5.1054
20	365.8	0.002036	0.005836	1785.6	2293.2	1826.3	583.7	2410.0	4.0146	0.9135	4.9281
22.088	374.136	0.003155	0.003155	2029.6	2029.6	2099.3	0.0	2099.3	4.4305	0.0000	4.4305

† Saturated liquid entropies have been adjusted to make the Gibbs functions of the liquid and vapor phases exactly equal. For this reason there are some small differences between values presented here and the original tables.

Sources: Reprinted by permission from William C. Reynolds and Henry C. Perkins, *Engineering Thermodynamics*, 2d ed. (New York: McGraw-Hill, 1977), pp. 624–625 (Table B-1b). Recalculated from equations given in Joseph H. Keenan, Frederick G. Keyes, Philip G. Hill, and Joan G. Moore, *Steam Tables* (New York: Wiley, 1969).

Appendix C.3a **Superheated water (English units)**†

p, psia (T_{sat}, °F)		Temperature, °F												
		100	200	300	400	500	600	700	800	900	1000	1100	1200	1300
0.2	v, ft³/lbm	1666.0	1964.0	2262.0	2560.0	2858.0	3156.0	3454.0	3752.0	4050.0	4347.0	4645.0	4943.0	5241.0
(53.1)	u, Btu/lbm	1043.9	1077.7	1112.1	1147.1	1182.8	1219.3	1256.7	1294.9	1334.0	1373.9	1414.8	1456.7	1499.4
	h, Btu/lbm	1105.6	1150.4	1195.8	1241.9	1288.6	1336.1	1384.5	1433.7	1483.8	1534.8	1586.8	1639.6	1693.4
	s, Btu/(lbm·R)	2.1550	2.2287	2.2928	2.3497	2.4011	2.4483	2.4919	2.5326	2.5708	2.6070	2.6414	2.6743	2.7058
0.5	v, ft³/lbm	665.9	785.5	904.8	1024.0	1143.0	1262.0	1382.0	1501.0	1620.0	1739.0	1858.0	1977.0	2096.0
(79.5)	u, Btu/lbm	1043.7	1077.6	1112.0	1147.1	1182.8	1219.3	1256.7	1294.9	1334.0	1373.9	1414.8	1456.7	1499.4
	h, Btu/lbm	1105.3	1150.3	1195.8	1241.8	1288.6	1336.1	1384.5	1433.7	1483.8	1534.8	1586.8	1639.6	1693.4
	s, Btu/(lbm·R)	2.0537	2.1276	2.1917	2.2487	2.3001	2.3472	2.3909	2.4316	2.4698	2.5060	2.5404	2.5733	2.6048
1	v, ft³/lbm		392.5	452.3	511.9	571.5	631.1	690.7	750.3	809.9	869.5	929.0	988.6	1048.0
(101.7)	u, Btu/lbm		1077.5	1112.0	1147.0	1182.8	1219.3	1256.7	1294.9	1333.9	1373.9	1414.8	1456.7	1499.4
	h, Btu/lbm		1150.1	1195.6	1241.7	1288.5	1336.1	1384.5	1433.7	1483.8	1534.8	1586.8	1639.6	1693.4
	s, Btu/(lbm·R)		2.0510	2.1152	2.1722	2.2237	2.2708	2.3144	2.3551	2.3934	2.4296	2.4640	2.4969	2.5283
2	v, ft³/lbm		196.0	226.0	255.9	285.7	315.5	345.3	375.1	404.9	434.7	464.5	494.3	524.1
(126.0)	u, Btu/lbm		1077.2	1111.8	1146.9	1182.7	1219.3	1256.6	1294.8	1333.9	1373.9	1414.8	1456.7	1499.4
	h, Btu/lbm		1149.7	1195.4	1241.6	1288.4	1336.0	1384.4	1433.7	1483.8	1534.8	1586.7	1639.6	1693.4
	s, Btu/(lbm·R)		1.9741	2.0386	2.0957	2.1472	2.1944	2.2380	2.2787	2.3170	2.3532	2.3876	2.4205	2.4519
5	v, ft³/lbm		78.15	90.24	102.2	114.2	126.1	138.1	150.0	161.9	173.9	185.8	197.7	209.6
(162.2)	u, Btu/lbm		1076.2	1111.3	1146.6	1182.5	1219.1	1256.5	1294.7	1333.8	1373.8	1414.8	1456.6	1499.4
	h, Btu/lbm		1148.6	1194.8	1241.2	1288.2	1335.8	1384.3	1433.5	1483.7	1534.7	1586.7	1639.5	1693.3
	s, Btu/(lbm·R)		1.8717	1.9369	1.9943	2.0460	2.0932	2.1369	2.1776	2.2159	2.2522	2.2866	2.3194	2.3509
10	v, ft³/lbm		38.85	44.99	51.03	57.04	63.03	69.01	74.98	80.95	86.91	92.88	98.84	104.8
(193.2)	u, Btu/lbm		1074.7	1110.4	1146.1	1182.2	1218.8	1256.3	1294.6	1333.7	1373.7	1414.7	1456.5	1499.3
	h, Btu/lbm		1146.6	1193.7	1240.5	1287.7	1335.5	1384.0	1433.3	1483.5	1534.6	1586.5	1639.4	1693.2
	s, Btu/(lbm·R)		1.7929	1.8594	1.9173	1.9692	2.0166	2.0603	2.1011	2.1394	2.1757	2.2101	2.2430	2.2745
14.7	v, ft³/lbm			30.52	34.67	38.77	42.86	46.93	51.00	55.07	59.13	63.19	67.25	71.30
(212.0)	u, Btu/lbm			1109.6	1145.6	1181.8	1218.6	1256.1	1294.4	1333.6	1373.6	1414.6	1456.5	1499.3
	h, Btu/lbm			1192.6	1239.9	1287.3	1335.2	1383.8	1433.1	1483.3	1534.4	1586.4	1639.3	1693.2
	s, Btu/(lbm·R)			1.8159	1.8743	1.9264	1.9739	2.0177	2.0586	2.0969	2.1332	2.1676	2.2005	2.2320

† Saturated liquid entropies have been adjusted to make the Gibbs functions of the liquid and vapor phases exactly equal. For this reason there are some small differences between values presented here and the original tables.

Sources: Reprinted by permission from William C. Reynolds and Henry C. Perkins, *Engineering Thermodynamics*, 2d ed. (New York: McGraw-Hill, 1977), pp. 634–637 (Table B-2). Recalculated from equations given in Joseph H. Keenan, Frederick G. Keyes, Philip G. Hill, and Joan G. Moore, *Steam Tables* (New York: Wiley, 1969).

Appendix C.3a Superheated water (English units)[†]—*continued*

p, psia (T_{sat}, °F)		Temperature, °F 300	400	500	600	700	800	900	1000	1100	1200	1300	1400	1500
20	v, ft³/lbm	22.36	25.43	28.46	31.47	34.47	37.46	40.45	43.44	46.42	49.41	52.39	55.37	58.35
(227.9)	u, Btu/lbm	1108.7	1145.1	1181.5	1218.3	1255.9	1294.3	1333.5	1373.5	1414.5	1456.4	1499.2	1542.9	1587.6
	h, Btu/lbm	1191.4	1239.2	1286.8	1334.8	1383.5	1432.2	1483.2	1534.3	1586.3	1639.2	1693.1	1747.8	1803.5
	s, Btu/(lbm·R)	1.7807	1.8397	1.8921	1.9397	1.9836	2.0245	2.0629	2.0991	2.1336	2.1665	2.1980	2.2283	2.2574
40	v, ft³/lbm	11.04	12.62	14.16	15.69	17.20	18.70	20.20	21.70	23.20	24.69	26.18	27.68	29.17
(267.2)	u, Btu/lbm	1105.1	1143.0	1180.1	1217.3	1255.1	1293.7	1333.0	1373.1	1414.2	1456.1	1498.9	1542.7	1587.4
	h, Btu/lbm	1186.8	1236.4	1284.9	1333.4	1382.4	1432.1	1482.5	1533.7	1585.9	1638.9	1692.8	1747.6	1803.3
	s, Btu/(lbm·R)	1.6995	1.7608	1.8142	1.8623	1.9065	1.9476	1.9861	2.0224	2.0570	2.0899	2.1214	2.1517	2.1809
60	v, ft³/lbm	7.260	8.353	9.399	10.42	11.44	12.45	13.45	14.45	15.45	16.45	17.45	18.45	19.44
(292.7)	u, Btu/lbm	1101.3	1140.8	1178.6	1216.3	1254.4	1293.0	1332.5	1372.7	1413.8	1455.8	1498.7	1542.5	1587.2
	h, Btu/lbm	1181.9	1233.5	1283.0	1332.1	1381.4	1431.2	1481.8	1533.2	1585.4	1638.5	1692.4	1747.3	1803.0
	s, Btu/(lbm·R)	1.6497	1.7136	1.7680	1.8167	1.8611	1.9024	1.9410	1.9775	2.0121	2.0450	2.0766	2.1069	2.1361
80	v, ft³/lbm		6.217	7.017	7.794	8.561	9.321	10.08	10.83	11.58	12.33	13.08	13.83	14.58
(312.0)	u, Btu/lbm		1138.5	1177.2	1215.3	1253.6	1292.4	1332.0	1372.3	1413.5	1455.5	1498.4	1542.3	1587.0
	h, Btu/lbm		1230.6	1281.1	1330.7	1380.3	1430.4	1481.1	1532.6	1584.9	1638.1	1692.1	1747.0	1802.8
	s, Btu/(lbm·R)		1.6792	1.7348	1.7840	1.8287	1.8702	1.9089	1.9455	1.9801	2.0131	2.0447	2.0751	2.1043
100	v, ft³/lbm		4.934	5.587	6.216	6.834	7.445	8.053	8.657	9.260	9.861	10.46	11.06	11.66
(327.8)	u, Btu/lbm		1136.2	1175.7	1214.2	1252.8	1291.8	1331.4	1371.9	1413.1	1455.2	1498.2	1542.0	1586.8
	h, Btu/lbm		1227.5	1279.1	1329.3	1379.2	1429.6	1480.5	1532.1	1584.5	1637.7	1691.8	1746.7	1802.5
	s, Btu/(lbm·R)		1.6519	1.7087	1.7584	1.8035	1.8451	1.8840	1.9206	1.9553	1.9884	2.0200	2.0504	2.0796
140	v, ft³/lbm		3.466	3.952	4.412	4.860	5.301	5.739	6.173	6.605	7.036	7.466	7.895	8.324
(353.1)	u, Btu/lbm		1131.4	1172.7	1212.1	1251.2	1290.5	1330.4	1371.0	1412.4	1454.6	1497.7	1541.6	1586.4
	h, Btu/lbm		1221.2	1275.1	1326.4	1377.1	1427.9	1479.1	1531.0	1583.5	1636.9	1691.1	1746.1	1802.0
	s, Btu/(lbm·R)		1.6090	1.6684	1.7193	1.7650	1.8070	1.8461	1.8829	1.9178	1.9509	1.9826	2.0130	2.0423
180	v, ft³/lbm		2.648	3.042	3.409	3.763	4.110	4.453	4.793	5.131	5.467	5.802	6.137	6.471
(373.1)	u, Btu/lbm		1126.2	1169.6	1210.0	1249.6	1289.3	1329.4	1370.2	1411.7	1454.0	1497.2	1541.2	1586.0
	h, Btu/lbm		1214.4	1270.9	1323.5	1374.9	1426.2	1477.7	1529.8	1582.6	1636.1	1690.4	1745.6	1801.5
	s, Btu/(lbm·R)		1.5751	1.6374	1.6895	1.7359	1.7783	1.8177	1.8546	1.8896	1.9229	1.9546	1.9851	2.0144

[†] Saturated liquid entropies have been adjusted to make the Gibbs functions of the liquid and vapor phases exactly equal. For this reason there are some small differences between values presented here and the original tables.

Sources: Reprinted by permission from William C. Reynolds and Henry C. Perkins, *Engineering Thermodynamics*, 2d ed. (New York: McGraw-Hill, 1977), pp. 634–637 (Table B-2). Recalculated from equations given in Joseph H. Keenan, Frederick G. Keyes, Philip G. Hill, and Joan G. Moore, *Steam Tables* (New York: Wiley, 1969).

Appendix C.3a Superheated water (English units)[†]—*continued*

p, psia (T_{sat}, °F)		Temperature, °F												
		400	500	600	700	800	900	1000	1100	1200	1300	1400	1500	1600
200	v, ft^3/lbm	2.361	2.724	3.058	3.379	3.693	4.003	4.310	4.615	4.918	5.220	5.521	5.822	6.123
(381.8)	u, Btu/lbm	1123.5	1168.0	1208.9	1248.8	1288.6	1328.9	1369.8	1411.4	1453.7	1496.9	1540.9	1585.8	1631.6
	h, Btu/lbm	1210.8	1268.8	1322.0	1373.8	1425.3	1477.0	1529.3	1582.1	1635.7	1690.1	1745.3	1801.3	1858.1
	s, Btu/(lbm·R)	1.5602	1.6240	1.6769	1.7236	1.7662	1.8057	1.8427	1.8778	1.9111	1.9429	1.9734	2.0027	2.0310
250	v, ft^3/lbm		2.150	2.426	2.688	2.943	3.193	3.440	3.685	3.929	4.172	4.414	4.655	4.896
(401.0)	u, Btu/lbm		1163.8	1206.1	1246.7	1287.0	1327.6	1368.7	1410.5	1453.0	1496.3	1540.4	1585.3	1631.1
	h, Btu/lbm		1263.3	1318.3	1371.1	1423.2	1475.3	1527.9	1581.0	1634.8	1689.3	1744.6	1800.7	1857.6
	s, Btu/(lbm·R)		1.5950	1.6496	1.6972	1.7403	1.7801	1.8174	1.8526	1.8860	1.9179	1.9485	1.9779	2.0062
300	v, ft^3/lbm		1.766	2.004	2.227	2.442	2.653	2.860	3.066	3.270	3.473	3.675	3.877	4.078
(417.4)	u, Btu/lbm		1159.5	1203.2	1244.6	1285.4	1326.3	1367.7	1409.6	1452.2	1495.6	1539.8	1584.8	1630.7
	h, Btu/lbm		1257.5	1314.5	1368.3	1421.0	1473.6	1526.4	1579.8	1633.8	1688.4	1743.8	1800.0	1857.0
	s, Btu/(lbm·R)		1.5703	1.6268	1.6753	1.7189	1.7591	1.7966	1.8319	1.8655	1.8975	1.9281	1.9575	1.9859
400	v, ft^3/lbm		1.284	1.476	1.650	1.816	1.978	2.136	2.292	2.446	2.599	2.752	2.904	3.055
(444.7)	u, Btu/lbm		1150.1	1197.3	1240.4	1282.1	1323.7	1365.5	1407.8	1450.7	1494.3	1538.7	1583.8	1629.8
	h, Btu/lbm		1245.2	1306.6	1362.5	1416.6	1470.1	1523.6	1577.4	1631.8	1686.8	1742.4	1798.8	1855.9
	s, Btu/(lbm·R)		1.5284	1.5894	1.6398	1.6846	1.7254	1.7634	1.7991	1.8329	1.8650	1.8958	1.9253	1.9537
600	v, ft^3/lbm		0.7947	0.9456	1.073	1.190	1.302	1.411	1.517	1.622	1.726	1.829	1.931	2.033
(486.3)	u, Btu/lbm		1128.0	1184.5	1231.5	1275.4	1318.4	1361.2	1404.2	1447.7	1491.7	1536.4	1581.8	1628.0
	h, Btu/lbm		1216.2	1289.5	1350.6	1407.6	1462.9	1517.8	1572.7	1627.8	1683.4	1739.5	1796.3	1853.7
	s, Btu/(lbm·R)		1.4594	1.5322	1.5874	1.6345	1.6768	1.7157	1.7521	1.7863	1.8188	1.8499	1.8796	1.9082
800	v, ft^3/lbm			0.6776	0.7829	0.8764	0.9640	1.048	1.130	1.210	1.289	1.367	1.445	1.522
(518.3)	u, Btu/lbm			1170.1	1222.1	1268.4	1312.9	1356.7	1400.5	1444.6	1489.1	1534.2	1579.8	1626.2
	h, Btu/lbm			1270.4	1338.0	1398.2	1455.6	1511.9	1567.8	1623.8	1680.0	1736.6	1793.7	1851.5
	s, Btu/(lbm·R)			1.4863	1.5473	1.5971	1.6410	1.6809	1.7180	1.7527	1.7856	1.8169	1.8469	1.8756
1000	v, ft^3/lbm			0.5140	0.6080	0.6878	0.7610	0.8305	0.8976	0.9630	1.027	1.090	1.153	1.215
(544.7)	u, Btu/lbm			1153.7	1212.0	1261.2	1307.3	1352.2	1396.8	1441.5	1486.4	1531.9	1577.8	1624.4
	h, Btu/lbm			1248.8	1324.5	1388.5	1448.1	1505.9	1562.9	1619.7	1676.5	1733.7	1791.2	1849.3
	s, Btu/(lbm·R)			1.4452	1.5137	1.5666	1.6122	1.6532	1.6910	1.7263	1.7595	1.7911	1.8212	1.8501

[†] Saturated liquid entropies have been adjusted to make the Gibbs functions of the liquid and vapor phases exactly equal. For this reason there are some small differences between values presented here and the original tables.

Sources: Reprinted by permission from William C. Reynolds and Henry C. Perkins, *Engineering Thermodynamics*, 2d ed. (New York: McGraw-Hill, 1977), pp. 634–637 (Table B-2). Recalculated from equations given in Joseph H. Keenan, Frederick G. Keyes, Philip G. Hill, and Joan G. Moore, *Steam Tables* (New York: Wiley, 1969).

Appendix C.3a Superheated water (English units)[†]—*continued*

p, psia (T_{sat}, °F)		Temperature, °F 800	900	1000	1100	1200	1300	1400	1500	1600	1700	1800	1900	2000
2000	v, ft^3/lbm	0.3071	0.3534	0.3945	0.4325	0.4685	0.5031	0.5368	0.5697	0.6020	0.6340	0.6656	0.6971	0.7284
(636.0)	u, Btu/lbm	1220.1	1276.8	1328.1	1377.2	1425.2	1472.7	1520.2	1567.6	1615.4	1663.5	1712.0	1761.0	1810.6
	h, Btu/lbm	1333.8	1407.6	1474.1	1537.2	1598.6	1659.0	1718.8	1778.5	1838.2	1898.1	1958.3	2019.0	2080.1
	s, Btu/(lbm·R)	1.4564	1.5128	1.5600	1.6019	1.6400	1.6753	1.7084	1.7397	1.7694	1.7978	1.8251	1.8513	1.8767
3000	v, ft^3/lbm	0.1757	0.2160	0.2485	0.2772	0.3036	0.3285	0.3524	0.3754	0.3978	0.4198	0.4416	0.4631	0.4844
(695.5)	u, Btu/lbm	1167.6	1241.8	1301.7	1356.2	1408.0	1458.5	1508.1	1557.3	1606.3	1655.3	1704.5	1754.0	1803.9
	h, Btu/lbm	1265.2	1361.7	1439.6	1510.0	1576.6	1640.8	1703.7	1765.6	1827.1	1888.4	1949.6	2011.1	2072.8
	s, Btu/(lbm·R)	1.3677	1.4416	1.4969	1.5436	1.5850	1.6226	1.6573	1.6897	1.7203	1.7494	1.7771	1.8037	1.8293
4000	v, ft^3/lbm	0.1052	0.1462	0.1752	0.1995	0.2213	0.2414	0.2603	0.2784	0.2959	0.3129	0.3296	0.3462	0.3625
	u, Btu/lbm	1095.0	1201.5	1272.9	1333.9	1390.1	1443.7	1495.7	1546.7	1597.1	1647.2	1697.1	1747.1	1797.3
	h, Btu/lbm	1172.9	1309.7	1402.6	1481.6	1553.9	1622.4	1688.4	1752.8	1816.1	1878.8	1941.1	2003.3	2065.6
	s, Btu/(lbm·R)	1.2742	1.3791	1.4451	1.4975	1.5425	1.5825	1.6190	1.6528	1.6843	1.7140	1.7422	1.7691	1.7950
5000	v, ft^3/lbm	0.05933	0.1038	0.1312	0.1530	0.1720	0.1892	0.2052	0.2203	0.2348	0.2489	0.2626	0.2761	0.2895
	u, Btu/lbm	987.2	1155.1	1242.0	1310.6	1371.6	1428.6	1483.2	1536.1	1587.9	1639.0	1689.7	1740.3	1790.8
	h, Btu/lbm	1042.1	1251.1	1363.4	1452.2	1530.8	1603.7	1673.0	1739.9	1805.2	1869.3	1932.7	1995.7	2058.6
	s, Btu/(lbm·R)	1.1586	1.3192	1.3990	1.4579	1.5068	1.5495	1.5878	1.6228	1.6553	1.6857	1.7144	1.7417	1.7678
6000	v, ft^3/lbm	0.03942	0.07588	0.1021	0.1222	0.1393	0.1545	0.1685	0.1817	0.1942	0.2063	0.2180	0.2295	0.2409
	u, Btu/lbm	896.9	1102.9	1209.1	1286.4	1352.7	1413.3	1470.5	1525.4	1578.7	1630.9	1682.4	1733.4	1784.3
	h, Btu/lbm	940.6	1187.2	1322.4	1422.1	1507.3	1584.9	1657.6	1727.1	1794.3	1859.9	1924.5	1988.3	2051.7
	s, Btu/(lbm·R)	1.0710	1.2601	1.3563	1.4224	1.4754	1.5208	1.5610	1.5974	1.6309	1.6620	1.6912	1.7189	1.7452
7000	v, ft^3/lbm	0.03341	0.05760	0.08172	0.1004	0.1161	0.1299	0.1425	0.1542	0.1653	0.1759	0.1862	0.1963	0.2062
	u, Btu/lbm	855.0	1049.7	1175.0	1261.7	1333.5	1397.8	1457.7	1514.6	1569.4	1622.8	1675.0	1726.7	1777.8
	h, Btu/lbm	898.3	1124.3	1280.9	1391.8	1483.9	1566.1	1642.3	1714.4	1783.5	1850.7	1916.3	1981.0	2045.0
	s, Btu/(lbm·R)	1.0321	1.2049	1.3163	1.3899	1.4471	1.4953	1.5374	1.5751	1.6096	1.6414	1.6711	1.6991	1.7257
8000	v, ft^3/lbm	0.03061	0.04657	0.06722	0.08445	0.09892	0.1116	0.1231	0.1337	0.1437	0.1533	0.1625	0.1715	0.1803
	u, Btu/lbm	830.7	1003.7	1141.0	1236.8	1314.2	1382.3	1444.9	1503.8	1560.1	1614.6	1667.7	1719.9	1771.4
	h, Btu/lbm	876.0	1072.6	1240.5	1361.9	1460.6	1547.5	1627.1	1701.7	1772.9	1841.5	1908.3	1973.7	2038.4
	s, Btu/(lbm·R)	1.0098	1.1598	1.2793	1.3598	1.4212	1.4720	1.5160	1.5552	1.5906	1.6231	1.6533	1.6817	1.7085

[†] Saturated liquid entropies have been adjusted to make the Gibbs functions of the liquid and vapor phases exactly equal. For this reason there are some small differences between values presented here and the original tables.

Sources: Reprinted by permission from William C. Reynolds and Henry C. Perkins, *Engineering Thermodynamics*, 2d ed. (New York: McGraw-Hill, 1977), pp. 634–637 (Table B-2). Recalculated from equations given in Joseph H. Keenan, Frederick G. Keyes, Philip G. Hill, and Joan G. Moore, *Steam Tables* (New York: Wiley, 1969).

Appendix C.3b Superheated water (metric units)[†]

p, MPa (T_{sat}, °C)		Temperature, °C: 50	100	150	200	250	300	350	400	500	600	700	800	900
0.002	v, m³/kg	74.52	86.08	97.63	109.2	120.7	132.3	143.8	155.3	178.4	201.5	224.6	247.6	270.7
(17.5)	u, kJ/kg	2445.2	2516.3	2588.3	2661.6	2736.2	2812.2	2889.8	2969.0	3132.3	3302.5	3479.7	3663.9	3855.1
	h, kJ/kg	2594.3	2688.4	2783.6	2879.9	2977.6	3076.7	3177.4	3279.6	3489.1	3705.5	3928.8	4159.1	4396.5
	s, kJ/(kg·K)	8.9227	9.1936	9.4328	9.6479	9.8442	10.0251	10.1935	10.3513	10.6414	10.9044	11.1465	11.3718	11.5832
0.005	v, m³/kg	29.78	34.42	39.04	43.66	48.28	52.90	57.51	62.13	71.36	80.59	89.82	99.05	108.3
(32.9)	u, kJ/kg	2444.7	2516.0	2588.1	2661.4	2736.1	2812.2	2889.8	2968.9	3132.3	3302.5	3479.6	3663.9	3855.0
	h, kJ/kg	2593.6	2688.1	2783.3	2879.8	2977.5	3076.6	3177.3	3279.6	3489.1	3705.4	3928.8	4159.1	4396.5
	s, kJ/(kg·K)	8.4982	8.7699	9.0095	9.2248	9.4212	9.6022	9.7706	9.9284	10.2185	10.4815	10.7236	10.9489	11.1603
0.01	v, m³/kg	14.87	17.20	19.51	21.83	24.14	26.45	28.75	31.06	35.68	40.29	44.91	49.53	54.14
(45.8)	u, kJ/kg	2443.9	2515.5	2587.9	2661.3	2736.0	2812.1	2889.7	2968.9	3132.3	3302.5	3479.6	3663.8	3855.0
	h, kJ/kg	2592.6	2687.5	2783.0	2879.5	2977.3	3076.5	3177.2	3279.5	3489.0	3705.4	3928.7	4159.1	4396.4
	s, kJ/(kg·K)	8.1757	8.4487	8.6890	8.9046	9.1010	9.2821	9.4506	9.6084	9.8985	10.1616	10.4037	10.6290	10.8404
0.02	v, m³/kg		8.585	9.748	10.91	12.06	13.22	14.37	15.53	17.84	20.15	22.45	24.76	27.07
(60.1)	u, kJ/kg		2514.5	2587.3	2660.9	2735.7	2811.9	2889.5	2968.8	3132.2	3302.4	3479.6	3663.8	3855.0
	h, kJ/kg		2686.2	2782.3	2879.1	2977.0	3076.3	3177.0	3279.4	3488.9	3705.3	3928.7	4159.1	4396.4
	s, kJ/(kg·K)		8.1263	8.3678	8.5839	8.7807	8.9619	9.1304	9.2884	9.5785	9.8417	10.0838	10.3091	10.5205
0.05	v, m³/kg		3.418	3.889	4.356	4.820	5.284	5.747	6.209	7.134	8.057	8.981	9.904	10.83
(81.3)	u, kJ/kg		2511.6	2585.6	2659.8	2735.0	2811.3	2889.1	2968.4	3131.9	3302.2	3479.5	3663.7	3854.9
	h, kJ/kg		2682.5	2780.1	2877.6	2976.0	3075.5	3176.4	3278.9	3488.6	3705.1	3928.5	4158.9	4396.3
	s, kJ/(kg·K)		7.6955	7.9409	8.1588	8.3564	8.5380	8.7069	8.8650	9.1554	9.4186	9.6608	9.8861	10.0975
0.07	v, m³/kg		2.434	2.773	3.108	3.441	3.772	4.103	4.434	5.095	5.755	6.415	7.074	7.734
(89.9)	u, kJ/kg		2509.6	2584.5	2659.1	2734.5	2811.0	2888.8	2968.2	3131.8	3302.1	3479.4	3663.6	3854.9
	h, kJ/kg		2680.0	2778.6	2876.7	2975.3	3075.0	3176.1	3278.6	3488.4	3704.9	3928.4	4158.8	4396.2
	s, kJ/(kg·K)		7.5349	7.7829	8.0020	8.2001	8.3821	8.5511	8.7094	8.9999	9.2632	9.5054	9.7307	9.9422
0.1	v, m³/kg		1.696	1.936	2.172	2.406	2.639	2.871	3.103	3.565	4.028	4.490	4.952	5.414
(99.6)	u, kJ/kg		2506.6	2582.7	2658.0	2733.7	2810.4	2888.4	2967.8	3131.5	3301.9	3479.2	3663.5	3854.8
	h, kJ/kg		2676.2	2776.4	2875.3	2974.3	3074.3	3175.5	3278.1	3488.1	3704.7	3928.2	4158.7	4396.1
	s, kJ/(kg·K)		7.3622	7.6142	7.8351	8.0341	8.2165	8.3858	8.5442	8.8350	9.0984	9.3406	9.5660	9.7775

[†] Saturated liquid entropies have been adjusted to make the Gibbs functions of the liquid and vapor phases exactly equal. For this reason there are some small differences between values presented here and the original tables.

Sources: Reprinted by permission from William C. Reynolds and Henry C. Perkins, *Engineering Thermodynamics*, 2d ed. (New York: McGraw-Hill, 1977), pp. 626–629 (Table B-2). Recalculated from equations given in Joseph H. Keenan, Frederick G. Keyes, Philip G. Hill, and Joan G. Moore, *Steam Tables* (New York: Wiley, 1969).

Appendix C.3b **Superheated water (metric units)**† ***—continued***

p, MPa (T_{sat}, °C)		Temperature, °C 150	200	250	300	350	400	450	500	550	600	700	800	900
0.15	v, m³/kg	1.285	1.444	1.601	1.757	1.912	2.067	2.222	2.376	2.530	2.685	2.993	3.301	3.609
(111.4)	u, kJ/kg	2579.8	2656.2	2732.5	2809.5	2887.7	2967.3	3048.4	3131.1	3215.6	3301.6	3479.0	3663.4	3854.6
	h, kJ/kg	2772.6	2872.9	2972.7	3073.0	3174.5	3277.3	3381.7	3487.6	3595.1	3704.3	3927.9	4158.5	4395.9
	s, kJ/(kg·K)	7.4201	7.6441	7.8446	8.0278	8.1975	8.3562	8.5057	8.6473	8.7821	8.9109	9.1533	9.3787	9.5903
0.2	v, m³/kg	0.9596	1.080	1.199	1.316	1.433	1.549	1.665	1.781	1.897	2.013	2.244	2.475	2.706
(120.2)	u, kJ/kg	2576.9	2654.4	2731.2	2808.6	2886.9	2966.7	3047.9	3130.7	3215.2	3301.4	3478.8	3663.2	3854.5
	h, kJ/kg	2768.8	2870.5	2971.0	3071.8	3173.5	3276.5	3381.0	3487.0	3594.7	3704.0	3927.7	4158.3	4395.8
	s, kJ/(kg·K)	7.2803	7.5074	7.7094	7.8934	8.0636	8.2226	8.3723	8.5140	8.6489	8.7778	9.0203	9.2458	9.4574
0.4	v, m³/kg	0.4708	0.5342	0.5951	0.6548	0.7139	0.7726	0.8311	0.8893	0.9475	1.006	1.121	1.237	1.353
(143.6)	u, kJ/kg	2564.5	2646.8	2726.1	2804.8	2884.0	2964.4	3046.0	3129.2	3213.9	3300.2	3477.9	3662.5	3853.9
	h, kJ/kg	2752.8	2860.5	2964.2	3066.7	3169.6	3273.4	3378.4	3484.9	3592.9	3702.4	3926.5	4157.4	4395.1
	s, kJ/(kg·K)	6.9307	7.1714	7.3797	7.5670	7.7390	7.8992	8.0497	8.1921	8.3274	8.4566	8.6995	8.9253	9.1370
0.6	v, m³/kg		0.3520	0.3938	0.4344	0.4742	0.5137	0.5529	0.5920	0.6309	0.6697	0.7472	0.8245	0.9017
(158.9)	u, kJ/kg		2638.9	2720.9	2801.0	2881.1	2962.0	3044.1	3127.6	3212.5	3299.1	3477.1	3661.8	3853.3
	h, kJ/kg		2850.1	2957.2	3061.6	3165.7	3270.2	3375.9	3482.7	3591.1	3700.9	3925.4	4156.5	4394.4
	s, kJ/(kg·K)		6.9673	7.1824	7.3732	7.5472	7.7086	7.8600	8.0029	8.1386	8.2682	8.5115	8.7375	8.9494
0.8	v, m³/kg		0.2608	0.2931	0.3241	0.3544	0.3843	0.4139	0.4433	0.4726	0.5018	0.5601	0.6181	0.6761
(170.4)	u, kJ/kg		2630.6	2715.5	2797.1	2878.2	2959.7	3042.2	3125.9	3211.2	3297.9	3476.2	3661.1	3852.8
	h, kJ/kg		2839.2	2950.0	3056.4	3161.7	3267.1	3373.3	3480.6	3589.3	3699.4	3924.3	4155.7	4393.6
	s, kJ/(kg·K)		6.8167	7.0392	7.2336	7.4097	7.5723	7.7245	7.8680	8.0042	8.1341	8.3779	8.6041	8.8161
1	v, m³/kg		0.2060	0.2327	0.2579	0.2825	0.3066	0.3304	0.3541	0.3776	0.4011	0.4478	0.4943	0.5407
(179.9)	u, kJ/kg		2621.9	2709.9	2793.2	2875.2	2957.3	3040.2	3124.3	3209.8	3296.8	3475.4	3660.5	3852.2
	h, kJ/kg		2827.9	2942.6	3051.2	3157.7	3263.9	3370.7	3478.4	3587.5	3697.9	3923.1	4154.8	4392.9
	s, kJ/(kg·K)		6.6948	6.9255	7.1237	7.3019	7.4658	7.6188	7.7630	7.8996	8.0298	8.2740	8.5005	8.7127
1.5	v, m³/kg		0.1325	0.1520	0.1697	0.1866	0.2030	0.2192	0.2352	0.2510	0.2668	0.2981	0.3292	0.3603
(198.3)	u, kJ/kg		2598.1	2695.3	2783.1	2867.6	2951.3	3035.3	3120.3	3206.4	3293.9	3473.2	3658.7	3850.8
	h, kJ/kg		2796.8	2923.2	3037.6	3147.4	3255.8	3364.1	3473.0	3582.9	3694.0	3920.3	4152.6	4391.2
	s, kJ/(kg·K)		6.4554	6.7098	6.9187	7.1025	7.2697	7.4249	7.5706	7.7083	7.8393	8.0846	8.3118	8.5243

† Saturated liquid entropies have been adjusted to make the Gibbs functions of the liquid and vapor phases exactly equal. For this reason there are some small differences between values presented here and the original tables.

Sources: Reprinted by permission from William C. Reynolds and Henry C. Perkins, *Engineering Thermodynamics*, 2d ed. (New York: McGraw-Hill, 1977), pp. 626–629 (Table B-2). Recalculated from equations given in Joseph H. Keenan, Frederick G. Keyes, Philip G. Hill, and Joan G. Moore, *Steam Tables* (New York: Wiley, 1969).

Appendix C.3*b* **Superheated water (metric units)**[†]**—*continued***

p, MPa (T_{sat}, °C)		Temperature, °C 250	300	350	400	450	500	550	600	650	700	750	800	900
2	v, m³/kg	0.1114	0.1255	0.1386	0.1512	0.1635	0.1757	0.1877	0.1996	0.2114	0.2232	0.2350	0.2467	0.2700
(212.4)	u, kJ/kg	2679.6	2772.6	2859.8	2945.2	3030.4	3116.2	3203.0	3290.9	3380.2	3471.0	3563.2	3657.0	3849.3
	h, kJ/kg	2902.5	3023.5	3137.0	3247.6	3357.5	3467.6	3578.3	3690.1	3803.1	3917.5	4033.2	4150.4	4389.4
	s, kJ/(kg·K)	6.5461	6.7672	6.9571	7.1279	7.2853	7.4325	7.5713	7.7032	7.8290	7.9496	8.0656	8.1774	8.3903
3	v. m³/kg	0.07058	0.08114	0.09053	0.09936	0.1079	0.1162	0.1244	0.1324	0.1404	0.1484	0.1563	0.1641	0.1798
(233.9)	u, kJ/kg	2644.0	2750.0	2843.7	2932.7	3020.4	3107.9	3196.0	3285.0	3375.2	3466.6	3559.4	3653.6	3846.5
	h, kJ/kg	2855.8	2993.5	3115.3	3230.8	3344.0	3456.5	3569.1	3682.3	3796.5	3911.7	4028.2	4146.0	4385.9
	s, kJ/(kg·K)	6.2880	6.5398	6.7436	6.9220	7.0842	7.2346	7.3757	7.5093	7.6364	7.7580	7.8747	7.9871	8.2008
4	v, m³/kg		0.05884	0.06645	0.07341	0.08003	0.08643	0.09269	0.09885	0.1049	0.1109	0.1169	0.1229	0.1347
(250.4)	u, kJ/kg		2725.3	2826.6	2919.9	3010.1	3099.5	3189.0	3279.1	3370.1	3462.1	3555.5	3650.1	3843.6
	h, kJ/kg		2960.7	3092.4	3213.5	3330.2	3445.2	3559.7	3674.4	3789.8	3905.9	4023.2	4141.6	4382.3
	s, kJ/(kg·K)		6.3622	6.5828	6.7698	6.9371	7.0908	7.2343	7.3696	7.4981	7.6206	7.7381	7.8511	8.0655
6	v, m³/kg		0.03616	0.04223	0.04739	0.05214	0.05665	0.06101	0.06525	0.06942	0.07352	0.07758	0.08160	0.08958
(275.6)	u, kJ/kg		2667.2	2789.6	2892.8	2988.9	3082.2	3174.6	3266.9	3359.6	3453.2	3547.6	3643.1	3837.8
	h, kJ/kg		2884.2	3043.0	3177.2	3301.8	3422.1	3540.6	3658.4	3776.2	3894.3	4013.1	4132.7	4375.3
	s, kJ/(kg·K)		6.0682	6.3342	6.5415	6.7201	6.8811	7.0296	7.1685	7.2996	7.4242	7.5433	7.6575	7.8735
8	v, m³/kg		0.02426	0.02995	0.03432	0.03817	0.04175	0.04516	0.04845	0.05166	0.05481	0.05791	0.06097	0.06702
(295.1)	u, kJ/kg		2590.9	2747.7	2863.8	2966.7	3064.3	3159.8	3254.4	3349.0	3444.0	3539.6	3636.1	3832.1
	h, kJ/kg		2785.0	2987.3	3138.3	3272.0	3398.3	3521.0	3642.0	3762.3	3882.5	4002.9	4123.8	4368.3
	s, kJ/(kg·K)		5.7914	6.1309	6.3642	6.5559	6.7248	6.8786	7.0214	7.1553	7.2821	7.4027	7.5182	7.7359
10	v m³/kg			0.02242	0.02641	0.02975	0.03279	0.03564	0.03837	0.04101	0.04358	0.04611	0.04859	0.05349
(311.1)	u, kJ/kg			2699.2	2832.4	2943.3	3045.8	3144.5	3241.7	3338.2	3434.7	3531.5	3629.0	3826.3
	h, kJ/kg			2923.4	3096.5	3240.8	3373.6	3500.9	3625.3	3748.3	3870.5	3992.6	4114.9	4361.2
	s, kJ/(kg·K)			5.9451	6.2127	6.4197	6.5974	6.7569	6.9037	7.0406	7.1696	7.2919	7.4086	7.6280
12	v, m³/kg			0.01721	0.02108	0.02412	0.02680	0.02929	0.03164	0.03390	0.03610	0.03824	0.04034	0.04447
(324.8)	u, kJ/kg			2641.1	2798.3	2918.8	3026.6	3128.9	3228.7	3327.2	3425.3	3523.4	3621.8	3820.6
	h, kJ/kg			2847.6	3051.2	3208.2	3348.2	3480.3	3608.3	3734.0	3858.4	3982.3	4105.9	4354.2
	s, kJ/(kg·K)			5.7604	6.0754	6.3006	6.4879	6.6535	6.8045	6.9445	7.0757	7.1998	7.3178	7.5390

[†] Saturated liquid entropies have been adjusted to make the Gibbs functions of the liquid and vapor phases exactly equal. For this reason there are some small differences between values presented here and the original tables.

Sources: Reprinted by permission from William C. Reynolds and Henry C. Perkins, *Engineering Thermodynamics*, 2d ed. (New York: McGraw-Hill, 1977), pp. 626–629 (Table B-2). Recalculated from equations given in Joseph H. Keenan, Frederick G. Keyes, Philip G. Hill, and Joan G. Moore, *Steam Tables* (New York: Wiley, 1969).

Appendix C.3b Superheated water (metric units)†—*continued*

p, MPa (T_{sat}, °C)		Temperature, °C												
		400	450	500	550	600	650	700	750	800	850	900	950	1000
15	v, m^3/kg	0.01565	0.01845	0.02080	0.02293	0.02491	0.02680	0.02861	0.03037	0.03210	0.03379	0.03546	0.03711	0.03875
(342.2)	u, kJ/kg	2740.7	2879.5	2996.5	3104.7	3208.6	3310.4	3410.9	3511.0	3611.0	3711.2	3811.9	3913.2	4015.4
	h, kJ/kg	2975.4	3156.2	3308.5	3448.6	3582.3	3712.3	3840.1	3966.6	4092.4	4218.0	4343.8	4469.9	4596.6
	s, kJ/(kg·K)	5.8819	6.1412	6.3451	6.5207	6.6784	6.8232	6.9580	7.0848	7.2048	7.3192	7.4288	7.5340	7.6356
20	v, m^3/kg	0.00994	0.01270	0.01477	0.01656	0.01818	0.01969	0.02113	0.02251	0.02385	0.02516	0.02645	0.02771	0.02897
(365.8)	u, kJ/kg	2619.2	2806.2	2942.8	3062.3	3174.0	3281.5	3386.5	3490.0	3592.7	3695.1	3797.4	3900.0	4003.1
	h, kJ/kg	2818.1	3060.1	3238.2	3393.4	3537.6	3675.3	3809.1	3940.3	4069.8	4198.3	4326.4	4454.3	4582.5
	s, kJ/(kg·K)	5.5548	5.9025	6.1409	6.3356	6.5056	6.6591	6.8002	6.9317	7.0553	7.1723	7.2839	7.3907	7.4933
22.088	v, m^3/kg	0.00818	0.01104	0.01305	0.01475	0.01627	0.01768	0.01901	0.02029	0.02152	0.02272	0.02389	0.02505	0.02619
(374.136)	u, kJ/kg	2552.9	2772.1	2919.0	3043.9	3159.1	3269.1	3376.1	3481.1	3585.0	3688.3	3791.4	3894.5	3998.0
	h, kJ/kg	2733.7	3015.9	3207.2	3369.6	3518.4	3659.6	3796.0	3929.2	4060.3	4190.1	4319.1	4447.9	4576.6
	s, kJ/(kg·K)	5.4013	5.8072	6.0634	6.2670	6.4426	6.5998	6.7437	6.8772	7.0024	7.1206	7.2330	7.3404	7.4436
30	v, m^3/kg	0.00279	0.00674	0.00868	0.01017	0.01145	0.01260	0.01366	0.01466	0.01562	0.01655	0.01745	0.01833	0.01920
	u, kJ/kg	2067.3	2619.3	2820.7	2970.3	3100.5	3221.0	3335.8	3447.0	3555.6	3662.6	3768.5	3873.8	3978.8
	h, kJ/kg	2151.0	2821.4	3081.0	3275.4	3443.9	3598.9	3745.7	3886.9	4024.3	4159.0	4291.9	4423.6	4554.7
	s, kJ/(kg·K)	4.4736	5.4432	5.7912	6.0350	6.2339	6.4066	6.5614	6.7030	6.8341	6.9568	7.0726	7.1825	7.2875
40	v, m^3/kg	0.00191	0.00369	0.00562	0.00698	0.00809	0.00906	0.00994	0.01076	0.01152	0.01226	0.01296	0.01365	0.01432
	u, kJ/kg	1854.5	2365.1	2678.4	2869.7	3022.6	3158.0	3283.6	3402.9	3517.9	3629.8	3739.4	3847.5	3954.6
	h, kJ/kg	1930.8	2512.8	2903.3	3149.1	3346.4	3520.6	3681.3	3833.1	3978.8	4120.0	4257.9	4393.6	4527.6
	s, kJ/(kg·K)	4.1143	4.9467	5.4707	5.7793	6.0122	6.2063	6.3759	6.5281	6.6671	6.7957	6.9158	7.0291	7.1365
60	v, m^3/kg	0.00163	0.00208	0.00296	0.00396	0.00483	0.00560	0.00627	0.00689	0.00746	0.00800	0.00851	0.00900	0.00948
	u, kJ/kg	1745.3	2053.9	2390.5	2658.8	2861.1	3028.8	3177.2	3313.6	3441.6	3563.6	3681.0	3795.0	3906.4
	h, kJ/kg	1843.4	2179.0	2567.9	2896.2	3151.2	3364.5	3553.6	3726.8	3889.1	4043.3	4191.5	4335.0	4475.2
	s, kJ/(kg·K)	3.9325	4.4128	4.9329	5.3449	5.6460	5.8838	6.0832	6.2569	6.4118	6.5523	6.6814	6.8012	6.9135
80	v, m^3/kg	0.00152	0.00177	0.00219	0.00276	0.00339	0.00398	0.00452	0.00502	0.00548	0.00591	0.00632	0.00671	0.00709
	u, kJ/kg	1687.0	1944.9	2218.9	2483.9	2711.8	2904.7	3073.2	3225.3	3365.7	3497.3	3622.3	3742.1	3857.8
	h, kJ/kg	1808.3	2086.9	2393.9	2704.9	2982.7	3222.8	3434.7	3626.6	3803.8	3970.1	4127.9	4279.1	4425.2
	s, kJ/(kg·K)	3.8338	4.2328	4.6432	5.0331	5.3609	5.6284	5.8521	6.0445	6.2137	6.3652	6.5026	6.6289	6.7459

† Saturated liquid entropies have been adjusted to make the Gibbs functions of the liquid and vapor phases exactly equal. For this reason there are some small differences between values presented here and the original tables.

Sources: Reprinted by permission from William C. Reynolds and Henry C. Perkins, *Engineering Thermodynamics*, 2d ed. (New York: McGraw-Hill, 1977), pp. 626–629 (Table B-2). Recalculated from equations given in Joseph H. Keenan, Frederick G. Keyes, Philip G. Hill, and Joan G. Moore, *Steam Tables* (New York: Wiley, 1969).

Appendix C.4a Compressed water (English units)

Temp. °F	v ft³/lbm	u Btu/lbm	h Btu/lbm	s Btu/(lbm·R)	v ft³/lbm	u Btu/lbm	h Btu/lbm	s Btu/(lbm·R)	v ft³/lbm	u Btu/lbm	h Btu/lbm	s Btu/(lbm·R)
	p = 500 psia (467.13°F)				p = 1000 psia (544.75°F)				p = 1500 psia (596.39°F)			
Sat	0.019 748	447.70	449.53	0.649 04	0.021 591	538.39	542.38	0.743 20	0.023 461	604.97	611.48	0.808 24
32	0.015 994	0.00	1.49	0.000 00	0.015 967	0.03	2.99	0.000 05	0.015 939	0.05	4.47	0.000 07
50	0.015 998	18.02	19.50	0.035 99	0.015 972	17.99	20.94	0.035 92	0.015 946	17.95	22.38	0.035 84
100	0.016 106	67.87	69.36	0.129 32	0.016 082	67.70	70.68	0.129 01	0.016 058	67.53	71.99	0.128 70
150	0.016 318	117.66	119.17	0.214 57	0.016 293	117.38	120.40	0.214 10	0.016 268	117.10	121.62	0.213 64
200	0.016 608	167.65	169.19	0.293 41	0.016 580	167.26	170.32	0.292 81	0.016 554	166.87	171.46	0.292 21
250	0.016 972	217.99	219.56	0.367 02	0.016 941	217.47	220.61	0.366 28	0.016 910	216.96	221.65	0.365 54
300	0.017 416	268.92	270.53	0.436 41	0.017 379	268.24	271.46	0.435 52	0.017 343	267.58	272.39	0.434 63
350	0.017 954	320.71	322.37	0.502 49	0.017 909	319.83	323.15	0.501 40	0.017 865	318.98	323.94	0.500 34
400	0.018 608	373.68	375.40	0.566 04	0.018 550	372.55	375.98	0.564 72	0.018 493	371.45	376.59	0.563 43
450	0.019 420	428.40	430.19	0.627 98	0.019 340	426.89	430.47	0.626 32	0.019 264	425.44	430.79	0.624 70
500					0.020 36	483.8	487.5	0.6874	0.020 24	481.8	487.4	0.6853
550									0.021 58	542.1	548.1	0.7469
	p = 2000 psia (636.00°F)				p = 3000 psia (695.52°F)				p = 5000 psia			
Sat	0.025 649	662.40	671.89	0.862 27	0.034 310	783.45	802.50	0.973 20				
32	0.015 912	0.06	5.95	0.000 08	0.015 859	0.09	8.90	0.000 09	0.015 755	0.11	14.70	−0.000 01
50	0.015 920	17.91	23.81	0.035 75	0.015 870	17.84	26.65	0.035 55	0.015 773	17.67	32.26	0.035 08
100	0.016 034	67.37	73.30	0.128 39	0.015 987	67.04	75.91	0.127 77	0.015 897	66.40	81.11	0.126 51
200	0.016 527	166.49	172.60	0.291 62	0.016 476	165.74	174.89	0.290 46	0.016 376	164.32	179.47	0.288 18
300	0.017 308	266.93	273.33	0.433 76	0.017 240	265.66	275.23	0.432 05	0.017 110	263.25	279.08	0.428 75
400	0.018 439	370.38	377.21	0.562 16	0.018 334	368.32	378.50	0.559 70	0.018 141	364.47	381.25	0.555 06
450	0.019 191	424.04	431.14	0.623 13	0.019 053	421.36	431.93	0.620 11	0.018 803	416.44	433.84	0.614 51
500	0.020 14	479.8	487.3	0.6832	0.019 944	476.2	487.3	0.6794	0.019 603	469.8	487.9	0.6724
560	0.021 72	551.8	559.8	0.7565	0.021 382	546.2	558.0	0.7508	0.020 835	536.7	556.0	0.7411
600	0.023 30	605.4	614.0	0.8086	0.022 74	597.0	609.6	0.8004	0.021 91	584.0	604.2	0.7876
640					0.024 75	654.3	668.0	0.8545	0.023 34	634.6	656.2	0.8357
680					0.028 79	728.4	744.3	0.9226	0.025 35	690.6	714.1	0.8873
700									0.026 76	721.8	746.6	0.9156

Source: Reprinted from Gordon J. Van Wylen and Richard E. Sonntag, *Fundamentals of Classical Thermodynamics*, 3d ed. (New York: Wiley, 1986), p. 632 (Table A.1.4E).

Appendix C.4*b* Compressed water (metric units)

Temp. °C	*v* m³/kg	*u* kJ/kg	*h* kJ/kg	*s* kJ/(kg·K)	*v* m³/kg	*u* kJ/kg	*h* kJ/kg	*s* kJ/(kg·K)	*v* m³/kg	*u* kJ/kg	*h* kJ/kg	*s* kJ/(kg·K)
	p = 5 MPa (263.99°C)				p = 10 MPa (311.06°C)				p = 15 MPa (342.24°C)			
Sat.	.001 285 9	1147.8	1154.2	2.9202	.001 452 4	1393.0	1407.6	3.3596	.001 658 1	1585.6	1610.5	3.6848
0	.000 997 7	.04	5.04	.0001	.000 995 2	.09	10.04	.0002	.000 992 8	.15	15.05	.0004
20	.000 999 5	83.65	88.65	.2956	.000 997 2	83.36	93.33	.2945	.000 995 0	83.06	97.99	.2934
40	.001 005 6	166.95	171.97	.5705	.001 003 4	166.35	176.38	.5686	.001 001 3	165.76	180.78	.5666
60	.001 014 9	250.23	255.30	.8285	.001 012 7	249.36	259.49	.8258	.001 010 5	248.51	263.67	.8232
80	.001 026 8	333.72	338.85	1.0720	.001 024 5	332.59	342.83	1.0688	.001 022 2	331.48	346.81	1.0656
100	.001 041 0	417.52	422.72	1.3030	.001 038 5	416.12	426.50	1.2992	.001 036 1	414.74	430.28	1.2955
120	.001 057 6	501.80	507.09	1.5233	.001 054 9	500.08	510.64	1.5189	.001 052 2	498.40	514.19	1.5145
140	.001 076 8	586.76	592.15	1.7343	.001 073 7	584.68	595.42	1.7292	.001 070 7	582.66	598.72	1.7242
160	.001 098 8	672.62	678.12	1.9375	.001 095 3	670.13	681.08	1.9317	.001 091 8	667.71	684.09	1.9260
180	.001 124 0	759.63	765.25	2.1341	.001 119 9	756.65	767.84	2.1275	.001 115 9	753.76	770.50	2.1210
200	.001 153 0	848.1	853.9	2.3255	.001 148 0	844.5	856.0	2.3178	.001 143 3	841.0	858.2	2.3104
220	.001 186 6	938.4	944.4	2.5128	.001 180 5	934.1	945.9	2.5039	.001 174 8	929.9	947.5	2.4953
240	.001 226 4	1031.4	1037.5	2.6979	.001 218 7	1026.0	1038.1	2.6872	.001 211 4	1020.8	1039.0	2.6771
260	.001 274 9	1127.9	1134.3	2.8830	.001 264 5	1121.1	1133.7	2.8699	.001 255 0	1114.6	1133.4	2.8576
280					.001 321 6	1220.9	1234.1	3.0548	.001 308 4	1212.5	1232.1	3.0393
300					.001 397 2	1328.4	1342.3	3.2469	.001 377 0	1316.6	1337.3	3.2260
320									.001 472 4	1431.1	1453.2	3.4247
340									.001 631 1	1567.5	1591.9	3.6546

Source: Reprinted from Gordon J. Van Wylen and Richard E. Sonntag, *Fundamentals of Classical Thermodynamics*, 3d ed. (New York: Wiley, 1986), pp. 649–650 (Table A.1.4).

Appendix C.4*b* Compressed water (metric units)—*continued*

Temp. °C	*v* m³/kg	*u* kJ/kg	*h* kJ/kg	*s* kJ/(kg·K)	*v* m³/kg	*u* kJ/kg	*h* kJ/kg	*s* kJ/(kg·K)	*v* m³/kg	*u* kJ/kg	*h* kJ/kg	*s* kJ/(kg·K)
	p = 20 MPa (365.81°C)				p = 30 MPa				p = 50 MPa			
Sat.	.002 036	1785.6	1826.3	4.0139								
0	.000 990 4	.19	20.01	.0004	.000 985 6	.25	29.82	.0001	.000 976 6	.20	49.03	−.0014
20	.000 992 8	82.77	102.62	.2923	.000 988 6	82.17	111.84	.2899	.000 980 4	81.00	130.02	.2848
40	.000 999 2	165.17	185.16	.5646	.000 995 1	164.04	193.89	.5607	.000 987 2	161.86	211.21	.5527
60	.001 008 4	247.68	267.85	.8206	.001 004 2	246.06	276.19	.8154	.000 996 2	242.98	292.79	.8052
80	.001 019 9	330.40	350.80	1.0624	.001 015 6	328.30	358.77	1.0561	.001 007 3	324.34	374.70	1.0440
100	.001 033 7	413.39	434.06	1.2917	.001 029 0	410.78	441.66	1.2844	.001 020 1	405.88	456.89	1.2703
120	.001 049 6	496.76	517.76	1.5102	.001 044 5	493.59	524.93	1.5018	.001 034 8	487.65	539.39	1.4857
140	.001 067 8	580.69	602.04	1.7193	.001 062 1	576.88	608.75	1.7098	.001 051 5	569.77	622.35	1.6915
160	.001 088 5	665.35	687.12	1.9204	.001 082 1	660.82	693.28	1.9096	.001 070 3	652.41	705.92	1.8891
180	.001 112 0	750.95	773.20	2.1147	.001 104 7	745.59	778.73	2.1024	.001 091 2	735.69	790.25	2.0794
200	.001 138 8	837.7	860.5	2.3031	.001 130 2	831.4	865.3	2.2893	.001 114 6	819.7	875.5	2.2634
220	.001 169 3	925.9	949.3	2.4870	.001 159 0	918.3	953.1	2.4711	.001 140 8	904.7	961.7	2.4419
240	.001 204 6	1016.0	1040.0	2.6674	.001 192 0	1006.9	1042.6	2.6490	.001 170 2	990.7	1049.2	2.6158
260	.001 246 2	1108.6	1133.5	2.8459	.001 230 3	1097.4	1134.3	2.8243	.001 203 4	1078.1	1138.2	2.7860
280	.001 296 5	1204.7	1230.6	3.0248	.001 275 5	1190.7	1229.0	2.9986	.001 241 5	1167.2	1229.3	2.9537
300	.001 359 6	1306.1	1333.3	3.2071	.001 330 4	1287.9	1327.8	3.1741	.001 286 0	1258.7	1323.0	3.1200
320	.001 443 7	1415.7	1444.6	3.3979	.001 399 7	1390.7	1432.7	3.3539	.001 338 8	1353.3	1420.2	3.2868
340	.001 568 4	1539.7	1571.0	3.6075	.001 492 0	1501.7	1546.5	3.5426	.001 403 2	1452.0	1522.1	3.4557
360	.001 822 6	1702.8	1739.3	3.8772	.001 626 5	1626.6	1675.4	3.7494	.001 483 8	1556.0	1630.2	3.6291
380					.001 869 1	1781.4	1837.5	4.0012	.001 588 4	1667.2	1746.6	3.8101

Source: Reprinted from Gordon J. Van Wylen and Richard E. Sonntag, *Fundamentals of Classical Thermodynamics*, 3d ed. (New York: Wiley, 1986), pp. 649–650 (Table A.1.4).

Appendix C.5a Saturated ammonia (English units)

		Specific volume ft^3/lbm			Enthalpy Btu/lbm			Entropy Btu/(lbm · R)		
Temp. °F	Abs. press. psia p	Sat. liquid v_f	Evap. v_{fg}	Sat. vapor v_g	Sat. liquid h_f	Evap. h_{fg}	Sat. vapor h_g	Sat. liquid s_f	Evap. s_{fg}	Sat. vapor s_g
−60	5.55	0.022 80	44.707	44.73	−21.2	610.8	589.6	−0.0517	1.5286	1.4769
−55	6.54	0.022 90	38.357	38.38	−15.9	607.5	591.6	−0.0386	1.5017	1.4631
−50	7.67	0.023 00	33.057	33.08	−10.6	604.3	593.7	−0.0256	1.4753	1.4497
−45	8.95	0.023 10	28.597	28.62	−5.3	600.9	595.6	−0.0127	1.4495	1.4368
−40	10.41	0.023 22	24.837	24.86	0	597.6	597.6	0.000	1.4242	1.4242
−35	12.05	0.023 33	21.657	21.68	5.3	594.2	599.5	0.0126	1.3994	1.4120
−30	13.90	0.023 50	18.947	18.97	10.7	590.7	601.4	0.0250	1.3751	1.4001
−25	15.98	0.023 60	16.636	16.66	16.0	587.2	603.2	0.0374	1.3512	1.3886
−20	18.30	0.023 70	14.656	14.68	21.4	583.6	605.0	0.0497	1.3277	1.3774
−15	20.88	0.023 81	12.946	12.97	26.7	580.0	606.7	0.0618	1.3044	1.3664
−10	23.74	0.023 93	11.476	11.50	32.1	576.4	608.5	0.0738	1.2820	1.3558
−5	26.92	0.024 06	10.206	10.23	37.5	572.6	610.1	0.0857	1.2597	1.3454
0	30.42	0.024 19	9.092	9.116	42.9	568.9	611.8	0.0975	1.2377	1.3352
5	34.27	0.024 32	8.1257	8.150	48.3	565.0	613.3	0.1092	1.2161	1.3253
10	38.51	0.024 46	7.2795	7.304	53.8	561.1	614.9	0.1208	1.1949	1.3157
15	43.14	0.024 60	6.5374	6.562	59.2	557.1	616.3	0.1323	1.1739	1.3062
20	48.21	0.024 74	5.8853	5.910	64.7	553.1	617.8	0.1437	1.1532	1.2969
25	53.73	0.024 88	5.3091	5.334	70.2	548.9	619.1	0.1551	1.1328	1.2879
30	59.74	0.025 03	4.8000	4.825	75.7	544.8	620.5	0.1663	1.1127	1.2790
35	66.26	0.025 18	4.3478	4.373	81.2	540.5	621.7	0.1775	1.0929	1.2704
40	73.32	0.025 33	3.9457	3.971	86.8	536.2	623.0	0.1885	1.0733	1.2618
45	80.96	0.025 48	3.5885	3.614	92.3	531.8	624.1	0.1996	1.0539	1.2535
50	89.19	0.025 64	3.2684	3.294	97.9	527.3	625.2	0.2105	1.0348	1.2453
55	98.06	0.025 81	2.9822	3.008	103.5	522.8	626.3	0.2214	1.0159	1.2373
60	107.6	0.025 97	2.7250	2.751	109.2	518.1	627.3	0.2322	0.9972	1.2294
65	117.8	0.026 14	2.4939	2.520	114.8	513.4	628.2	0.2430	0.9786	1.2216
70	128.8	0.026 32	2.2857	2.312	120.5	508.6	629.1	0.2537	0.9603	1.2140
75	140.5	0.026 50	2.0985	2.125	126.2	503.7	629.9	0.2643	0.9422	1.2065
80	153.0	0.026 68	1.9283	1.955	132.0	498.7	630.7	0.2749	0.9242	1.1991
85	166.4	0.026 87	1.7741	1.801	137.8	493.6	631.4	0.2854	0.9064	1.1918
90	180.6	0.027 07	1.6339	1.661	143.5	488.5	632.0	0.2958	0.8888	1.1846
95	195.8	0.027 27	1.5067	1.534	149.4	483.2	632.6	0.3062	0.8713	1.1775
100	211.9	0.027 47	1.3915	1.419	155.2	477.8	633.0	0.3166	0.8539	1.1705
105	228.9	0.027 69	1.2853	1.313	161.1	472.3	633.4	0.3269	0.8366	1.1635
110	247.0	0.027 90	1.1891	1.217	167.0	466.7	633.7	0.3372	0.8194	1.1566
115	266.2	0.028 13	1.0999	1.128	173.0	460.9	633.9	0.3474	0.8023	1.1497
120	286.4	0.028 36	1.0186	1.047	179.0	455.0	634.0	0.3576	0.7851	1.1427
125	307.8	0.028 60	0.9444	0.973	185.1	448.9	634.0	0.3679	0.7679	1.1358

Sources: Reprinted from Gordon J. Van Wylen and Richard E. Sonntag, *Fundamentals of Classical Thermodynamics*, 3d ed. (New York: Wiley, 1986), pp. 652–653 (Table A.2.1E). Copyright © 1986 John Wiley & Sons. Reprinted by permission of John Wiley & Sons, Inc. Also reprinted from National Bureau of Standards Circular No. 142, *Tables of Thermodynamic Properties of Ammonia*.

Appendix C.5*b* Saturated ammonia (metric units)[a]

		Specific volume m³/kg			Enthalpy kJ/kg			Entropy kJ/(kg·K)		
Temp. °C	Abs. press. kPa p	Sat. liquid v_f	Evap. v_{fg}	Sat. vapor v_g	Sat. liquid h_f	Evap. h_{fg}	Sat. vapor h_g	Sat. liquid s_f	Evap. s_{fg}	Sat. vapor s_g
−50	40.88	0.001 424	2.6239	2.6254	−44.3	1416.7	1372.4	−0.1942	6.3502	6.1561
−48	45.96	0.001 429	2.3518	2.3533	−35.5	1411.3	1375.8	−0.1547	6.2696	6.1149
−46	51.55	0.001 434	2.1126	2.1140	−26.6	1405.8	1379.2	−0.1156	6.1902	6.0746
−44	57.69	0.001 439	1.9018	1.9032	−17.8	1400.3	1382.5	−0.0768	6.1120	6.0352
−42	64.42	0.001 444	1.7155	1.7170	−8.9	1394.7	1385.8	−0.0382	6.0349	5.9967
−40	71.77	0.001 449	1.5506	1.5521	0.0	1389.0	1389.0	0.0000	5.9589	5.9589
−38	79.80	0.001 454	1.4043	1.4058	8.9	1383.3	1392.2	0.0380	5.8840	5.9220
−36	88.54	0.001 460	1.2742	1.2757	17.8	1377.6	1395.4	0.0757	5.8101	5.8858
−34	98.05	0.001 465	1.1582	1.1597	26.8	1371.8	1398.5	0.1132	5.7372	5.8504
−32	108.37	0.001 470	1.0547	1.0562	35.7	1365.9	1401.6	0.1504	5.6652	5.8156
−30	119.55	0.001 476	0.9621	0.9635	44.7	1360.0	1404.6	0.1873	5.5942	5.7815
−28	131.64	0.001 481	0.8790	0.8805	53.6	1354.0	1407.6	0.2240	5.5241	5.7481
−26	144.70	0.001 487	0.8044	0.8059	62.6	1347.9	1410.5	0.2605	5.4548	5.7153
−24	158.78	0.001 492	0.7373	0.7388	71.6	1341.8	1413.4	0.2967	5.3864	5.6831
−22	173.93	0.001 498	0.6768	0.6783	80.7	1335.6	1416.2	0.3327	5.3188	5.6515
−20	190.22	0.001 504	0.6222	0.6237	89.7	1329.3	1419.0	0.3684	5.2520	5.6205
−18	207.71	0.001 510	0.5728	0.5743	98.8	1322.9	1421.7	0.4040	5.1860	5.5900
−16	226.45	0.001 515	0.5280	0.5296	107.8	1316.5	1424.4	0.4393	5.1207	5.5600
−14	246.51	0.001 521	0.4874	0.4889	116.9	1310.0	1427.0	0.4744	5.0561	5.5305
−12	267.95	0.001 528	0.4505	0.4520	126.0	1303.5	1429.5	0.5093	4.9922	5.5015
−10	290.85	0.001 534	0.4169	0.4185	135.2	1296.8	1432.0	0.5440	4.9290	5.4730
−8	315.25	0.001 540	0.3863	0.3878	144.3	1290.1	1434.4	0.5785	4.8664	5.4449
−6	341.25	0.001 546	0.3583	0.3599	153.5	1283.3	1436.8	0.6128	4.8045	5.4173
−4	368.90	0.001 553	0.3328	0.3343	162.7	1276.4	1439.1	0.6469	4.7432	5.3901
−2	398.27	0.001 559	0.3094	0.3109	171.9	1269.4	1441.3	0.6808	4.6825	5.3633
0	429.44	0.001 566	0.2879	0.2895	181.1	1262.4	1443.5	0.7145	4.6223	5.3369
2	462.49	0.001 573	0.2683	0.2698	190.4	1255.2	1445.6	0.7481	4.5627	5.3108
4	497.49	0.001 580	0.2502	0.2517	199.6	1248.0	1447.6	0.7815	4.5037	5.2852
6	534.51	0.001 587	0.2335	0.2351	208.9	1240.6	1449.6	0.8148	4.4451	5.2599
8	573.64	0.001 594	0.2182	0.2198	218.3	1233.2	1451.5	0.8479	4.3871	5.2350
10	614.95	0.001 601	0.2040	0.2056	227.6	1225.7	1453.3	0.8808	4.3295	5.2104
12	658.52	0.001 608	0.1910	0.1926	237.0	1218.1	1455.1	0.9136	4.2725	5.1861
14	704.44	0.001 616	0.1789	0.1805	246.4	1210.4	1456.8	0.9463	4.2159	5.1621
16	752.79	0.001 623	0.1677	0.1693	255.9	1202.6	1458.5	0.9788	4.1597	5.1385
18	803.66	0.001 631	0.1574	0.1590	265.4	1194.7	1460.0	1.0112	4.1039	5.1151
20	857.12	0.001 639	0.1477	0.1494	274.9	1186.7	1461.5	1.0434	4.0486	5.0920
22	913.27	0.001 647	0.1388	0.1405	284.4	1178.5	1462.9	1.0755	3.9937	5.0692
24	972.19	0.001 655	0.1305	0.1322	294.0	1170.3	1464.3	1.1075	3.9392	5.0467
26	1033.97	0.001 663	0.1228	0.1245	303.6	1162.0	1465.6	1.1394	3.8850	5.0244
28	1098.71	0.001 671	0.1156	0.1173	313.2	1153.6	1466.8	1.1711	3.8312	5.0023
30	1166.49	0.001 680	0.1089	0.1106	322.9	1145.0	1467.9	1.2028	3.7777	4.9805
32	1237.41	0.001 689	0.1027	0.1044	332.6	1136.4	1469.0	1.2343	3.7246	4.9589
34	1311.55	0.001 698	0.0969	0.0986	342.3	1127.6	1469.9	1.2656	3.6718	4.9374
36	1389.03	0.001 707	0.0914	0.0931	352.1	1118.7	1470.8	1.2969	3.6192	4.9161
38	1469.92	0.001 716	0.0863	0.0880	361.9	1109.7	1471.5	1.3281	3.5669	4.8950
40	1554.33	0.001 726	0.0815	0.0833	371.7	1100.5	1472.2	1.3591	3.5148	4.8740
42	1642.35	0.001 735	0.0771	0.0788	381.6	1091.2	1472.8	1.3901	3.4630	4.8530
44	1734.09	0.001 745	0.0728	0.0746	391.5	1081.7	1473.2	1.4209	3.4112	4.8322
46	1829.65	0.001 756	0.0689	0.0707	401.5	1072.0	1473.5	1.4518	3.3595	4.8113
48	1929.13	0.001 766	0.0652	0.0669	411.5	1062.2	1473.7	1.4826	3.3079	4.7905
50	2032.62	0.001 777	0.0617	0.0635	421.7	1052.0	1473.7	1.5135	3.2561	4.7696

Sources: Reprinted from Gordon J. Van Wylen and Richard E. Sonntag, *Fundamentals of Classical Thermodynamics*, 3d ed. (New York: Wiley, 1986), pp. 658–659 (Table A.2.1). Copyright © 1986 John Wiley & Sons. Reprinted by permission of John Wiley & Sons, Inc. Also reprinted from National Bureau of Standards Circular No. 142, *Tables of Thermodynamics Properties of Ammonia.*

Appendix C.6a Superheated ammonia (English units)

Units are: v – ft^3/lbm, h – Btu/lbm, s – Btu/(lbm·R).

Abs. press. psia (Sat. temp.)		Temperature, °F 0	20	40	60	80	100	120	140	160	180	200	220
10	v	28.58	29.90	31.20	32.49	33.78	35.07	36.35	37.62	38.90	40.17	41.45	
	h	618.9	629.1	639.3	649.5	659.7	670.0	680.3	690.6	701.1	711.6	722.2	
(−41.34)	s	1.477	1.499	1.520	1.540	1.559	1.578	1.596	1.614	1.631	1.647	1.664	
15	v	18.92	19.82	20.70	21.58	22.44	23.31	24.17	25.03	25.88	26.74	27.59	
	h	617.2	627.8	638.2	648.5	658.9	669.2	679.6	690.0	700.5	711.1	721.7	
(−27.29)	s	1.427	1.450	1.471	1.491	1.511	1.529	1.548	1.566	1.583	1.599	1.616	
20	v	14.09	14.78	15.45	16.12	16.78	17.43	18.08	18.73	19.37	20.02	20.66	21.3
	h	615.5	626.4	637.0	647.5	658.0	668.5	678.9	689.4	700.0	710.6	721.2	732.0
(−16.64)	s	1.391	1.414	1.436	1.456	1.476	1.495	1.513	1.531	1.549	1.565	1.582	1.598
25	v	11.19	11.75	12.30	12.84	13.37	13.90	14.43	14.95	15.47	15.99	16.50	17.02
	h	613.8	625.0	635.8	646.5	657.1	667.7	678.2	688.8	699.4	710.1	720.8	731.6
(−7.96)	s	1.362	1.386	1.408	1.429	1.449	1.468	1.486	1.504	1.522	1.539	1.555	1.571
30	v	9.25	9.731	10.20	10.65	11.10	11.55	11.99	12.43	12.87	13.30	13.73	14.16
	h	611.9	623.5	634.6	645.5	656.2	666.9	677.5	688.2	698.8	709.6	720.3	731.1
(−.57)	s	1.337	1.362	1.385	1.406	1.426	1.446	1.464	1.482	1.500	1.517	1.533	1.550
35	v	—	8.287	8.695	9.093	9.484	9.869	10.25	10.63	11.00	11.38	11.75	12.12
	h	—	622.0	633.4	644.4	655.3	666.1	676.8	687.6	698.3	709.1	719.9	730.7
(5.89)	s	—	1.341	1.365	1.386	1.407	1.427	1.445	1.464	1.481	1.498	1.515	1.531
40	v	—	7.203	7.568	7.922	8.268	8.609	8.945	9.278	9.609	9.938	10.27	10.59
	h	—	620.4	632.1	643.4	654.4	665.3	676.1	686.9	697.7	708.5	719.4	730.3
(11.66)	s	—	1.323	1.347	1.369	1.390	1.410	1.429	1.447	1.465	1.482	1.499	1.515
45	v	—	6.363	6.694	7.014	7.326	7.632	7.934	8.232	8.528	8.822	9.115	9.406
	h	—	618.8	630.8	642.3	653.5	664.6	675.5	686.3	697.2	708.0	718.9	729.9
(16.87)	s	—	1.307	1.331	1.354	1.375	1.395	1.414	1.433	1.450	1.468	1.485	1.501
50	v	—	—	5.988	6.280	6.564	6.843	7.117	7.387	7.655	7.921	8.185	8.448
	h	—	—	629.5	641.2	652.6	663.7	674.7	685.7	696.6	707.5	718.5	729.4
(21.67)	s	—	—	1.317	1.340	1.361	1.382	1.401	1.420	1.437	1.455	1.472	1.488
60	v	—	—	4.933	5.184	5.428	5.665	5.897	6.126	6.352	6.576	6.798	7.019
	h	—	—	626.8	639.0	650.7	662.1	673.3	684.4	695.5	706.5	717.5	728.6
(30.21)	s	—	—	1.291	1.315	1.337	1.358	1.378	1.397	1.415	1.432	1.449	1.466

(*Continued*)

Appendix C.6a Superheated ammonia (English units)—*continued*

Units are: v – ft^3/lbm, h – Btu/lbm, s – Btu/(lbm·R).

Abs. press. psia (Sat. temp.)		Temperature, °F 60	80	100	120	140	160	180	200	240	280	320	360
	v	4.401	4.615	4.822	5.025	5.224	5.420	5.615	5.807	6.187	6.563	—	—
70	h	636.6	648.7	660.4	671.8	683.1	694.3	705.5	716.6	738.9	761.4	—	—
(37.7)	s	1.294	1.317	1.338	1.358	1.377	1.395	1.413	1.430	1.463	1.494	—	—
	v	3.812	4.005	4.190	4.371	4.548	4.722	4.893	5.063	5.398	5.73	—	—
80	h	634.3	646.7	658.7	670.4	681.8	693.2	704.4	715.6	738.1	760.7	—	—
(44.4)	s	1.275	1.298	1.320	1.340	1.360	1.378	1.396	1.414	1.447	1.478	—	—
	v	3.353	3.529	3.698	3.862	4.021	4.178	4.332	4.484	4.785	5.081	—	—
90	h	631.8	644.7	657.0	668.9	680.5	692.0	703.4	714.7	737.3	760.0	—	—
(50.47)	s	1.257	1.281	1.304	1.325	1.344	1.363	1.381	1.400	1.432	1.464	—	—
	v	2.985	3.149	3.304	3.454	3.600	3.743	3.883	4.021	4.294	4.562	—	—
100	h	629.3	642.6	655.2	667.3	679.2	690.8	702.3	713.7	736.5	759.4	—	—
(56.05)	s	1.241	1.266	1.289	1.310	1.331	1.349	1.368	1.385	1.419	1.451	—	—
	v	—	2.166	2.288	2.404	2.515	2.622	2.727	2.830	3.030	3.227	3.420	—
140	h	—	633.8	647.8	661.1	673.7	686.0	698.0	709.9	733.3	756.7	780.0	—
(74.79)	s	—	1.214	1.240	1.263	1.284	1.305	1.324	1.342	1.376	1.409	1.440	—
	v	—	—	1.720	1.818	1.910	1.999	2.084	2.167	2.328	2.484	2.637	—
180	h	—	—	639.9	654.4	668.0	681.0	693.6	705.9	730.1	753.9	777.7	—
(89.78)	s	—	—	1.999	1.225	1.248	1.269	1.289	1.308	1.344	1.377	1.408	—
	v	—	—	—	1.443	1.525	1.601	1.675	1.745	1.881	2.012	2.140	2.265
220	h	—	—	—	647.3	662.0	675.8	689.1	701.9	726.8	751.1	775.3	779.5
(102.42)	s	—	—	—	1.192	1.217	1.239	1.260	1.280	1.317	1.351	1.383	1.413
	v	—	—	—	1.302	1.380	1.452	1.521	1.587	1.741	1.835	1.954	2.069
240	h	—	—	—	643.5	658.8	673.1	686.7	699.8	725.1	749.8	774.1	798.4
(108.09)	s	—	—	—	1.176	1.203	1.226	1.248	1.268	1.305	1.339	1.371	1.402
	v	—	—	—	1.182	1.257	1.326	1.391	1.453	1.572	1.686	1.796	1.904
260	h	—	—	—	639.5	655.6	670.4	684.4	697.7	723.4	748.4	772.9	797.4
(113.42)	s	—	—	—	1.162	1.189	1.213	1.235	1.256	1.294	1.329	1.361	1.391
	v	—	—	—	1.078	1.151	1.217	1.279	1.339	1.451	1.558	1.661	1.762
280	h	—	—	—	635.4	652.2	667.6	681.9	695.6	721.8	747.0	771.7	796.3
(118.45)	s	—	—	—	1.147	1.176	1.201	1.224	1.245	1.283	1.318	1.351	1.382

Source: Reprinted from Gordon J. Van Wylen and Richard E. Sonntag, *Fundamentals of Classical Thermodynamics*, 3d ed. (New York: Wiley, 1986), pp. 654–657 (Table A.22.E).

Appendix C.6*b* **Superheated ammonia (metric units)**

Units are: v – m^3/kg, h – kJ/kg, s – kJ/(kg·K).

Abs. press. kPa (Sat. temp.) °C		Temperature, °C											
		−20	−10	0	10	20	30	40	50	60	70	80	100
	v	2.4474	2.5481	2.6482	2.7479	2.8473	2.9464	3.0453	3.1441	3.2427	3.3413	3.4397	
50	h	1435.8	1457.0	1478.1	1499.2	1520.4	1541.7	1563.0	1584.5	1606.1	1627.8	1649.7	
(−46.54)	s	6.3256	6.4077	6.4865	6.5625	6.6360	6.7073	6.7766	6.8441	6.9099	6.9743	7.0372	
	v	1.6233	1.6915	1.7591	1.8263	1.8932	1.9597	2.0261	2.0923	2.1584	2.2244	2.2903	
75	h	1433.0	1454.7	1476.1	1497.5	1518.9	1540.3	1561.8	1583.4	1605.1	1626.9	1648.9	
(−39.18)	s	6.1190	6.2028	6.2828	6.3597	6.4339	6.5058	6.5756	6.6434	6.7096	6.7742	6.8373	
	v	1.2110	1.2631	1.3145	1.3654	1.4160	1.4664	1.5165	1.5664	1.6163	1.6659	1.7155	1.8145
100	h	1430.1	1452.2	1474.1	1495.7	1517.3	1538.9	1560.5	1582.2	1604.1	1626.0	1648.0	1692.6
(−33.61)	s	5.9695	6.0552	6.1366	6.2144	6.2894	6.3618	6.4321	6.5003	6.5668	6.6316	6.6950	6.8177
	v	0.9635	1.0059	1.0476	1.0889	1.1297	1.1703	1.2107	1.2509	1.2909	1.3309	1.3707	1.4501
125	h	1427.2	1449.8	1472.0	1493.9	1515.7	1537.5	1559.3	1581.1	1603.0	1625.0	1647.2	1691.8
(−29.08)	s	5.8512	5.9389	6.0217	6.1006	6.1763	6.2494	6.3201	6.3887	6.4555	6.5206	6.5842	6.7072
	v	0.7984	0.8344	0.8697	0.9045	0.9388	0.9729	1.0068	1.0405	1.0740	1.1074	1.1408	1.2072
150	h	1424.1	1447.3	1469.8	1492.1	1514.1	1536.1	1558.0	1580.0	1602.0	1624.1	1646.3	1691.1
(−25.23)	s	5.7526	5.8424	5.9266	6.0066	6.0831	6.1568	6.2280	6.2970	6.3641	6.4295	6.4933	6.6167
	v		0.6199	0.6471	0.6738	0.7001	0.7261	0.7519	0.7774	0.8029	0.8282	0.8533	0.9035
200	h		1442.0	1465.5	1488.4	1510.9	1533.2	1555.5	1577.7	1599.9	1622.2	1644.6	1689.6
(−18.86)	s		5.6863	5.7737	5.8559	5.9342	6.0091	6.0813	6.1512	6.2189	6.2849	6.3491	6.4732
	v		0.4910	0.5135	0.5354	0.5568	0.5780	0.5989	0.6196	0.6401	0.6605	0.6809	0.7212
250	h		1436.6	1461.0	1484.5	1507.6	1530.3	1552.9	1575.4	1597.8	1620.3	1642.8	1688.2
(−13.67)	s		5.5609	5.6517	5.7365	5.8165	5.8928	5.9661	6.0368	6.1052	6.1717	6.2365	6.3613
	v			0.4243	0.4430	0.4613	0.4792	0.4968	0.5143	0.5316	0.5488	0.5658	0.5997
300	h			1456.3	1480.6	1504.2	1527.4	1550.3	1573.0	1595.7	1618.4	1641.1	1686.7
(−9.23)	s			5.5493	5.6366	5.7186	5.7963	5.8707	5.9423	6.0114	6.0785	6.1437	6.2693
	v			0.3605	0.3770	0.3929	0.4086	0.4239	0.4391	0.4541	0.4689	0.4837	0.5129
350	h			1451.5	1476.5	1500.7	1524.4	1547.6	1570.7	1593.6	1616.5	1639.3	1685.2
(−5.35)	s			5.4600	5.5502	5.6342	5.7135	5.7890	5.8615	5.9314	5.9990	6.0647	6.1910
	v			0.3125	0.3274	0.3417	0.3556	0.3692	0.3826	0.3959	0.4090	0.4220	0.4478
400	h			1446.5	1472.4	1497.2	1521.3	1544.9	1568.3	1591.5	1614.5	1637.6	1683.7
(−1.89)	s			5.3803	5.4735	5.5597	5.6405	5.7173	5.7907	5.8613	5.9296	5.9957	6.1228
	v			0.2752	0.2887	0.3017	0.3143	0.3266	0.3387	0.3506	0.3624	0.3740	0.3971
450	h			1441.3	1468.1	1493.6	1518.2	1542.2	1565.9	1589.3	1612.6	1635.8	1682.2
(1.26)	s			5.3078	5.4042	5.4926	5.5752	5.6532	5.7275	5.7989	5.8678	5.9345	6.0623

(*Continued*)

Appendix C.6*b* Superheated ammonia (metric units)—*continued*

Units are: v – m^3/kg, h – kJ/kg, s – kJ/(kg·K).

Abs. press. kPa (Sat. temp.) °C		Temperature, °C 20	30	40	50	60	70	80	100	120	140	160	180
	v	0.2698	0.2813	0.2926	0.3036	0.3144	0.3251	0.3357	0.3565	0.3771	0.3975		
500	h	1489.9	1515.0	1539.5	1563.4	1587.1	1610.6	1634.0	1680.7	1727.5	1774.7		
(4.14)	s	5.4314	5.5157	5.5950	5.6704	5.7425	5.8120	5.8793	6.0079	6.1301	6.2472		
	v	0.2217	0.2317	0.2414	0.2508	0.2600	0.2691	0.2781	0.2957	0.3130	0.3302		
600	h	1482.4	1508.6	1533.8	1558.5	1582.7	1606.6	1630.4	1677.7	1724.9	1772.4		
(9.29)	s	5.3222	5.4102	5.4923	5.5697	5.6436	5.7144	5.7826	5.9129	6.0363	6.1541		
	v	0.1874	0.1963	0.2048	0.2131	0.2212	0.2291	0.2369	0.2522	0.2672	0.2821		
700	h	1474.5	1501.9	1528.1	1553.4	1578.2	1602.6	1626.8	1674.6	1722.4	1770.2		
(13.81)	s	5.2259	5.3179	5.4029	5.4826	5.5582	5.6303	5.6997	5.8316	5.9562	6.0749		
	v	0.1615	0.1696	0.1773	0.1848	0.1920	0.1991	0.2060	0.2196	0.2329	0.2459	0.2589	
800	h	1466.3	1495.0	1522.2	1548.3	1573.7	1598.6	1623.1	1671.6	1719.8	1768.0	1816.4	
(17.86)	s	5.1387	5.2351	5.3232	5.4053	5.4827	5.5562	5.6268	5.7603	5.8861	6.0057	6.1202	
	v		0.1488	0.1559	0.1627	0.1693	0.1757	0.1820	0.1942	0.2061	0.2178	0.2294	
900	h		1488.0	1516.2	1543.0	1569.1	1594.4	1619.4	1668.5	1717.1	1765.7	1814.4	
(21.54)	s		5.1593	5.2508	5.3354	5.4147	5.4897	5.5614	5.6968	5.8237	5.9442	6.0594	
	v		0.1321	0.1388	0.1450	0.1511	0.1570	0.1627	0.1739	0.1847	0.1954	0.2058	0.2162
1000	h		1480.6	1510.0	1537.7	1564.4	1590.3	1615.6	1665.4	1714.5	1763.4	1812.4	1861.7
(24.91)	s		5.0889	5.1840	5.2713	5.3525	5.4292	5.5021	5.6392	5.7674	5.8888	6.0047	6.1159
	v			0.1129	0.1185	0.1238	0.1289	0.1338	0.1434	0.1526	0.1616	0.1705	0.1792
1200	h			1497.1	1526.6	1554.7	1581.7	1608.0	1659.2	1709.2	1758.9	1808.5	1858.2
(30.96)	s			5.0629	5.1560	5.2416	5.3215	5.3970	5.5379	5.6687	5.7919	5.9091	6.0214
	v			0.0944	0.0995	0.1042	0.1088	0.1132	0.1216	0.1297	0.1376	0.1452	0.1528
1400	h			1483.4	1515.1	1544.7	1573.0	1600.2	1652.8	1703.9	1754.3	1804.5	1854.7
(36.28)	s			4.9534	5.0530	5.1434	5.2270	5.3053	5.4501	5.5836	5.7087	5.8273	5.9406
	v				0.0851	0.0895	0.0937	0.0977	0.1053	0.1125	0.1195	0.1263	0.1330
1600	h				1502.9	1534.4	1564.0	1592.3	1646.4	1698.5	1749.7	1800.5	1851.2
(41.05)	s				4.9584	5.0543	5.1419	5.2232	5.3722	5.5084	5.6355	5.7555	5.8699
	v				0.0739	0.0781	0.0820	0.0856	0.0926	0.0992	0.1055	0.1116	0.1177
1800	h				1490.0	1523.5	1554.6	1584.1	1639.8	1693.1	1745.1	1796.5	1847.7
(45.39)	s				4.8693	4.9715	5.0635	5.1482	5.3018	5.4409	5.5699	5.6914	5.8069
	v				0.0648	0.0688	0.0725	0.0760	0.0824	0.0885	0.0943	0.0999	0.1054
2000	h				1476.1	1512.0	1544.9	1575.6	1633.2	1687.6	1740.3	1792.4	1844.1
(49.38)	s				4.7834	4.8930	4.9902	5.0786	5.2371	5.3793	5.5104	5.6333	5.7499

Source: Reprinted from Gordon J. Van Wylen and Richard E. Sonntag, *Fundamentals of Classical Thermodynamics*, 3d ed. (New York: Wiley, 1986), pp. 660–663 (Table A.2.2).

Appendix C.7a Saturated refrigerant-12 (English units)

Temp. °F T	Abs. press. psia p	Specific volume ft³/lbm Sat. liquid v_f	Evap. v_{fg}	Sat. vapor v_g	Enthalpy Btu/lbm Sat. liquid h_f	Evap. h_{fg}	Sat. vapor h_g	Entropy Btu/(lbm·R) Sat. liquid s_f	Evap. s_{fg}	Sat. vapor s_g
−130	0.412 24	0.009 736	70.7203	70.730	−18.609	81.577	62.968	−0.049 83	0.247 43	0.197 60
−120	0.641 90	0.009 816	46.7312	46.741	−16.565	80.617	64.052	−0.043 72	0.237 31	0.193 59
−110	0.970 34	0.009 899	31.7671	31.777	−14.518	79.663	65.145	−0.037 79	0.227 80	0.190 02
−100	1.4280	0.009 985	21.1541	22.164	−12.466	78.714	66.248	−0.032 00	0.218 83	0.186 83
−90	2.0509	0.010 073	15.8109	15.821	−10.409	77.764	67.355	−0.026 37	0.210 34	0.183 98
−80	2.8807	0.010 164	11.5228	11.533	−8.3451	76.812	68.467	−0.020 86	0.202 29	0.181 43
−70	3.9651	0.010 259	8.5584	8.5687	−6.2730	75.853	69.580	−0.015 48	0.194 64	0.179 16
−60	5.3575	0.010 357	6.4670	6.4774	−4.1919	74.885	70.693	−0.010 21	0.187 16	0.177 14
−50	7.1168	0.010 459	4.9637	4.9742	−2.1011	73.906	71.805	−0.005 06	0.180 38	0.175 33
−40	9.3076	0.010 564	3.8644	3.8750	0	72.913	72.913	0	0.173 73	0.173 73
−30	11.999	0.010 674	3.0478	3.0585	2.1120	71.903	74.015	0.004 96	0.167 33	0.172 29
−20	15.267	0.010 788	2.4321	2.4429	4.2357	70.874	75.110	0.009 83	0.161 19	0.171 02
−10	19.189	0.010 906	1.9628	1.9727	6.3716	69.824	76.196	0.014 62	0.155 27	0.169 89
0	23.849	0.011 030	1.5979	1.6089	8.5207	68.750	77.271	0.019 32	0.149 56	0.168 88
10	29.335	0.011 160	1.3129	1.3241	10.684	67.651	78.335	0.023 95	0.144 03	0.167 98
20	35.736	0.011 296	1.0875	1.0988	12.863	66.522	79.385	0.028 52	0.138 67	0.167 19
30	43.148	0.011 438	0.907 36	0.918 80	15.058	65.361	80.419	0.033 01	0.133 47	0.166 48
40	51.667	0.011 588	0.761 98	0.773 57	17.273	64.163	81.436	0.037 45	0.128 41	0.165 86
50	61.394	0.011 746	0.643 62	0.655 37	19.507	62.926	82.433	0.041 84	0.234 46	0.165 30
60	72.433	0.011 913	0.546 48	0.558 39	21.766	61.643	83.409	0.046 18	0.118 61	0.164 79
70	84.888	0.012 089	0.466 09	0.478 18	24.050	60.309	84.359	0.050 48	0.113 86	0.164 34
80	98.870	0.012 277	0.399 07	0.411 35	26.365	58.917	85.282	0.054 75	0.109 17	0.163 92
90	114.49	0.012 478	0.342 81	0.355 29	28.713	57.461	86.174	0.059 00	0.104 53	0.163 53
100	131.86	0.012 693	0.295 25	0.307 94	31.100	55.929	87.029	0.063 23	0.099 92	0.163 15
110	151.11	0.012 924	0.255 77	0.267 69	33.531	54.313	87.844	0.067 45	0.095 34	0.162 79
120	172.35	0.013 174	0.220 19	0.233 26	36.013	52.597	88.610	0.071 68	0.090 73	0.162 41
130	195.71	0.013 447	0.190 19	0.203 64	38.553	50.768	89.321	0.075 83	0.086 09	0.162 02
140	221.32	0.013 746	0.164 24	0.177 99	41.162	48.805	89.967	0.080 21	0.081 38	0.161 59
150	249.31	0.014 078	0.141 56	0.155 64	43.850	46.684	90.534	0.084 53	0.076 57	0.161 10
160	279.82	0.014 449	0.121 59	0.136 04	46.633	44.373	91.006	0.088 93	0.072 60	0.160 53
170	313.00	0.014 871	0.103 86	0.118 73	49.529	41.830	91.359	0.093 42	0.066 43	0.159 85
180	349.00	0.015 360	0.087 94	0.103 30	52.562	38.999	91.561	0.098 04	0.060 96	0.159 00
190	387.98	0.015 942	0.073 476	0.089 418	55.769	35.792	91.561	0.102 84	0.055 11	0.157 93
200	430.09	0.016 659	0.060 069	0.076 728	59.203	32.075	91.278	0.107 89	0.048 62	0.156 51
210	475.52	0.017 601	0.047 242	0.064 843	62.959	27.599	90.558	0.113 32	0.039 21	0.154 53
220	524.43	0.018 986	0.035 154	0.053 140	67.246	21.790	89.036	0.119 43	0.032 06	0.151 49
230	577.03	0.021 854	0.017 581	0.039 435	72.893	12.229	85.122	0.127 39	0.017 73	0.145 12
233.6 (critical)	596.9	0.028 70	0	0.028 70	78.86	0	78.86	0.135 90	0	0.135 90

Sources: Gordon J. Van Wylen and Richard E. Sonntag, *Fundamentals of Classical Thermodynamics*, 3d ed. (New York: Wiley, 1986), pp. 664–665 (Table A.3.1E). Copyright © 1986 John Wiley & Sons. Reprinted by permission of John Wiley & Sons, Inc. Also, copyright 1955 and 1956 E. I. du Pont de Nemours & Company, Inc. Courtesy E. I. du Pont de Nemours & Company.

Appendix C.7b Saturated refrigerant-12 (metric units)

		Specific volume m^3/kg			Enthalpy kJ/kg			Entropy kJ/(kg·K)		
Temp. °C	Abs. press. MPa p	Sat. liquid v_f	Evap. v_{fg}	Sat. vapor v_g	Sat. liquid h_f	Evap. h_{fg}	Sat. vapor h_g	Sat. liquid s_f	Evap. s_{fg}	Sat. vapor s_g
−90	0.0028	0.000 608	4.414 937	4.415 545	−43.243	189.618	146.375	−0.2084	1.0352	0.8268
−85	0.0042	0.000 612	3.036 704	3.037 316	−38.968	187.608	148.640	−0.1854	0.9970	0.8116
−80	0.0062	0.000 617	2.137 728	2.138 345	−34.688	185.612	150.924	−0.1630	0.9609	0.7979
−75	0.0088	0.000 622	1.537 030	1.537 651	−30.401	183.625	153.224	−0.1411	0.9266	0.7855
−70	0.0123	0.000 627	1.126 654	1.127 280	−26.103	181.640	155.536	−0.1197	0.8940	0.7744
−65	0.0168	0.000 632	0.840 534	0.841 166	−21.793	179.651	157.857	−0.0987	0.8630	0.7643
−60	0.0226	0.000 637	0.637 274	0.637 910	−17.469	177.653	160.184	−0.0782	0.8334	0.7552
−55	0.0300	0.000 642	0.490 358	0.491 000	−13.129	175.641	162.512	−0.0581	0.8051	0.7470
−50	0.0391	0.000 648	0.382 457	0.383 105	−8.772	173.611	164.840	−0.0384	0.7779	0.7396
−45	0.0504	0.000 654	0.302 029	0.302 682	−4.396	171.558	167.163	−0.0190	0.7519	0.7329
−40	0.0642	0.000 659	0.241 251	0.241 910	−0.000	169.479	169.479	−0.0000	0.7269	0.7269
−35	0.0807	0.000 666	0.194 732	0.195 398	4.416	167.368	171.784	0.0187	0.7027	0.7214
−30	0.1004	0.000 672	0.158 703	0.159 375	8.854	165.222	174.076	0.0371	0.6795	0.7165
−25	0.1237	0.000 679	0.130 487	0.131 166	13.315	163.037	176.352	0.0552	0.6570	0.7121
−20	0.1509	0.000 685	0.108 162	0.108 847	17.800	160.810	178.610	0.0730	0.6352	0.7082
−15	0.1826	0.000 693	0.090 326	0.091 018	22.312	158.534	180.846	0.0906	0.6141	0.7046
−10	0.2191	0.000 700	0.075 946	0.076 646	26.851	156.207	183.058	0.1079	0.5936	0.7014
−5	0.2610	0.000 708	0.064 255	0.064 963	31.420	153.823	185.243	0.1250	0.5736	0.6986
0	0.3086	0.000 716	0.054 673	0.055 389	36.022	151.376	187.397	0.1418	0.5542	0.6960
5	0.3626	0.000 724	0.046 761	0.047 485	40.659	148.859	189.518	0.1585	0.5351	0.6937
10	0.4233	0.000 733	0.040 180	0.040 914	45.337	146.265	191.602	0.1750	0.5165	0.6916
15	0.4914	0.000 743	0.034 671	0.035 413	50.058	143.586	193.644	0.1914	0.4983	0.6897
20	0.5673	0.000 752	0.030 028	0.030 780	54.828	140.812	195.641	0.2076	0.4803	0.6879
25	0.6516	0.000 763	0.026 091	0.026 854	59.653	137.933	197.586	0.2237	0.4626	0.6863
30	0.7449	0.000 774	0.022 734	0.023 508	64.539	134.936	199.475	0.2397	0.4451	0.6848
35	0.8477	0.000 786	0.019 855	0.020 641	69.494	131.805	201.299	0.2557	0.4277	0.6834
40	0.9607	0.000 798	0.017 373	0.018 171	74.527	128.525	203.051	0.2716	0.4104	0.6820
45	1.0843	0.000 811	0.015 220	0.016 032	79.647	125.074	204.722	0.2875	0.3931	0.6806
50	1.2193	0.000 826	0.013 344	0.014 170	84.868	121.430	206.298	0.3034	0.3758	0.6792
55	1.3663	0.000 841	0.011 701	0.012 542	90.201	117.565	207.766	0.3194	0.3582	0.6777
60	1.5259	0.000 858	0.010 253	0.011 111	95.665	113.443	209.109	0.3355	0.3405	0.6760
65	1.6988	0.000 877	0.008 971	0.009 847	101.279	109.024	210.303	0.3518	0.3224	0.6742
70	1.8858	0.000 897	0.007 828	0.008 725	107.067	104.255	211.321	0.3683	0.3038	0.6721
75	2.0874	0.000 920	0.006 802	0.007 723	113.058	99.068	212.126	0.3851	0.2845	0.6697
80	2.3046	0.000 946	0.005 875	0.006 821	119.291	93.373	212.665	0.4023	0.2644	0.6667
85	2.5380	0.000 976	0.005 029	0.006 005	125.818	87.047	212.865	0.4201	0.2430	0.6631
90	2.7885	0.001 012	0.004 246	0.005 258	132.708	79.907	212.614	0.4385	0.2200	0.6585
95	3.0569	0.001 056	0.003 508	0.004 563	140.068	71.658	211.726	0.4579	0.1946	0.6526
100	3.3440	0.001 113	0.002 790	0.003 903	148.076	61.768	209.843	0.4788	0.1655	0.6444
105	3.6509	0.001 197	0.002 045	0.003 242	157.085	49.014	206.099	0.5023	0.1296	0.6319
110	3.9784	0.001 364	0.001 098	0.002 462	168.059	28.425	196.484	0.5322	0.0742	0.6064
112	4.1155	0.001 792	0.000 005	0.001 797	174.920	0.151	175.071	0.5651	0.0004	0.5655

Sources: Gordon J. Van Wylen and Richard E. Sonntag, *Fundamentals of Classical Thermodynamics*, 3d ed. (New York: Wiley, 1986), pp. 670–671 (Table A.3.1).

Appendix C.8a Superheated refrigerant-12 (English units)

Temp. °F	v ft³/lbm	h Btu/lbm	s Btu/(lbm·R)	v ft³/lbm	h Btu/lbm	s Btu/(lbm·R)	v ft³/lbm	h Btu/lbm	s Btu/(lbm·R)
		5 lbf/in²			10 lbf/in²			15 lbf/in²	
0	8.0611	78.582	0.196 63	3.9809	78.246	0.184 71	2.6201	77.902	0.177 51
20	8.4265	81.309	0.202 44	4.1691	81.024	0.190 61	2.7494	80.712	0.183 49
40	8.7903	84.090	0.208 12	4.3556	83.828	0.196 35	2.8770	83.561	0.189 31
60	9.1528	86.922	0.213 67	4.5408	86.689	0.201 97	3.0031	86.451	0.194 98
80	9.5142	89.806	0.219 12	4.7248	89.596	0.207 46	3.1281	89.383	0.200 51
100	9.8747	92.738	0.224 45	4.9079	92.548	0.212 83	3.2521	92.357	0.205 93
120	10.234	95.717	0.229 68	5.0903	95.546	0.218 09	3.3754	95.373	0.211 22
140	10.594	98.743	0.234 81	5.2720	98.586	0.223 25	3.4981	98.429	0.216 40
160	10.952	101.812	0.239 85	5.4533	101.669	0.228 30	3.6202	101.525	0.221 48
180	11.311	104.925	0.244 79	5.6341	104.793	0.233 26	3.7419	104.661	0.226 46
200	11.668	108.079	0.249 64	5.8145	107.957	0.238 13	3.8632	107.835	0.231 35
220	12.026	111.272	0.254 41	5.9946	111.159	0.242 91	3.9841	111.046	0.236 14
		20 lbf/in²			25 lbf/in²			30 lbf/in²	
20	2.0391	80.403	0.178 29	1.6125	80.088	0.174 14	1.3278	79.765	0.170 65
40	2.1373	83.289	0.184 19	1.6932	83.012	0.180 12	1.3969	82.730	0.176 71
60	2.2340	86.210	0.189 92	1.7723	85.965	0.185 91	1.4644	85.716	0.182 57
80	2.3295	89.168	0.195 50	1.8502	88.950	0.191 55	1.5306	88.729	0.188 26
100	2.4241	92.164	0.200 95	1.9271	91.968	0.197 04	1.5957	91.770	0.193 79
120	2.5179	95.198	0.206 28	2.0032	95.021	0.202 40	1.6600	94.843	0.199 18
140	2.6110	98.270	0.211 49	2.0786	98.110	0.207 63	1.7237	97.948	0.204 45
160	2.7036	101.380	0.216 59	2.1535	101.234	0.212 76	1.7868	101.086	0.209 60
180	2.7957	104.528	0.221 59	2.2279	104.393	0.217 78	1.8494	104.258	0.214 63
200	2.8874	107.712	0.226 49	2.3019	107.588	0.222 69	1.9116	107.464	0.219 57
220	2.9789	110.932	0.231 30	2.3756	110.817	0.227 52	1.9735	110.702	0.224 40
240	3.0700	114.186	0.236 02	2.4491	114.080	0.232 25	2.0351	113.973	0.229 15
		35 lbf/in²			40 lbf/in²			50 lbf/in²	
40	1.1850	82.442	0.173 75	1.0258	82.148	0.171 12	0.802 48	81.540	0.166 55
60	1.2442	85.463	0.179 68	1.0789	85.206	0.177 12	0.847 13	84.676	0.172 71
80	1.3021	88.504	0.185 42	1.1306	88.277	0.182 92	0.890 25	87.811	0.178 62
100	1.3589	91.570	0.191 00	1.1812	91.367	0.188 54	0.932 16	90.953	0.184 34
120	1.4148	94.663	0.196 43	1.2309	94.480	0.194 01	0.973 13	94.110	0.189 88
140	1.4701	97.785	0.201 72	1.2798	97.620	0.199 33	1.0133	97.286	0.195 27
160	1.5248	100.938	0.206 89	1.3282	100.788	0.204 53	1.0529	100.485	0.200 51
180	1.5789	104.122	0.211 95	1.3761	103.985	0.209 61	1.0920	103.708	0.205 63
200	1.6327	107.338	0.216 90	1.4236	107.212	0.214 57	1.1307	106.958	0.210 64
220	1.6862	110.586	0.221 75	1.4707	110.469	0.219 44	1.1690	110.235	0.215 53
240	1.7394	113.865	0.226 51	1.5176	113.757	0.224 20	1.2070	113.539	0.220 32
260	1.7923	117.175	0.231 17	1.5642	117.074	0.228 88	1.2447	116.871	0.225 02
		60 lbf/in²			70 lbf/in²			80 lbf/in²	
60	0.692 10	84.126	0.168 92	0.580 88	83.552	0.165 56	—	—	—
80	0.729 64	87.330	0.174 97	0.614 58	86.832	0.171 75	0.527 95	86.316	0.168 85
100	0.765 88	90.528	0.180 79	0.646 85	90.091	0.177 68	0.557 34	89.640	0.174 89
120	0.801 10	93.731	0.186 41	0.678 03	93.343	0.183 39	0.585 56	92.945	0.180 70
140	0.835 51	96.945	0.191 86	0.708 36	96.597	0.188 91	0.612 86	96.242	0.186 29
160	0.869 28	100.776	0.197 16	0.738 00	99.862	0.194 27	0.639 43	99.542	0.191 70
180	0.902 52	103.427	0.202 33	0.767 08	103.141	0.199 48	0.665 43	102.851	0.196 96
200	0.935 31	106.700	0.207 36	0.795 71	106.439	0.204 55	0.690 95	106.174	0.202 07
220	0.967 75	109.997	0.212 29	0.823 97	109.756	0.209 51	0.716 09	109.513	0.207 06
240	0.999 88	113.319	0.217 10	0.851 91	113.096	0.214 35	0.740 90	112.872	0.211 93
260	1.031 80	116.666	0.221 82	0.879 59	116.459	0.219 09	0.765 44	116.251	0.216 69
280	1.063 40	120.039	0.226 44	0.907 05	119.846	0.223 73	0.789 75	119.652	0.221 35

(*Continued*)

Appendix C.8a Superheated refrigerant-12 (English units)—*continued*

Temp. °F	*v* ft³/lbm	*h* Btu/lbm	*s* Btu/(lbm·R)	*v* ft³/lbm	*h* Btu/lbm	*s* Btu/(lbm·R)	*v* ft³/lbm	*h* Btu/lbm	*s* Btu/(lbm·R)
		90 lbf/in²			100 lbf/in²			125 lbf/in²	
100	0.487 49	89.175	0.172 34	0.431 38	88.694	0.169 96	0.329 43	87.407	0.164 55
120	0.513 46	92.536	0.178 24	0.455 62	92.116	0.175 97	0.350 86	91.008	0.170 87
140	0.538 45	95.879	0.183 91	0.478 81	95.507	0.181 72	0.370 98	94.537	0.176 86
160	0.562 68	99.216	0.189 38	0.501 18	98.884	0.187 26	0.390 15	98.023	0.182 58
180	0.586 29	102.557	0.194 69	0.522 91	102.257	0.192 62	0.408 57	101.484	0.188 07
200	0.609 41	105.905	0.199 84	0.544 13	105.633	0.197 82	0.426 42	104.934	0.193 38
220	0.632 13	109.267	0.204 86	0.564 92	109.018	0.202 87	0.443 80	108.380	0.198 53
240	0.654 51	112.644	0.209 76	0.585 38	112.415	0.207 80	0.460 81	111.829	0.203 53
260	0.676 62	116.040	0.214 55	0.605 54	115.828	0.212 61	0.477 50	115.287	0.208 40
280	0.698 49	119.456	0.219 23	0.625 46	119.258	0.217 31	0.493 94	118.756	0.213 16
300	0.720 16	122.892	0.223 81	0.645 18	122.707	0.221 91	0.510 16	122.238	0.217 80
320	0.741 66	126.349	0.228 30	0.664 72	126.176	0.226 41	0.526 19	125.737	0.222 35
		150 lbf/in²			175 lbf/in²			200 lbf/in²	
120	0.280 07	89.800	0.166 29	—	—	—	—	—	—
140	0.298 45	93.498	0.172 56	0.245 95	92.373	0.168 59	0.205 79	91.137	0.164 80
160	0.315 66	97.112	0.178 49	0.261 98	96.142	0.174 78	0.221 21	95.100	0.171 30
180	0.332 00	100.675	0.184 15	0.276 97	99.823	0.180 62	0.235 35	98.921	0.177 37
200	0.347 69	104.206	0.189 58	0.291 20	103.447	0.186 20	0.248 60	102.652	0.183 11
220	0.362 85	107.720	0.194 83	0.304 85	107.036	0.191 56	0.261 17	106.325	0.188 60
240	0.377 61	111.226	0.199 92	0.318 04	110.605	0.196 74	0.273 23	109.962	0.193 87
260	0.392 03	114.732	0.204 85	0.330 87	114.162	0.201 75	0.284 89	113.576	0.198 96
280	0.406 17	118.242	0.209 67	0.343 39	117.717	0.206 62	0.296 23	117.178	0.203 90
300	0.420 08	121.761	0.214 36	0.355 67	121.273	0.211 37	0.307 30	120.775	0.208 70
320	0.433 79	125.290	0.218 94	0.367 73	124.835	0.215 99	0.318 15	124.373	0.213 37
340	0.447 33	128.833	0.223 43	0.379 63	128.407	0.220 52	0.328 81	127.974	0.217 93
		250 lbf/in²			300 lbf/in²			400 lbf/in²	
160	0.162 49	92.717	0.164 62	—	—	—	—	—	—
180	0.176 05	96.925	0.171 30	0.134 82	94.556	0.165 37	—	—	—
200	0.188 24	100.930	0.177 47	0.146 97	98.975	0.172 17	0.091 005	93.718	0.160 92
220	0.199 52	104.809	0.183 26	0.157 74	103.136	0.178 38	0.103 16	99.046	0.168 88
240	0.210 14	108.607	0.188 77	0.167 61	107.140	0.184 19	0.113 00	103.735	0.175 68
260	0.200 27	112.351	0.194 04	0.176 85	111.043	0.189 69	0.121 63	108.105	0.181 83
280	0.230 01	116.060	0.199 13	0.185 62	114.879	0.194 95	0.129 49	112.286	0.187 56
300	0.239 44	119.747	0.204 05	0.194 02	118.670	0.200 00	0.136 80	116.343	0.192 98
320	0.248 62	123.420	0.208 82	0.202 14	122.430	0.204 89	0.143 72	120.318	0.198 14
340	0.257 59	127.088	0.213 46	0.210 02	126.171	0.209 63	0.150 32	124.235	0.203 10
360	0.226 39	130.754	0.217 99	0.217 70	129.900	0.214 23	0.156 68	128.112	0.207 89
380	0.275 04	134.423	0.222 41	0.225 22	133.624	0.218 72	0.162 85	131.961	0.212 58
		500 lbf/in²			600 lbf/in²				
220	0.064 207	92.397	0.156 83	—	—	—			
240	0.077 620	99.218	0.166 72	0.047 488	91.024	0.153 35			
260	0.087 054	104.526	0.174 21	0.061 922	99.741	0.165 66			
280	0.094 923	109.277	0.180 72	0.070 859	105.637	0.173 74			
300	0.101 90		0.186 66	0.078 059	110.729	0.180 53			
320	0.108 29		0.192 21	0.084 333	115.420	0.186 63			
340	0.114 26	122.143	0.197 46	0.090 017	119.871	0.192 27			
360	0.119 92	126.205	0.202 47	0.095 289	124.167	0.197 57			
380	0.125 33	130.207	0.207 30	0.100 25	128.355	0.202 62			
400	0.130 54	134.166	0.211 96	0.104 98	132.466	0.207 46			
420	0.135 59	138.096	0.216 48	0.109 52	136.523	0.212 13			
440	0.140 51	142.004	0.220 87	0.113 91	140.539	0.216 64			

Source: Gordon J. Van Wylen and Richard E. Sonntag, *Fundamentals of Classical Thermodynamics*, 3d ed. (New York: Wiley, 1986), pp. 666–669 (Table A.3.2E).

Appendix C.8*b* **Superheated refrigerant-12 (metric units)**

Temp. °C	*v* m^3/kg	*h* kJ/kg	*s* kJ/(kg·K)	*v* m^3/kg	*h* kJ/kg	*s* kJ/(kg·K)	*v* m^3/kg	*h* kJ/kg	*s* kJ/(kg·K)
		0.05 MPa			**0.10 MPa**			**0.15 MPa**	
−20.0	0.341 857	181.042	0.7912	0.167 701	179.861	0.7401	—	—	—
−10.0	0.356 227	186.757	0.8133	0.175 222	185.707	0.7628	0.114 716	184.619	0.7318
0.0	0.370 508	192.567	0.8350	0.182 647	191.628	0.7849	0.119 866	190.660	0.7543
10.0	0.384 716	198.471	0.8562	0.189 994	197.628	0.8064	0.124 932	196.762	0.7763
20.0	0.398 863	204.469	0.8770	0.197 277	203.707	0.8275	0.129 930	202.927	0.7977
30.0	0.412 959	210.557	0.8974	0.204 506	209.866	0.8482	0.134 873	209.160	0.8186
40.0	0.427 012	216.733	0.9175	0.211 691	216.104	0.8684	0.139 768	215.463	0.8390
50.0	0.441 030	222.997	0.9372	0.218 839	222.421	0.8883	0.144 625	221.835	0.8591
60.0	0.455 017	229.344	0.9565	0.225 955	228.815	0.9078	0.149 450	228.277	0.8787
70.0	0.468 978	235.774	0.9755	0.233 044	235.285	0.9269	0.154 247	234.789	0.8980
80.0	0.482 917	242.282	0.9942	0.240 111	241.829	0.9457	0.159 020	241.371	0.9169
90.0	0.496 838	248.868	1.0126	0.247 159	248.446	0.9642	0.163 774	248.020	0.9354
		0.20 MPa			**0.25 MPa**			**0.30 MPa**	
0.0	0.088 608	189.669	0.7320	0.069 752	188.644	0.7139	0.057 150	187.583	0.6984
10.0	0.092 550	195.878	0.7543	0.073 024	194.969	0.7366	0.059 984	194.034	0.7216
20.0	0.096 418	202.135	0.7760	0.076 218	201.322	0.7587	0.062 734	200.490	0.7440
30.0	0.100 228	208.446	0.7972	0.079 350	207.715	0.7801	0.065 418	206.969	0.7658
40.0	0.103 989	214.814	0.8178	0.082 431	214.153	0.8010	0.068 049	213.480	0.7869
50.0	0.107 710	221.243	0.8381	0.085 470	220.642	0.8214	0.070 635	220.030	0.8075
60.0	0.111 397	227.735	0.8578	0.088 474	227.185	0.8413	0.073 185	226.627	0.8276
70.0	0.115 055	234.291	0.8772	0.091 449	233.785	0.8608	0.075 705	233.273	0.8473
80.0	0.118 690	240.910	0.8962	0.094 398	240.443	0.8800	0.078 200	239.971	0.8665
90.0	0.122 304	247.593	0.9149	0.097 327	247.160	0.8987	0.080 673	246.723	0.8853
100.0	0.125 901	254.339	0.9332	0.100 238	253.936	0.9171	0.083 127	253.530	0.9038
110.0	0.129 483	261.147	0.9512	0.103 134	260.770	0.9352	0.085 566	260.391	0.9220
		0.40 MPa			**0.50 MPa**			**0.60 MPa**	
20.0	0.045 836	198.762	0.7199	0.035 646	196.935	0.6999	—	—	—
30.0	0.047 971	205.428	0.7423	0.037 464	203.814	0.7230	0.030 422	202.116	0.7063
40.0	0.050 046	212.095	0.7639	0.039 214	210.656	0.7452	0.031 966	209.154	0.7291
50.0	0.052 072	218.779	0.7849	0.040 911	217.484	0.7667	0.033 450	216.141	0.7511
60.0	0.054 059	225.488	0.8054	0.042 565	224.315	0.7875	0.034 887	223.104	0.7723
70.0	0.056 014	232.230	0.8253	0.044 184	231.161	0.8077	0.036 285	230.062	0.7929
80.0	0.057 941	239.012	0.8448	0.045 774	238.031	0.8275	0.037 653	237.027	0.8129
90.0	0.059 846	245.837	0.8638	0.047 340	244.932	0.8467	0.038 995	244.009	0.8324
100.0	0.061 731	252.707	0.8825	0.048 886	251.869	0.8656	0.040 316	251.016	0.8514
110.0	0.063 600	259.624	0.9008	0.050 415	258.845	0.8840	0.041 619	258.053	0.8700
120.0	0.065 455	266.590	0.9187	0.051 929	265.862	0.9021	0.042 907	265.124	0.8882
130.0	0.067 298	273.605	0.9364	0.053 430	272.923	0.9198	0.044 181	272.231	0.9061
		0.70 MPa			**0.80 MPa**			**0.90 MPa**	
40.0	0.026 761	207.580	0.7148	0.022 830	205.924	0.7016	0.019 744	204.170	0.6982
50.0	0.028 100	214.745	0.7373	0.024 068	213.290	0.7248	0.020 912	211.765	0.7131
60.0	0.029 387	221.854	0.7590	0.025 247	220.558	0.7469	0.022 012	219.212	0.7358
70.0	0.030 632	228.931	0.7799	0.026 380	227.766	0.7682	0.023 062	226.564	0.7575
80.0	0.031 843	235.997	0.8002	0.027 477	234.941	0.7888	0.024 072	233.856	0.7785
90.0	0.033 027	243.066	0.8199	0.028 545	242.101	0.8088	0.025 051	241.113	0.7987
100.0	0.034 189	250.146	0.8392	0.029 588	249.260	0.8283	0.026 005	248.355	0.8184
110.0	0.035 332	257.247	0.8579	0.030 612	256.428	0.8472	0.026 937	255.593	0.8376
120.0	0.036 458	264.374	0.8763	0.031 619	263.613	0.8657	0.027 851	262.839	0.8562
130.0	0.037 572	271.531	0.8943	0.032 612	270.820	0.8838	0.028 751	270.100	0.8745
140.0	0.038 673	278.720	0.9119	0.033 592	278.055	0.9016	0.029 639	277.381	0.8923
150.0	0.039 764	285.946	0.9292	0.034 563	285.320	0.9189	0.030 515	284.687	0.9098

(*Continued*)

Appendix C.8*b* **Superheated refrigerant-12 (metric units)—*continued***

Temp. °C	*v* m³/kg	*h* kJ/kg	*s* kJ/(kg·K)	*v* m³/kg	*h* kJ/kg	*s* kJ/(kg·K)	*v* m³/kg	*h* kJ/kg	*s* kJ/(kg·K)
	1.00 MPa			**1.20 MPa**			**1.40 MPa**		
50.0	0.018 366	210.162	0.7021	0.014 483	206.661	0.6812	—	—	—
60.0	0.019 410	217.810	0.7254	0.015 463	214.805	0.7060	0.012 579	211.457	0.6876
70.0	0.020 397	225.319	0.7476	0.016 368	222.687	0.7293	0.013 448	219.822	0.7123
80.0	0.021 341	232.739	0.7689	0.017 221	230.398	0.7514	0.014 247	227.891	0.7355
90.0	0.022 251	240.101	0.7895	0.018 032	237.995	0.7727	0.014 997	235.766	0.7575
100.0	0.023 133	247.430	0.8094	0.018 812	245.518	0.7931	0.015 710	243.512	0.7785
110.0	0.023 993	254.743	0.8287	0.019 567	252.993	0.8129	0.016 393	251.170	0.7988
120.0	0.024 835	262.053	0.8475	0.020 301	260.441	0.8320	0.017 053	258.770	0.8183
130.0	0.025 661	269.369	0.8659	0.021 018	267.875	0.8507	0.017 695	266.334	0.8373
140.0	0.026 474	276.699	0.8839	0.021 721	275.307	0.8689	0.018 321	273.877	0.8558
150.0	0.027 275	284.047	0.9015	0.022 412	282.745	0.8867	0.018 934	281.411	0.8738
160.0	0.028 068	291.419	0.9187	0.023 093	290.195	0.9041	0.019 535	288.946	0.8914
	1.60 MPa			**1.80 MPa**			**2.00 MPa**		
70.0	0.011 208	216.650	0.6959	0.009 406	213.049	0.6794	—	—	—
80.0	0.011 984	225.177	0.7204	0.010 187	222.198	0.7057	0.008 704	218.859	0.6909
90.0	0.012 698	233.390	0.7433	0.010 884	230.835	0.7298	0.009 406	228.056	0.7166
100.0	0.013 366	241.397	0.7651	0.011 526	239.155	0.7524	0.010 035	236.760	0.7402
110.0	0.014 000	249.264	0.7859	0.012 126	247.264	0.7739	0.010 615	245.154	0.7624
120.0	0.014 608	257.035	0.8059	0.012 697	255.228	0.7944	0.011 159	253.341	0.7835
130.0	0.015 195	264.742	0.8253	0.013 244	263.094	0.8141	0.011 676	261.384	0.8037
140.0	0.015 765	272.406	0.8440	0.013 772	270.891	0.8332	0.012 172	269.327	0.8232
150.0	0.016 320	280.044	0.8623	0.014 284	278.642	0.8518	0.012 651	277.201	0.8420
160.0	0.016 864	287.669	0.8801	0.014 784	286.364	0.8698	0.013 116	285.027	0.8603
170.0	0.017 398	295.290	0.8975	0.015 272	294.069	0.8874	0.013 570	292.822	0.8781
180.0	0.017 923	302.914	0.9145	0.015 752	301.767	0.9046	0.014 013	300.598	0.8955
	2.50 MPa			**3.00 MPa**			**3.50 MPa**		
90.0	0.006 595	219.562	0.6823						
100.0	0.007 264	229.852	0.7103	0.005 231	220.529	0.6770	—	—	—
110.0	0.007 837	239.271	0.7352	0.005 886	232.068	0.7075	0.004 324	222.121	0.6750
120.0	0.008 351	248.192	0.7582	0.006 419	242.208	0.7336	0.004 959	234.875	0.7078
130.0	0.008 827	256.794	0.7798	0.006 887	251.632	0.7573	0.005 456	245.661	0.7349
140.0	0.009 273	265.180	0.8003	0.007 313	260.620	0.7793	0.005 884	255.524	0.7591
150.0	0.009 697	273.414	0.8200	0.007 709	269.319	0.8001	0.006 270	264.846	0.7814
160.0	0.010 104	281.540	0.8390	0.008 083	277.817	0.8200	0.006 626	273.817	0.8023
170.0	0.010 497	289.589	0.8574	0.008 439	286.171	0.8391	0.006 961	282.545	0.8222
180.0	0.010 879	297.583	0.8752	0.008 782	294.422	0.8575	0.007 279	291.100	0.8413
190.0	0.011 250	305.540	0.8926	0.009 114	302.597	0.8753	0.007 584	299.528	0.8597
200.0	0.011 614	313.472	0.9095	0.009 436	310.718	0.8927	0.007 878	307.864	0.8775
	4.00 MPa								
120.0	0.003 736	224.863	0.6771						
130.0	0.004 325	238.443	0.7111						
140.0	0.004 781	249.703	0.7386						
150.0	0.005 172	259.904	0.7630						
160.0	0.005 522	269.492	0.7854						
170.0	0.005 845	278.684	0.8063						
180.0	0.006 147	287.602	0.8262						
190.0	0.006 434	296.326	0.8453						
200.0	0.006 708	304.906	0.8636						
210.0	0.006 972	313.380	0.8813						
220.0	0.007 228	321.774	0.8985						
230.0	0.007 477	330.108	0.9152						

Source: Gordon J. Van Wylen and Richard E. Sonntag, *Fundamentals of Classical Thermodynamics*, 3d ed. (New York: Wiley, 1986), pp. 672–675 (Table A.3.2SI).

Appendix C.9a Saturated refrigerant-22 (English units)

Temp. °F T	Abs. press. psia p	Specific volume (ft³/lbm) Sat. liq. v_f	Evap. v_{fg}	Sat. vap. v_g	Internal energy (Btu/lbm) Sat. liq. u_f	Evap. u_{fg}	Sat. vap. u_g
−150	0.2716	0.01018	141.22	141.23	−25.98	106.40	80.42
−140	0.4469	0.01027	88.522	88.532	−23.73	105.09	81.36
−130	0.7106	0.01037	57.346	57.356	−21.46	103.77	83.31
−120	1.0954	0.01046	38.270	38.280	−10.19	102.45	83.26
−110	1.6417	0.01056	26.231	26.242	−16.89	101.11	84.22
−100	2.3989	0.01066	18.422	18.433	−14.57	99.76	85.19
−90	3.4229	0.01077	13.224	13.235	−12.22	98.38	86.16
−80	4.7822	0.01088	9.6840	9.6949	−9.85	96.98	87.13
−70	6.5522	0.01100	7.2208	7.2318	−7.49	95.59	88.10
−60	8.8180	0.01111	5.4733	5.4844	−5.01	94.08	89.07
−50	11.674	0.01124	4.2112	4.2224	−2.54	92.56	90.02
−40	15.222	0.01136	3.2843	3.2957	−0.03	91.01	90.97
−30	19.773	0.01150	2.5934	2.6049	2.51	89.40	91.91
−20	24.845	0.01163	2.0710	2.0826	5.13	87.82	92.95
−10	31.162	0.01178	1.6707	1.6825	7.68	86.07	93.75
0	38.657	0.01193	1.3604	1.3723	10.32	84.33	94.65
10	47.464	0.01209	1.1169	1.1290	13.00	82.53	95.53
20	57.727	0.01226	0.92405	0.93631	15.71	80.67	96.38
30	69.591	0.01243	0.76956	0.78208	18.45	78.76	97.21
40	83.206	0.01262	0.64491	0.65753	21.23	76.79	98.02
50	98.727	0.01281	0.54325	0.55606	24.04	74.75	98.79
60	116.31	0.01302	0.45970	0.47272	26.80	72.65	99.54
70	136.12	0.01325	0.39048	0.40373	29.78	70.46	100.24
80	158.33	0.01349	0.33272	0.34621	32.71	68.20	100.91
90	183.09	0.01375	0.28414	0.29789	35.69	65.84	101.53
100	210.60	0.01404	0.24298	0.25702	38.72	63.37	102.09
110	241.04	0.01435	0.20787	0.22222	41.81	60.78	102.59
120	274.60	0.01469	0.17768	0.19238	44.96	58.05	103.01
130	311.50	0.01508	0.15153	0.16661	48.19	55.14	103.33
140	351.94	0.01552	0.12866	0.14418	51.52	52.02	103.54
150	396.19	0.01602	0.10846	0.12448	54.97	48.63	103.60
160	444.53	0.01663	0.09038	0.10701	58.58	44.88	103.46
170	497.26	0.01737	0.07391	0.09128	62.42	40.62	103.04
180	554.78	0.01833	0.05846	0.07679	66.62	35.57	102.19
190	617.59	0.01973	0.04311	0.06284	71.46	29.09	100.55
200	686.36	0.02244	0.02500	0.04744	78.30	19.13	97.43
204.81	721.91	0.03053	0	0.03053	87.25	0	87.25

(Continued)

Appendix C.9a Saturated refrigerant-22 (English units)*—*continued*

Temp. °F T	Enthalpy (Btu/lbm)* Sat. liq. h_f	Evap. h_{fg}	Sat. vapor h_g	Entropy (Btu/(lbm·R))* Sat. liq. s_f	Evap. s_{fg}	Sat. vapor s_g
−150	−25.97	113.49	87.52	−0.07147	0.36648	0.29501
−140	−23.72	112.40	88.68	−0.06432	0.35161	0.28729
−130	−21.46	111.31	89.85	−0.05736	0.33763	0.28027
−120	−19.19	110.21	91.02	−0.05055	0.32443	0.27388
−110	−16.89	109.09	92.20	−0.04389	0.31194	0.26805
−100	−14.56	107.93	93.37	−0.03734	0.30008	0.26274
−90	−12.22	106.76	94.54	−0.03091	0.28878	0.25787
−80	−9.84	105.55	95.71	−0.02457	0.27799	0.25342
−70	−7.43	104.30	96.87	−0.01832	0.26764	0.24932
−60	−4.99	103.00	98.01	−0.01214	0.25770	0.24556
−50	−2.51	101.65	99.14	−0.00604	0.24813	0.24209
−40	0	100.26	100.26	0.00000	0.23888	0.23888
−30	2.55	98.80	101.35	0.00598	0.22993	0.23591
−20	5.13	97.29	102.42	0.01189	0.22126	0.23315
−10	7.75	95.70	103.45	0.01776	0.21282	0.23058
0	10.41	94.06	104.47	0.02357	0.20460	0.22817
10	13.10	92.34	105.44	0.02932	0.19660	0.22592
20	15.84	90.54	106.38	0.03503	0.18876	0.22379
30	18.61	88.67	107.28	0.04070	0.18108	0.22178
40	21.42	86.72	108.14	0.04632	0.17354	0.21986
50	24.27	84.68	108.95	0.05190	0.16613	0.21803
60	27.17	82.54	109.71	0.05745	0.15882	0.21627
70	30.12	80.29	110.41	0.06296	0.15160	0.21456
80	33.11	77.94	111.05	0.06846	0.14442	0.21288
90	36.16	75.46	111.62	0.07394	0.13728	0.21122
100	39.27	72.84	112.11	0.07942	0.13014	0.20956
110	42.45	70.05	112.50	0.08491	0.12296	0.20787
120	45.70	67.08	112.78	0.09042	0.11571	0.20613
130	49.06	63.88	112.94	0.09598	0.10833	0.20431
140	52.53	60.40	112.93	0.10163	0.10072	0.20235
150	56.14	56.59	112.73	0.10739	0.09281	0.20020
160	59.95	52.31	112.26	0.11334	0.08442	0.19776
170	64.02	47.40	111.42	0.11959	0.07531	0.19490
180	68.50	41.57	110.07	0.12635	0.06498	0.19133
190	73.71	34.02	107.73	0.13409	0.05237	0.18646
200	80.86	21.99	102.85	0.14460	0.03334	0.17794
204.81	91.33	0	91.33	0.16016	0	0.16016

* The enthalpy and entropy of saturated liquid R-22 are taken as zero at a temperature of −40 °F.

Source: Reprinted by permission from William L. Haberman and James E. A. John, *Engineering Thermodynamics* (Boston: Allyn & Bacon, 1980), pp. 414–415 (Table A.10).

Appendix C.9b Saturated refrigerant-22 (metric units)

Temp. °C T	Abs. press. (kPa) p	Specific volume (m³/kg) Sat. liq. v_f	Evap. v_{fg}	Sat. vapor v_g	Internal energy (kJ/kg) Sat. liq. u_f	Evap. u_{fg}	Sat. vapor u_g
−100	2.0750	0.0006366	8.0083	8.0089	−59.37	246.86	187.49
−95	3.2323	0.0006418	5.2845	5.2851	−54.66	244.12	189.46
−90	4.8994	0.0006470	3.5804	3.5810	−49.92	241.36	191.36
−85	7.2412	0.0006525	2.4847	2.4854	−45.16	238.59	193.43
−80	10.461	0.0006581	1.7626	1.7633	−40.36	235.80	195.44
−75	14.794	0.0006638	1.2757	1.2764	−35.52	233.00	197.48
−70	20.523	0.0006697	0.94033	0.94100	−30.62	230.13	199.51
−65	27.965	0.0006758	0.69876	0.70552	−25.68	227.21	201.53
−60	37.480	0.0006821	0.53649	0.53717	−20.68	224.25	203.57
−55	49.474	0.0006885	0.41416	0.41485	−15.62	221.22	205.60
−50	63.139	0.0006952	0.32387	0.32457	−10.50	218.52	208.02
−45	82.701	0.0007022	0.25630	0.25700	−5.32	214.94	209.62
−40	104.943	0.0007093	0.20505	0.20576	−0.07	211.68	211.61
−35	131.669	0.0007168	0.16569	0.16569	5.24	208.33	213.57
−30	163.470	0.0007245	0.13513	0.13585	10.60	204.91	215.51
−25	200.968	0.0007325	0.11113	0.11186	16.01	233.45	217.44
−20	244.814	0.0007409	0.092106	0.092847	21.55	197.77	219.32
−15	295.686	0.0007496	0.076878	0.077628	27.11	194.07	221.18
−10	354.284	0.0007587	0.064583	0.065342	32.74	190.25	222.99
−5	421.330	0.0007683	0.054573	0.055341	35.52	189.24	224.76
0	497.567	0.0007783	0.046359	0.047137	44.20	182.30	226.50
5	583.756	0.0007889	0.039568	0.040357	50.02	178.15	228.17
10	680.673	0.0008000	0.033915	0.034715	55.92	173.87	229.79
15	789.117	0.0008118	0.029177	0.029989	61.88	169.48	231.36
20	909.899	0.0008243	0.025180	0.026004	67.92	164.92	232.84
25	1043.856	0.0008376	0.021787	0.022625	74.04	160.22	234.26
30	1191.842	0.0008519	0.018891	0.019743	80.23	155.36	235.59
35	1354.741	0.0008673	0.016400	0.017267	86.52	150.30	236.82
40	1533.466	0.0008839	0.018859	0.015137	92.90	145.04	237.94
45	1728.969	0.0009020	0.012384	0.013286	99.40	139.53	238.93
50	1942.254	0.0009219	0.010751	0.011672	106.04	133.73	239.77
55	2174.382	0.0009440	0.009440	0.010257	112.81	127.62	240.43
60	2426.496	0.0009687	0.0080321	0.0090008	119.83	121.01	240.84
65	2699.843	0.0009970	0.0068907	0.0078877	127.04	113.93	240.97
70	2995.810	0.0010298	0.0058593	0.0068891	134.53	106.23	240.76
75	3316.03	0.0010691	0.0049144	0.0059835	142.43	97.62	240.05
80	3662.29	0.0011181	0.0040307	0.0051488	150.92	87.70	238.62
85	4036.81	0.0011832	0.0031751	0.0043583	160.31	75.79	236.10
90	4442.50	0.0012822	0.0022823	0.0035645	171.50	59.90	231.40
95	4883.49	0.0015205	0.0010311	0.0025516	188.92	29.92	218.84
96.006	4977.39	0.0019056	0	0.0019056	203.09	0	203.09

(*Continued*)

Appendix C.9*b* Saturated refrigerant-22 (metric units)—*continued*

Temp. °C T	Enthalpy (kJ/kg)* Sat. liq. h_f	Enthalpy (kJ/kg)* Evap. h_{fg}	Enthalpy (kJ/kg)* Sat. vapor h_g	Entropy (kJ/(kg·K))* Sat. liq. s_f	Entropy (kJ/(kg·K))* Evap. s_{fg}	Entropy (kJ/(kg·K))* Sat. vapor s_g
−100	−59.37	263.48	204.11	−0.29317	1.52159	1.22842
−95	−54.66	261.20	206.54	−0.26426	1.46397	1.19971
−90	−49.92	258.91	208.98	−0.24016	1.41356	1.17340
−85	−45.16	256.59	211.43	−0.21447	1.36369	1.14922
−80	−40.35	254.25	213.89	−0.18928	1.31624	1.12696
−75	−35.51	251.87	216.36	−0.16452	1.27098	1.10646
−70	−30.61	249.42	218.82	−0.14012	1.22771	1.08759
−65	−25.66	246.92	221.26	−0.11611	1.18621	1.07010
−60	−20.65	244.35	223.70	−0.09234	1.14629	1.05395
−55	−15.59	241.70	226.12	−0.06891	1.10792	1.03901
−50	−10.46	238.96	228.51	−0.04569	1.07081	1.02512
−45	−5.26	236.13	230.87	−0.02276	1.03495	1.01219
−40	0.00	233.20	233.20	0.00000	1.00014	1.00014
−35	5.33	230.15	235.48	0.02251	0.96638	0.98889
−30	10.72	227.00	237.72	0.04485	0.93354	0.97839
−25	16.19	223.72	239.92	0.06699	0.90152	0.96851
−20	21.73	220.33	242.05	0.08895	0.87032	0.95927
−15	27.33	216.79	244.13	0.11075	0.83977	0.95052
−10	33.01	213.13	246.14	0.13234	0.80990	0.94224
−5	38.76	209.32	248.08	0.15380	0.78057	0.93437
0	44.59	205.36	249.95	0.17178	0.75178	0.92688
5	50.48	201.24	251.73	0.19627	0.72346	0.91973
10	56.46	196.96	253.42	0.21727	0.69559	0.91286
15	62.52	192.49	255.02	0.23819	0.66802	0.90621
20	68.67	187.84	256.50	0.25899	0.64074	0.89973
25	74.91	182.97	257.88	0.27970	0.61367	0.89337
30	81.25	177.87	259.12	0.30037	0.58676	0.88713
35	87.69	172.52	260.22	0.32104	0.55982	0.88086
40	94.26	166.89	261.15	0.34167	0.53291	0.87458
45	100.96	160.94	261.90	0.36233	0.50585	0.86818
50	107.83	154.62	262.44	0.38313	0.47844	0.86157
55	114.86	147.86	262.73	0.40409	0.45058	0.85467
60	122.18	140.50	262.68	0.42547	0.42171	0.84718
65	129.73	132.54	262.27	0.44714	0.39200	0.83914
70	137.62	123.77	261.40	0.46944	0.36071	0.83015
75	145.98	113.90	259.89	0.49267	0.32714	0.81981
80	155.01	102.47	257.48	0.51735	0.29016	0.80751
85	165.09	88.60	253.69	0.54446	0.24736	0.79182
90	177.04	70.04	247.24	0.57664	0.19288	0.76952
95	196.35	34.96	231.30	0.62731	0.09493	0.72224
96.006	212.57	0	212.57	0.67090	0	0.67090

* The enthalpy and the entropy of saturated liquid R-22 are taken as zero at a temperature of −40 °C.

Source: Reprinted by permission from William L. Haberman and James E. A. John, *Engineering Thermodynamics* (Boston: Allyn & Bacon, 1980), pp. 472–473 (Table B.10).

Appendix C.10a Superheated refrigerant-22 (English units)

Abs. press. (psia)	Sat. temp. (°F)	Sat. vapor	Temperature (°F)					
p	T		−100	0	100	200	300	400
			Specific volume, v (ft^3/lbm)					
		v_g						
0.2	−155.80	188.29	223.01	285.14	347.22	409.32	471.37	533.42
0.5	−137.64	79.698	89.095	114.00	138.85	163.70	188.55	213.37
1	−122.16	41.678	44.458	56.949	69.397	81.83	94.27	106.68
2	−104.87	21.831	22.139	28.426	34.668	40.893	47.12	53.34
5	−78.62	9.3011		11.311	13.831	16.333	18.83	21.34
10	−55.58	4.8778		5.6060	6.8855	8.1464	9.399	10.65
15	−40.57	3.3412		3.7037	4.5701	5.4174	6.256	7.10
20	−29.12	2.5527		2.7521	3.4122	4.0529	4.685	5.325
40	1.63	1.3285			1.6749	2.0060	2.3281	2.657
60	22.03	0.90222			1.0952	1.3235	1.5424	1.767
80	37.76	0.68318			0.80477	0.98209	1.1495	1.323
100	50.77	0.54908			0.63003	0.77712	0.91372	1.046
120	61.95	0.45822			0.51309	0.64036	0.75651	0.8678
140	71.83	0.39243			0.42911	0.54258	0.64419	0.7409
160	80.71	0.34249			0.36568	0.46914	0.55993	0.6447
180	88.81	0.30323			0.31587	0.41194	0.49437	0.5715
200	96.27	0.27150			0.27553	0.36609	0.44190	0.51218
250	112.76	0.21351				0.28325	0.34740	0.40549
300	126.98	0.17400				0.22759	0.28431	0.33436
350	139.54	0.14514				0.18738	0.23917	0.28356
400	150.82	0.12297				0.15674	0.20524	0.24546
500	170.50	0.09053				0.11220	0.15757	0.19212
			Internal energy, u (Btu/lbm)					
		u_g						
0.2	−155.80	79.88	85.37	96.49	109.20	123.42	139.07	156.01
0.5	−137.64	81.58	85.34	96.47	109.19	123.42	139.06	156.00
1	−122.16	83.05	85.30	96.45	109.18	123.40	139.04	155.98
2	−104.87	84.72	85.22	96.41	109.15	123.38	139.02	155.95
5	−78.62	87.27		96.30	109.07	123.33	138.96	155.87
10	−55.58	89.49		96.04	108.93	123.24	138.86	155.78
15	−40.57	90.92		95.81	108.80	123.15	138.80	155.69
20	−29.12	92.00		95.57	108.66	123.06	138.74	155.60
40	1.63	94.79			108.09	122.69	138.49	155.28
60	22.03	96.55			107.50	122.32	138.23	155.02
80	37.76	97.84			106.89	121.94	137.96	154.86
100	50.77	98.85			106.25	121.55	137.70	154.77
120	61.95	99.68			105.59	121.16	137.43	154.58
140	71.83	100.37			104.89	120.75	137.15	154.41
160	80.71	100.96			104.16	120.34	136.88	154.24
180	88.81	101.46			103.38	119.92	136.60	154.07
200	96.27	101.89			102.55	119.49	136.31	153.82
250	112.76	102.71				118.36	135.59	153.29
300	126.98	103.24				117.15	134.84	152.75
350	139.54	103.54				115.85	134.06	152.20
400	150.82	103.60				114.42	133.26	151.64
500	170.50	103.01				111.05	131.55	150.48

(*Continued*)

Appendix C.10a Superheated refrigerant-22 (English units)—*continued*

Abs. press. (psia)	Sat. temp. (°F)	Sat. vapor	Temperature (°F)					
p	T		−100	0	100	200	300	400
			Enthalpy, h (Btu/lbm)					
		h_g						
0.2	−155.80	86.85	93.62	107.04	122.05	138.57	156.52	175.75
0.5	−137.64	88.96	93.59	107.02	122.04	138.56	156.51	175.74
1	−122.16	90.77	93.53	106.99	122.02	138.54	156.49	175.72
2	−104.87	92.80	93.42	106.93	121.98	138.51	156.46	175.69
5	−78.62	95.87		106.74	121.87	138.44	156.38	175.61
10	−55.58	98.52		106.41	121.67	138.31	156.26	175.49
15	−40.57	100.19		106.09	121.48	138.18	156.16	175.39
20	−29.12	101.44		105.76	121.28	138.06	156.08	175.31
40	1.63	104.63			120.49	137.54	155.72	174.95
60	22.03	106.57			119.66	137.01	155.35	174.64
80	37.76	107.95			118.80	136.48	154.98	174.45
100	50.77	109.01			117.91	135.93	154.61	174.13
120	61.95	109.85			116.98	135.38	154.23	173.85
140	71.83	110.54			116.01	134.81	153.84	173.60
160	80.71	111.10			114.99	134.23	153.46	173.33
180	88.81	111.56			113.90	133.64	153.06	173.10
200	96.27	111.93			112.75	133.03	152.67	172.78
250	112.76	112.59				131.46	151.66	172.05
300	126.98	112.90				129.78	150.62	171.31
350	139.54	112.94				127.98	149.55	170.57
400	150.82	112.70				126.02	148.45	169.81
500	170.50	111.38				121.43	146.13	168.26
			Entropy, s (Btu/(lbm·R))					
		s_g						
0.2	−155.80	0.29985	0.32028	0.35311	0.38261	0.40982	0.43515	0.45889
0.5	−137.64	0.28557	0.29917	0.33204	0.36155	0.38878	0.41411	0.43785
1	−122.16	0.27521	0.28314	0.31607	0.34561	0.37274	0.39807	0.42193
2	−104.87	0.26527	0.26700	0.30005	0.32964	0.35679	0.38212	0.40590
5	−78.62	0.25283		0.27872	0.30845	0.33566	0.36099	0.38477
10	−55.58	0.24399		0.26230	0.29229	0.31961	0.34494	0.36872
15	−40.57	0.23906		0.25248	0.28273	0.31016	0.33553	0.35931
20	−29.12	0.23566		0.24535	0.27588	0.30342	0.32884	0.35262
40	1.63	0.22780			0.25893	0.28694	0.31259	0.33637
60	22.03	0.22337			0.24855	0.27706	0.30293	0.32679
80	37.76	0.22029			0.24083	0.26987	0.29598	0.31998
100	50.77	0.21790			0.23454	0.26415	0.29050	0.31464
120	61.95	0.21593			0.22912	0.25936	0.28595	0.31024
140	71.83	0.21425			0.22428	0.25520	0.28205	0.30648
160	80.71	0.21276			0.21984	0.25149	0.27862	0.30320
180	88.81	0.21142			0.21566	0.24813	0.27554	0.30026
200	96.27	0.21018			0.21165	0.24503	0.27274	0.29760
250	112.76	0.20740				0.23814	0.26665	0.29186
300	126.98	0.20487				0.23204	0.26146	0.28705
350	139.54	0.20244				0.22641	0.25688	0.28286
400	150.82	0.20001				0.22104	0.25273	0.27914
500	170.50	0.19474				0.21034	0.24532	0.27267

Source: Reprinted by permission from William L. Haberman and James E. A. John, *Engineering Thermodynamics* (Boston: Allyn & Bacon, 1980), pp. 416–417 (Table A.11).

Appendix C.10*b* Superheated refrigerant-22 (metric units)

Abs. press. (kPa)	Sat. temp. (°C)	Sat. vapor	Temperature (°C)					
	T_g		−50	0	50	100	150	200
					Specific volume, v (m^3/kg)			
		v_g						
1	−107.61	15.885	21.455	26.263	31.070	35.876	40.685	45.492
5	−89.79	3.519	4.283	5.248	6.211	7.176	8.137	9.098
10	−80.64	1.8411	2.137	2.621	3.104	3.588	4.069	4.549
20	−70.41	0.9646	1.064	1.308	1.550	1.794	2.034	2.275
40	−58.86	0.5059	0.527	0.651	0.773	0.897	1.017	1.138
60	−51.37	0.3468	0.349	0.432	0.514	0.596	0.673	0.759
80	−45.68	0.2652		0.323	0.385	0.446	0.510	0.570
100	−41.03	0.2152		0.257	0.307	0.356	0.407	0.455
200	−25.12	0.1123		0.1260	0.1519	0.1770	0.2020	0.2260
300	−14.61	0.0766		0.0822	0.1001	0.1172	0.1331	0.1497
400	−6.52	0.0582		0.0598	0.0739	0.0871	0.0994	0.118
500	0.15	0.0469			0.0586	0.0694	0.0796	0.0895
600	5.88	0.0393			0.0482	0.0573	0.0660	0.0744
700	10.93	0.0338			0.0408	0.0488	0.0564	0.0637
800	15.47	0.0296			0.0347	0.0418	0.0489	0.0555
900	19.61	0.0263			0.0307	0.0373	0.0434	0.0493
1000	23.42	0.0237			0.0272	0.0333	0.0388	0.0442
1500	39.10	0.0155			0.0168	0.0213	0.0253	0.0294
2000	51.28	0.0113				0.0153	0.0184	0.0214
2500	61.38	0.0087				0.0116	0.0144	0.0169
3000	70.07	0.0069				0.0091	0.0117	0.0138
					Internal energy, u (kJ/kg)			
		u_g						
1	−107.61	184.53	208.93	233.47	260.97	290.87	323.67	358.81
5	−89.79	191.51	208.88	233.44	260.95	290.86	323.66	358.80
10	−80.64	195.18	208.78	233.39	260.92	290.84	323.64	358.79
20	−70.41	199.32	208.56	233.24	260.82	290.82	323.63	358.77
40	−58.86	204.01	208.09	232.94	260.59	290.79	323.62	358.75
60	−51.37	207.04	207.64	232.66	260.40	290.73	323.58	358.72
80	−45.68	209.33		232.38	260.21	290.66	323.52	358.65
100	−41.03	211.19		232.11	260.02	290.52	323.43	358.56
200	−25.12	217.40		230.84	259.29	290.07	323.13	358.41
300	−14.61	221.31		229.38	258.36	289.42	322.77	358.11
400	−6.52	224.22		227.99	257.48	288.76	322.30	357.91
500	0.15	226.55			256.66	288.25	321.90	357.60
600	5.88	228.45			255.67	287.67	321.45	357.23
700	10.93	230.07			254.80	287.02	320.94	356.75
800	15.47	231.48			253.97	286.75	320.60	356.43
900	19.61	232.72			252.84	285.86	320.05	355.93
1000	23.42	233.75			251.61	285.04	319.61	355.51
1500	39.10	237.74			245.91	281.80	317.28	353.30
2000	51.28	239.94				278.10	315.07	352.20
2500	61.38	240.85				274.17	312.35	350.21
3000	70.07	240.68				269.41	309.39	348.33

(Continued)

Appendix C.10*b* Superheated refrigerant-22 (metric units)—*continued*

Abs. press. (kPa)	Sat. temp. (°C) T_g	Sat. vapor	Temperature (°C) −50	0	50	100	150	200
			Enthalpy, h (kJ/kg)					
		h_g						
1	−107.61	200.41	230.38	259.73	292.04	326.75	364.35	404.30
5	−89.79	209.10	230.29	259.68	292.00	326.74	364.34	404.29
10	−80.64	213.59	230.15	259.60	291.96	326.72	364.33	404.28
20	−70.41	218.61	229.84	259.40	291.82	326.70	364.32	404.27
40	−58.86	224.25	229.17	258.98	291.51	326.67	364.31	404.26
60	−51.37	227.85	228.56	258.59	291.25	326.51	364.30	404.25
80	−45.68	230.55		258.22	291.01	326.34	364.28	404.23
100	−41.03	232.71		257.81	290.81	326.12	364.08	404.05
200	−25.12	239.86		256.04	289.67	325.47	363.53	403.60
300	−14.61	244.29		254.04	288.39	324.58	362.72	403.02
400	−6.52	247.50		251.91	287.04	323.60	362.08	402.62
500	0.15	250.00			285.96	322.95	361.70	402.37
600	5.88	252.03			284.59	322.05	361.05	401.87
700	10.93	253.73			283.36	321.18	360.42	401.32
800	15.47	255.16			281.73	320.19	359.72	400.82
900	19.61	256.39			280.47	319.43	359.11	400.31
1000	23.42	257.45			278.81	318.34	358.41	399.66
1500	39.10	260.99			271.11	313.75	355.23	397.40
2000	51.28	262.54				308.70	351.87	395.00
2500	61.38	262.60				303.17	348.35	392.46
3000	70.07	261.38				296.71	344.49	389.73
			Entropy, s (kJ/(kg·K))					
		s_g						
1	−107.61	1.27520	1.43157	1.55006	1.65851	1.75784	1.85237	1.94160
5	−89.79	1.17223	1.27655	1.39517	1.50370	1.60310	1.69763	1.78686
10	−80.64	1.12969	1.20937	1.32828	1.43689	1.53645	1.63098	1.72049
20	−70.41	1.08905	1.14178	1.26115	1.36998	1.46981	1.56434	1.65417
40	−58.86	1.05047	1.07252	1.19285	1.30205	1.40317	1.49770	1.58763
60	−51.37	1.02880	1.03197	1.15310	1.26268	1.36402	1.45855	1.54858
80	−45.68	1.01390		1.12447	1.23451	1.33601	1.43054	1.52067
100	−41.03	1.00240		1.10201	1.21251	1.31426	1.40924	1.49902
200	−25.12	0.96876		1.03090	1.14387	1.25603	1.35131	1.44089
300	−14.61	0.94985		0.98699	1.10230	1.20627	1.30160	1.39123
400	−6.52	0.93671		0.95345	1.07131	1.17637	1.27173	1.36163
500	0.15	0.92667			1.04749	1.15389	1.25125	1.34573
600	5.88	0.91851			1.02686	1.13460	1.23263	1.32711
700	10.93	0.91160			1.00967	1.11845	1.21698	1.31146
800	15.47	0.90558			0.99155	1.10218	1.20155	1.29603
900	19.61	0.90022			0.97826	1.09031	1.19035	1.28483
1000	23.42	0.89537			0.96455	1.07831	1.17906	1.27354
1500	39.10	0.87571			0.90752	1.03033	1.13463	1.22911
2000	51.28	0.85985				0.99257	1.10115	1.19750
2500	61.38	0.84625				0.96324	1.07357	1.17206
3000	70.07	0.83002				0.92890	1.04919	1.15023

Source: Reprinted by permission from William L. Haberman and James E. A. John, *Engineering Thermodynamics* (Boston: Allyn & Bacon, 1980), pp. 474–475 (Table B.11).

Appendix C.11a Saturated mercury (English units)

Sat. press., psia	Sat. temp., °F	Specific volume, ft³/lbm v_f	v_g	Enthalpy, Btu/lbm h_f	h_{fg}	h_g	Entropy, Btu/(lbm·R) s_f	s_{fg}	s_g
0.01	233.57	1.21×10^{-3}	3637	6.668	127.732	134.400	0.01137	0.18428	0.19565
0.02	259.88	1.21	1893	7.532	127.614	135.146	0.01259	0.17735	0.18994
0.03	276.22	1.21	1292	8.068	127.540	135.608	0.01332	0.17332	0.18664
0.05	297.97	1.21	799	8.778	127.442	136.220	0.01427	0.16821	0.18248
0.1	329.73	1.22	416	9.814	127.300	137.114	0.01561	0.16126	0.17687
0.2	364.25	1.22×10^{-3}	217.3	10.936	127.144	138.080	0.01699	0.15432	0.17131
0.3	385.92	1.22	148.6	11.639	127.047	138.686	0.01783	0.15024	0.16807
0.4	401.98	1.22	113.7	12.159	126.975	139.134	0.01844	0.14736	0.16580
0.5	415.00	1.22	92.18	12.568	126.916	139.484	0.01892	0.14511	0.16403
0.6	425.82	1.23	77.84	12.929	126.868	139.797	0.01932	0.14328	0.16260
0.8	443.50	1.23×10^{-3}	59.58	13.500	126.788	140.288	0.01994	0.14038	0.16032
1	457.72	1.24	48.42	13.959	126.724	140.683	0.02045	0.13814	0.15859
2	504.93	1.24	25.39	15.476	126.512	141.988	0.02205	0.13116	0.15321
3	535.25	1.24	17.50	16.439	126.377	142.816	0.02302	0.12706	0.15008
5	575.7	1.24	10.90	17.741	126.193	143.934	0.02430	0.12188	0.14618
7	604.7	1.25×10^{-3}	8.04	18.657	126.065	144.722	0.02516	0.11846	0.14362
10	637.0	1.25	5.81	19.685	125.919	145.604	0.02610	0.11483	0.14093
20	706.0	1.26	3.09	21.864	125.609	147.473	0.02800	0.10779	0.13579
40	784.4	1.27	1.648	24.345	125.255	149.600	0.03004	0.10068	0.13072
60	835.7	1.28	1.144	25.940	125.024	150.964	0.03127	0.09652	0.12779
80	874.8	1.29×10^{-3}	0.885	27.149	124.849	152.008	0.03218	0.09356	0.12574
100	906.8	1.29	0.725	28.152	124.706	152.858	0.03290	0.09127	0.12417
150	969.4	1.30	0.507	30.090	124.424	154.514	0.03425	0.08707	0.12132
200	1017.2	1.31	0.392	31.560	124.209	155.769	0.03523	0.08411	0.11934
250	1057.2	1.31	0.322	32.784	124.029	156.813	0.03603	0.08178	0.11781
300	1091.2	1.32×10^{-3}	0.276	33.824	123.876	157.700	0.03669	0.07989	0.11658
400	1148.4	1.32	0.215	35.565	123.620	159.185	0.03775	0.07688	0.11463
450	1173.2	1.32	0.194	36.315	123.509	159.824	0.03820	0.07566	0.11386
500	1196.0	1.33	0.177	37.006	123.406	160.412	0.03861	0.07455	0.11316
600	1236.8	1.34	0.151	38.245	123.221	161.466	0.03932	0.07264	0.11196
700	1273.3	1.34×10^{-3}	0.132	39.339	123.058	162.397	0.03993	0.07102	0.11095
800	1306.1	1.34	0.118	40.324	122.910	163.234	0.04047	0.06961	0.11008
900	1336.2	1.35	0.106	41.226	122.775	164.001	0.04095	0.06837	0.10932
1000	1364.0	1.35	0.098	42.056	122.649	164.705	0.04139	0.06726	0.10865
1100	1390.0	1.36	0.090	42.828	122.533	165.361	0.04179	0.06625	0.10804

Sources: Reprinted by permission from Lucian A. Sheldon, *Thermodynamic Properties of Mercury Vapor*, General Electric Company. Liquid densities from WADC TR-59-598. Also from William C. Reynolds and Henry C. Perkins, *Engineering Thermodynamics*, 2d ed. (New York: McGraw-Hill, 1977), p. 638 (Table B-3).

Appendix C.11*b* **Saturated mercury (metric units)**

Sat. press., MPa	Sat. temp., °C	Specific volume, m^3/kg v_g	Enthalpy, kJ/kg h_f	h_{fg}	h_g	Entropy, kJ/(kg·K) s_f	s_{fg}	s_g
0.000 06	109.2	259.6	15.13	297.20	312.33	0.0466	0.7774	0.8240
0.000 07	112.3	224.3	15.55	297.14	312.69	0.0477	0.7709	0.8186
0.000 08	115.0	197.7	15.93	297.09	313.02	0.0487	0.7654	0.8141
0.000 09	117.5	176.8	16.27	297.04	313.31	0.0496	0.7604	0.8100
0.000 10	119.7	160.1	16.58	297.00	313.58	0.0503	0.7560	0.8063
0.0002	134.9	83.18	18.67	296.71	315.38	0.0556	0.7271	0.7827
0.0004	151.5	43.29	20.93	296.40	317.33	0.0610	0.6981	0.7591
0.0006	161.8	29.57	22.33	296.21	318.54	0.0643	0.6811	0.7454
0.0008	169.4	22.57	23.37	296.06	319.43	0.0666	0.6690	0.7356
0.0010	175.5	18.31	24.21	295.95	320.16	0.0685	0.6596	0.7281
0.002	195.6	9.570	26.94	295.57	322.51	0.0744	0.6305	0.7049
0.004	217.7	5.013	29.92	295.15	325.07	0.0806	0.6013	0.6819
0.006	231.6	3.438	31.81	294.89	326.70	0.0843	0.5842	0.6685
0.008	242.0	2.632	33.21	294.70	327.91	0.0870	0.5721	0.6591
0.010	250.3	2.140	34.33	294.54	328.87	0.0892	0.5627	0.6519
0.02	278.1	1.128	38.05	294.02	332.07	0.0961	0.5334	0.6295
0.04	309.1	0.5942	42.21	293.43	335.64	0.1034	0.5039	0.6073
0.06	329.0	0.4113	44.85	293.06	337.91	0.1078	0.4869	0.5947
0.08	343.9	0.3163	46.84	292.78	339.62	0.1110	0.4745	0.5855
0.1	356.1	0.2581	48.45	292.55	341.00	0.1136	0.4649	0.5785
0.2	397.1	0.1377	53.87	291.77	345.64	0.1218	0.4353	0.5571
0.3	423.8	0.095 51	57.38	291.27	348.65	0.1268	0.4179	0.5447
0.4	444.1	0.073 78	60.03	290.89	350.92	0.1305	0.4056	0.5361
0.5	460.7	0.060 44	62.20	290.58	352.78	0.1334	0.3960	0.5294
0.6	474.9	0.051 37	64.06	290.31	354.37	0.1359	0.3881	0.5240
0.7	487.3	0.044 79	65.66	290.08	355.74	0.1380	0.3815	0.5195
0.8	498.4	0.039 78	67.11	289.87	356.98	0.1398	0.3757	0.5155
0.9	508.5	0.035 84	68.42	289.68	358.10	0.1415	0.3706	0.5121
1.0	517.8	0.032 66	69.61	289.50	359.11	0.1429	0.3660	0.5089
1.2	534.4	0.027 81	71.75	289.19	360.94	0.1455	0.3581	0.5036
1.4	549.0	0.024 29	73.63	288.92	362.55	0.1478	0.3514	0.4992
1.6	562.0	0.021 61	75.37	288.67	364.04	0.1498	0.3456	0.4954
1.8	574.0	0.019 49	76.83	288.45	365.28	0.1515	0.3405	0.4920
2.0	584.9	0.017 78	78.23	288.24	366.47	0.1531	0.3359	0.4890
2.2	595.1	0.016 37	79.54	288.05	367.59	0.1546	0.3318	0.4864
2.4	604.6	0.015 18	80.75	287.87	368.62	0.1559	0.3280	0.4839
2.6	613.5	0.014 16	81.89	287.70	369.59	0.1571	0.3245	0.4816
2.8	622.0	0.013 29	82.96	287.54	370.50	0.1583	0.3212	0.4795
3.0	630.0	0.012 52	83.97	287.39	371.36	0.1594	0.3182	0.4776
3.5	648.5	0.010 96	86.33	287.04	373.37	0.1619	0.3115	0.4734
4.0	665.1	0.009 78	88.43	286.73	375.16	0.1641	0.3056	0.4697
4.5	680.3	0.008 85	90.35	286.44	376.79	0.1660	0.3004	0.4664
5.0	694.4	0.008 09	92.11	286.18	378.29	0.1678	0.2958	0.4636
5.5	707.4	0.007 46	93.76	285.93	379.69	0.1694	0.2916	0.4610
6.0	719.7	0.006 93	95.30	285.70	381.00	0.1709	0.2878	0.4587
6.5	731.3	0.006 48	96.75	285.48	382.23	0.1723	0.2842	0.4565
7.0	742.3	0.006 09	98.12	285.28	383.40	0.1736	0.2809	0.4545
7.5	752.7	0.005 75	99.42	285.08	384.50	0.1748	0.2779	0.4527

Source: Reprinted by permission from B. V. Karlekar, *Thermodynamics for Engineers* (Englewood Cliffs, N.J.: Prentice-Hall, 1983), pp. 554–555 (Appendix E). Also reprinted by permission from Lucian A. Sheldon, *Thermodynamic Properties of Mercury Vapor*, General Electric Company.

Appendix C.12a Critical point data (English units)

Substance	Formula	Molecular mass	Temp. R	Pressure psia	Volume, ft^3/lb mole
Air	—	28.97	238.3	547.6	1.481
Ammonia	NH_3	17.03	729.8	1636	1.16
Argon	Ar	39.948	272	705	1.20
Bromine	Br_2	159.808	1052	1500	2.17
Carbon dioxide	CO_2	44.01	547.5	1071	1.51
Carbon monoxide	CO	28.011	240	507	1.49
Chlorine	Cl_2	70.906	751	1120	1.99
Deuterium (normal)	D_2	4.00	69.1	241	—
Helium	He	4.003	9.5	33.2	0.926
Helium^3	He	3.00	6.01	16.9	—
Hydrogen (normal)	H_2	2.016	59.9	188.1	1.04
Krypton	Kr	83.80	376.9	798	1.48
Neon	Ne	20.183	80.1	395	0.668
Nitrogen	N_2	28.013	227.1	492	1.44
Nitrous oxide	N_2O	44.013	557.4	1054	1.54
Oxygen	O_2	31.999	278.6	736	1.25
Sulfur dioxide	SO_2	64.063	775.2	1143	1.95
Water	H_2O	18.015	1165.3	3204	0.90
Xenon	Xe	131.30	521.55	852	1.90
Benzene	C_6H_6	78.115	1012	714	4.17
n-Butane	C_4H_{10}	58.124	765.2	551	4.08
Carbon tetrachloride	CCl_4	153.82	1001.5	661	4.42
Chloroform	$CHCl_3$	119.38	965.8	794	3.85
Dichlorodifluoromethane	CCl_2F_2	120.91	692.4	582	3.49
Dichlorofluoromethane	$CHCl_2F$	102.92	813.0	749	3.16
Ethane	C_2H_6	30.020	549.8	708	2.37
Ethyl alcohol	C_2H_5OH	46.07	929.0	926	2.68
Ethylene	C_2H_4	28.054	508.3	742	1.99
n-Hexane	C_6H_{14}	86.178	914.2	439	5.89
Methane	CH_4	16.043	343.9	673	1.59
Methyl alcohol	CH_3OH	32.042	923.7	1154	1.89
Methyl chloride	CH_3Cl	50.488	749.3	968	2.29
Propane	C_3H_8	44.097	665.9	617	3.20
Propene	C_3H_6	42.081	656.9	670	2.90
Propyne	C_3H_4	40.065	722	776	—
Trichlorofluoromethane	CCl_3F	137.37	848.1	635	3.97

Sources: Reprinted with permission from K. A. Kobe and R. E. Lynn, Jr., *Chemical Reviews*, 52: 117–236 (1953). Copyright 1953 American Chemical Society. Also reprinted from Gordon J. Van Wylen and Richard E. Sonntag, *Fundamentals of Classical Thermodynamics*, 3d ed. (New York: Wiley, 1986), p. 684 (Table A.6E). Copyright © 1986 John Wiley & Sons. Reprinted by permission of John Wiley & Sons, Inc.

Appendix C.12b Critical point data (metric units)

Substance	Formula	Molecular mass	Temp. K	Pressure MPa	Volume m^3/kgmole
Air	—	28.97	132.41	3.774	.0923
Ammonia	NH_3	17.03	405.5	11.28	.0724
Argon	Ar	39.948	151	4.86	.0749
Bromine	Br_2	159.808	584	10.34	.1355
Carbon dioxide	CO_2	44.01	304.2	7.39	.0943
Carbon monoxide	CO	28.011	133	3.50	.0930
Chlorine	Cl_2	70.906	417	7.71	.1242
Deuterium (normal)	D_2	4.00	38.4	1.66	—
Helium	He	4.003	5.3	0.23	.0578
$Helium^3$	He	3.00	3.3	0.12	—
Hydrogen (normal)	H_2	2.016	33.3	1.30	.0649
Krypton	Kr	83.80	209.4	5.50	.0924
Neon	Ne	20.183	44.5	2.73	.0417
Nitrogen	N_2	28.013	126.2	3.39	.0899
Nitrous oxide	N_2O	44.013	309.7	7.27	.0961
Oxygen	O_2	31.999	154.8	5.08	.0780
Sulfur dioxide	SO_2	64.063	430.7	7.88	.1217
Water	H_2O	18.015	647.3	22.09	.0568
Xenon	Xe	131.30	289.8	5.88	.1186
Benzene	C_6H_6	78.115	562	4.92	.2603
n-Butane	C_4H_{10}	58.124	425.2	3.80	.2547
Carbon tetrachloride	CCl_4	153.82	556.4	4.56	.2759
Chloroform	$CHCl_3$	119.38	536.6	5.47	.2403
Dichlorodifluoromethane	CCl_2F_2	120.91	384.7	4.01	.2179
Dichlorofluoromethane	$CHCl_2F$	102.92	451.7	5.17	.1973
Ethane	C_2H_6	30.070	305.5	4.88	.1480
Ethyl alcohol	C_2H_5OH	46.07	516	6.38	.1673
Ethylene	C_2H_4	28.054	282.4	5.12	.1242
n-Hexane	C_6H_{14}	86.178	507.9	3.03	.3677
Methane	CH_4	16.043	191.1	4.64	.0993
Methyl alcohol	CH_3OH	32.042	513.2	7.95	.1180
Methyl chloride	CH_3Cl	50.488	416.3	6.68	.1430
Propane	C_3H_8	44.097	370	4.26	.1998
Propene	C_3H_6	42.081	365	4.62	.1810
Propyne	C_3H_4	40.065	401	5.35	—
Trichlorofluoromethane	CCl_3F	137.37	471.2	4.38	.2478

Sources: Reprinted with permission from K. A. Kobe and R. E. Lynn, Jr., *Chemical Reviews*, 52: 117–236 (1953). Copyright 1953 American Chemical Society. Also reprinted from Gordon J. Van Wylen and Richard E. Sonntag, *Fundamentals of Classical Thermodynamics*, 3d ed. (New York: Wiley, 1986), p. 685 (Table A.6SI). Copyright © 1986 John Wiley & Sons. Reprinted by permission of John Wiley & Sons, Inc.

Appendix C.13a Gas constant data (English units)[†]

Substance	M lbm/lbmole	c_p Btu/(lbm·R)	$\bar{c}_p$ Btu/(lbmole·R)	c_v Btu/(lbm·R)	$\bar{c}_v$ Btu/(lbmole·R)	R ft·lbf/(lbm·R)	R Btu/(lbm·R)	$k = c_p/c_v$
Argon, Ar	39.94	0.125	4.99	0.075	3.00	38.69	0.0497	1.67
Helium, He	4.003	1.24	4.96	0.744	2.97	386.0	0.4961	1.67
Hydrogen, H_2	2.016	3.42	6.89	2.435	4.90	766.5	0.9850	1.40
Nitrogen, N_2	28.02	0.248	6.95	0.177	4.96	55.15	0.0709	1.40
Oxygen, O_2	32.00	0.219	7.01	0.157	5.02	48.29	0.0621	1.39
Carbon monoxide, CO	28.01	0.249	6.97	0.178	4.98	55.17	0.0709	1.40
Air	28.97	0.240	6.95	0.172	4.96	53.34	0.0685	1.40
Water vapor, H_2O	18.016	0.446	8.04	0.336	6.05	85.78	0.1102	1.33
Methane, CH_4	16.04	0.532	8.53	0.408	6.54	96.3	0.1238	1.30
Carbon dioxide, CO_2	44.01	0.202	8.89	0.157	6.90	35.1	0.0451	1.29
Sulfur dioxide, SO_2	64.07	0.154	9.87	0.123	7.88	24.1	0.0310	1.25
Acetylene, C_2H_2	26.04	0.409	10.65	0.333	8.66	59.3	0.0763	1.23
Ethylene, C_2H_4	28.05	0.410	11.50	0.339	9.51	55.1	0.0708	1.21
Ethane, C_2H_6	30.07	0.422	12.69	0.356	10.70	51.4	0.0660	1.19
Propane, C_3H_8	44.09	0.404	17.81	0.358	15.82	35.0	0.0450	1.13
Isobutane, C_4H_{10}	58.12	0.420	24.41	0.386	22.42	26.0	0.0342	1.09

[†] $R = \mathscr{R}/M$ and $c_v = c_p - R$.

Source: Reprinted with permission from William C. Reynolds and Henry C. Perkins, *Engineering Thermodynamics*, 2d ed. (New York: McGraw-Hill, 1977), p. 641 (Table B-6a).

Appendix C.13b Gas constant data (metric units)[†]

Substance	M kg/kgmole	c_p kJ/(kg·K)	$\bar{c}_p$ kJ/(kgmole·K)	c_v kJ/(kg·K)	$\bar{c}_v$ kJ/(kgmole·K)	R kJ/(kg·K)	k c_p/c_v
Argon, Ar	39.94	0.523	20.89	0.315	12.57	0.208	1.67
Helium, He	4.003	5.200	20.81	3.123	12.50	2.077	1.67
Hydrogen, H_2	2.016	14.32	28.86	10.19	20.55	4.124	1.40
Nitrogen, N_2	28.02	1.038	29.08	0.742	20.77	0.296	1.40
Oxygen, O_2	32.00	0.917	29.34	0.657	21.03	0.260	1.39
Carbon monoxide, CO	28.01	1.042	29.19	0.745	20.88	0.297	1.40
Air	28.97	1.004	29.09	0.718	20.78	0.286	1.40
Water vapor, H_2O	18.016	1.867	33.64	1.406	25.33	0.461	1.33
Carbon dioxide, CO_2	44.01	0.845	37.19	0.656	28.88	0.189	1.29
Sulfur dioxide, SO_2	64.07	0.644	41.26	0.514	32.94	0.130	1.25
Methane, CH_4	16.04	2.227	35.72	1.709	27.41	0.518	1.30
Propane, C_3H_8	44.09	1.691	74.56	1.502	66.25	0.189	1.13

[†] The R values in this table were determined from $R = \mathscr{R}/M$, and the c_v values from $c_v = c_p - R$. For purposes of internal consistency more digits have been reported than justified by the experimental data. In calculations of entropy changes using the perfect-gas equation of state, it is recommended that the value of k be computed to calculator accuracy.

Source: Reprinted with permission from William C. Reynolds and Henry C. Perkins, *Engineering Thermodynamics*, 2d ed. (New York: McGraw-Hill, 1977), p. 642 (Table B-6b).

Appendix C.14a Constant pressure specific heat ideal gas temperature relations (English units)

$$\bar{c}_p = \frac{\text{Btu}}{\text{lbmole}\cdot\text{R}} \qquad \theta = \frac{T(\text{Rankine})}{180}$$

Gas		Range R	Max error %
N_2	$\bar{c}_p = 9.3355 - 122.56\theta^{-1.5} + 256.38\theta^{-2} - 196.08\theta^{-3}$	540–6300	0.43
O_2	$\bar{c}_p = 8.9465 + 4.8044 \times 10^{-3}\theta^{1.5} - 42.679\theta^{-1.5} + 56.615\theta^{-2}$	540–6300	0.30
H_2	$\bar{c}_p = 13.505 - 167.96\theta^{-0.75} + 278.44\theta^{-1} - 134.01\theta^{-1.5}$	540–6300	0.60
CO	$\bar{c}_p = 16.526 - 0.16841\theta^{0.75} - 47.985\theta^{-0.5} + 42.246\theta^{-0.75}$	540–6300	0.42
OH	$\bar{c}_p = 19.490 - 14.185\theta^{0.25} + 4.1418\theta^{0.75} - 1.0196\theta$	540–6300	0.43
NO	$\bar{c}_p = 14.169 - 0.40861\theta^{0.5} - 16877\theta^{-0.5} + 17.899\theta^{-1.5}$	540–6300	0.34
H_2O	$\bar{c}_p = 34.190 - 43.868\theta^{0.25} + 19.778\theta^{0.5} - 0.88407\theta$	540–6300	0.43
CO_2	$\bar{c}_p = -0.89286 + 7.2967\theta^{0.5} - 0.98074\theta + 5.7835 \times 10^{-3}\theta^2$	540–6300	0.19
NO_2	$\bar{c}_p = 11.005 + 51.650\theta^{-0.5} - 86.916\theta^{-0.75} + 55.580\theta^{-2}$	540–6300	0.26
CH_4	$\bar{c}_p = -160.82 + 105.10\theta^{0.25} - 5.9452\theta^{0.75} + 77.408\theta^{-0.5}$	540–3600	0.15
C_2H_4	$\bar{c}_p = -22.800 + 29.433\theta^{0.5} - 8.5185\theta^{0.75} + 43.683\theta^{-3}$	540–3600	0.07
C_2H_6	$\bar{c}_p = 1.648 + 4.124\theta - 0.153\theta^2 + 1.74 \times 10^{-3}\theta^3$	540–2700	0.83
C_3H_8	$\bar{c}_p = -0.966 + 7.279\theta - 0.3755\theta^2 + 7.58 \times 10^{-3}\theta^3$	540–2700	0.40
C_4H_{10}	$\bar{c}_p = 0.945 + 8.873\theta - 0.438\theta^2 + 8.36 \times 10^{-3}\theta^3$	540–2700	0.54

Sources: Reprinted by permission of the authors from T. C. Scott and R. E. Sonntag, University of Michigan, unpublished (1971), except C_2H_6, C_3H_8, C_4H_{10} from K. A. Kobe, *Petroleum Refiner* 28, no. 2, 113 (1949). Also reprinted from Gordon J. Van Wylen and Richard E. Sonntag, *Fundamentals of Classical Thermodynamics*, 3d ed. (New York: Wiley, 1986), p. 688 (Table A.9E) Copyright © 1986 John Wiley & Sons. Reprinted by permission of John Wiley & Sons, Inc.

Appendix C.14*b* Constant pressure specific heat ideal gas temperature relations (metric units)

$$\bar{c}_p = \frac{\text{kJ}}{\text{kgmole}\cdot\text{K}} \qquad \theta = \frac{T(\text{Kelvin})}{100}$$

Gas		Range K	Max. error %
N_2	$\bar{c}_p = 39.060 - 512.79\theta^{-1.5} + 1072.7\theta^{-2} - 820.40\theta^{-3}$	300–3500	0.43
O_2	$\bar{c}_p = 37.432 + 0.020\,102\theta^{1.5} - 178.57\theta^{-1.5} + 236.88\theta^{-2}$	300–3500	0.30
H_2	$\bar{c}_p = 56.505 - 702.74\theta^{-0.75} + 1165.0\theta^{-1} - 560.70\theta^{-1.5}$	300–3500	0.60
CO	$\bar{c}_p = 69.145 - 0.704\,63\theta^{0.75} - 200.77\theta^{-0.5} + 176.76\theta^{-0.75}$	300–3500	0.42
OH	$\bar{c}_p = 81.546 - 59.350\theta^{0.25} + 17.329\theta^{0.75} - 4.2660\theta$	300–3500	0.43
NO	$\bar{c}_p = 59.283 - 1.7096\theta^{0.5} - 70.613\theta^{-0.5} + 74.889\theta^{-1.5}$	300–3500	0.34
H_2O	$\bar{c}_p = 143.05 - 183.54\theta^{0.25} + 82.751\theta^{0.5} - 3.6989\theta$	300–3500	0.43
CO_2	$\bar{c}_p = -3.7357 + 30.529\theta^{0.5} - 4.1034\theta + 0.024\,198\theta^2$	300–3500	0.19
NO_2	$\bar{c}_p = 46.045 + 216.10\theta^{-0.5} - 363.66\theta^{-0.75} + 232.550\theta^{-2}$	300–3500	0.26
CH_4	$\bar{c}_p = -672.87 + 439.74\theta^{0.25} - 24.875\theta^{0.75} + 323.88\theta^{-0.5}$	300–2000	0.15
C_2H_4	$\bar{c}_p = -95.395 + 123.15\theta^{0.5} - 35.641\theta^{0.75} + 182.77\theta^{-3}$	300–2000	0.07
C_2H_6	$\bar{c}_p = 6.895 + 17.26\theta - 0.6402\theta^2 + 0.007\,28\theta^3$	300–1500	0.83
C_3H_8	$\bar{c}_p = -4.042 + 30.46\theta - 1.571\theta^2 + 0.031\,71\theta^3$	300–1500	0.40
C_4H_{10}	$\bar{c}_p = 3.954 + 37.12\theta - 1.833\theta^2 + 0.034\,98\theta^3$	300–1500	0.54

Sources: Reprinted by permission of the authors from T. C. Scott and R. E. Sonntag, University of Michigan, unpublished (1971), except C_2H_6, C_3H_8, C_4H_{10} from K. A. Kobe, *Petroleum Refiner* 28, no. 2, 113 (1949). Also reprinted from Gordon J. Van Wylen and Richard E. Sonntag, *Fundamentals of Classical Thermodynamics*, 3d ed. (New York: Wiley, 1986), p. 688 (Table A.9SI). Copyright © 1986 John Wiley & Sons. Reprinted by permission of John Wiley & Sons, Inc.

Appendix C.15a Equation of state constants (English units)

Gas	van der Waal constants[a]		
	R, ft·lbf/(lbm·R)	a, ft^4·lbf/lbm^2	b, ft^3/lbm
Air	53.34	867	0.020
Ammonia	90.74	7809	0.035
Butane (n)	26.59	2199	0.032
Carbon dioxide	35.11	1012	0.016
Carbon monoxide	55.17	1004	0.023
Helium	386.04	1132	0.093
Hydrogen	766.53	32820	0.212
Methane	96.32	4763	0.043
Nitrogen	55.16	933	0.022
Oxygen	48.29	721	0.016
Propane	35.04	2585	0.033
Refrigerant-12	12.78	393	0.013
Water vapor	85.78	9130	0.027

[a] The values of R, a, and b can be obtained from $R = \mathscr{R}/M$, $a = (27/64)(RT_c)^2/p_c$, and $b = RT_c/(8p_c)$, where M is the molecular mass and T_c and p_c are the temperature and pressure at the critical state.

Appendix C.15a Equation of state constants (English units)—*continued*

Gas	Beattie-Bridgeman constants				
	$a \times 10^3$, ft^3/lbm	A_o, ft^4·lbf/lbm^2	$b \times 10^3$, ft^3/lbm	$B_o \times 10^2$, ft^3/lbm	$c \times 10^{-6}$, (ft·R)^3/lbm
Air	10.7	842.7	−24.7	0.255	0.1398
Ammonia	160.0	4480.7	179.8	3.21	26.1656
Butane (n)	33.5	286.1	26.0	6.79	5.6266
Carbon dioxide	26.0	1404.3	26.3	3.81	1.4008
Carbon monoxide	14.9	930.6	−0.395	2.88	0.1399
Helium	239.0	733.2	0.0	5.60	0.0009
Hydrogen	−40.2	26338.5	−346.2	16.67	0.0234
Methane	18.5	4809.8	−15.8	5.58	0.7469
Nitrogen	14.9	929.9	−3.96	2.88	0.1398
Oxygen	12.8	790.7	2.11	0.232	0.1400
Propane	26.6	333.0	15.6	6.58	2.5430

(Continued)

Appendix C.15a **Equation of state constants (English units)—*continued***

Gas	Redlich-Kwong constants[b] a, $(ft^3/lbm)^2(R)^{1/2}$ (psia)	b, ft^3/lbm
Air	13520	0.01397
Ammonia	214970	0.02435
Butane (n)	61700	0.02222
Carbon dioxide	23970	0.01080
Carbon monoxide	15900	0.01571
Helium	3707	0.06646
Hydrogen	257500	0.14690
Methane	89750	0.02961
Nitrogen	14270	0.01532
Oxygen	12190	0.01100
Propane	67590	0.02275
Refrigerant-12	10510	0.00915
Water vapor	316030	0.01877

[b] These can be calculated from critical state data as $a = (2.9686 \times 10^{-3})(R^2 T_c^{2.5}/p_c)$ and $b = (6.0167 \times 10^{-4})(RT_c/p_c)$, where R is the specific gas constant in ft·lbf/(lbm·R), T_c is in R, and p_c is in psia.

Source: Reprinted from Gordon J. Van Wylen and Richard E. Sonntag, *Fundamentals of Classical Thermodynamics, SI Version*, 2d ed. (New York: Wiley, 1978). Copyright © 1978 John Wiley & Sons. Reprinted by permission of John Wiley & Sons, Inc.

Appendix C.15*b* **Equations of state constants (SI units)**

Gas	van der Waal constants[a] R, kJ/(kg·K)	a, $kN \cdot m^4/kg^2$	$b \times 10^3$, m^3/kg
Air	0.287	0.162	1.25
Ammonia	0.488	1.457	2.18
Butane (n)	0.143	0.410	2.00
Carbon dioxide	0.189	0.189	1.00
Carbon monoxide	0.297	0.187	1.44
Helium	2.077	0.211	5.81
Hydrogen	4.124	6.125	13.24
Methane	0.518	0.889	2.68
Nitrogen	0.297	0.174	1.37
Oxygen	0.260	0.135	1.00
Propane	0.189	0.482	2.06
Refrigerant-12	0.069	0.073	0.81
Water vapor	0.462	1.704	1.69

[a] The values of R, a, and b can be obtained from $R = \mathcal{R}/M$, $a = (27/64)(RT_c)^2/p_c$, and $b = RT_c/(8p_c)$, where M is the molecular mass and T_c and p_c are the temperature and pressure at the critical state.

(*Continued*)

Appendix C.15*b* Equations of state constants (SI units)—*continued*

Gas	Beattie-Bridgeman constants				
	$a \times 10^4$, m^3/kg	A_o, $m^4 \cdot kN/kg^2$	$b \times 10^4$, m^3/kg	B_o, m^3/kg	$c \times 10^{-6}$, $(m \cdot K)^3/kg$
Air	6.66	0.157	−15.3	0.159	14.98
Ammonia	100.1	0.836	112.0	0.200	2800.82
Butane (*n*)	20.92	0.053	16.2	0.424	602.29
Carbon dioxide	16.22	0.262	16.5	0.238	149.94
Carbon monoxide	9.35	0.174	−0.25	0.180	14.96
Helium	149.3	0.137	0.0	0.350	0.0997
Hydrogen	−25.1	4.914	−216.0	1.042	2.50
Methane	11.53	0.897	−9.85	0.349	79.93
Nitrogen	9.35	0.173	−2.47	0.180	14.96
Oxygen	8.00	0.147	1.31	0.145	15.00
Propane	16.60	0.062	9.73	0.411	272.22

(*Continued*)

Appendix C.15*b* Equations of state constants (SI units)—*continued*

Gas	Redlich-Kwong constants[b]	
	a, $(m^3/kg)^2(K)^{1/2}(kPa)$	$b \times 10^3$, m^3/kg
Air	1.881	0.8721
Ammonia	29.91	1.520
Butane (*n*)	8.584	1.387
Carbon dioxide	3.335	0.6742
Carbon monoxide	2.212	0.9808
Helium	0.5157	4.149
Hydrogen	35.82	9.169
Methane	12.49	1.848
Nitrogen	1.985	0.9564
Oxygen	1.696	0.6867
Propane	9.403	1.420
Refrigerant-12	1.462	0.5711
Water vapor	43.97	1.172

[b] These can be calculated from critical state data as $a = 0.42748(R^2 T_c^{2.5}/p_c)$ and $b = 0.08664(RT_c/p_c)$, where R is the specific gas constant in kJ/(kg·K), T_c is in K, and p_c is in kPa.

Source: Reprinted from Gordon J. Van Wylen and Richard E. Sonntag, *Fundamentals of Classical Thermodynamics, SI Version*, 2d ed. (New York: Wiley, 1978).

Appendix C.16a **Air tables (English units)**
Reference level: 0 R and 1 atm
Absolute entropies may be calculated from

$$s = \phi - \mathscr{R}\ln(p/p^{\circ}) + 1.0 \text{ Btu/(lbm·R)}$$

where p° is the reference pressure of 1 atm.

Temp., R	h Btu/lbm	p_r	u Btu/lbm	v_r	ϕ Btu/(lbm·R)
200	47.67	0.04320	33.96	1714.9	0.36303
220	52.46	0.06026	37.38	1352.5	0.38584
240	57.25	0.08165	40.80	1088.8	0.40666
260	62.03	0.10797	44.21	892.0	0.42582
280	66.82	0.13986	47.63	741.6	0.44356
300	71.61	0.17795	51.04	624.5	0.46007
320	76.40	0.22290	54.46	531.8	0.47550
340	81.18	0.27545	57.87	457.2	0.49002
360	85.97	0.3363	61.29	396.6	0.50369
380	90.75	0.4061	64.70	346.6	0.51663
400	95.53	0.4858	68.11	305.0	0.52890
420	100.32	0.5760	71.52	270.1	0.54058
440	105.11	0.6776	74.93	240.6	0.55172
460	109.90	0.7913	78.36	215.33	0.56235
480	114.69	0.9182	81.77	193.65	0.57255
500	119.48	1.0590	85.20	174.90	0.58233
520	124.27	1.2147	88.62	158.58	0.59173
540	129.06	1.3860	92.04	144.32	0.60078
560	133.86	1.5742	95.47	131.78	0.60950
580	138.66	1.7800	98.90	120.70	0.61793
600	143.47	2.005	102.34	110.88	0.62607
620	148.28	2.249	105.78	102.12	0.63395
640	153.09	2.514	109.21	94.30	0.64159
660	157.92	2.801	112.67	87.27	0.64902
680	162.73	3.111	116.12	80.96	0.65621
700	167.56	3.446	119.58	75.25	0.66321
720	172.39	3.806	123.04	70.07	0.67002
740	177.23	4.193	126.51	65.38	0.67665
760	182.08	4.607	129.99	61.10	0.68312
780	186.94	5.051	133.47	57.20	0.68942
800	191.81	5.526	136.97	53.63	0.69558
820	196.69	6.033	140.47	50.35	0.70160
840	201.56	6.573	143.98	47.34	0.70747
860	206.46	7.149	147.50	44.57	0.71323
880	211.35	7.761	151.02	42.01	0.71886
900	216.26	8.411	154.57	39.64	0.72438
920	221.18	9.102	158.12	37.44	0.72979
940	226.11	9.834	161.68	35.41	0.73509
960	231.06	10.610	165.26	33.52	0.74030
980	236.02	11.430	168.83	31.76	0.74540
1000	240.98	12.298	172.43	30.12	0.75042
1020	245.97	13.215	176.04	28.59	0.75536
1040	250.95	14.182	179.66	27.17	0.76019
1060	255.96	15.203	183.29	25.82	0.76496
1080	260.97	16.278	186.93	24.58	0.76964
1100	265.99	17.413	190.58	23.40	0.77426
1120	271.03	18.604	194.25	22.30	0.77880
1140	276.08	19.858	197.94	21.27	0.78326
1160	281.14	21.18	201.63	20.293	0.78767
1180	286.21	22.56	205.33	19.377	0.79201
1200	291.30	24.01	209.05	18.514	0.79628
1220	296.41	25.53	212.78	17.700	0.80050
1240	301.52	27.13	216.53	16.932	0.80466
1260	306.65	28.80	220.28	16.205	0.80876

(*Continued*)

Appendix C.16a Air tables (English units)—*continued*

Temp., R	h Btu/lbm	p_r	u Btu/lbm	v_r	ϕ Btu/(lbm·R)
1280	311.79	30.55	224.05	15.518	0.81280
1300	316.94	32.39	227.83	14.868	0.81680
1320	322.11	34.31	231.63	14.253	0.82075
1340	327.29	36.31	235.43	13.670	0.82464
1360	332.48	38.41	239.25	13.118	0.82848
1380	337.68	40.59	243.08	12.593	0.83229
1400	342.90	42.88	246.93	12.095	0.83604
1420	348.14	45.26	250.79	11.622	0.83975
1440	353.37	47.75	254.66	11.172	0.84341
1460	358.63	50.34	258.54	10.743	0.84704
1480	363.89	53.04	262.44	10.336	0.85062
1500	369.17	55.86	266.34	9.948	0.85416
1520	374.47	58.78	270.26	9.578	0.85767
1540	379.77	61.83	274.20	9.226	0.86113
1560	385.08	65.00	278.13	8.890	0.86456
1580	390.40	68.30	282.09	8.569	0.86794
1600	395.74	71.73	286.06	8.263	0.87130
1620	401.09	75.29	290.04	7.971	0.87462
1640	406.45	78.99	294.03	7.691	0.87791
1660	411.82	82.83	298.02	7.424	0.88116
1680	417.20	86.82	302.04	7.168	0.88439
1700	422.59	90.95	306.06	6.924	0.88758
1720	428.00	95.24	310.09	6.690	0.89074
1740	433.41	99.69	314.13	6.465	0.89387
1760	438.83	104.30	318.18	6.251	0.89697
1780	444.26	109.08	322.24	6.045	0.90003
1800	449.71	114.03	326.32	5.847	0.90308
1820	455.17	119.16	330.40	5.658	0.90609
1840	460.63	124.47	334.50	5.476	0.90908
1860	466.12	129.95	338.61	5.302	0.91203
1880	471.60	135.64	342.73	5.134	0.91497
1900	477.09	141.51	346.85	4.974	0.91788
1920	482.60	147.59	350.98	4.819	0.92076
1940	488.12	153.87	355.12	4.670	0.92362
1960	493.64	160.37	359.28	4.527	0.92645
1980	499.17	167.07	363.43	4.390	0.92926
2000	504.71	174.00	367.61	4.258	0.93205
2020	510.26	181.16	371.79	4.130	0.93481
2040	515.82	188.54	375.98	4.008	0.93756
2060	521.39	196.16	380.18	3.890	0.94026
2080	526.97	204.02	384.39	3.777	0.94296
2100	532.55	212.1	388.60	3.667	0.94564
2120	538.15	220.5	392.83	3.561	0.94829
2140	543.74	229.1	397.05	3.460	0.95092
2160	549.35	238.0	401.29	3.362	0.95352
2180	554.97	247.2	405.53	3.267	0.95611
2200	560.59	256.6	409.78	3.176	0.95868
2220	566.23	266.3	414.05	3.088	0.96123
2240	571.86	276.3	418.31	3.003	0.96376
2260	577.51	286.6	422.59	2.921	0.96626
2280	583.16	297.2	426.87	2.841	0.96876
2300	588.82	308.1	431.16	2.765	0.97123
2320	594.49	319.4	435.46	2.691	0.97369
2340	600.16	330.9	439.76	2.619	0.97611
2360	605.84	342.8	444.07	2.550	0.97853
2380	611.53	355.0	448.38	2.483	0.98092
2400	617.22	367.6	452.70	2.419	0.98331

Sources: Abridged from Joseph H. Keenan and Joseph Kaye, *Gas Tables* (New York: Wiley, 1948). Copyright © 1948 John Wiley & Sons. Reprinted by permission of John Wiley & Sons, Inc. Also reprinted by permission from J. P. Holman, *Thermodynamics*, 3d ed. (New York: McGraw-Hill, 1980), pp. 745–747 (Table A-17).

Appendix C.16*b* **Air tables (metric units)**
Reference level: 0 K and 1 atm
Absolute entropies may be calculated from

$$s = \phi - \mathcal{R} \ln(p/p^{\circ}) + 4.1869 \text{ kJ/(kg·K)}$$

where p° is the reference pressure of 1 atm.

T, K	h, kJ/kg	p_r	u, kJ/kg	v_r	ϕ kJ/(kg·K)
100	99.76	0.029 90	71.06	2230	1.4143
110	109.77	0.041 71	78.20	1758.4	1.5098
120	119.79	0.056 52	85.34	1415.7	1.5971
130	129.81	0.074 74	92.51	1159.8	1.6773
140	139.84	0.096 81	99.67	964.2	1.7515
150	149.86	0.123 18	106.81	812.0	1.8206
160	159.87	0.154 31	113.95	691.4	1.8853
170	169.89	0.190 68	121.11	594.5	1.9461
180	179.92	0.232 79	128.28	515.6	2.0033
190	189.94	0.281 14	135.40	450.6	2.0575
200	199.96	0.3363	142.56	396.6	2.1088
210	209.97	0.3987	149.70	351.2	2.1577
220	219.99	0.4690	156.84	312.8	2.2043
230	230.01	0.5477	163.98	280.0	2.2489
240	240.03	0.6355	171.15	251.8	2.2915
250	250.05	0.7329	178.29	227.45	2.3325
260	260.09	0.8405	185.45	206.26	2.3717
270	270.12	0.9590	192.59	187.74	2.4096
280	280.14	1.0889	199.78	171.45	2.4461
290	290.17	1.2311	206.92	157.07	2.4813
300	300.19	1.3860	214.09	144.32	2.5153
310	310.24	1.5546	221.27	132.96	2.5483
320	320.29	1.7375	228.45	122.81	2.5802
330	330.34	1.9352	235.65	113.70	2.6111
340	340.43	2.149	242.86	105.51	2.6412
350	350.48	2.379	250.05	98.11	2.6704
360	360.58	2.626	257.23	91.40	2.6987
370	370.67	2.892	264.47	85.31	2.7264
380	380.77	3.176	271.72	79.77	2.7534
390	390.88	3.481	278.96	74.71	2.7796
400	400.98	3.806	286.19	70.07	2.8052
410	411.12	4.153	293.45	65.83	2.8302
420	421.26	4.522	300.73	61.93	2.8547
430	431.43	4.915	308.03	58.34	2.8786
440	441.61	5.332	315.34	55.02	2.9020
450	451.83	5.775	322.66	51.96	2.9249
460	462.01	6.245	329.99	49.11	2.9473
470	472.25	6.742	337.34	46.48	2.9693
480	482.48	7.268	344.74	44.04	2.9909
490	492.74	7.824	352.11	41.76	3.0120
500	503.02	8.411	359.53	39.64	3.0328
510	513.32	9.031	366.97	37.65	3.0532
520	523.63	9.684	374.39	35.80	3.0733
530	533.98	10.372	381.88	34.07	3.0930
540	544.35	11.097	389.40	32.45	3.1124
550	554.75	11.858	396.89	30.92	3.1314
560	565.17	12.659	404.44	29.50	3.1502
570	575.57	13.500	411.98	28.15	3.1686
580	586.04	14.382	419.56	26.89	3.1868
590	596.53	15.309	427.17	25.70	3.2047
600	607.02	16.278	434.80	24.58	3.2223
610	617.53	17.297	442.43	23.51	3.2397
620	628.07	18.360	450.13	22.52	3.2569
630	638.65	19.475	457.83	21.57	3.2738
640	649.21	20.64	465.55	20.674	3.2905

(*Continued*)

Appendix C.16b Air tables (metric units)—*continued*

T, K	h, kJ/kg	p_r	u, kJ/kg	v_r	ϕ kJ/(kg·K)
650	659.84	21.86	473.32	19.828	3.3069
660	670.47	23.13	481.06	19.026	3.3232
670	681.15	24.46	488.88	18.266	3.3392
680	691.82	25.85	496.65	17.543	3.3551
690	702.52	27.29	504.51	16.857	3.3707
700	713.27	28.80	512.37	16.205	3.3861
710	724.01	30.38	520.26	15.585	3.4014
720	734.20	31.92	527.72	15.027	3.4156
730	745.62	33.72	536.12	14.434	3.4314
740	756.44	35.50	544.05	13.900	3.4461
750	767.30	37.35	552.05	13.391	3.4607
760	778.21	39.27	560.08	12.905	3.4751
770	789.10	41.27	568.10	12.440	3.4894
780	800.03	43.35	576.15	11.998	3.5035
790	810.98	45.51	584.22	11.575	3.5174
800	821.94	47.75	592.34	11.172	3.5312
810	832.96	50.08	600.46	10.785	3.5449
820	843.97	52.49	608.62	10.416	3.5584
830	855.01	55.00	616.79	10.062	3.5718
840	866.09	57.60	624.97	9.724	3.5850
850	877.16	60.29	633.21	9.400	3.5981
860	888.28	63.09	641.44	9.090	3.6111
870	899.42	65.98	649.70	8.792	3.6240
880	910.56	68.98	658.00	8.507	3.6367
890	921.75	72.08	666.31	8.233	3.6493
900	932.94	75.29	674.63	7.971	3.6619
910	944.15	78.61	682.98	7.718	3.6743
920	955.38	82.05	691.33	7.476	3.6865
930	966.64	85.60	699.73	7.244	3.6987
940	977.92	89.28	708.13	7.020	3.7108
950	989.22	93.08	716.57	6.805	3.7227
960	1000.53	97.00	725.01	6.599	3.7346
970	1011.88	101.06	733.48	6.400	3.7463
980	1023.25	105.24	741.99	6.209	3.7580
990	1034.63	109.57	750.48	6.025	3.7695
1000	1046.03	114.03	759.02	5.847	3.7810
1020	1068.89	123.12	775.67	5.521	3.8030
1040	1091.85	133.34	793.35	5.201	3.8259
1060	1114.85	143.91	810.61	4.911	3.8478
1080	1137.93	155.15	827.94	4.641	3.8694
1100	1161.07	167.07	845.34	4.390	3.8906
1120	1184.28	179.71	862.85	4.156	3.9116
1140	1207.54	193.07	880.37	3.937	3.9322
1160	1230.90	207.24	897.98	3.732	3.9525
1180	1254.34	222.2	915.68	3.541	3.9725
1200	1277.79	238.0	933.40	3.362	3.9922
1220	1301.33	254.7	951.19	3.194	4.0117
1240	1324.89	272.3	969.01	3.037	4.0308
1260	1348.55	290.8	986.92	2.889	4.0497
1280	1372.25	310.4	1004.88	2.750	4.0684
1300	1395.97	330.9	1022.88	2.619	4.0868
1320	1419.77	352.5	1040.93	2.497	4.1049
1340	1443.61	375.3	1059.03	2.381	4.1229
1360	1467.50	399.1	1077.17	2.272	4.1406
1380	1491.43	424.2	1095.36	2.169	4.1580
1400	1515.41	450.5	1113.62	2.072	4.1753
1420	1539.44	478.0	1131.90	1.9808	4.1923
1440	1563.49	506.9	1150.23	1.8942	4.2092
1460	1587.61	537.1	1168.61	1.8124	4.2258
1480	1611.80	568.8	1187.03	1.7350	4.2422
1500	1635.99	601.9	1205.47	1.6617	4.2585

Sources: Adapted to SI units from Joseph H. Keenan and Joseph Kaye, *Gas Tables* (New York: Wiley, 1948). Copyright © 1948 John Wiley & Sons. Reprinted by permission of John Wiley & Sons, Inc. Also reprinted by permission from J. P. Holman, *Thermodynamics*, 3d ed. (New York: McGraw-Hill, 1980), pp. 748–750 (Table A-17M).

Appendix C.16c Other gases (English units)[†]

Reference level: 0 R and 1 atm; h in Btu/lbm mol; ϕ in Btu/(lbmole·R)

Absolute entropies at other pressures may be calculated from

$$\bar{s} = \bar{\phi} - \mathscr{R} \ln(p/p^{o}) \text{ Btu/(lbmole·R)}$$

where p^{o} is the reference pressure of 1 atm.

Temp., R	Products of combustion, 400% theoretical air		Products of combustion, 200% theoretical air		Nitrogen		Oxygen		Water vapor		Carbon dioxide		Hydrogen		Carbon monoxide	
	$\bar{h}$	$\bar{\phi}$	$\bar{h}$	$\bar{\phi}$	$\bar{h}$	$\bar{\phi}$	$\bar{h}$	$\bar{\phi}$	$\bar{h}$	$\bar{\phi}$	$\bar{h}$	$\bar{\phi}$	$\bar{h}$	$\bar{\phi}$	$\bar{h}$	$\bar{\phi}$
537	3746.8	46.318	3774.9	46.300	3729.5	45.755	3725.1	48.986	4258.3	45.079	4030.2	51.032	3640.3	31.194	3729.5	47.272
600	4191.9	47.101	4226.3	47.094	4167.9	46.514	4168.3	49.762	4764.7	45.970	4600.9	52.038	4075.6	31.959	3168.0	48.044
700	4901.7	48.195	4947.7	48.207	4864.9	47.588	4879.3	50.858	5575.4	47.219	5552.0	53.503	4770.2	33.031	4866.0	49.120
800	5617.5	49.150	5676.3	49.179	5564.4	48.522	5602.0	51.821	6396.9	48.316	6552.9	54.839	5467.1	33.961	5568.2	50.058
900	6340.3	50.002	6413.0	50.047	6268.1	49.352	6337.9	52.688	7230.9	49.298	7597.6	56.070	6165.3	34.784	6276.4	50.892
1000	7072.1	50.773	7159.8	50.833	6977.9	50.099	7087.5	53.477	8078.9	50.191	8682.1	57.212	6864.5	35.520	6992.2	51.646
1100	7812.9	51.479	7916.4	51.555	7695.0	50.783	7850.4	54.204	8942.0	51.013	9802.6	58.281	7564.6	36.188	7716.8	52.337
1200	8563.4	52.132	8683.6	52.222	8420.0	51.413	8625.8	54.879	9820.4	51.777	10955.3	59.283	8265.8	36.798	8450.8	52.976
1300	9324.1	52.741	9461.7	52.845	9153.9	52.001	9412.9	55.508	10714.5	52.494	12136.9	60.229	8968.7	37.360	9194.6	53.571
1400	10095.0	53.312	10250.7	53.430	9896.9	52.551	10210.4	56.099	11624.8	53.168	13344.7	61.124	9673.8	37.883	9948.1	54.129
1500	10875.6	53.851	11050.2	53.981	10648.9	53.071	11017.1	56.656	12551.4	53.808	14576.0	61.974	10381.5	38.372	10711.1	54.655
1600	11665.6	54.360	11859.6	54.504	11409.7	53.561	11832.5	57.182	13494.9	54.418	15829.0	62.783	11092.5	38.830	11483.4	55.154
1700	12464.3	54.844	12678.6	55.000	12178.9	54.028	12655.6	57.680	14455.4	54.999	17101.4	63.555	11807.4	39.264	12264.3	55.628
1800	13271.7	55.306	13507.0	55.473	12956.3	54.472	13485.8	58.155	15433.0	55.559	18391.5	64.292	12526.8	39.675	13053.2	56.078
1900	14087.2	55.747	14344.1	55.926	13741.6	54.896	14322.1	58.607	16427.5	56.097	19697.8	64.999	13250.9	40.067	13849.8	56.509
2000	14910.3	56.169	15189.3	56.360	14534.4	55.303	15164.0	59.039	17439.0	56.617	21018.7	65.676	13980.1	40.441	14653.2	56.922
2100	15740.5	56.574	16042.4	56.777	15334.0	55.694	16010.9	59.451	18466.9	57.119	22352.7	66 327	14714.5	40.799	15463.3	57.317
2200	16577.1	56.964	16902.5	57.177	16139.8	56.068	16862.6	59.848	19510.8	57.605	23699.0	66.953	15454.4	41.143	16279.4	57.696
2300	17419.8	57.338	17769.3	57.562	16951.2	56.429	17718.8	60.228	20570.6	58.077	25056.3	67.557	16199.8	41.475	17101.0	58.062
2400	18268.0	57.699	18642.1	57.933	17767.9	56.777	18579.2	60.594	21645.7	58.535	26424.0	68.139	16950.6	41.794	17927.4	58.414
2500	19121.4	58.048	19520.7	58.292	18589.5	57.112	19443.4	60.946	22735.4	58.980	27801.2	68.702	17707.3	42.104	18758.8	58.754

[†] To convert this table to metric units use the conversion factors 1 Btu/lbmole = 2.3258 kJ/kgmole, 1 Btu/(lbmole·R) = 4.1865 kJ/(kgmole·K), and 1 R = $\frac{5}{9}$ K.

(Continued)

Appendix C.16c Other gases (English units)† —*continued*

Temp., R	Products of combustion, 400% theoretical air		Products of combustion, 200% theoretical air		Nitrogen		Oxygen		Water vapor		Carbon dioxide		Hydrogen		Carbon monoxide	
	$\bar{h}$	$\bar{\phi}$	$\bar{h}$	$\bar{\phi}$	$\bar{h}$	$\bar{\phi}$	$\bar{h}$	$\bar{\phi}$	$\bar{h}$	$\bar{\phi}$	$\bar{h}$	$\bar{\phi}$	$\bar{h}$	$\bar{\phi}$	$\bar{h}$	$\bar{\phi}$
2600	19979.7	58.384	20404.6	58.639	19415.8	57.436	20311.4	61.287	23839.5	59.414	29187.1	69.245	18469.7	42.403	19594.3	59.081
2700	20842.8	58.710	21293.8	58.974	20246.4	57.750	21182.9	61.616	24957.2	59.837	30581.2	69.771	19237.8	42.692	20434.0	59.398
2800	21709.8	59.026	22187.5	59.300	21081.1	58.053	22057.8	61.934	26088.0	60.248	31982.8	70.282	20011.8	42.973	21277.2	59.705
2900	22581.4	59.331	23086.0	59.615	21919.5	58.348	22936.1	62.242	27231.2	60.650	33391.5	70.776	20791.5	43.247	22123.8	60.002
3000	23456.6	59.628	23988.5	59.921	22761.5	58.632	23817.1	62.540	28386.3	61.043	34806.6	71.255	21576.9	43.514	22973.4	60.290
3100	24335.5	59.916	24895.3	60.218	23606.8	58.910	24702.5	62.831	29552.8	61.426	36227.9	71.722	22367.7	43.773	23826.0	60.569
3200	25217.8	60.196	25805.6	60.507	24455.0	59.179	25590.5	63.113	30730.2	61.801	37654.7	72.175	23164.1	44.026	24681.2	60.841
3300	26102.9	60.469	26719.2	60.789	25306.0	59.442	26481.6	63.386	31918.2	62.167	39086.7	72.616	23965.5	44.273	25539.0	61.105
3400	26991.4	60.734	27636.4	61.063	26159.7	59.697	27375.9	63.654	33116.0	62.526	40523.6	73.045	24771.9	44.513	26399.3	61.362
3500			28556.8	61.329	27015.9	59.944	28273.3	63.914	34323.4	62.876	41965.2	73.462	25582.9	44.748	27261.8	61.612
3600			29479.9	61.590	27874.4	60.186	29173.9	64.168	35540.1	63.221	43411.0	73.870	26398.5	44.978	28126.6	61.855
3700			30406.0	61.843	28735.1	60.422	30077.5	64.415	36765.4	63.557	44860.6	74.267	27218.5	45.203	28993.5	62.093
3800			31334.8	62.091	29597.9	60.652	30984.1	64.657	37998.9	63.887	46314.0	74.655	28042.8	45.423	29862.3	62.325
3900			32266.2	62.333	30462.8	60.877	31893.6	64.893	39240.2	64.210	47771.0	75.033	28871.1	45.638	30732.9	62.551
4000					31329.4	61.097	32806.1	65.123	40489.1	64.528	49231.4	75.404	29703.5	45.849	31605.2	62.772
4100					32198.0	61.310	33721.6	65.350	41745.4	64.839	50695.1	75.765	30539.8	46.056	32479.1	62.988
4200					33068.1	61.520	34639.9	65.571	43008.4	65.144	52162.0	76.119	31379.8	46.257	33354.4	63.198
4300					33939.9	61.726	35561.1	65.788	44278.0	65.444	53632.1	76.464	32223.5	46.456	34231.2	63.405
4400					34813.1	61.927	36485.0	66.000	45553.9	65.738	55105.1	76.803	33070.9	46.651	35109.2	63.607
4500					35687.8	62.123	37411.8	66.208	46835.9	66.028	56581.0	77.135	33921.6	46.842	35988.6	63.805
4600					36563.8	62.316	38341.4	66.413	48123.6	66.312	58059.7	77.460	34775.7	47.030	36869.3	63.998
4700					37441.1	62.504	39273.6	66.613	49416.9	66.591	59541.1	77.779	35633.0	47.215	37751.0	64.188
4800					38319.5	62.689	40208.6	66.809	50715.5	66.866	61024.9	78.091	36493.4	47.396	38633.9	64.374
4900					39199.1	62.870	41146.1	67.003	52019.0	67.135	62511.3	78.398	37356.9	47.574	39517.8	64.556
5000					40079.8	63.049	42086.3	67.193	53327.4	67.401	64000.0	78.698	38223.8	47.749	40402.7	64.735
5100					40961.6	63.223	43029.1	67.380	54640.3	67.662	65490.9	78.994	39092.8	47.921	41288.6	64.910
5200					41844.4	63.395	43974.3	67.562	55957.4	67.918	66984.0	79.284	39965.1	48.090	42175.2	65.082
5300					42728.3	63.563	44922.2	67.743	57278.7	68.172	68479.1	79.569	40840.2	48.257	43063.2	65.252

† To convert this table to metric units use the conversion factors 1 Btu/lbmole = 2.3258 kJ/kgmole, 1 Btu/(lbmole·R) = 4.1865 kJ/(kgmole·K), and 1 R = $\frac{5}{9}$ K.

Sources: Abridged from Joseph H. Keenan and Joseph Kaye, *Gas Tables* (New York: Wiley, 1948). Copyright © 1948 John Wiley & Sons. Reprinted by permission of John Wiley & Sons, Inc. Also reprinted by permission from J. P. Holman, *Thermodynamics*, 3d ed. (New York: McGraw-Hill, 1980), pp. 751–752 (Table A-18).

Appendix C.17 **Base 10 logarithms of the equilibrium constants K_e for the reaction**

$$v_1 C_1 + v_2 C_2 \rightleftarrows v_3 C_3 + v_4 C_4 \qquad K_e = \frac{\chi_3^{v_3} \chi_4^{v_4}}{\chi_1^{v_1} \chi_2^{v_2}} \left(\frac{p}{p_o}\right)^{v_3 + v_4 - v_1 - v_2} \qquad (p_o = 1 \text{ atm})$$

T, K	$H_2 \rightleftarrows 2H$	$O_2 \rightleftarrows 2O$	$H_2O \rightleftarrows H_2 + \frac{1}{2}O_2$	$H_2O \rightleftarrows OH + \frac{1}{2}H_2$	$CO_2 \rightleftarrows CO + \frac{1}{2}O_2$	$N_2 \rightleftarrows 2N$	$\frac{1}{2}O_2 + \frac{1}{2}N_2 \rightleftarrows NO$	$Na \rightleftarrows Na^+ + e^-$	$Cs \rightleftarrows Cs^+ + e^-$
298	−71.210	−80.620	−40.047	−46.593	−45.043	−119.434	−15.187	−32.3	−25.1
400	−51.742	−58.513	−29.241	−33.910	−32.41	−87.473	−11.156	−24.3	−17.5
600	−32.667	−36.859	−18.663	−21.470	−20.07	−56.206	−7.219	−14.6	−10.0
800	−23.074	−25.985	−13.288	−15.214	−13.90	−40.521	−5.250	−9.58	−6.15
1000	−17.288	−19.440	−10.060	−11.444	−10.199	−31.084	−4.068	−6.54	−3.79
1200	−13.410	−15.062	−7.896	−8.922	−7.742	−24.619	−3.279	−4.47	−2.18
1400	−10.627	−11.932	−6.334	−7.116	−5.992	−20.262	−2.717	−2.97	−1.010
1600	−8.530	−9.575	−5.175	−5.758	−4.684	−16.869	−2.294	−1.819	−0.108
1800	−6.893	−7.740	−4.263	−4.700	−3.672	−14.225	−1.966	−0.913	+0.609
2000	−5.579	−6.269	−3.531	−3.852	−2.863	−12.016	−1.703	−0.175	+1.194
2200	−4.500	−5.064	−2.931	−3.158	−2.206	−10.370	−1.488	+0.438	+1.682
2400	−3.598	−4.055	−2.429	−2.578	−1.662	−8.992	−1.309	+0.956	+2.098
2600	−2.833	−3.206	−2.003	−2.087	−1.203	−7.694	−1.157	+1.404	+2.46
2800	−2.176	−2.475	−1.638	−1.670	−0.807	−6.640	−1.028	+1.792	+2.77
3000	−1.604	−1.840	−1.322	−1.302	−0.469	−5.726	−0.915	+2.13	+3.05
3200	−1.104	−1.285	−1.046	−0.983	−0.175	−4.925	−0.817	+2.44	+3.29
3500	−0.458	−0.571	−0.693	−0.557	+0.201	−3.893	−0.692	+2.84	+3.62
4000	+0.406	+0.382	−0.221	−0.035	+0.699	−2.514	−0.526	+3.38	+4.07
4500	+1.078	+1.125	+0.153	+0.392	+1.081	−1.437	−0.345	+3.82	+4.43
5000	+1.619	+1.719	+0.450	+0.799	+1.387	−0.570	−0.298	+4.18	+4.73

Source: Reprinted by permission from William C. Reynolds and Henry C. Perkins, *Engineering Thermodynamics*, 2d ed. (New York: McGraw-Hill, 1977), p. 652 (Table B-14).

Appendix C.18 Isentropic compressible flow tables for air ($k = 1.4$)

M	p/p_{os}	T/T_{os}	ρ/ρ_{os}	A/A^*	M^*
0.10000	0.99303	0.99800	0.99502	5.82183	0.10944
0.20000	0.97250	0.99206	0.98028	2.96352	0.21822
0.30000	0.93947	0.98232	0.95638	2.03506	0.32572
0.40000	0.89561	0.96899	0.92427	1.59014	0.43133
0.50000	0.84302	0.95238	0.88517	1.33984	0.53452
0.60000	0.78400	0.93284	0.84045	1.18820	0.63481
0.70000	0.72093	0.91075	0.79158	1.09437	0.73179
0.80000	0.65602	0.88652	0.73999	1.03823	0.82514
0.90000	0.59126	0.86059	0.68704	1.00886	0.91460
1.00000	0.52828	0.83333	0.63394	1.00000	1.00000
1.10000	0.46835	0.80515	0.58170	1.00793	1.08124
1.20000	0.41238	0.77640	0.53114	1.03044	1.15828
1.30000	0.36091	0.74738	0.48290	1.06630	1.23114
1.40000	0.31424	0.71839	0.43742	1.11493	1.29987
1.50000	0.27240	0.68966	0.39498	1.17617	1.36458
1.60000	0.23527	0.66138	0.35573	1.25023	1.42539
1.70000	0.20259	0.63371	0.31969	1.33761	1.48247
1.80000	0.17404	0.60680	0.28682	1.43898	1.53598
1.90000	0.14924	0.58072	0.25699	1.55526	1.58609
2.00000	0.12780	0.55556	0.23005	1.68750	1.63299
2.10000	0.10935	0.53135	0.20580	1.83694	1.67687
2.20000	0.09352	0.50813	0.18405	2.00497	1.71791
2.30000	0.07997	0.48591	0.16458	2.19313	1.75629
2.40000	0.06840	0.46468	0.14720	2.40310	1.79218
2.50000	0.05853	0.44444	0.13169	2.63672	1.82574
2.60000	0.05012	0.42517	0.11787	2.89597	1.85714
2.70000	0.04295	0.40683	0.10557	3.18301	1.88653
2.80000	0.03685	0.38941	0.09463	3.50012	1.91404
2.90000	0.03165	0.37286	0.08489	3.84976	1.93981
3.00000	0.02722	0.35714	0.07623	4.23456	1.96396
3.50000	0.01311	0.28986	0.04523	6.78962	2.06419
4.00000	0.00659	0.23810	0.02766	10.71875	2.13809
4.50000	0.00346	0.19802	0.01745	16.56220	2.19360
5.00000	0.00189	0.16667	0.01134	25.00000	2.23607
5.50000	0.00107	0.14184	0.00758	36.86897	2.26913
6.00000	0.00063	0.12195	0.00519	53.17981	2.29528
6.50000	0.00039	0.10582	0.00364	75.13433	2.31626
7.00000	0.00024	0.09259	0.00261	104.14290	2.33333
7.50000	0.00016	0.08163	0.00190	141.84140	2.34738
8.00000	0.00010	0.07246	0.00141	190.10930	2.35907
8.50000	0.00007	0.06472	0.00107	251.08620	2.36889
9.00000	0.00005	0.05814	0.00082	327.18930	2.37722
9.50000	0.00003	0.05249	0.00063	421.13160	2.38433
10.00000	0.00002	0.04762	0.00049	535.93780	2.39046

Appendix C.19 Normal shock tables for air ($k = 1.4$)

M_x	M_y	p_y/p_x	T_y/T_x	ρ_y/ρ_x	p_{osy}/p_{osx}	p_{osy}/p_x
0.00000	1.00000	1.00000	1.00000	1.00000	1.00000	1.89293
0.10000	0.91177	1.24500	1.06494	1.16908	0.99893	2.13285
0.20000	0.84217	1.51333	1.12799	1.34162	0.99280	2.40750
0.30000	0.78596	1.80500	1.19087	1.51570	0.97937	2.71359
0.40000	0.73971	2.12000	1.25469	1.68966	0.95820	3.04924
0.50000	0.70109	2.45833	1.32022	1.86207	0.92979	3.41327
0.60000	0.66844	2.82000	1.38797	2.03175	0.89520	3.80497
0.70000	0.64054	3.20500	1.45833	2.19772	0.85572	4.22383
0.80000	0.61650	3.61333	1.53158	2.35922	0.81268	4.66951
0.90000	0.59562	4.04500	1.60792	2.51568	0.76736	5.14178
1.00000	0.57735	4.50000	1.68750	2.66667	0.72087	5.64044
2.10000	0.56128	4.97833	1.77045	2.81190	0.67420	6.16538
2.20000	0.54706	5.48000	1.85686	2.95122	0.62814	6.71648
2.30000	0.53441	6.00500	1.94680	3.08455	0.58329	7.29368
2.40000	0.52312	6.55333	2.04033	3.21190	0.54014	7.89691
2.50000	0.51299	7.12500	2.13750	3.33333	0.49901	8.52613
2.60000	0.50387	7.72000	2.23834	3.44898	0.46012	9.18130
2.70000	0.49563	8.33833	2.34289	3.55899	0.42359	9.86240
2.80000	0.48817	8.98000	2.45117	3.66355	0.38946	10.56938
2.90000	0.48138	9.64500	2.56321	3.76286	0.35773	11.30224
3.00000	0.47519	10.33333	2.67901	3.85714	0.32834	12.06095
3.50000	0.45115	14.12500	3.31505	4.26087	0.21295	16.24199
4.00000	0.43496	18.50000	4.04687	4.57143	0.13876	21.06808
4.50000	0.42355	23.45833	4.87509	4.81188	0.09170	26.53866
5.00000	0.41523	29.00000	5.80000	5.00000	0.06172	32.65346
5.50000	0.40897	35.12500	6.82180	5.14894	0.04236	39.41235
6.00000	0.40416	41.83333	7.94059	5.26829	0.02965	46.81519
6.50000	0.40038	49.12500	9.15643	5.36508	0.02115	54.86198
7.00000	0.39736	57.00000	10.46939	5.44445	0.01535	63.55261
7.50000	0.39491	65.45834	11.87948	5.51020	0.01133	72.88713
8.00000	0.39289	74.50000	13.38672	5.56522	0.00849	82.86546
8.50000	0.39121	84.12500	14.99113	5.61165	0.00645	93.48763
9.00000	0.38980	94.33333	16.69273	5.65116	0.00496	104.75360
9.50000	0.38860	105.12500	18.49152	5.68504	0.00387	116.66340
10.00000	0.38758	116.50000	20.38750	5.71429	0.00304	129.21690

Appendix C.20 The elements

Name	Symbol	Atomic number	International atomic mass, 1966	Name	Symbol	Atomic number	International atomic mass, 1966
Actinium	Ac	89	—	Curium	Cm	96	—
Aluminum	Al	13	26.9815	Dysprosium	Dy	66	162.50
Americium	Am	95	—	Einsteinium	Es	99	—
Antimony,			—	Erbium	Er	68	167.26
stibium	Sb	51	121.75	Europium	Eu	63	151.96
Argon	Ar	18	39.948	Fermium	Fm	100	—
Arsenic	As	33	74.9216	Fluorine	F	9	18.9984
Astatine	At	85	—	Francium	Fr	87	—
Barium	Ba	56	137.34	Gadolinium	Gd	64	157.25
Berkelium	Bk	97	—	Gallium	Ga	31	69.72
Beryllium	Be	4	9.0122	Germanium	Ge	32	72.59
Bismuth	Bi	83	208.980	Gold, aurum	Au	79	196.967
Boron	B	5	10.811	Hafnium	Hf	72	178.49
Bromine	Br	35	79.904	Helium	He	2	4.0026
Cadmium	Cd	48	112.40	Holmium	Ho	67	164.930
Calcium	Ca	20	40.08	Hydrogen	H	1	1.00797
Californium	Cf	98	—	Indium	In	49	114.82
Carbon	C	6	12.01115	Iodine	I	53	126.9044
Cerium	Ce	58	140.12	Iridium	Ir	77	192.2
Cesium	Cs	55	132.905	Iron, ferrum	Fe	26	55.847
Chlorine	Cl	17	35.453	Krypton	Kr	36	83.80
Chromium	Cr	24	51.996	Lanthanum	La	57	138.91
Cobalt	Co	27	58.9332	Lawrencium	Lr	103	(257)
Columbium, see			—	Lead, plumbum	Pb	82	207.19
niobium				Lithium	Li	3	6.939
Copper	Cu	29	63.546	Lutetium	Lu	71	174.97

Source: Reprinted by permission from William C. Reynolds and Henry C. Perkins, *Engineering Thermodynamics*, 2d ed. (New York: McGraw-Hill, 1977), p. 653 (Table B-15).

D Appendix D: Thermodynamic Charts

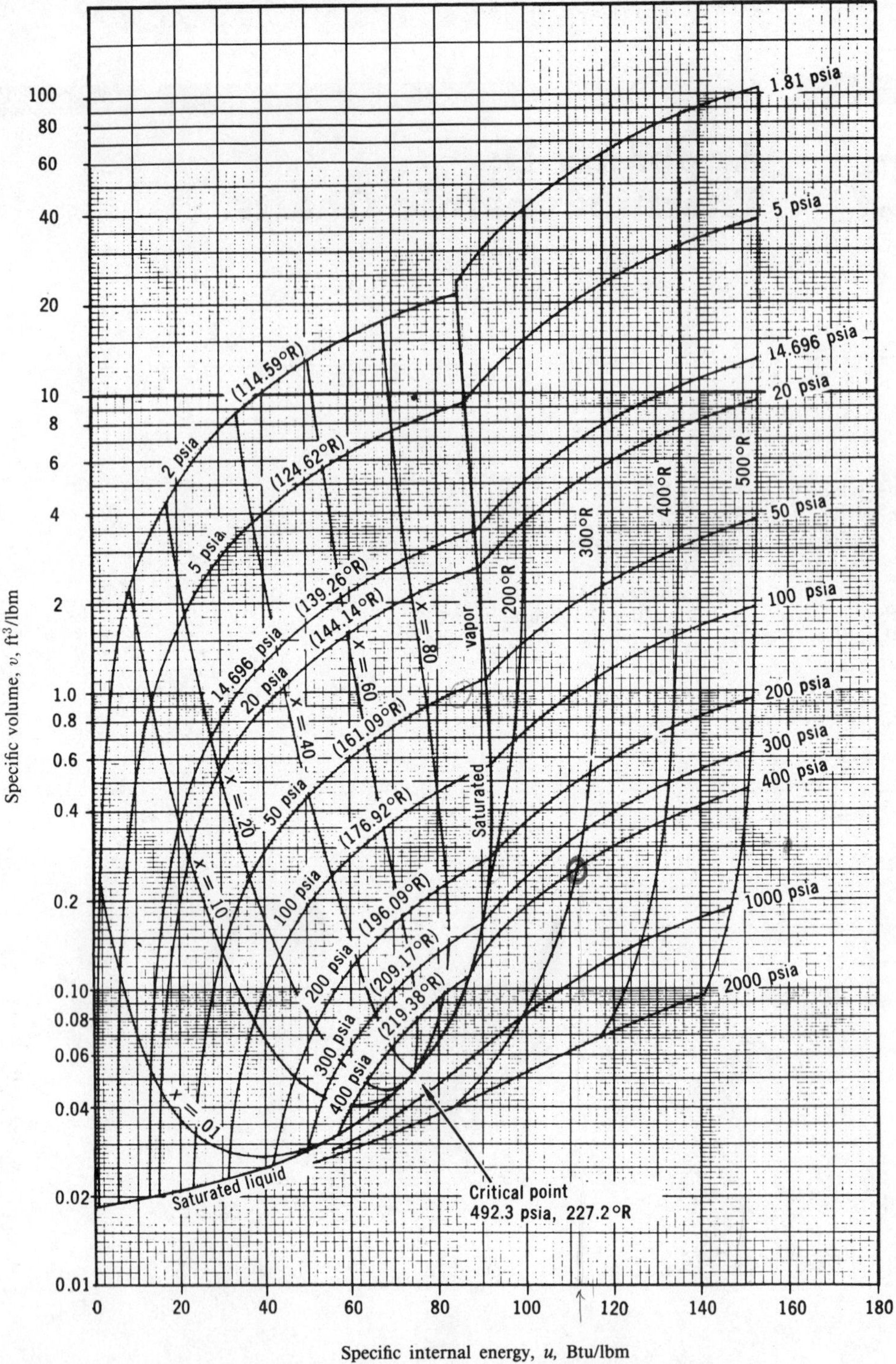

Appendix D.1 *v-u* chart for nitrogen. Based on National Bureau of Standards TN 129A.
Sources: Reprinted by permission from William C. Reynolds and Henry C. Perkins, *Engineering Thermodynamics*, 2d ed. (New York: McGraw-Hill, 1977), p. 605 (Figure B-4).

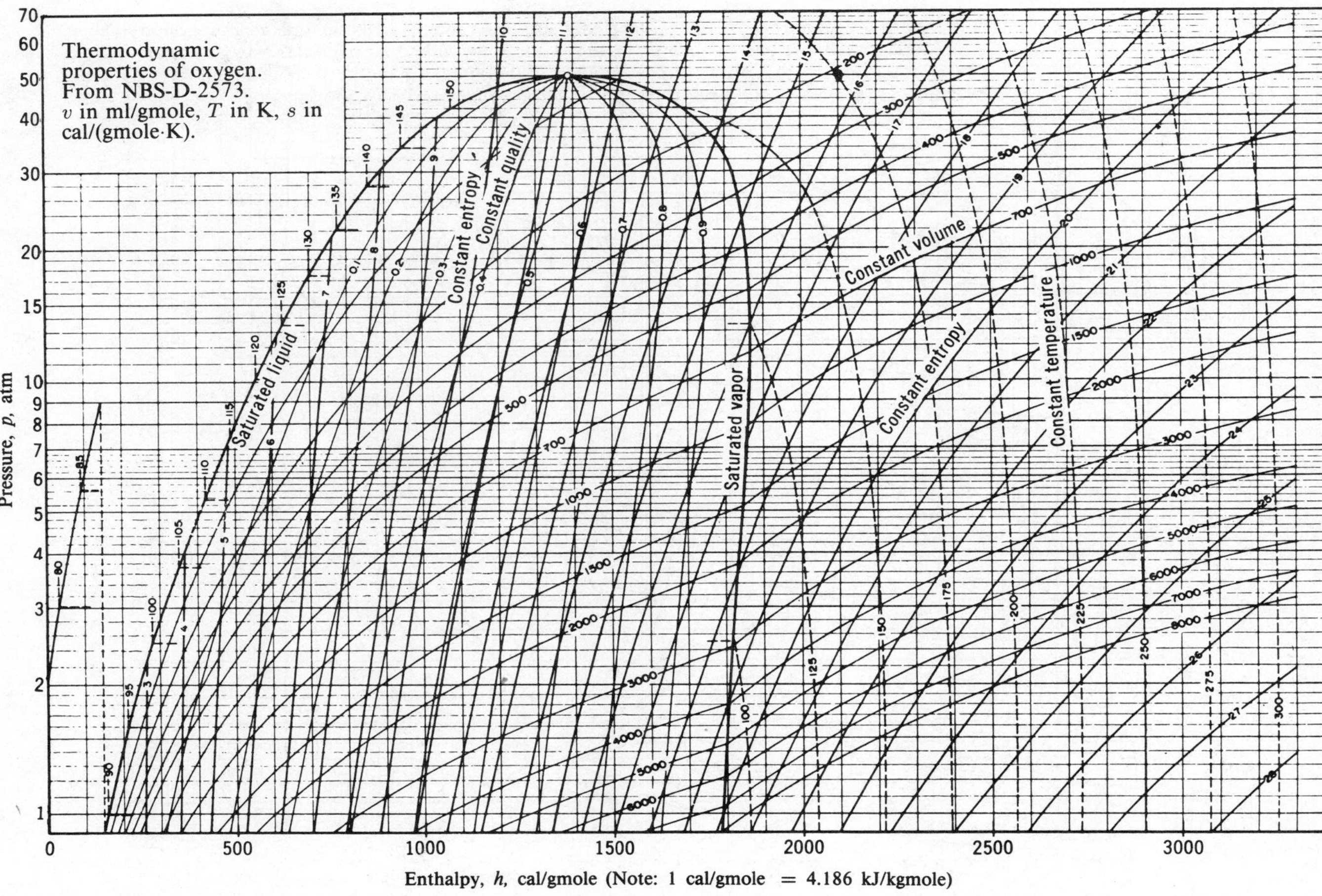

Appendix D.2 *p-h* chart for oxygen. From NBS D-2573. 1 cal = 4.184 joules, v in mL/gmole, T in K, s in cal/(gmole-K). *Sources:* From National Bureau of Standards D-2573. Also reprinted by permission from William C. Reynolds and Henry C. Perkins, *Engineering Thermodynamics*, 2d ed. (New York: McGraw-Hill, 1977), p. 606 (Figure B-5).

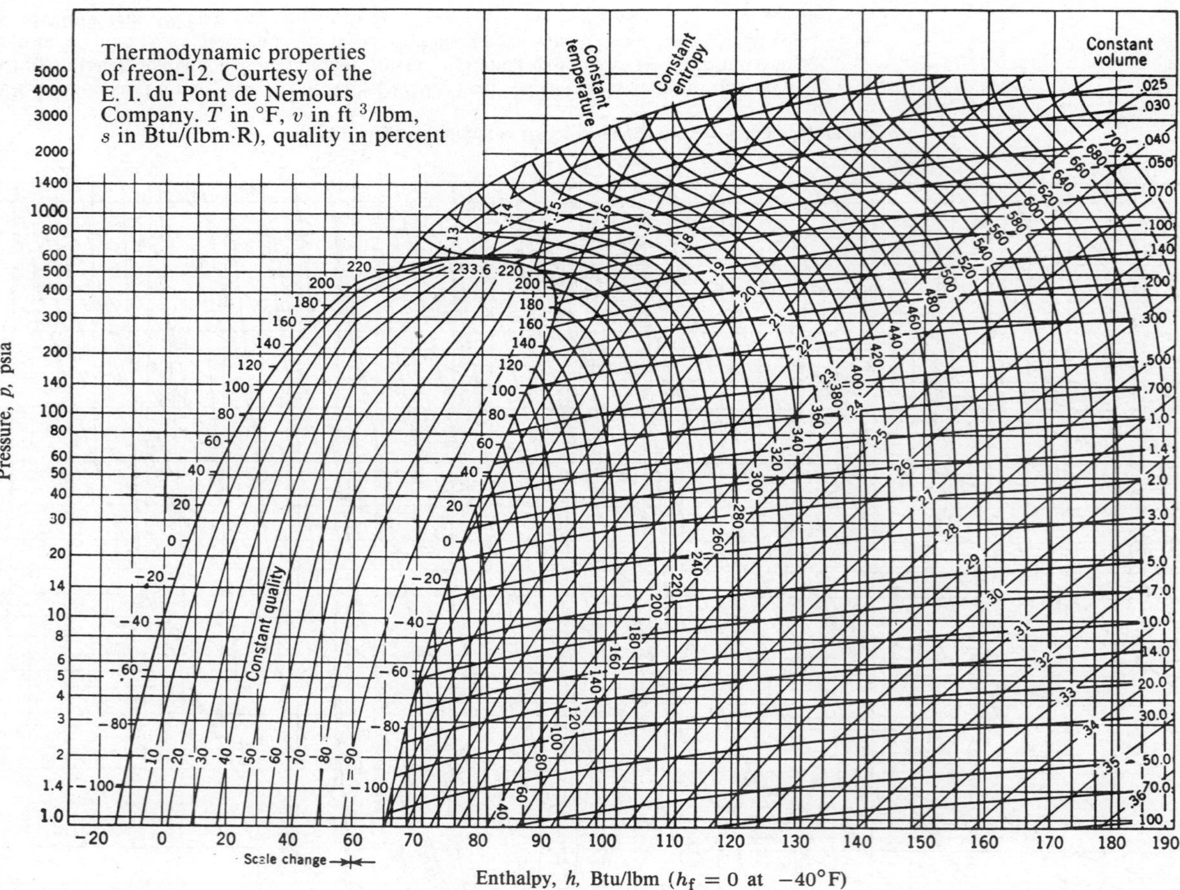

Appendix D.3 *p-h* chart for Refrigerant-12. Courtesy of the E. I. du Pont de Nemours Company. T in °F, v in ft^3/lbm, s in Btu/(lbm·R), quality in percent. *Sources*: Courtesy of E. I. du Pont de Nemours & Co. Also reprinted by permission from William C. Reynolds and Henry C. Perkins, *Engineering Thermodynamics*, 2d ed. (New York: McGraw-Hill, 1977), p. 608 (Figure B-7).

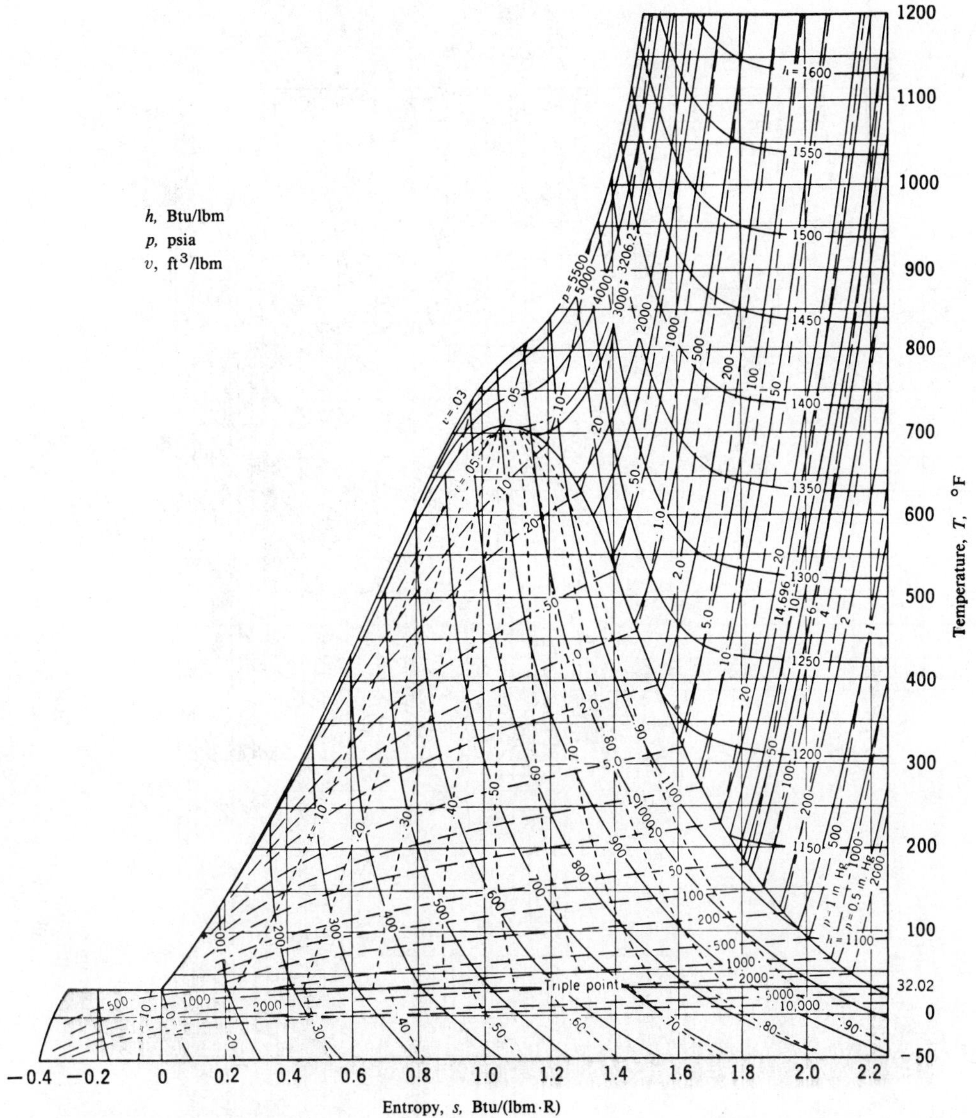

Appendix D.4 *T-s* chart for water. *Sources*: Reprinted from Joseph H. Keenan and Joseph Keyes, *Thermodynamics Properties of Steam* (New York: Wiley, 1936). Copyright © 1936 John Wiley & Sons. Reprinted by permission of John Wiley & Sons, Inc. As adapted by Joachim E. Lay, *Thermodynamics* Charles E. Merrill, Inc., Englewood Cliffs, N.J., 1963, by permission. Also reprinted from William C. Reynolds and Henry C. Perkins, *Engineering Dynamics*, 2d ed. (New York: McGraw-Hill, 1977), p. 604 (Figure B-3).

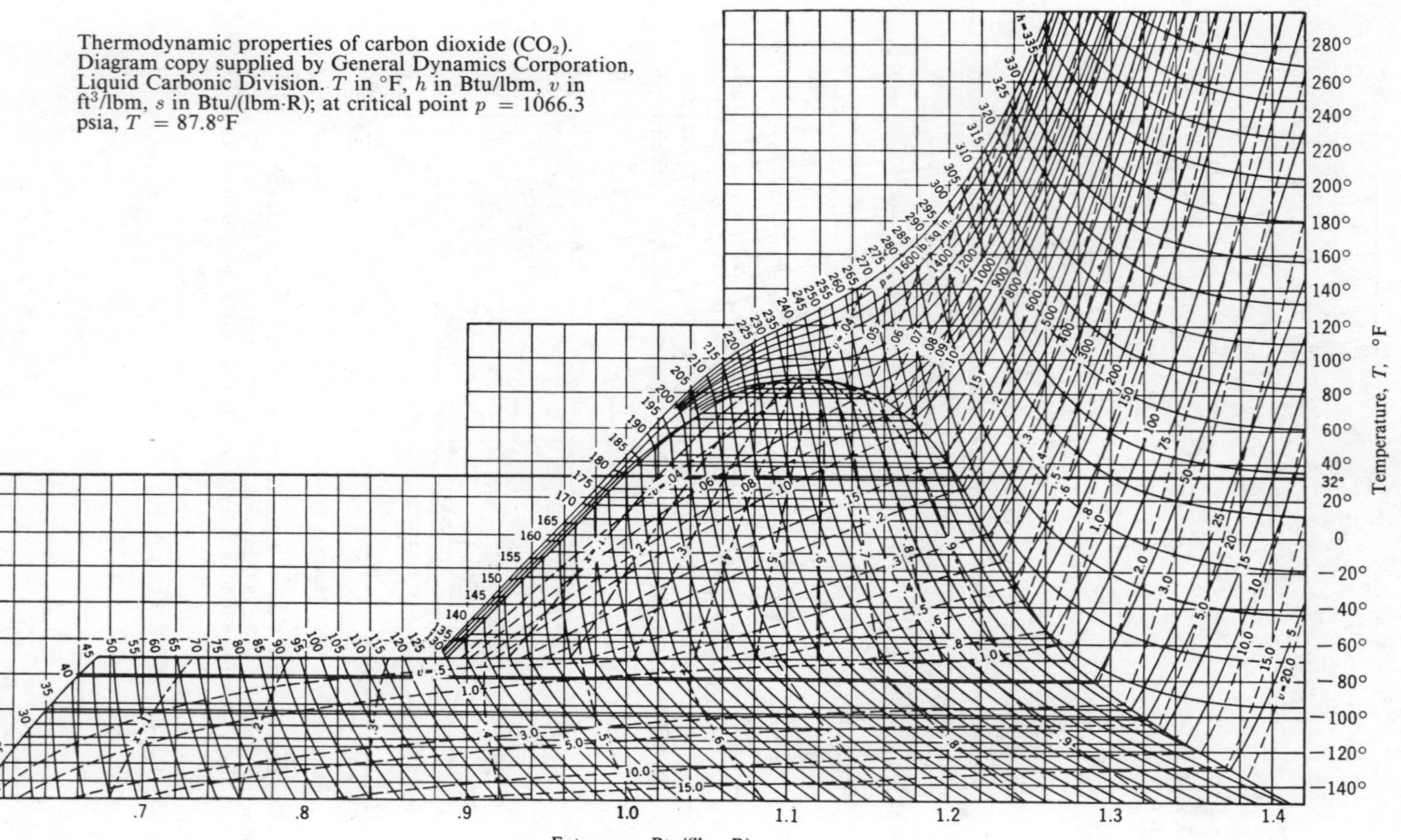

Appendix D.5 *T-s* chart for carbon dioxide. Diagram copy supplied by General Dynamics Corporation, Liquid Carbonic Division. T in °F, h in Btu/lbm, v in ft^3/lbm, s in Btu/(lbm·R); at critical point p = 1066.3 psia, T = 87.8 °F. *Sources*: Reprinted by permission of General Dynamics Corporation, Liquid Carbonic Division. Also reprinted from William C. Reynolds and Henry C. Perkins, *Engineering Thermodynamics*, 2d ed. (New York: McGraw-Hill, 1977), p. 607 (Figure B-6).

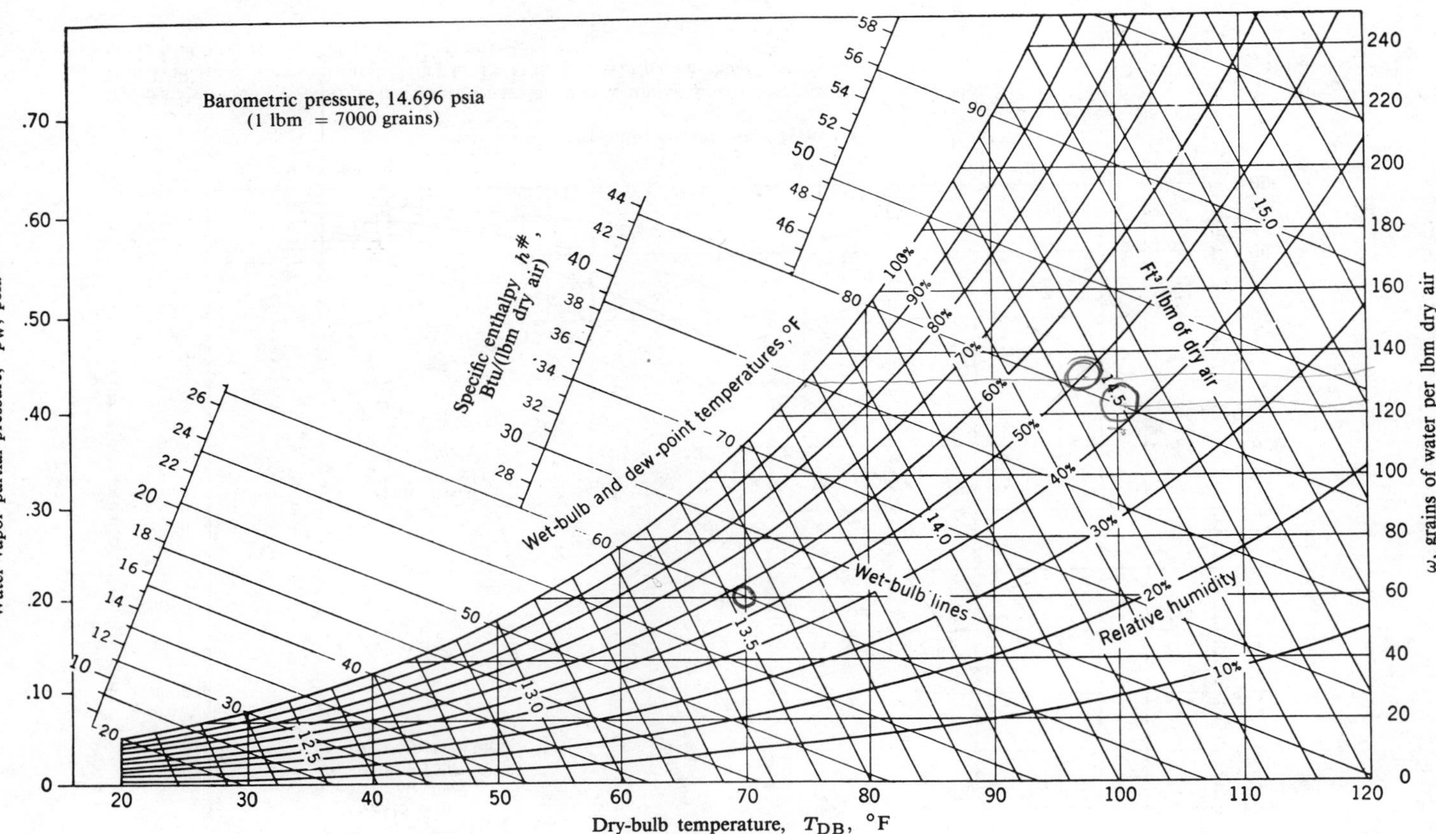

Appendix D.6a Psychrometric chart for water (English units). Courtesy of the General Electric Company. Barometric pressure, 14.696 lbf/in² (1 lbm = 7000 grains) *Sources*: Courtesy of the General Electric Company. Also reprinted from William C. Reynolds and Henry C. Perkins, *Engineering Thermodynamics*, 2d ed. (New York: McGraw-Hill, 1977), p. 614 (Figure B-13a).

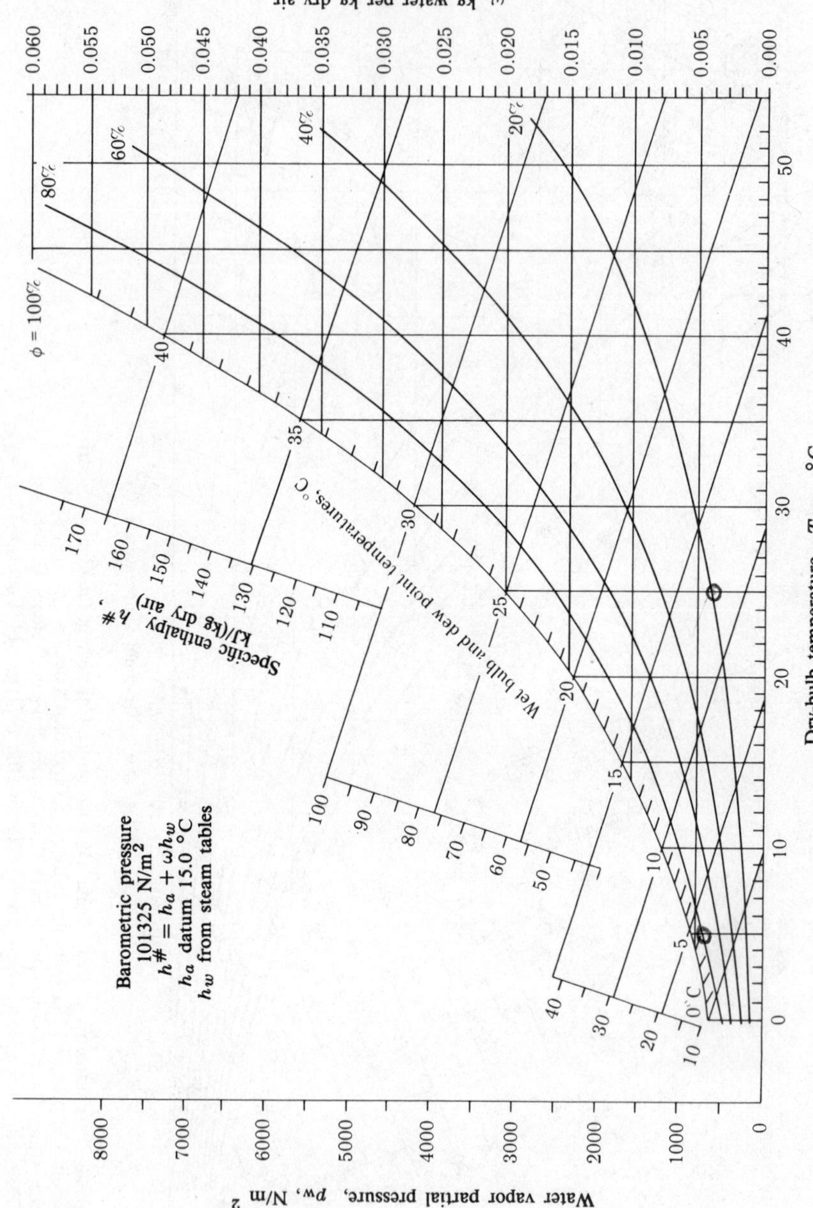

Appendix D.6b Psychrometric chart for water (metric units). *Source*: Reprinted by permission from William C. Reynolds and Henry C. Perkins, *Engineering Thermodynamics*, 2d ed. (New York: McGraw-Hill, 1977), p. 615 (Figure B-13b).

Index

Software to accompany THERMODYNAMICS

TO RUN THE PROGRAM: Insert the disk in Drive A. At the > prompt type the word THERMO (or THERMO/M if you have a monochrome monitor and a Color Graphics Adapter) and then press the RETURN (or ENTER) key. The program should then load and show the opening title screen. This screen will be replaced by the menu screen after a few seconds (how long it stays up depends on the clock speed of your computer), or you can press any key and it will be immediately replaced by the menu screen. Use the arrow keys or the menu item numbers to choose the desired program.

TO SEE THE README FILE: Insert the disk in Drive A. At the > prompt type README and then press the RETURN (or ENTER) key. Each page of the README file will then be displayed on the screen (pressing any key will bring up the next page). To get a hard copy of the README file on your printer just type PRINT README.TXT and then press RETURN (or ENTER) at the > prompt.